Creative Publications

ALGEBRA

TEACHER'S EDITION

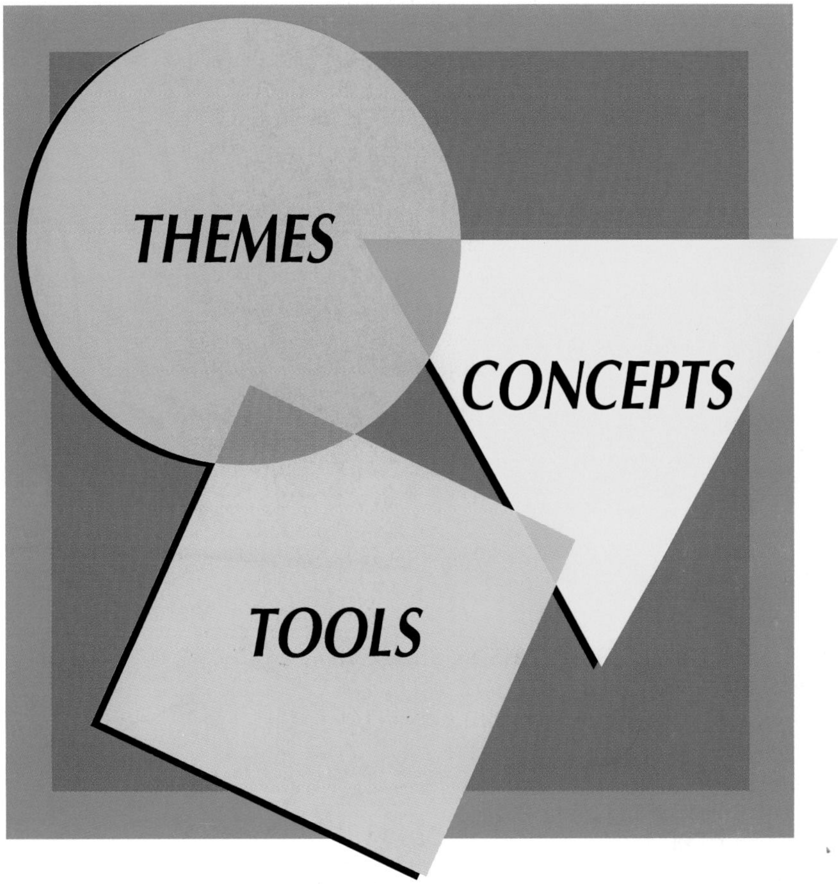

Anita Wah
Henri Picciotto

Creative Publications
Mountain View, California

ACKNOWLEDGEMENTS

Page	Credit
Cover (girl on bicycle)	Lori Adamski Peek/Tony Stone Worldwide
Cover (aircraft in flight)	Randy Jolly/Comstock
Cover (planet earth)	Terje Kveen/The Image Bank
Cover (money symbol)	Michel Tcherevkoff/The Image Bank
2	Linda Dufurrena/Grant Heilman Photography, Inc.
42	©Comstock, Inc.
80	Science Source • Division of Photo Researchers
122	James H. Carmichael/The Image Bank
164	Garry Gay/The Image Bank West
204	Peter Grumann/The Image Bank West
244	Chris Bjornberg/Science Source • Division of Photo Researchers
284	Barry Runk, Stan Schoenberger/ Grant Heilman Photography, Inc.
326	©W. Cody/West Light
366	Don Landwehrle/The Image Bank West
396	©Jim Zuckerman/West Light
424	Gabriel Covian/The Image Bank West
456	Chris Collins/The Stock Market
482	Michael Sciulli/The Image Bank West

Text excerpt "When Mrs. Frederick C. Little's second son...cigarette box," from *Stuart Little* by E. B. White. Copyright 1945 by E. B. White. Text copyright renewed ©1973 by E. B. White. Selection reprinted by permission of HarperCollins Publishers.

Managing Editor • George William Bratton III
Project Editor • Ann Roper
Project Art Director and Graphic Designer • Hyru Gau
Production Manager • Vickie Self
Art Director • JoAnne K. Hammer
Math Content Editor • Lyn Savage
Solutions Editor • Terry Whittier
Technical Illustrator for Solutions • Joseph Parenteau
Indexer • Steven Sorensen
Cover Design • Hyru Gau
Composition and Film • GTS Graphics, Inc.

1300 Villa Street
Mountain View, California 94041-1197

ISBN: 1-56107-252-4
2 3 4 5 6 7 8 9 10 B 99 98 97 96 95 94 93

AUTHORS

Anita Wah received her Bachelor's Degree in Mathematics from Oberlin College and a Master's Degree in Biostatistics from Harvard. She attended and taught as a master teacher at the Woodrow Wilson Algebra Institute and has over ten years of teaching experience at the high school and college levels. She has been involved as a curriculum consultant and staff development trainer for the State of California.

Henri Picciotto has been teaching mathematics for over twenty years at every level from counting to calculus. He has developed curriculum for the Lawrence Hall of Science at the University of California and has consulted for many schools, districts, and university departments of education across the country. He received his Bachelor's Degree, as well as his Master's Degree in Mathematics from the University of California at Berkeley. He is currently the mathematics coordinator for The Urban School of San Francisco, California.

A Word From the Authors

We would like to acknowledge the many people without whom this book would not have been possible.

These math teachers and authors had a significant influence on our teaching or on the ideas that led to this book: Abraham Arcavi, Richard Brown, G.D. Chakerian, Calvin Crabill, Zoltan Dienes, Lew Douglas, Martin Flashman, Paul Foerster, Donna Gaarder, Martin Gardner, Harold Jacobs, Mary Laycock, Sidney Rachlin, Peter Rasmussen, Sherman Stein, Daniel Teague, Joel Teller, Zalman Usiskin.

We also learned a lot from the following curriculum development projects: Change from Within, the Hawaii Algebra Learning Project, the Interactive Math Project, the Lane County Mathematics Project, the Shell Centre for Mathematical Education, and the Quantitative Literacy Project.

We received valuable suggestions from Phil Mallinson, Neil Picciotto, and especially Lyn Savage.

These teachers used the preliminary version of this book in their classes, and helped us iron out the difficulties: Alan Fishman, Mark Gordon, Richard Lautze, Kem Morehead, Hoang Nguyen, and Beau Leonhart. We are grateful to have had their enthusiastic support as the course was being developed.

And of course, our spouses: Alan Fishman and Irva Hertz-Picciotto.

Heartfelt thanks to all!

Dedication

This book is dedicated to our students and colleagues at The Urban School of San Francisco, a great place for involvement, collaboration, and challenge.

TEACHER'S EDITION CONTENTS

WHY WE WROTE THIS BOOK

A quick look through this textbook will make one thing obvious—it is very different from traditional algebra textbooks. While most of the topics of the traditional course are included, there are many new topics, there are changes in emphasis, many more connections are made with future math classes, and a broad array of new learning tools is deployed to engage and support students' thinking.

Like many of you, we have taught the traditional algebra course. Over the years we have tried a variety of textbooks, but some difficulties would not go away. Traditional textbooks:

- did not provide enough exposure to algebra concepts. Many important and difficult ideas were seen for only the duration of one chapter, which is not enough for most students to understand them.
- did not provide enough motivation. By failing to reveal connections with other parts of mathematics and with the real world, they made algebra concepts appear to be useless and made the course boring for many students.
- restricted access. Their narrow focus on rules and symbol manipulation shut out many students who would do better in a visual, exploratory, hands-on environment.

MATHEMATICS REFORM

Meanwhile, we were inspired by the *Standards* of the National Council of Teachers of Mathematics. In this important document, and in the movement that it engendered, we saw the possibility for an exciting renewal in the teaching of mathematics in general, and of algebra in particular.

The changes that are being asked of math teachers are all-encompassing. We are told to de-emphasize some topics and increase the attention to some others; to reveal connections within mathematics with science and real life; to integrate calculators and manipulatives into our teaching; to do more group work and student-oriented discovery lessons and less lecturing; to use more writing assignments, projects, and alternative methods of assessment; and finally to teach algebra to students who had traditionally not been encouraged to study it.

In the past few years, we have been deeply involved in implementing these changes in our classes. We were able to find some excellent ideas by conducting fishing expeditions into assorted textbooks and supplementary materials. And when we did not find what we were looking for, we developed our own material. This was a lot of work and we spent much time at the photocopier. Since we knew we weren't the only teachers with these needs, we decided to develop a brand new textbook that would be the core of a new course. This book would provide new content and new pedagogy all in one place. It would provide the support needed by teachers who, like us, are trying to participate in the reform movement.

Towards the Algebra of Tomorrow

We still believe the core concepts of algebra are of central importance and that they need to be learned at some point in grades 7-10. In a way, we see this book as a transition to the algebra course of tomorrow. Because it is not too drastic a departure from the traditional course, it can be used now. Students who use this book can continue their education in a traditional course. Teachers can start using it right away.

On the other hand, we are too committed to change and the reform movement to create a superficial remake of the traditional textbook. While there is a place for books that take only timid steps, this book would not belong there.

Among textbooks that do represent a break with tradition, many break along a single dimension. They may emphasize real-world applications, or incorporate a problem-solving approach, or be suitable for cooperative learning, or support the use of graphing calculators or manipulatives, or encourage writing. Or perhaps they do a couple of those things. This book is different because it does all those things, and more.

This is not because we could not make up our minds between competing theories. It is because we realize that since students have different learning styles, we need to cast a broad net to catch as many students as possible. Limiting ourselves to any one approach and retaining the traditional approach otherwise, would be turning our backs on too many great ideas we have learned about in the past few years.

This book constitutes a major rethinking of the traditional Algebra 1 course, with new connections, new content, and new approaches. You will be able to use it for years to come, growing into it step by step. It will challenge you as well as your students. Prepare for an exciting time!

Guiding Principles

This book is based on three big ideas that have been guiding principles in our teaching.

In order to learn to reason flexibly and independently about the abstract concepts of algebra, students need **tools** to think with. These tools should be designed to support students' work with the main ideas of algebra: variables, operations, equations, functions, and so on.

Learning mathematics should be based on solving interesting **problems**, but problem solving need not be separated from the acquisition of skills.

Most students will not remember concepts if they are explained once or twice by a teacher and practiced in isolation over a short period of time. Students must be **involved** in their own learning and have experience with ideas in many forms and formats over an **extended** period of time. They must experiment, conjecture, discover, and write about what they are thinking.

These principles are reflected in the style, content, and organization of this book.

▶ Style

This book puts thinking and **problem solving** at the heart of almost every lesson. Students get a lot of practice, but most of it is in the context of worthwhile activities, rather than in the traditional drill and practice format. In particular, developing students' **communication** skills is intimately linked to the development of their mathematical competence.

▶ Content

In choosing the content for the book, we were guided by the following principles:

The work should, as much as possible, be interesting to both students and teachers.

It should reveal connections with other branches of mathematics and science.

It should prepare students for future math classes.

Finally, the book should have enough traditional content to allow teachers to be comfortable in teaching it and enough new content to remain relevant for years to come.

While the book's title is *Algebra*, its content is far more **integrated** than other algebra textbooks. There is a substantial geometric strand running throughout, with a particular emphasis on similar figures, measurement, and the Pythagorean theorem. These ideas are woven into the fabric of the course and are used to support algebraic ideas—not just tacked on. In addition, there are lessons on proportion, data analysis, number theory, mathematical modeling, unit conversions, abstract algebra, and more.

▶ Organization

The organizing principle of this book, as indicated by its title, is the interaction of themes, tools, and concepts. The **concepts** are the mathematical ideas students need to learn. The **themes** furnish the context in which the concepts are learned. And the **tools** assist in the learning process. This approach allows us to follow a **spiraling** method where any important concept is approached again and again all year, not just for the duration of a chapter or unit.

Who is This Book For?

▶ Teachers

This book has been written for teachers who want to implement the NCTM *Standards*, who are ready to experiment with new curriculum ideas, who want to use student-centered pedagogy, and who have a good understanding of mathematics.

▶ Students

This book is suitable for a broad spectrum of students and was actually written for use in heterogeneous classes. The traditional distinctions between students who are good at math and those who are not become blurred when writing and learning tools enter the picture. Students who are more verbal than quantitative, who are more visual or hands-on learners, who are good collaborators, and who enjoy working with calculators and computers have talents that are often undervalued in the traditional math class. The multiple approaches supported by this book allow all these students to work from their strengths and to expand into the areas where they are less comfortable.

While the use of cooperative learning, tools, and writing helps guarantee access to algebra for average and weaker students, the same methods help challenge traditionally strong math students to become more reflective and improve their communication skills. Just getting the answer is no longer sufficient; being able to explain it and being able to ask the next question are just as important.

In addition, the book offers a large number of open-ended and more complex problems and puzzles. These are important for challenging the strong students in a heterogeneous class. However, more complex or more difficult problems should not be seen as hurting the average or weaker students. In fact, such problems give those students something to strive for. Some research shows that the best way to help students having difficulty with problems of average difficulty is not remedial work, but to give them support and encouragement to tackle tougher problems.

▶ Grade Levels

The majority of the book can be covered in a first-year algebra course in grades 8 or 9. Alternatively, it can be used as the backbone of a two-year algebra course in grades 7 and 8, or it can be used as a two-year pre-algebra course in grades 7 and 8 by working slowly through the first nine chapters, placing special emphasis on manipulatives. The book can also be used as a two-year course in grades 9 and 10 as part of an integrated algebra-geometry sequence, using the whole book and supplementing it with some additional work in geometry.

Why is This Book Different?

There are substantial differences between the content of this book and the more traditional algebra course. The reasons for the differences in this book were based on:

▶ Technology

Technological changes such as calculators, graphing calculators, and the soon-to-come symbol manipulators have changed the priorities of math education.

▶ Priorities

Too much energy has been spent on unimportant topics (such as the simplification of complicated radical expressions) and not enough on essential topics (such as real-world applications).

▶ Pedagogy

Some traditional topics (such as using symbol manipulation to solve absolute value inequalities) have proven to be too difficult for beginners, and some topics which were thought to be too difficult (such as functions) are now accessible.

▶ Connections

Connections with other parts of math and applications have been lacking.

▶ Preview

The preview of important concepts from subsequent courses has also been lacking.

In order to make room for more emphasis on real-world applications and modeling, interpretation of graphs, functions, geometry, reasoning, and mathematical structure, we had to take something out. What we reduced or removed was in line with the recommendations of the National Council of Teachers of Mathematics and every other professional organization involved in mathematics education.

▶ What was Reduced

Factoring as a skill, though the book includes a strong development of factoring as a concept; *complicated symbol manipulation,* such as simplifying complex rational and radical expressions.

▶ What was Removed

Simplifying radical expressions containing variables, which at this level requires oversimplifying the problem by assuming all variables to be nonnegative, causing later confusion; *solving inequalities that involve absolute value,* which is too complicated for Algebra 1; *word problems by type,* though the book emphasizes the development of problem-solving strategies needed to solve all kinds of problems.

▶ What was Replaced

Formal proofs, with a drastically increased emphasis on reasoning and mathematical thinking; *FOIL,* with much more powerful and general methods; *long division of polynomials,* with more emphasis on dividing polynomials by a monomial—an area of considerable confusion for students; *standard rules for solving inequalities,* with plenty of practice using nonstandard methods.

WHAT ABOUT GEOMETRY AND ALGEBRA 2?

You may wonder whether this book will adequately prepare your students for geometry and Algebra 2. The answer is that they will be far better prepared. Your students will enter geometry with unusually strong preparation, since the most important and difficult topics in many high school geometry courses (similar figures and the Pythagorean theorem) will have been substantially previewed in this course. In addition, two very important concepts in which geometry students are often found to be insufficiently prepared (square roots and proportions) have been given extra attention.

It is unfortunately true that most students entering Algebra 2 have forgotten much of what they learned in Algebra 1. Because this book provides extended exposure to the important ideas, emphasizes understanding, and stresses a few fundamental concepts, it is likely that the students will retain what they learned much longer. In addition, their preparation will be strengthened by the fact that they will have had early exposure to some of the more challenging ideas of Algebra 2, such as functions.

The above discussion assumes a traditional geometry and Algebra 2 curriculum. But as those courses change to reflect the growing reform movement, your students will be even better prepared. The increased emphasis on open-ended problems, on writing, on mathematical reasoning, on functions, on technology, and so on, that will be transforming the rest of the high school curriculum will already have been part of your students' Algebra 1 background. The increasing emphasis on discrete math will have been foreshadowed by this book's number theory, abstract algebra, and probability lessons. And the increased emphasis on probability and statistics will have been previewed by work on proportions and data analysis.

This book is also designed to strengthen students' preparation for science classes. The emphasis on number sense, interpretation of graphs, scientific notation, proportional thinking, and the use of calculators is substantially greater than in a traditional algebra course.

Finally, this book is not merely preparation for the future. It is designed to provide meaningful and engaging work now. Teachers who used the preliminary versions of the book reported that they had never seen students as engaged and interested in algebra.

How is the Book Organized?

The book is divided into 14 chapters. Most chapters contain 12 numbered lessons. Each lesson concentrates on one or two ideas which are explored in a concentrated way through various types of problems. The types of problems can be classified as:

▶ Explorations

Explorations are often, but not always, at the beginning of a lesson. They are intended to give students a chance to familiarize themselves with a problem, working on their own.

▶ Guided Investigations

Most unlabeled problems in the body of a lesson are parts of guided investigations. They offer a systematic and structured approach to the material.

▶ Generalizations

These problems, which are useful for assessment, allow students to think about what they learned in the previous exercises in a broader context. Sometimes, it may be the transition from specific numerical cases to variables. At other times, it may be the recognition of a pattern or the movement from a specific application to a general rule. In any case, it is a crucial mathematical process, which is to a great extent what algebra is about.

▶ Summaries

These questions ask students to summarize explicitly what they learned and are an excellent assessment tool. Anything they can write about, they must understand. And if they cannot write about it, they can look back at the work they did, get help from their group, or from you. Merely "discovering" something does not guarantee it will be understood or remembered. Writing about it helps assure understanding and retention.

Key Problems

These problems are identified by a red key. They are not summaries or generalizations, but do require a little writing and are crucial to a thorough understanding of the concepts covered. They also provide another tool for assessment.

Reports

These activities are more ambitious writing assignments that can constitute the backbone of student assessment. Each report should be a one- or two-page illustrated essay about an important idea or application.

Challenges

Indicated by a yellow light bulb, these problems are more difficult than other problems. It isn't expected that most students will be able to solve them quickly or by themselves.

Projects and Research

These activities require more initiative from the students. Projects involve some independent mathematical thinking on the part of the students. Research requires them to look for information from the real world, usually numerical information that can be the basis for some applied math.

Thinking/Writing

Following every fourth numbered lesson, there is a shorter lesson labeled *Thinking/Writing A, B,* or *C*. These lessons always end in a report. Their purpose is to apply what was learned in the previous lessons in such a way as to lead students to reflect upon it and develop a deeper understanding.

Below the Line

Most lessons are followed by material that is not part of any particular lesson. The problems in this section are numbered consecutively with the problems in the body of the lesson but, because they focus on a different subject, they are clearly separated from the main lesson by a colorful horizontal bar, hence they are referred to as being *below the line*. This material consists of problems for **review** of past work, **preview** of work to come, as well as **discoveries** (side trips), and **puzzles**.

Essential Ideas

Each chapter ends with a set of problems under this title. The problems were selected to review the ideas students can be expected to have mastered by that point in the course.

Other Features

Core vs. Optional Material

It is likely that there is more material in this book than you can cover in one year. As a way to guide you through it, especially during the first year you use the book, we have indicated what we consider optional, or noncore material, by shading it in light beige. For more on how to sequence the material and what parts you can consider skipping, see the *Course Planning Guide* in the back of this book.

Subsidiary Strands

At the end of most chapters, there are one or two lessons that do not fit the main theme or concept of the chapter. These lessons are in one of three areas: abstract algebra, number theory, and lessons requiring geoboards. The geoboard lessons are a crucial part of the core of the course and have essentially two functions: to help develop proportional reasoning and to lay the groundwork for a geometric approach to square roots and measurement introduced in Chapter 9.

The abstract algebra and number theory lessons are optional, but highly recommended. The number theory lessons are built around challenging problems for which there is no "canned" solution. The abstract algebra lessons provide insights into the common mathematical structure of systems that look very different from each other. Both types of lessons provide a change of pace, and have a fanciful, recreational flavor that makes them appealing to students.

▶ The Teacher's Guide

Each page from the student text is reproduced in its entirety in reduced form in this Teacher's Edition beginning on page 2. Each chapter and lesson is accompanied by notes in the margin surrounding the reduced student pages. These notes provide suggestions on timing, level of difficulty, and clarify the role of the lesson in the big picture of the whole course. At the beginning of the teacher notes for each lesson, core sequence problems are identified, as well as problems suitable for homework. In addition, problems useful for assessment are also indicated.

Solutions to the problems are also provided. If you want to provide your students with answers, you may allow them access to this Teacher's Edition. However, we have found that students comparing answers with each other is a good way to promote cooperation and to quickly identify a source of difficulty.

WHAT ARE THEMES, TOOLS, AND CONCEPTS?

*T*his book is organized around the interaction of **themes**, **tools**, and **concepts**.

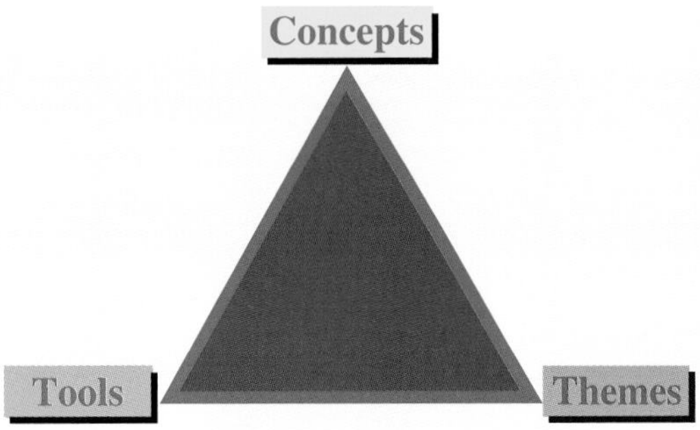

This organizational scheme differs dramatically from the straightforward, topical organization of a traditional algebra textbook. Mathematics is a rich subject, and the interaction of these three components enables the beginning algebra student to get a glimpse of that richness. Using different tools and themes, we can revisit a concept repeatedly, with tools providing the medium for exploration, and themes the motivation. Students' understanding of a concept can deepen gradually as they work with it in new contexts and with a variety of representations.

THEMES

The tools help students learn algebra, but for most of them to want to learn it, algebra must be seen to have a connection with reality. Themes are mathematics-rich contexts, drawn from real-world or fanciful problems, where algebra concepts can be introduced, explored, developed, and reviewed. Well-chosen themes can bring algebra to life, uncover connections to other parts of mathematics, and support the claim that algebra does indeed have applications.

We selected a half-dozen themes: *dimensions*, *measurement*, *making comparisons*, *growth and change*, *optimization*, and *motion*. Some are the focus of one chapter, others appear again and again throughout the book.

▶ Making Connections

In addition to providing a context and motivation for algebraic work, the thematic approach makes it possible to reveal connections with science, culture, and daily life. Most ideas are introduced by starting with a problem outside of mathematics which leads to the realization that it is best solved with the help of algebra. For example, Chapter 3 begins with a get-rich-quick scheme designed to introduce inverse operations. Chapter 6 opens with a comparison of car rental prices which sets the stage for a series of lessons on solving equations and inequalities. In Chapter 7, identities involving squares are introduced through a problem about square windows. In Chapter 8, slope is introduced by analyzing data on children's growth rates, which allows the introduction of the laws of exponents through population growth problems. In Chapter 10, techniques for solving simultaneous equations are developed through a whole series of applications, from organizing a van pool, to making cranberry-apple juice.

Connections are made within algebra through a spiraling curriculum, where important algebraic ideas are tackled again and again. This is in contrast to the topical organization of more traditional textbooks where a topic is addressed only within the confines of its chapter. Thus, connections are made between apparently unrelated topics that turn out to have the same underlying mathematical structure. For example, in some traditional textbooks, almost everything about lines and linear functions is covered in a few sections, usually in a chapter on graphing. In this text, students encounter linear functions and their graphs repeatedly in Chapters 1 through 5.

Connections are made with other parts of mathematics throughout the book, such as exploratory lessons in number theory, with advanced algebra (through work with nonlinear functions and graphs and the graphical solution of equations and inequalities), with probability and data analysis modeling, with calculus, and especially with a full geometry strand.

▶ Integrating the Mathematics Curriculum

Merely juxtaposing traditional lessons in algebra and geometry does not mean a curriculum is integrated. In fact, it could just mean a hodgepodge of unrelated lessons. The interweaving of algebra and geometry in this text is always meaningful. The geometry topics originate in the study of perimeter, area, and volume. These topics are used to develop algebraic generalizations from numerical data, and form the basis of our approach to the distributive law and factoring. Later, they develop into lessons on similarity, which support algebraic work on proportions and slope. A geometric approach to square roots leads to a better understanding of the algebraic rules for the manipulation of radicals. And finally, the work on the Pythagorean theorem is grounded in work on distance in the Cartesian plane.

In this way, the introduction of geometric ideas is not a distraction from the teaching of algebra. In fact, it enhances it. These intimate links between algebra and geometry were at the core of ancient Greek mathematics, but have unfortunately vanished from our algebra classes.

▶ Mathematical Modeling

The final benefit of the thematic approach is that it makes it possible to start from data. Again and again we ask students to analyze data and develop mathematical models with the help of various tools: in-out tables, graphics, function diagrams, and calculators. It is this work with numbers that is the essence of the scientific enterprise, and it is in this kind of work that mathematical patterns emerge both for the professional scientist and for the algebra student.

Because this is an introductory course, we use fairly "well-behaved" data, and some of it is admittedly contrived, to fit the needs of the lessons. But we also include raw, real-world data in many lessons and occasionally encourage you and your students to collect your own data and conduct your own experiments.

Sophisticated statistical techniques are premature at this level, but we do include some work on averages and on fitting the median-median line.

With the exception of a few problems in Chapter 12, we avoid the type of applications in which a formula is supplied and students are simply given a few questions to answer by manipulating symbols. Although these applications may convince them that algebra is useful, they do little to promote students' ability to use it. We concentrate instead on mathematical modeling, in which a situation is presented and students are guided in making a mathematical analysis of it. This has several advantages for students. It immerses them in the mathematics. It involves them in the decisions that need to be made to simplify a real-world situation, in order to make a mathematical model. And it convinces them not only that mathematics is useful, but that they are capable of using it.

▶ Recreational Mathematics

As indicated in the previous paragraphs, we support the moves to make mathematics relevant. However, some reformers are getting carried away with this, and forgetting that *mathematics is worth pursuing not only because it is powerful, but also because it is beautiful and entertaining*. As the world's leading recreational mathematician, Martin Gardner, put it, "...there must be an interplay of seriousness and frivolity. The frivolity keeps the reader alert. The seriousness makes the play worthwhile."

To keep this in mind, we have included many puzzles from recreational mathematics, and many lessons are motivated not by real-world problems, but by mathematical questions that are interesting for their own sake.

Tools

The extensive use of math tools is probably the most distinguishing feature of this book. Our experience with electronic and manipulative tools has shown us that they can be the key to a student-centered classroom. They can help transform any math class into a lab course, where students experiment and make discoveries. They can help students build on their areas of competence, such as visual, electronic, or manipulative talents, and they can help provide an environment where students can improve their communication and reasoning abilities.

▶ Why Tools?

Our interest in the tool-based approach was inspired in part by the ideas of Seymour Papert. In the introduction to his book *Mindstorms,* Papert described how his early fascination with gears gave him an *object-to-think-with* while he was learning mathematics as a child in school. He then explains his belief in the importance of such objects for all children.

What an individual can learn, and how he learns it, depends on what models he has available....The gear can be used to illustrate many powerful "advanced" mathematical ideas, such as groups or relative motion. But it does more than this. As well as connecting with the formal knowledge of mathematics, it also connects with the "body knowledge"...of a child....It is this double relationship—both abstract and sensory—that gives the gear the power to carry powerful mathematics into the mind.

We must ask why some learning takes place so early and spontaneously while some is delayed many years or does not happen at all without...formal instructions....If we really look at the "child as builder" we are on our way to an answer. All builders need materials to build with....In some cases the culture supplies them in abundance, thus facilitating constructive Piagetian learning. But in many cases where Piaget would explain the slower development of a particular concept by its great complexity or formality, I see the critical factor as the relative poverty of the culture in those materials that would make the concept simple and concrete.

Papert's proposals are centered around the computer, but as he illustrates in his story about gears, *objects-to-think-with* need not be electronic. Our definition of tools for learning mathematics includes manipulative and paper-and-pencil tools, as well as electronic ones. All of them are *objects-to-discuss* and *objects-to-write-about*, as well as *objects-to-think-with.* Using a wide variety of tools makes algebra accessible to students with a wide variety of learning styles.

▶ Which Tools?

In order to give students a wide range of algebraic experiences, we use eleven different tools. Some of them are familiar to all math teachers, others may be new to you. Some tools are used throughout the course, others only in a few lessons. In all cases, we have found the tools to be helpful in getting students involved in, and thinking about, the major concepts of algebra.

The tools can be roughly divided into three main groups: **manipulatives** (geoboards, the Lab Gear, *radical gear)*, **pencil-and-paper tools** (grid paper, dot paper, Cartesian graphing, function diagrams, tables of values, symbol manipulation), and **electronic tools** (calculators, and, optionally, graphing calculators). A calculator, ruler, and paper and pencil are assumed to be available at all times. If manipulatives, special paper, or a graphing calculator are needed for a lesson, it is noted at the beginning.

▶ How Are Tools Used?

■ Cartesian Graphing

The Cartesian graph has had an enormous influence on how we teach, and even how we understand, mathematics. (For example, think about the use of the word *slope* to describe the rate of change of a function.) Most of us recognize it as a profound and powerful tool for visualizing algebra.

In the traditional Algebra 1 course, however, graphing is usually taught as an end in itself, just another topic to be studied briefly before moving on to something else. In this course, Cartesian graphing is introduced at the very beginning and used as a tool to analyze and visualize almost every important concept in the course, from operations with signed numbers to the quadratic formula.

Early in the course, lessons are designed to give students a thorough understanding of the relationship between three representations of functions: equation, graph, and number pairs. Throughout the book, we emphasize the application of graphing in an applied setting, giving students plenty of practice choosing appropriate scales for the axes and working with different units of measurement.

■ Graphing Calculators and Computers

The advent of graphing calculators and graphing software has made it possible to revolutionize the teaching of functions. The ability to graph any function rapidly and accurately in any domain where it is defined, and the increasing availability of the tools to do it, means that traditional paper-and-pencil graphing, as a skill, no longer deserves the central place it once occupied in our curriculum.

We are enthusiastic proponents of electronic graphing and have been involved in it for many years. In fact, a Logo grapher programmed by one of us (part of *Logo Math: Tools and Games,* published by Terrapin, Inc.) was used to generate many of the graphs for this book. Having been intimately involved with this new technology for several years has given us a good sense of both its strengths and limitations.

This book contains a number of lessons which would be enhanced by the use of graphing calculators. However, since many teachers still do not have access to them, we have designed the book so that it does not require their use.

While graphing by hand is no longer an essential skill, it can be a crucial step in the learning process If it is accompanied by discussion and reflection, paper-pencil graphing can help reveal fundamental ideas, such as the relationship between the fact that a number pair satisfies an equation, and that the point that represents it is on the graph of the function. Using a graphing calculator well involves making some judicious choices about when and where to introduce it.

■ Other Function Tools

Function Diagrams: One thing that makes Cartesian graphs powerful, but also difficult for beginners to understand, is the fact that the two axes are perpendicular. Function diagrams are another representation of functions which is based on parallel x- and y-number lines. Function diagrams complement Cartesian graphing by emphasizing different features of functions. For example, domain and range, the definition of function, inverse function, and rate of change, are easier to understand with the help of this tool than with Cartesian graphs. In fact, function diagrams make it possible to talk about many features of functions that were previously postponed until Algebra 2 or pre-calculus.

In-Out Tables: The function diagram is actually a graphic representation of a table of x- and y-values. The table of values is an essential tool from the toolbox of the traditional algebra course. It requires no special equipment. It helps students learn how to detect patterns in numerical data. A strong understanding of functions is impossible without facility in using this representation.

■ The Lab Gear®

The tools we have discussed thus far offer different representations of the concept of function. However, algebra is far more than the study of functions, and the beginning algebra student also needs tools for understanding the crucial concepts of variables, operations, equations, and inequalities. The Lab Gear is a powerful tool for studying these ideas, providing a comprehensive algebra manipulative environment.

The Lab Gear has been designed to be used for learning and understanding the distributive law, factoring, equation solving, completing the square, and many other topics of beginning algebra. Most importantly, it helps improve the discourse about symbols, by providing something concrete to manipulate and talk about. As with any of the tools, you will need to learn it yourself before trying to teach with it.

Because algebra is an extension of arithmetic, the Lab Gear has been designed as an extension of the most successful and effective manipulative used to teach arithmetic—Base Ten Blocks. The Lab Gear is completely compatible with Base Ten Blocks—in fact, the two can be used in conjunction with each other to teach algebra, arithmetic, or both. The inclusion of blue blocks to represent variables allows the Lab Gear to be used at a higher level of abstraction. The sizes of the x-blocks and y-blocks were carefully chosen to prevent the confusion that arises when a block such as the Base Ten rod, having whole number dimensions, is used to represent a variable.

The Lab Gear is an extension of the development of algebra manipulatives that has taken place over many years. Zoltan Dienes, who was an early promoter of Base Ten Blocks, was the first to see their potential as a manipulative for algebra. Mary Laycock extended his ideas in work with multi-base blocks and popularized the "upstairs" representation of minus. Peter Rasmussen came up with the important idea of an x-block that is not a multiple of 1 and with the precursor of the corner piece.

The Lab Gear incorporates the best of its predecessors' designs, but it goes further, by including features that have advantages over other algebra manipulatives:

The corner piece: Helps organize the rectangle model of multiplication and division in two or three dimensions.

The workmat: Provides an environment used for equation solving and for operations with signed numbers.

A powerful combination of **two methods to represent minus** (the minus area on the workmat, and "upstairs"). This model is mathematically superior to the two-color model (see the section *Computing With Signed Numbers* on pages 579–591).

The use of **two variables** (x and y) adds flexibility and makes it possible to work with problems involving two variables, including the solution of simultaneous equations.

The use of **three-dimensional blocks** rather than tiles, which makes it possible to represent quantities such as x^2y and y^3 and to show the product of three factors.

All of these unique features work together to create a unified concrete environment in which to learn many concepts of algebra.

■ Grid Tools

This book often uses geometric topics as a source of data for algebraic generalizations. Much of this work is done with the help of three grid tools:

Graph paper: An important use of graph paper is as an environment in which to study perimeter and area, topics that lend themselves to interesting algebraic questions. Of course, graph paper also serves as a background for Cartesian graphing, and it can be used to construct function diagrams.

Geoboards: These tools provide another environment in which we study area. By including approximately one geoboard lesson in each of the first nine chapters, we gradually build the necessary background for a geometric introduction to proportion and slope, the concept of square root, and justification for the rules used in manipulating radicals.

Dot paper: While geoboards are initially very popular, students gradually realize that the same work can be pursued very well on dot paper, with less trouble and more accuracy. Moreover, dot paper can be cut to create *radical gear,* a manipulative for learning about the manipulation of radicals in Chapter 9.

■ Calculators

Calculators, computers, and other computational devices are everywhere. In all contemporary institutions, with the unfortunate exception of some schools, electronic methods are replacing paper-and-pencil computation.

■ Algebraic Symbols

The last tool we will discuss is the use of algebraic symbols. The manipulation of symbols used to be the nearly exclusive subject of the beginning algebra course. In this book, algebraic symbols still have an important place, but the emphasis is on the ideas they embody. Key structural rules, such as the distributive law and the laws of exponents, are important to understand, not only because of their importance in the manipulation of symbols, but also because they offer insights into the meaning of the operations.

We do not expect students to be able to understand algebraic symbols spontaneously. For most students, it takes a lot of work to get to the point of being able to use algebraic notation well. The work is essentially the process of abstracting structure from numerical data. This movement from the specific to the general is one of the essential activities of mathematics and science. Symbol sense is not assumed at the beginning of the course, but developing it is one of our main goals.

Concepts

While symbol manipulation is a useful tool, accurate and/or speedy manipulation is no longer defensible as a central goal of the new algebra. Instead, the goal should be understanding of concepts. Tools and themes are the means, not the end. Their purpose is to help create a course where students can learn algebra concepts such as functions, numbers, variables, operations, equations, and more generally, mathematical structure.

As for mathematical terminology and notation, we have tried to navigate a middle course; too much jargon is intimidating and premature, but some ideas cannot be expressed precisely without using correct mathematical language.

The following is an overview of some of the major concepts in the book.

▶ Number Sense

To understand symbols, one must understand numbers. As a result, this book includes quite a lot of work with numbers, but the work is spread out through the year, and is geared to problem solving and real-world applications, not arithmetic algorithms. For example, we review percent in an interesting applied context, connecting it with the use of exponents, and we use graphs to throw light on the arithmetic of signed numbers.

The main extensions of students' number sense beyond the material they are likely to have seen before is in the work with scientific notation, and the work with square roots. We give these topics plenty of attention.

If some students have difficulties with basic arithmetic, help them use their calculators to solve problems. For example, you will be very popular if you teach students how to use the fractions-processing capabilities of their calculators. Many problems, interspersed throughout the book, directly address students' misconceptions about numbers. For example, their lack of clarity about multiplication and division by numbers between -1 and 1.

Avoid dwelling on arithmetic algorithms, such as signed number and fraction arithmetic, at the beginning of the school year. By the time students take algebra, most are happy to be done with their study of arithmetic, either because they already understand it, or because they have never understood it and see no reason to expect that they will. When discussing real-world problems, treat the necessary review of fractions, decimals, and percent with a light touch. Put the main emphasis on the algebraic structure of the problem and on discussion of the reasonableness of the numerical results. (If, however, you work on the rules of signed number arithmetic, you can use the reproducible Lab Gear-based lessons in the back of this book.)

▶ Function Sense

The concept of function is addressed throughout the book, not just in one lesson or chapter. We approach functions in many ways, through real-world applications, graphs, in-out tables, and function diagrams. Proficiency in using several representations of function and the ability to move from one representation to another are the foundation of a solid understanding.

We introduce composition of functions, inverse functions, and transformations of graphs, concepts that are usually postponed until Algebra 2 or pre-calculus. Because our approach is supported by effective tools, we have found these subjects to be well within the grasp of Algebra 1 students at an exploratory level.

Providing a strong foundation in functions and making these more advanced concepts understandable has a worthwhile pay-off: we use them to create a conceptual approach to many Algebra 1 topics that have been traditionally taught through the learning of rules. We use functions and their graphs to help students understand operations with signed numbers, equation solving, inequalities, the laws of exponents, square roots, and many other topics.

▶ Equation Solving and Inequalities

Traditional algebra courses often introduce the solving of linear equations too early in the semester. This forces students who have no sense of what variables are, much less equations, to memorize algorithms that have no meaning to them. Our approach is to spread the introduction of linear equations over the entire first semester, or even longer, in the case of a two-year course.

Instead of a standard procedure, we introduce a multiplicity of techniques.

Trial and error (also known by many teachers as guess and check): First and foremost, because it throws the most light on the meaning of the question, and empowers the students to seek the solution on their own.

The cover-up method: Mostly useful to highlight the concept of inverse operations.

Through graphing: This is particularly useful with the help of electronic calculators, and has the advantage of being useful for solving any equation whatsoever, even one like $x^3 + 2^x - 3/x = 456$.

With the Lab Gear®: This is strictly a transitional environment, intended to provide an opportunity for students to create their equation-solving techniques and rules.

By applying rules of algebra: This is the closest to the traditional technique, though we never impose a particular sequence, leaving it up to students to develop their own strategies.

As for inequalities, we do some work with them, but limit ourselves to trial and error, graphing, and Lab Gear approaches. We believe that it is counter-productive to teach rules for solving inequalities in Algebra 1, since students almost always remember them incorrectly. Instead, we provide several possible approaches and, in optional exercises, hint at some rules that students might develop for themselves.

▶ Proportional Thinking

The absence of experience using proportional thinking in traditional algebra courses means that students studying similar triangles in geometry, and later applying what they learned in trigonometry, are under-prepared. Similarly, students in science classes, where proportional thinking is essential, need solid grounding in the mathematics of proportions. We address this need by using geometric and real-world contexts in lessons that are spread throughout the book. Direct variation is emphasized early in the book, and approached from several different angles. We also cover unit conversion from a mathematical standpoint, a topic that is usually relegated to science classes. We contrast comparing by ratio to comparing by difference, an idea which is important in many applications, but usually overlooked in algebra courses.

▶ Mathematical Structure

By this we refer primarily to an understanding of the algebraic structures underlying the real number system, meaning especially an understanding of the operations and their relationships to each other. This includes the distributive law, the laws of exponents, and the rules for operations with radicals. We avoid the overly abstract approach of the *new math,* and instead, concentrate on developing students' understanding through examples and models.

We also put this understanding in a broader context through some optional lessons on abstract algebra (via specific examples well within students' reach) and the relationship between different types of numbers (real, rational, irrational, integers, natural) and different types of equations.

▶ Symbol Sense

We emphasize some of the topics about symbols that were not taught effectively in the traditional course such as the gradual process of replacing numbers with variables when thinking of a real-world problem, and the meaning of parameters, especially in certain basic forms such as $y = kx$, $xy = k$, $x + y = k$, $y = mx + b$.

As students' understanding of algebraic concepts deepens, they are gaining symbol sense—an appreciation for the power of symbolic thinking, an understanding of when and how to apply it, and a feel for mathematical structure. Symbol sense is a level of mathematical literacy beyond number sense, which it subsumes. It is the true prerequisite for further work in math and science, and the real purpose of the new algebra course. As the NCTM puts it, Algebra is the language through which most of mathematics is communicated. It also provides a means of operating with concepts at an abstract level, and then applying them, a process that often fosters generalizations and insights beyond the original context.

Achieving Mathematical Power

Tools and themes create an environment in which students are empowered and motivated, when problem solving, discovery, and cooperative learning can thrive, and where skills can develop naturally and in context. Our goal is to help students develop the mathematical skills necessary for future math courses as well as for the world of work.

▶ How Tools Help

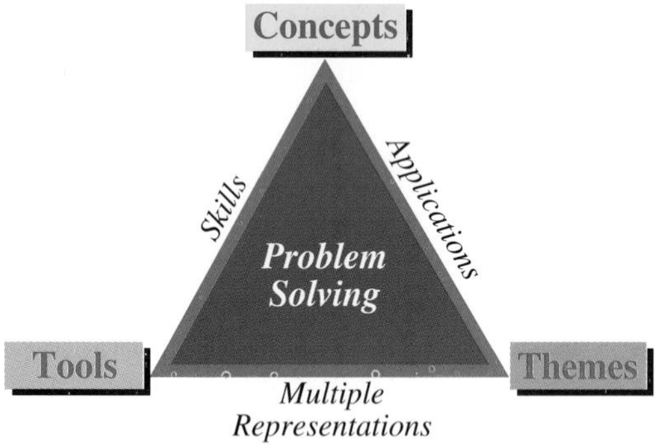

The multi-tool approach has four advantages over more traditional methods.

Access: By providing immediate feedback, these tools make it possible for all students to get involved with significant mathematical concepts. This is not to say that tools make algebra easy. Algebra is abstract and difficult for most students. It takes persistent effort to develop mastery. But tools do make algebra accessible to all who are willing to work at it.

Discourse: The tools also facilitate the transition from a traditional class format into one where discovery learning, problem solving, and cooperative work are the norm. Instead of the teacher's authority being the sole arbiter of correctness, tools make it possible for students to use reasoning and discussion about a concrete reference as a way to judge the validity of mathematical statements.

Independence: As students work with tools over time and develop more and more understanding of the concepts of algebra, they have less and less need of certain tools (such as manipulatives or function diagrams), which have merely served as a bridge to understanding abstract ideas. On the other hand, they become more sophisticated users of other tools (such as calculators and electronic graphing devices), which will remain useful throughout their mathematical careers. In both cases, the students are more self-reliant, and therefore, more self-confident.

Multiple Representations: There is a synergy in the interaction of math tools. For example, a student who has thought about square roots in a multidimensional way, with the help of geoboards, dot paper, radical gear, calculators, and graphing calculators, has much more depth of understanding, particularly if the relationships among the representations have been made explicit, than a student who has practiced only disembodied operations with radicals.

In a multi-tool environment, students will develop specialties. Some will be Lab Gear experts, while others will be most comfortable with the use of calculators or function diagrams. This is normal, and cooperative learning allows all students to benefit from each other's strengths.

Finally, this book does not depend on any one tool. If at first you are uncomfortable with function diagrams, or with the Lab Gear, you should de-emphasize those lessons until you have become better acquainted with the tool. Of course, you will get the most out of this book if you take some time to familiarize yourself with all the tools.

▶ Algebra as a Web

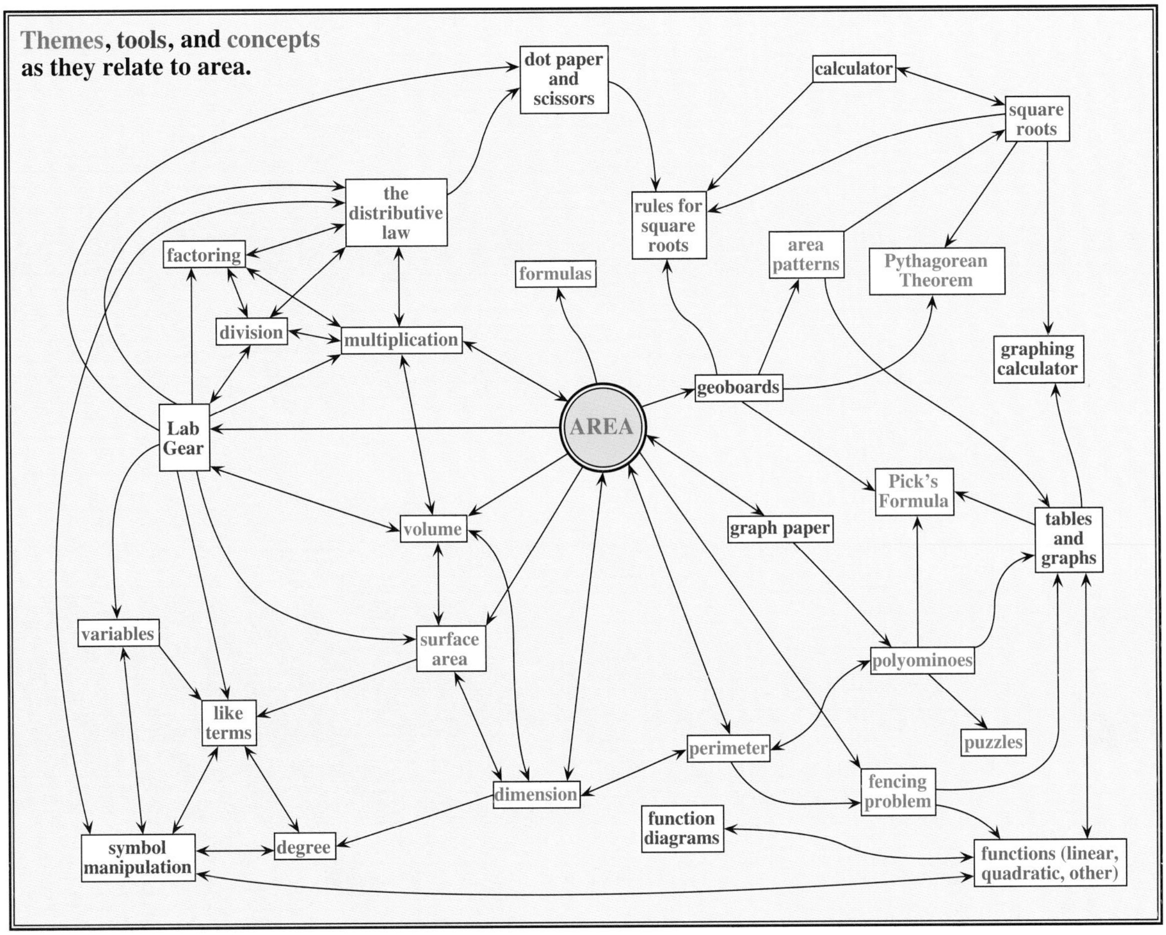

Themes, tools, and **concepts** are interwoven in a complex web. This map was constructed by starting from area, a sub-theme of measurement, then showing the connections between algebra topics, between algebra and geometry, and between algebra and the real world. The map does not include the whole book, but it does reveal how our approach goes about making these connections. In the traditional curriculum, which assumes an arbitrary sequence within algebra, these connections are masked, and the geometric connections aren't made at all.

Contrast it with the corresponding map for the traditional course shown here.

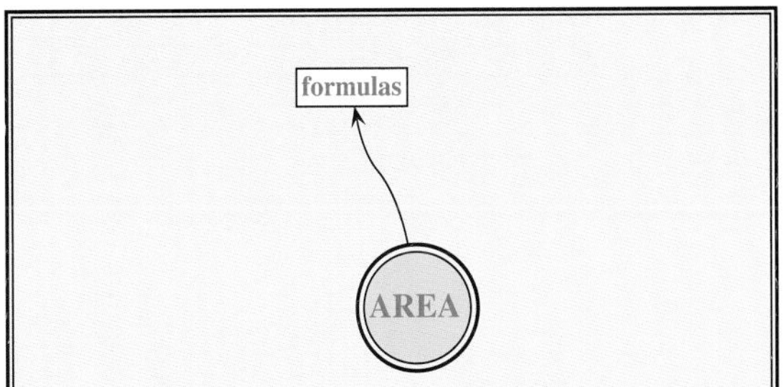

Area in the Traditional Algebra Course

CONCLUSION

*T*he traditional algebra course we used to teach suffered from five main shortcomings.

One-dimensionality: The course's overwhelming emphasis on the manipulation of symbols was too abstract for many students; for others, it was boring. Lacking a concrete context for communication, classes became divided into two groups: those who "got it" and those who didn't.

Authoritarianism: All knowledge came from the teacher. The goal was to manipulate symbols, and the teacher was the sole source of information about how to manipulate them correctly. Students depended upon memorizing algorithms, and since that is a task better suited to computers than to humans, they often forgot, and found themselves helpless.

Apparent pointlessness: The work seemed completely unrelated to situations students might realistically encounter outside the classroom, or even in other branches of mathematics or science.

Skills/enrichment dichotomy: Problem solving was relegated to the role of enrichment and divorced from the main purpose of the course, which was the acquisition of narrow skills through repetitive drill.

Topical organization: Topics were taught in self-contained chapters. Students had insufficient time to absorb one new idea before going on to the next. Even word problems were usually constructed to test a single skill, rather than to draw on and to exercise the students' entire reservoir of mathematical knowledge.

These shortcomings were both curricular and pedagogical. They could not be addressed by piecemeal change—we needed a revolution.

▶ Strategies for Change

As you embark on the process of making changes, you may run into resistance from many quarters. Students may feel that the course involves too much work, and particularly, too much writing. Some even complain it requires too much thinking. Parents may worry because the course is different from the one they took. More significantly, students, parents, and colleagues may be concerned about whether students will be prepared for the next course, which may be quite traditional. Some may feel anxiety about the suitability of the course for strong (or weak) students.

We have tried to respond to these concerns in this introduction. In these closing comments, we will make a few suggestions about strategy.

Start with the changes in pedagogy and be more gradual about making changes in content. As students become more involved in their own learning, and the results are obvious to all, and as national, state, and local requirements change, it will become easier to implement content changes.

Make sure your stronger students are challenged. They, and their parents, are among your most important allies in the process of change.

If you have trouble with certain lessons or types of lessons, de-emphasize them, and fall back on more familiar material.

Work closely with other teachers who agree with you about the need for change. In particular, try to find other teachers who use this book, and help each other out.

As your students become more skillful at writing, have them polish reports and projects and display them on bulletin boards. Publish outstanding write-ups on real-world problems in school or PTA newsletters.

▶ The Rewards

Making change is difficult, but rewarding. Here are some statements from teachers who used preliminary versions of this book.

This book is so rich, there is so much to do, you cannot do it from A to Z. You start investigating something that seems trivial, that all students can get into, and soon you are challenging your top students.

It's so concrete, it's a whole new way of doing algebra. When someone makes a statement, you can say, "Show me."

The only problem I have with class control is that everyone wants to participate.

Students get so involved in a problem that they won't want to leave at the end of the period. That used to happen in art class, not math class.

The book supports discovery. It takes the teacher away from being the center of attention. I feel less pressure; I'm just another participant in the learning environment. I can step back and be more aware of what's going on and where the kids are, so I can be more helpful.

This book meets students where they are and brings them along from there. They develop so much confidence. We ask them to do things they've never done before, but since they're used to that, they just plunge in confidently.

A lot of problems don't have just one answer. I like that. It means that a lot of students can get into it and feel as if they're doing something right. The book supports conjecturing. Kids are not so attached to having the one "right" answer.

Using the Lab Gear helps us appeal to all kinds of students. Several students told me, "If it weren't for this, I'd never understand algebra." Some of them even bought their own set of Lab Gear to use at home. A few resisted the Lab Gear, but then we'd find some of those same students going to get it during a test! It really helped when we set up the classroom as a lab, so that the tools were always accessible for those who needed them.

The hardest thing about using this book was getting used to writing and explaining. So often at first when the book said, "Explain," students would ask, "What does this mean? What do they want?" I had to really think about how to answer them and I realized that it helped me understand, too! I like all the writing. Writing is hard for me, but when I write about something, it helps me internalize the ideas and really understand them. It does the same for the students.

It took us a while to learn how to incorporate writing, but it was well worth the time and effort. Our students had to get used to writing and to our standards for good writing, but once they got the idea they were so proud of their work. We learned to be careful not to assign too much, and to give them enough time to work on it so that they could do high quality work. They put a lot of effort into their Thinking/Writing assignments. After a while, those assignments generated a lot of enthusiasm.

Dear Parent,

This book is different from the book you used if you took algebra. It certainly is different from the books we used. We have taught from many algebra textbooks over the years, and are well acquainted with the traditional algebra course. The course had many problems: there were many Ds and Fs, and even students who got good grades often did not really understand what they were doing. In addition, the development of calculator and computer technology has made it imperative to change the emphasis of the course. Moreover, as a profession, math teachers now have a better understanding of how students learn.

This book is based on three big ideas, which have been guiding principles in our teaching:

- In order to learn to reason flexibly and independently about the abstract concepts of algebra, students need tools to think with. These tools should be designed to support students' work with the main ideas of algebra: variables, operations, equations, functions, and so on. We use manipulative, electronic, and old-fashioned pencil-and-paper tools.

- Learning mathematics should be based on solving interesting problems. Students' skills develop best if they are given an interesting context to practice them in. Look through the book at the wide variety of problems we address: air travel, get-rich-quick schemes, telephone billing plans, children's growth rates, making cranberry-apple juice, car and bicycle trips, and on and on.

- Most students will not remember concepts if they are explained once or twice by a teacher and practiced in isolation over a short period of time. Students must be involved in their own learning, and have experience with ideas in many forms and formats over an extended period of time. They must experiment, conjecture, discover, and write about what they are thinking. In this book, important ideas are returned to over and over, and much work is expected of the student — hard work, but work that is more varied and interesting than the traditional drill and practice.

After using this book, your child will be exceptionally well prepared for future courses, because we have made a point of giving extra emphasis to the areas that are most important to the rest of secondary school math and science: square roots, proportions, scientific notation, functions, and symbol sense. In addition, the emphasis on thinking, communication, and writing skill will help across the whole curriculum.

If you have any questions about this course, we are sure your student's teacher will be glad to help answer them. The biggest help you can provide is to make sure that your student does algebra homework every day.

Sincerely,

Anita Wah and Henri Picciotto

Dear Student,

In arithmetic you have learned to work with numbers. Algebra is an extension of arithmetic, where you learn to work with symbols. It is the language of all of mathematics and science, and a tool for solving problems in business and engineering.

In the future more and more algebra will be done by computer. But what good would it do you to have a computer ready to do the algebra for you if you didn't understand what algebra is? It would be as useful as a calculator to someone who didn't know the meaning of numbers.

Algebra is difficult to learn, but it is the key to so many possibilities in your life that it is worth the effort. You cannot learn algebra just by listening to your teacher. You need to be much more involved: do your homework every day, read the book carefully, and if necessary, get help from your teacher. Good work habits are essential if you want to succeed in this class.

Most importantly, be ready to discuss difficult problems with your classmates, sometimes to help them, and sometimes to get help from them. Talking is the best way to sort out what you understand from what you don't understand, and explaining is the best way to improve your understanding. While learning math and problem solving, you will also be improving your ability to communicate with other people.

You may be surprised at how much writing will be expected from you. Almost every lesson requires you to explain something, and you will have to write reports on a regular basis. This is difficult at first, but it will help you in the long run, by making you not only a better mathematician, but also a better thinker, and a better writer.

Good work habits, communicating, thinking, and writing will help you no matter what you do in the future. But of course, as math teachers, we would like you to stick with it, and take many more math classes. To convince you of this, we have tried to write a book that you will find interesting and that puts you, the student, in the center of the action.

Sincerely,

Anita Wah and Henri Picciotto

CONTENTS

Chapter 1
Perimeter and Area Patterns

Overview of the Chapter

Theme: The theme of this chapter is *perimeter and area patterns*. This unorthodox opener makes it possible to achieve an enormous amount of interesting work right away.

1. **Introduction of New Tools:**

   These will be used throughout the course, so it is important to get familiar with them.
   - The Lab Gear
   - Graphing
   - Geoboards

2. **Algebra Concepts Emphasized:**

   Students will *begin* to have some mastery of these by the end of this chapter. Nevertheless, they will be reviewed abundantly in future chapters.
   - Variables and constants
   - Substitution and evaluation
   - Combining like terms
   - Degree
   - Operations: addition and multiplication
   - Polynomials
   - The area/volume model for multiplication
   - Order of operations

3. **Algebra Concepts Previewed:**

   These concepts will be just touched on, to prepare students for a more in-depth approach later.
   - Signed numbers
   - Equations and identities
   - Cartesian coordinates
   - Perfect squares
   - The distributive law
   - Factoring
   - Inferring a function from data
   - Linear functions
   - The function $y = x^2$

4. **Problem-Solving Techniques:**

   These techniques are emphasized, but others will no doubt come into play.
   - Organized searches
   - Trial and error
   - Looking for patterns
   - Using tables

CHAPTER 1

The spiral shape of a ram's horn

Coming in this chapter:

Exploration If you draw a closed shape by following the lines on graph paper, you can find its area and perimeter by counting. For a given area, what perimeters are possible?

PERIMETER AND AREA PATTERNS

5. **Connections and Context:**

   These concepts are not central to the algebra curriculum. In some cases they come from other parts of mathematics, and in other cases they come from more advanced algebra courses. They are here because they help motivate and apply the Algebra 1 concepts listed above.

   - Polyominoes, polycubes
   - Dimension
   - Optimization
   - Area, perimeter
   - Volume, surface area
   - Triangular numbers
   - Fibonacci numbers

As this list makes clear, there is a lot going on in this first chapter. It is the jumping-off point for the whole course, and it must get students involved with algebra.

Involved: They will see that this is not a spectator sport. They will build up their understanding through their own struggles and discoveries.

With Algebra: They will immediately get involved with variables and problem solving. It is terribly costly to student morale to start the course with arithmetic review.

Because much of the work in the chapter comes from the very concrete departure point of area and perimeter, students tend to accept the legitimacy of pursuing it. A few real-world applications help give the chapter some relevance even beyond that.

Minus

Note that we hold off on the introduction of minus until Chapter 2. Too many mistakes are associated with this, especially early on, and we want students to get a solid start before tackling it.

▼ 1.1
Polyominoes

Core Sequence: 1-11, 13-14

Suitable for Homework: 7-12, 15-16

What this Lesson is About:

- First experience with area and perimeter, which will be used throughout the course as a place to discover and apply algebraic ideas
- Introduction to the idea of dimensions, which is important for understanding how the Lab Gear is used as a concrete representation of abstract ideas

*T*his lesson is drawn from the world of recreational mathematics.

Background: Though the first pentomino puzzle was published in 1907, polyominoes were rediscovered and named by mathematician Solomon W. Golomb at Harvard University in 1953. Since then polyominoes have become one of the most popular branches of recreational mathematics. Mathematicians have created and solved hundreds of polyomino problems. They have proved others to be insoluble. (This branch of math is called *combinatorial geometry*.) Computer programmers have used computers to solve some of the tougher puzzles. Commercial manufacturers have marketed variations of polyomino games, including very popular video games (*Tetris* and its variations). Teachers at all levels have found polyominoes a valuable addition to their curriculum.

*I*n this book, polyominoes and related topics will be used to introduce a number of algebra concepts. In this chapter they provide a substantial problem to work on, a first look at perimeter and area, a first introduction to optimization problems, and a first experience with graphing. In future chapters they will be used to discuss similarity and proportion.

DISCOVERING POLYOMINOES

*T*hese activities work well in a cooperative-learning setup, where students can compare their answers and help each other. (See **Cooperative Learning** in this Teacher's Guide.)

LESSON 1.1

Polyominoes

You will need: graph paper

Definition: *Polyominoes* are shapes that are made by joining squares edge-to-edge. The best known example is the *domino.*

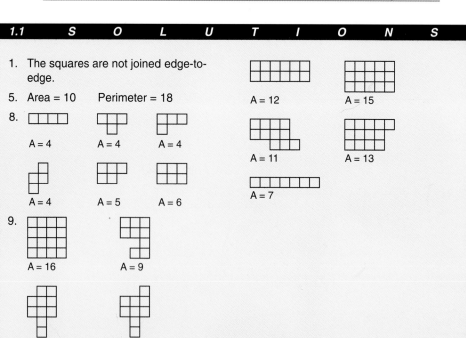

Using three squares, you can find two different *trominoes*, the straight one and the bent one.

There are only two trominoes. The bent one is shown in different positions.

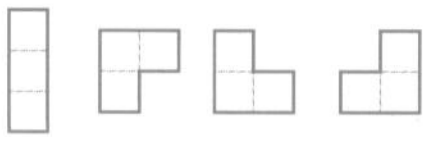

The following shapes are *not* polyominoes.

1. What part of the definition do they violate?

DISCOVERING POLYOMINOES

2. *Tetrominoes* are made up of four squares. There are five different tetrominoes. Find all of them.
3. Guess how many squares make up a *pentomino*. Find all twelve pentominoes. Make sure you do not "find" the same one more than once!
4. Find as many *hexominoes* as you can.

AREA AND PERIMETER

Large polyominoes may have holes in them, as in this 11-omino (i.e. polyomino of area 11).

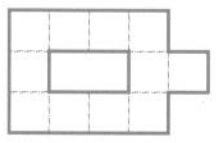

In this book, we will not discuss polyominoes with holes.

Definitions: The *area* of a two-dimensional figure is the number of unit squares it would take to cover it. The *perimeter* of a figure is the distance around it.

For example, the area of the domino is 2, and its perimeter is 6.

In this book, area and perimeter will provide you with many opportunities to discover and apply algebra concepts.

5. Here is a 10-omino. What is its area? What is its perimeter?

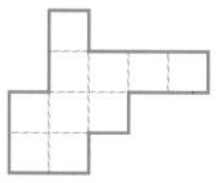

6. Draw some 10-ominoes, and find the perimeter of each one. It would take too long to find all of the 10-ominoes, but try to find every possible 10-omino perimeter.
7. Repeat problem 6 for 16-ominoes.
8. Draw as many polyominoes as you can having 10 units of perimeter, and find the area of each one.
9. Find some polyominoes having perimeter 16. It would take too long to find all of them, but try to find every possible area.

1.1 SOLUTIONS

1. The squares are not joined edge-to-edge.
5. Area = 10 Perimeter = 18
8.

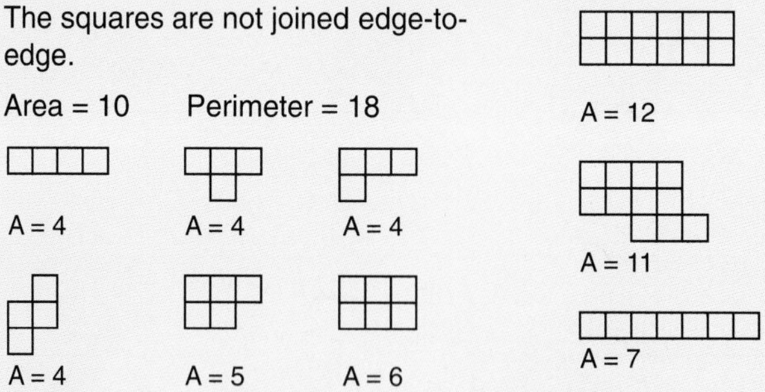

9.

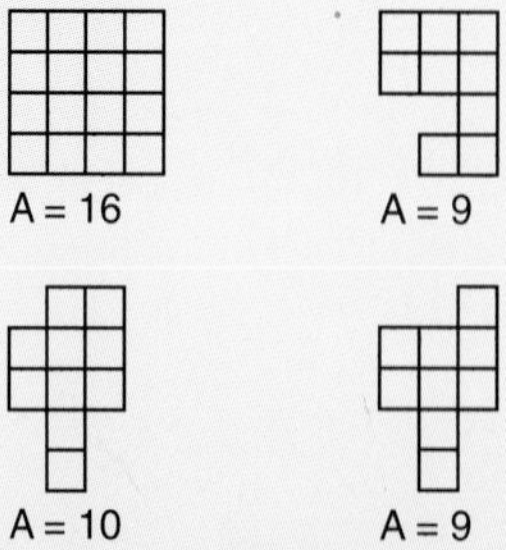

10. **Summary** Describe any patterns you noticed when working on this lesson.

11. Have you found any polyominoes having an odd-number perimeter? If you have, check your work. If you haven't, explain why.

Area and perimeter of polyominoes are related. It is not a simple relationship: for a given area, there may be more than one perimeter possible. For a given perimeter, there may be more than one area.

12. **Project** The words *polyomino, tetromino, pentomino, hexomino* all end the same way, but they start with different prefixes.
   a. Find other words (not just from mathematics) that start with the prefixes *poly-, tetr-, pent-,* and *hex-*. Tell the meaning of each word.
   b. What are the prefixes for 7, 8, 9, and 10? Find words that begin with those prefixes. Tell the meaning of each word.
   c. Write a story using as many of the words you found as possible.

PREVIEW *DIMENSIONS*

- The following are one-dimensional: a line, the boundary of a soccer field.
- The following are two-dimensional: the surface of a lake, the paper wrapped around a present.
- The following are three-dimensional: an apple, a person.

An object like a sheet, while it does have some thickness and therefore is three-dimensional, can be thought of as a model of a two-dimensional surface with no thickness. Similarly, a wire or even a pencil can be thought of as a model of a one-dimensional line.

13. Divide the following into three groups: one-, two-, or three-dimensional.
   a. a book
   b. a lake
   c. a map
   d. a piece of paper
   e. a piece of string
   f. an algebra student
   g. Mickey Mouse
   h. the boundary of a county
   i. the water in a glass
   j. the paint on a house

14. Name three objects of each kind.
   a. one-dimensional
   b. two-dimensional
   c. three-dimensional

Getting comfortable with the concept of dimension will help you with some of the algebra concepts that you will study later in this course.

15. Draw a picture that incorporates several of your objects of different dimensions.

16. Write a short paragraph explaining what 3-D glasses are used for.

1.1 SOLUTIONS

10. Answers will vary. Here are some examples:

    All perimeters are even numbers. For a given number of squares, the largest perimeter occurs when the squares are arranged like a train; the smallest perimeter occurs when the squares are arranged into a large square or rectangle with odd pieces on one side.

11. No. There are no polyominoes with an odd perimeter. For every polyomino, each edge has an opposite edge and there are no unmatched edges, so the perimeters are always even.

12. Answers will vary.

    The prefixes for 7, 8, 9, and 10 are hept-, oct-, nona-, and deca-, respectively.

13. 1-D: e, h
    2-D: c, d, j
    3-D: a, b, f, g, i

14. Answers will vary.

15. Answers will vary.

16. Answers will vary.

It is possible to discover polyominoes using graph paper, but your students will have an easier time if you supply them with square tiles or cubes to experiment with. The Lab Gear 1-blocks or x^2-blocks can be used. However, even if the shapes are found with manipulatives, students need to keep a record on graph paper.

If your students use cubes, make sure to limit their search to two-dimensional figures. (Every cube must touch the table.) The search will be expanded into three dimensions in Lesson 10.

If you have access to interlocking cubes, use them. They are particularly convenient because, once a shape is found, it can be rotated and flipped over, which makes it easier to recognize duplicates. Note that it is *tromino* not the more euphonious *triomino*, because the latter is copyrighted as the name of a triangular domino.

AREA AND PERIMETER

Area and perimeter will be used throughout the book to motivate, discover, illustrate, or apply algebraic concepts. The work in this lesson serves as a reminder of the meaning of those two words.

Project The prefixes *poly-*, *di-*, *tri-*, *tetr-*, *pent-*, *hex-*, *hept-*, *oct-*, *non-*, and *dec-* will come up again when your students study geometry.

Some students may object to vocabulary-building and creative writing in a math class. Insist that this is as important as any other exercise. Remember that for some students this may be the most comfortable area.

PREVIEW *DIMENSIONS*

This topic is new for Algebra 1. It is an important strand in this chapter, where it helps students grasp the concept of degree, and it lays the groundwork for understanding the difference between linear and quadratic functions later in the course. Moreover, it comes up naturally when working with the Lab Gear manipulatives.

▼ 1.2
Perimeter of Polyominoes

Core Sequence: 1-22

Suitable for Homework: 21-22

What this Lesson is About:

- Looking for patterns, using tables, using graphs
- Dimensions, units, and measurement

SHORTEST AND LONGEST PERIMETER

At first this seems to be a big project, but a pattern quickly emerges for the longest perimeters. The shortest perimeters are more difficult to understand, but they usually generate a great deal of curiosity.

MAKING PREDICTIONS

These exercises are the students' opportunity to articulate the patterns they discovered while making the table. Insist on full explanations in numbers 4 and 6. Do not stress spelling and punctuation here. When working through a lesson, writing is used as a help to thinking, and students should be uninhibited about putting ideas on paper. (See **Writing** on page 541.)

LESSON 1.2

Perimeter of Polyominoes

You will need: graph paper

SHORTEST AND LONGEST PERIMETER

For polyominoes with a given area, there may be more than one perimeter. In this section, you will try to find the shortest and the longest perimeter for each given area.

1. Copy this table, extend it to area 24, and fill it out. (A few rows have been done for you.) Experiment on graph paper as much as you need to, and look for patterns.

	Perimeter	
Area	**Shortest**	**Longest**
1	4	4
2	6	6
3		
4	8	10
5		
...		

2. What patterns do you notice in the table? Explain.

3. Describe the pattern for the perimeter of a polyomino of area *A*, having:

a. the longest perimeter;

b. the shortest perimeter.

4. For a polyomino having a given area, what perimeters are possible between the shortest and longest? (For example, for area 4, the minimum perimeter is 8, and the maximum is 10. Is it possible to have a perimeter of 9?)

5. What perimeters are possible for area 9?

MAKING PREDICTIONS

Mathematics is the science of patterns. Discovering a pattern can help you make predictions.

6. Predict the longest possible perimeters for polyominoes having these areas. If the number is not too big, experiment on graph paper to test your predictions.

a. 36 b. 40 c. 100
d. 99 e. 101 f. 1000

7. Explain your method for answering problem 6.

8. Predict the shortest possible perimeters for polyominoes having these areas. If the number is not too big, experiment on graph paper to test your predictions.

a. 36 b. 40 c. 100
d. 99 e. 101 f. 1000

9. Explain your method for answering problem 8.

MAKING A GRAPH

10. On graph paper, draw a horizontal axis and a vertical axis. Label the horizontal axis *Area* and the vertical axis *Perimeter,* as in the following graph. Extend them as far as you can, to at least 25 units for area and 55 units for perimeter.

1.2 SOLUTIONS

1.

	Perimeter	
Area	**Shortest**	**Longest**
1	4	4
2	6	6
3	8	8
4	8	10
5	10	12
6	10	14
7	12	16
8	12	18
9	12	20
10	14	22
11	14	24
12	14	26
13	16	28
14	16	30
15	16	32
16	16	34
17	18	36
18	18	38
19	18	40
20	18	42
21	20	44
22	20	46
23	20	48
24	20	50
25	20	52

2. In the shortest column, the numbers start at 4 and increase by 2 at certain intervals. For example, the next number is 6 and the next is a group of two 8s, a group of two 10s, a group of three 12s, a group of three 14s, a group of four 16s, a group of four 18s, etc.

   In the longest column, the numbers are consecutive, even integers starting at 4.

3. a. Longest perimeter = $2 \cdot A + 2$
   b. No general formula. When the area is a perfect square, the shortest perimeter is four times the square root of the area.

4. From Lesson 1, #11, the possible perimeters are even numbers between the shortest and longest perimeters.

5. Shortest P = 12
   Longest P = 20
   Possible perimeters: 12, 14, 16, 18, 20

6. Use the formula; longest perimeter $= 2 \cdot A + 2$
   a. $2 \cdot 36 + 2 = 74$
   b. $2 \cdot 40 + 2 = 82$
   c. $2 \cdot 100 + 2 = 202$
   d. $2 \cdot 99 + 2 = 200$

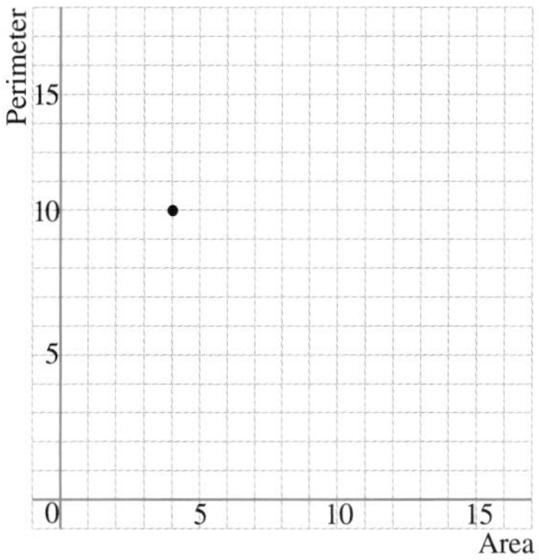

Definition: The point where the axes meet is called the *origin*.

For the following problems, you will need the numbers you found in the table in problem 1.

11. For each area, there is one number for the longest perimeter. For example, the longest perimeter for an area of 4 is 10. This gives us the number pair (4, 10). Put a dot on the graph at the corresponding point. (Count 4 spaces to the right of the origin, and 10 spaces up.) Do this for all the *area and longest perimeter* points on the table.

12. Describe what the graph looks like.

13. Using the same axes, repeat problem 1 with the numbers for area and shortest perimeter. One dot would be at (4, 8).

14. Describe what the graph looks like.

INTERPRETING THE GRAPH

15. Explain why the first set of points is higher on the graph than the second set.

16. As the area grows, which grows faster, the longest perimeter or the shortest perimeter? What happens to the gap between the two?

17. Use the graph to figure out how many different perimeters are possible for an area of 25. Explain how you did it.

18. Use the table you made in problem 1 to answer problem 17. Explain how you did it.

19. Use the graph to check whether there is a polyomino having area 15 units and perimeter 20. Explain how you did it.

20. Use the table you made in problem 1 to answer problem 19. Explain how you did it.

In this lesson you used patterns, tables, and graphs to help you think about a problem. This is an important skill which you will develop throughout this course.

MAKING A GRAPH

*T*his is the first of many graphs for the year. Make sure that the students are setting up the axes correctly, and that they understand how to locate points.

INTERPRETING THE GRAPH

*Y*ou may want to discuss these problems with the whole class. Tables and graphs are alternate representations for the same data. Students should develop facility with both.

1.2 SOLUTIONS

e. $2 \cdot 101 + 2 = 204$
f. $2 \cdot 1000 + 2 = 2002$

7. Answers will vary. Students can use sketches or the formula as in #6.

8. For perfect squares the shortest perimeter is four times the square root of the area.

   a. 24 b. 26 c. 40
   d. 40 e. 42 f. 128

9. Answers will vary. Students can use sketches or the formula as in #8.

10., 11., 13.

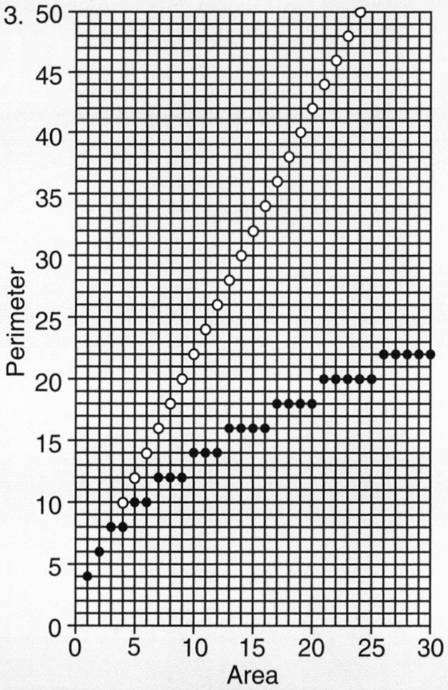

12. The graph is a straight line which goes diagonally up from left to right.

14. The graph looks like a flight of stairs going up from left to right.

15. The longest perimeter is increasing for each additional area. The shortest perimeter clumps in groups before increasing.

16. As the area grows, the longest perimeter grows faster and the gap between the shortest and longest perimeter grows larger.

17. Find the number 25 on the area axis. Trace a vertical line until it intersects both graphs.

    For each intersection point, trace a horizontal line to the perimeter axis and read the shortest and longest perimeter. (Shortest P = 20, longest P = 52)

PREVIEW ***UNITS AND DIMENSIONS***

Length is measured in linear units, such as the inch (in.) or centimeter (cm). Length refers to one dimension.

Area is measured in square units, such as the square inch (in.^{2}, or sq in.) or square centimeter (cm^2). Area refers to two dimensions.

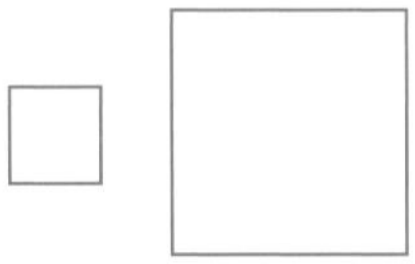

Volume is measured in cubic units, such as the cubic inch (in.^{3}, or cu in.) or cubic centimeter (cm^3, or cc). Volume refers to three dimensions.

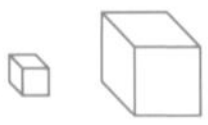

21. Divide the following units into three groups according to what they measure: length, area, or volume.

a. acre
b. fluid ounce
c. foot
d. gallon
e. kilometer
f. liter
g. meter
h. mile
i. pint
j. quart
k. yard

22. For each unit listed in problem 21, name something that might be measured with it. For example, for (a), the area of a farm could be measured in acres.

1.2 S O L U T I O N S

Possible perimeters are 20, 22, 24, ..., 52

18. Extend the table to area = 25 and fill in the shortest and longest perimeter, using the patterns found previously.

Go down to 25 under the area column and read the shortest and longest perimeter.

Possible perimeters are 20, 22, 24, ..., 52

19. Find the number 15 on area axis. Trace a vertical line until it intersects both graphs.

For each intersection point, trace a horizontal line to the perimeter axis and read the shortest and longest perimeter. (Shortest P = 16, longest P = 32).

20. Go down to 15 under the area column and read the shortest and longest perimeters.

Since 20 is even and is between 16 and 32, there exists a polyomino of area 15.

21. Length: c, e, g, h, k
Area: a
Volume: b, d, f, i, j

22. Answers will vary.

LESSON 1.3

Introduction to the Lab Gear

You will need:

the Lab Gear 

The Lab Gear blocks come in two colors, yellow and blue.

THE YELLOW BLOCKS

The yellow blocks represent whole numbers, such as 1, 5, or 25.

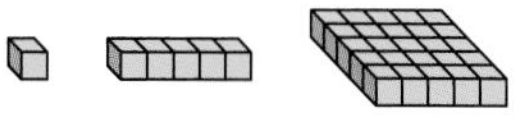

1. Use the Lab Gear to represent these quantities. Write down what blocks you used.
   a. 13   b. 21
2. Find as many different numbers as possible that can be represented by using exactly three yellow blocks.
3. Write some numbers that *cannot* be represented by the Lab Gear. Explain why you believe this to be true.

You will soon learn to use the Lab Gear for negative numbers. Later, you will use the Lab Gear to work with fractions.

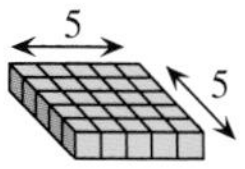

Notice that the block that represents 25 is a 5-by-5 square.

> **Notation:** In algebra, the multiplication 5 times 5 is written $5 \cdot 5 = 25$, or $5(5) = 25$. Do not use **x** to indicate multiplication—it could be confused with the letter x. When handwriting, use a dot, and when typing or using a computer, use an asterisk: $5 * 5 = 25$. In this book, we will use the dot.

THE BLUE BLOCKS

The blue blocks represent *variables*.
All the Lab Gear variables are related to these two blocks.

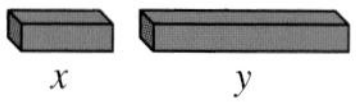

Variables are usually named by letters. Since the names x and y are used most often in algebra, they have been chosen to name the variables in the Lab Gear.

4. Write a way to remember which block is x and which block is y.

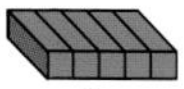

$5x$

This block represents $5 \cdot x$ (which is usually written as $5x$). The reason it is $5x$ can be seen by counting the number of x's that make it. Another way to see it is to notice that it is a rectangle. In a rectangle, the area is equal to the length times the width. Using the corner piece, we can measure the $5x$ block, and see that its dimensions are 5 and x, and its area is $5x$ square units.

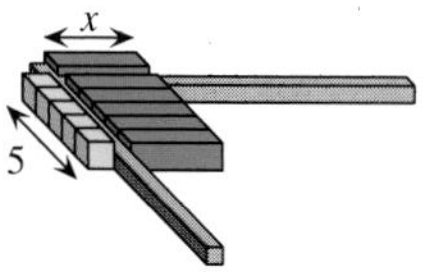

▼ 1.3
Introduction to the Lab Gear

Core Sequence: 1-11

Suitable for Homework: 10-12

Useful for Assessment: 10-11

What this Lesson is About:

- The first experience with the Lab Gear, our central tool for much of the course
- An application of area and a preview of volume
- A digression about triangular numbers, to help students develop problem-solving techniques

*I*f you are not used to using manipulatives, read **The Algebra Lab Gear** on pages 551-552.

THE YELLOW BLOCKS

*N*ote that the yellow blocks are based on base-10 blocks, which may be familiar to some of your students from elementary school days. If so, those students can be asked to make a presentation to the class about base-10 blocks and how they used the blocks to help them learn arithmetic.

1.3 SOLUTIONS

1. a. 2 five-blocks and 3 one-blocks
   b. 4 five-blocks and 1 one-block
2. 3, 7, 11, 15, 27, 31, 35, 51, 55, 75
3. At this stage, the Lab Gear cannot represent zero, negative numbers, or fractions. Later on, students will learn how to show zero and negative numbers. Fractions cannot be shown with the blocks.
4. The x-block is shorter than the y-block.

THE BLUE BLOCKS

The concept of variable is one of the most subtle in mathematics. Instead of hoping for immediate understanding, we want students to start working with variables and to get comfortable with them. The Lab Gear allows for such a gradual process.

Length and width for a rectangle, and length, width, and height for a box are crucial concepts in this course and in mathematics. Using the corner piece is a way to help see these concepts. A fuller discussion of dimension and area can be found in Lessons 5 and 6. A fuller discussion of volume will start in Lesson 10.

DISCOVERY HANDSHAKES

The handshakes problem is not directly related to the main thrust of the lesson or the chapter. It is a preview of later work on triangular numbers, and an opportunity to develop problem-solving skills. (Two approaches are suggested in the hint, use of diagrams and starting with an easier problem.)

5. Using the corner piece, find the measurements of each of these blocks in terms of x and y. Sketch each block. Label each one with its dimensions and area.

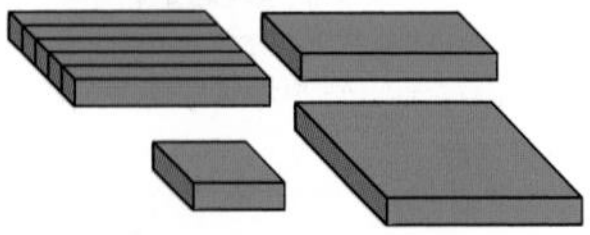

Notation: In algebra, $5 \cdot x$ is written $5x$, and $x \cdot y$ is written xy. (When no operation is indicated, multiplication is understood.) $x \cdot x$ is abbreviated x^2, and read *x squared*, or *the square of x*.

6. Explain why x^2 is read *the square of x*.

The following figure shows $x \cdot x \cdot x$ in the corner piece. There is a block whose measurements in three dimensions (length, width, height) match those shown.

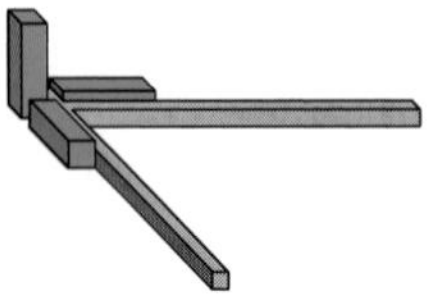

7. Which block would fit in the corner piece with those measurements? What shape is it?

8. In algebra the quantity $x \cdot x \cdot x$ is read *x cubed*, or *the cube of x*. Why do you think it is called that?

9. Use the corner piece to find the length, width, and height of each of the remaining blocks in terms of x and y.

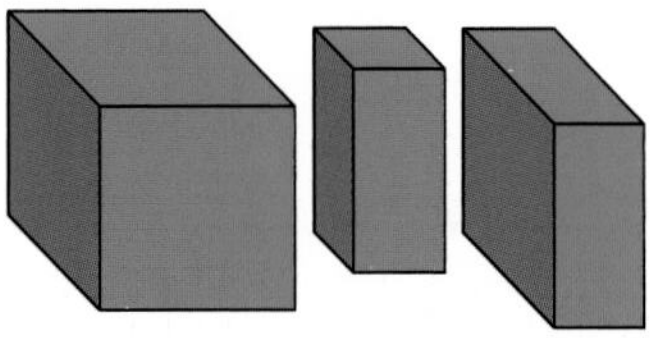

10. Summary Sketch each Lab Gear block, and label it with its name. Keep these labeled sketches in your notebook for future reference. (However, if you forget the name of a block, you don't need to look it up. Just measure it, using the corner piece.)

11. Sketch what each of the following would look like with the Lab Gear. If an expression is impossible to show with the Lab Gear, explain why.

a. $x^2 + x^2 + 3$
b. $x^2y + xy$
c. $x + x^2 + x^3$
d. $x^3 + x^4$

DISCOVERY HANDSHAKES

12. There are nine teachers at a math department meeting. They decide to shake hands with each other before starting the meeting. Each teacher is to shake hands exactly once with each other teacher. How many handshakes does it take? Explain your answer and how you arrived at it.

(Hint: You may use sketches to help you solve the problem. A good approach is to start out by counting the handshakes if there are two, three, four, five people at the meeting, and by looking for a pattern.)

1.3 SOLUTIONS

5. Name of block = its area

Area	Width	Length
$5y$	5	y
xy	x	y
x^2	x	x
y^2	y	y

6. The area represented by x^2 is the area of a square.

7. The x^3-block, which has the shape of a cube

8. The volume represented by x^3 is the volume of a cube.

9. Name of block = its volume

Volume	Width	Length	Height
y^3	y	y	y
x^2y	x	x	y
y^2x	x	y	y

11. a.

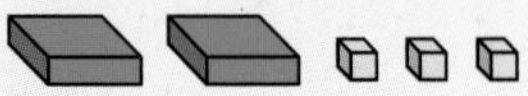

b.

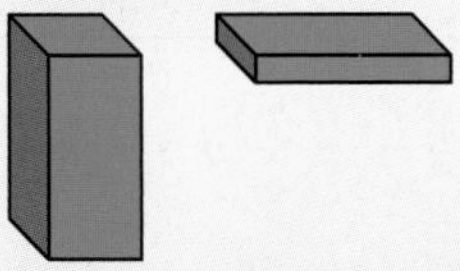

c.

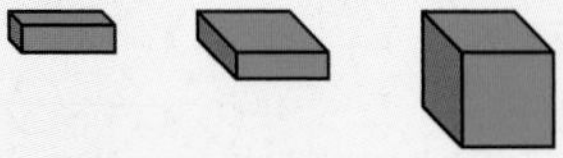

d. Impossible since there is no x^4-block.

12. 36 handshakes —The first teacher shakes eight hands. The second teacher shakes seven new hands since s/he already shook the first teacher's hand. The third teacher shakes six new hands. Continue the pattern,
$8 + 7 + 6 + 5 + 4 + 3 + 2 + 1 = 36$.

LESSON 1.4

Variables and Constants

You will need:

the Lab Gear 

Variables are one of the most important concepts of algebra. A variable can stand for different numbers at different times. For example, x could be a positive or a negative number or 0. It could be greater than y, less than y, or equal to y.

Because they do not change, numbers are called *constants.*

SUBSTITUTING

Definition: Replacing a variable by a constant amount is called *substitution.*

Example: The figure shows how the Lab Gear can be used to show the substitution $x = 2$ for the expressions x, $x + 2$, $3x$, x^2, and x^3.

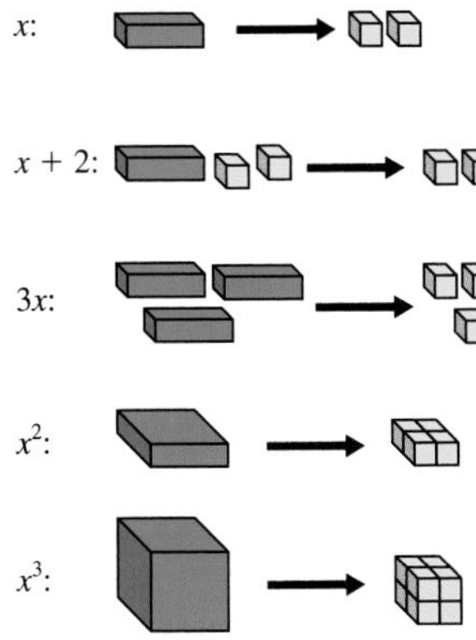

1. Sketch what $x + 2$ looks like modeled with the Lab Gear. Then sketch what it looks like if the following substitution is done.
   a. $x = 5$ b. $x = 1$
   c. $x = 3$ d. $x = 0$
2. Repeat problem 1 for x^2.
3. Repeat problem 1 for x^3.
4. Repeat problem 1 for $3x$.

An expression that involves x can have many different values, depending on the value of x.

EVALUATING

Definition: To *evaluate* an expression means to find its value for a particular value of x.

Looking back at the figure in the previous section, you can see the value of each expression when $x = 2$. The figure shows that $x + 2 = 4$, $3x = 6$, $x^2 = 4$, and $x^3 = 8$.

In the following problems:

- Put out blocks to match each figure.
- Replace the variables (represented by blue blocks) with the given constants (represented by yellow blocks).
- Evaluate each expression by counting what you have.

5. Evaluate for :
   a. $y = 1$; b. $y = 2$; c. $y = 0$.

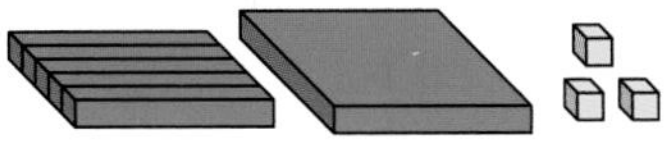

▼ 1.4 Variables and Constants

Core Sequence: 1-21

Suitable for Homework: 8-11, 13-22

What this Lesson is About:

- Beginning to develop a sense of the meaning of variable, by using substitution to evaluate expressions

Using substitution to evaluate a polynomial, or more generally, a formula, is a daily occurrence in many walks of life from science and engineering to financial planning. This is often done using programmable calculators or computer spreadsheets. Electronic evaluation of expressions has the advantage of being fast and free of careless mistakes.

Because of the existence of this new technology, we must change our emphasis in Algebra 1. First, it is more important than ever to teach the concepts behind substitution, specifically the concepts of variables and operations. Second, we must teach students how to use the technology. This part depends on what equipment you have available and, at any rate, should not be addressed this early in the course. At this stage the goal is for students to understand how substitution works and what it means. The use of the Lab Gear is a good way to begin.

1.4 SOLUTIONS

1–4: Sketches should show the following numbers of blocks:

1. a. 7
   b. 3
   c. 5
   d. 2
2. a. 25
   b. 1
   c. 9
   d. 0
3. a. 125
   b. 1
   c. 27
   d. 0
4. a. 15
   b. 3
   c. 9
   d. 0
5. a. 9
   b. 17
   c. 3

SUBSTITUTING, EVALUATING

You may want to demonstrate the example on the overhead.

It is most effective to make a copy of the original expression and to work on the copy, replacing the blue blocks with their values in yellow blocks. This allows you to see the original expression while working, and makes it easier to avoid mistakes.

FINDING x

Do not teach equation-solving techniques. These are deliberately saved for much later in the course. Students need to develop many algebra skills prior to tackling equation solving through symbol manipulation. They need many opportunities to use trial and error, as in these problems.

THE SUBSTITUTION RULE

Make sure to have time for group and/or class discussion of these problems, even if some or all of problems 13-22 were done as homework.

Besides reinforcing the concepts of variables, substitution, and the operations, these problems preview the concepts of equations and identities.

The final Report, by making a connection with the Lab Gear, helps focus on the concept of identity.

6. Evaluate for :
a. $x = 1$; b. $x = 5$; c. $x = 0$.

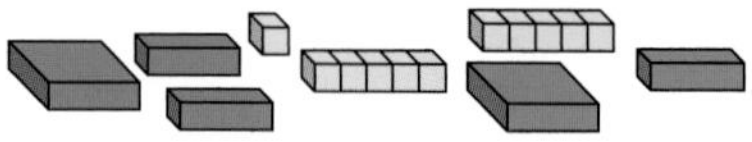

7. Evaluate for :
a. $x = 5$ and $y = 4$
b. $x = 4$ and $y = 0$

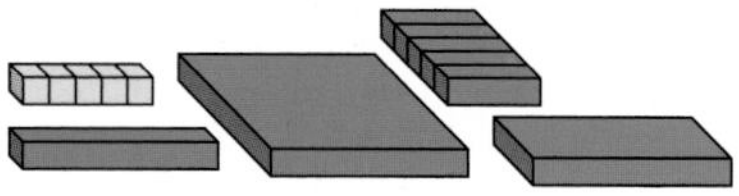

Evaluate these expressions without using the Lab Gear. You may want to use your calculator.

8. $y^2 + 5y + 3$ if $y = 1.3$

9. $y^2 + xy + 5x + y + 5$ if $x = \frac{1}{2}$ and $y = 4$

Evaluating expressions is important in many walks of life, from science and engineering to business and finance. It is usually done with the help of calculators and computers. In this course you will learn some of the ideas that are built into calculators and computers.

FINDING X

Use trial and error for these problems.

10. If $x + 2 = 18$, what is x?

11. What is x if
a. $3x = 18$? b. $x^2 = 64$?
c. $x^3 = 64$?

In a sense, finding x is the reverse of substituting. In future chapters you will learn many methods for finding the value of a variable.

THE SUBSTITUTION RULE

In the following equations, there are two place-holders, a diamond and a triangle. The **substitution rule** is that, within one expression or equation, the same number is placed in all the diamonds, and the same number is placed in all the triangles. (The number in the diamonds may or may not equal the number in the triangles.)

For example, in the equation

$$\Diamond + \Diamond + \Diamond + \Delta = \Delta + \Delta$$

if you place 2 in the $\Diamond$ and 3 in the Δ, you get

$$2 + 2 + 2 + 3 = 3 + 3.$$

Note that even though the diamond and triangle were replaced according to the rule, the resulting equation is *not* true.

12. **Exploration** The equation

$$\Diamond + \Diamond + \Diamond + \Delta = \Delta + \Delta$$

is not true with 2 in the $\Diamond$ and 3 in the Δ. Find as many pairs of numbers as possible that can be put in the $\Diamond$ and in the Δ to make the equation true. For example, 0 in both the Δ and $\Diamond$ makes it true. Arrange your answers in a table like this:

$\Diamond$	Δ
0	0
...	...

Describe any pattern you notice. Explain why the pattern holds.

1.4 S O L U T I O N S

6. a. 16
   b. 76
   c. 11
7. a. 70
   b. 25
8. 11.19
9. 29.5
10. 16
11. a. 6
    b. 8
    c. 4
12. Answers will vary. Students will find different patterns, but the key is that each triangle is worth three diamonds.

For the following equations, experiment with various numbers for ◊ and Δ. (Remember the substitution rule.) For each equation, try to give three examples of values that make it true. If you can give only one, or none, explain why.

13. ◊ + ◊ + ◊ = 3 · ◊

14. ◊ + ◊ + ◊ = 4 · ◊

15. Δ + Δ + Δ = 3 · Δ

16. ◊ + ◊ + 2 = 3 · ◊

17. ◊ + ◊ + 2 = 2 · ◊

18. ◊ · Δ = Δ · ◊

19. ◊ · Δ = Δ + ◊

20. ◊ · ◊ · ◊ = 3 · ◊

21. ◊ · ◊ · Δ = ◊ + ◊ + Δ

22. **Report** Say that ◊ is x and Δ is y. For each equation above, show both sides with a sketch of Lab Gear blocks. In some cases, the sketches may help you explain whether the equations are always true or not. For example, for problem 13 both sides would look like this.

But, for problem 14 the right side would look like this. Write an illustrated report about what you did.

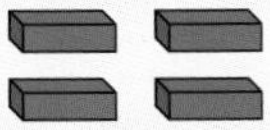

1.4 SOLUTIONS

13. Any number will work.
14. Only ◊ = 0 will work.
15. Any number will work.
16. Only ◊ = 2 will work.
17. None.
18. Any number will work.
19.

Diamond	Triangle
0	0
2	2
3	3/2
4	4/3
5	5/4
6	6/5
x	$x/(x-1)$

20. Only ◊ = 0 will work.

21.

Diamond	Triangle
0	0
2	4/3
3	3/4
4	8/15
5	5/12
x	$2x/(x^2-1)$

22. Reports will vary. Here is a brief summary.

There are three types of equations: always, sometimes, and never true. $x + x + x = 3x$ is an example of an always true equation, which is an identity. Most students will try positive integers but they should be encouraged to try negative numbers and fractions. $x + x + 2 = 2x$ is an example of a never true equation. The Lab Gear is a very effective visual way to show why this is so. Lastly, $x + x + x = 3y$ is an example of a sometimes true equation.

$x + x + x = 3x$

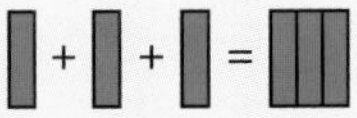

$x + x + 2 \neq 2x$

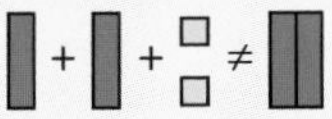

$x + x + x = 3y$

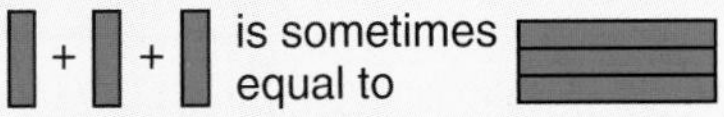

THINKING WRITING 1.A Graphing Rectangle Areas

Core Sequence: the whole assignment

Suitable for Homework:
the whole assignment

Useful for Assessment: 6

What this Assignment is About:

- Preview of $y = mx$ and $y = x^2$ functions

*T*his lesson takes off from the concept of area of a rectangle, but actually it is a preview of the functions $y = mx$ and $y = x^2$. Students are encouraged to develop their skills in observing and interpreting graphs, one of the central skills in Algebra 1.

*T*his is the first of many writing assignments in this book. Many students will not have done writing in math class before, and will not know how to begin. To help students with the format, some teachers have used the **Guidelines for Thinking/Writing Assignments** on page 558.

*Y*our standards in writing assignments can be higher than for day-to-day writing. Spelling, punctuation, and neatness should reflect the best of the students' ability. However, remember that the most important thing, especially at the beginning, is for students to develop a good attitude towards writing, perhaps the most powerful thinking and communication tool they will develop in high school. Make your standards clear but be supportive and encouraging.

*S*tudents will vary greatly in the level of sophistication with which they approach the problem. Some will merely make *observations* about the graphs. Others will be able to make *connections* between the graphs and the geometry of the problem. Still others will be able to *interpret* the graphs, explaining not only how they are different, but why.

*S*ince there is no single right answer or method, it is important for students to see a wide range of approaches. Having a class discussion of examples of student work helps convince students that writing is important and is another way for you to communicate your expectations. Some teachers have found it helpful to encourage, or even require, students to rewrite the first assignment until it meets their standards for writing assignments. This is time consuming for both teachers and students, but is well worth it in the long run.

THINKING WRITING 1.A Graphing Rectangle Areas

How does the area of a rectangle change if you vary either the length or the width and leave the other dimension unchanged? How does the area of a rectangle change if you vary both the length and the width? Tables and graphs will help you investigate these questions and notice patterns.

1. What is the area of a rectangle having the following dimensions?
a. 1 by 9 b. 2 by 9
c. 3 by 9 d. 9 by 9

2. What is the area of a rectangle having the following dimensions, if $x = 10$?
a. 1 by x b. 2 by x
c. 3 by x d. x by x

3. Make a table like this, extending it to $x = 6$.

	Area of rectangle having dimensions:			
x	1 by x	2 by x	3 by x	x by x
1	1	2	3	1
2	...	...	...	...

4. Draw axes, with x on the horizontal axis, and area on the vertical axis. Plot the points you obtained in problem 3 for the area of 1-by-x rectangles. For example, (1, 1) will be on the graph.

5. Does it make sense to connect the points you plotted? What would be the meaning of points on the line, in between the ones you got from your table? Label your graph *1 by x*.

6. On the same axes, graph the data you obtained for 2-by-x, 3-by-x, and x-by-x rectangles. For more accuracy on the last one, you may use your calculator to find points for $x = 0.5$, 1.5, and so on. Label your graphs *2 by x, 3 by x....*

7. **Report** Write about the four graphs. Describe them and compare them. Your report should reflect what you learned in the above investigation. It should consist of three parts: a problem statement, a detailed explanation, and a conclusion. It should include, but not be limited to, answers to the following questions.

- What is the shape of each graph?
- Which ones are alike? Different? Why?
- How do the first three graphs differ from each other? What is the meaning of that difference?
- What is special about the fourth? Why?
- Do the graphs ever intersect each other? What is the meaning of the points of intersection?
- Where do they cross the vertical axis, and what is the meaning of that point?
- Where does the fourth one cross the others, and what are the meanings of those points?
- Which area grows the fastest? Why?

1.A SOLUTIONS

1. a. 9 square units
b. 18 square units
c. 27 square units
d. 81 square units

2. a. 10 b. 20 c. 30 d. 100

3.

	Area of rectangle having dimensions:			
x	1 by x	2 by x	3 by x	x by x
1	1	2	3	1
2	2	4	6	4
3	3	6	9	9
4	4	8	12	16
5	5	10	15	25
6	6	12	18	36

4., 6.

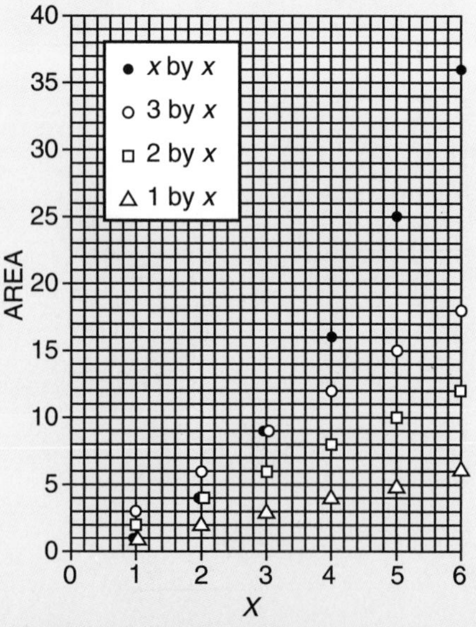

5. Yes, it does make sense to connect the points. Any point on one of the lines or the curve represents a rectangle with noninteger dimensions.

(Solutions continued on page 509)

LESSON 1.5 Dimensions

You will need:

the Lab Gear 

DIMENSIONS AND THE LAB GEAR

Of course, all the Lab Gear blocks are three-dimensional, (as are all objects in the real world). However, we sometimes use the x-block, or the 5-block as a **model** of a one-dimensional object. That is, as a model of a line segment of length x, or 5. Similarly, we can use the x^2- or xy-blocks as models of two-dimensional, flat objects.

1. Some blocks, such as the x^3, cannot be used as models of one- or two-dimensional objects. Make a list of these blocks, which we will call the 3-D blocks.

When making sketches of the Lab Gear, if 3-D blocks or three-dimensional arrangements are not involved, it is much more convenient to work with two-dimensional sketches of the blocks **as seen from above.**

2. Which blocks do these figures represent?

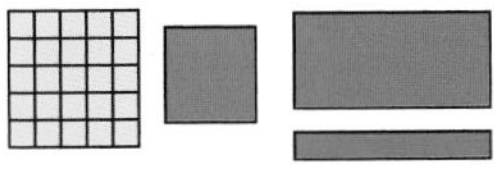

3. Make a 2-D sketch of each of the ten "flat" blocks as seen from above.
4. On your sketch, write *1* on the blocks that model one-dimensional line segments, and *2* on the blocks that model two-dimensional figures.
5. Which block can be thought of as a model of a zero-dimensional point?
6. Sketch the following:
   a. four x-blocks arranged to model a one-dimensional line segment;
   b. four x-blocks arranged to model a two-dimensional rectangle;
   c. four x-blocks arranged to model a three-dimensional box.
7. Sketch the following:
   a. three x^2-blocks arranged to represent a two-dimensional rectangle;
   b. three x^2-blocks arranged to represent a three-dimensional box.

FACES OF THE LAB GEAR

The x^2-block, **as seen from the side**, looks just like the x-block seen from the side, since in either case you see an x-by-1 rectangle.

8. a. Make an x-by-1 rectangle by tracing an x-block.
   b. Place the x^2-block on the rectangle you traced. For it to fit, you will have to stand it on edge.
   c. Which other two blocks can be placed on the rectangle?
9. a. Using a block, trace another rectangle (or square).
   b. Find all the blocks that fit on it.
10. Repeat problem 9, until you have found five more groups of blocks. List each group. Some blocks will appear on more than one list.

In the next sections, when putting blocks next to each other, join them along matching faces.

▼ 1.5 Dimensions

Core Sequence: 1-27

Suitable for Homework: 28-30

What this Lesson is About:

- Looking at the Lab Gear blocks in terms of their dimensions and faces
- First experience with Lab Gear rectangles, a central tool for later understanding of the distributive law
- Preview— a model of opposites, and the addition of signed numbers

Note that two (related) meanings of the word *dimensions* are addressed: the dimensionality of a given block (3, 2, 1, or 0 dimensions) and dimensions as linear measurements (length, width, and height).

This lesson lays the groundwork for much upcoming material by giving students concrete manipulative and perceptual experiences. Do not expect instant mastery of the underlying ideas.

DIMENSIONS AND THE LAB GEAR

This section prepares students for the concept of degree, which will be defined in the next lesson.

In the context of the Lab Gear, we can think of a thickness of one unit as not contributing to the dimensions of a block or collection of blocks.

1.5 SOLUTIONS

1. x^3-block
   y^3-block
   x^2y-block
   xy^2-block
2. 25, x^2, xy, and y
5. 1-block
6. a. 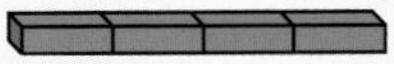
   b. 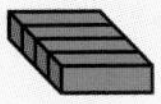
   c. 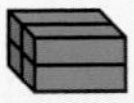
7. a. 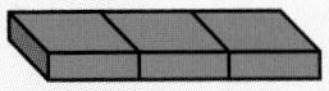
   b. 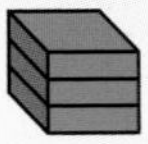
8. c. xy-block and $5x$-block
9. Answers will vary.
10. Blocks that will fit a y-by-y trace:
    y^2, xy^2, y^3
    Blocks that will fit a y-by-x trace:
    xy^2, x^2y, xy
    Blocks that will fit a y-by-1 trace:
    y, y^2, $5y$, xy
    Blocks that will fit a 5-by-1 trace:
    5, 25, $5x$, $5y$
    Blocks that will fit a 1-by-1 trace:
    1, 5, x, y

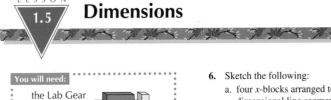

*N*ote that there are no overhead 3-D blocks.

FACES OF THE LAB GEAR

*T*his section prepares students for the concept of surface area. More importantly for the purposes of this course, it develops some basic familiarity with the Lab Gear blocks which will be essential when working on **Make a Rectangle** and **Make a Square** problems. (See below.)

MAKE A RECTANGLE
MAKE A SQUARE

*T*hese sections preview the concepts of the distributive law and factoring. These concepts will take about a semester to consolidate, so do not expect miracles from these problems. At this stage, it is important for students

- to realize that the area of a rectangle or square can be obtained by just enumerating the blocks it is built with, and
- to be able to use the corner piece to identify the length and width of a rectangle.

*W*e will return to the area model of multiplication in Lesson 9.

*E*ncourage students to work in pairs. If a pair is stumped, they can get help from other students in the class.

MAKE A RECTANGLE

11. Exploration Build each shape and sketch it, showing which blocks you used.

a. Use only blue blocks; make a rectangle that is not a square.

b. Use both yellow and blue blocks; make a rectangle that is not a square.

c. Use both yellow and blue blocks; make a square.

d. Use only blue blocks; make a square.

12. Use 1-blocks to make as many different rectangles as you can, having area:

a. 12	b. 13	c. 14
d. 30	e. 31	f. 32

13. Make and sketch as many Lab Gear rectangles as you can having area:

a. $8x$ b. $6xy$

You can rearrange the blocks $2x^2 + 12x$ into a rectangle like this.

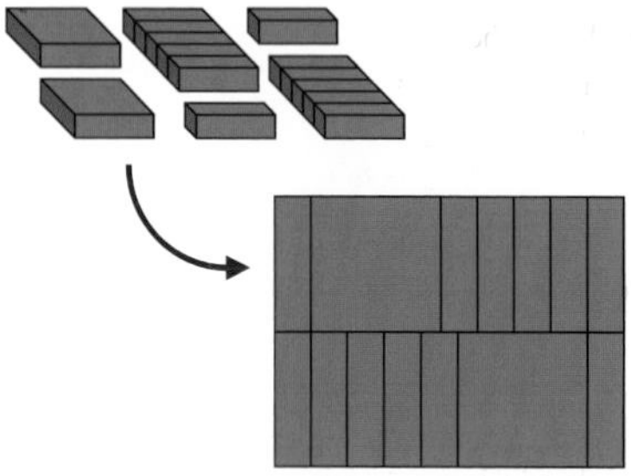

The length and width of this rectangle are $x + 6$ and $2x$, which can be seen better if you organize the blocks logically and use the corner piece, as shown. (Notice that you could also turn the rectangle so that the length and width are exchanged. This is considered to be the same rectangle.) The area of the rectangle $2x^2 + 12x$ can be found by just counting the blocks.

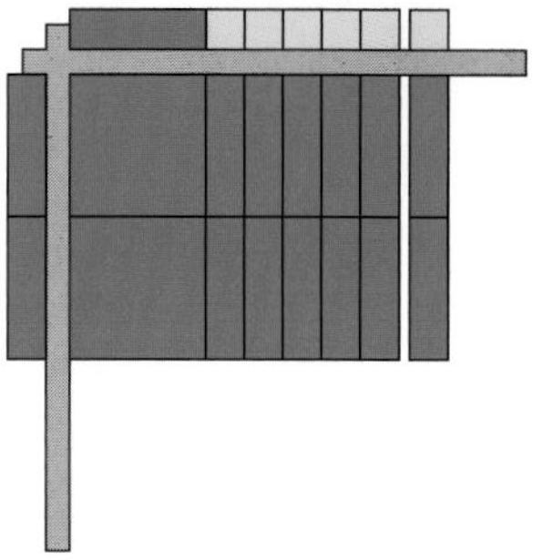

14. There is another rectangular arrangement of the same blocks which has different dimensions. Find it.

For each problem:

a. Arrange the given blocks into a rectangle in the corner piece.

b. Sketch it (as seen from above).

c. Write the length, width, and area.

Find two different solutions for problem 17.

15. 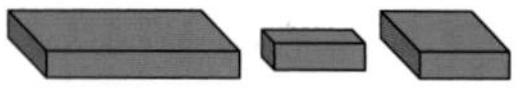

16. 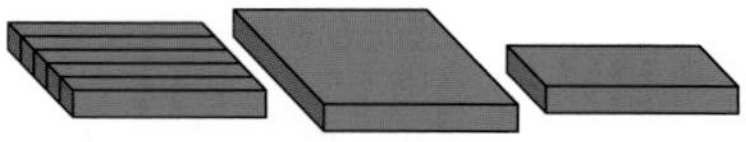

17. 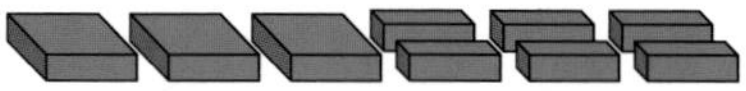

By now you should be able to find the length, width, and area of any Lab Gear rectangle. This will be a useful skill throughout this course.

1.5 SOLUTIONS

11. Answers will vary.

12. a. 3 b. 1 c. 2
d. 4 e. 1 f. 3

13. There are 5 possibilities. Here are some:

a. Use a $5x$-block and three x-blocks.

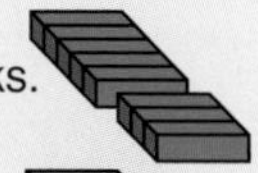

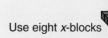

Use eight x-blocks

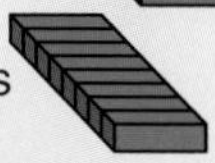

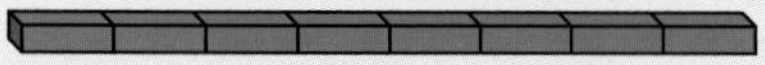

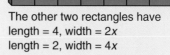

The other two rectangles have
length = 4, width = $2x$
length = 2, width = $4x$

b. Use six xy-blocks and arrange to form four different rectangles:
length = $6x$, width = y
length = x, width = $6y$
length = $2x$, width = $3y$
length = $3x$, width = $2y$

14. length = x, width = $2x + 12$

15. length = $x + y + 1$
width = x
area = $x^2 + xy + x$

16. length = $y + x + 5$
width = y
area = $y^2 + xy + 5y$

17. length = $3x + 6$ or, length = $3x$
width = x width = $x + 2$
area = $3x^2 + 6x$ area = $3x^2 + 6x$

For each problem, the area of a rectangle is given.

a. Get the blocks that are named.
b. Make the rectangle.
c. Write the length and width.

One problem is impossible. Explain why.

18. $3x^2 + 9x$ **19.** $3xy + 2x + x^2$

20. $4x^2 + 9y$ **21.** $x^2 + 5x$

MAKE A SQUARE

For each problem, the area of a square is given.

a. Get the blocks.
b. Make the square.
c. Write the side length.

One problem is impossible. Explain why.

22. 36 **23.** 49

24. 40 **25.** $4x^2$

26. $9x^2$ **27.** $x^2 + 2x + 1$

PREVIEW ***THE ZERO MONSTER***

The Zero Monster eats zeroes. However, all I have to feed it are cups ($\cup$), and caps ($\cap$). It will not eat cups or caps, but it can put one $\cup$ together with one $\cap$ to create a zero, which it eats.

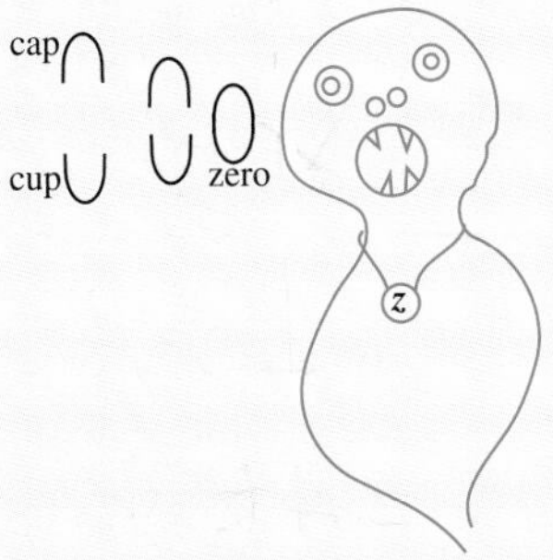

For example, if there are three cups and five caps, it will make and eat three zeroes, leaving two caps. This can be written like this:

$$\cup\cup\cup + \cap\cap\cap\cap\cap = \cap\cap$$

or like this:

$$3\cup + 5\cap = 2\cap$$

28. Find out how many zeroes the Zero Monster ate. What was left after it finished eating? Fill in the blanks.

a. $9\cup + 6\cap =$ ___
b. $9\cup + 6\cup =$ ___
c. $9\cap + 6\cap =$ ___
d. $9\cap + 6\cup =$ ___

29. Fill in the blanks.

a. $4\cup +$ ___ $= 8\cap$
b. $4\cup +$ ___ $= 8\cup$
c. $4\cap +$ ___ $= 8\cap$
d. $4\cap +$ ___ $= 8\cup$

30. Fill in the blanks.

a. $7\cup +$ ___ $= 1\cap$
b. $7\cup +$ ___ $= 1\cup$
c. $7\cap +$ ___ $= 1\cap$
d. $7\cap +$ ___ $= 1\cup$

$2\cap$ and $2\cup$ are examples of *opposites,* because when you add them, you get zero. The concept of opposite is important in algebra, and we will return to it in Chapter 2.

Insist that *near-rectangles* are not good enough. Demand perfect fit. Also let students know that a rectangle can extend beyond the physical limits of the corner piece.

PREVIEW ***THE ZERO MONSTER***

This is a Preview of work on addition and subtraction of signed numbers. Do not bring up rules for signed number arithmetic. Let students work the problems any way they want at this stage, and encourage group or class discussion of the approaches they used. (You may also use the problem to obtain discreetly a partial assessment of students' arithmetic readiness.)

1.5 SOLUTIONS

18. length = $3x$, width = $x + 3$ or, length = $3x + 9$, width = x
19. length = $3y + 2 + x$, width = x
20. Impossible. The x^2-block and y-block do not have edges of common length.
21. length = $x + 5$, width = x
22. side = 6
23. side = 7
24. Impossible. No (integer) number times itself equals 40.
25. side = $2x$
26. side = $3x$
27. side = $x + 1$
28. a. 6 zeroes, 3 $\cup$ left.
    b. No zeroes, 15 $\cup$ left.
    c. No zeroes, 15 $\cap$ left.
    d. 6 zeroes, 3 $\cap$ left
29. a. 12 $\cap$
    b. 4 $\cup$
    c. 4 $\cap$
    d. 12 $\cup$
30. a. 8 $\cap$
    b. 6 $\cap$
    c. 6 $\cup$
    d. 8 $\cup$

▼ 1.6
Coming to Terms

Core Sequence: 1-9, 14-22

Suitable for Homework: 1, 6, 10-13, 21-22

Useful for Assessment: 1, 7-9, 22

What this Lesson is About:

- The concept of degree is developed from the concept of dimensions
- Combining like terms

DEGREE

This is a new way to define degree. It is a subtle definition based entirely on the Lab Gear model. The goal of the lesson is for students to reach a generalization that is independent of the blocks. (However, a thorough mastery of the concept of degree is not central to the development of the course.)

LESSON 1.6

Coming to Terms

You will need:

the Lab Gear 

1. Name a Lab Gear block that can be used as a model for an object with:
   a. three dimensions;
   b. two dimensions;
   c. one dimension;
   d. zero dimensions.

Definitions: In the expression

$$x^3 + 2xy - 3x + 4,$$

four quantities are added or subtracted, so we say that there are four *terms:* x^3, $2xy$, $3x$, and 4. Note that a term is a product of numbers and variables. The sum or difference of one or more terms is called a *polynomial.*

Note that polynomials do not involve division by variables. For example, $(1/x) + x$ is not a polynomial.

DEGREE

The *degree* of an expression, in terms of the Lab Gear, is the **lowest dimension** in which you can arrange the blocks. For example, take the expression $3x$. These blocks can be arranged in a rectangle (two dimensions) or in a line (one dimension).

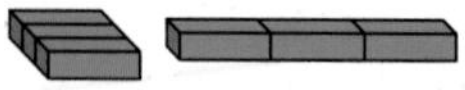

The lowest dimension is one, so the degree of $3x$ is one.

2. Show how the term $2xy$ could be arranged as a box (three dimensions) or as a rectangle (two dimensions). What is the degree of $2xy$?

Of course, x^3 cannot be shown in less than three dimensions, so its degree is 3.

3. Write the degree of each blue block.

The degree of a constant expression (any combination of yellow blocks) is considered to be 0. The reason for this is that the yellow blocks can be separated into 1-blocks, which model zero-dimensional points, with no length, width, or height. See the figure below, which shows how the number 8 can be shown in three ways.

Three dimensions

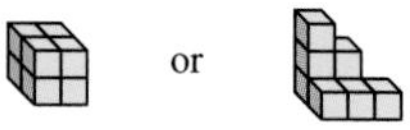

Two dimensions

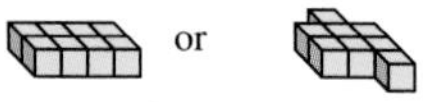

One dimension

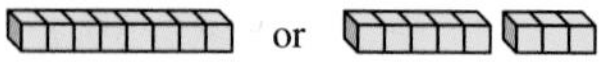

Zero dimensions

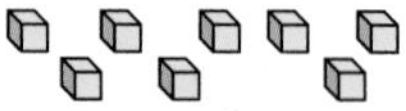

4. What is the degree of these terms?
   a. $4y$ b. $5x^2$
   c. $2xy^2$ d. 7

The degree of a polynomial can be found in the same way. For example, the figures below show how the blocks x^2 and y can be arranged in figures of two or three dimensions. However note that they cannot be arranged into figures of zero or one dimension.

1.6 SOLUTIONS

1. Answers will vary. One possible solution is given.
   a. x^3-block
   b. xy-block
   c. 5-block
   d. 1-block
2. Degree of $2xy = 2$

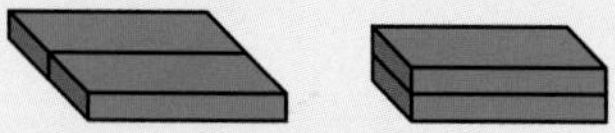

3.

Block	Degree
x^3	3
y^3	3
x^2y	3
y^2x	3
xy	2
x^2	2
y^2	2
x	1
y	1
$5x$	1
$5y$	1

4. a. 1
   b. 2
   c. 3
   d. 0

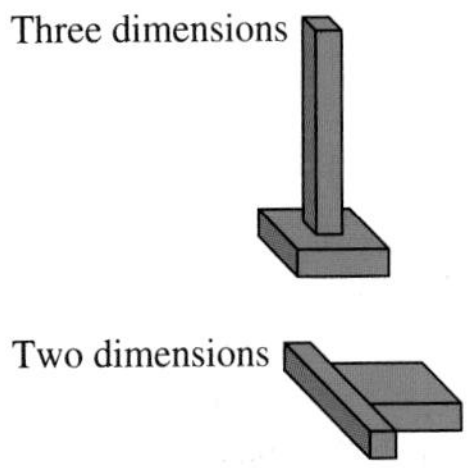

5. What is the degree of $x^2 + y$?

6. What is the degree of these polynomials?
   a. $4y + 3$ b. $x^3 + 5x^2$
   c. $2xy^2 + x^2$ d. $xy + 7$

Definition: The 2 in the term $2xy$ is called the *coefficient.* A term like x^3 has an invisible coefficient, a 1, since $1x^3$ is usually written just x^3.

7. **Generalizations** If two terms differ only by their coefficients (like $2x$ and $5x$) what can you say about their degrees?

8. How can you find the degree of a term without using the Lab Gear? Explain, using examples.

9. How can you find the degree of a polynomial without using the Lab Gear? Explain, using examples.

HIGHER DEGREE

10. Why is it impossible to show $x^2 \cdot x^2$ with the Lab Gear?

11. What is the product of x^2 and x^2?

12. Even though there are only three dimensions in space, terms can be of degree 4. Write as many different terms of degree 4 as you can, using 1 for the coefficient and x and y for the variables.

13. Which of these expressions cannot be shown with the blocks? Explain.
    a. $5x^2$ b. $2x^5$ c. $\frac{2}{x^5}$ d. $\frac{5}{x^2}$

COMBINING LIKE TERMS

There are many ways you can write an expression that names a collection of Lab Gear blocks. When you put blocks of the same size and shape together and name them according to the arrangement, you are combining *like terms*. Look at these examples.

This quantity is written $x + x + x$,

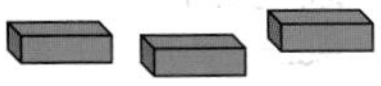

or $3x$, after combining like terms.

This quantity is written $y + x + y$,

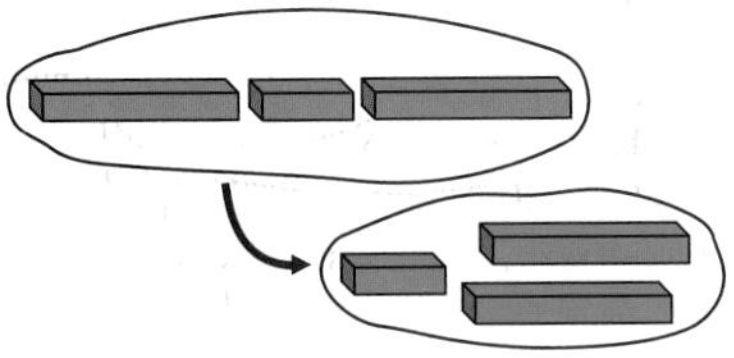

or $x + 2y$, after combining like terms.

This quantity is written $x^2 + 5 + x + x^2 + x + x^2$,

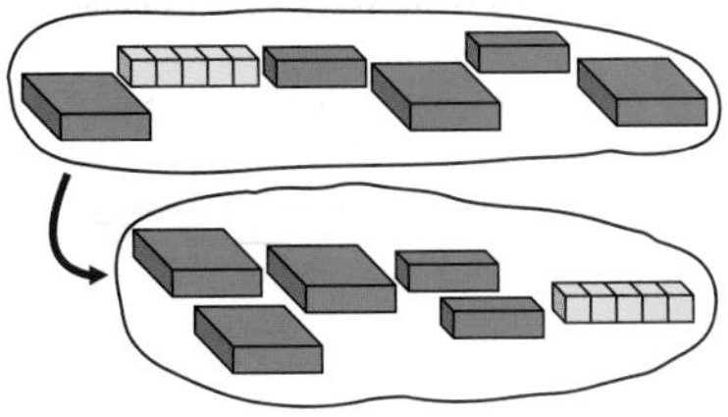

or $3x^2 + 2x + 5$, after combining like terms.

HIGHER DEGREE

*S*ome students are fascinated with the fourth dimension. Encourage them to read *Flatland*, by Edwin Abbott, and to make an oral report to the class. Other references: *The Fourth Dimension: Toward a Geometry of Higher Reality* by Rudy Rucker (Houghton Mifflin, 1984); *Sphereland* by Dionys Burger (Thomas Y. Crowell Co, NY, 1965).

COMBINING LIKE TERMS

*T*his activity should help prevent mistakes of the type $x + x = x^2$. If students want to do this lesson by looking at the figures, without using actual blocks, let them. However, first make sure they are able to identify the blocks on sight. (If so, problems 13-19 could be assigned as homework.) At this stage, do not use abstract arguments like the distributive law to explain combining like terms — the blocks make it clear enough.

1.6 SOLUTIONS

5. 2
6. a. 1
   b. 3
   c. 3
   d. 2
7. They are the same.
8. Add the exponents of the variables. For example, xy^2 has degree three.
9. The degree of a polynomial is the degree of its highest degree term. For example, $5xy^2 + 2x + 3$ has degree three.
10. $x^2 \cdot x^2$ would require four dimensions which cannot be shown by the Lab Gear.
11. x^4
13. $2x^5$ and $2/x^5$ cannot be shown by the blocks because we cannot model five-dimensional objects with three-dimensional blocks.
    Also, $5/x^2$ cannot be shown. The blocks cannot model fractions.

Of course, a 5x-block, when combining like terms, is equivalent to 5 separate x-blocks. For example, it can be combined with two x-blocks to make 7x.

For each example, show the figure with your blocks, combine like terms, then write the quantity the short way.

14.

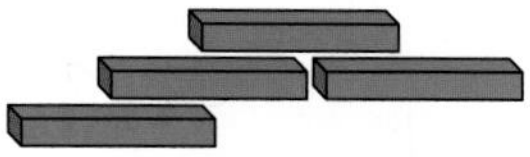

15.

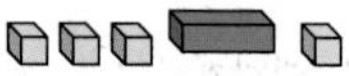

16.

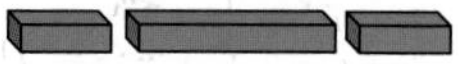

17.

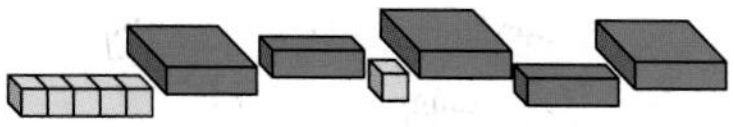

18.

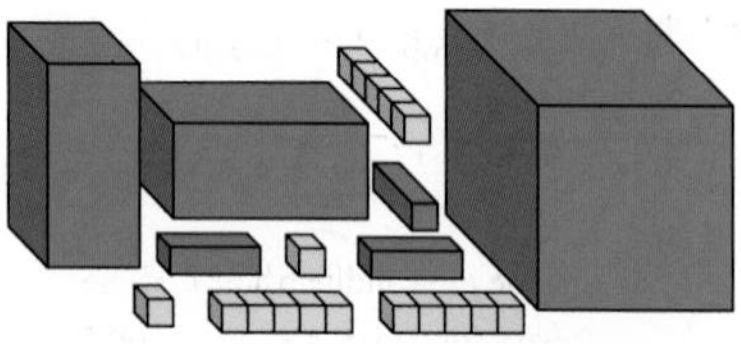

19.

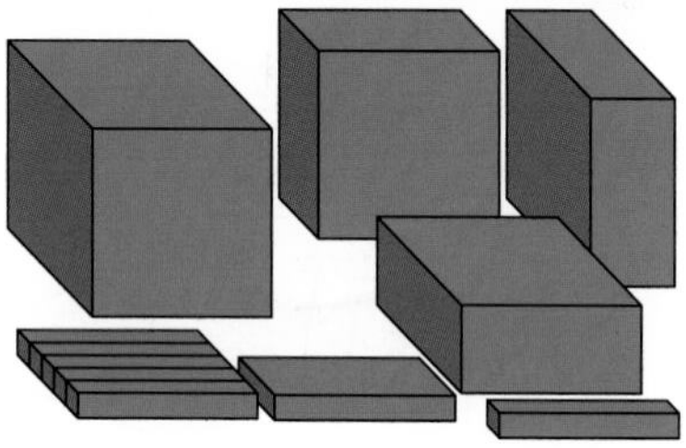

20.

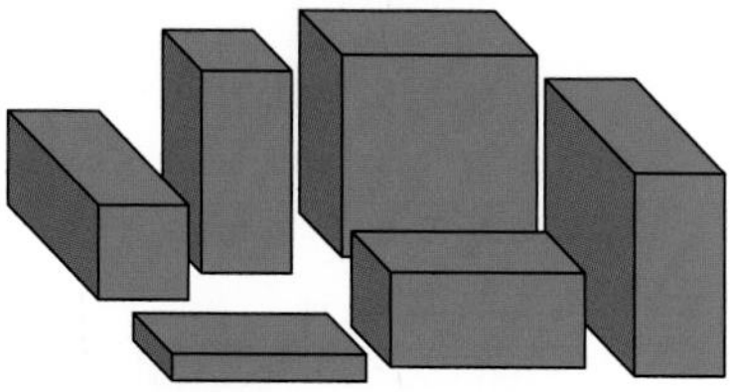

21. What terms are missing? (More than one term is missing in each problem.)

a. $3x^2 + 4x +$ ___ $= 9x^2 + 8x + 7$

b. $x^2y + 6xy +$ ___ $= 9x^2y + 8xy$

22. **Summary** Explain, with examples, the words *degree, coefficient, polynomial,* and *like terms*. Use sketches of the Lab Gear as well as explanations in words and symbols.

1.6 SOLUTIONS

14. 4y
15. $x + 4$
16. $y + 2x$
17. $3x^2 + 2x + 6$
18. $y^3 + 2x^2y + 3x + 17$
19. $y^3 + 3xy^2 + xy + 6y$
20. $3x^2y + 2xy^2 + xy$
21. a. $6x^2$, $4x$, 7
    b. $8x^2y$, $2xy$
22. Answers will vary.
    A term is a product of numbers and variables. A polynomial is a sum or difference of one or more terms. The degree of a term is the sum of the exponents of all the variables in that term. The degree of a polynomial is the degree of its highest degree term. In terms of the Lab Gear, the degree of an expression is the lowest dimension that the blocks can be arranged in. A coefficient is the number that multiplies a term. Like terms are two or more expressions with the same variables and exponents.

LESSON 1.7

Perimeter

You will need:

the Lab Gear 

graph paper 

PERIMETER OF LAB GEAR BLOCKS

When we discuss the perimeter and area of the Lab Gear blocks, we will be thinking of the tops of the "flat" blocks, which are two-dimensional figures. For example, if you look at the 5-block from above, you would see this figure. Its area is 5 cm^2, and its perimeter is 12 cm.

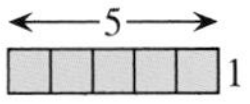

Area: 5 cm^2
Perimeter:
$5 + 1 + 5 + 1 = 12$ cm

Find and write the area and perimeter of these figures, which are the top faces of groups of yellow blocks.

1.

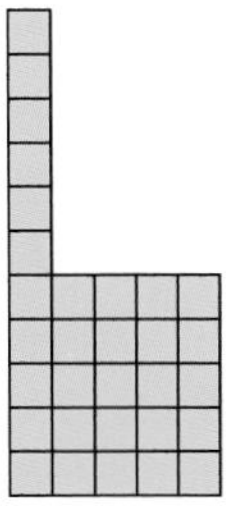

2.

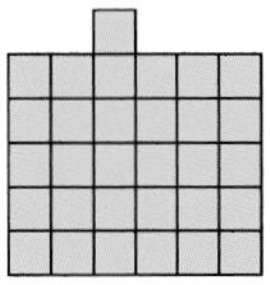

3.

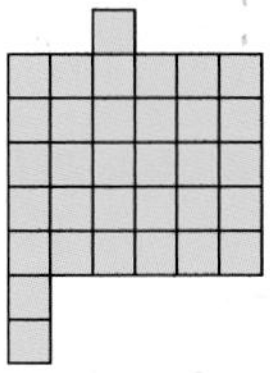

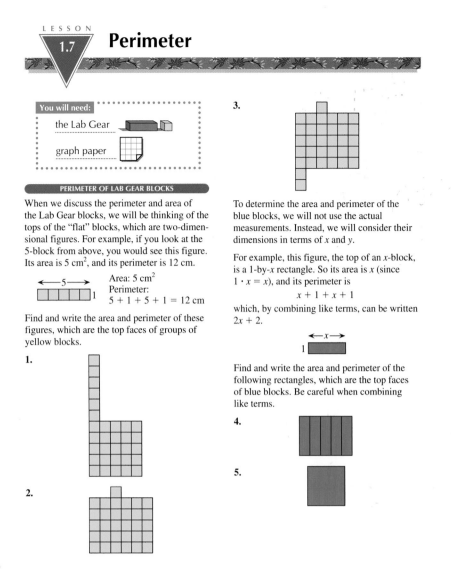

To determine the area and perimeter of the blue blocks, we will not use the actual measurements. Instead, we will consider their dimensions in terms of x and y.

For example, this figure, the top of an x-block, is a 1-by-x rectangle. So its area is x (since $1 \cdot x = x$), and its perimeter is

$$x + 1 + x + 1$$

which, by combining like terms, can be written $2x + 2$.

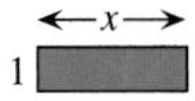

Find and write the area and perimeter of the following rectangles, which are the top faces of blue blocks. Be careful when combining like terms.

4.

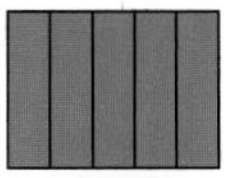

5.

▼ 1.7 Perimeter

Core Sequence: 1-20

Suitable for Homework: 1-15, 21-31

Useful for Assessment: 21-28

What this Lesson is About:

- An application of combining like terms in an interesting problem-solving context
- More patterns, tables, and graphs, previewing linear functions

Perimeter in itself is not a core concept in an algebra class. The reason it is part of the core sequence for this course is that it offers an opportunity to discover and apply algebraic ideas.

PERIMETER OF LAB GEAR BLOCKS

An opportunity to practice combining like terms

1.7 SOLUTIONS

1. A = 31 cm^2
   P = 32 cm
2. A = 31 cm^2
   P = 24 cm
3. A = 33 cm^2
   P = 28 cm
4. A = $5x$
   P = $2x + 10$
5. A = x^2
   P = $4x$

PERIMETER OF LAB GEAR FIGURES

Students devise various strategies to find the perimeters. Class discussion may be helpful here, so let students share and compare their approaches.

The convention that x is between 1 and 5, and y is between 5 and 10 is necessary, because otherwise the figures would look different, and actually have different perimeters.

MAKING FIGURES

The problems do not have to be done in order. If students accidentally solve 19 while working on 17, encourage them to record the solution.

Reversing the process (finding a figure of given perimeter, instead of the usual finding the perimeter of a given figure) is necessary to a solid, nonrote understanding of perimeter.

6. 

7. 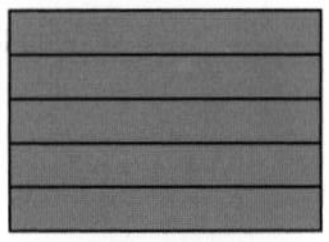

8. 

9. 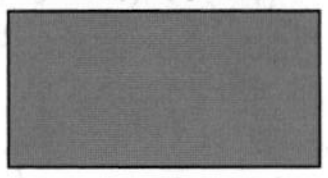

PERIMETER OF LAB GEAR FIGURES

In these problems, assume that x and y are positive. In fact, assume that x is between 1 and 5, and y is between 5 and 10.

Find the perimeter of these figures.

10. 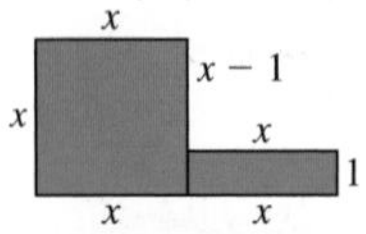

11. 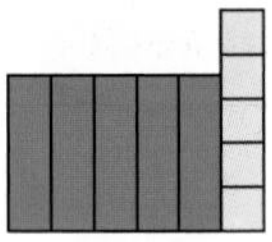

12. 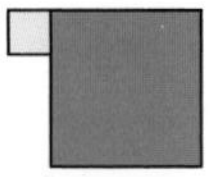

13. 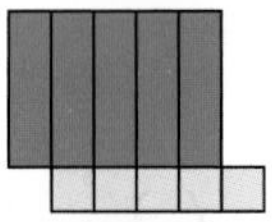

14. 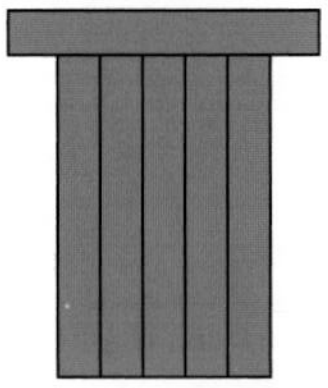

15. 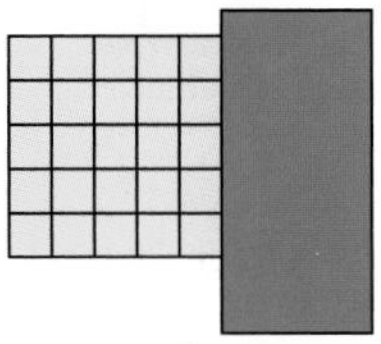

MAKING FIGURES

Use an xy-block and a 5-block to make figures having these perimeters. (These can be any shape. They do not have to be rectangles.) Sketch the figure in each case.

16. $2x + 2y + 2$

17. $2x + 2y + 10$

18. $2y + 12$

19. Repeat the last three problems using a y-block and a $5x$-block.

1.7 SOLUTIONS

6. $A = y$
   $P = 2y + 2$
7. $A = 5y$
   $P = 2y + 10$
8. $A = y^2$
   $P = 4y$
9. $A = xy$
   $P = 2x + 2y$
10. $P = 6x$
11. $P = 22$
12. $P = 4x + 2$
13. $P = 2x + 14$
14. $P = 4y + 2$
15. $P = 2y + 2x + 10$

For #16-19, answers will vary. One possible solution is given.

16. 

17. 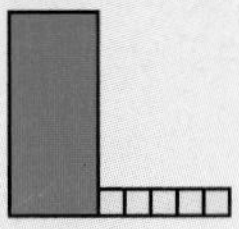

18. 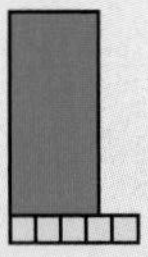

19. a) 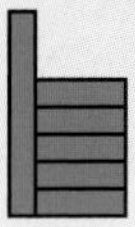

b) 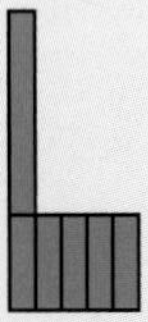

c) 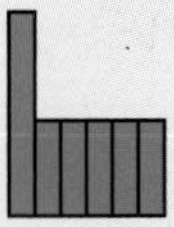

20.
a. Use another combination of blocks to get a perimeter of $2x + 2y + 2$.
b. Use another combination of blocks to get a perimeter of $2x + 2y + 10$.
c. Use another combination of blocks to get a perimeter of $2y + 12$.

PENTOMINO STRIPS

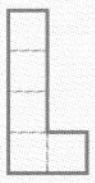

21. What is the perimeter of the L pentomino?

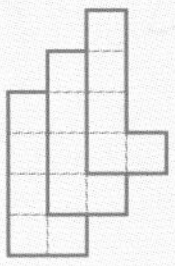

22. Draw a strip of L pentominoes, as shown in the figure above. What is the perimeter if you've used 3 L's?

23. Make a table like this, extending it to 7 rows.

L's	Perimeter
1	...
2	16
3	...

24. Explain how you would find the perimeter of a 100-L strip without drawing it.

25. How many L's were used if the perimeter was 92?

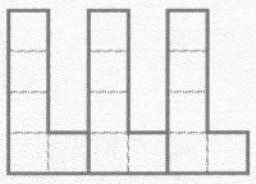

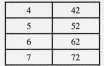

26. Repeat problems 22-25 for an arrangement like the one above.

27. You can use graphs to compare the perimeter patterns for the two pentomino strip arrangements.
a. Draw a pair of axes. Label the horizontal axis *Number of L's* and the vertical axis *Perimeter.*
b. Graph all the number pairs from your first table. For example, since the 2-L strip has a perimeter of 16, you would plot the point (2, 16).
c. On the same pair of axes, graph all the number pairs from your second table.
d. Compare the graphs. How are they the same? How are they different?

28. Repeat problems 22-25 using another pentomino.

POLYOMINO AREA AND PERIMETER

29. Arrange three blocks so that the perimeter of the resulting figure is $6x + 2y$. Find all the solutions you can.

30. Arrange four blocks so that the perimeter of the resulting figure is $8x + 18$. Find all the solutions you can.

31. Arrange five blocks so that the perimeter of the resulting figure is $2y + 2x + 12$. Find all the solutions you can.

PENTOMINO STRIPS

*T*his activity combines the search for patterns with an opportunity to use what has been learned about perimeter, graphing, and polyominoes. It previews later work on linear functions. It could be skipped for now and assigned any time before the end of Chapter 3.

POLYOMINO AREA AND PERIMETER

*O*f course comparing quantities that are measured in different units is not physically meaningful. We propose this exploration anyway, because the question does come up when thinking about area and perimeter. Questions of unit and dimension were discussed explicitly in Lessons 2 and 5.

1.7 S O L U T I O N S

21. P = 12

22. P = 20

23.

L's	Perimeter
1	12
2	16
3	20
4	24
5	28
6	32
7	36

24. The pattern is Perimeter = 4L + 8.
100-L strip: P = 4(100) + 8 = 408

25. L = 21

26. a.

L's	Perimeter
1	12
2	22
3	32
4	42
5	52
6	62
7	72

b. P = 10L + 2
100-L strip: P = 1002
c. L = 9

27. d. Both graphs are points that lie on diagonal lines going up from left to right. One line is steeper than the other.

28. Answers will vary.

31. Answers will vary.
Two possible solutions are given.

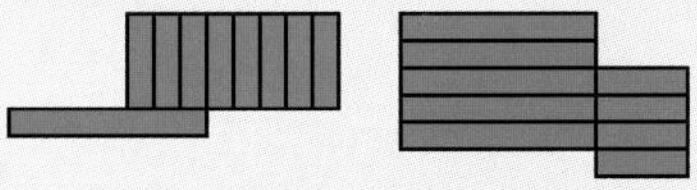

27. a., b., c.

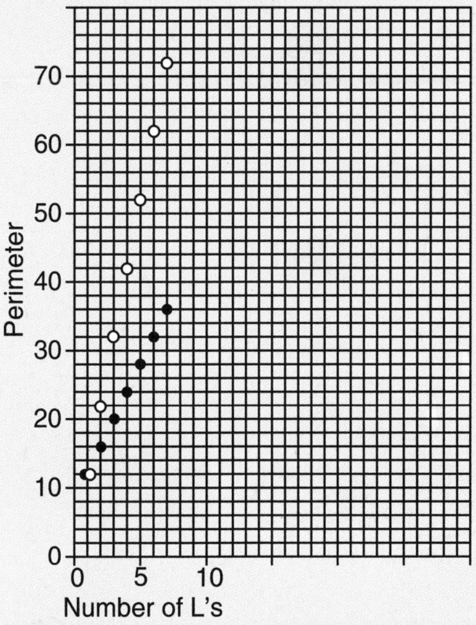

▼ 1.8
Window-Shopping

Core Sequence: 1-4

Suitable for Homework: 2-7

What this Lesson is About:

- A challenging problem based on area and perimeter. Students must infer a function from data, a very important skill in applied mathematics.
- A digression based on polyominoes that previews the Fibonacci number sequence

WINDOWS

The exploration is difficult, but it is within students' reach. If they are floundering, insist that they use the hints. These are not only *important*, they are necessary for a problem this tough. (The difficulty stems from the fact that this is a function of two variables, and especially from the fact that the students do not know what the variables are.)

It is preferable that you give no help, or rather, your help should be on the procedure of the search for the pattern, not on the substance. Encourage the students to make tables, to share their work with each other, to keep detailed notes, and so on.

Not all problems should be possible to solve quickly. Students need to develop tenacity and perseverance at least as much as they need to learn algebra.

LESSON 1.8

Window-Shopping

On weekends, Lara works at the A.B. GLARE window store. One day a customer, Mr. Alvin Cutterball, asked for an explanation of how the prices were chosen. Lara did not know. Later she asked her supervisor. The supervisor looked very busy and told her not to worry about it. Lara concluded that he probably didn't know and decided she would figure it out herself.

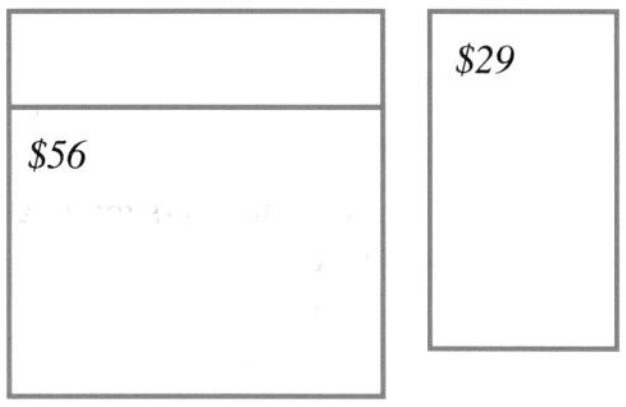

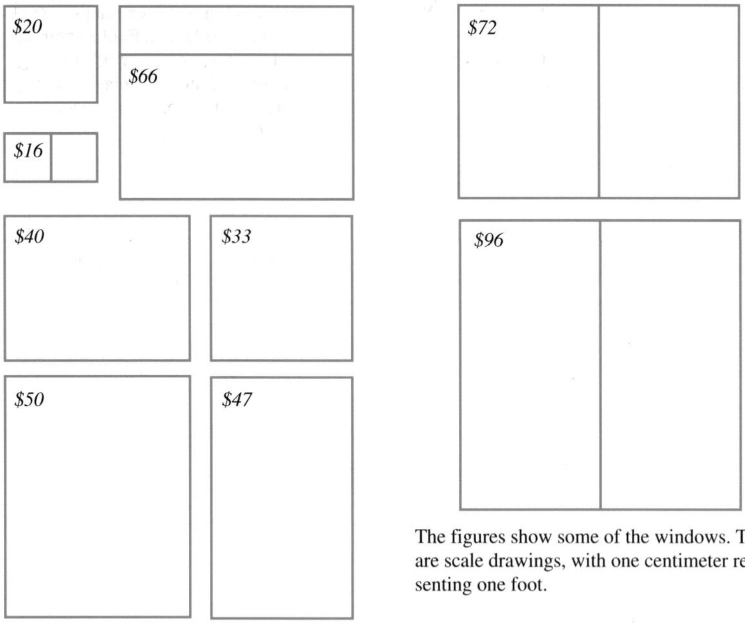

The figures show some of the windows. They are scale drawings, with one centimeter representing one foot.

1.8 SOLUTIONS

1. Answers will vary.
   The formula for double pane windows is Cost = $2P + A$, where P is the perimeter plus the length of the middle line and A is the area. For single pane windows, the formula is the same, but there is no middle line to add to the perimeter.
2. The $50 window is on sale. The regular price is $56.

1. **Exploration** The price of almost all the windows was calculated by following the same principle. Figure out how it was done.

   Important hints:
   - Work with other students.
   - Think about what numbers might affect pricing. (Some possibilities: length, width, area of glass, perimeter of window, number of panes, etc.…)
   - Keep an organized record of the numbers you come across in your exploration.
   - Keep a record of ideas you try, even if they end up not working.

2. One window is on sale and priced below what the system would indicate. Which one is it? How much does it cost when not on sale?

3. Draw scale models of windows that would cost the amounts below. Explain how you got your answers.

   a. $32 b. $84

4. **Report** Summarize your solutions to problems 1, 2, and 3 by writing an explanation of how window prices are calculated. Make it so clear that even Lara's supervisor could understand it. Explain how you figured out the pricing system, showing tables, lists, calculations, diagrams, or anything else that helped you solve the problem.

DISCOVERY A DOMINO PROBLEM

The figure shows all the ways to cover a two-by-four strip with dominoes.

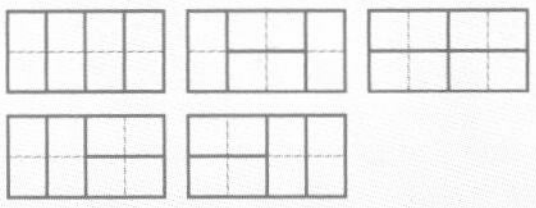

5. Find out how many ways there are to cover a two-by-five strip with dominoes. Sketch each way, making sure that you do not show the same way more than once.

6. Make a table like this one about strips of width 2, extending it to length 8. Note that there is only one way to cover a strip of length zero, and that is not to cover it!

Length of strip	Number of ways to cover it with dominoes
0	1
1	1
2	...
3	...
4	5
5	...

7. Look for the pattern in the numbers in the second column. Use the pattern to extend the table to length 10.

The Exploration could be assigned as a *problem of the week*, giving students several days to crack it if initial classroom efforts fail.

DISCOVERY A DOMINO PROBLEM

This is an enrichment activity based on polyominoes. It previews the Fibonacci number sequence, which will reappear in Chapter 2 and beyond.

In a Fibonacci sequence each term is the sum of the previous two terms.

The reason this is a Fibonacci sequence is that all the coverings for a strip of length n can be obtained by adding a vertical domino to the coverings of length $n - 1$, or by adding a horizontal pair of dominoes to the coverings of length $n - 2$. (Students do not need to understand this.)

1.8 SOLUTIONS

3. Answers will vary. Some students will use trial and error, but here's a systematic way.

   Let's assume we want to make a model of a single pane window that will cost $C. Since $P = 2L + 2W$ and $A = LW$, substituting into the equation $C = 2P + A$, we get $C = 2(2L + 2W) + LW$. Now choose a L or W and solve for the other side.

   Now, let's consider a double pane window and assume that the middle line is along the length of the window. Since $P = 3L + 2W$, we get $C = 2(3L + 2W) + LW$. Again, choose one of the sides and solve for the other.

   Here are examples of single and double pane windows that cost $32.

   Choose $L = 2$ for both windows

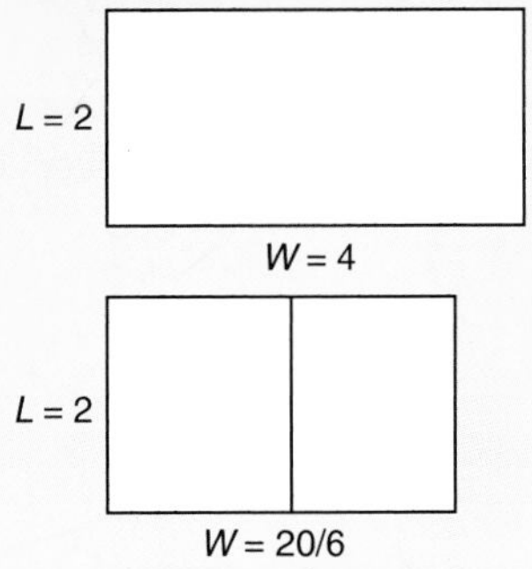

4. Answers will vary. The formula is given in #1.

5. There are eight ways. Four are shown.

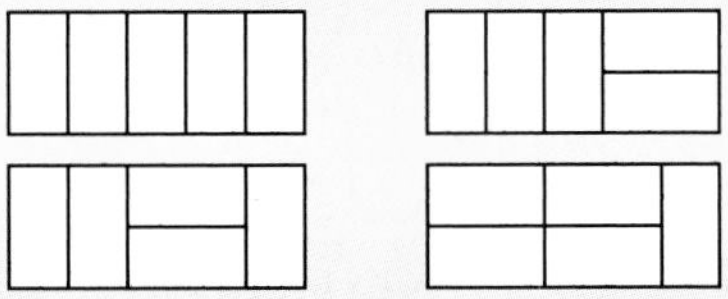

6.

Length of strip	Number of ways to cover it with dominoes
0	1
1	1
2	2
3	3
4	5
5	8
6	13
7	21
8	34
9	55
10	89

7. This is the Fibonacci sequence.

THINKING WRITING 1.B Drapes

Core Sequence: 1-4

Suitable for Homework:
the whole assignment

Useful for Assessment:
the whole assignment

What this Assignment is About:

- Applying a theme of the chapter to a real-world problem

*T*his is a fairly realistic application of area to a real-world problem. (The project allows you to make it even more realistic.) It is complicated enough to demand careful and organized work, but simple enough to be understandable.

THINKING WRITING 1.B Drapes

The A.B. GLARE window store also sells drapes. They stock full-length drapes that go down to the floor, as well as window-length drapes that just cover the window.

One day a customer, Ms. Phoebe Tall, came in with a list of the windows for which she needed drapes.

> **Window-length drapes:**
> three 2-by-3-ft windows
> two 3-by-3-ft windows
>
> **Full-length drapes:**
> two 3-by-7-ft door-windows
>
> **Undecided:**
> four 3-by-4-ft windows
> six 3-by-5-ft windows
>
> (The second number represents the height.)

The material Ms. Tall selected is priced at $3 per square foot. All her windows (except the door-windows, of course) are 3 feet above the floor.

She asked Lara to help her figure out what the cost of various options would be. She wanted to know the smallest amount she could spend. She also wanted to know how much it would cost if she used full-length drapes for all the "undecided" windows. After listening to Lara's explanations, she revealed that she was planning to spend no more than $800. Figure out what Lara should advise her to do.

1. Figure out the smallest amount Ms. Tall could spend, assuming that all the undecided windows are covered with window-length drapes. (Hint: First find the total area. Drawing sketches might help.)
2. Figure out the largest amount she could spend, assuming that all the undecided windows are covered with full-length drapes.
3. If she were planning to spend no more than $800, how many of the undecided windows could she cover with full-length drapes?
4. **Report** Write a full explanation of the results of your investigation. Include sketches that Lara could use to explain the options to Ms. Tall. Your report should consist of three parts: a problem statement, a detailed explanation, and a conclusion.
5. **Project** Find out how drapes are actually sold, and answer Ms. Tall's questions with information from a store in your area.

1.B SOLUTIONS

1. $648
2. $918
3. Answers will vary.
   Examples: four 3-by-4 ft. windows
   four 3-by-5 ft. windows
   $26 left over

   Or, two 3-by-4 ft. windows
   six 3-by-5 ft. windows
   $8 left over
4. Answers will vary.
   Students should organize their results. There is a fixed cost associated with the "decided" drapes. The "undecided" drapes is what Lara has to solve. Some combinations will have more left-over money than others. Students should justify their solutions.
5. Answers will vary.

LESSON 1.9

Adding and Multiplying

You will need:

the Lab Gear 

ADDITION

Using the Lab Gear, the addition $y + 5$ can be modeled in two ways. You can show two collections of blocks, y and 5. Or you can line up the blocks to get a figure that has length $y + 5$. Both methods are shown here.

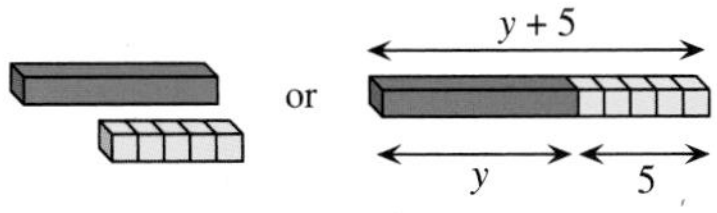

1. Sketch this addition both ways, $3x + 2$.

MULTIPLICATION

The multiplication $3 \cdot (2x + 1)$ can be modeled in two ways. One way is to show three collections of $2x + 1$.

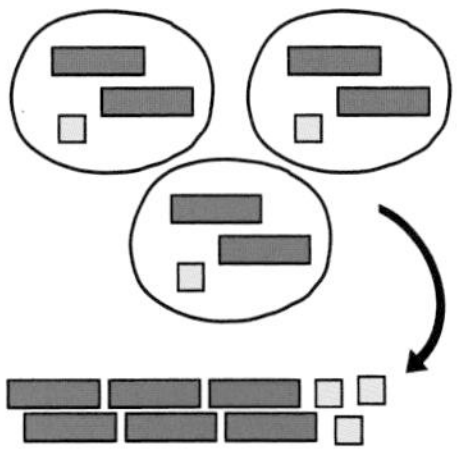

As you can see in the figure,
$3 \cdot (2x + 1) = 6x + 3$.

The other way is to use the corner piece. First set up the factors (3 and $2x + 1$) on the outside.

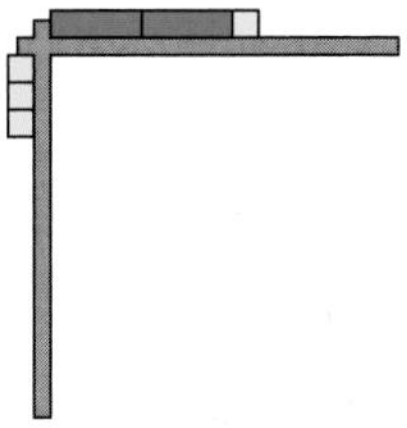

Then make a rectangle having those dimensions.

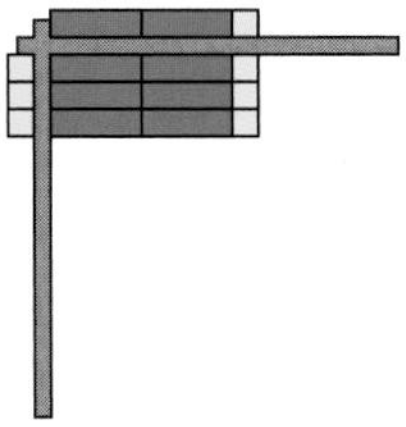

The rectangle represents the product. Again you see that $3 \cdot (2x + 1) = 6x + 3$. This is the familiar *length* · *width* = *area* formula for a rectangle.

2. Sketch this multiplication two ways, $2 \cdot (x + 3)$.
   a. Use collections of blocks.
   b. Use the corner piece.
3. What were the length, width, and area of the rectangle in problem 2?

▼ 1.9 Adding and Multiplying

Core Sequence: the whole lesson

Suitable for Homework: 14
(Problems 15-22 could be done at home, using sketches. But it would be better to assign the Pentomino Strips investigation from Lesson 7, the Domino Problem from Lesson 8, or the Word Figures material from Lesson 11 for homework, so the students will have the Lab Gear within reach when working on this lesson.)

What this Lesson is About:

- Lab Gear models for addition and multiplication (when no minus signs are involved)
- Order of operations
- Common algebra mistakes

ADDITION
MULTIPLICATION

How to model addition and multiplication was implied in previous chapters. Here it is addressed explicitly. Other operations will be discussed in Chapter 2.

Notice that there are two approaches: one based on collections of blocks, and another based on a careful rectangular arrangement of the blocks. Neither model works in every situation, and both should be mastered by students.

1.9 SOLUTIONS

3. $L = 2$
   $W = x + 3$
   $A = 2x + 6$

ORDER OF OPERATIONS

This issue comes up naturally when writing multiplications such as the ones in the preceding section. Note that we introduce order of operations one step at a time. Subtraction, division, and exponents will be treated in later chapters.

You should decide on the degree of complexity you want for the Exploration. Should students be allowed to use as many pairs of parentheses as they want? If so, the problem is more difficult, but it is also more informative, because there could be discussions of how to handle nested parentheses.

Most scientific and programmable calculators allow several levels of parentheses, and that feature can be used when working on this problem.

With any factors of degree 0 or 1, you can model the multiplication in the corner piece.

4. What multiplication is shown in this figure?

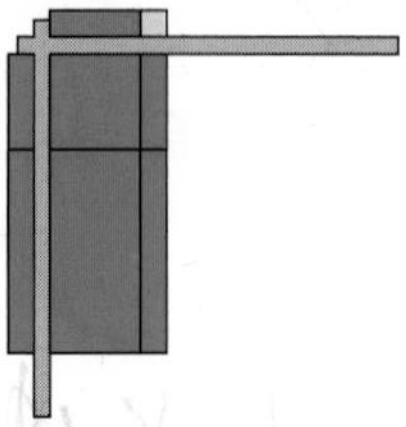

5. Multiplying the x by the x gave x^2. What other multiplications do you see in the figure above?

6. Multiply with the corner piece.
a. $3x \cdot 2$ b. $3 \cdot 2x$
c. $2x \cdot 3$ d. $2x \cdot 3y$

7. Multiply with the corner piece.
a. $5(x + 1)$ b. $x(x + 3)$

8. Find the area of a rectangle having the sides given below. For each write an equation of the form *length times width = area.*
a. 5 and $x + 3$
b. x and $2x + 5$

9. Find the sides of a rectangle having the given area. Each problem has at least two solutions. Find as many of them as you can and write an equation for each.
a. $6x$ b. $6x^2 + 3x$

10. These equations are of the form *length times width = area.* Use the Lab Gear to help you fill in the blanks.
a. $y \cdot$ _____ $= y^2 + xy$
b. $(x + 2) \cdot$ _____ $= 3x + 6$
c. (_____ $+ 3) \cdot x = 2xy + 3x$

Understanding the area model of multiplication will help you avoid many common algebra errors.

ORDER OF OPERATIONS

The figure above showed a multiplication. Some students write it like this: $x + 1 \cdot x + y$. Unfortunately, someone else might read it as *add the three terms*: x, $1 \cdot x$, and y. Simplified, this would be $x + x + y$, or $2x + y$. But the intended meaning was equivalent to $x^2 + xy + x + y$, as you can see on the figure. To avoid this kind of confusion, mathematicians have agreed on the following rule.

> **Rule:** When the operations of multiplication and addition (or subtraction) appear in the same expression, *multiplication should be performed first.* If we want to change this order, we have to use parentheses.

This means that one correct way to write the multiplication in the figure is $(x + 1)(x + y)$, which can mean only *multiply* $x + 1$ *by* $x + y$.

11. a. Show $2 \cdot x + 5$ with the Lab Gear. Sketch.
b. Next to your sketch show $2 \cdot (x + 5)$ with the Lab Gear. Sketch it. Keep the blocks on the table for the next problem.

12. a. Copy both collections of blocks from problem 11, substituting 1 for x. What is each expression equal to?
b. Repeat, using 5 for x.
c. Repeat, using 0 for x.

13. Can you find a value of x for which $2 \cdot x + 5 = 2 \cdot (x + 5)$? If so, what is the value? If not, why can't you find a value?

1.9 SOLUTIONS

4. $(x + y)(x + 1)$
5. $x \cdot 1$, $y \cdot x$, $y \cdot 1$
6. a. $6x$
b. $6x$
c. $6x$
d. $6xy$
7. a. $5x + 5$
b. $x^2 + 3x$
8. a. $5(x + 3) = 5x + 15$
b. $x(2x + 5) = 2x^2 + 5x$
9. a. 1 by $6x$, $1 \cdot 6x = 6x$
6 by x, $6 \cdot x = 6x$
2 by $3x$, $2 \cdot 3x = 6x$
3 by $2x$, $3 \cdot 2x = 6x$
b. 3 by $(2x^2 + x)$, $3(2x^2 + x) = 6x^2 + 3x$
x by $(6x + 3)$, $x(6x + 3) = 6x^2 + 3x$
$3x$ by $(2x + 1)$, $3x(2x + 1) = 6x^2 + 3x$

10. a. $y + x$
b. 3
c. $2y$
12. a. 7, 12
b. 15, 20
c. 5, 10
13. No, since $2(x + 5) = 2x + 10$, which is always five more than $2x + 5$, no matter what value of x we use

14. **Exploration** Insert parentheses in each expression, so as to get many different values. What are the greatest and smallest values you can find for each one?
   a. $0 \cdot 1 + 2 \cdot 3 + 4 \cdot 5 + 6 \cdot 7 + 8 \cdot 9$
   b. $0 + 1 \cdot 2 + 3 \cdot 4 + 5 \cdot 6 + 7 \cdot 8 + 9$

THE SAME OR DIFFERENT?

Students sometimes confuse $3 + x$ with $3x$. With the Lab Gear, it is easy to see the difference. $3 + x$ involves addition.

or

$3x$ involves multiplication.

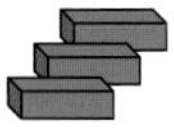

or

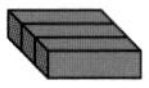

15. Find the value of $3 + x$ when:
   a. $x = 0$ b. $x = 5$
   c. $x = 0.5$

16. Find the value of $3x$ when :
   a. $x = 0$ b. $x = 5$
   c. $x = 0.5$

17. For most values of x, $3x$ does not equal $3 + x$. In fact there is only one number you can substitute for x that will make $3 + x$ equal to $3x$. Use trial and error to find this number.

18. Build these expressions with the Lab Gear. Sketch. Which two are the same?
   a. $6xy$ b. $2x + 3y$
   c. $2x \cdot 3y$ d. $5xy$

19. Build and sketch these two expressions with the Lab Gear.
   a. $2x + 3y$ b. $2xy + 3$

20. Use trial and error to find a pair of values of x and y that will make the two expressions in problem 19 have the same value.

21. Use the Lab Gear to show each expression. Sketch.
   a. $5 + x + y$ b. $5 + xy$
   c. $5x + y$ d. $5xy$

22. Choose values for x and y so that all four expressions in problem 21 have different values.

THE SAME OR DIFFERENT?

These problems provide practice with basic operations and substituting. They are based on traditional mistakes made by algebra students. The Lab Gear makes it easier to grasp which expressions are the same, and which are different.

1.9 SOLUTIONS

14. a. smallest is 0: $0(1 + 2 \cdot 3 + 4 \cdot 5 + 6 \cdot 7 + 8 \cdot 9)$
   greatest is 20,790: $(0 \cdot 1) + 2 \cdot (3 + 4) \cdot (5 + 6) \cdot (7 + 8) \cdot 9$
   b. smallest is 109: $0 + (1 \cdot 2) + (3 \cdot 4) + (5 \cdot 6) + (7 \cdot 8) + 9$
   greatest is 9,945: $0 + 1 \cdot (2 + 3) \cdot (4 + 5) \cdot (6 + 7) \cdot (8 + 9)$
15. a. 3
   b. 8
   c. 3.5
16. a. 0
   b. 15
   c. 1.5
17. 1.5
18. Sketches will vary. a. and c. are the same.
19. Sketches will vary.
   a.
   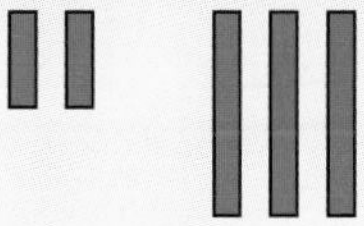
   b.
   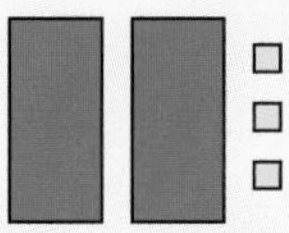
20. When $x = 3/2$, y can be any number and when $y = 1$, x can be any number.
22. Answers will vary.

▼ 1.10 Three Dimensions

Core Sequence: 1-10, 22-24

Suitable for Homework: 20-24

What this Lesson is About:

- More work with multiplication, previewing the distributive law and factoring
- Surface area problems provide more practice combining like terms
- A digression with polycubes, the 3-D version of polyominoes
- This lesson starts students thinking in three dimensions, an important skill if they are to pursue mathematics or science.

VOLUME

Volume, like area, provides a model of multiplication and the distributive law. A fuller discussion of volume will take place in Chapter 2.

MAKE A BOX

This gives students practice with recognizing the dimensions of a box. This will be important later on, as the volume model of multiplication is used to explore the distributive law and factoring.

LESSON 1.10 Three Dimensions

You will need: the Lab Gear

VOLUME

Definition: The *volume* of a solid is the number of unit cubes it would take to build it.

1. What is the volume of this box? Explain how you got your answer.

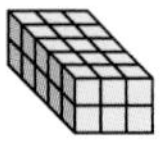

You can find the volume of a Lab Gear building by just adding the volume of each block. For example, both of these buildings have volume $x^3 + x^2$.

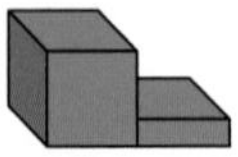

or

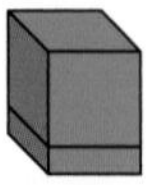

2. What is the volume of each of these buildings?

a

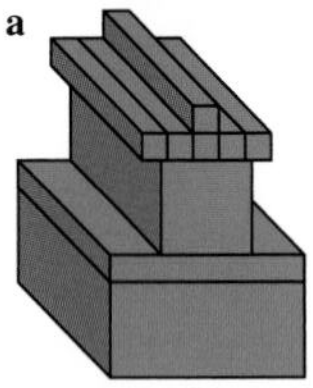

b

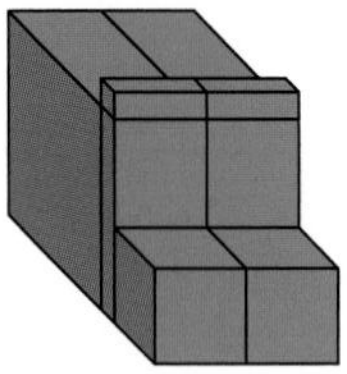

MAKE A BOX

Example: This box has volume $y^3 + xy^2 + y^2 + xy$, length $y + x$, width y, and height $y + 1$.

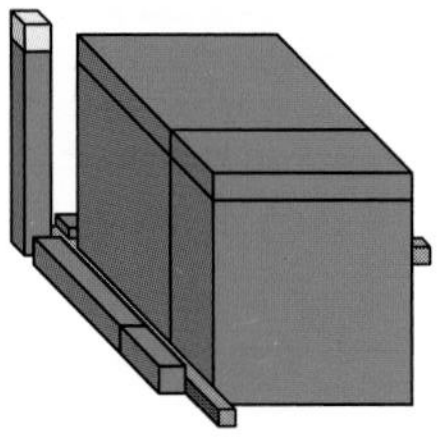

For each problem, the volume of a box is given.

a. Get the blocks.
b. Use them to make a box.
c. Write the length, width, and height.

3. $3xy + x^2y + xy^2$
4. $xy^2 + 2y^2$
5. $x^2y + 2xy + y$
6. $x^2y + xy^2 + xy + y^2$
7. $y^3 + y^2 + xy^2$
8. $x^3 + x^2y + 2x^2 + xy + x$

We will return to the volume of boxes in a future chapter.

SURFACE AREA

Definition: The *surface area* of a solid is the number of unit squares it would take to cover all its faces (including the bottom).

1.10 SOLUTIONS

1. 30 cube units. Count the 1-cubes or multiply the dimensions, $5 \cdot 3 \cdot 2 = 30$.
2. $y^2x + y^2 + yx^2 + 6y$, $2x^3 + 2y^2x + 2xy + 2x$
3. length = $y + x + 3$
   width = y
   height = x
4. length = $x + 2$
   width = y
   height = y
5. length = $x + 1$
   width = $x + 1$
   height = y
6. length = $x + 1$
   width = y
   height = $x + y$
7. length = $x + y + 1$
   width = y
   height = y
8. length = $x + 1$
   width = x
   height = $y + x + 1$

In simple cases, to figure out the surface area it helps to think of a paper jacket that would cover the whole block. The area of such a jacket is the surface area of the block.

For example, the surface area of the 5-block is 22 cm². Its volume, of course, is 5 cm³.

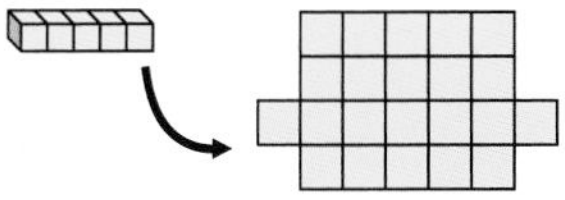

9. Find the surface area of the 25-block.

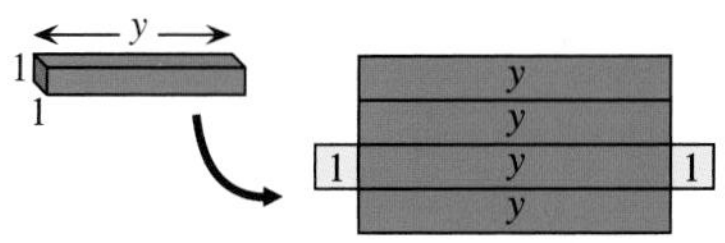

The surface area of the blue blocks can also be figured out by thinking of their jackets. For example, the y-block has a surface area of $4y + 2$.

10. Find the surface area of each of the other blue Lab Gear blocks.

DISCOVERY ***POLYCUBES***

Definition: *Polycubes* are obtained by joining cubes together face-to-face. They are the three-dimensional equivalent of polyominoes. Here is a *tetracube*.

There is just one *monocube*, and one *dicube*. There are two *tricubes* and eight *tetracubes*.

All of these polycubes look just like the corresponding polyominoes, except three of the tetracubes, which are really three-dimensional.

11. Find all the polycubes, monocube to eight tetracubes, with your blocks and try to sketch them. Hint: Two of the three-dimensional tetracubes are mirror images of each other.

12. Find the surface area of the polycubes you found in problem 11.

13. Find polycubes having volume 8 and as many different surface areas as possible. There are five different solutions.

14. Were any of your surface areas odd numbers? If yes, check your work. If no, explain why not.

15. For a given number of cubes, how would you assemble them to get the largest surface area? The smallest?

16. What would the largest possible surface area be for a polycube having volume 100?

17. Explain in words how you would find the largest possible surface area for a given volume.

18. For each of the following volumes, find the smallest possible surface area.

a. 12 b. 18 c. 20
d. 24 e. 27 f. 30

19. Explain in words how you would find the smallest possible surface area for a given volume.

SURFACE AREA

This is traditionally seen as a difficult topic, even though it is taught in middle school. What usually makes it difficult is that students are asked to visualize three-dimensional objects without getting any hands-on experience with them. Here, the availability of the Lab Gear blocks and the fact that students have done a lot of thinking, talking, and writing about dimension, makes surface area more accessible.

Again, keep in mind that this is not a core topic in an algebra class. You certainly should not teach surface area formulas. The point of this work is to provide an environment in which to do algebraic work, specifically combining like terms.

DISCOVERY ***POLYCUBES***

This is a three-dimensional equivalent to Lessons 1 and 2.

1.10 SOLUTIONS

9. 70 square units

10.

Block	Surface Area
y	$4y + 2$
x	$4x + 2$
x^2	$2x^2 + 4x$
y^2	$2y^2 + 4y$
$5x$	$12x + 10$
$5y$	$12y + 10$
xy	$2xy + 2x + 2y$
x^2y	$2x^2 + 4xy$
xy^2	$2y^2 + 4xy$
x^3	$6x^2$
y^3	$6y^2$

11., 12.

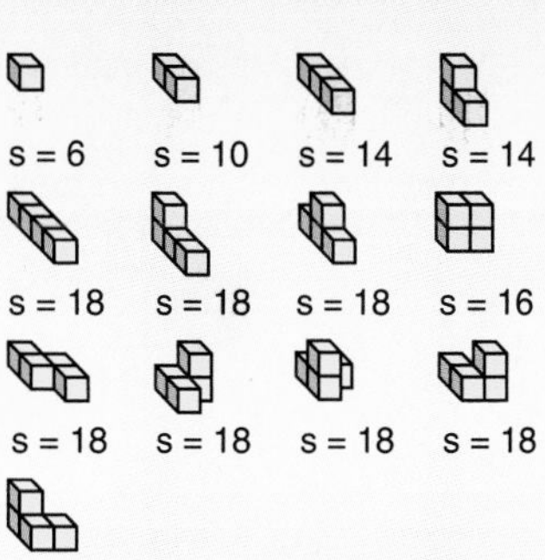

13.

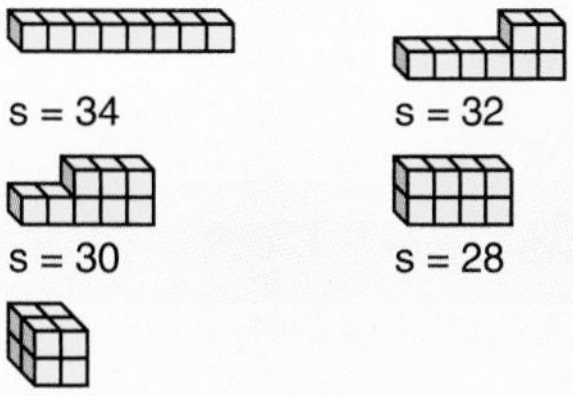

14. No. This is similar to the polyominoes. Since every face has an opposite face and there are no unmatched faces, the surface area is an even number.

15. For a given number of cubes, the smallest surface area occurs when the cubes are arranged into a large cube or a rectangular solid with as few odd pieces as possible. The largest surface area occurs when the cubes are arranged like a train.

16. largest surface area $= 4 \cdot \text{volume} + 2 = 402$

17. same as number 15.

18. a. 32 b. 42 c. 48
d. 52 e. 54 f. 62

19. same as number 15

MORE ON POLYCUBES

*M*ore three-dimensional thinking. Once again, interlocking cubes would be helpful.

*S*tudents need not have completed all of Lesson 10. These problems depend solely on 10 and the text preceding it.

REVIEW *PERIMETER*

*T*his is homework material, since the students probably won't need to manipulate the blocks to find the perimeters.

MORE ON POLYCUBES

20. Find all the polycubes having volume less than 5. Put aside all the ones that are box-shaped. The remaining pieces should have a total volume of 27. Using wooden cubes and glue, make a set of puzzle pieces out of these polycubes. Assemble them into a 3-by-3-by-3 cube. (This classic puzzle is called the Soma® Cube.)

21. There are 29 pentacubes. Twelve look like the pentominoes, and 17 are "truly" three-dimensional. Find them all and sketch them.

REVIEW *PERIMETER*

Find the perimeter of each figure.

22.

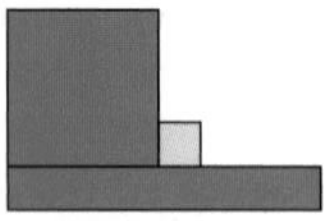

23.

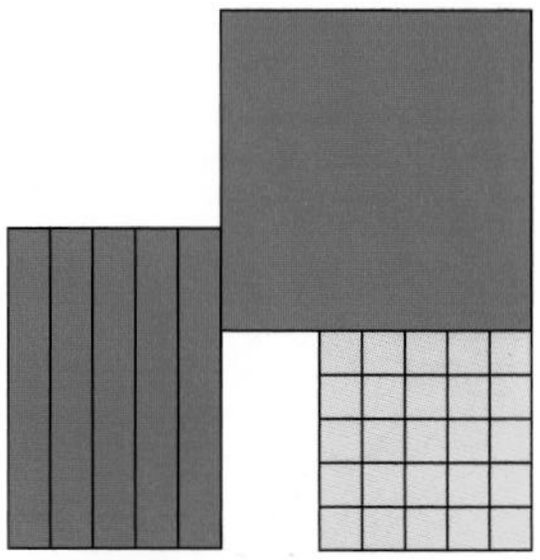

24.

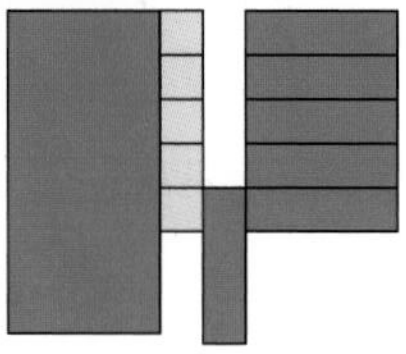

1.10 SOLUTIONS

20. Be patient. It will probably take many tries to build this Soma® Cube.
21. Some of the 17 "truly" three-dimensional pentacubes have mirror images. There are five that do not have mirror images.
22. $2x + 2y + 2$
23. $4y + 30$
24. $4x + 4y + 2$

LESSON 1.11 Word Figures

WORD TRIANGLES

Imagine you have a supply of letter tiles, and you use them to make word triangles like this one.

A
L A
A L E
R E A L

Rules: Each row contains the letters of the previous one, plus one more. It's OK to scramble the letters from one row to the next.

1. Extend this word triangle.
2. Make a word triangle with your own letters.
3. How many letter tiles are used in a five-row word triangle?
4. Make a table like this, extending it to ten rows.

Rows	Tiles
1	1
2	3
3	6
4	...

5. The numbers you found in problem 4 (1, 3, 6, ...) are called the *triangular numbers*. Explain how they are calculated.
6. Extend the above word triangle up to **ARGUABLE**. (Along the way, you might use **ALGEBRA**.)

WORD LADDERS

Rules: From one row to the next, change one letter only. It's OK to scramble the letters.

For example:

R E A L
L E A D
L O A D
F O L D
F O O D

7. Make up a word ladder with your own letters. Choose your word length, and use as many rows as you need. It's fun to choose related words for the beginning and end of the ladder, like **CAR** and **BUS**.

The above example, from **REAL** to **FOOD**, took four steps (and five rows). It is an example of a *perfect* word ladder. For a word ladder to be called perfect, two things must be true:

a. Every letter from the original word must be changed in the final word.
b. If the word has n letters, the ladder must take exactly n steps.

For a five-letter word, a perfect ladder would take five steps (one per letter) and therefore six rows.

8. How many tiles would a five-letter perfect word ladder require?
9. Make a table of the number of tiles required for perfect word ladders, extended to word length 10.

▼ 1.11 Word Figures

Core Sequence: none of the lesson

Suitable for Homework: the whole lesson

What this Lesson is About:

- A digression that starts with word puzzles and ends up with a method for calculating triangular numbers

Word puzzles may appeal to students who do not necessarily like math (though your students may be surprised to learn that mathematicians often like word puzzles).

This is a short lesson that leads to an interesting general approach to how to calculate triangular numbers. This previews some of the work in Chapter 5 on sums of arithmetic sequences.

The lesson can be used as a source of homework when no other homework seems practical, because you are in a lesson that relies heavily on the manipulatives.

WORD TRIANGLES

Problem 1 can easily be answered by just adding one line to the triangle, but you or your students may want to up the ante. If so, problem 6 offers a stiffer challenge.

WORD LADDERS

Word ladders were invented by Lewis Carroll, under the name *doublets*.

1.11 SOLUTIONS

1. Answers will vary.
2. Answers will vary.
3. 15
4.

Rows	Tiles
1	1
2	3
3	6
4	10
5	15
6	21
7	28
8	36
9	45
10	55

5. Add the number of rows to the previous number of tiles.
6. A
L A
A L E
R E A L
L A R G E
G A R B L E
A L G E B R A
A R G U A B L E
7. Answers will vary.
8. (5 steps)(6 rows) = 30 tiles
9.

Rows	Tiles
1	1
2	6
3	12
4	20
5	30
6	42
7	56
8	72
9	90
10	110

PUTTING IT TOGETHER

This is the mathematical payoff of the lesson. At this stage, it is enough for students to figure out a strategy for the calculation of the nth triangular number based on the graphic method shown. They should also be able to express it in words, and to apply it.

Of course the lesson can lead to a formula, if the class is sophisticated enough, but this is definitely not to be expected in the first chapter of Algebra 1.

POLYOMINO PUZZLES

The puzzles are not very difficult, once the pieces are made. (Interlocking cubes are a big help if you have access to them.)

Problem 2, once again, is an experience with triangular numbers. Recognizing that the same pattern underlies problems that appear different is what mathematics is all about.

Problem 3 incorporates review of whole number factoring and prime numbers.

The rectangle puzzles are not particularly difficult, but there are many of them. Students can be encouraged to divide up the work.

The puzzle-solution records can be colored and displayed on a bulletin board.

Word Length	Tiles
1	2
2	6
3	12
4	...

10. The numbers you found in problem 9 (1, 6, 12, ...) are called the *rectangular numbers*. Explain how they can be calculated.

11. Make up a word ladder from **MATH** to **GAME**.

PUTTING IT TOGETHER

12. This figure shows the third triangular number.

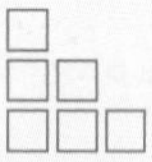

Draw a sketch of two copies of this triangle, arranged together to make a rectangle.

13. This figure shows the fourth rectangular number.

Show how you could divide it into two equal triangular numbers.

14. **Summary** Describe the relationship between triangular numbers and rectangular numbers.

15.
a. Explain how to calculate triangular numbers by first calculating rectangular numbers.
b. Calculate the 100th triangular number.

POLYOMINO PUZZLES

16. Using graph paper and scissors, or interlocking cubes, make a set of polyominoes having area greater than 1 and less than 5. You should have one domino, two triominoes, and five tetrominoes, for a total of eight puzzle pieces with no duplicates.

17. Using the same unit as you used for the puzzle pieces, draw staircases with base 3, 4, 5, 6, and 7. The first one is shown here.

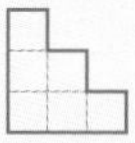

Now cover each staircase in turn with some of your puzzle pieces. Record your solutions on graph paper. For the last staircase, you will need all of your pieces.

18. Make a list of all the rectangles, including squares, having area 28 or less. Their dimensions (length and width) should be *whole numbers greater than 1.* (In other words, the shortest sides should be 2.) There are 25 such rectangles.

19. Draw these rectangles, and use the puzzle pieces to cover them. Record your solutions on graph paper. (It is impossible to cover one of the rectangles.)

POLYOMINO AREA AND PERIMETER

Think of the monomino. Its area is 1 and its perimeter is 4. Think of the domino. Its area is 2 and its perimeter is 6.

1.11 SOLUTIONS

10. Multiply the word length by one plus the word length.

11. Answers will vary.

12.

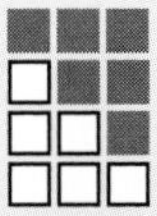

13.

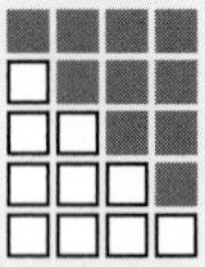

14. Each rectangular number is twice its corresponding triangular number.

15. a. To get the triangular number, divide the rectangular number by 2.
b. rectangular number = 100(101) = 10,100
triangular number = 10100/2
= 5050

18.

Area	Length	Width
28	14	2
28	7	4
27	9	3
26	13	2
25	5	5
24	12	2
24	6	4
24	8	3
22	11	2
21	7	3
20	5	4
20	10	2
18	9	2
18	6	3
16	8	2
16	4	4
15	5	3
14	7	2
12	4	3
12	6	2
10	5	2
9	3	3
8	4	2
6	3	2
4	2	2

19. The 9-by-3 rectangle is impossible to do since no combination of the puzzle pieces will have a total area of 27.

The areas representing the pieces are: 2, 3, 3, 4, 4, 4, 4, 4.

To cover a rectangle, find combinations of these areas that will add up

20. **Exploration** Is the number representing the perimeter of a given polyomino always greater than the number representing its area, or can it be equal to it, or even smaller? Look over your notes and sketches from Lesson 2, and experiment some more on graph paper if you need to. Then write a paragraph to answer this question fully, with examples and graph paper illustrations.

21. Find out if there are polyominoes having both area and perimeter equal to
    a. 14 b. 15 c. 16
    d. 17 e. 18 f. 20

WORD SQUARES

This is a word square.

	a	b	c	d
a	M	A	T	H
b	A	C	R	E
c	T	R	E	E
d	H	E	E	L

Note that the words can be read across or down. The largest word square in the English language took years of hard work to discover. It is made up of obscure ten-letter words.

22. How many letter tiles are used in the word square above?

23. Make a table showing the number of tiles required for word squares, extended to word length 10.

Word Length	Tiles
1	1
2	4
3	9
4	...

24. The numbers you found in problem 11 (1, 4, 9, ...) are called the *square numbers*. Explain how they can be calculated.

25. There is an interesting pattern based on adding pairs of consecutive triangular numbers (1 + 3, 3 + 6, ...) Explain it.

26. Draw a sketch of the third triangular number put together with the fourth triangular number (upside down) to show a square number.

27. What do you think the 100th triangular number and the 101st triangular number add up to?

28. Make a word square using these clues. The answer words are all four letters long and can be read both across and down.
    a. Made to be played.
    b. You learned about it in this chapter.
    c. Don't make one!
    d. A piece of cake.

Note: The 3-by-9 rectangle puzzle is possible only if you allow the use of the monomino (a single square) as a puzzle piece.

For more puzzles of this type, incorporating many math lessons, see *Pentomino Activities*, by Henri Picciotto (Creative Publications, 1984).

WORD SQUARES

More problem solving with words and numbers. Work with square and triangular numbers.

1.11 SOLUTIONS

to the area of the rectangle. Some rectangles have more than one combination.

20. Answers will vary. Here is one explanation.
    Draw the line perimeter = area ($y = x$).
    Draw a vertical line at the given area. Look at the intersection of the vertical line and the line $y = x$. If the intersection is between the shortest and longest perimeter graphs, inclusive, and the area is even, there exists a polyomino with the area equal to the perimeter.

    If there are even perimeters on this vertical line between the line $y = x$ and the longest perimeter graph, there exists a polyomino with perimeter greater than the area.

    If there are even perimeters on this vertical line between the line $y = x$ and the shortest perimeter graph, there exists a polyomino with perimeter less than the area.

21. a. No b. No c. Yes
    d. No e. Yes f. Yes

22. 16

23.

Word Length	Tiles
1	1
2	4
3	9
4	16
5	25
6	36
7	49
8	64
9	81
10	100

24. Square the word length to get the number of tiles.

25. Adding the consecutive triangular numbers will give the square numbers.

26.
```
• ○ ○ ○
• • ○ ○
• • • ○
• • • •
```

27. The sum of 100th and 101st triangular numbers give the 101st square number. To get the square number, take the term number and square it. So the 101st square number is 10,201.

28. g a m e
    a r e a
    m e s s
    e a s y

▼ 1.12
Area on the Geoboard

Core Sequence: the whole lesson

Suitable for Homework:
(using dot paper) 4-6, 14-16

Useful for Assessment: 16

What this Lesson is About:

- First experience with a tool that will be crucial to our development of ideas of proportional thinking, slope, and square root

There will be a geoboard lesson in each chapter, in a sequence intended to provide a hands-on base on which to build the concepts of proportion and square roots. This lesson emphasizes area, in accordance with the theme of the chapter. Geoboard area will eventually lead to work with square roots.

The initial Exploration is designed to get students involved with area as counting, a necessary prerequisite to a more sophisticated understanding. Another purpose of the activity is to introduce the concept of area of shapes that include angles other than 90 degrees.

TRIANGLES
VERTICES

These problems are there to get students familiar with this new geometric environment, and with the use of coordinates on the geoboard.

LESSON 1.12
Area on the Geoboard

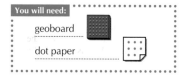

You will need:
- geoboard
- dot paper

This geoboard shape has area 18.

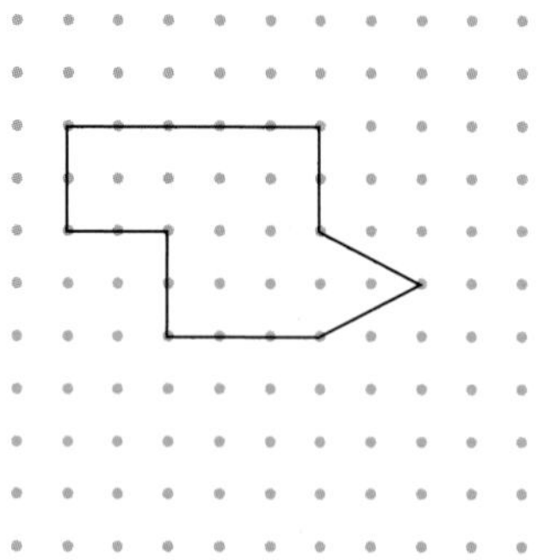

1. **Exploration** Find as many geoboard shapes having area 18 as you can. They do not need to be rectangles. You are allowed to stretch the rubber band in any direction whatsoever, including diagonals. Sketch each shape on dot paper.

TRIANGLES

2. On your geoboard make three triangles, each one satisfying one of the following conditions. Sketch each triangle on dot paper.
   a. One side is horizontal, and one is vertical.
   b. One side is horizontal, no side is vertical.
   c. No side is horizontal or vertical.

3. Repeat problem 2 for these conditions.
   a. Two sides are of equal length, one horizontal and the other vertical.
   b. Two sides are of equal length, but neither is horizontal or vertical.

VERTICES

Definition: The corners of geometric figures such as triangles and rectangles are called *vertices.* (Singular: *vertex.*)

4. Make a figure on the geoboard having vertices in order at (4, 6), (7, 5), (8, 3), (8, 2), (6, 0), (2, 0), (0, 2), (0, 3), (1, 5).

5. Do not remove the rubber band from problem 4. Using another rubber band, make a figure having vertices in order at (2, 2), (6, 2), (5, 1), (3, 1).

6. Add eyes to the face. What are the coordinates of their vertices?

AREA TECHNIQUES

7. Make a triangle having vertices at (0, 0), (0, 10), and (10, 0). What is its area? Explain how you figured it out.

8. Make a triangle having vertices at (0, 10), (0, 6), and (3, 6).
   a. With another rubber band, make a rectangle that shares three of its vertices with the triangle. What are the coordinates of the fourth vertex of the rectangle?
   b. What is the area of the rectangle?
   c. What is the area of the triangle?

9. Find the area of a triangle having vertices at (0, 10), (0, 5), and (7, 5).

1.12 SOLUTIONS

1. Answers will vary
2. Answers will vary.
3. Answers will vary.

4., 5.

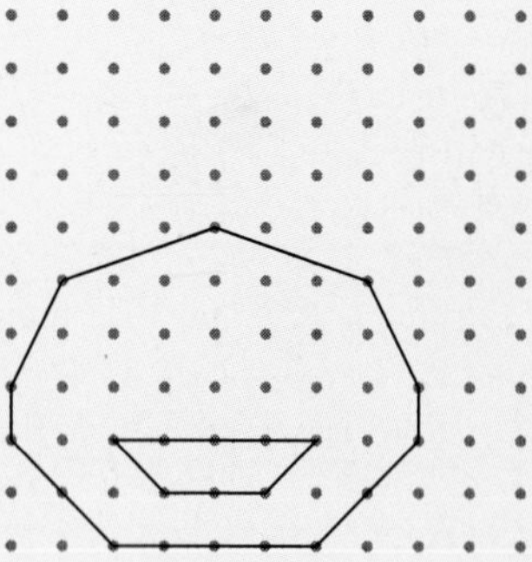

(0, 0)

6. Answers will vary.
7. 50 square units. Since the area of the triangle is half the area of the geoboard, divide the area of the geoboard by two.
8. The area of the rectangle is 12 square units. Since the area of the triangle is half that of the rectangle, the area of the triangle is 6 square units.
9. 17.5 square units

10. On your geoboard, make two different-shaped triangles that satisfy these conditions: one horizontal and one vertical side, and area 10. Record your solutions on dot paper.

11. Repeat problem 10 for area 9.

12. Copy these figures on your geoboard (or on dot paper). Find the area of each one. Explain how you did it.

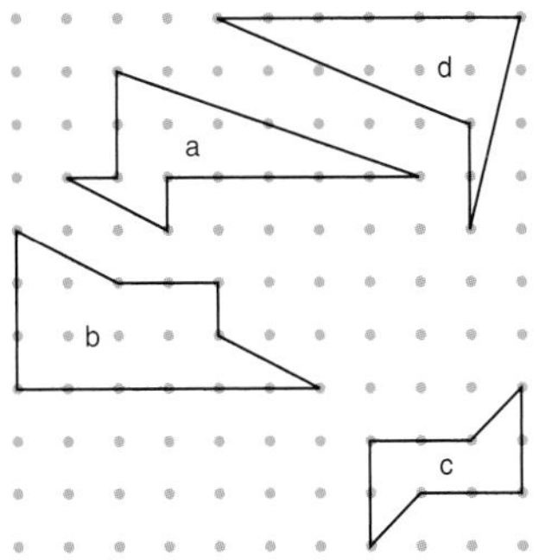

13. On your geoboard, make the triangle having vertices at (0, 10), (0, 4), and (3, 6).
    a. With another rubber band, divide the triangle into two smaller triangles, such that they each have one horizontal and one vertical side. Find the area of all three triangles.
    b. With another rubber band, make the smallest rectangle that covers the original triangle. What is the area of the rectangle?

14. Find the area of the triangle having vertices at (0, 0), (0, 7), and (3, 5).

15. Record your solutions on dot paper.
    a. Make five triangles having a horizontal side of length 6 and area 15.
    b. Make five triangles having a horizontal side of length other than 6 and area 15.
    c. Make five triangles having a vertical side of length 7 and area 10.5.

16. Find the area of the triangle having vertices at (0, 0), (0, 5), and (3, 7).

17. **Summary** Explain how one finds the area of a geoboard triangle having one horizontal or vertical side.

AREA TECHNIQUES

This is the heart of the lesson. Students develop an approach to finding the area of many geoboard shapes.

It is essential that you avoid teaching area formulas here. In later chapters, when dealing with triangles without any horizontal or vertical sides, knowledge of a formula involving the base and height of a triangle will be entirely useless, or more likely destructive, because students will know neither base nor height.

Finding area by addition and subtraction of known pieces will allow students to find any geoboard area, and reinforce the actual meaning of area, which for many students is hidden by formulas. (For example, they believe that "area is when you multiply," which is at best a partial truth, and at worst misleading because it is not based on a full understanding. Area can be found by addition, subtraction, multiplication, or division, depending on the context.)

1.12 SOLUTIONS

10. Any triangle with horizontal and vertical sides of 1 and 20, 20 and 1, 4 and 5, 5 and 4, 2 and 10, or 10 and 2

11. Any triangle with horizontal and vertical sides of 1 and 18, 18 and 1, 2 and 9, 9 and 2, 6 and 3, or 3 and 6

12. The general procedure is to split the figure into triangles first, having horizontal and vertical sides. Find the area of each rectangle that shares all three vertices of these triangles. Divide these areas by two. The area of the figure is the sum of these halves.
    a. 7 square units b. 10 square units
    c. 4 square units d. 7 square units

13. a. This is called the addition method. Find the area of the smaller triangles and add them up to get the area of the original triangle.
    Answers: 6 square units, 3 square units, 9 square units
    b. This is called the rectangular method. Draw the rectangle so that it shares the vertical side (or horizontal side) of the triangle. The area of the rectangle is twice the area of the triangle.
    Answer: 18 square units

14. 10.5 square units

15. Answers will vary. Students will do this problem in different ways, but here's one way to proceed. Students can double the given area. Then find a rectangle that has this area and satisfies the stated condition. The triangles that share one common side with the rectangle and the other vertex anywhere on the opposite side have the same area.
    This transformation is called *shearing*. See figure.

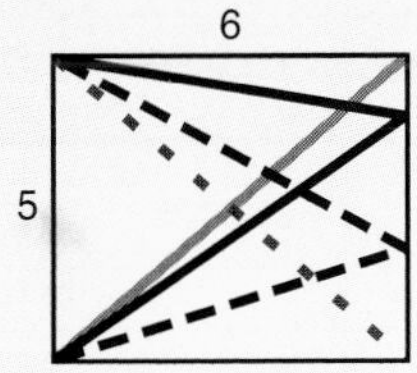

16. 7.5 square units

17. Answers will vary.
    The two methods are called the addition and rectangular method of finding the area of triangles with horizontal or vertical sides. See #13 for more details. Students can also use the formula, *area of a triangle = half the base times the height*, if they've discovered it.

THINKING WRITING **1.C**

More Window Prices

Core Sequence: none of the assignment

Suitable for Homework:
the whole assignment

Useful for Assessment:
the whole assignment

What this Assignment is About:

- Another example of looking for a pattern in real-world data

This time, the amount of data is smaller, but with the experience from Lesson 8 this should be quite straightforward.

This assignment is a perfect way to assess what individual students learned from the cooperative work in Lesson 8.

THINKING WRITING

1.C More Window Prices

In Lesson 8 you figured out how window prices were determined in an imaginary store. Real prices are probably not determined this way.

Window manufacturers use a special four-number code for describing the size of standard two-pane windows like those shown below. The first two numbers give the width in feet and inches, and the last two numbers give the height. For example, the code 2636 means that the window is 2 feet 6 inches wide and 3 feet 6 inches high.

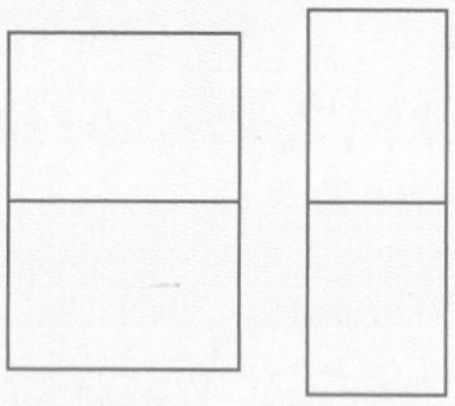

2636 1640

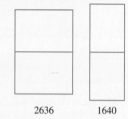

The prices for some windows are given below. You will investigate how the price depends on the dimensions of the window.

Code	Price
3030	$108.00
4030	$135.00
3040	$130.50
4040	$162.00

1. What are the dimensions of a 1640 window?
2. Use the code to figure out the dimensions of the windows. Make a table showing the code, the dimensions, and the price. You may also want to include other measurements, like the perimeter or area.
3. Experiment to figure out how the prices were determined. (The formula is not the same as the one used by the A.B. GLARE window store.) Try to find a pattern. According to your pattern, what should a 3050 window cost?
4. **Report** Write a report about this problem.
   - First, clearly state the problem you are solving.
   - Next, explain the results of your investigation. Include the table you made and explain how you used it to find a formula relating the code to the price. Include sketches and show your calculations in a systematic way. Give a couple of examples to illustrate that your formula really works. Explain why the order of the numbers in the code is important. For example, compare the cost of a 3050 window with the cost of a 5030 window. Make another price list showing what some other windows should cost.
   - Write a brief conclusion commenting on your results. Explain why this method of pricing makes sense. Would it still make sense for very large or very small windows? If you do not think so, can you think of a better way?

1.C SOLUTIONS

1. 1 foot 6 inches wide and 4 feet high
2.

Code	Width (feet)	Height (feet)	Area (sq. ft.)	Perim.* (feet)	Price ($)
3030	3	3	9	15	$108.00
4030	4	3	12	18	$135.00
3040	3	4	12	17	$130.50
4040	4	4	16	20	$162.00

* Note: The perimeter here includes the center line.
$P = 2(w + h) + w = 3w + 2h$

3. Price = $4.5P + 4.5A$, where P is the perimeter and A is the area.
A 3050 window costs $153.00

4. Answers will vary.
   - Since the formula is Price = $4.5P + 4.5A$ and $P = 3W + 2H$, the order of the numbers in the code is important. The first two digits in the code represent the width, and since the perimeter is $3W + 2H$, windows with the same area but larger width will cost more.
   - We do not know which window is easier to manufacture. But this method of pricing makes sense because larger width windows will need more material for the middle line and thus should cost more.

Essential Ideas

VARIABLES AND CONSTANTS

1. Explain, with examples, how to figure out the names of the other blue blocks by using 5-blocks, x-blocks, y-blocks, and the corner piece.

If $x = 5$ and $y = 3$, we can use the Lab Gear to think of xy, x^2y, xy^2.

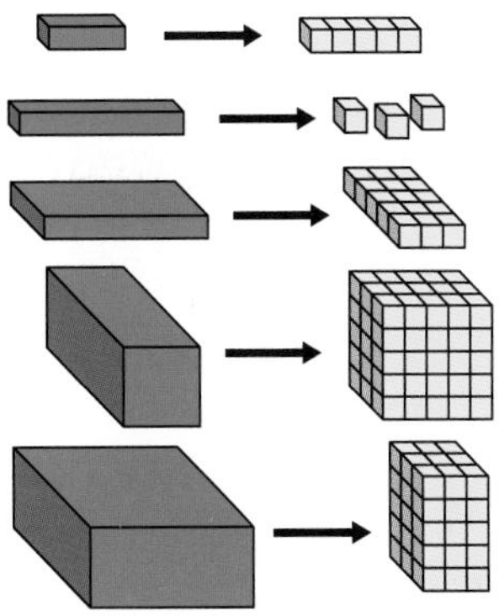

Here is $x^3 + x^2 + 3x + 5$, if $x = 2$.

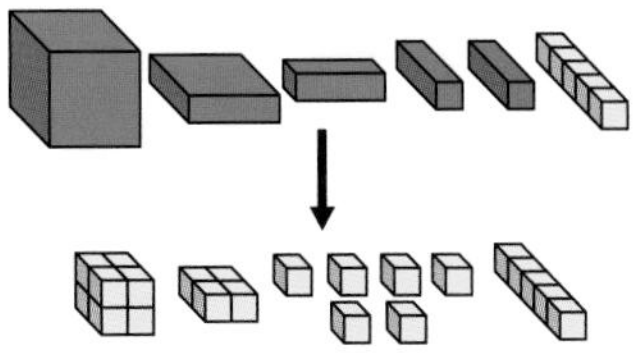

For each problem, write what the blocks show in terms of the variables x and y, then use substitution to evaluate them for:

a. $x = 0$ and $y = 2$;
b. $x = 5$ and $y = 1$;
c. $x = 2$ and $y = 3$.

2.

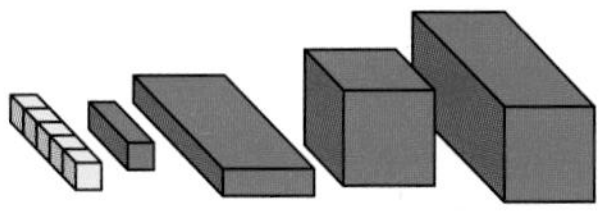

3.

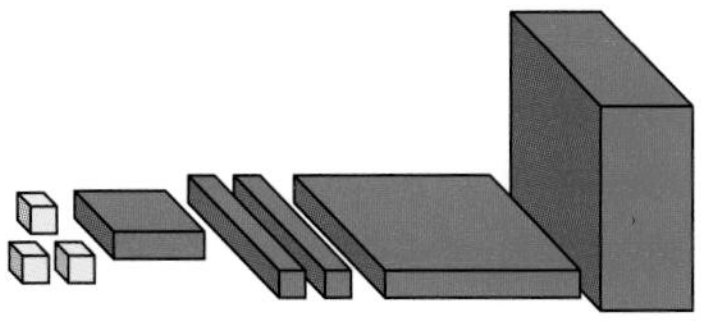

LIKE TERMS

Combine like terms.

4.

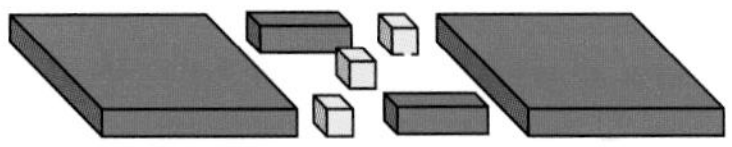

5.

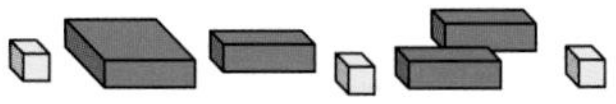

6.

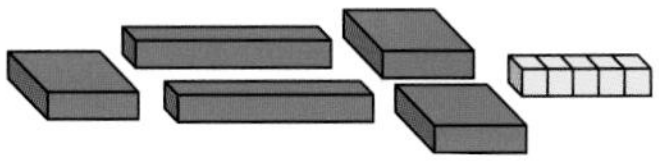

7.

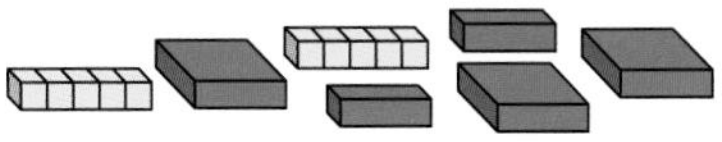

8.

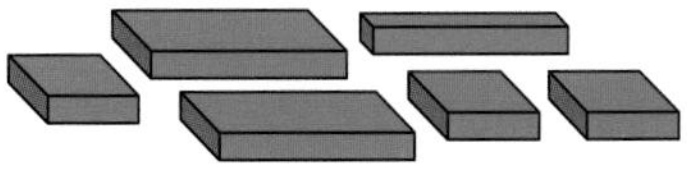

◆ Essential Ideas

*T*his is a review of the essential ideas. It could be useful in preparing for the test. These are the algebra concepts that students should be starting to master.

*M*ost of the problems avoid being exact replicas of the ones in the body of the chapter. Instead, they take the central ideas in a slightly more developed form, or simply in a slightly different context.

◆ SOLUTIONS

1. The names of blue blocks that model two-dimensional figures are determined by multiplying length by width. The blue blocks that model three-dimensional figures are determined by multiplying length, width, and height.
2. a. 5
   b. 165
   c. 33
3. a. 11
   b. 36
   c. 40
4. $2y^2 + 2x + 3$
5. $x^2 + 3x + 3$
6. $3x^2 + 2y + 5$
7. $3x^2 + 2x + 10$
8. $3x^2 + 2xy + y$

9.

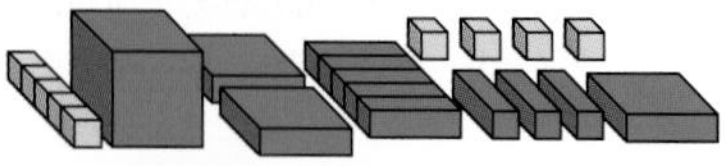

10.

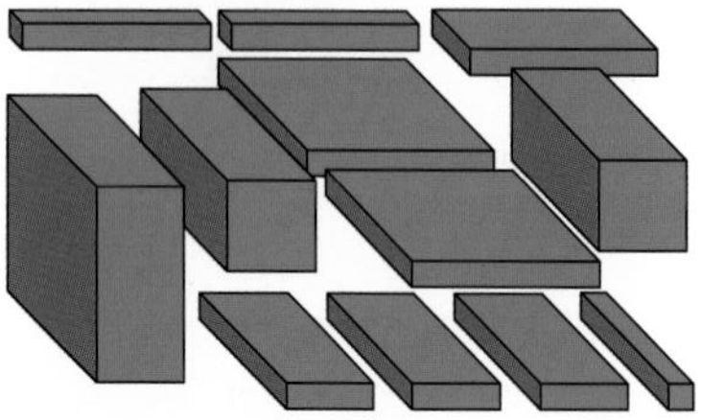

11.

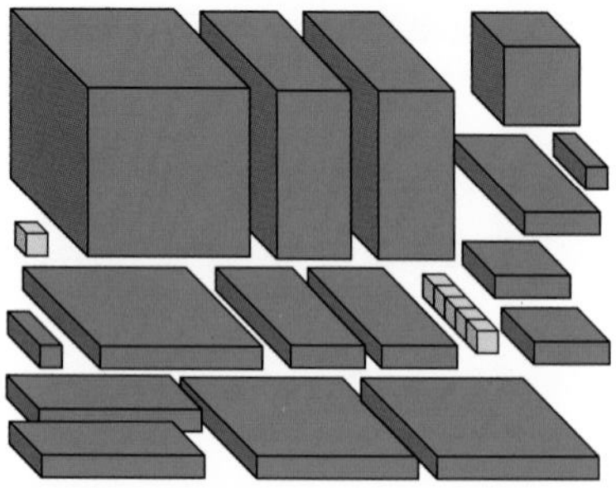

UNLIKE TERMS

12. My student Al *doesn't* like terms. He missed every problem on the Algebra Quiz. Please help poor Al with his algebra. For each problem, give the correct answer and explain what Al did wrong. Use Lab Gear sketches when possible.

a. $x^2 + x = x^3$

b. $3x + x = 3x^2$

c. $x^2 + x^2 + x^2 + x^2 = x^8$

d. $y \cdot 6 = y^6$

e. $2x + 3y = 5xy$

ADDING AND MULTIPLYING

13. Use the Lab Gear to show each expression. Sketch.

a. $2 + x + y$

b. $2 + xy$

c. $2x + y$

d. $2xy$

14. a. Find values for x and y so that all four expressions in problem 13 have different values.

b. Find values for x and y so that as many as possible of the given expressions are equal to each other.

15. Use the Lab Gear to show each expression. Sketch. (Hint: Use the corner piece for the last one.)

a. $x + y^2$

b. $x^2 + y$

c. $x^2 + y^2$

d. $(x + y)^2$

16. Find values for x and y so that all four expressions in problem 15 have different values.

ORDER OF OPERATIONS

17. Use the Lab Gear to show $2 + 5y$ and $(2 + 5)y$. Sketch each one.

18. a. Use trial and error to find a value of y such that $2 + 5y = (2 + 5)y$.

b. If $y = 0$, which is greater, $2 + 5y$ or $(2 + 5)y$?

c. If $y = 2$, which is greater, $2 + 5y$ or $(2 + 5)y$?

SOLUTIONS

9. $x^3 + 3x^2 + 8x + 9$

10. $2x^2y + y^2x + 4xy + 3y + 2y^2$

11. $x^3 + 2x^2 + 2xy^2 + 5xy + 2x + y^3 + 3y^2 + 6$

12. The Lab Gear is very effective since students can see that the right side does not equal the left side.
   a. $x^2 + x$
   b. $4x$
   c. $4x^2$
   d. $6y$
   e. $2x + 3y$

14. a. Answers will vary.
   b. Answers will vary. When $x = 1$ and $y = 2$, #13b, 13c, and 13d are equal.

16. Answers will vary.

18. a. $y = 1$
   b. $2 + 5y$
   c. $(2 + 5)y$

AREA AND MULTIPLICATION

Use the corner piece for problems 19-21.

19. Find the area of a rectangle having the sides given below. For each problem write a multiplication of the form *length times width = area.*

a. 3 and 5   b. 3 and x

c. 3 and $x + 5$ d. x and $x + 5$

20. Find the sides of a rectangle having the following areas. Each problem has at least two solutions. Find as many of them as you can and write an equation for each.

a. $4x$ b. $4x^2 + 8x$

c. $3xy + 6x^2 + 9x$

21. These equations are of the form *length times width = area.* Use the blocks to help you fill in the blanks.

a. $x \cdot$ _____ $= x^2 + xy$

b. $(y + 1) \cdot$ _____ $= 5y + 5$

c. (_____ $+ 3) \cdot y = 2xy + 3y$

d. $2x \cdot$ _____ $= 4x + 2xy + 6x^2$

22. Use the Lab Gear to build all the rectangles (or squares) you can find having the following perimeters. For each one, sketch your answer and write the length, width, and area.

a. $8x$

b. $6x + 2y$

c. $4x + 4y$

23. What is the area of the triangle in the figure if

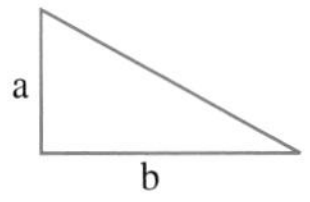

a. a = 7 and b = 9?

b. a = $4x$ and b = y?

◆ S O L U T I O N S

19. a. $3 \cdot 5 = 15$
    b. $3 \cdot x = 3x$
    c. $3(x + 5) = 3x + 15$
    d. $x(x + 5) = x^2 + 5x$

20. a. $4 \cdot x$, $2 \cdot 2x$, $1 \cdot 4x$
    b. $x(4x + 8)$, $4x(x + 2)$, $2x(2x + 4)$
    c. $x(3y + 6x + 9)$, $3x(y + 2x + 3)$

21. a. $x + y$
    b. 5
    c. $2x$
    d. $2 + y + 3x$

22. a. length = $2x$
    width = $2x$
    area = $4x^2$
    b. length = y
    width = $3x$
    area = $3xy$
    c. length = $2y$
    width = $2x$
    area = $4xy$

23. a. 31.5 square units
    b. $2xy$

Chapter 2
FUNCTIONS AND OPERATIONS

Overview of the Chapter

*T*his chapter begins with lessons using the Lab Gear to model operations, followed by a lesson using the calculator to explore exponents. Functions are introduced through some interesting real-world situations, and tables and function diagrams are used as a tool to understand both functions and operations.

*T*he main themes are motion, growth, and change, but at the end of the chapter students take a more sophisticated look at some perimeter and area problems related to those in Chapter 1, using what they now know about functions.

1. Introduction of New Tools:

- Two ways to show minus with the Lab Gear
- The scientific calculator (though your students may have been using this tool, this is the first time the book explicitly asks them to do so)
- The function diagram

2. Algebra Concepts Emphasized:

- Three meanings of minus
- Additive property of zero
- Opposites
- Operations with integers
- Commutative and associative laws for addition and multiplication
- The length model of addition and subtraction
- The distributive law
- Simplifying expressions
- Definition of exponents
- Functions of one and two variables

3. Algebra Concepts Reviewed:

- The volume and area model for multiplication
- Combining like terms
- Order of operations
- Using variables to gain insights into number patterns
- Inferring a function from data

CHAPTER 2

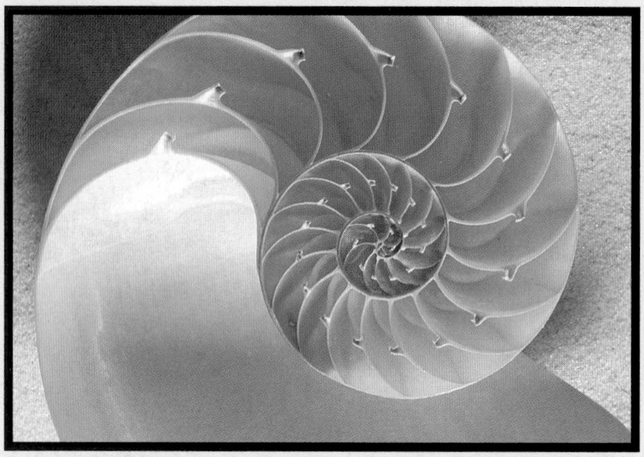
The equiangular spiral of a nautilus shell

Coming in this chapter:

Exploration 1, 1, 2, 3, 5, 8, 13, 21, 34, 55, 89, 144, 233, 377…
There are many patterns in this sequence of numbers. Find as many as you can, using addition, subtraction, multiplication, and division.

Operations and Functions

4. Algebra Concepts Previewed:

- Distributing a minus sign
- Factoring
- Multiplying binomials (++, +−, −+)
- Functions of two variables
- Linear and exponential functions
- Arithmetic sequences
- Step functions
- Exponential growth
- Linear equations
- Inverse operations
- Inverse functions
- Parameters

5. Problem-Solving Techniques:

- Trial and error
- Looking for patterns
- Using tables
- Sketching figures
- Reducing a problem to an easier version
- Systematic search

6. Connections and Context:

- Polyominoes
- Area, perimeter
- Area of geoboard triangles
- Motion — time, distance, rate
- The role of assumptions in modeling
- Growth and change
- Square and rectangular numbers
- Fibonacci numbers

Note About Homework: Because Lessons 1-4 and Lesson 10 involve the Lab Gear, you may need other sources of homework while working on them. In addition to end-of-lesson problems in Lessons 2 and 4, you may use material you skipped in Chapter 1. From further ahead in Chapter 2, you may use the Fibonacci material (problems 8-24 in Lesson 6), or **Thinking/Writing 2.C**.

▼ 2.1
Minus and Opposites

Core Sequence: 1-11

Suitable for Homework:
reading about **Upstairs** and **The Minus Area**, problems 10-16

Useful for Assessment: 5, 11

What this Lesson is About:

- The three meanings of minus
- The two ways to represent them with the Lab Gear
- The additive property of zero and the definition of opposites

This lesson involves much reading. Because of the importance of the concepts and techniques introduced, it is crucial to have a whole-class discussion about the three meanings of minus and the two ways of showing it with the Lab Gear, perhaps using the overhead blocks. **Note:** The workmat is referred to in this lesson for the first time. You may wish to make copies of the Lab Gear Workmat on page 592 for your students before beginning the lesson. Remind the students to keep their workmats for use in future lessons.

Do not *choose* one or the other method of showing minus. It is only by combining the two methods that a rich enough model for distributing the minus sign, simplifying polynomial expressions, and equation solving can be developed in later chapters.

Be aware of the fact that the 3-D blocks, while useful for the visualization of monomials of degree 3, cannot be easily used with the *upstairs* method, and in fact are probably best left out of work that involves minus.

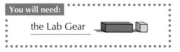

LESSON 2.1

Minus and Opposites

You will need:

the Lab Gear 

THREE MEANINGS OF MINUS

The *minus* sign can mean three different things, depending on the context.

- It can mean **negative**. In front of a positive number, and only there, it means negative. Example: -2 can mean negative 2.
- It can mean **opposite**. The opposite of a number is what you add to it to get zero. Example: -2 can mean the opposite of 2, which is negative 2, since $2 + {}^-2 = 0$. Likewise, ^-x means the opposite of x, and $x + {}^-x = 0$.
- It can mean **subtract.** Between two expressions, it means subtract the second expression from the first one. For example, $x - 3$ means subtract 3 from x.

1. For each of the following, write an explanation of what the minus sign means.

a. $y - 5$ b. $^-(5x + 1)$
c. -2 d. ^-x

2. Write the value of ^-x if:

a. $x = 2$; b. $x = {}^-3$.

3. True or False? (Explain your answers.)

a. ^-x is always negative.
b. ^-x can be positive.

Notation: In this book, the minus sign meaning *negative* or *opposite* will be smaller than the one for subtract. In handwriting, this is not necessary. However some calculators use different keys for the two meanings: [−] for subtraction, and [(−)] or [+/−] for *negative* or *opposite*.

There are two ways of showing minus with the Lab Gear: upstairs and the minus area.

UPSTAIRS

Rule: Any blocks placed on top of other blocks are preceded by a minus sign.

This figure shows $5 - 2$. Notice that the *uncovered* part of the bottom block equals 3. If you remove matching upstairs and downstairs blocks, you will be left with three downstairs blocks. This is how we show $5 - 2 = 3$ with upstairs and downstairs blocks.

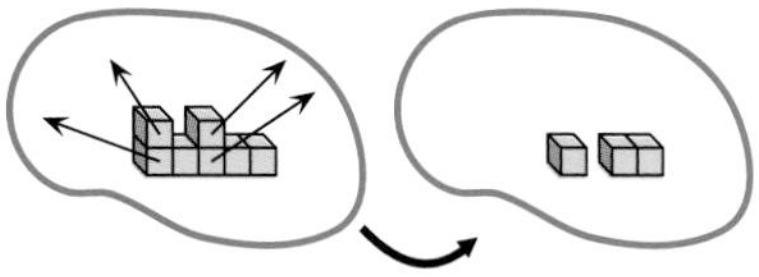

This figure shows $2 - 5$. If you mentally remove matching blocks downstairs and upstairs, you are left with 3 upstairs blocks, or -3. We can only do this mentally, however, since blocks cannot float in mid-air.

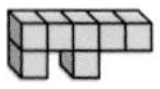 $2 - 5 = {}^-3$

Do not stack Lab Gear blocks more than two levels high. Two levels are enough to illustrate many ideas of algebra and will keep things clear. More would be confusing.

Subtraction with variables is shown in the same way. The amount being subtracted must be placed upstairs. Note that upstairs blocks are shaded in the 2-D sketch.

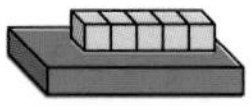

2.1 SOLUTIONS

1. a. subtract
   b. opposite
   c. negative or opposite
   d. opposite
2. a. -2
   b. 3
3. a. False
   b. True
   Since x may be positive or negative, then ^-x may be positive or negative. For example, if $x = {}^-7$ then $^-x = 7$.

The upstairs method of showing minus is important and useful, but it is limited; it cannot easily be used to show minus when it means *negative* or *opposite*.

THE MINUS AREA

Look at your workmat. The rectangles with rounded corners represent the **minus areas**. The whole collection of blocks inside the minus area is preceded by a minus sign. For example, $2 - 5$ can be shown this way. (Here the minus sign means *subtract*.)

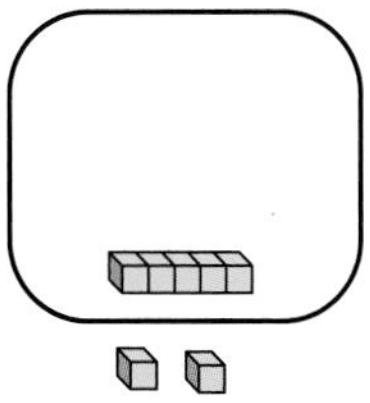

If you remove the matching blocks inside and outside the minus area, you will be left with three blocks inside the minus area, or $^-3$. (Here the minus sign means *negative*.)

4. Sketch how you would show each quantity on the workmat. You may need to use upstairs in some of the problems.
   a. $5 - x$ b. $x - 5$
   c. $^-(x + 5)$ d. $^-(5 - x)$
   e. $^-5$

5. **Summary**
   a. Explain, using examples, how the minus area can show all three meanings of minus.
   b. Which of the three meanings does the upstairs method show best? Explain.
   c. Put some blocks in the minus area, including some blocks upstairs. Sketch. What quantity does this arrangement represent?

REMOVING OPPOSITES

When the quantities inside and outside the minus area are the same, they add up to zero and can be removed. For example, the figure shows that $5 + x + 1 - (x + 1) = 5$.

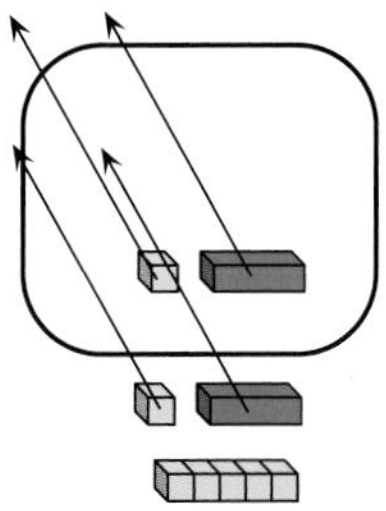

Similarly, matching upstairs and downstairs quantities add up to zero, and can be removed.

6. Two of these four figures represent the same quantity. Which two? Explain.

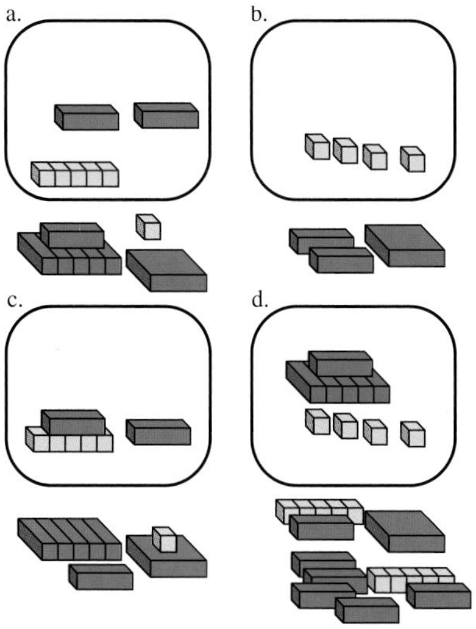

THREE MEANINGS OF MINUS

The concept of minus is the source of many mistakes for algebra students. This is partially due to insufficient clarity about the meanings of minus. We introduce all three meanings at once, so that students do not get stuck with a dominant interpretation.

We do not start with an introduction to negative numbers. By the time they are in an algebra class, students have been introduced to negative numbers many times. One more introduction is not needed. If they do not fully understand negative numbers yet, students find the subject discouraging. If they do, they are bored.

UPSTAIRS

The *upstairs* method is the more concrete of the two, as it visibly and meaningfully shows all three quantities involved in the subtraction: the original quantity, what is being removed, and the resulting difference. Since the subtraction meaning of minus is the most familiar to students, this is a good place to start.

In a complicated figure, with many blocks upstairs, it is most convenient to think of each of them as preceded by a minus sign.

The upstairs method will be refined in Lesson 3. It will be essential to help model the product of polynomials that involve minus signs.

2.1 SOLUTIONS

6. Parts a and b signify $2x + x^2 - 4$.

THE MINUS AREA

*I*t is most convenient to think of all the blocks in the minus area as representing one quantity, the whole quantity being preceded by a minus sign. When writing an expression involving the minus area, parentheses can be used, as in the text following the subtitle **Removing Opposites**.

*C*onversely, when building an expression such as $5x - 2 - (xy + 5 - x)$, it is convenient to place the 2 upstairs, on top of the $5x$. The whole quantity in parentheses should be built in the minus area, with xy and 5 downstairs and the x upstairs. It is helpful to build examples of expressions like this one on the overhead, with all-class discussion, to make sure all students understand how to use both methods of showing minus at the same time.

REMOVING OPPOSITES

ADDING ZERO

*T*hese are two crucial Lab Gear techniques, which will be used extensively in simplifying expressions and equation solving. They are based on the additive properties of zero ($a + 0 = a$, and $a - 0 = a$) and on the definition of opposites.

MINUS PUZZLES

*T*his is simple work with signed numbers, providing more practice with the two techniques mentioned above.

ADDING ZERO

The number 2 can be shown most simply with two 1-blocks outside the minus area. However, sometimes it is useful to show the number 2 using more blocks.

For example, after adding a five-block in the minus area and a five-block outside, the figure still shows 2. Since 5 and -5 are opposites, their sum is zero, so we really added zero. The technique of adding zero is useful in many situations.

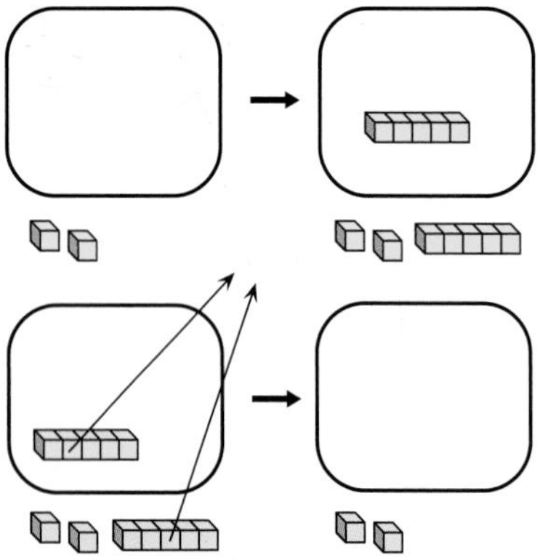

7. Sketch two other ways to show the number 2.

8. Sketch or explain how to show -9 with:
a. three blocks; b. five blocks;
c. seven blocks.

9. Sketch or explain how you would show 5 with:
a. 3 blocks; b. 11 blocks.

10. Can you show 5 with any number of blocks? Can you show it with 100 blocks? With 101 blocks? Explain your answers.

11. a. Show $x - 1$ in at least three different ways. Sketch or explain.
b. Show $1 - x$ in at least three different ways. Sketch or explain.

MINUS PUZZLES

12. Nineteen numbers can be shown with exactly two yellow blocks. What are they?

13. Find three ways to show -4 using only a 5-block and a 1-block. Sketch or explain.

14. Find four ways to show 3 with three blocks. Sketch or explain.

15. Find four ways to show -8 with four blocks. Sketch or explain.

16. Make up a puzzle like the above for a classmate. Solve a classmate's puzzle.

2.1 SOLUTIONS

10. It can be shown only with an odd number of blocks. We can construct 5 with only an odd number of blocks and if we add zero to 5 then we would be adding an even number of blocks. Even plus odd is odd.

11. b.

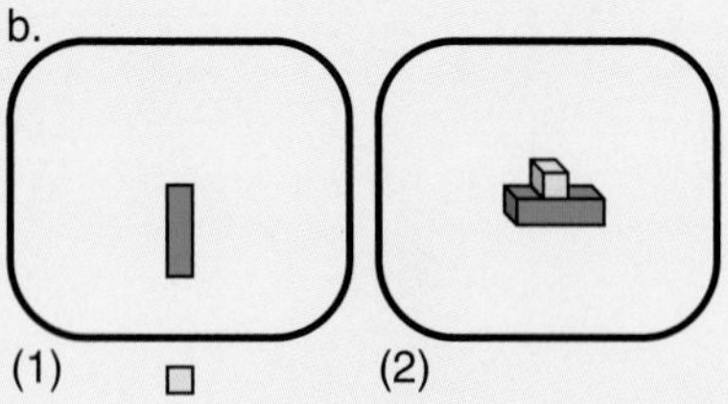

(1) (2)

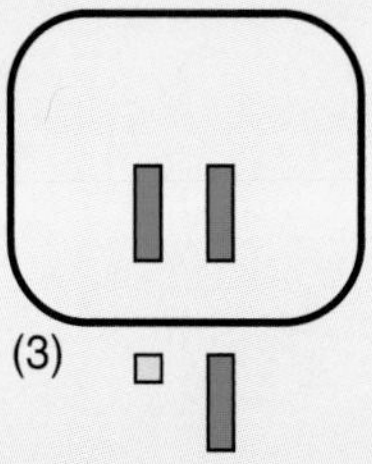

(3)

12. -50, -30, -26, -24, -20, -10, -6, -4, -2, 0, 2, 4, 6, 10, 20, 24, 26, 30, 50.

13. Answers will vary. Two possible solutions are given.

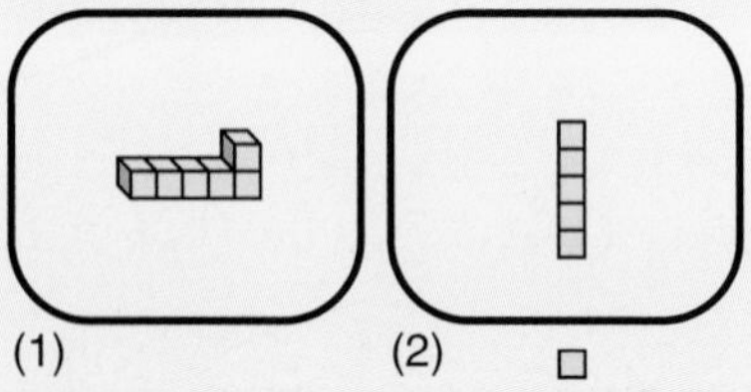

(1) (2)

16. Answers will vary.

LESSON 2.2 Adding and Subtracting

You will need:

the Lab Gear 

ASSOCIATIVE AND COMMUTATIVE LAWS

As you know, addition can be modeled with the Lab Gear by putting together collections of blocks on the workmat. For example, $x + 5$ means *put together x and 5* and $(x + 5) + {-1}$ means *put together x + 5 and -1*. This expression can be simplified by removing opposites, which would give us $x + 4$.

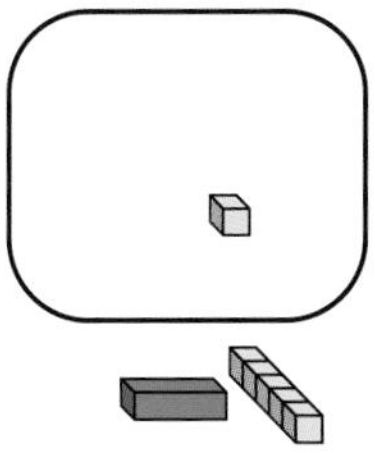

Note that the same figure could have been used to represent $x + (5 + {-1})$. This is because, in an addition, quantities can be grouped in any way. This is called the *associative law for addition.*

The same figure could have been used to represent $-1 + (x + 5)$, or $(5 + x) + {-1}$. This is because in an addition, you can change the order of the terms. This is called the *commutative law for addition.*

Finally, because of the commutative and associative properties, the -1 could have been shown upstairs on top of the x, or on top of the 5, instead of in the minus area. In every case, the expression would simplify to $x + 4$.

1. After simplifying these expressions, one will be different from the rest. Which one? Explain.

a.

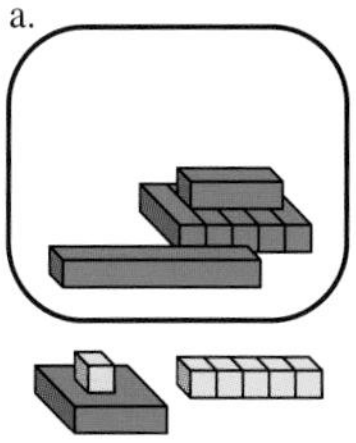

b.

c.

d.

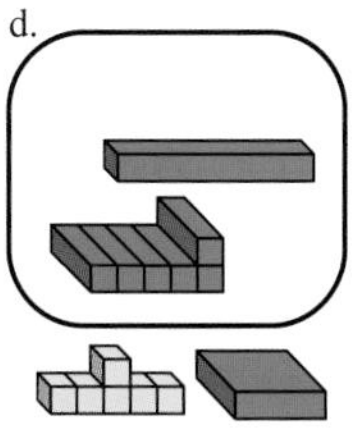

Add these polynomials. (In other words, remove opposites and combine like terms.) It may help to use the Lab Gear.

2. $(xy + 3x + 1) + (2x + 3)$
3. $(xy - 3x + 1) + (-2x - 3)$
4. $(xy + 3x - 1) + (-2x + 3)$
5. $(3 - 2x + xy) + (3x - 1)$
6. What do you notice about problems 4 and 5? Explain.

2.2 Adding and Subtracting

Core Sequence: 1-19

Suitable for Homework: none of it (See the **Note About Homework** in the chapter overview.)

Useful for Assessment: 6, 12, 17

What this Lesson is About:

- Simplifying on the workmat
- Preview of distributing a minus sign

ASSOCIATIVE AND COMMUTATIVE LAWS

The commutative and associative properties of addition are not interesting to students, because they are self-evident. Do not dwell on this terminology, but make sure the students understand problems 1 and 4-6, which are applications of these laws.

Problems 2-5 are essentially review, since they consist of combining like terms, as in Chapter 1, and removing opposites, as in Lesson 1.

2.2 SOLUTIONS

1. Part c is a different quantity. Part c is $x^2 - 6x - y + 6$ whereas parts a, b, and d are $x^2 - 4x - y + 4$.
2. $xy + 5x + 4$
3. $xy - 5x - 2$
4. $xy + x + 2$
5. $xy + x + 2$
6. They are equivalent because of the associative and commutative laws of addition.

UPSTAIRS BLOCKS IN THE MINUS AREA

*T*he purpose of this section is to lead students to a discovery of the rule for distributing minus signs. Do not teach any rules at the beginning. Instead, explain the adding zero/removing opposites strategy, perhaps by doing an example on the overhead. The students should be able to discover the rule on their own by working through problems 7-11. Encourage discussion throughout this section, especially about problem 12.

*N*ote that some students may not yet have mastered distributing the minus sign without using the Lab Gear. This technique, and the terminology to describe it, will be reviewed in Chapter 3.

UPSTAIRS BLOCKS IN THE MINUS AREA

Here is a useful technique. To simplify upstairs blocks in the minus area, you can add zero, then remove opposites. For example, this figure shows how to simplify

$$-(y^2 - y).$$

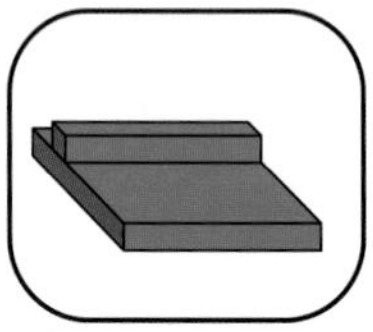

- **Add zero** by adding y inside and outside the minus area.

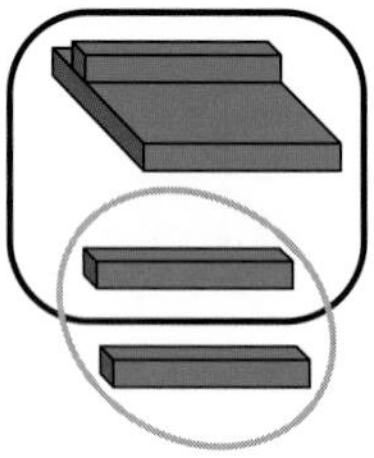

- **Remove opposites,** the matching blocks upstairs and downstairs.

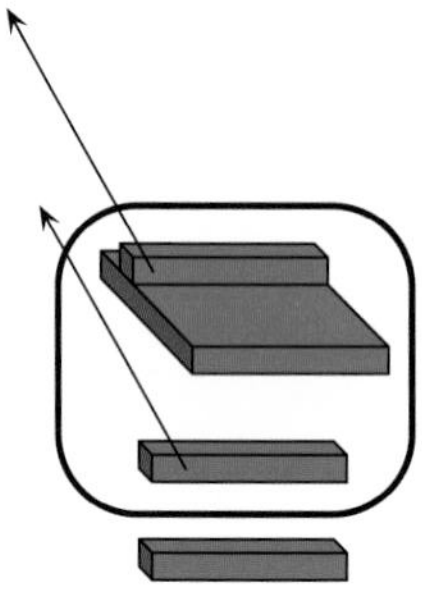

- The simplified form is $-y^2 + y$. All the blocks are downstairs.

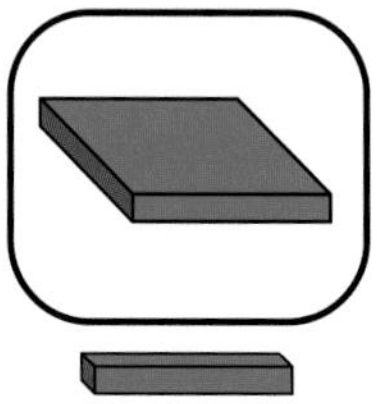

When working with the Lab Gear on the workmat, *simplifying* usually means
- removing opposites;
- combining like terms; and
- getting everything downstairs.

7. Model each expression using the Lab Gear. You will have to use both the minus area and upstairs blocks. Then simplify.
a. $-(5 - x)$ b. $-(x - 5)$
c. $3 - (x - 2)$ d. $(x - 2) - 3$

For problems 8–11 below:
- Build the first expression with the Lab Gear on the left side of the workmat.
- Next, compare each of the expressions a, b, c, and d to the original expression. (To make the comparison, build the expression on the right side of the workmat and simplify as needed.)

8. Which of these expressions are equivalent to $-(x + y)$?
a. $-x + (-y)$ b. $-x - y$
c. $-x + y$ d. $y - x$

9. Which of these expressions are equivalent to $-(x - y)$?
a. $-x + y$ b. $-x - y$
c. $-(y - x)$ d. $y - x$

2.1 SOLUTIONS

7. a. $-5 + x$
   b. $-x + 5$
   c. $5 - x$
   d. $x - 5$
8. Parts a and b are equivalent.
9. Parts a and d are equivalent.

10. Which of these expressions are equivalent to $-(y - x)$?
   a. $x - y$ b. $-x + y$
   c. $-y + x$ d. $-y - x$

11. Which of these expressions are equivalent to $-(-x + y)$?
   a. $-x + y$ b. $-y - x$
   c. $x - y$ d. $y - x$

12. **Generalization** For each expression below, write an equivalent one without parentheses. Do not use the Lab Gear.
   a. $-(a + b)$ b. $-(a - b)$
   c. $-(-a + b)$

SUBTRACTION

The figure shows the subtraction

$(x + 5 - 1) - (5x - 2)$.

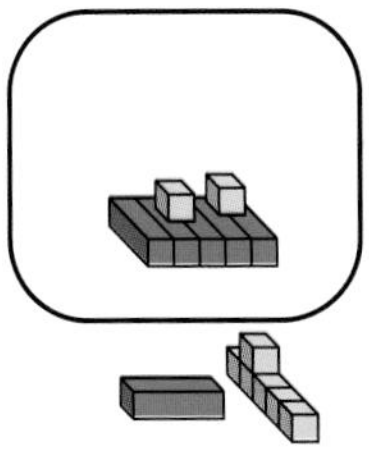

13. Use what you learned in the previous section to simplify it.

14. Simplify, using the Lab Gear.
   a. $x - (5x + 2)$ b. $x - (5x - 2)$

15. Simplify, with or without the Lab Gear.
   a. $(6x + 2) - (3x + 1)$
   b. $(3x - 2) - (6x + 1)$
   c. $(6x - 1) - (3x - 2)$
   d. $(3x - 2) - (6x - 1)$

16. In (a-c) find the missing expression. It may help to use the Lab Gear.
   a. $-3x -$ ____ $= -4x$
   b. $-3y -$ ____ $= -6y$
   c. $-3y -$ ____ $= -2x - 4y$

17. **Summary**
   a. Write a subtraction problem that you could model with the Lab Gear by putting blocks upstairs in the minus area.
   b. Simplify this subtraction without using the Lab Gear. Explain the rule you are using.

18. How could you show the subtraction

$y - -x$

with the Lab Gear? (Hint: Remember about adding zero.) What would it look like after it is simplified? What is a rule you could use without the blocks to simplify this kind of expression?

19. Simplify without the blocks, $-(-a - b)$. Explain your answer.

REVIEW *MINUS PUZZLE*

20. a. Using the Lab Gear, show -4 in five different ways.
   b. What numbers of blocks can and cannot be used to show -4?

SUBTRACTION

In this section, students apply what they learned in the previous one. Problems 16-19 are particularly interesting.

For problem 18, students have suggested adding zero in the form of (for example) y^2 in and out of the minus area, thereby creating "platforms." Then a y-block can be placed outside, and an x-block upstairs in the minus area. From there on the problem is straightforward.

REVIEW *MINUS PUZZLE*

An optional review of some material from Lesson 1.

2.2 SOLUTIONS

10. Parts a and c are equivalent.

11. Only part c is equivalent.

12. a. $-a - b$
   b. $-a + b$
   c. $a - b$

13. $-4x + 6$

14. a. $-4x - 2$
   b. $-4x + 2$

15. a. $3x + 1$
   b. $-3x - 3$
   c. $3x + 1$
   d. $-3x - 1$

16. a. x
   b. $3y$
   c. $y + 2x$

17. Answers will vary.

18. Put y in the plus region. Add zero by putting x in both the plus and minus regions. Now, take out an x from the minus region leaving $y + x$. Since a minus sign can mean the "opposite of," we can interpret $y - (-x)$ to mean take the opposite of $-x$ and add it to y to get $y + x$.

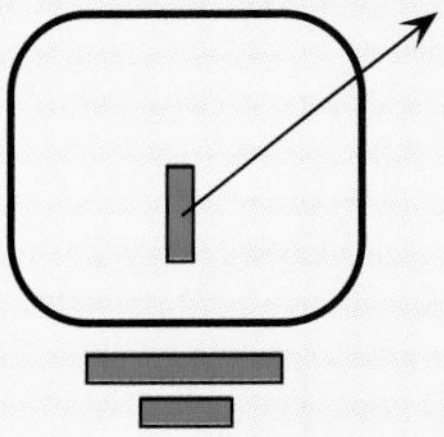

19. $-(-a - b) = a + b$

20. a. Answers will vary. One possible solution is given.

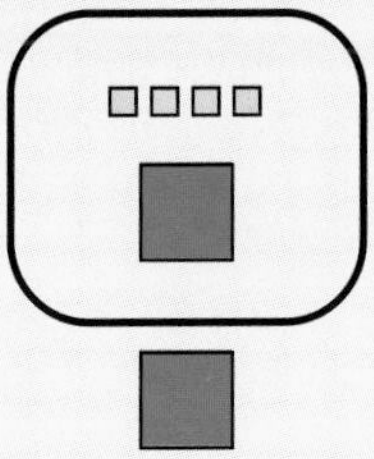

▼ 2.3 Multiplying

Core Sequence: 1-18

Useful for Assessment: 1, 4, 16

What this Lesson is About:

- The volume and area models of multiplication
- Review of terms and like terms
- Preview of the distributive law and factoring

*M*inus is not used in this lesson in an effort to make the visual models of multiplication and the distributive law as clear as possible. The same material, with minus, will be tackled in the next lesson.

THREE DIMENSIONS

*Y*ou could throw light on this by doing a version of problem 1 with a numerical example, such as $2 \cdot 3 \cdot 5$. This would allow you to review exactly how one finds the volume of a box, including both versions:

length · width · height

and *(area of base) · height.*

ASSOCIATIVE AND COMMUTATIVE LAWS

*A*gain, the laws themselves are not that interesting at this level, but it is important for students to be able to visualize the different ways to show a product of several factors.

LESSON 2.3

Multiplying

You will need:

the Lab Gear 

THREE DIMENSIONS

Just as we used the area of a rectangle to help us model multiplication of two factors, we can use the volume of a box to help us model multiplication of three factors.

For example, $5 \cdot x \cdot y$ can be shown like this.

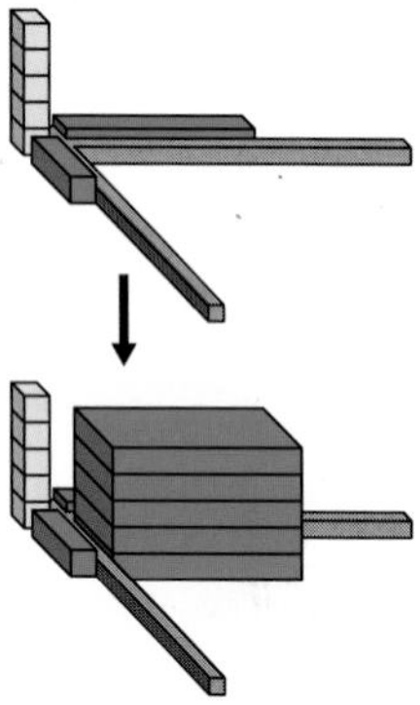

But another way to show it could be:

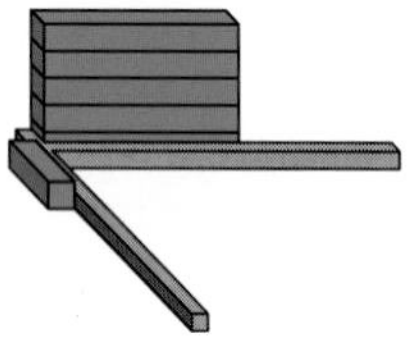

1. Use the Lab Gear to show how x^2y can be seen as a product of:
   a. three factors;
   b. two factors;
   c. two factors in another way.

ASSOCIATIVE AND COMMUTATIVE LAWS

In a multiplication the factors can be grouped in any way. For example, $(-2 \cdot 3) \cdot 4 = -2 \cdot (3 \cdot 4)$. This is called *the associative law for multiplication.*

In a multiplication the factors can be multiplied in any order. For example, $5 \cdot (-6) = (-6) \cdot 5$. This is called *the commutative law for multiplication.*

2. Using six xy-blocks, it is possible to make a rectangle in four different ways. Find all four rectangles, and write a multiplication equation for each.
3. Using six xy-blocks, it is also possible to make a three-dimensional box. There are many such boxes. Find five, and write at least two multiplications for each one.
4. **Summary** Explain how problems 2-3 about $6xy$ provide examples of the associative and commutative laws for multiplication.

HOW MANY TERMS?

5. **Exploration** After combining like terms, how many terms does the product have for each of the following multiplications? Is there a pattern? You may use the Lab Gear.
   a. $2x \cdot 3x$
   b. $2(x + 3)$
   c. $2x(x + 3x)$
   d. $(3 + x)(x + 2)$

2.3 SOLUTIONS

For problems 1-4, the answers will vary. One possible solution is given for each one.

1. a. An x-block is both the height and length. A y-block is the width.
   b. An x^2-block is the length and a y-block is the width.
2. i. Six x-blocks are on the length and a y-block is on the width. $(6x) \cdot y = 6xy$
   ii. Two x-blocks are on the length and three y-blocks are on the width. $(2x) \cdot (3y) = 6xy$
   iii. 3 x-blocks are on the length and 2 y-blocks are on the width. $(3x) \cdot (2y) = 6xy$
   iv. 6 y-blocks are on the length and an x-block is on the width. $x \cdot (6y) = 6xy$
3. There are 9 boxes possible. The dimensions are:
   (1) $6 \cdot x \cdot y$
   (2) $3 \cdot 2x \cdot y$
   (3) $3 \cdot x \cdot 2y$
   (4) $2 \cdot 3x \cdot y$
   (5) $2 \cdot x \cdot 3y$
   (6) $1 \cdot 3x \cdot 2y$
   (7) $1 \cdot 2x \cdot 3y$
   (8) $1 \cdot x \cdot 6y$
   (9) $1 \cdot 6x \cdot y$
4. The volume of the box remains constant even though the dimensions are interchanged.
5. a. one term
   b. two terms
   c. one term
   d. three terms

Some patterns are: The product of two monomials is a monomial. The product of a monomial and a binomial is a binomial. The product of two binomials is a trinomial.

The figure shows $(x + 3)(x + 5)$.

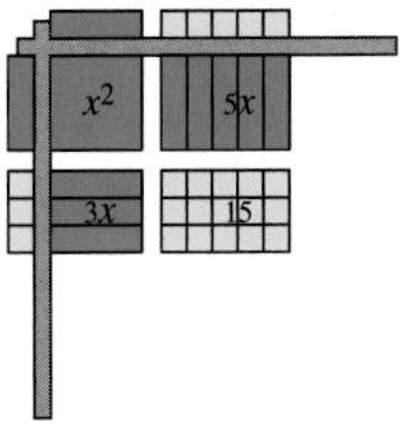

The resulting rectangle is made up of four smaller rectangles. The area of each one is shown in the figure.

6. a. Which two rectangles are made up of the same kind of block?

b. What is the answer to the multiplication $(x + 3)(x + 5)$? Combine like terms in your answer. How many terms are in your final answer?

7. a. Use the corner piece to model the multiplication $3x(x + 5)$. Sketch it, showing the resulting rectangle.

b. On your sketch, write the area of each of the smaller rectangles that make up the larger rectangle.

c. Write the result of the multiplication $3x(x + 5)$. Combine like terms.

d. How many terms are in your final answer?

8. Repeat problem 7 for

$$(x + 3)(x + y + 5).$$

9. Repeat problem 7 for

$$(x + y + 3)(x + y + 5).$$

10. Use the Lab Gear to model a multiplication problem that has four terms in the final answer. Sketch the blocks and write the multiplication.

MAKE A RECTANGLE

Take blocks for each expression.

a. Arrange them into a rectangle.

b. Write a multiplication equation of the form *length times width equals area.*

11. $xy + 5y$ **12.** $xy + 7x$

13. $7y + 7x$ **14.** $x^2 + 7x$

15. $x^2 + 7x + xy$

16. Do not use the Lab Gear for this problem. Write the addition

$$y^2 + 2xy + 3y$$

as a multiplication. Explain how you solved the problem.

In problems 17 and 18, take blocks for each expression.

a. Arrange them into a rectangle.

b. Write a multiplication equation of the form *length times width equals area.*

17. $x^2 + 7x + 6$

18. $x^2 + 7x + 10$

HOW MANY TERMS?

This section simultaneously reviews terms and like terms, and previews the distributive law, which will be learned explicitly in the next lesson.

MAKE A RECTANGLE

This section previews factoring in the case where there is a common factor. Problem 16 asks the students to be able to factor without using the blocks. It may be good to have a class discussion of this problem, to facilitate the transition to paper-and-pencil factoring.

Problems 17 and 18 are much more challenging than the previous six. They are a preview of trinomial factoring and make a good geometric puzzle. Use these as an extra challenge. There is no need to dwell on trinomial factoring at this early stage.

2.3 SOLUTIONS

6. a. $3x$; $5x$
   b. $x^2 + 8x + 15$. three terms
7. c. $3x(x + 5) = 3x^2 + 15x$
   d. two terms
8. c. $x^2 + 8x + xy + 3y + 15$
   d. five terms
9. c. $x^2 + 2xy + 8x + 8y + y^2 + 15$
   d. six terms
10. Answers will vary.
16. $y(y + 2x + 3)$. Notice that y is in every term. So y should be one side of the rectangle. Now think of what you would multiply y by to get the area.

▼ 2.4 The Distributive Law

Core Sequence: 1-25, 27

Suitable for Homework: 27
(See the **Note About Homework** in the chapter overview.)

Useful for Assessment: 9, 25

What this Lesson is About:

- The length model of addition and subtraction
- The area model of multiplication, with minus signs in one of the factors
- The distributive law
- Preview of factoring when there is a common factor

LINEAR ADDITION AND SUBTRACTION

This is probably easy, and for many students it will not require a lot of effort. Nevertheless, it is important that this model be mastered, as it is a necessary component of multiplication in the corner piece.

THE UNCOVERED RECTANGLE

This concept will need a discussion, using the overhead projector.

THE DISTRIBUTIVE LAW

This law has been previewed, but this is the first time that minus appears in one of the factors, and it is the first time that the law is articulated.

The law is difficult to put in words, but it is all right for students to use symbols, as in problem 10, to explain it. Be sure that all students understand problem 10 before continuing.

Many students may be able to do problems 11 and 12 without using the Lab Gear.

LESSON 2.4

The Distributive Law

LINEAR ADDITION AND SUBTRACTION

In the case of x, y, and constant blocks — in other words quantities of degree 1 or 0 — you can think of adding as putting together blocks end-to-end *in a line*. For example, $2x + 5$ is shown by connecting the two x-blocks and the 5-block on their 1-by-1 faces.

Similarly, subtraction of quantities of degree 0 and 1 can be shown linearly, by making sure that the uncovered area models a single line segment. The figure shows $y - 5$.

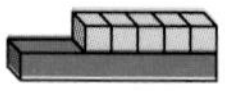

This representation is based on a *length* model of addition and subtraction.

1. Sketch these sums, showing length.
   a. $y + 2$ b. $3x + 1$
2. Sketch these differences, showing length.
   a. $y - 2$ b. $3x - 1$

THE UNCOVERED RECTANGLE

It is possible to use the corner piece for multiplication when minus signs are involved. For example, this figure shows the multiplication $5(5 - 2)$.

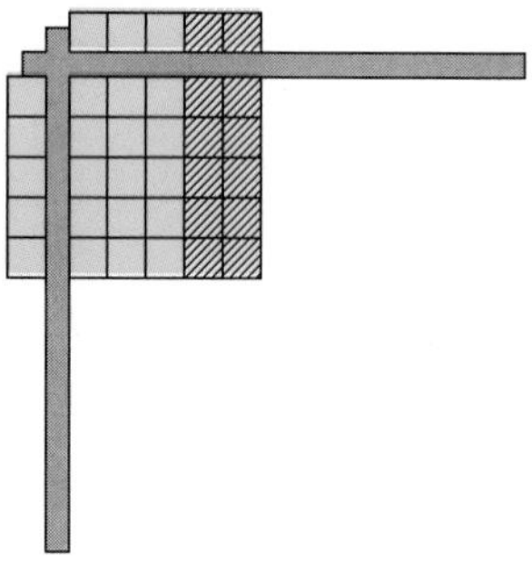

Remember that the shaded blocks are upstairs. Look at the part of the downstairs blocks that are not covered by upstairs blocks. The answer to the multiplication is represented by the **uncovered rectangle** with dimensions 5 and $5 - 2$. Of course, the product is 5 times 3, or 15, which is the answer you get when you simplify upstairs and downstairs blocks.

THE DISTRIBUTIVE LAW

Find these products, using the Lab Gear. Remember to use upstairs for minus.

3. $x(5 + y)$
4. $(5 - x)y$
5. $5(x + y)$
6. $(y - 5)x$
7. $y(5 + x)$
8. $(y - x)5$
9. **Summary** Explain how you can correctly remove parentheses from an algebraic expression when they are preceded or followed by a multiplication, and when there is more than one term in the parentheses.
10. Remove the parentheses.
    a. $a(b + c)$ b. $(a - b)c$

The rule you have discovered in this section is called *the distributive law of multiplication over addition and subtraction.*

Use the distributive law to multiply. You may use the Lab Gear to check your work.

11. a. $2x(x + 1)$ b. $2x(x - 1)$
12. a. $2x(x + y + 5)$
    b. $2x(x + y - 5)$
    c. $2x(-x + y + 5)$
    d. $2x(x - y + 5)$

2.4 SOLUTIONS

3. $5x + xy$
4. $5y - xy$
5. $5x + 5y$
6. $xy - 5x$
7. $5y + xy$
8. $5y - 5x$
9. Multiply the monomial term by each term in the polynomial. Take the sum of all these products.
10. a. $ab + ac$
    b. $ac - bc$
11. a. $2x^2 + 2x$
    b. $2x^2 - 2x$
12. a. $2x^2 + 2xy + 10x$
    b. $2x^2 + 2xy - 10x$
    c. $-2x^2 + 2xy + 10x$
    d. $2x^2 - 2xy + 10x$

For problems 13-18:

a. Show the quantity with the Lab Gear, using upstairs to show minus.

b. Arrange the blocks so the uncovered part is a rectangle.

c. Write a multiplication of the type, *length times width* = *area* for the uncovered rectangle.

13. $xy - 2y$ **14.** $xy - 2x$

15. $xy - x^2$ **16.** $xy + x - x^2$

17. $y^2 + xy - 5y$ **18.** $y^2 - xy - y$

19. Explain how someone might have done problem 18 without the Lab Gear.

20. Write $x^2 - xy - x$ as a multiplication of the type, *length times width* = *area,* for the uncovered rectangle.

RELATED PRODUCTS

21. Use the corner piece to show
$(3x + 1)(2x - 1)$.

This figure shows the product $(3x + 1)(2x - 1)$.

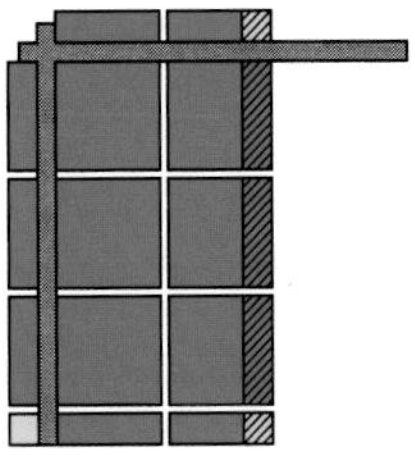

Notice that, inside the corner piece, the uncovered rectangle has dimensions $3x + 1$ and $2x - 1$. These are the original factors. This tells you that we did the multiplication correctly. But the product can be simplified, as shown below.

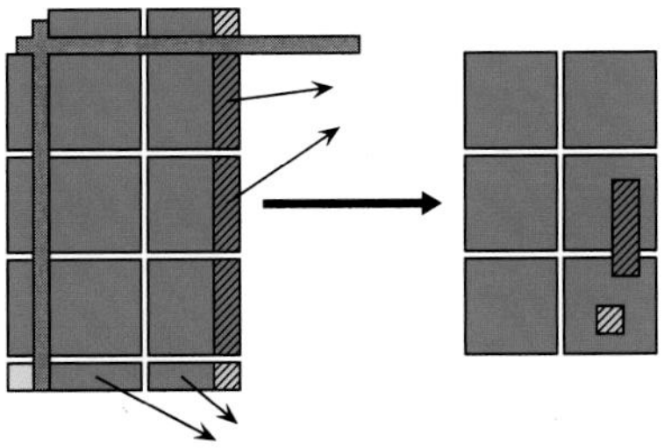

22. a. Explain what was done to the blocks in problem 21 after using the corner piece. Which blocks were removed, and why?

b. Write the final answer, combining like terms.

23. Use the Lab Gear to find the product: $(3x - 1)(2x + 1)$. Sketch the process as was done for problem 21.

24. a. Show the multiplication $(3x + 2)(2x + 5)$ with the Lab Gear. Write the product.

b. Write two more multiplications, both involving minus, that use the same blocks as $(3x + 2)(2x + 5)$. In each case write the product.

The factoring problems, 13-18, are there to make sure the main point of the lesson (the distributive law) has been mastered. The terminology (common factor, factoring) will be introduced in Chapter 3. You may use it when discussing these problems, but do not expect your students to master it now.

RELATED PRODUCTS

This is about multiplying two binomials by each other with the Lab Gear, except in the case where there is a minus in both factors.

Many students learned how to multiply binomials in pre-algebra, and they may resent learning the Lab Gear model. They should still learn it, as they can generalize it to trinomials, and it leads to a better understanding of the distributive law.

Even if they are in reality unable to solve it, such students should enjoy struggling with problem 26, which is extremely difficult.

2.4 SOLUTIONS

19. This is using the distributive property going backwards. Notice that y is in every term, so y will be the width. That makes $(y - x - 1)$ the length. Therefore,
$y(y - x - 1) = y^2 - xy - y$.

20. $x(x - y - 1) = x^2 - xy - x$

22. a. Simplify terms. Since
$2x + (-2x) = 0$,
we can remove these blocks.

b. $6x^2 - x - 1$

25. **Summary** You can use the same blocks to show all three of these products with the Lab Gear. Explain why the products are different, even though the same blocks are used. Include sketches as part of your explanation.

a. $(2x + 3)(3x + 5)$
b. $(2x + 3)(3x - 5)$
c. $(2x - 3)(3x + 5)$

26. You will learn how to model

$$(2x - 3)(3x - 5)$$

with the Lab Gear in a later chapter. Try to find a way to do this without looking ahead in the book.

REVIEW *UNLIKE TERMS*

27. Al *still* doesn't like terms. For each problem, give the correct answer, if possible, and explain what Al did wrong. Use Lab Gear sketches or substitute numbers.

a. $x^2 - x = x$
b. $3x - x = 3$
c. $9x - 4y = 5(x - y)$

2.4 SOLUTIONS

27. a. $x^2 - x$ is not equal to x.

minus 

is not equal to 

b. $3x - x$ is not equal to 3.

 minus 

is not equal to 

c. $9x - 4y$ is not equal to $5(x - y)$.

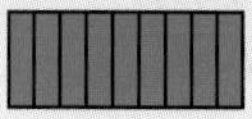 minus 

is not equal to

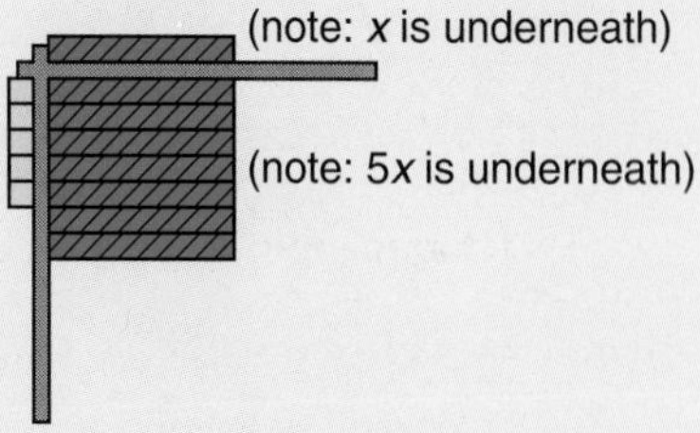

2.A Solutions

1. a. Martin multiplied $2 \cdot 3$.
   b. $2^3 = 2 \cdot 2 \cdot 2$ not $2 \cdot 3$
   c. 8
2. a. Martin multiplies $3x \cdot x$.
   b. $3x + x \neq 3x^2$ since

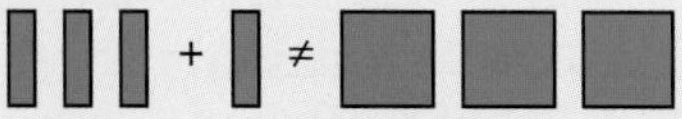

   c. $4x$
3. a. Martin subtracted as if they were similar terms. He also subtracted the exponents.
   b. You cannot simplify dissimilar terms.
   c. $2x^3 - x^2 = 2x^3 - x^2$

THINKING WRITING

2.A Operations

The teacher had just returned the math test, and no one was looking very happy. Martin had missed *all* the problems.

Test Name: Martin P.

Operations

1. $2^3 = 6$
2. $3x + x = 3x^2$
3. $2x^3 - x^2 = x$
4. $5 - 2x = 3x$
5. $4 - 2 \cdot 6x = 12x$
6. $(2x - 3) - (x - 2) = x + 5$
7. $6x - (x^2 - 4x) = 2x - x^2$
8. $-(y^2 - x^2) = -y^2 - x^2$
9. $(2x + 1)(3x - 5) = 6x^2 - 5$
10. $2x(-y + 5) = 2x - y + 5$
11. $2y + 3x = 5xy$
12. $6 - 2(x + 3) = 4x + 12$

"I hate math tests," Martin groaned. "I'd rather have my teeth pulled out." Mary would not show her test to anyone, but she looked miserable, too. "I'll need a brain transplant to pass this course," she moaned. Lew, the math whiz, grimaced at his test score and glared at his crutches. He was used to getting everything right, but he had just had an operation on his knee after an injury on the playing field. Math had been the last thing on his mind when he took the test.

Then the teacher did an unusual thing. He handed out these instructions:

Free Points!

You can get extra points on the **Operations** test if you can correct your mistakes. This is what you need to do:

a. For each problem, explain your mistake. Try to figure out what you were thinking. Most of your mistakes have to do with operations.

b. Show me you now know how to do the problem correctly. Use sketches of the Lab Gear or explain a rule you have learned. Don't just give me the answer.

c. Finally, write the correct answer to the problem.

What should Martin write to get his free points? Write out the corrections for him.

THINKING WRITING

2.A Operations

Core Sequence: 1-12

Suitable for Homework: the whole assignment

Useful for Assessment: the whole assignment

What this Assignment is About:

- Review of like terms
- Review of order of operations
- Review of the distributive law
- Distributing a minus sign

This is a chance to review all the work on operations by thinking about some of the most popular types of student errors. If students can answer parts (a) and (b) for any of Martin's mistakes, they are unlikely to make the same mistakes themselves.

Note that parts (a) and (b) make this assignment substantially longer than one which would consist solely of finding the correct answers, but the extra writing should pay off by yielding better understanding. In the long run, the time spent writing will help reduce the time spent practicing the skills.

2.A SOLUTIONS

4. a. Martin was thinking they were similar terms.
   b. $5 - 2x \neq 3x$
   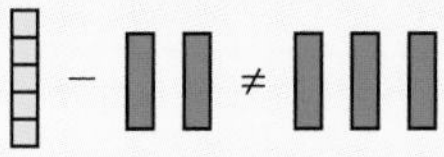
   c. $5 - 2x = 5 - 2x$.
5. a. Martin subtracted 2 from 4 and then multiplied by 6. This is an incorrect order of operations.
   b. First multiply 2 by $6x$ which is $12x$, then subtract it from 4.
   c. $4 - 12x$
6. a. Martin saw two minus signs and made everything positive.
   b. Distribute the minus sign: $2x - 3 - (x - 2) = 2x - 3 - x + 2$
   c. $x - 1$
7. a. Martin confused subtraction with multiplication. Distribute the minus sign.
   b. $6x - (x^2 - 4x) = 6x - x^2 + 4x$
   c. $10x - x^2$
8. a. He forgot to distribute the minus sign.
   b. Distribute the minus sign: $-(y^2 - x^2) = -y^2 - (-x^2)$
   c. $-y^2 + x^2$
9. a. Martin forgot to multiply all the terms.
   c. $6x^2 - 7x - 5$
10. a. He confused subtraction with multiplication and did not distribute $2x$.
    b. Distribute $2x$: $2x(-y + 5) = 2x(-y) + 2x \cdot 5$
    c. $-2xy + 10x$
11. a. He confused the operation of addition with multiplication.
    b. $2y + 3x \neq 5xy$
    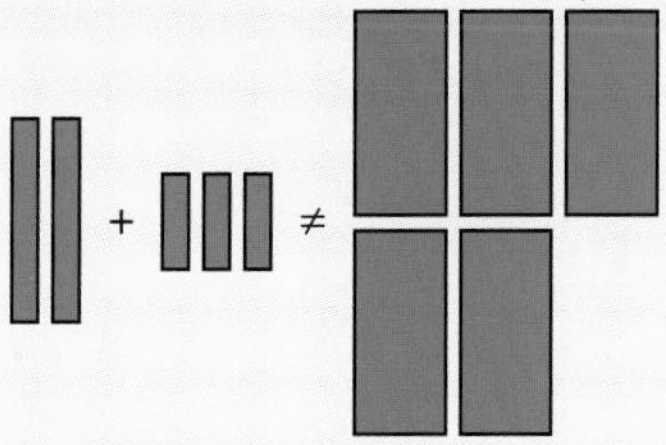
    c. $2y + 3x = 2y + 3x$
12. a. Martin did not distribute the -2, and he combined dissimilar terms.
    b. First distribute the -2: $6 - 2(x + 3) = 6 - 2x - 6$, then combine similar terms.
    c. $-2x$

▼ 2.5 Powers

Core Sequence: 1-13

Suitable for Homework: 6-17

Useful for Assessment: 5, 15-17

What this Lesson is About:

- Introduction to exponents
- Preview of exponential growth
- Making assumptions

DOING DISHES

This problem provides motivation for the concept of exponents. Exponents are not actually needed until problem 5, since students can use repeated multiplication to answer problems 1-4. However, they will find that the use of exponents (and calculators) makes the problem much easier.

EXPONENTS

EXPONENTIAL NOTATION

This is just an introduction. Exponents will be addressed in much greater depth in Chapters 7 and 8. At this point, it is necessary for students to master only the notation, and how to use their calculators to work with exponents.

The **Doing Dishes** table, or the use of calculators, may help you preview the exponent 0. Of course, do not expect mastery of that idea.

Problem 7f is intended to introduce gently the use of minus in the context of powers. All of problem 7 previews some of the laws of exponents. Again, do not expect mastery.

LESSON 2.5

Powers

DOING DISHES

Abe agreed to do the dishes daily in exchange for one cent on April 1st, two cents on April 2nd, four cents on April 3rd, and so on, doubling the amount every day.

1. To find out how much money Abe was earning, make a table like this one, for at least the first ten days.

Day #	Cents	Total
1	1	1
2	2	3
3	4	7
4	...	...

2. How are the numbers in the *Cents* column calculated?
3. How much money did Abe get paid on April 30? Explain how you figured out the answer. Do you think you could talk your parents into an arrangement like this?
4. a. Study the table, looking for a pattern in the *Total* column. Describe the pattern.
   b. How much money did Abe make altogether during the month of April?

Definitions: Exponents

Exponentiation, or *raising to a power,* is the operation of multiplying a number by itself repeatedly. The number that is multiplied is called the *base.* The number of factors is called the *exponent.*

Examples:

- The expression $2 \cdot 2 \cdot 2 \cdot 2 \cdot 2$ is written 2^5, where 2 is the base and 5 is the exponent.
- You are already familiar with squaring and cubing, which are special cases of exponentiation in the case of raising to the second and third powers.
- The numbers in the Cents column in the above table are called the *powers of 2,* because they can be obtained by raising 2 to different powers.

Notation:

- On calculators, it is not possible to use this notation. Instead, 2^5 is entered as 2 [y^x] 5, 2 [x^y] 5, or 2 [^] 5.
- On computers, most word processors allow the user to type exponents (called *superscripts*).
- Computer programming languages use 2^5, 2**5, or `POWER 2 5`.

5. **Generalization**
   a. How much money did Abe make on the nth day of April? (Watch out.)
   b. What is the number in the *Total* column on day n? Explain.

EXPONENTIAL NOTATION

The number 64 can be written in exponential notation as 2^6 or 8^2. (Check this with your calculator or by mental multiplication.)

6. Find another way to write 64 in exponential notation.
7. Write each of these numbers in exponential notation. Do not use 1 as an exponent. If possible, find more than one way. It may help to use your calculator.
   a. 81 b. 1
   c. 1024 d. 625
   e. 6561 f. 💡 -512

2.5 SOLUTIONS

1.

Day. No.	Cents	Total
1	1	1
2	2	3
3	4	7
4	8	15
5	16	31
6	32	63
7	64	127
8	128	255
9	256	511
10	512	1023

2. The amount for each day is doubled from the previous day.
3. 2^{29} = $5,368,709.12
4. a. The earning on day n is 1 cent more than the accumulated earning on day $n - 1$.
   b. $2^{30} - 1$ = earnings for the whole month of April, which is $10,737,418.23
5. a. 2^{n-1}
   b. $2^{n+1} - 1$
   Look at #4 for an explanation.
6. 4^3
7. a. 9^2
   b. $x^0, x \neq 0$
   c. 2^{10}
   d. 5^4
   e. 9^4
   f. -2^9

CHAIN LETTER

Lara received this letter.

> *Dear Lara,*
>
> *Send copies of this letter to five people, or the most terrible bad luck will afflict you. One man broke the chain, and a flower-pot fell on his head, giving him a terrible headache which continues to this day.*
>
> *Don't look a gift-horse in the eye. Rome was not built in a pond. Don't cry over spilt tears.*
>
> *Please do not break the chain! It was started in 1919 by a psychic.*
>
> *Bea*

Assume that the chain is not broken, and that each person who receives it takes a week to send out five copies.

8. After one week, five people receive Lara's letter. After another week, how many people receive the letter? Make a table like the following for the first ten weeks.

Week #	Letters received this week	Total number received so far
1	5	5
2	25	30
3	...	...

9. How many weeks until the number of letters received that week is greater than the population of the United States?

10. How many letters were received in the nth week?

11. If each person made six copies of the letter instead of five, how would your answer to problem 10 change?

12. Do you think that the chain was started in 1919? Explain why or why not.

13. How do the assumptions we made to solve this problem compare with what happens in the real world with chain letters?

GETTING HELP

Assume Lara gave a copy of the letter to Lea and they each sent five copies in the first week.

14. If everything continues as in the previous section, how many people receive the letter? Make a table like the following for the first five weeks.

Week #	Letters received this week	Total number received so far
1	10	10
2	50	60
3	...	...

15. Write the number of letters received in the 10th week as an expression *using exponents.*

16. How many letters were received in the nth week?

17. If each person asked a friend to help in the same way, how would your answers to problems 14-16 change?

CHAIN LETTER

Exponents allow us to model what happens with chain letters only at the cost of assumptions which oversimplify the phenomenon. The reality is that not every recipient complies with the admonitions not to break the chain, and that many recipients have common friends, so that the same person may receive more than one copy of the letter.

These ideas are explored in problems 12 and 13. Students should remember that mathematical models are no more reliable than the assumptions that they are built upon.

The pattern for the *Total* column is much harder to see than in the case of successive sums of powers of two, so do not ask students to generalize. If some of your students want to pursue this, encourage them to start by studying sums of successive powers of 1, 2, 3, and 4 before tackling 5. They should be able to discover that there is a pattern for the sums of successive powers of b: Each total can be obtained from the previous total by multiplying by b and adding 1. However, a formula for the nth term is too difficult to find at this level.

GETTING HELP

This section previews order of operations with exponents (which will be discussed explicitly in Chapter 7). Students should see that $2 \cdot 5^n$ is different from $(2 \cdot 5)^n$.

2.5 SOLUTIONS

8.

Week No.	Letters received	Total received
1	5	5
2	25	30
3	125	155
4	625	780
5	3125	3905
6	15,625	19,530
7	78,125	97,655
8	390,526	488,280
9	1,953,125	2,441,405
10	9,765,625	12,207,030

9. If we take the U.S. population at 250,000,000 then by the 13th week the population is surpassed since $5^{13} = 1{,}220{,}703{,}125$.

10. 5^n

11. 6^n

12. It probably did not start in 1919 since that would mean there would have been 5^{7396} letters, which is many times the present world population.

13. Answers will vary.

14.

Week No.	Letters received	Total received
1	10	10
2	50	60
3	250	310
4	1250	1560
5	6250	7810

15. $2 \cdot 5^{10}$

16. $2 \cdot 5^n$

17. If n is the number of the week, then instead of the number of letters received being $2 \cdot 5^n$, it would be $2^n \cdot 5^n$. This is because the number of letters is being doubled each week.

▼ 2.6 Finding Patterns

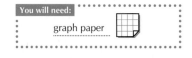

Core Sequence: 1-6, 28

Suitable for Homework: 11-29

Useful for Assessment: 4-6, 20-21

What this Lesson is About:

- Patterns in numerical data
- Preview of step functions
- Using variables to understand mathematical patterns

You could save some of problems 11-24 to serve as a source of homework when working on a lesson that requires manipulatives, such as Lesson 10, Lesson 12, or several of the lessons in Chapter 3.

PARKING RATES

There's a lot to this section. Students should probably work in groups for best results.

An all-class discussion may be necessary about problem 7, as students may never have seen a step function. (It is not necessary for them to learn this word or any generalities about step functions but, with help, they should be able to graph the rates correctly.)

LESSON 2.6

Finding Patterns

You will need: graph paper

PARKING RATES

Two downtown parking garages charge different amounts, as shown by the following signs.

Ball Garage	
up to:	'U' pay:
1/2 hour	35 cents
1 hour	70 cents
1 1/2 hr	$1.05
2 hours	$1.40
3 hours	$2.65
4 hours	$3.90
5 hours	$5.15
6 hours	$6.40
7 hours	$7.65
all day	$8.90

Bear Garage	
up to:	fee:
1 hour	$1.05
2 hours	$2.10
3 hours	$3.15
4 hours	$4.20
5 hours	$5.25
6 hours	$6.30
all day	$7.25

1. If you park for two hours and five minutes, you have to pay the three-hour fee. How much is that at each garage?
2. People who work downtown tend to use one of the garages, and people who shop there tend to use the other. Explain why, with examples.
3. Lara notices that for the amount of time she is planning to park, the cost difference between the two garages is less than a quarter. How long is she planning to park?
4. The parking fees at the Bear Garage mostly fit a pattern. Describe the pattern in words. Where does it break down?
5. The parking fees at the Ball Garage fit a more complicated pattern. Describe the pattern in words. Why might the owner of Ball Garage have chosen a complicated pattern?

Analyzing numbers can be useful in making intelligent decisions. Here is an example.

6. Zalman owns an empty lot. He decides to convert it to a parking garage. He wants to charge a fee that is not too expensive. He decides on these rules:
   - The fee should increase by a constant amount for each half-hour.
   - For parking times from a half-hour to nine hours, the fee should never be more than 25 cents higher than either Ball's or Bear's fee.
   - The fee should be the highest possible fee that satisfies these rules.

   a. Explain why Zalman might have chosen each rule.

   b. What rate should he choose? (For convenience in making change, it should be a multiple of 5 cents.) Explain.
7. Graph the parking fees for all three garages. Put *time* on the horizontal axis, and *cost* on the vertical axis.

2.6 SOLUTIONS

1. Ball: $2.65
   Bear: $3.15
2. Workers use the Bear Garage since the all-day fee is cheaper, whereas shoppers will usually not need all-day parking. So Ball Parking would be cheaper for shoppers up to five hours.
3. Between 5 and 6 hours.
4. The cost is $1.05 per hour through 6 hours. This pattern breaks down after 6 hours.
5. From 0 to 2 hours, the charge is 35 cents per half hour. After 2 hours, the charge is $1.25 per hour. The owner is encouraging short-time use.
6. a. Answers will vary.
   b. 40 cents per half hour
7. 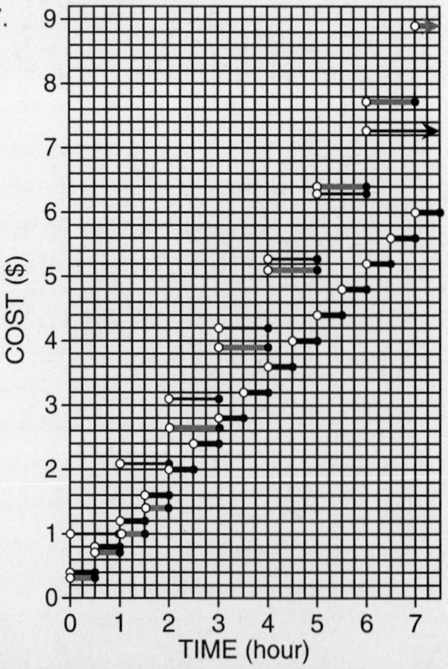

FIBONACCI SEQUENCES

The following numbers are called *Fibonacci numbers* after the Italian mathematician who first studied them:

1, 1, 2, 3, 5, 8, 13, 21...

8. Describe the pattern. Then give the next five Fibonacci numbers. (As a hint, if you have not yet discovered the pattern, look at the *Lucas numbers* — named after another mathematician — which follow the same principle: 1, 3, 4, 7, 11, 18, 29, 47, 76, 123...)

9. **Exploration** Look for patterns in the Fibonacci numbers. You may use addition, subtraction, or multiplication.

Definition: A *sequence* is an ordered list of numbers or expressions.

10. You can create your own Fibonacci-like sequence. Choose any two numbers, and use them as the starting values for a sequence like the ones described in problem 8. Name the sequence after yourself. Have a classmate check that your sequence is correct.

11. a. Find the first ten terms in a new sequence by adding the Fibonacci and the Lucas numbers. (The sequence should start: 2, 4, 6, 10, 16...) Is the resulting sequence a Fibonacci-like sequence? (Does it follow the same rule?)
b. Find the first ten terms in a new sequence by subtracting the Fibonacci numbers from the Lucas numbers. Compare your answer to the one in (a).
c. Find the first ten terms in a new sequence by dividing the sequence in (b) by 2. The result should be familiar.

12. Look for odd/even patterns in Fibonacci-like sequences including the original one, the Lucas sequence, and three named after students in your class. Explain.

13. Extend the Fibonacci and Lucas sequences to the left. In other words, what number should come before the first number? What number should come before that, and so on? Describe the resulting patterns.

MISSING NUMBERS

The following Fibonacci-like sequence fragments have numbers missing. Copy the sequences and fill in the blanks.

14. a. 0.5, 1.1, ___, ___, ___
b. 5, -4, ___, ___, ___
c. -6, -7, ___, ___, ___

15. a. ___, ___, ___, 11, 20
b. 2, ___, 7, ___, ___
c. ___, 3, ___, 9, ___

You may need to use trial and error for these.

16. a. 1, ___, ___, 11, ___
b. 12, ___, ___, 13, ___
c. ___, 8, ___, ___, 10

17. a. 1, ___, ___, ___, 11
b. 1, ___, ___, ___, 20
c. 2, ___, ___, ___, 19

18. a. 3, ___, ___, ___, ___, 29
b. 5, ___, ___, ___, ___, ___, 17

FIBONACCI SEQUENCES

These exercises only scratch the surface. There are countless wonderful patterns in the Fibonacci sequence.

Some hints for problem 9: What happens when you add strings of consecutive Fibonacci numbers? What happens when you multiply Fibonacci numbers that are separated by one number? (For example, the third and the fifth Fibonacci numbers, or the fourth and the sixth.)

Can problem 12 be generalized for multiples of 3, 4, 5, and so on?

We hold off on introducing subscripts until Chapter 5. If you want your students to learn to use subscripts before tackling some or all of problems 8-24, you can postpone them until then.

2.6 SOLUTIONS

8. The sum of the previous two numbers equals the subsequent number.
   34, 55, 89, 144, 233

10. Answers will vary.

11. a. 2, 4, 6, 10, 16, 26, 42, 68, 110, 178. It is Fibonacci-like.
    b. 0, 2, 2, 4, 6, 10, 16, 26, 42, 68. It is Fibonacci-like.
    c. 0, 1, 1, 2, 3, 5, 8, 13, 21, 34

12. Answers will vary.

13. Fibonacci: ..., -3, 2, -1, 1, 0, 1, 1, 2, 3
    Lucas: ..., 7, -4, 3, -1, 2, 1, 3, 4, 7
    Both the Fibonacci and Lucas sequences will alternate between positive and negative numbers.

14. a. 1.6, 2.7, 4.3
    b. 1, -3, -2
    c. -13, -20, -33

15. a. 7, 2, 9, 11, 20
    b. 2, 5, 7, 12, 19
    c. 3, 3, 6, 9, 15

16. a. 1, 5, 6, 11, 17
    b. 12, 0.5, 12.5, 13, 25.5
    c. -7, 8, 1, 9, 10

17. a. 1, 3, 4, 7, 11
    b. 1, 6, 7, 13, 20
    c. 2, 5, 7, 12, 19

18. a. 3, 4, 7, 11, 18, 29
    b. 5, -1, 4, 3, 7, 10, 17

MISSING NUMBERS

USING VARIABLES

FIBONACCI PUZZLE

*T*rial and error is an important problem-solving skill which is necessary for problems 16-18. If your students are getting frustrated, you may lead an all-class discussion to help the students develop trial-and-error techniques. For example, with problem 16a, students should be encouraged to keep a record of what the fourth number is for each value of the second number. They should observe whether the fourth number gets larger when the second one does. They can then adjust the second number appropriately.

*M*ost classes would not be ready this early in the course for an equation-solving approach to these problems. (Equation-solving techniques are introduced in Chapter 3 and emphasized in Chapter 6.) However, an algebraic approach to pattern recognition is explored in problems 19-23.

*S*tudents may want to use Lab Gear blocks to work on problems 20 and 21.

*I*f your students are frustrated by problem 24, suggest that they conduct a systematic search. They can try starting a sequence with 1, 1; 1, 2; 1, 3; and so on. Then 2, 1; 2, 2; and so on. As they work, they will find ways to speed up the search.

USING VARIABLES

19. Look at problem 17. Describe the relationship between the middle number and the outer numbers.

20. Create a five-term Fibonacci-like sequence in which the first two terms are x and y.

21. Check whether the pattern you noticed in problem 19 works for the sequence you just created. Explain.

22. Fill in the blanks for this Fibonacci-like sequence. -123, ___, ___, ___, 456

23. Extend the sequence you started in problem 20. Look for patterns.

FIBONACCI PUZZLE

24. How many Fibonacci-like sequences can you find that involve only positive whole numbers and include your age *in fourth place or later?* How about your teacher's age, or the age of a parent or adult friend?

DISCOVERY ***PERIMETER ARRANGEMENTS***

25. **Exploration** Make sketches of some different ways that you could put together an x-block and an x^2-block in two dimensions. (They have to touch each other, but they don't have to make a rectangle.) Use your imagination. There are more than two arrangements possible. Is it possible to sketch all the arrangements you think up?

26. Find the perimeters of the arrangements you sketched in problem 19. Write each perimeter next to the sketch. Make sure you have found the largest and smallest perimeters possible.

27. Find two arrangements that have the same perimeter, but look as different from each other as possible.

REVIEW ***MISSING TERMS***

28. What terms are missing? More than one term may be missing in each problem.

a. $3x^2 - 4x +$ ___ $= -9x^2 + 8x + 7$

b. $-x^2y + 6xy +$ ___ $= 9x^2y + 8y$

c. $3x^2 - 4x - ($ ___ $) = -9x^2 + 8x + 7$

d. $-x^2y + 6xy - ($ ___ $) = 9x^2y + 8y$

PUZZLE ***MAGIC TRIANGLE***

29. Put an integer from -4 to 4 in each circle to get equal sums along each side of the triangle. Find as many different sums as you can.

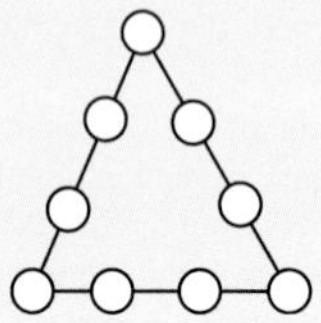

2.6 S O L U T I O N S

19. Sum of the two outer numbers (the number on the left side and the one on the right side) is divisible by the middle number.

20. x, y, $x + y$, $x + 2y$, $2x + 3y$, $3x + 5y$

21. Pattern should be the same.

22. -123, 234, 111, 345, 456

23. $5x + 8y$, $8x + 13y$, $13x + 21y$, ... One pattern to note is that the coefficient of each successive x-term is the same as the coefficient of the preceding y-term.

24. Answers will vary.

25. Answers will vary. Two possible solutions are given.

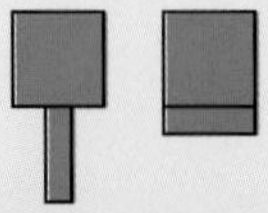

26. Answers will vary.

27. Answers will vary.

28. a. $-12x^2 + 12x + 7$

b. $10x^2y - 6xy + 8y$

c. $12x^2 - 12x - 7$

d. $-10x^2y + 6xy - 8y$

29. A possible solution is:

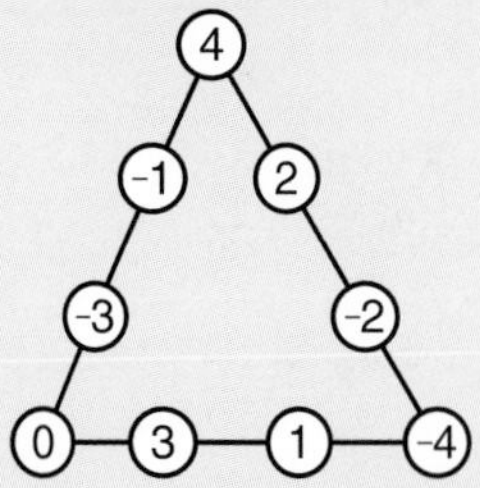

LESSON 2.7

Functions and Function Diagrams

You will need:

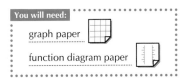

- graph paper
- function diagram paper

FUNCTIONS FROM IN-OUT TABLES

Definition: The following tables are called input-output tables, or *in-out tables.*

The number that is put in is x, and y is the number that comes out. Each table has a rule that allows you to get y from x. For example, the rule for the table in problem 1 is *to get y, add three to x.* We say that y can be written *as a function of x:* $y = x + 3$.

Definition: A *function* is a rule that assigns a single output to each input.

For each of the following problems:

a. Copy the table.
b. Describe the rule that allows you to get y from x.
c. Use the rule to find the missing numbers. (In some cases, the missing numbers may be difficult to find; use trial and error and a calculator to make it easier.)
d. Write y as a function of x.

1.

x	y
-5	-2
7	10
5	
	-7

2.

x	y
7	3.8
10	6.8
0	
	10

3.

x	y
5	20
3	12
1	
	-1

4.

x	y
7	40
1	16
-2	4
-5	
	-12

5.

x	y
3	8
4	13
1	-2
7	
	20

6.

x	y
5	15
2	-6
-1	-9
6	
	54

7. **Exploration** Find as many functions as possible that assign the y value 4 to the x value 1.

FUNCTION DIAGRAMS

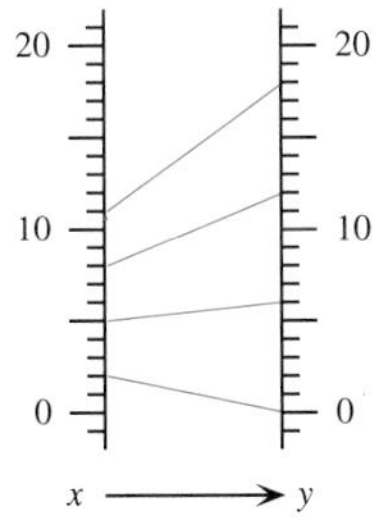

The figure above shows a function diagram for this table.

x	y
2	0
5	6
8	12
11	18

2.7 SOLUTIONS

1.

x	y
-5	-2
7	10
5	8
-10	-7

Add 3 to x to get y. $y = x + 3$.

2.

x	y
7	3.8
10	6.8
0	-3.2
13.2	10

Subtract 3.2 from x to get y. $y = x - 3.2$

3.

x	y
5	20
3	12
1	4
-.25	-1

Multiply x by 4 to get y. $y = 4x$

4.

x	y
7	40
1	16
-2	4
-5	-8
-6	-12

Multiply x by 4 then add 12 to get y. $y = 4x + 12$.

5.

x	y
3	8
4	13
1	-2
7	28
27/5	20

Multiply x by 5 then subtract 7 to get y. $y = 5x - 7$.

2.7 Functions and Function Diagrams

Core Sequence: 1-17

Suitable for Homework: 4-7, 14-23

What this Lesson is About:

- Introduction of function diagrams, a new tool
- Preview of linear functions
- Preview of linear equations

FUNCTIONS FROM IN-OUT TABLES

You could introduce this lesson by playing a game of *What's my function?* with the class. In that game, you ask students for input numbers, and respond with the output that a secret function would give. The students have to guess the function. Both the suggested inputs and the outputs are written on the chalkboard or on the overhead screen, in an in-out table.

Any functions can be used in the game. The easiest require only one operation. Examples: functions of the form $y = mx$, $y = x + b$, $y = x^2$.

More challenging are functions that require two operations. Examples: functions of the form $y = mx + b$, $y = ax^2$, $y = x^2 + c$, $y = x(x + b)$.

When students have guesses about the function, they can be asked to supply the outputs, instead of immediately letting the cat out of the bag and revealing the rule. This will give their classmates a chance to guess the function for themselves.

Once the function has been found, the game can continue by giving students inputs and asking for outputs, and finally by giving students outputs and asking for the inputs that would have produced them.

Problem 7 should produce a long list of possible functions. A good discussion could follow: How could one tell which one is correct? Trying other inputs, of course, would quickly rule out most of them.

FUNCTION DIAGRAMS

The authors would like to acknowledge Dr. Martin Flashman of Humboldt State University, Arcata, California, for his insights into the pedagogical power of the function diagram.

A reproducible page of blank function diagrams can be found on page 564. These are useful, especially when beginning to work with function diagrams. Later, students will make their own diagrams on graph paper.

This is the first of three lessons on function diagrams. A function diagram is essentially a graphical representation of an in-out table. As a learning tool, it has some advantages over the Cartesian graph. The following ideas are easier to see on a function diagram than on a Cartesian graph: definition of function, domain and range, inverse function, rate of change.

Of course, the function diagram does not replace the Cartesian graph, which is still one of the most powerful models we have to understand and apply mathematics. We have already worked with Cartesian graphs, and we will return to them in Chapter 4.

For clarity, we talk about the *x*- and *y*-number lines in the context of function diagrams, while we use the words *x*- and *y*-axes in the context of Cartesian graphs.

I SEE WHERE YOU'RE COMING FROM

Most of these problems cannot be solved by just looking at the diagram. Students will have to figure out some strategy for problems whose answers are not directly readable. The most effective approach is to start by identifying the function represented by the diagram, but your students may find other ways.

For problem 17, do not teach equation-solving techniques. The purpose of the problem is to develop the students' ability to work with equations by trial and error. This is a necessary step for understanding what equations are. Preview of equation solving will continue in Chapter 3. Formal equation-solving techniques will be introduced in Chapter 6.

UPS AND DOWNS

Problems 18-20 can be solved visually.

Problem 21 can be solved by trial and error, assuming the function was identified in the previous section. Make sure that your students do not think that problem 21a is a repeat of 15a or 17d.

8. What is the function illustrated in the previous function diagram?

For each function in problems 9-12:

a. Make a table, using at least five in-out pairs.

b. Make a function diagram, using the scale shown below.

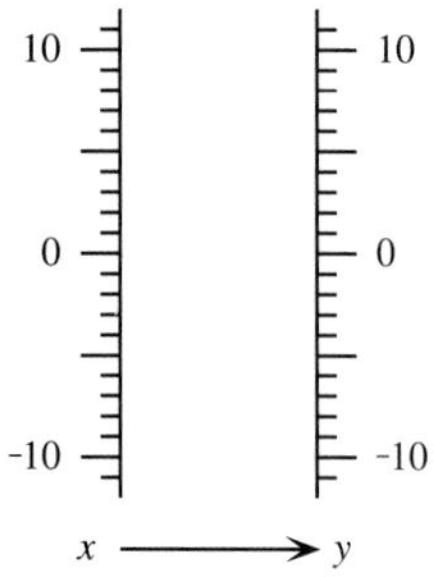

9. $y = x + 2$ **10.** $y = x - 2$

11. $y = 2x$ **12.** $y = x/2$

13. Make a function diagram for each of the tables in problems 1, 2, and 3. You will have to decide what scale to use on the *x*- and *y*-number lines. (For each problem, use the same scale on both number lines.)

Function diagrams are an important way of understanding functions. We will use them throughout this course.

I SEE WHERE YOU'RE COMING FROM

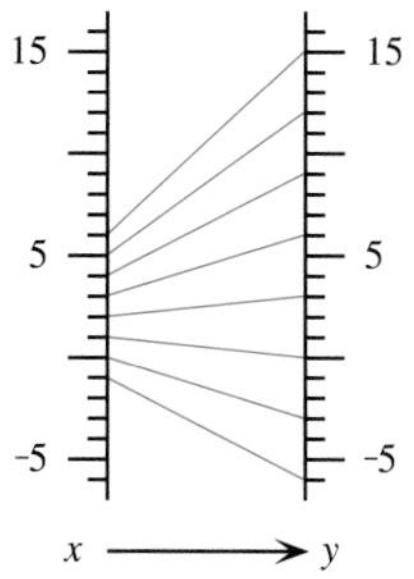

The following problems are about the above function diagram. Assume that more in-out lines could be added, following the same pattern.

14. Find the output when the input is:
a. 0 b. 5 c. -5

15. Find the output when the input is:
a. 99 b. -100 c. 1000

16. Find the output when the input is:
a. 1/2 b. 1/3 c. 1/6

For the following problem, you may need to use trial and error.

17. Find the input when the output is:
a. 0 b. 5 c. -5
d. 99 e. -100 f. 1000

2.7 SOLUTIONS

6.

x	y
5	15
2	-6
-1	-9
6	26
8	54

Square *x* then subtract 10 to get *y*.
$y = x^2 - 10$

7. Answers will vary

8. $y = 2x - 4$

For problems 9-12, one possible function diagram is given.

9. $y = x + 2$

x	y
3	5
-2	0
5	7
8	10
0	2

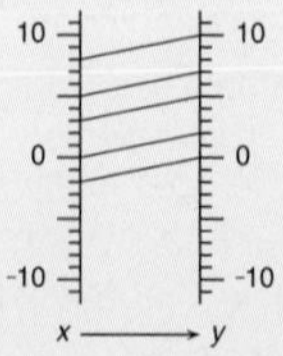

10. $y = x - 2$

x	y
7	5
0	-2
5	3
-5	-7
10	8

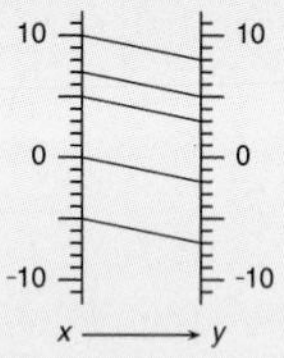

11. $y = 2x$

x	y
0	0
3	6
5	10
-3	-6
-5	-10

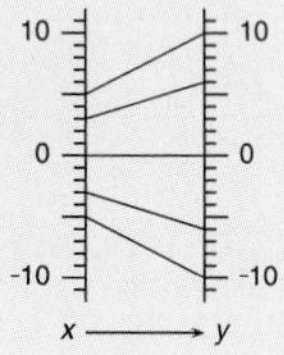

12. $y = x/2$

x	y
0	0
6	3
10	5
-6	-3
-10	-5

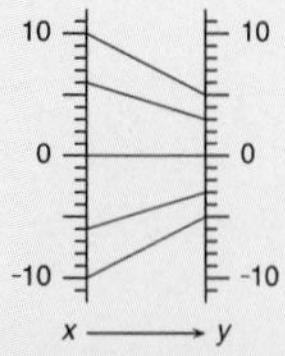

UPS AND DOWNS

Each line in a function diagram connects an input point on the x-number line to its output point on the y-number line. We use the notation (x, y) to refer to such a line. Notice that in the previous diagram some of the lines go up, and some go down. For example: (5, 12) goes up, and (0, -3) goes down.

18. If you were to draw additional lines in the function diagram, could you correctly draw one that goes neither up nor down? Where would it start?

19. In describing the diagram, one might say 5 goes to 12, "moving" up 7 units. Which point "moves" down 5 units?

20. Find a point that moves
a. up 3 units; b. down 3 units;
c. up 6 units; d. down 4 units.

21. Use trial and error to find a point that moves
a. up 99 units;
b. down 100 units.

22. **Generalization** If you know of a point that moves up n units in the previous diagram, how would you find a point that moves down n units? Write a full explanation.

DISCOVERY *SURFACE AREA OF A BOX*

The volume of a box is given by the formula
volume = length · width · height.

23. Write the surface area of a box as a function of length, width, and height. Compare your function with the ones found by some of your classmates.

Students may find a pattern for how much a given x goes up or down. Such a pattern would be useful for solving problem 21, but it is not necessary.

In a way, problems 19-21 preview simultaneous linear equations, since x and y have to satisfy two constraints: the linear relationship given in the function diagram, and the amount given for the value to "move" up or down.

Problem 22 depends on seeing the symmetry in the function diagram. The ordered pair discovered in problem 18 gives the line of symmetry. This problem is quite a challenge, and any attempts to solve it should be praised. Class discussion may be needed to achieve some closure on this problem.

DISCOVERY ***SURFACE AREA OF A BOX***

This problem is a good opportunity to see how comfortable your students are with using variables to represent relationships. It is also interesting to compare the different formulas that are likely to be found, and discuss how to check whether they are equivalent. (One way is to check if they give the same answers when used to find the surface area of a certain box.)

Students do not need to memorize the formulas they obtain.

2.7 SOLUTIONS

For problems 14-17, the function is $y = 3x - 3$:

14. a. -3
b. 12
c. -18

15. a. 294
b. -303
c. 2997

16. a. -3/2
b. -2
c. -5/2

17. a. 1
b. 8/3
c. -2/3
d. 34
e. -97/3
f. 1003/3

18. Yes; 3/2

19. -1 moves down 5 units to -6.

20. a. (3, 6)
b. (0, -3)
c. (9/2, 21/2)
d. (-1/2, -9/2)

21. a. (51, 150)
b. (-97/2, -297/2)

22. Find the horizontal line of symmetry such that when you fold over this line all the input-output lines coincide. From this fold, determine how many spaces there will be on the x-line where the output will be *up n* spaces. To find desired location on the x-line count *down* the same number of spaces from the fold on the x-line. Do the same to find the location on the y-line.

23. The surface area is 2 · length · width + 2 · height · length + 2 · width · height.

▼ 2.8
Time, Distance, Speed

Core Sequence: 1-10

Useful for Assessment: 4

What this Lesson is About:

- Introduction to motion problems
- Interpreting function diagrams in an applied context

Seeing function diagrams applied to real-world data may help motivate their use by providing a context.

MOTION PICTURES

Real-world data is simplified in order to provide us with a workable example of traveling at a constant rate. The main point of this activity is to see the relationship between the three quantities of time, distance, and speed.

You may return to this section at the end of the lesson and discuss with your class what the function diagrams might actually look like for a real race. Which of the participants is most likely to tire? In fact, what sort of duration is realistic? How fast should they run to be able to maintain their speed for a full hour? What if the race was over a certain distance rather than a certain duration?

LESSON 2.8

Time, Distance, Speed

MOTION PICTURES

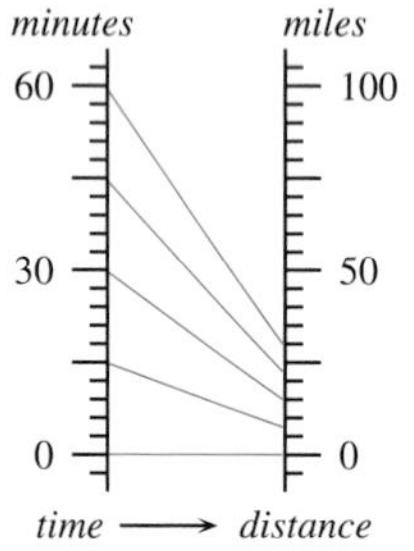

Roller Skater

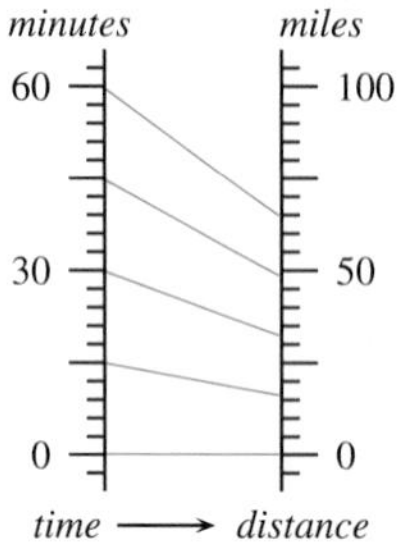

Cheetah

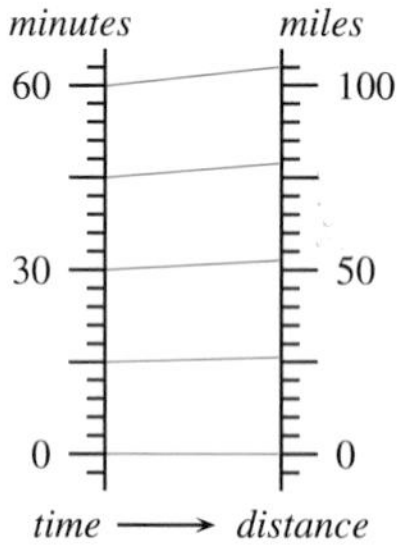

Needletail

The above function diagrams represent the motion of three living creatures: a fast roller skater; a cheetah (one of the world's fastest mammals, it's a large, wild cat that lives in Africa); and a white-throated needletail (one of the world's fastest birds, it lives in Australia).

The diagrams assume that the three creatures ran a one-hour race, and were able to maintain their top speed for the full hour. (This is not realistic, but then neither is the idea of a roller skater racing with a cheetah and a bird.)

Each diagram shows minutes on the x-number line, and miles on the y-number line.

1. Use the diagrams to estimate how far each went in an hour.
2. After thirty minutes, approximately
   a. how far is the needletail ahead of the cheetah?
   b. how far is the cheetah ahead of the skater?
3. Estimate each speed
   a. in miles per hour;
   b. in miles per minute.
4. 🔑 Explain how time-distance function diagrams allow you to compare speeds. Time is on the x-number line, distance is on the y-number line. Where is speed?

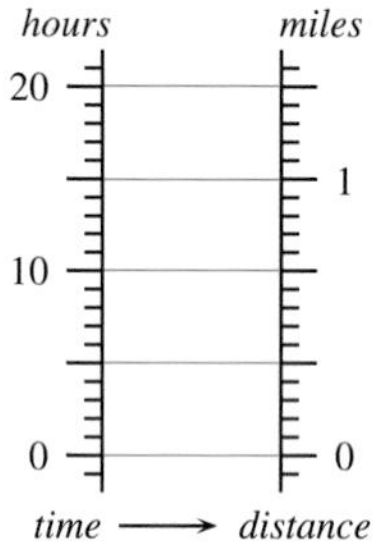

Sloth

2.8 SOLUTIONS

1. roller skater: 30 miles
   cheetah: 65 miles
   needletail: 105 miles
2. (After 30 minutes, the roller skater has gone 15 miles, the cheetah 32.5, and the needletail 52.5.)
   a. 20 miles
   b. 17.5 miles
3. roller skater: 30 miles/hour
   cheetah: 65 miles/hour
   needletail: 105 miles/hour
4. To determine speed, find the distance associated with 60 minutes. This is the speed in miles per hour. Using the same scale we note that the steeper the lines going down from left to right, the slower the speed. If the lines are going up from left to right, then we note that this denotes a faster speed than the previous ones.

5. The preceding diagram shows the hypothetical progress of a sloth. The x-number line represents time in hours, and the y-number line represents distance in miles. Compare the sloth's motion to the motion of the skater, cheetah, and needletail. How fast is it going per hour? Per minute?

6. Explain why someone comparing the sloth's speed to the needletail's might make a mistake and take the diagrams to mean the sloth is almost as fast as the needletail.

THE BALL

In a physics experiment, a ball is launched straight up by some device, and its height above the ground is recorded at one-second intervals. The resulting information is displayed in the function diagram below, where the x-number line represents time in seconds, and the y-number line represents distance from the ground at that time in meters.

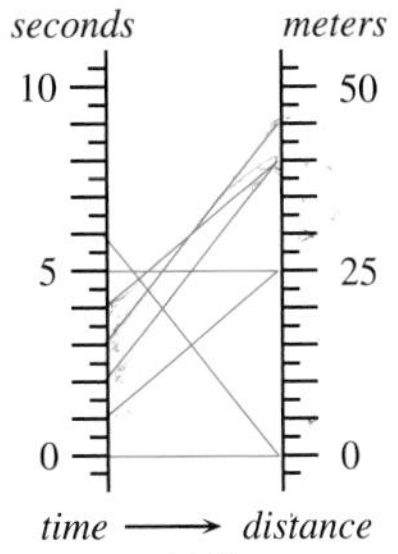

Ball

On the function diagram, follow the motion of the ball with your finger on the y-number line, second by second.

7. During which one-second interval(s) did the ball move the fastest? The slowest?

8. At what time did the ball change direction?

9. Make a table like this one, showing the height of the ball at one-second intervals. Extend the table until you have included all the information given on the function diagram.

Time (seconds)	Height (meters)
0	0
1	25
2	...

10. Estimate the times when the ball was at the following heights. (Give two times for each part, one on the way up, and one on the way down.)
a. 40 m　　b. 30 m
c. 20 m　　d. 10 m

THE BALL

*T*his activity previews quadratic functions, though the questions can be answered totally visually, without finding the actual function that describes the ball's trajectory.

*N*otice how a function diagram highlights the varying rate of change of a quadratic function.

2.8 S O L U T I O N S

5. 1/15 mile per hour; 1/900 mile per minute
6. The needletail's function diagram lines are almost horizontal like the sloth's. However, their scales are different.
7. fastest: between 0 and 1 second, also between 5 and 6 seconds
slowest: between 2 and 3 seconds, also between 3 and 4 seconds
8. at 3 seconds
9.

Time (seconds)	Height (meters)
0	0
1	25
2	40
3	45
4	40
5	25
6	0

10. a. 2 seconds, 4 seconds
b. between 1 and 2 seconds and between 4 and 5 seconds
c. Just below 1 second and just after 5 seconds
d. Under 0.5 seconds and over 5.5 seconds

THINKING WRITING **2.B**

The Car Trip

Core Sequence: none of the assignment

Suitable for Homework: 1-2

Useful for Assessment: 1-2

What this Assignment is About:

- Reading a data-based function diagram
- Relationship of time, distance, and rate
- Creating a data-based function diagram

This is an extension of the work in Lesson 8. However, instead of a mathematical function, we have one derived from plausible data.

Nevertheless, a number of mathematical concepts are subsumed in it, the most important being that of rate of change. When the car's position moves fast, slowly, or not at all, this is reflected in the rate of change of the y-value as a function of time (the x-value).

You might discuss with your students what it means for two in-out lines to meet on the y-number line. What would it mean if two in-out lines in a *car trip* function diagram crossed between the x- and y-number lines?

For problem 2, you may be able to get a class set of road maps for your students from an automobile club or your State Department of Transportation.

THINKING WRITING

2.B The Car Trip

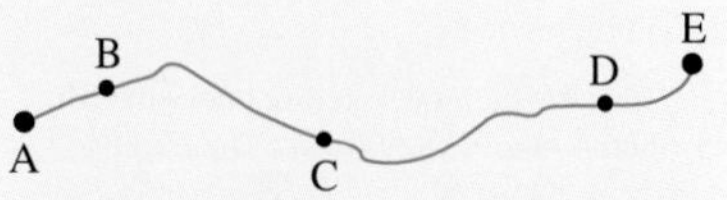

A family is traveling by car from City A, in Cool County, towards City E. On this diagram, the x-number line represents the time of day, with 9 A.M. near the bottom, and 7 P.M. near the top; the y-number line represents distance from City A in miles.

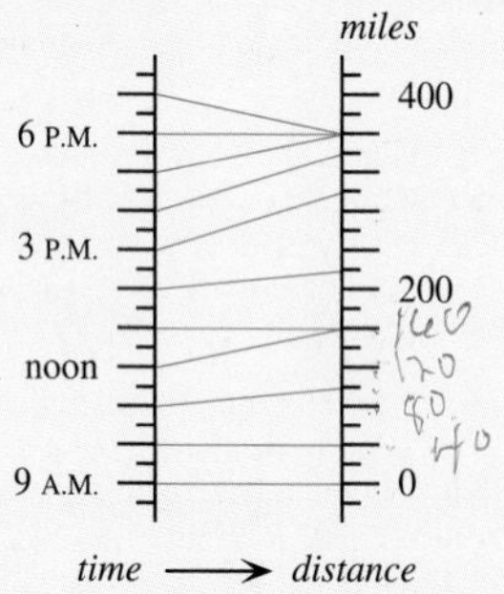

Car Trip

1. **Report** Describe the trip as best you can from the information on the function diagram. In your paragraph, make clear what you get from the diagram and where you are making guesses to interpret the information. Your paragraph should include answers to the following questions, but should not be limited to them.
   - What time did the trip start?
   - What happened from 12 to 1? Where did it happen?
   - When did the family drive faster than the speed limit? How fast were they going then?
   - How could you explain the changes in speed that are evident from the diagram?
   - What time did they arrive at their destination?
   - How far is City E from City A?

2. **Project**
   a. Using real towns and distances (perhaps taken from a road map), draw a map and a function diagram for another car trip.
   b. Get the map and function diagram that one of your classmates made in part (a). Write a paragraph describing the trip shown. Discuss your description with the person who made the map and diagram. Do you agree on what the figures convey? If you disagree, is one of you misinterpreting the figures? Or are both interpretations correct?

2.B SOLUTIONS

1. - The trip started at 9 A.M.
   - From 12-1, they had a lunch break perhaps. They did not go any distance during this time. They are 160 miles from home during this time.
   - They traveled faster than the speed limit between 2 and 3 P.M. They were going 80 mph.
   - Explanations of changes in speed will vary.
   - They arrived at their destinations at 5 P.M.
   - The distance from City A to City E is 360 miles.
2. Answers will vary.

LESSON 2.9

Operations and Function Diagrams

You will need:

graph paper

function diagram paper

ADDITION

1. Draw a function diagram to represent each of these functions.

a. $y = x + 6$ b. $y = x + 3$

c. Compare the two diagrams. How are they alike? How are they different?

The two function diagrams you just drew both represented functions of the form $y = x + b$, where b is a constant. In the first case, b was 6. In the second case, b was 3.

2. Draw three other function diagrams of the form $y = x + b$. Be sure to try at least one negative value of b.

3. a. Draw a function diagram for the function $y = x$.

b. The function $y = x$ is also of the form $y = x + b$. What is b?

4. The function diagrams you drew in problems 1-3 represent addition. In each case, to get the value of y, you added the number b to x. How are all of these diagrams alike? How are they different? How does the value of b affect the diagram?

MULTIPLICATION

5. Draw a function diagram to represent each of these functions.

a. $y = 2x$ b. $y = 3x$

c. Compare the two diagrams. How are they alike? How are they different?

The two function diagrams you just drew both represented functions of the form $y = mx$, where m is a constant. In the first case, m was 2. In the second case, m was 3.

6. Draw three other function diagrams of the form $y = mx$. Be sure to try at least one negative value of m and one value of m between 0 and 1.

7. The function $y = x$, for which you already have a diagram, is also of the form $y = mx$. What is m?

8. The function diagrams you just drew represent multiplication. In each case, to get the value of y you multiplied x by a number. How are all of these diagrams the same? How are they different?

9. Look at your multiplication diagrams. For each one, as the value of x increases from the bottom of its number line, follow the value of y on its number line with your finger.

a. For what values of m does the value of y go up? Down?

b. Is there a value of m for which y goes neither up nor down, but remains unchanged?

c. For what values of m does the value of y change faster than x? More slowly?

d. Is there a value of m for which y changes at the same rate as x?

2.9 Operations and Function Diagrams

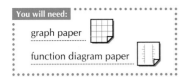

Core Sequence: 1-17

Suitable for Homework: 11-17

Useful for Assessment: 16

What this Lesson is About:

- The relationship between addition and subtraction, multiplication and division
- Preview of inverse functions
- Using parameters

This straightforward lesson completes the introduction to function diagrams.

ADDITION

MULTIPLICATION

The parameters in the linear function $y = mx + b$ are m and b. In Chapters 3 and beyond we will look at linear functions using both parameters at one time. In this lesson, we deal with them separately for the most part.

For $y = x + b$, the diagrams consist of parallel lines. As a geometric transformation of the number line, this function is a translation.

For $y = mx$, the diagrams consist of concurrent lines. (The lines all meet at one point. Your students may not notice this. They do not need to at this stage; we will return to the function diagrams of linear

2.9 SOLUTIONS

1. Numbers chosen on each axis will vary. Possible examples are given.

a. 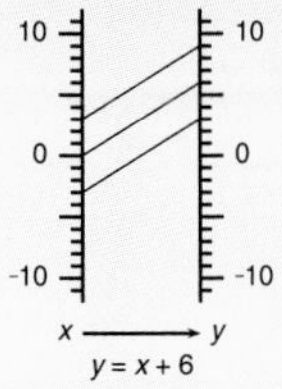

b. 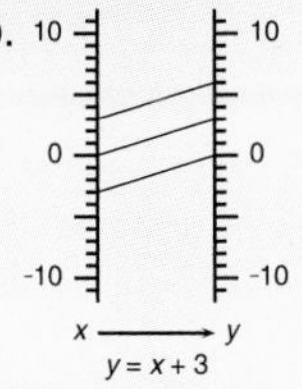

c. Both function diagrams have parallel lines. The lines for $y = x + 6$ have a steeper slope than the lines for $y = x + 3$.

2. Answers will vary.

3. Numbers chosen on each axis will vary. Possible examples are given.

a. 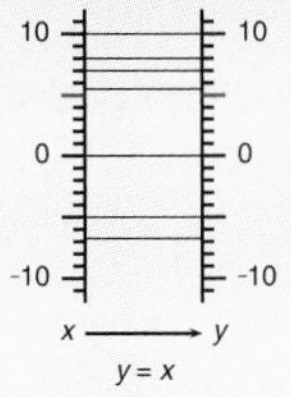

b. $b = 0$

4. The diagrams are alike in that the function diagram lines are parallel. They differ in the slopes of the function diagram lines. The parameter b affects the slope of the function diagram lines.

5. Numbers chosen on each axis will vary. Possible examples are given.

a. 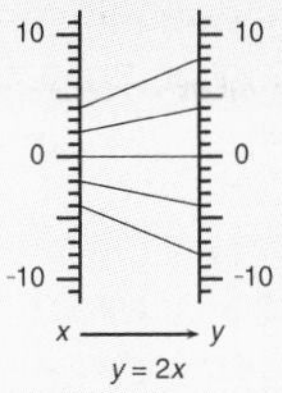

b. 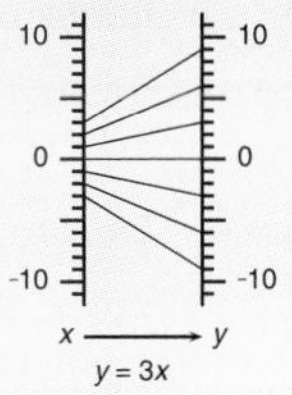

c. Both diagrams have similar shapes in that the slopes of the lines increase the farther up you go from 0 and decrease the farther down from 0. $y = 3x$ increases more quickly.

6. Answers will vary.

7. $m = 1$

functions in Chapter 6.) As a geometric transformation of the number line, this function is a dilation.

*P*roblem 9 focuses on the concept of rate of change. In Chapter 8, we will connect this understanding of rate of change with the concept of slope in a Cartesian graph. (Slope will be introduced in Chapter 5.)

MIRROR IMAGE DIAGRAMS

*T*he mirror is a vertical line between the two number lines. (Reflection across a horizontal mirror would yield a diagram that would correspond to the same function as the original diagram.)

*W*e will return to mirror image function diagrams in Chapter 3, when we work on inverse functions.

*T*he most difficult part of problem 16, and the one most worthy of class discussion is about $y = mx$ and $y = x/m$, when m is between 0 and 1. Values of m between -1 and 0 are not mentioned in the student text, in order to keep the statement of problem 16 from being even longer than it already is, but of course students can discuss those values as well.

*P*roblem 17 provides an opportunity to preview linear functions, with $m = -1$ and different values for the parameter b.

*W*e do not look at the function diagrams for functions of the form $y = m/x$ until Chapter 5, because they are quite complicated.

MIRROR IMAGE DIAGRAMS

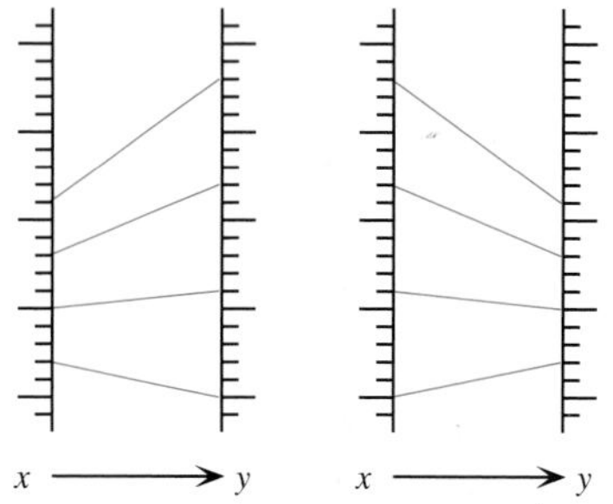

The two function diagrams above are mirror images of each other.

10. Explain how to draw the mirror image of a function diagram.

For each of the following functions:

a. Draw the function diagram, using the same scale on the x- and y-number lines.

b. Draw the mirror image diagram.

c. Find the function corresponding to the mirror image.

11. $y = x + 3$ **12.** $y = 4x$

13. $y = x - 4$ **14.** $y = x/3$

15. Explain the relationship between the function corresponding to the mirror image and the original function.

16. Report Write a report summarizing what you learned in this lesson. Illustrate your report with examples of function diagrams. Your report should include, but not be limited to, answers to the following questions:

- Addition can be represented by functions of the form $y = x + b$. What do their function diagrams look like if $b = 0$? What if b is greater than 0? Less than 0?
- Subtraction can be represented by functions of the form $y = x - b$. How do their function diagrams compare with those of addition?
- Multiplication can be represented by functions of the form $y = mx$. What do their function diagrams look like if m is negative? If m is positive? What if m is a number between 0 and 1?
- Division can be represented by functions of the form $y = x/m$. How do their function diagrams compare with those of multiplication? What if m is positive? Negative? What if m is a number between 0 and 1?

17. Compare function diagrams of the form $y = b - x$ with those of the form $y = x - b$.

2.9 SOLUTIONS

8. Analyzing $y = mx$: When $m = 1$, all lines are parallel and horizontal. When $m = 2$, all lines starting on the x-axis above zero will go up from left to right. All the lines starting below zero go down from left to right. As m becomes more positive, the lines become steeper. In all cases, if the function lines were extended, they would intersect on the left side of the x-axis. If m is negative, the lines intersect in one point between the x- and y-axes. If $0 < m < 1$ and we extend the function diagram lines, they would intersect on the right side of the y-axis.

9. a. $m > 0$; $m < 0$
   b. $m = 0$
   c. $m > 1$, $m < -1$; $-1 < m < 1$
   d. $m = 1$

10. Interchange the x- and y-values.

11. Numbers chosen on each axis will vary. Possible examples are given.

a. 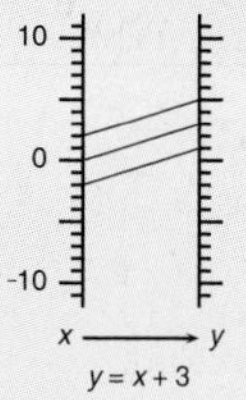

b. 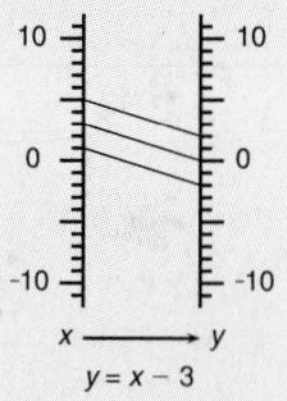

c. $y = x - 3$

12. Numbers chosen on each axis will vary. Possible examples are given.

a. 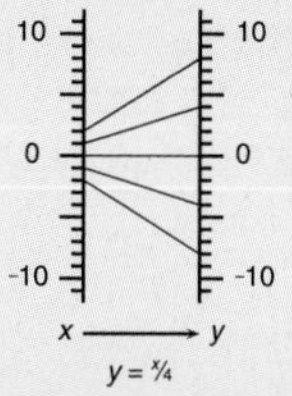

b. 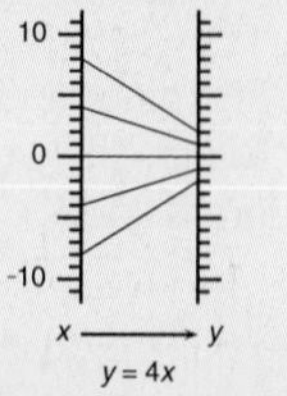

c. $y = (1/4)x$

13. Numbers chosen on each axis will vary. Possible examples are given.

a. 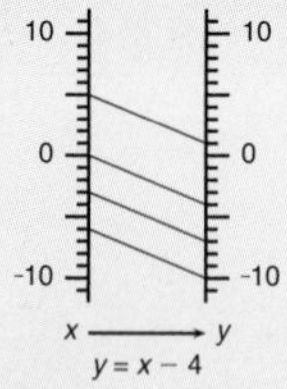

b. 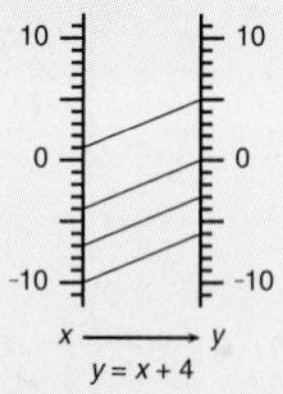

c. $y = x + 4$

14. Numbers chosen on each axis will vary. Possible examples are given.

a. 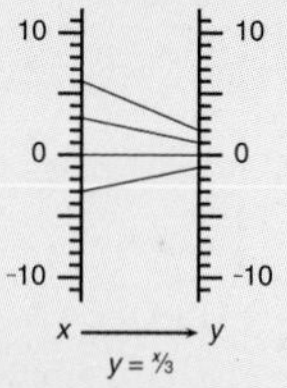

b. 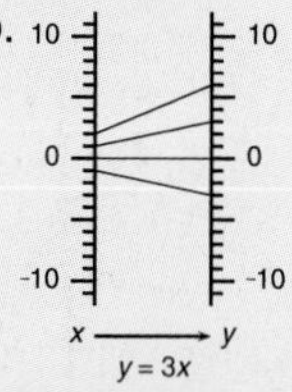

c. $y = 3x$

(Solutions continued on page 509)

LESSON 2.10

Perimeter and Surface Area Functions

You will need:

the Lab Gear 

PERIMETER

1. Look at this sequence of block figures. Think about how it would continue, following the pattern. Then:
   a. Sketch the next figure in the sequence.
   b. Copy and complete the table below.
   c. Describe the pattern in words.

Figure #	Perimeter
1	4
2	6
3	8
4	...
10	...
100	...
n	...

Repeat problem 1 for each of these sequences.

2. 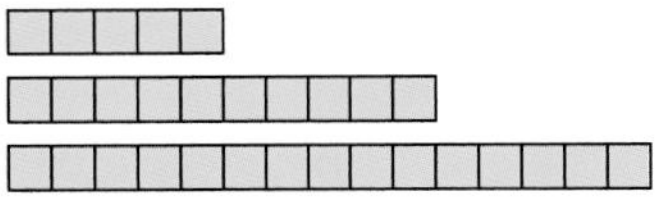

3. 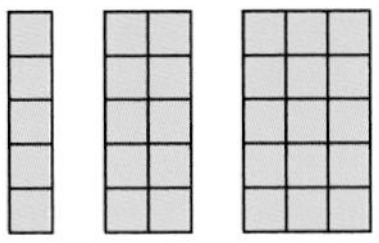

4. 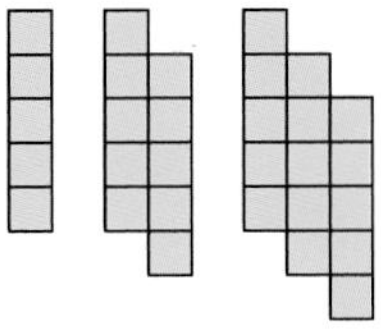

5. 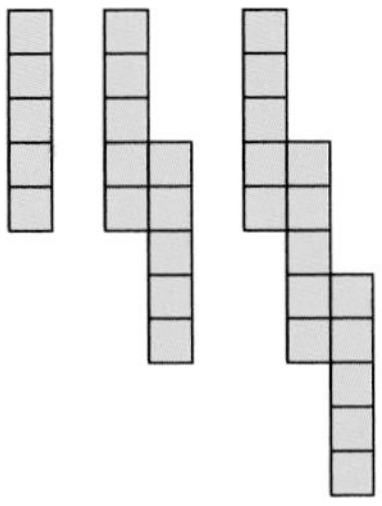

6. 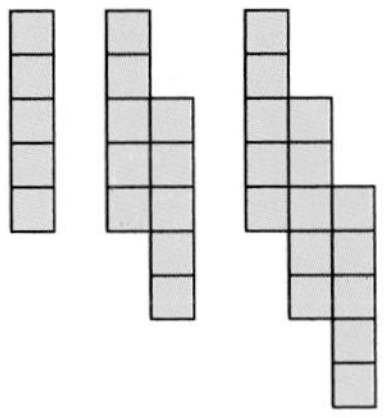

If you have trouble answering questions 7-8 by trial and error, try making graphs from the data in your tables, with the figure number (n) on the horizontal axis and the perimeter on the vertical axis.

7. In problem 1, which figure would have perimeter 50?

8. Is it possible to have perimeter 50 for any of the patterns in problems 2-6?

2.10 Perimeter and Surface Area Functions

Core Sequence: 1-12

Suitable for Homework: 1-8, 23-24

Useful for Assessment: 11

What this Lesson is About:

- Recognizing number patterns in a geometric context
- Using variables and functions to represent and understand numeric and geometric information
- Preview of arithmetic sequences, linear functions, and linear equations

In this lesson the Lab Gear is a source of an interesting problem, rather than a tool used to model a given algebra technique.

PERIMETER

Problems 1-8 provide opportunities to recognize a number pattern in a sequence of perimeters. Actually, the sequence is an arithmetic sequence, and the function is linear. The n line in the table is an opportunity to express the pattern algebraically.

Problems 9-12 are an interesting manipulative generalization, using a blue-blocks figure to model each sequence, with x standing in for n.

2.10 SOLUTIONS

1.

Figure #	Perimeter
1	4
2	6
3	8
4	10
10	22
100	202
n	$2n + 2$

Perimeter is two times the figure number plus two.

2.

Figure #	Perimeter
1	12
2	22
3	32
4	42
10	102
100	1002
n	$10n + 2$

Perimeter is ten times the figure number plus two.

3.

Figure #	Perimeter
1	12
2	14
3	16
4	18
10	30
100	210
n	$10 + 2n$

Perimeter is twice the figure number plus ten.

4.

Figure #	Perimeter
1	12
2	16
3	20
4	24
10	48
100	408
n	$4n + 8$

Perimeter is four times the figure number plus eight.

5.

Figure #	Perimeter
1	12
2	20
3	28
4	36
10	84
100	804
n	$8n + 4$

Perimeter is eight times the figure number plus four.

6.

Figure #	Perimeter
1	12
2	18
3	24
4	30
10	66
100	606
n	$6n + 6$

Perimeter is six times the figure number plus six.

7. Figure number 24 in table

SURFACE AREA

MORE SURFACE AREA

These problems are algebraically very much the same, but they are visually a little more difficult to handle. Many students would have trouble solving these without having the manipulatives at hand. For that reason, you may reverse the order of the lesson: Start with problems 13-16, next do problems 1-12, then return to problems 17-22. Doing things this way allows you to start in class with the blocks, to continue at home, and to finish in class the next day.

You may also save problems 18-22 for review at some later date.

9. Look at the x-block.

a. What is the perimeter of its top face?

b. What is its perimeter if $x = 1, 2, 3, 4, 10$? Make a table like the ones above.

c. Compare your table with those in problems 1-6. It should be the same as one of them. Which one? Explain why you think this works.

10. a. This figure represents the tops of five x-blocks. What is its perimeter?

b. What is its perimeter if $x = 1, 2, 3, 4, 10$? Make a table like the ones above.

c. This figure is related to one of problems 2-6. Which one? Explain.

Note that in problems 9 and 10, just one figure represents a whole infinite sequence of figures, because of the use of variables.

11. Find the blue block that is related to problem 3. Explain.

12. For each of problems 4-6, build a related figure made of blue blocks. Check your answer by making a table.

SURFACE AREA

13. Look at the sequence of cube figures. Think about how it would continue, following the pattern. Then:

a. Sketch the next figure in the sequence.

b. Copy and complete the following table.

c. Describe the pattern in words.

Figure #	Surface Area
1	6
2	10
3	14
4	...
10	...
100	...
n	...

Repeat problem 13 for each of these sequences.

14. 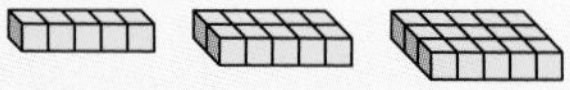

15. 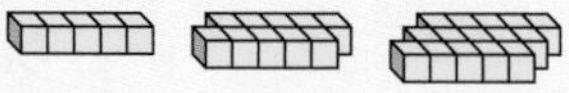

16. 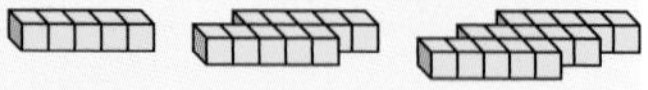

17. For each of problems 13-16, build a related figure made of blue blocks. Check your answers by making a table.

MORE SURFACE AREA

18. Look at the sequence. Think about how it continues, following the pattern. Then:

a. Sketch the next figure.

b. Make a table like the following one.

2.10 SOLUTIONS

8. Figure number 20 from problem #3.

9. a. $2x + 2$

b.

x	Perimeter
1	4
2	6
3	8
4	10
10	22

c. It's the same as problem #1 since both have the same rule for the perimeter, which is $2n + 2$.

10. a. $10x + 2$

b.

x	Perimeter
1	12
2	22
3	32
4	42
10	102

c. This is the same as #2 since both have the same rule for the perimeter, which is $10n + 2$.

11. 5x-block since 2D perimeter is $10 + 2x$, which is the same rule for the perimeter in #3.

12. i. 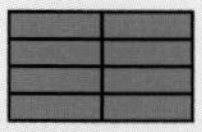 $4x + 8$

ii. 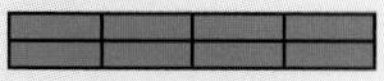 $8x + 4$

iii.  $6x + 6$

13.

Figure #	Surface Area
1	6
2	10
3	14
4	18
10	42
100	402
n	$4n + 2$

Each one-block has a surface area of six, so for the nth figure we get $6n$. Each time we add a new one-block, we lose a surface area of two. So the total surface area is $6n - 2(n - 1) = 6n - 2n + 2 = 4n + 2$.

14.

Figure #	Surface Area
1	22
2	34
3	46
4	58
10	130
100	1210
n	$12n + 10$

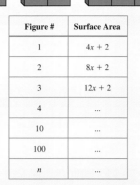

Figure #	Surface Area
1	$4x + 2$
2	$8x + 2$
3	$12x + 2$
4	...
10	...
100	...
n	...

c. Describe the pattern in words.

Repeat problem 18 for each of these sequences.

19. 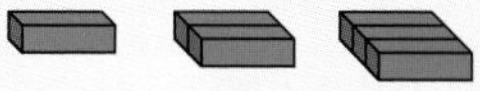

20. 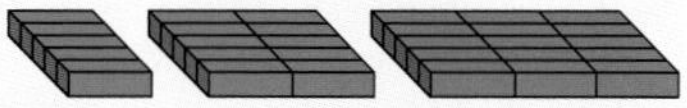

21. 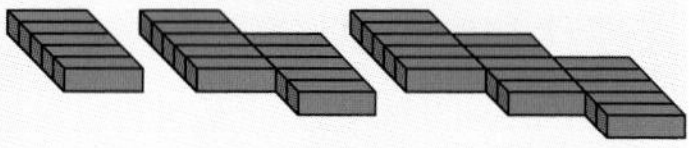

22. Make a figure out of blue blocks such that by substituting 1, 2, 3, … for y in its surface area you get the same sequence as you did in problem 19. Check your work by making a table.

GAME SPROUTS

This is a game for two players. Start with three dots on a piece of paper. These represent towns. Players take turns. To make a move:

- Join a town to itself or to another town with a *road* (a line).
- Place another town somewhere on the road you just created.

Rules:

- A road cannot cross itself, another road, or an existing town.
- No town can have more than three roads coming out of it.

The winner is the last person able to make a legal move.

23. Play the game with a classmate.

24. What is the maximum number of moves possible in a game?

GAME SPROUTS

See Chapter 1 of *Mathematical Carnival*, by Martin Gardner (New York, 1965), for more information on this game.

In a way, the game previews **Thinking/Writing 2.C**. You do not have to assign it before the students do C.

2.10 SOLUTIONS

Each five-block has a surface area of 22, so for the nth figure we get $22n$. Each time we add a new five block, we lose a surface area of 10. So the total surface area is $22n - 10(n - 1) = 22n - 10n + 10 = 12n + 10$.

15.

Figure #	Surface Area
1	22
2	36
3	50
4	64
10	148
100	1408
n	$14n + 8$

Each five-block has a surface area of 22, so for the nth figure we get $22n$. Each time we add a new five-block, we lose a surface area of eight. So the total surface area is $22n - 8(n - 1) = 14n + 8$.

16.

Figure #	Surface Area
1	22
2	38
3	54
4	70
10	166
100	1606
n	$16n + 6$

Each five-block has a surface area of 22, so for the nth figure we get $22n$. Each successive time we add a new five-block, we lose a surface area of six. So the total surface area is $22n - 6(n - 1) = 16n + 6$.

17. i. 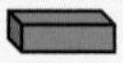 $4n + 2$

ii. 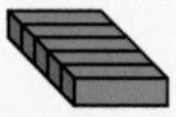 $12n + 10$

iii. 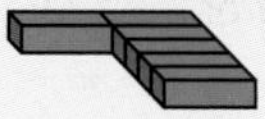 $14n + 8$

iv. 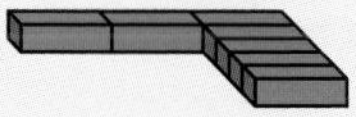 $16n + 6$

18.

Figure #	Surface Area
1	$4x + 2$
2	$8x + 2$
3	$12x + 2$
4	$16x + 2$
10	$40x + 2$
100	$400x + 2$
n	$4nx + 2$

Each x-block has a surface area of $4x + 2$, so for the nth figure we get $n(4x + 2)$. Each time we add a new x-block, we lose a surface area of two. So the total surface area is $n(4x + 2) - 2(n - 1) = 4nx + 2$.

(Solutions continued on page 509.)

▼ 2.11
Polyomino Functions

Core Sequence: none of the lesson

Suitable for Homework: 2-7, 12-17

Useful for Assessment: 17

What this Lesson is About:

- More number patterns from a geometric context, generalized with variables
- A function of two variables
- Square and rectangular numbers

The lesson wraps up the question of the relationship between polyomino area and perimeter that was opened in Chapter 1, Lessons 1 and 2.

POLYOMINO EYES

Polyomino eyes are the second variable that accounts for the range of possible polyomino perimeters possible for a given area.

Problems 1-2 help students organize their research by keeping area constant, in order to highlight the relationship between perimeter and eyes. If the Exploration is very successful, problem 2 can be skipped. If, on the other hand, you do not want to spend too much time on this lesson, you may skip problem 1, and provide more guidance, so as to get to the formula in problem 5 more rapidly.

LESSON 2.11

Polyomino Functions

You will need: graph paper

POLYOMINO EYES

Definition: The points of intersection of the grid lines inside a polyomino are called *eyes.*

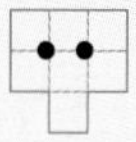

1. **Exploration** Any polyomino has an area, a perimeter, and a number of eyes. Is there a relationship between the three numbers? Can you express the perimeter as a function of the area and the number of eyes? (Hint: To find out, draw several polyominoes *that have the same area,* but different perimeters. For each one, write the number of eyes and the perimeter. As the number of eyes increases, does the perimeter get longer or shorter? Repeat the process for a different area.) Write a paragraph telling what you discover.

2. Complete the table shown at the top of the next column. Use data from these figures.

3. Write a formula for the perimeter of a polyomino having area 12 and e eyes.

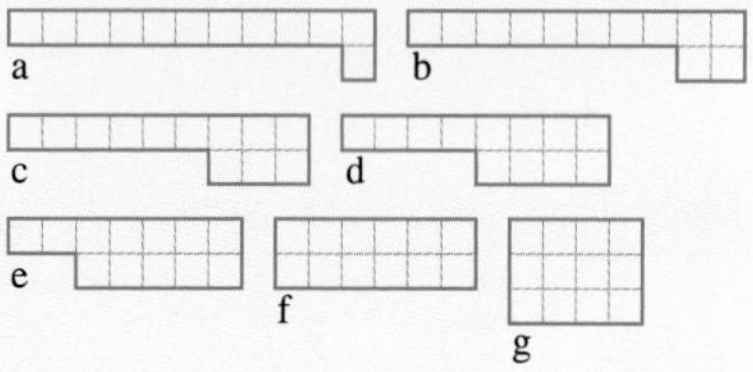

Figure	Eyes	Area	Perimeter
a	0	12	...
b	...	...	...

4. Fill out a similar table for another area. Write a formula for the perimeter as a function of the number of eyes for your area.

5. If you know that a polyomino has 0 eyes, and area 100, how could you get its perimeter?

6. Answer question 5 using area 100 and 10 eyes.

7. **Generalization** Write a formula for the perimeter p of a polyomino having area a and e eyes. (This formula is a function of two variables, a and e.)

8. For a given area, what is the maximum number of eyes? Find a pattern by experimenting with areas 4 and greater.

A GRAPH PAPER SPIRAL

9. Make a polyomino spiral on your graph paper by shading in one square at a time. See the figure below.

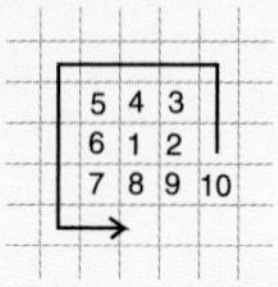

2.11 SOLUTIONS

1. Answers may vary. One can express the perimeter as a function of the area and the number of eyes. See the formula for this function in #7.

2.

Figure	Eyes	Area	Perimeter
a	0	12	26
b	1	12	24

3. perimeter = $26 - 2e$
4. Answers may vary.
5. perimeter = $2 \cdot 100 + 2 = 202$
6. perimeter = $202 - 2 \cdot 10 = 182$
7. perimeter = $2 \cdot a + 2 - 2e$
8. If area is n^2, then the maximum number of eyes is $(n-1)^2$.

9.

Area	Perimeter
1	4
2	6
3	8
4	8
5	10
6	10
7	12
8	12
9	12
10	14

Every time you shade a square, write the perimeter of the figure in a table like the following. Continue until you see a pattern.

Area	Perimeter
1	4
2	6
3	8
...	...

10. Describe the pattern you see.

11. Now make a new spiral the same way. This time record *only* the areas of squares and rectangles that you get along the way, in two tables like those below, continuing until you see a pattern in all the columns.

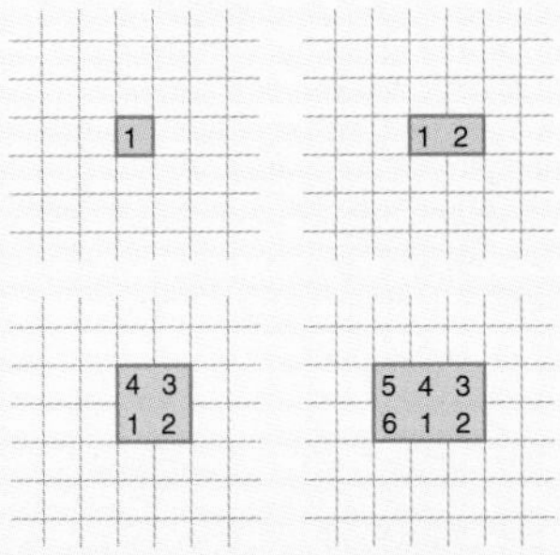

Square #	Area	Perimeter
1	1	4
2	4	8
3	...	...

Rectangle #	Area	Perimeter
1	2	6
2	6	10
3	...	...

12. Describe the patterns you see in each column.

13. What will the area and perimeter be for square #100?

14. Write a function for:

a. the area of square #*x*;

b. the perimeter of square #*x*.

15. What will the area and perimeter be for rectangle #100?

16. Write a function for:

a. the area of rectangle #*x*;

b. the perimeter of rectangle #*x*.

17. Report What do you know about the relationship between area and perimeter of polyominoes? You may draw information from this lesson, as well as from Chapter 1, Lessons 1 and 2. Use graphs and illustrations.

*T*he formula is called Pick's formula. (Since they are unlikely ever to need it, students should not memorize it.)

*T*he pattern in problem 8 is hard to find, but pretty. The maximum number of eyes is related to the minimum perimeter which was investigated in Chapter 1, Lesson 2, and to some of the issues investigated in the next section.

A GRAPH PAPER SPIRAL

*T*his is yet another way to think about the problem of the minimum perimeter for polyominoes of given area.

*A*long the way, students get to work with square and rectangular numbers and to use variables and functions. Rectangular numbers first appeared in Chapter 1, Lesson 11.

*P*roblem 17 asks students to summarize all they have learned about polyomino area and perimeter. Once again, what is important here is not the specific content that was covered. That content is *pure mathematics*, in that it has no immediately obvious applications. What mattered was the process of the investigation. A large and complex problem was approached from various angles, over a period of weeks, before it was completely understood. In the process, students both used and learned algebra.

*P*olyominoes will return in Chapter 7.

2.11 SOLUTIONS

10. Upon completing a rectangle, your next perimeter will remain two higher than the previous one until you have completed a new rectangle again.

11.

Square #	Area	Perimeter
1	1	4
2	4	8
3	9	12
4	16	16
5	25	20
6	36	24

Rectangle #	Area	Perimeter
1	2	6
2	6	10
3	12	14
4	20	18
5	30	22

12. The patterns for the square are as follows: Area equals the square of the square number. The perimeter is four times the square number. The patterns for the rectangle are as follows: The area is the quantity of the rectangle number plus one times the rectangle number. The perimeter is four times the rectangle number plus two.

13. Area = 10,000. Perimeter = 400.

14. a. Area = x^2.
b. Perimeter = $4x$

15. Area = 10,100. Perimeter = 402.

16. a. Area = $(x + 1) \cdot x$
b. Perimeter = $4x + 2$

17. Answers will vary. However for both the rectangular and square polyominos, the area starts out less than the perimeter but soon will overtake the perimeter. The area will equal the perimeter in the square polyomino when $n^2 = 4n$. For the rectangle, the area will equal the perimeter when $n(n + 1) = 4n + 2$.

▼ 2.12
Geoboard Triangles

Core Sequence: 1-18

Suitable for Homework: (using dot paper) 10-12, 14-18

Useful for Assessment: 10-12, 18

What this Lesson is About:

- Learning to find the area of any geoboard triangle
- Using operations in a concrete context
- Using variables and functions to express relationships
- Solving a difficult problem by breaking it down into smaller problems

This lesson is a necessary part of the process that will lead to a geometric approach to square roots later in the course.

The lesson is long and does not have to be covered at once. For example, you may save problems 13-18 for later. Just make sure to do them before Chapter 3, Lesson 12, the next geoboard lesson.

Do not teach or remind the students about the formula for the area of a triangle. It is important at this stage that they learn to find areas by their own methods, and that several approaches for the same figure be compared. For some geoboard triangles, the formula *(base times height divided by two)* is useless or even misleading, because neither base nor height are known. Yet student-devised methods will work even in those cases.

LESSON 2.12

Geoboard Triangles

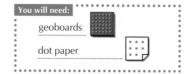

You will need:
- geoboards
- dot paper

1. **Exploration** If many triangles have one vertical side in common, how is their area related to the position of the third vertex? To find out, make many triangles having vertices at (0, 0) and (0, 8). For each one, keep a record of the coordinates of the third vertex and the area. Look for patterns. Write a paragraph explaining what you found out. Use sketches.

HORIZONTAL *AND* VERTICAL SIDES

2. Make a triangle having a horizontal side of length 6 and a vertical side of length 4. What is its area?

3. In this problem, use triangles having a horizontal side of 6.
   a. Make a table like the following. All triangles should have a horizontal side of length 6, but the length of the vertical side will vary. Extend the table all the way to vertical side of length 10.

Vertical Side	Area
0	...
1	...
2	6
...	...

   b. Explain how you could find the area of a triangle having horizontal side 6 and vertical side 100.
   c. Express the area as a function of the vertical side.

4. Repeat problem 3 for a horizontal side of length 9.

ONE HORIZONTAL *OR* VERTICAL SIDE

5. Make a triangle having vertices at (0, 0) and (0, 7) and the third vertex at (1, 4). What is its area?

6. Make a table like the following for triangles having vertices at (0, 0) and (0, 7) and the third vertex as indicated. Extend the table all the way to vertex (7, 4).

3rd Vertex	Area
(0, 4)	...
(1, 4)	...
(2, 4)	...
...	...

7. Write the area as a function of the *x*-coordinate of the third vertex.

8. a. Make the triangle having vertices (0, 0), (0, 7), and (9, 4). Guess its area.
   b. With another rubber band, make the smallest rectangle that covers the triangle. If you did it correctly, you should now see two new triangles. Find the area of the rectangle and the area of the two new triangles.
   c. Find the area of the original triangle. This should match your guess from part (a).

2.12 SOLUTIONS

1. Answers will vary. The area turns out to be 1/2 · 8 · the *x*-coordinate of the third vertex. See #6 & 7 for a table and a similar formula.
2. Area = 12
3. a.

Vertical Side	Area
0	0
1	3
2	6
3	9
4	12
5	15
6	18
7	21
8	24
9	27
10	30

   b. Area = 300. The rectangle that goes around this triangle has an area of 600; the triangle is one half the area of the rectangle.
   c. Area = 3 · vertical side
4. a.

Vertical Side	Area
0	0
1	4.5
2	9
3	13.5
4	18
5	22.5
6	27
7	31.5
8	36
9	40.5
10	45

   b. Area = 450. Explanation is like problem #3b.
   c. Area = 4.5 · vertical side
5. Area = 7/2
6.

3rd Vertex	Area
(0, 4)	0
(1, 4)	7/2
(2, 4)	7
(3, 4)	21/2
(4, 4)	14
(5, 4)	35/2
(6, 4)	21
(7, 4)	49/2

7. Area = 7/2 · (*x*)
8. a. Area = 63/2
   b. Area of rectangle = 63
      Area of one triangle = 13.5 and the other triangle is 18.
   c. The area of the original triangle is 63/2.

9. How would you find the area of the triangle having vertices at (1, 0), (6, 0), and (9, 9)? Find it and explain what you did, using a sketch and a paragraph.

Generalizations

10. a. Make triangles having vertices at (0, 0) and (0, 6) and the third vertex at (*x*, 9), where *x* takes each of the whole number values from 0 to 10. Make a table of values to show the area as a function of *x*.
b. Make triangles having vertices at (0, 0) and (0, 6) and the third vertex at (9, *y*), where *y* takes each of the whole number values from 0 to 10. Make a table of values to show the area as a function of *y*.
c. How do the answers to (a) and (b) differ?

11. a. Make at least three triangles having vertices at (0, 1) and (0, 6) and the third vertex at (*x*, *y*), where *x* and *y* take whole number values from 1 to 8. Sketch each one and find its area.
b. Explain how you would find the area of a triangle having vertices at (0, 1), (0, 6), and (99, 99) without drawing a picture.

12. Explain how you would find the area of a triangle having vertices at (0, 0), (*b*, 0), and (*x*, *h*), where *b* and *h* are nonnegative.

NO HORIZONTAL OR VERTICAL SIDES

13. **Exploration** What is the area of the triangle having vertices (0, 6), (7, 8), and (6, 1)? Explain how you arrive at the answer. Use sketches on dot paper.

14. What is the area of the four-sided shape having vertices at (0, 7), (2, 10), (10, 5), (5, 0)? Hint: First find the area of the whole geoboard, then use subtraction.

15. Make a triangle having no horizontal or vertical sides and having vertices on the outside edges of the geoboard. Use subtraction to find its area.

16. Repeat problem 15 on another triangle.

17. What is the area of the triangle having vertices at (1, 8), (2, 4), and (9, 3)? Hint: You may use the triangles having these vertices.

(1, 8), (1, 3), (9, 3)
(2, 4), (1, 3), (9, 3)
(1, 8), (2, 4), (1, 3)

18. **Report** Write an illustrated report on how to find the area of any geoboard triangle. Give examples of the different techniques. Make sure you include examples of using division by two, addition, and subtraction.

Throughout the lesson, the key problem-solving technique is to reduce the given problem to a combination of easier problems.

Problem 1 prepares students for problems 2-9.

HORIZONTAL AND VERTICAL SIDES

The best strategy, which some student is sure to find, is to enclose the triangle in a rectangle with the horizontal and vertical sides as length and width. The area of the triangle is half the area of the rectangle.

ONE HORIZONTAL *OR* VERTICAL SIDE

Here at least two strategies are possible: one based on addition (splitting the triangle into two triangles of the type studied in the previous section); and one based on subtraction, as suggested in problem 8.

Only subtraction works for the example given in problem 9.

Problems 10-12 guide students into an algebraic representation. In particular, students may recognize the usual formula for the area of a triangle as the outcome of problem 12.

NO HORIZONTAL OR VERTICAL SIDES

For these cases again, only subtraction works, (in combination with other methods).

The Report (problem 18) summarizes the whole lesson.

2.12 SOLUTIONS

9. Area = 27. One way is to put a rectangle around the triangle. Find the area of the rectangle and then subtract the areas of the two new triangles that are formed.

10. a.

3rd Vertex	Area
(0, 9)	0
(1, 9)	3
(2, 9)	6
(3, 9)	9
(4, 9)	12
(5, 9)	15
(6, 9)	18
(7, 9)	21
(8, 9)	24
(9, 9)	27
(10, 9)	30

b.

3rd Vertex	Area
(9, 0)	45
(9, 1)	45
(9, 2)	45
(9, 3)	45
(9, 4)	45
(9, 5)	45
(9, 6)	45
(9, 7)	45
(9, 8)	45
(9, 9)	45
(9, 10)	45

c. In part a the area is increasing, while in part b the area is constant.

11. a. The area for all triangles is (1/2) · (5) · (*x*-coordinate). It does not matter what the *y*-coordinate is. Changing *y* shears the triangle but does not change its area.
b. The area is (1/2) · 5 · 99

12. Answers will vary. However, one explanation is similar to problem #9. Another interesting way is if we sheer the triangle until we get a right triangle with equal area. The right triangle will have vertices (0, *h*), (0, 0) and (*b*, 0). The area of both triangles will be 1/2 · *b* · *h*.

13. Area is 23.5. The solution is very similar to #9, except you need to subtract the area of three triangles from the area of the rectangle.

14. Area = 47. 15. Answers will vary.

16. Answers will vary. 17. Area = 13.5

18. Students' reports will vary. However explanations like problems #9, 12, and 13 should be included.

THINKING WRITING 2.C Towns, Roads, and Zones

Core Sequence: none of the assignment

Suitable for Homework: 2-8

Useful for Assessment: 7

What this Assignment is About:

- Using tables and variables to represent a number pattern
- Functions of two variables
- Preview of equivalent equations

It is best to do problem 1 in class. It is not likely that the whole problem will be solved in one sitting while working on this Exploration. Its purpose is to help the students become clear on the terminology and give them a chance to find their own strategies for solution. Problems 2-6 should help them get more specific.

The questions in problem 7 are intended to lead to three equivalent equations, each one solved for a different variable. Your students probably do not yet know how to transform equations into each other formally, but they should be able to do this based on their understanding of the numerical relationships between the three quantities.

THINKING WRITING 2.C Towns, Roads, and Zones

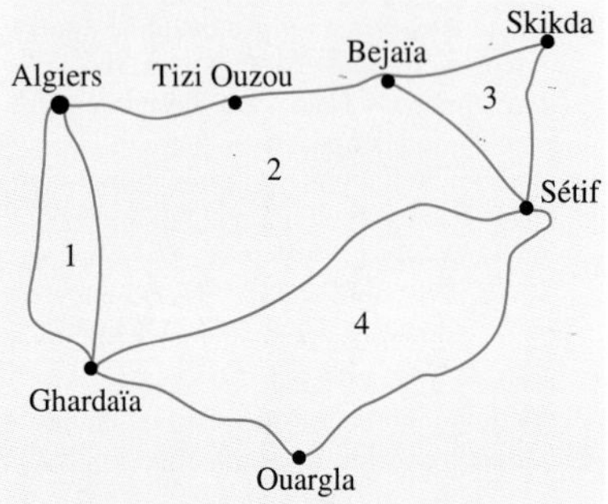

This is a simplified road map of part of Algeria. It shows 7 towns and 10 roads. For the purposes of this lesson we will call any area completely surrounded by roads, (and not crossed by any road,) a *zone*. As you can see, there are 4 zones on this map.

Rules: Each town is connected to all the others by roads (not necessarily a direct connection); all roads begin and end at a town. It is possible for a road to connect a town to itself. It is possible for more than one road to connect two towns.

In maps like this one there is a relationship between the number of towns, roads, and zones. Your goal in this lesson is to find it. The relationship was discovered by the Swiss mathematician and astronomer Leonhard Euler. It is part of a branch of geometry called *topology*, which he created.

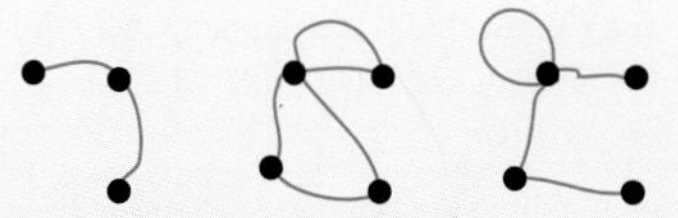

1. **Exploration** Make many different "maps" like the ones above. Keep track of the number of roads, towns, and zones in a table. Try to find a pattern in the relationship of the three numbers. (If you cannot find a relationship between all three numbers, keep one of the numbers constant and look for a relationship between the other two.)
2. Make at least six different three-town maps. What is the relationship between the number of roads and the number of zones? Express it in words, and write r (the number of roads) as a function of z (the number of zones).
3. Make at least six different four-town maps. What is the relationship between the number of roads and the number of zones? Express it in words and write a function.
4. Make at least six different five-road maps. What is the relationship between the number of towns and the number of zones? Express it in words and write a function.

2.C SOLUTIONS

1. There is a relationship between the numbers of towns, roads, and zones. Look at #7 for these formulas.
2. Roads = Zones + 2
3. Roads = Zones + 3
4. Towns + Zones = 6

5. Make at least six different six-road maps. What is the relationship between the number of towns and the number of zones? Express it in words and write a function.

6. Make at least six different four-zone maps. What is the relationship between the number of roads and the number of towns? Express it in words and write a function.

7. **Report** Write an illustrated report describing what you have learned about towns, roads, and zones. Give examples. Your report should answer the following questions, but not be limited to them:
   - If there are t towns and r roads, how many zones are there?
   - If there are t towns and z zones, how many roads are there?
   - If there are r roads and z zones, how many towns are there?

8. **Project** **Euler**
   Find out about Leonhard Euler and/or the Koenigsberg Bridge Problem. Prepare an oral presentation or a bulletin board display.

PROJECT: EULER

This should probably not be assigned to the whole class. But a student or group in need of extra credit, or someone particularly inspired by this assignment may want to pursue it. One source of information is *Men of Mathematics*, by E.T. Bell (© 1965, T.T. Bell). The problem can easily be split into two presentations or displays, one on Euler's life in general (he was an extraordinarily prolific mathematician and scientist), and the other on the Koenigsberg Bridge Problem (which is very accessible and interesting to students).

2.C SOLUTIONS

5. Towns + Zones = 7
6. Roads = Towns + 3
7. Zones = Roads − Towns + 1
   Roads = Towns + Zones − 1
   Towns = Roads − Zones + 1
8. Answers will vary.

◆ Essential Ideas

ADDING AND SUBTRACTING

MULTIPLYING

By now many students may not need the Lab Gear for these problems. If they do, let them have access to the blocks.

Essential Ideas

THREE MEANINGS OF MINUS

1. For each of the following, write an explanation of what the minus sign means.

a. -2 b. $-(2 + 2x)$

c. $x - 2$ d. $-y$

OPPOSITES

2. Find the opposite of each quantity. Remember: A quantity and its opposite add up to zero.

a. x b. 2

c. -2 d. $-x$

e. $x + 2$ f. $x - 2$

ADDING AND SUBTRACTING

In problems 3-4 you may want to make sketches or use the Lab Gear.

3. Simplify. (Add and combine like terms.)

a. $(y^2 + x^2 - 3y) + (y + 3x^2 - x^2)$

b. $x + (25 - yx - y^2) + (xy - y - x)$

4. Simplify. (Subtract; combine like terms.)

a. $(4 - x^2 - 5x) - 3x - 2$

b. $(4 - x^2 + 5x) - (3x - 2)$

c. $(4 + x^2 - 5x) - (3x + 2)$

d. $(-4 - x^2 - 5x) - (-3x + 2)$

MULTIPLYING

In problems 5-8 you may want to make sketches or use the Lab Gear.

5. Multiply.

a. $2x \cdot 4x$ b. $5x \cdot 6y$

c. $3xy \cdot 10$

6. The quantity $36xy$ can be written as the product $9x \cdot 4y$. Write $36xy$ as a product in at least four other ways.

7. Multiply.

a. $2(x + y - 5)$ b. $x(x + y + 5)$

c. $x(-x + y + 5)$

8. Choose two of the three multiplications in problem 7. Make a sketch of what they look like when modeled with the Lab Gear.

EXPONENTIAL NOTATION

9. Write each of these numbers in exponential notation. If possible, find more than one way. It may help to use your calculator.

a. 32 b. 64 c. 256

d. 4096 e. 1 f. 6561

FUNCTIONS AND FUNCTION DIAGRAMS

For each of the following problems:

a. Copy the table.

b. Describe the rule that allows you to get y from x.

c. Use the rule to find the missing numbers. (In some cases, the missing numbers may be difficult to find; use trial and error and a calculator to make it easier.)

d. Write y as a function of x.

10.

x	y
-1	-7
4	28
0	
	7

11.

x	y
3	4
12	1
6	3
	5

12.

x	y
5	2
3	4
1	
	-1

13. a. Make a function diagram in which the output (y) is always 4 more than the input (x).

b. Write a rule (function) for your function diagram.

◆ SOLUTIONS

1. a. negative number
   b. opposite of
   c. subtract
   d. opposite of

2. a. $-x$ b. -2 c. 2
   d. x e. $-x - 2$ f. $-x + 2$

3. a. $y^2 + 3x^2 - 2y$ b. $25 - y^2 - y$

4. a. $2 - x^2 - 8x$ b. $6 - x^2 + 2x$
   c. $2 + x^2 - 8x$ d. $-6 - x^2 - 2x$

5. a. $8x^2$ b. $30xy$ c. $30xy$

6. $4x \cdot 9y$; $6x \cdot 6y$; $12x \cdot 3y$; $18x \cdot 2y$

7. a. $2x + 2y - 10$
   b. $x^2 + xy + 5x$
   c. $-x^2 + xy + 5x$

8. a. length = 2; width = $x + y - 5$;
   area = $2x + 2y - 10$
   b. length = x; width = $x + y + 5$;
   area = $x^2xy + 5x$
   c. length = x; width = $-x + y + 5$;
   area = $-x^2 + xy + 5x$

9. Answers will vary. One example is given for each problem.
   a. 2^5 b. 8^2 c. 4^4
   d. 64^2 e. 1^{10000} f. 9^4

10.

x	y
-1	-7
4	28
0	0
1	7

$y = 7x$

11.

x	y
3	4
12	1
6	3
0	5

$y = (-1/3)x + 5$

12.

x	y
5	2
3	4
1	6
8	-1

$y = -x + 7$

13. a. Answers will vary
    b. $y = x + 4$

14. a. Answers will vary
    b. $y = 4x$

15. One possible diagram is:

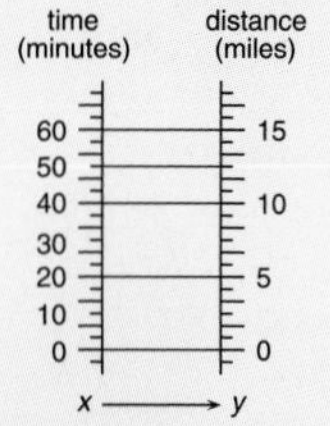

14. a. Make a function diagram in which the output (y) is always 4 times the input (x).
b. Write a rule (function) for your function diagram.

15. Make a function diagram with *time* on the x-number line (show one hour from the bottom to the top), and *distance* on the y-number line, to represent the motion of a cyclist riding at a constant speed of 15 miles per hour. Your diagram should have five in-out lines.

PATTERNS AND FUNCTIONS

16. Look at the sequence of figures. Think about how it would continue, following the pattern. Then:
a. Sketch the next figure in the sequence.
b. Copy and complete a table like the one below.
c. Describe the pattern in words.

Figure #	Perimeter
1	...
2	...
3	...
4	...
10	...
100	...
n	...

Repeat problem 16 for these sequences.

17. 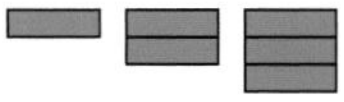

18. 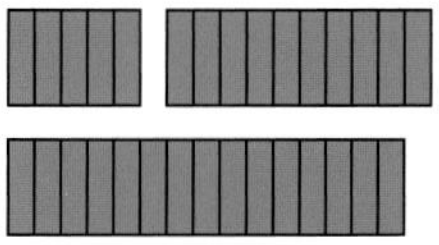

19. 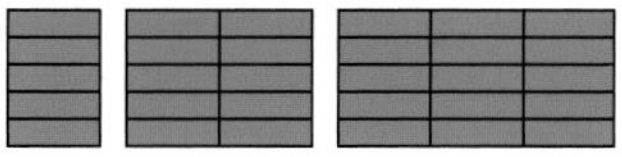

20. 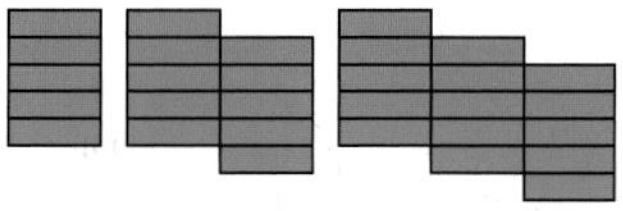

21. In problem 16, what figure would have a perimeter of $88x + 2$? Use trial and error if necessary.

22. Which sequence in problems 17-20, if any, contains a perimeter of
a. $2x + 100$?
b. $100x + 2$?
c. $100x + 100$?

23. Look at the xy-block.
a. What is the perimeter of its top face?
b. What is its perimeter if $y = 1, 2, 3, 4, 10$? (Do not substitute a number for x.) Arrange your answers in a table.
c. Compare your table with those in problems 16-20. It should be the same as one of them. Which one? Explain.

24. Use blue blocks to make a figure. Substitute 1, 2, 3, ... for y in its perimeter to get the same sequence as problem 18. Check your work; make a table.

GEOBOARD TRIANGLES

25. On dot paper, sketch triangles having area 18, and having
a. one horizontal and one vertical side;
b. one horizontal side, no vertical side;
c. no horizontal or vertical side.

PATTERNS AND FUNCTIONS

This section is based on Lesson 10.

The generalized formulas on line n of the tables will be expressed in terms of both x and n.

The generalization in problems 22-23 involves y standing in for n.

◆ SOLUTIONS

16.

Figure #	Perimeter
1	$2x + 2$
2	$4x + 2$
3	$6x + 2$
4	$8x + 2$
10	$20x + 2$
100	$200x + 2$
n	$2nx + 2$

Each x-block has a perimeter of $2x + 2$, so the nth figure's perimeter is $n(2x + 2)$. However, after each successive block is added we lose 2 units of perimeter. So we get $n(2x + 2) - (n - 1)2 = 2nx + 2$.

17.

Figure #	Perimeter
1	$2x + 2$
2	$2x + 4$
3	$2x + 6$
4	$2x + 8$
10	$2x + 20$
100	$2x + 200$
n	$2x + 2n$

The explanation is similar to #16 except we get $n(2x + 2) - (n - 1)2x = 2x + 2n$.

18.

Figure #	Perimeter
1	$10 + 2x$
2	$20 + 2x$
3	$30 + 2x$
4	$40 + 2x$
10	$100 + 2x$
100	$1000 + 2x$
n	$10n + 2x$

The explanation is similar to #16 except we get $n(2x + 10) - (n - 1)2x = 10n + 2x$.

19.

Figure #	Perimeter
1	$2x + 10$
2	$4x + 10$
3	$6x + 10$
4	$8x + 10$
10	$20x + 10$
100	$200x + 10$
n	$2nx + 10$

The explanation is similar to #16 except we have $n(2x + 10) - (n - 1)10 = 2nx + 10$.

(Solutions continued on page 509)

Chapter 3
WORKING BACKWARDS

Overview of the Chapter

*T*he chapter begins with an engaging problem about a "get rich quick" scheme. Students begin by using their calculators and trial and error, but they quickly see the need for developing more systematic techniques to solve the problem. The remainder of the chapter concentrates on developing these algebraic techniques.

*T*he problem-solving strategy of working backwards ties together many key topics: the arithmetic of signed numbers, inverse operations and functions, the uses of opposites and reciprocals. Mastery of these topics will help students develop an in-depth understanding of equation solving. In fact, near the end of the chapter, one equation-solving technique is introduced.

1. Introduction of New Tools:

- Arrows to represent functions
- Division in the Corner Piece
- A "table" technique for multiplying polynomials without the Lab Gear
- Using calculators for division

2. Algebra Concepts Emphasized:

- Cartesian graphing vocabulary
- Subtracting a negative number
- Multiplying by a negative number
- Multiplying by -1
- Distributing a minus sign
- Adding the opposite
- Combining functions
- Iteration of functions
- Inverse operations, especially multiplication and division
- Division by zero
- Understanding and using reciprocals
- Multiplication and division by numbers between 0 and 1

CHAPTER 3

The double helix of a DNA molecule

Coming in this chapter:

Exploration Algebank offers to double your money every month, in exchange for a monthly fee. Is this a good deal? Does the answer depend on the fee, on the amount of money you have to invest, or on both?

WORKING BACKWARDS

3. Algebra Concepts Reviewed:

- Understanding and using opposites
- Substitution
- The distributive law
- The associative and commutative laws
- Properties of zero and one
- Order of operations

4. Algebra Concepts Previewed:

- Iterating linear functions
- Solving linear equations
- Solving linear inequalities
- Applications of linear functions
- Factoring
- Slope
- Inverse functions
- Writing equations

5. Problem-Solving Techniques:

- Trial and error
- Working backwards
- Extending patterns
- Using variables to understand number patterns and real-world problems

6. Connections and Context:

- Mathematics as a tool for decision-making
- Modular arithmetic
- Cryptography
- Graphing data
- Finite groups

▼ 3.1 Instant Riches

Core Sequence: 1-12

Suitable for Homework: 5-15

Useful for Assessment: 12-15

What this Lesson is About:

- Iterating linear functions
- Solving a real-world problem by trial and error and by working backwards
- Using mathematics as a tool for decision-making

AMAZING OPPORTUNITY!

This problem is difficult enough to challenge all students, but simple enough to allow everyone to participate. A more fully algebraic discussion of the problem is saved for **Thinking/Writing 3.C**, at the end of the chapter.

The Exploration should lead to some interesting discussions, and will be a good way to make sure everyone understands the big question that this lesson addresses.

Students are likely to use trial and error for problem 2. Problem 3 should get the point across that the plan is advantageous to some, but not to others. In addition, it supplies students with a new tool, using arrows to represent functions.

RUNNING OUT OF MONEY

This section is a generalization of problem 2, and should lead students to see the benefits of working backwards for solving this sort of problem. (For example, in problem 4 it is easy to see that if subtracting $100 from Bea's balance left $0, then there must have been $100 in the account, which means that she must have started with $50.)

If some groups continue to use trial and error, a class discussion of different strategies could be helpful, so that everyone understands the strategy of working backwards. The arrow representation makes it easy to trace one's way backwards. The key is to understand that to travel backwards along an arrow, you have to use the inverse operation.

LESSON 3.1

Instant Riches

AMAZING OPPORTUNITY!

The following ad appeared in the school paper.

> Amazing investment opportunity at Algebank! Double your money instantly! Invest any amount! No amount is too small. Our bank will *double* the amount of money in your account every month. Watch your money grow!
>
> A service charge of $100 will be deducted from your account at the end of every month.

1. **Exploration** Do you think this is a good deal? Why or why not? Use some calculations to back up your opinion.

2. Reg was interested in this investment. After calling to make sure that the $100 fee would be deducted *after* his money was doubled, he decided to join. However, after his service charge was deducted at the end of the fourth month, he discovered that his bank balance was exactly $0! How much money did he start out with? Explain your answer.

Three other students invested their money. Gabe started with $45, Earl with $60, and Lara with $200. The figure shows a way to keep track of what happened to Lara's investment.

Month:
0 ... 1
(200) —·2→ 400 —−100→ (300) —·2→ 600…

3. a. Use arrows in this way to show what happened to Lara's, Gabe's, and Earl's investments for the first five months.
   b. Give advice to each of these students.

RUNNING OUT OF MONEY

4. Bea joined the plan, but discovered after one month that she had an account balance of exactly $0. How much money had she invested?

5. Lea discovered that she had an account balance of exactly $0 after two months. What was her initial investment?

6. Rea had an account balance of exactly $0 after three months. How much money did she start out with?

7. Summarize your answers to problems 4-6 by making a table like the one below. Then extend the table to show up to at least ten months.

Months to Reach a Zero-Dollar Balance

Months	Amount Invested
1	
2	
...	

8. Describe the pattern in your table.

GAINING AND LOSING

9. Mr. Lear joined the plan, but discovered that at the end of every month he had exactly the same amount of money as when he started. How much money is it? Explain how that happened.

3.1 SOLUTIONS

1. This is a good deal if more than $100 is invested. Anything under $100 will eventually be depleted.
2. $93.75
   Start at the end of the 4th month before the $100 was deducted. Work backwards for each month, adding the $100 to the amount and dividing the result by two.
3. a. Gabe

0: (45) —·2→ 90 —−100→ 1: (−10) —·2→ −20 —−100→ 2: (−120) —·2→ −240 —−100→ 3: (−340) —·2→ −680 —−100→ 4: (−780) —·2→ −1560 —−100→ 5: (−1660)

Earl

0: (60) —·2→ 120 —−100→ 1: (20) —·2→ 40 —−100→ 2: (−60) —·2→ −120 —−100→ 3: (−220) —·2→ −440 —−100→ 4: (−540) —·2→ −1080

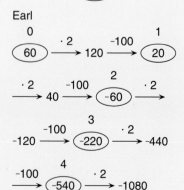

10. Algebank sends its customers statements quarterly (every three months). Several students were comparing their statements at the end of the first quarter. One had \$50, another had \$100, and a third had \$150 in the account.

a. What will happen to each student? Will all of them eventually gain money? What will their next quarterly statements look like? Explain.

b. Explain how you can figure out how much money each of them started with.

11. Find two initial investment amounts that differ by \$1, such that one of them will make money in this plan, and the other will lose money. How far apart will the amounts be in six months? Explain.

12. **Report** You have been asked to write an article on Algebank's investment plan for the Consumers' Guide column in the school paper. Write an article giving general advice to people wanting to join this plan. Describe the plan clearly and explain the pros and cons of joining it. Who will benefit from the plan? Who will lose in the long run? Explain, giving some examples. Make your article interesting, eye-catching, and readable.

13. **Generalization** Use what you have learned in this lesson to answer the following questions about plans with similar policies, but different numbers.

a. Give advice to people wanting to join a plan, if their money is *tripled* every month and the service charge is \$100.

b. Give advice to people wanting to join a plan if their money is doubled every month but the service charge is \$200.

14. Suppose Algebank were to deduct the service charge *before* doubling the money. How would this change your answers to problems 12 and 13b?

15. Describe another possible investment scheme and give advice to people about who should join and who should not.

GAINING AND LOSING

Problems 9-11 are intended to nudge the students towards a thorough understanding of who gains and who loses and why. The Report in problem 12 will give them a chance to show their understanding. However, if the Report does not include a mathematical explanation of the problem, insist that such an explanation be present in problems 9-11.

Problems 13-15 are optional extensions which you can use to explore this problem in more depth. In either case, **Thinking/ Writing 3.C** will be a chance to come back to the problem at a higher level of understanding.

Problem 15 is deliberately vague. It allows students to design plans that are similar to the one presented in this lesson. But very interesting mathematics can emerge from an open-ended question of this type. For example, a plan that doubles the investment and charges no fee will yield a geometric sequence. A plan where a certain amount is added to the account each month, but the fee is a percent of the account, behaves yet another way. If you do not want such an open-ended situation, skip the problem or specify the limits you want your students to respect.

3.1 SOLUTIONS

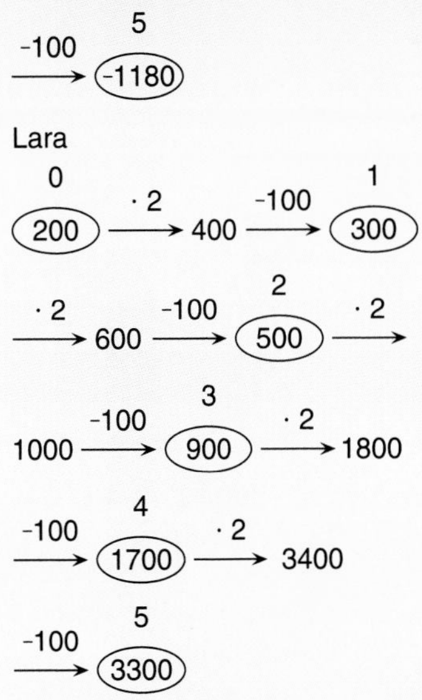

b. Gabe and Earl should not invest, but Lara made a good deal.

4. \$50 5. \$75 6. \$87.50

7.

Months to Reach a Zero Dollar Balance

Months	Amount invested
1	50
2	75
3	87.50
4	93.75
5	96.88
6	98.44
7	99.22
8	99.61
9	99.80
10	99.90

8. The amount invested is increased by half the difference between the two previous months' investments. e.g. (75 − 50)/2 + 75 = 87.50

9. \$100. At the end of each month, his money is doubled to \$200, but \$100 is deducted as service charge. So the amount invested remains the same, \$100.

10. a. The student with \$50 will lose all of it. The one with \$100 will neither gain nor lose. The third student with \$150 will make a profit. Next quarter's statement: -\$300, \$100, \$500

b. Starting with the amount on the statement, add \$100 and divide the result by two. Repeat adding \$100 and dividing two more times. The final result is the original investment.

(Solutions continued on page 510)

▼ 3.2
Two Negatives

Core Sequence: 1, 3-23

Suitable for Homework: 2-23

Useful for Assessment: 6, 11, 15-16, 22-23

What this Lesson is About:
- Cartesian graphing vocabulary
- Subtracting a negative number
- Multiplying by a negative number
- Multiplying by -1

These topics have not yet been addressed in this book. Your students are likely to have learned about operations and negative numbers more than once in their school careers. It would not be interesting or effective to go over the same ground again in the same way.

Instead, in this lesson we look at these topics from arithmetic through a distinctively algebraic perspective, by looking at the functions $y = 5 - x$ and $y = -3x$. We use two different tools to do this, Cartesian graphs and function diagrams. One benefit is that students who would react negatively to yet another review of signed number arithmetic will have something else to think about.

LESSON 3.2

Two Negatives

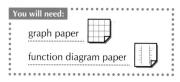

You will need:
- graph paper
- function diagram paper

1. **Exploration** Many people have heard the rule that *two negatives make a positive.* Investigate to decide whether this rule is always, sometimes, or never true when you *add* two negative numbers. Explain, giving examples. Then repeat your investigation for *subtracting, multiplying,* and *dividing* two negative numbers. Write a brief summary explaining your conclusions.

2. What does *not unilliterate* mean? What about *not uninteresting*? Look up *irregardless* in a dictionary.

SUBTRACTION

3. This function diagram represents a function of the type $y = b - x$. What is the value of b?

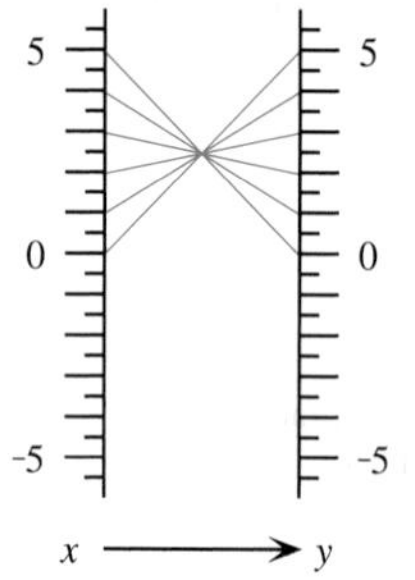

4. Make an in-out table for the in-out lines shown on the function diagram.

5. Copy the function diagram. Extend the table and the function diagram for negative values of x.

6. If you know the values of b and x, how can you calculate $b - x$ *by using addition?* Explain, using examples.

THE CARTESIAN COORDINATE SYSTEM

When you draw horizontal and vertical axes and plot points you are using a *Cartesian coordinate system.* It is named after the French mathematician and philosopher René Descartes. He is credited with bringing together algebra and geometry by using graphs to make geometric representations of algebraic equations.

An important skill in algebra is predicting what the graph will look like from the equation, or what the equation will be from the graph.

You should know the vocabulary of the Cartesian coordinate system.
- The horizontal number line is the *x-axis.*
- The vertical number line is the *y-axis.*
- The numbers (x, y) associated with a point are the *coordinates* of the point.
- The axes divide the coordinate system into four parts, called *quadrants.*
- The quadrants are numbered counterclockwise, as shown. In the first quadrant, the coordinates of every point are both positive.
- The point where the axes cross is called the *origin.* The coordinates of the origin are (0, 0).

3.2 SOLUTIONS

1. Answers will vary.
The sum of 2 negative numbers is a negative number.
The difference of 2 negative numbers can be either a negative, positive, or zero number. Let A and B be negative numbers. The difference, $A - B$, is negative if $B > A$, positive if $B < A$, zero if $B = A$. Examples:
$-3 - (-1) = -2$
$-2 - (-5) = 3$
$-9 - (-9) = 0$
The quotient of 2 negative numbers is a positive number, and the product of 2 negative numbers is also a positive number.

2. *Not unilliterate* means not being able to read or write.
Not uninteresting means interesting.
Though English teachers may object, some dictionaries define *irregardless* as meaning *regardless.* Other dictionaries call it nonstandard English, no such word.

3. $b = 5$

4.

x	y
5	0
4	1
3	2
2	3
1	4
0	5

5.

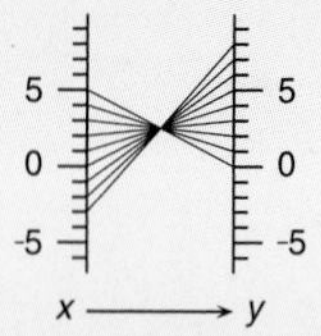

x	y
5	0
4	1
3	2
2	3
1	4
0	5
-1	6
-2	7
-3	8

6. Add b to the opposite of x.

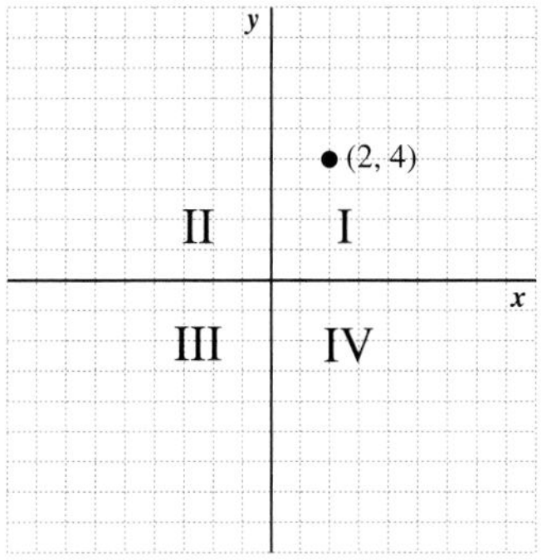

7. In which two quadrants does a graph lie if
   a. the second coordinate is always positive?
   b. the first coordinate is always positive?
   c. the two coordinates always have the same sign (both positive or both negative)?

8. What can you say about the signs of x and/or y if you know that (x, y) is in either
   a. the third or the fourth quadrant?
   b. the second or the fourth quadrant?
   c. the second or the third quadrant?

9. If a point is on the x-axis, what is its y-coordinate? If a point is on the y-axis, what is its x-coordinate?

Important: Zero, 0, is neither positive nor negative.

10. Make a Cartesian graph for the function from problem 3, using the in-out table you made in problems 4 and 5.

11. 🔑 Look at the part of the graph where the y-values are greater than 5. What are the x-values there? Explain what this says about *two negatives*.

MULTIPLICATION

The graph below shows the function $y = 3x$. The y-coordinate is always three times the x-coordinate. Three points are labeled.

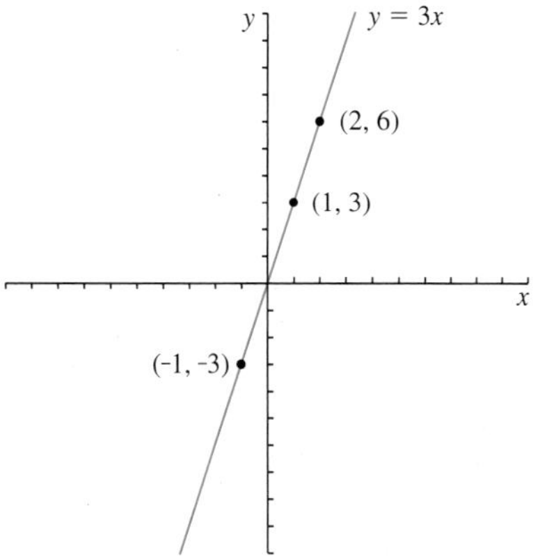

12. a. List three more (x, y) pairs that would be on the graph above, including at least one negative and one fractional value for x.
    b. In which two quadrants does the graph lie?
    c. In each (x, y) pair, how are the signs of the x-coordinate and the y-coordinate related?

13. This problem is about the function $y = -3x$.
    a. Make a table of at least six (x, y) values for this function. Use negative numbers and fractions as well as positive whole numbers.
    b. Write the multiplication fact that is represented by each (x, y) pair in your table.
    c. Use your table to make a graph of the function $y = -3x$.

Allow students to use their calculators for problem 1 if they want to. The purpose of the Exploration is not to test their grasp of signed number arithmetic, but to help them review it rapidly.

Encourage students to discuss problem 2 with an English teacher. Is it always better to simplify and say *interesting* instead of *not uninteresting*? The definition of *irregardless* in some dictionaries may surprise you.

SUBTRACTION

THE CARTESIAN COORDINATE SYSTEM

The rule for subtracting negative numbers is obtained by extending a pattern from subtracting positive numbers.

As indicated above, much of this lesson can be done as homework. However it is essential that problems 6 and 11 be discussed in class, because some students may find it difficult to interpret the diagram and the graph correctly.

The vocabulary about axes, coordinates, quadrants, and the origin is important.

3.2 SOLUTIONS

7. a. I, II b. I, IV c. I, III

8. a. x can be positive or negative but y can only be negative.
   b. x and y can be positive or negative.
   c. y can be positive or negative but x can only be negative.

9. If a point is on the x-axis, its y-coordinate is 0. If a point is on the y-axis, its x-coordinate is 0.

10.

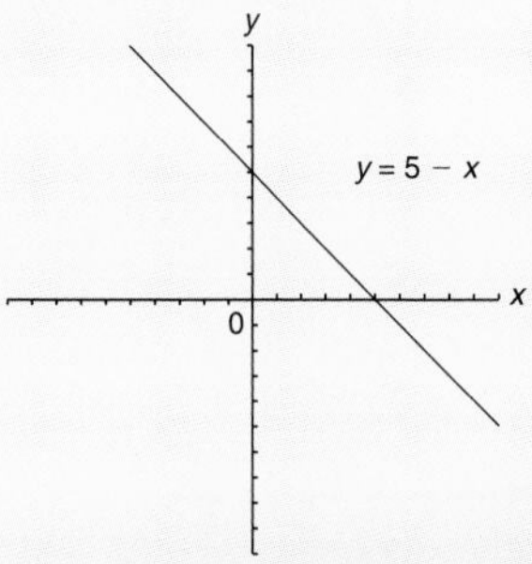

11. x-values are negative, when y-values are greater than 5. Since x is negative, $-x$ is positive, which shows that two negative numbers will multiply to give a positive number.

12. a. Answers will vary.
    b. I, III
    c. x- and y-coordinates have the same sign.

13. a. & b. Answers will vary. See table below.

x	y	Multiplication
-2	6	$-3(-2) = 6$
-1	3	$-3(-1) = 3$
0	0	$-3(0) = 0$
1/2	-3/2	$-3(1/2) = -3/2$
1	-3	$-3(1) = -3$
2	-6	$-3(2) = -6$

c.

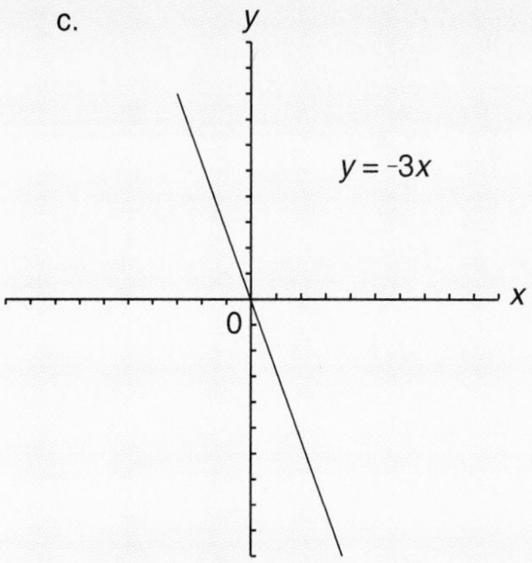

d. II, IV
e. The x- and y-coordinates have opposite signs except for (0, 0).

MULTIPLICATION

MULTIPLICATION BY -1

The same visual methods are applied to multiplication by a negative number.

If some students use their calculators for problem 16, make sure to have a class discussion of the shortcut other students probably discovered.

Problems 20-23 generalize the rules about multiplying signed numbers to multiplying monomials with negative coefficients.

d. In which two quadrants does the graph lie?

e. In each (x, y) pair in your table, how are the signs of the x-coordinate and the y-coordinate related?

14. a. Make a function diagram for the function $y = -3x$.

b. On the diagram, see how the signs of x and $-3x$ are related. When x is negative, what can you say about $-3x$?

15. What is the sign of the answer (positive or negative) when you

a. multiply a negative number and a positive number?

b. multiply two negative numbers?

c. multiply three negative numbers?

16. What is the sign of the answer? (You do not need to find the answer.)

a. $(-5)(-4)(-3)(-2)(-1)(0)(1)(2)(3)(4)(5)$

b. $(-9)(-87)(-7.65)(-43210)$

c. $(-9)^9$ d. $(-99)^{99}$

MULTIPLYING BY -1

Match each function diagram 17-19 with one or more functions from this list.

a. $y = 0$ b. $y = x$
c. $y = x + 0$ d. $y = 1 \cdot x$
e. $y = -x$ f. $y = -1 \cdot x$
g. $y = 0 \cdot x$ h. $y = 0 \cdot x^2$

17.

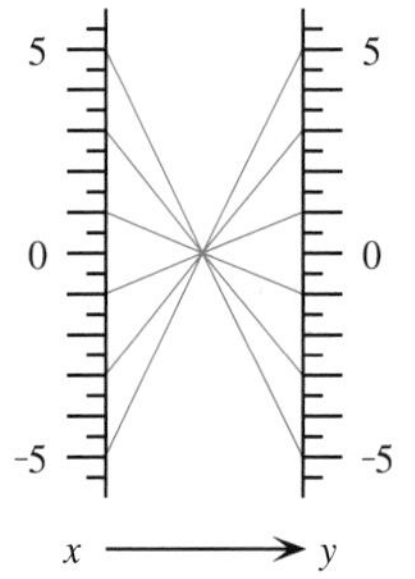

18.

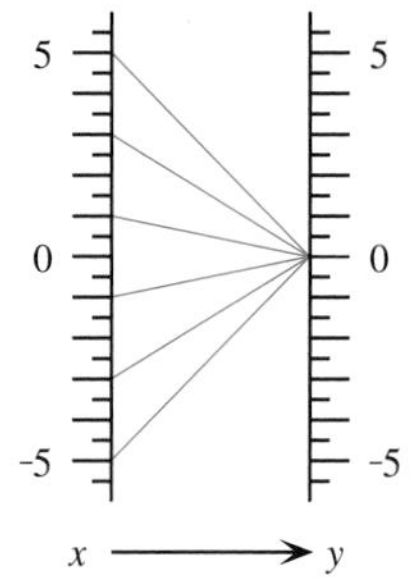

19.

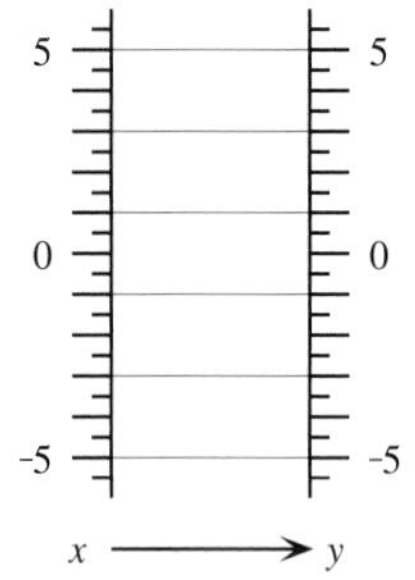

20. *Multiplying x by -1 is the same as taking the opposite of x.* Explain.

21. Generalization Explain each step of this calculation.

a. $(-x)(-y) = (-1)(x)(-1)(y)$

b. $= (-1)(-1)(x)(y)$

c. $= (1)(x)(y) = xy$

22. Simplify $(-a)(b)(-c)(-d)$ by the same method.

23. Find each product.

a. $-3 \cdot 5y(-x)$

b. $(-2y)(-3x)(-4)(12xy)$

c. $(-1.3x)(-7x^2)$

d. $(-3x)^2$

e. $(-3x)^3$

3.2 SOLUTIONS

14. a.

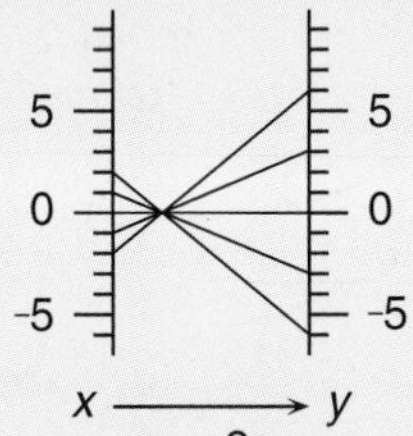

$y = -3x$

b. Where x is negative, $-3x$ is positive.

15. a. negative
b. positive
c. negative

16. a. zero
b. positive
c. negative
d. negative

17. e, f

18. a, g, h

19. b, c, d

20. Answers will vary. Multiplying x by -1 changes only the sign of x, except when $x = 0$. This is the same as taking the opposite of x.

21. a. Multiplying by -1 is the same as taking the opposite.
b. Commutative Law of Multiplication.
c. $(-1)(-1) = 1$ and 1 times any number is the same number.

22. $(-a)(b)(-c)(-d)$
$= (-1)(a)(b)(-1)(c)(-1)(d)$
$= (-1)(a)(b)(-1)(-1)(c)(d)$
$= (-1)(a)(b)(1)(c)(d)$
$= (-1)(a)(b)(c)(d)$
$= -abcd$

23. a. $15xy$
b. $-288x^2y^2$
c. $9.1x^3$
d. $9x^2$
e. $-27x^3$

LESSON 3.3

More on Minus

You will need:

the Lab Gear 

1. **Exploration** Choose several numbers and investigate the following questions. Write an explanation, using variables, of what you discover. What is the result when you
   a. add a number to its opposite?
   b. subtract a number from its opposite?
   c. multiply a number by its opposite?
   d. divide a number by its opposite?

MINUS AND THE DISTRIBUTIVE LAW

For each problem below:

- Use the Lab Gear to model the first expression on the left side of the workmat.
- If possible, simplify the expression by adding zero and removing matching blocks. Get all blocks downstairs.
- Then decide which of the expressions a, b, c, or d is equal to the given expression. Setting up each one in turn on the right side of the workmat may help. Explain your answers.

2. $x - (5 + 2x)$
   a. $x - 5 + 2x$ b. $x - 5 - 2x$
   c. $x + 5 + 2x$ d. $x + 5 - 2x$

3. $2x - (-4 + 3x)$
   a. $2x - 4 + 3x$ b. $2x - 4 - 3x$
   c. $2x + 4 + 3x$ d. $2x + 4 - 3x$

4. $3y + (5 - 2y)$
   a. $3y - 5 + 2y$ b. $3y - 5 - 2y$
   c. $3y + 5 + 2y$ d. $3y + 5 - 2y$

5. $x - (7 - 2y)$
   a. $x - 7 + 2y$ b. $x - 7 - 2y$
   c. $x + 7 + 2y$ d. $x + 7 - 2y$

6. $6x - (-3 - x)$
   a. $6x - 3 + x$ b. $6x + 3 + x$
   c. $6x - 3 - x$ d. $6x + 3 - x$

7. Write an equivalent expression without parentheses.
   a. $2x^2 - (4 - x - x^2)$
   b. $(2x^2 - 4) - (x - x^2)$
   c. $(y - 5) - 3x - 2$
   d. $y - 5 - (3x - 2)$

8. Write an expression containing at least one pair of parentheses that is equivalent to the given expression. (Do not put parentheses around the whole expression, or around a single term.)
   $$3x^3 - 6x + 2 - 5y$$

9. Compare your answers to problem 8 with your classmates. Try to find several different correct answers.

A minus sign preceding parentheses tells you to subtract or take the opposite of everything in the parentheses. Writing an equivalent expression without parentheses is called *distributing the minus sign.*

10. **Summary** Explain how to distribute a minus sign. Use examples.

11. Write an equivalent expression without parentheses.
    a. $-(r + s)$ b. $-(-r + s)$
    c. $-(r - s)$ d. $-(-r - s)$

12. Write an equivalent expression without parentheses.
    a. $-1(r + s)$ b. $-1(-r + s)$
    c. $-1(r - s)$ d. $-1(-r - s)$

You can see from these problems that distributing a minus sign is really just distributing -1.

3.3 More on Minus

Core Sequence: 1-29

Suitable for Homework: 10-21, 30

Useful for Assessment: 10, 16

What this Lesson is About:

- Distributing a minus sign
- Adding the opposite
- Review of the distributive law
- Preview of factoring

After this lesson, and certainly after this chapter, you should expect your students to have some degree of mastery of the basic rules of working with minus. However, experience shows that students often continue to make mistakes in this connection. Do not turn this into a life and death issue. There will be plenty of review of these techniques during the rest of the year. Keep things in perspective; correctly manipulating symbols is an important tool, but it's only a tool. Correctly manipulating symbols *under time pressure* is not important (except perhaps to do well on certain tests — but tests will be changing).

Problem 1 is not difficult, but it is interesting. It should reinforce the meaning of opposite, as well as give an opportunity to use various rules of working with signs. To get the most out of the Exploration, have a class discussion of it, highlighting the answers of those students who used variables.

3.3 SOLUTIONS

1. Let 5 be the number.
   a. 0, e.g. 5 + (-5) = 0
   b. The result is the opposite of twice the number, e.g. -5 − 5 = -10
   c. The result is the opposite of the number itself, e.g. (5)(-5) = -25
   d. The result is -1, e.g. 5/-5 = -1
2. b
3. d
4. d
5. a
6. b
7. Encourage students to combine like terms.
   a. $2x^2 - 4 + x + x^2 = 3x^2 + x - 4$
   b. $2x^2 - 4 - x + x^2 = 3x^2 - x - 4$
   c. $y - 5 - 3x - 2 = y - 3x - 7$
   d. $y - 5 - 3x + 2 = y - 3x - 3$
8. Answers will vary.
   e.g. $3x^3 + (-6x + 2) - 5y$
   $(3x^3 - 6x) + (2 - 5y)$
9. Answers will vary.
10. Answers will vary.
    Remove the minus sign in front of the parentheses. Change every sign inside the parentheses to its opposite sign.
11. a. $-r - s$
    b. $r - s$
    c. $-r + s$
    d. $r + s$
12. a. $-r - s$
    b. $r - s$
    c. $-r + s$
    d. $r + s$

MINUS AND THE DISTRIBUTIVE LAW

The distributive law and the relationship of opposites to multiplying by -1 laid the groundwork for distributing the minus sign, which is presented in this section.

Problem 6 is difficult to show with the Lab Gear. See the note about "platforms" in the Teacher's Guide for Chapter 2, Lesson 2, **Subtraction**.

ADDING THE OPPOSITE

Students have probably heard of the idea of adding the opposite in the context of operations with signed numbers. In fact, a specific case was seen in the last lesson in the context of subtracting negative numbers. In this lesson the emphasis is on algebraic expressions, and the method is presented in all its generality.

It is possible to use the method of adding zero and removing opposites to develop all the rules for signed numbers on the workmat. In particular, it is possible to use this approach to start with minus as "take away" and derive "adding the opposite" from there. We have omitted this work because too much focus on these rules in an algebra course is a mistake, particularly early in the year. It is not interesting to most students and can make the course bog down.

ADDING THE OPPOSITE

Find the expression that must be added or subtracted. It may help to use the Lab Gear.

13. a. $3x^2 + (-5x) + \_\_\_ = -(5x + x^2)$
b. $3x^2 + (-5x) - (\_\_\_) = -(5x + x^2)$

14. a. $-2xy + x + \_\_\_ = 6xy - 2x$
b. $-2xy + x - (\_\_\_) = 6xy - 2x$

15. a. $-12 + 4yx + \_\_\_ = 7xy - 15$
b. $-12 + 4yx - (\_\_\_) = 7xy - 15$

16. Compare your answers to parts (a) and (b) in problems 13-15. How are they related? Explain.

17. **Generalization** Problems 13-15 illustrated the following fact: *Subtracting is the same as adding the opposite.* For each subtraction, write an equivalent addition.
a. $y - (-x)$
b. $y - x$
c. $-y - x$

18. Find the sign of the answer. (You do not need to find the answer.)
a. 1646 − (-2459)
b. -2459 − 1646
c. -1646 − (-2459)
d. 2459 − (-1646)
e. -1646 − (2459)

19. Simplify each expression.
a. $6 - (-5)$
b. $-5 - (-7)$
c. $-21 - (-3x) + 15$
d. $-2x - (-12x) - 5xy$

20. Find each difference.
a. $2y - 7y$
b. $3xy - (-2xy)$
c. $-x^2 - 4x^2$
d. $2xy - 2x$

REVIEW AREA AND MULTIPLICATION

21. What is the other side of a rectangle, if one side is x and the area is
a. $5x$?
b. x^2?
c. $x^2 + 2xy$?
d. $x^2 + 2xy + 5x$?

The following equations are of the form *length times width = area of the rectangle.* Fill in the blanks. You may use the Lab Gear to help you. If you do, remember to use *upstairs* for minus and to build a figure with an *uncovered rectangle* of the required dimensions in the corner piece.

22. $x \cdot \_\_\_\_ = xy - x^2$

23. $(y - 2) \cdot \_\_\_\_ = 5y - 10$

24. $(\_\_\_\_ - 3) \cdot x = 2xy - 3x$

25. $2x \cdot \_\_\_\_ = 2xy + 4x^2 - 10x$

Use the Lab Gear for these.

26. $(x + \_\_\_)(y - 5) = xy + 5y - 5x - 25$

27. $(y - 1) \cdot \_\_\_\_ = xy + 5y - x - 5$

28. $(y + 2)(y - 1) = \_\_\_\_$ (Simplify.)

29. $(y - 1) \cdot \_\_\_\_ = y^2 + 4y - 5$ (Hint: Study problem 28.)

3.3 SOLUTIONS

13. a. $-4x^2$
b. $4x^2$

14. a. $-3x + 8xy$
b. $3x - 8xy$

15. a. $3xy - 3$
b. $-3xy + 3$

16. The expressions have opposite signs. In both parts (a) and (b), the expressions on the right side are the same. So the expressions needed on the left side are the same. But in part (b), there is a minus sign in front of the parentheses, which means taking the opposite or multiplying by -1. Therefore, the expressions in part (a) and (b) have opposite signs.

17. a. $y + x$
b. $y + (-x)$
c. $-y + (-x)$

18. a. positive
b. negative
c. positive
d. positive
e. negative

19. a. 11
b. 2
c. $3x - 6$
d. $10x - 5xy$

20. a. $-5y$
b. $5xy$
c. $-5x^2$
d. $2xy - 2x$

21. a. 5
b. x
c. $x + 2y$
d. $x + 2y + 5$

22. $(y - x)$

23. 5

24. $2y$

25. $(y + 2x - 5)$

26. 5

27. $(x + 5)$

28. $y^2 + y - 2$

29. $(y + 5)$

DISCOVERY *A SUBSTITUTION CODE*

This message has been coded by a *simple substitution code*.

Rules:

- Each letter is always replaced by the same letter throughout the message.
- No letter is ever replaced by itself.

QEB NRIB CLN QEFP GFKA LC TLAB FP QEHQ BHTE IBQQBN FP HISHUP NBMI-HTBA OU QEB PHJB IBQQBN QENLRDELRQ QEB JBPPHDB.

30. Try to break the code. (Copy the message carefully, leaving blank space between the lines. If you have a guess for a letter, enter it every place that letter appears. For clarity, use lower-case letters for your solution, and capitals for the coded message. Use a pencil and an eraser. Hint: The first word is a very common three-letter word.)

PREVIEW *MAKE A RECTANGLE*

31. For each problem make a Lab Gear rectangle having the given area. Write a multiplication equation.

a. $x^2 + 9x + 8$

b. $x^2 + 6x + 8$

*This is not to say that understanding operations with signed numbers is unimportant. In fact, we address these questions again with function diagrams and graphs in this chapter and in Chapters 5 and 6. Also, in many places throughout the book, you will find interesting number-oriented problems that students can explore with calculators. If you want to use the Lab Gear with signed numbers, see Chapter 2 in *The Algebra Lab, High School*, or Lessons 4-7 in *The Algebra Lab, Middle School*, (both by Creative Publications, 1990).

DISCOVERY *A SUBSTITUTION CODE*

This problem previews **Thinking/Writing 3.A**.

REVIEW *AREA AND MULTIPLICATION*

PREVIEW *MAKE A RECTANGLE*

Even though this is a review (of Chapter 2, Lesson 3), this section is difficult, and will take time. It can be skipped for now, but it must be done at some point before Lesson 6, which it previews.

The problems gradually increase in difficulty. It is important to have a class discussion of problems 28-29.

Problem 31 can be skipped, given as a challenge to those who finish early, or saved for the opening or closing of a future Lab Gear-based lesson.

3.3 SOLUTIONS

30. Decoded message: The rule for this kind of code is that each letter is always replaced by the same letter throughout the message.

31. a. $x^2 + 9x + 8 = (x + 8)(x + 1)$

b. $x^2 + 6x + 8 = (x + 4)(x + 2)$

▼ 3.4
Algebra Magic

Core Sequence: 1-13

Suitable for Homework: 6-9, 12-13

Useful for Assessment: 13

What this Lesson is About:

- Preview of composition of functions
- Using variables to understand number patterns
- Undoing operations (preview of equation solving)
- Review of the commutative law

MAGIC TRICKS

*I*f some of your students suggest using x instead of a number and carrying out the steps that way, that's great. Otherwise the idea will be suggested in the next section.

LAB GEAR MAGIC

*T*he Lab Gear helps make the transition to algebra. Some students will not need the blocks once they understand the basic idea, but others might find them useful throughout the rest of the lesson. You may challenge students to follow the algebra of tricks mentally. (Instead of picking a number, students all start with x. Then they carry out your instructions in their heads.)

LESSON 3.4

Algebra Magic

You will need:
the Lab Gear

MAGIC TRICKS

1. **Exploration** A magician asked everyone in the audience to think of a number. "Don't tell your number to anyone," she said. "Now do the following things to your number.

Step 1: Add the number to one more than the number.
Step 2: Add 7 to the result.
Step 3: Divide by 2.
Step 4: Subtract the original number.
Step 5: Divide by 4.

When you are finished, you should all have the same number"

What was the number, and how did the magician know it would be the same for everyone?

2. Try the following algebra magic problem. Record your result and compare it with others in your group. Do you all get the same answer, or does your answer depend on the number you started with?

1) Think of a number.
2) Multiply the number by 3.
3) Add 8 more than the original number.
4) Divide by 4.
5) Subtract the original number.

3. Do the same trick, but change the final step to *subtract* 2. Compare answers with your group members again. Are they the same or different? Explain.

LAB GEAR MAGIC

The following trick has been modeled with the Lab Gear.

1) Think of a number.

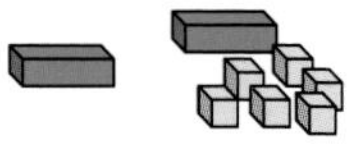

2) Add 6 more than the original number to the number.

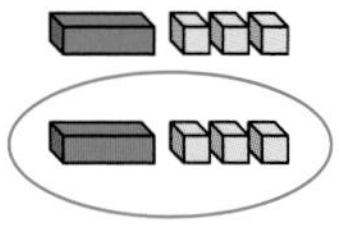

3) Divide by 2.
4) Subtract 2.

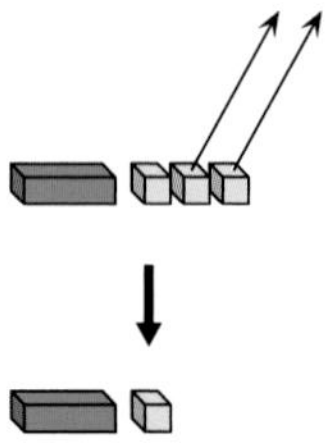

4. a. In this magic trick, do you think everyone should end up with the same or different answers? Explain.

b. How will a person's answer be related to his or her original number? Explain.

3.4 SOLUTIONS

1. The number is 1. The magician created this trick in such a way that the result is always 1 no matter what you pick as your number. Use a variable and show the trick with the Lab Gear.
2. All answers should be 2.
3. The answers students get will be the same number they started out with.
4. a. Since we end up with the x-block and the 1-block, everyone should have different answers depending on what value was chosen for x.
   b. The answers will be one more than the original number because the blocks show $x + 1$, where x can be any number.

5. Do the following magic trick with the Lab Gear. Start with an x-block, which represents the number a person chose. Sketch each step and write it algebraically.
   1) Start with any number.
   2) Multiply the number by 4.
   3) Add 5.
   4) Subtract 1.
   5) Divide by 4.
   6) Subtract one more than the original number.

   Should everyone have the same result? If yes, what is it?

REVISING MAGIC TRICKS

6. Change the magic trick in problem 5 by reversing the order of Steps (3) and (4). Do you get the same answer as you did before? Explain.
7. Change the magic trick in problem 5 by reversing the order of Steps (2) and (3). Was this harder or easier than reversing Steps (3) and (4)? Explain.
8. Change the last step in problem 5 so that everyone ends up with the number they started out with.
9. Do the following algebraic magic trick. Which steps can you reverse without changing the result? Why?
   1) Think of a number.
   2) Subtract 7.
   3) Add 3 more than the number.
   4) Add 4.
   5) Multiply by 3.
   6) Divide by 6.

   You should end up with the original number.

INVENTING MAGIC TRICKS

The following trick has one step missing.
1) Think of a number.
2) Take its opposite.
3) Multiply by 2.
4) Subtract 2.
5) Divide by 2.
6) ?????

10. Use the Lab Gear to model the first five steps of this trick. Use y to represent the original number. Then translate each step into an algebraic expression. Compare your result after step (5) with your classmates' answers.
11. Decide what step (6) should be, so that the given condition is satisfied.
    a. The final result is one more than the original number.
    b. The final result is the opposite of the original number.
    c. The final result is always zero.
    d. The final result is always -1.
12. For each of these conditions, (a-d), make up an algebra magic trick with at least five steps.
    a. The final result is the original number.
    b. The final result is 2, regardless of what the original number was.
    c. The final result is the same, whether you do the steps backward or forward.
    d. The trick uses all four operations (multiplication, division, addition, subtraction).
13. **Summary** Choose one of the tricks you wrote in problem 12. Test your trick with three numbers, including a negative number and a fraction. Show your work. Use algebra to explain the trick.

REVISING MAGIC TRICKS

Reversing the steps has no effect when the operation is addition or multiplication, since these operations are commutative. A subtle point is that if you reverse steps like:

add 3
subtract 5

you are changing $x + 3 - 5$ to $x - 5 + 3$. This is not commutativity for subtraction, but for adding 3, then -5. In fact, changing the order of the subtraction would have given $x + 5 - 3$, which is indeed a different amount. (It is not necessary to dwell on this.)

One way to organize thinking about these tricks is to draw arrows for each step in the way that was introduced in Lesson 1. For example, for problem 5:

x—(· 4)→ ... —(+5)→ ... —(-1)→ ... —(/4)→ ... —(-(x + 1))→ ...

INVENTING MAGIC TRICKS

Problems 10-11 prepare the students for the challenge of creating their own tricks, which they do in problem 12. Ask students to try their tricks on each other in their groups.

3.4 SOLUTIONS

5. Everyone should end up with 0.
6. Yes. Adding 5 and subtracting 1 is the same as adding 4. Reversing the order is also the same as adding 4.
7. Answers will vary.
8. Subtract 1
9. Steps 2 and 3, 3 and 4, 2 and 4 can be reversed without changing the result, because the order in which we subtract or add does not change the result.
10. $-y - 1$
11. a. Add two more than twice the original number.
    b. Add one.
    c. Add one more than the original number.
    d. Add the original number.
12. Answers will vary.
13. Answers will vary.

THINKING WRITING 3.A
Secret Codes

Core Sequence: none of the assignment

Suitable for Homework: 4-9

Useful for Assessment: 9

What this Assignment is About:

- An application of linear functions to cryptography
- Undoing operations
- Preview of inverse functions
- Modular arithmetic

Problem 30 at the end of Lesson 3 previewed this assignment. However, there is a difference between that code and the ones here. Both are simple substitution codes, but the ones in this assignment are limited to shifts in the alphabet, or to reversing the alphabet and then shifting. Nevertheless, the suggestions given in that problem about how to set up a decoding can be used. (Use pencil, skip lines, capitals for coded message, lower case for plaintext.)

Problems 1-3 should probably be done in class, to make sure everyone understands the assignment. The Report asks students to generalize. Most students should be able to include a formula for the decoding functions. If there is no class time to spend on problems 5-8, a description of decoding in words, based on specific examples, is acceptable.

More codes can be found in many Sunday papers, and in puzzle magazines such as *Games*.

THINKING WRITING
3.A Secret Codes

First we will use functions to create codes. Later we will use functions to break codes. Assign a number to each letter of the alphabet. A is 1, B is 2, and so on.

A	1	H	8	O	15	V	22
B	2	I	9	P	16	W	23
C	3	J	10	Q	17	X	24
D	4	K	11	R	18	Y	25
E	5	L	12	S	19	Z	26
F	6	M	13	T	20		
G	7	N	14	U	21		

Definition: The text of a message, before it is encoded, is called the *plaintext.*

The easiest code works by replacing each letter by one that follows it at a certain distance in the alphabet. For example, A (letter 1) is replaced with H (letter 8), B (2) is replaced with I (9), and so on. The function used in this example is $y = 7 + x$, where x is the number of the plaintext letter, and y is the number of the coded letter.

If the number of the coded letter is greater than 26, subtract 26 from it. For example, V's number is 22, $22 + 7 = 29$, $29 - 26 = 3$, so the code letter for V is C.

1. Copy and complete this table to show the $y = 7 + x$ code.

Plaintext	Code
A	H
B	I
C	...

2. Use $y = 7 + x$ to encode the words `smile, juggle, dance, puzzle.`
3. Choose a number, b, and use $y = b + x$ to encode a message for a classmate. (Let the classmate know the value of b so he or she will be able to decode the message quickly.)
4. Decode the following message, which has been encoded with $y = 10 + x$.
`DRSC COXDOXMO ECOC RKVP DRO VODDOBC SX DRO KVZRKLOD.`
5. Find the function that would decode the message in problem 4. Check your answer by actually using it on `DRSC`, and making sure it gives the expected plaintext.
6. a. Use the function $y = 27 - x$ to encode these names.
`Bernard, Carol, Ellen, Peter`
b. Describe in words the code obtained from this function.
7. a. Encode your name with $y = 30 - x$.
b. Now take the answer to (a) and encode it with $y = 30 - x$ again.
c. Comment on the result in (b).
8. a. Encode the word `bilingual` with $y = 8 - x$ and then with $y = x - 8$. Do you get the same answer? Explain.
b. Find a decoding function for each function in part (a).
9. **Report** In this lesson you learned about two kinds of coding functions. Some look like $y = 7 + x$, and others look like $y = 8 - x$. Write a report on how to decode messages coded by each kind of function and also by functions like $y = x - 8$. Give examples using other numbers for each of the three kinds of functions. Mention any special numbers. (For example, what happens when $y = x + 26$?)

3.A SOLUTIONS

1.

Plaintext	Code	Plaintext	Code
A	H	N	U
B	I	O	V
C	J	P	W
D	K	Q	X
E	L	R	Y
F	M	S	Z
G	N	T	A
H	O	U	B
I	P	V	C
J	Q	W	D
K	R	X	E
L	S	Y	F
M	T	Z	G

2. smile = ztpsl juggle = qbnnsl
dance = khujl puzzle = wbggsl
3. Answers will vary.
4. Decoded message: This sentence uses half of the letters in the alphabet.
5. $y = x - 10$, If $x - 10$ is a negative number, add it to 26 to get the decoded letter.
DRSC = THIS
6. a. Bernard = yvimziw Carol = xzilo
Ellen = voovm Peter = kvgvi
b. A is replaced by Z, B by Y, C by X, etc. A physical model can be built by writing the alphabet in a column or row. Then fold the paper between the letters M and N such that A is paired with Z, B with Y, etc. This can be used to

LESSON 3.5

Introduction to Inequalities

You will need:

the Lab Gear 

WHICH IS GREATER?

You can tell which of two numbers is greater by their positions on the number line.

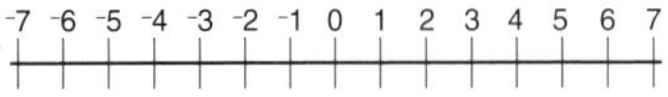

The number that is greater is farther to the right. The number that is less is farther to the left.

Notation: The symbol for *less than* is <. For example, -5 < 3, 0 < 7, and -6 < -2. The symbol for *greater than* is >. For example, 6 > 3, 0 > -2, and -5 > -9.

1. Use the correct symbol.
   a. -5 ? -7 b. -5 ? -1

This workmat shows two expressions.
$x + 4 - 5 - (x + 5)$ and $10 + 2x - 1 - (2x - 1)$

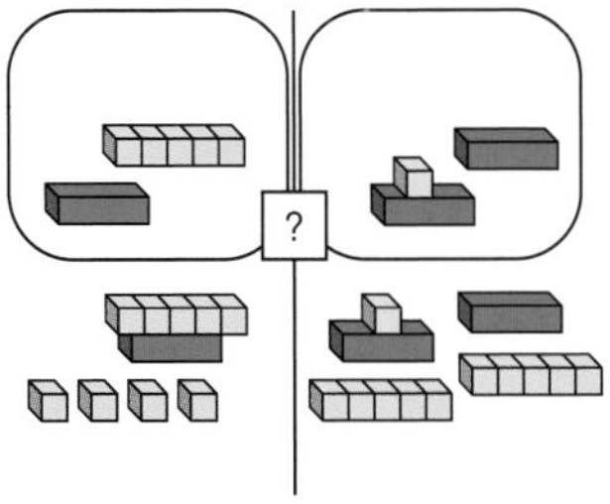

Which is greater? The question mark shows that this is unknown.

2. Put out blocks to match the figure. Simplify both sides. Write an expression for the blocks that remain on the left side. Write an expression for the blocks on the right side. Which side is greater? Show your answer by writing the correct *inequality sign* between the two expressions.

For each problem, put out blocks to match the figure, and
   a. write the two expressions;
   b. simplify both sides on the workmat;
   c. decide which side is greater or whether they are equal, and write the correct sign between the expressions.

3.

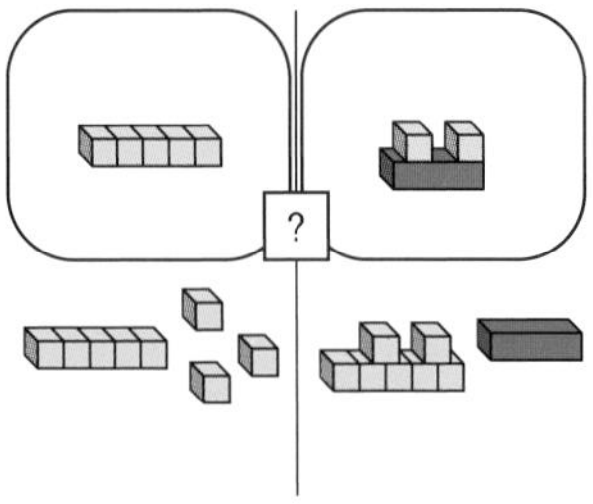

4.

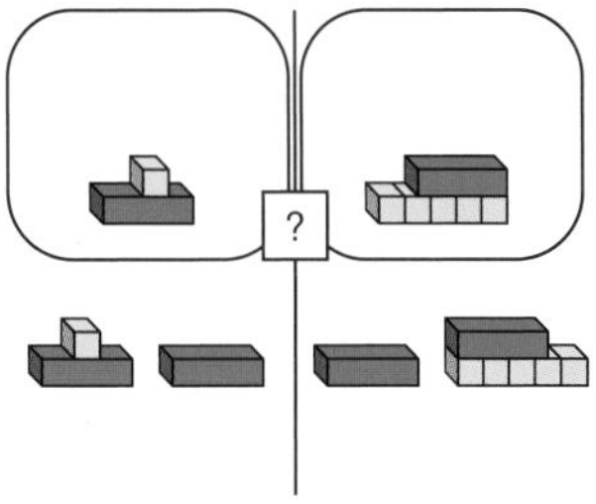

▼ 3.5
Introduction to Inequalities

Core Sequence: 1-31

Suitable for Homework: 12-31

What this Lesson is About:
- Preview of solving linear inequalities
- Review of substitution
- Review of distributing the minus sign and order of operations

This lesson is important, even though most of it is not directly related to the chapter's theme of Working Backwards. The reason we address inequalities early in the course is that, *with a tool-based approach*, they put equations in a broader context and thereby help students focus on the meaning of equations, instead of just on solving techniques.

3.5 SOLUTIONS

(3.A Solutions continued)
encode/decode words instead of $y = 27 - x$.

7. Answers will vary.
   The student will obtain his/her name again. $y = 30 - x$ is the encoding and decoding function.

8. a. $y = 8 - x$: bilingual = fyvytamgv
      $y = x - 8$: bilingual = tadafamsd
      The two functions are not the same, so we do not get the same decoded message.
   b. encode: $y = 8 - x$
      decode: $y = 8 - x$
      encode: $y = x - 8$
      decode: $y = x + 8$

9. Answers will vary. If we encode with $y = x - b$, then we decode with $y = x + b$. If we encode with $y = b - x$, then we decode with the same function.

1. a. -5 > -7
   b. -5 < -1

2. $4 + x - 5 - (x + 5)$?
   $10 + 2x - 1 - (2x - 1)$
   $-1 + x - x - 5$? $9 + 2x - 2x + 1$
   $-6 < 10$

3. 3 < 5

4. $x = x$

WHICH IS GREATER?

CAN YOU TELL?

*T*hese sections use the Lab Gear to introduce students to the concept of inequalities. This work will be picked up again in Chapter 6, when we concentrate on equations and equation solving. Be sure you have done these problems yourself before doing them in class, so you will be able to anticipate student questions.

5.

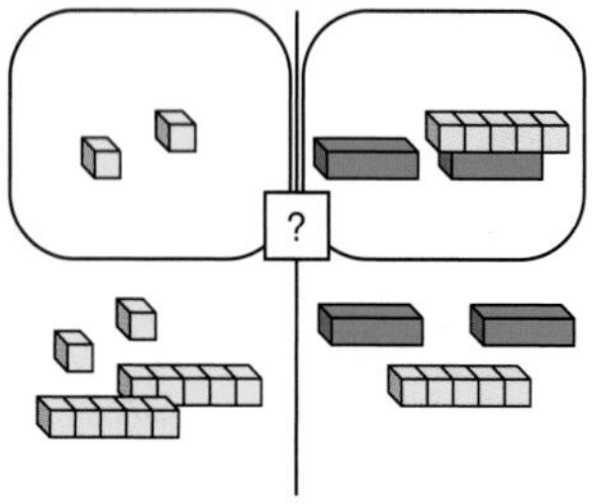

6.

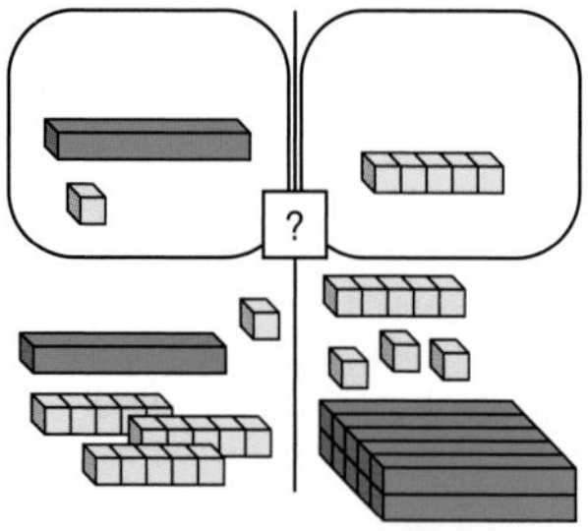

CAN YOU TELL?

To compare $2x - x + 5 - (5 - x)$ with $5 + 3x - 1 - (x - 3)$, first show the two expressions with the Lab Gear.

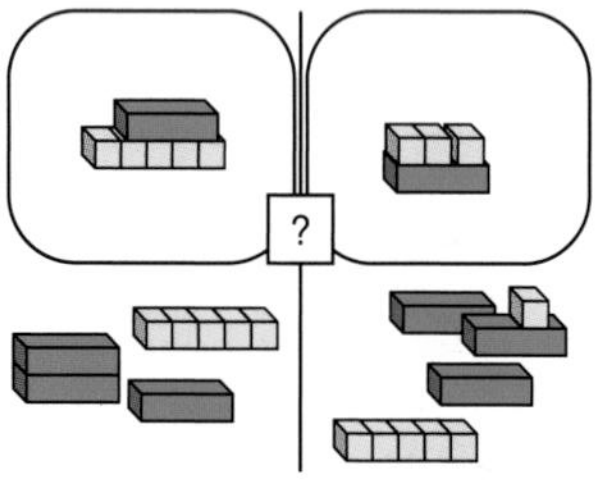

7. Simplify both sides, then arrange the blocks in a logical manner to determine which side is greater.

Your workmat should look like this.

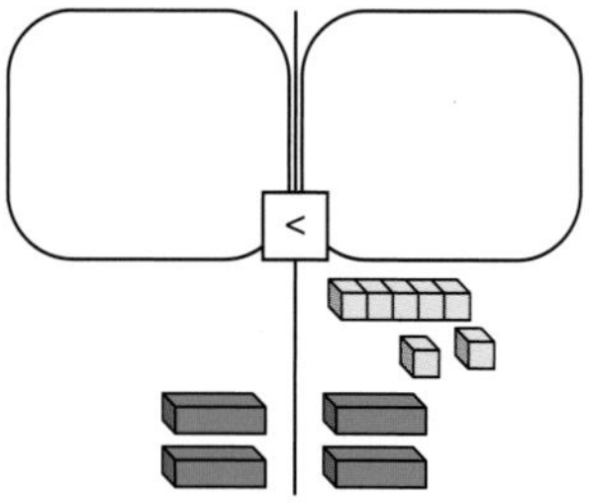

Both sides include $2x$, but the right side is greater, as it also includes 7 more units. So we can write

$$2x < 2x + 7.$$

Now compare these expressions.

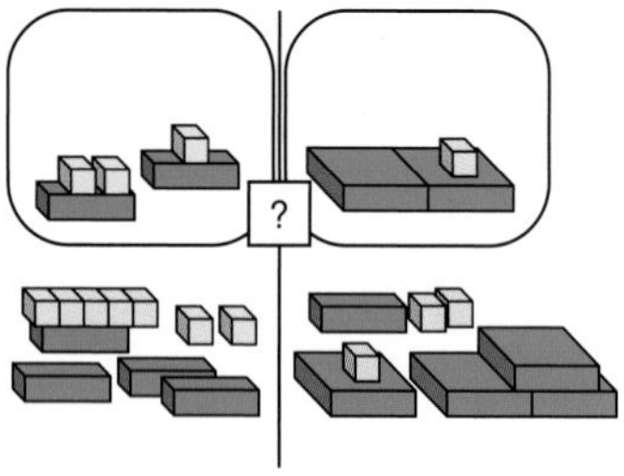

8. Write both expressions as they are shown in this figure.

9. Simplify both sides, then arrange the blocks in a logical manner to determine which side is greater.

3.5 SOLUTIONS

5. $10 = 10$
6. $15 > 3$
8. $4x + 2 - 5 - (2x - 3)?$
   $3x^2 - x^2 + x + 2 - 1 - (2x^2 - 1)$
9. $2x \; ? \; x + 2$
   $2x = x + 2$ if $x = 2$
   $2x > x + 2$ if $x > 2$
   $2x < x + 2$ if $x < 2$

Your workmat should look like this.

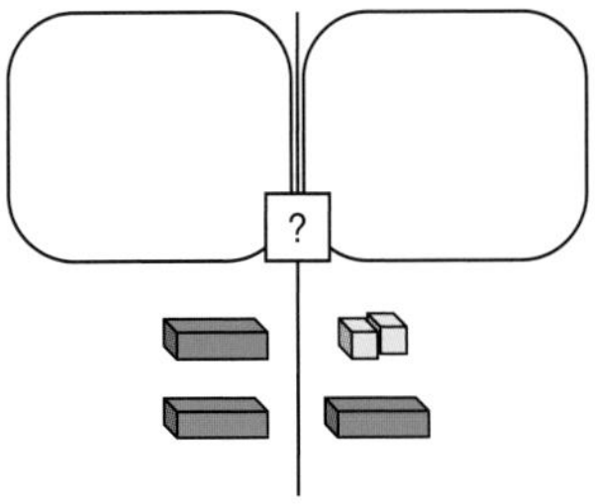

In this case, it is impossible to tell which side is greater, because we do not know whether x is greater or less than 2.

For problems 10-13, write both expressions as they are given. Then simplify, using your blocks, and write the expressions in simplified form. Decide which side is greater, whether they are equal, or whether it is impossible to tell. Write the correct symbol or ?.

10.

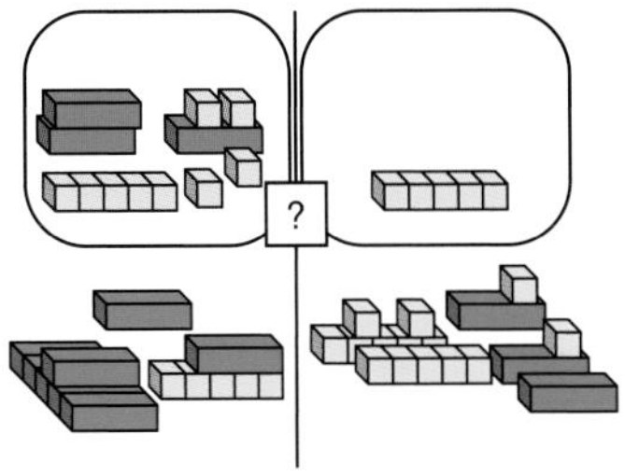

11.

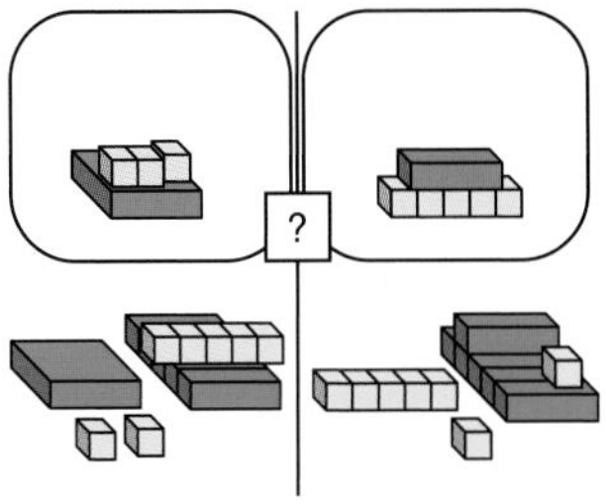

12.

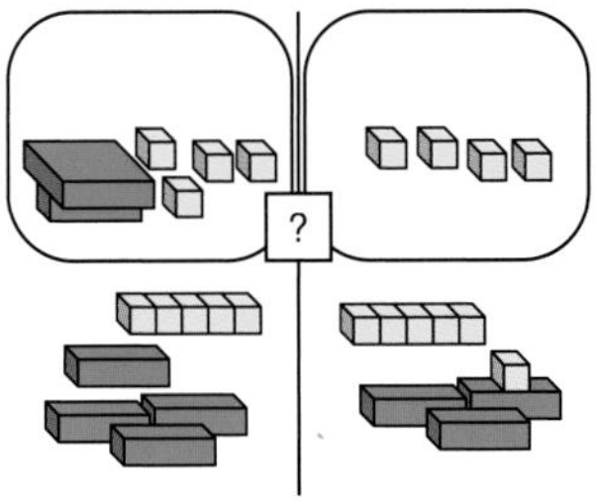

13.

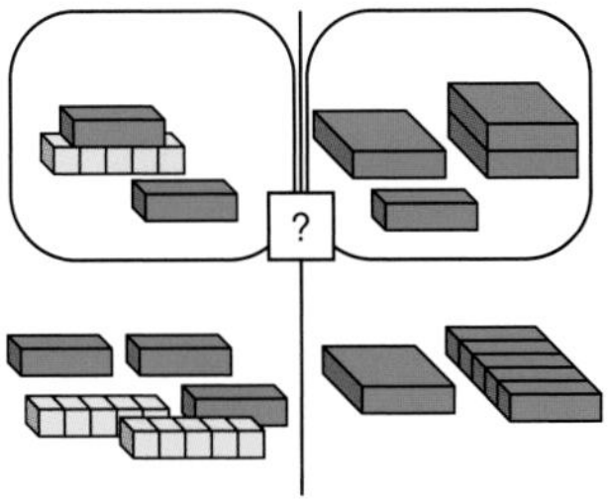

TESTING VALUES OF *X*

Look at these two expressions.

$2x - 5$ $\quad$ $-3x + 6$

Which is greater? The answer depends on the value of x.

14. a. Substitute -1 for x in both expressions and tell which is greater.
b. Substitute 3 for x in both expressions and tell which is greater.
c. Find another value for x which makes $2x - 5$ greater.
d. Find another value for x which makes $-3x + 6$ greater.

15. For each of the following pairs of expressions, find two values of x, one that makes the first expression greater and one that makes the second expression greater. Show all your calculations.
a. $7x - 4$ $\quad$ $3x - 2$
b. $-2x + 6$ $\quad$ $8x - 4$
c. x $\quad$ $-x$

TESTING VALUES OF *x*

*Your students may wonder whether there is a value of x that makes the two expressions equal. That is a good question. Suggest trial and error as an approach to seeking an answer. Other techniques will be introduced later (working backwards in Lesson 9, symbol manipulation in Chapter 6, graphing in Chapters 4 and 10.)

Note that problems 16-21 have a format similar to a standard SAT type of question. In addition to previewing inequalities, these questions test and develop students' understanding of variables and operations.

3.5 S O L U T I O N S

10. $3x < 3x + 1$
11. $5x = 5x$
12. $3x + x^2 + 1 > 3x$
(because $x^2 + 1$ is positive)
13. $3x + 5$ and $4x$; impossible to tell
14. a. $-7 < 9$
b. $1 > -3$
c. Any number greater than 11/5.
d. Any number less than 11/5.
15. Answers will vary.

For problems 23-25, there are infinite numbers of solutions. Class discussion of student answers to problems of this type can be extremely useful.

DISCOVERY ***MORE CODES***

This section extends the work with coding functions. It focuses on the issue of whether a function has an inverse, which was mostly avoided in the body of the chapter.

DISCOVERY ***SUMMING UP***

This section does not require having done **Thinking/Writing 3.A,** as it does not rely on functions. (However, your students will need to use the table of letter values.)

For each pair of expressions, write

A if the expression in column A is greater;
B if the expression in column B is greater;
? if you would have to know the value of x in order to know which is greater.

Remember that x can have negative and fractional values. It may help to think about the Lab Gear. In each case *explain your answer*, giving test values of x if it helps your explanation.

	A	B
16.	$7x$	$7x - 1$
17.	$7x + 1$	$-7x + 1$
18.	$7x + 1$	$7x - 1$
19.	$7x - 1$	$-7x - 1$
20.	$7x + 1$	$-7x - 1$
21.	$7x^2 - 1$	$7x - 1$

22. Compare your answers to problems 16-21 with other students' answers. Discuss your disagreements. If you disagree with another student, try to find an example to show which answer is not correct.

23. Write an expression containing x, that is less than 4 when x is less than 9.

24. Write an expression containing x, that is less than 4 when x is more than 9.

25. Write an expression containing x, that is less than 4 for all values of x.

DISCOVERY ***MORE CODES***

If the coding function is of the form $y = mx$, it is more difficult to encode and decode. (For the letter values, see **Thinking/Writing 3.A**.)

26. a. Encode the word `extra` using $y = 3x$.
b. What did you do when $3x$ was larger than 26?

27. Decode the following sentence which was encoded with $y = 3x$. It may help to make a table showing the matching of the plaintext and coded alphabet.

`APIBOCEO HXO VOCIO.`

28. Encode the word `multiplication` with:
a. $y = x$; b. $y = 2x$;
c. $y = 13x$; d. $y = 26x$.

29.
a. Decode the following message, which was encoded with $y = 2x$. It may help to make a table showing the matching of the plaintext and coded alphabet.

`HD NPJ JRNPN NPRBN. DPN PDT FBB XDP NJXX TPBN'L JRNPN?`

b. What makes $y = 2x$ a difficult code to crack?

DISCOVERY ***SUMMING UP***

Say that the sum of a word is the sum of the numbers corresponding to its letters. (For the letter values, see **Thinking/Writing 3.A**.) For example, the word `topic` has value

$$20 + 15 + 16 + 9 + 3 = 63.$$

30. What is the sum of the word `algebra`?

31. Find as many words as possible having sum 100.

3.5 SOLUTIONS

16. A
17. ?
18. A
19. ?
20. ?
21. ?
22. Answers will vary.
23. Answers will vary. Possible solutions are expressions of the form $x - b$, where $b \geq 5$.
24. Answers will vary. Possible solutions are expressions of the form $-x + b$, where $b \leq 13$.
25. Answers will vary. Possible solutions are expressions of the form $4 - (x^2 + b^2 + 1)$; where b is a real number.
26. a. othbc
b. When $3x$ is larger than 26, one way to deal with this is to divide the number by 26 and use only the remainder to encode the letter. Another way is to keep subtracting 26 until you get an integer between 1 and 26.
27. Decoded message: Increase the peace.
The decode function is $y = x/3$. If x is not a multiple of 3, add 26 to it until the result is a multiple of 3. Now divide the number by 3 and use the quotient to decode the letter.
28. a. multiplication
b. zpxnrfxrfbnrdb
c. mmzzmzzmmmzmmz
d. multiplicztion
29. a. Decoded message: Do the right thing. But how can you tell what's right?
b. Each letter could be decoded to 2 letters. So we have to rely on the context and use the trial and error method to decode a word.
30. 46
31. Answers will vary.

LESSON 3.6

Multiplication and Division

You will need:

the Lab Gear

Notation: In algebra, the symbol ÷ is not used, perhaps because it looks too much like a + sign. To show division, use the format of a fraction.

$$\frac{6}{2} = 3$$

Or, if you're using a typewriter or computer, write it with a slash, 6/2 = 3.

In this book we will write division both ways.

ONE MULTIPLICATION, TWO DIVISIONS

For most multiplication equations, there are two division equations. For example, corresponding to $7 \cdot 3 = 21$, we have

21/7 = 3 and 21/3 = 7.

With the Lab Gear, you can use a rectangle to model multiplication and division.

Arrange your corner piece and blocks to match this figure.

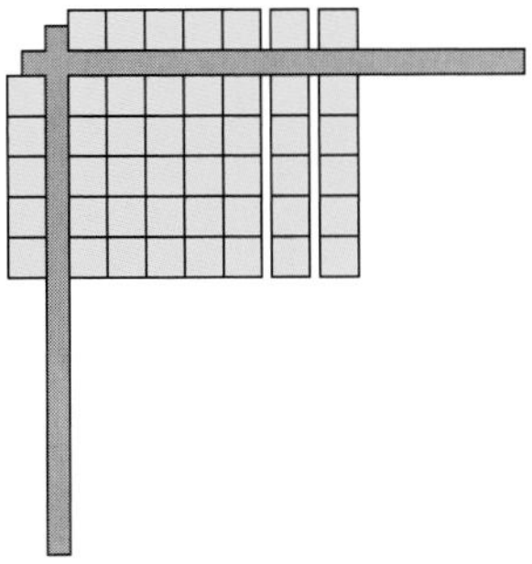

1. Write the multiplication equation that is shown by the figure.
2. Write the two division equations that are shown by the figure.
3. You could use the corner piece to set up several different divisions having numerator 12. For each, write the division equation and the corresponding multiplication equation.
4. Explain why it is impossible to set up the division 12/0 with the Lab Gear.
5. Some algebra students believe that 12/0 = 0. Explain why they are *wrong* by discussing the multiplication that would correspond to this division.
6. a. Using the corner piece, multiply $(x + 4)(x + 3)$.
   b. Write two division equations related to the multiplication.

DIVISION IN THE CORNER PIECE

Here is an example of dividing in the corner piece.

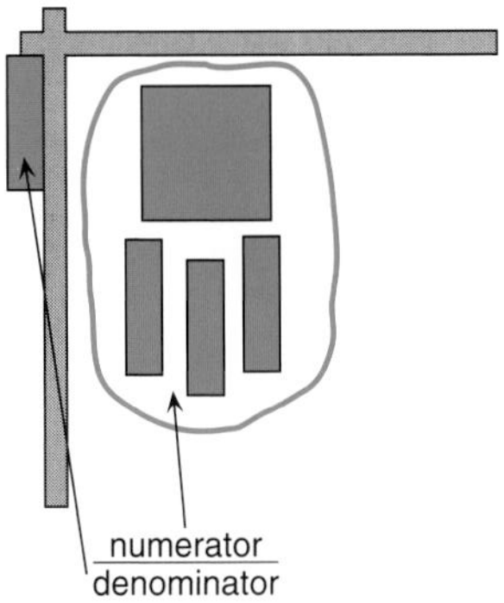

▼ 3.6 Multiplication and Division

Core Sequence: 1-22

Suitable for Homework: 13-20, 22

Useful for Assessment: 5, 18-19

What this Lesson is About:

- The relationship between multiplication and division
- A geometric model for division
- Division by zero
- A technique for multiplying polynomials without the Lab Gear

ONE MULTIPLICATION, TWO DIVISIONS

DIVISION IN THE CORNER PIECE

This is a straightforward extension of the area model for multiplication to an area model for division. It was previewed at the end of Lesson 3 in the *what is the other side*? and missing term problems, 22-29.

The arrangement of the blocks in the corner piece is the same as the arrangement of the divisor, dividend, and quotient in the traditional long division layout.

Problem 11 is difficult, but some of your students should be able to solve it with the help of the 3-D blocks. It is a preview of more work on multiplication and division, which will take place in Chapter 5.

3.6 SOLUTIONS

1. $5 \cdot 7 = 35$
2. 35/5 = 7
   35/7 = 5
3. $1 \cdot 12 = 12$
   12/1 = 12
   12/12 = 1

   $2 \cdot 6 = 12$
   12/6 = 2
   12/2 = 6

   $3 \cdot 4 = 12$
   12/4 = 3
   12/3 = 4
4. We cannot build a rectangle having width or length zero.
5. If 12/0 = 0, then we can write $0 \cdot 0 = 12$, but $0 \cdot 0$ equals 0 not 12. Therefore $12/0 \neq 0$.
6. a. $x^2 + 7x + 12$
   b. $\frac{x^2 + 7x + 12}{x + 4} = x + 3$
   $\frac{x^2 + 7x + 12}{x + 3} = x + 4$

MULTIPLICATION WITHOUT THE LAB GEAR

The "table" method for multiplying polynomials looks very much like multiplication in the corner piece. It is less concrete but more convenient than using the corner piece, since it does not require blocks. In addition, minus is somewhat easier to deal with.

However, to use the method correctly, students must see polynomials as sums of terms, and make sure that terms that are preceded by a minus sign are written with their minus sign in the table.

This method is much superior to "FOIL," since it works with absolute generality to multiply any two polynomials (not just binomials).

MULTIPLICATION PUZZLES

These should help your students consolidate what they have learned in the previous section.

REVIEW WHAT'S YOUR SIGN?

This easy problem reviews the rules for multiplying by negative numbers and previews the Zero Product Property.

- Put the denominator to the left of the corner piece.
- Make a rectangle out of the numerator and place it inside the corner piece so that one side of the rectangle matches the denominator.

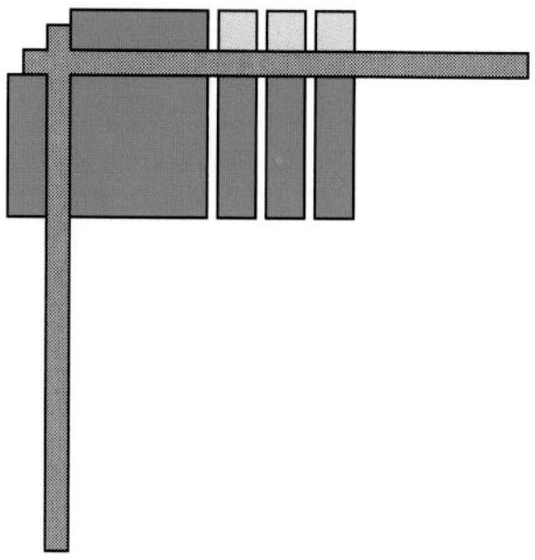

- Finally, to get the answer, figure out what blocks go along the top of the corner piece.

7. Write the division equation shown by the figure.

The denominator was a factor of the numerator, and a rectangle was formed with no pieces left over. However, in some cases, there will be a remainder. Here is an example.

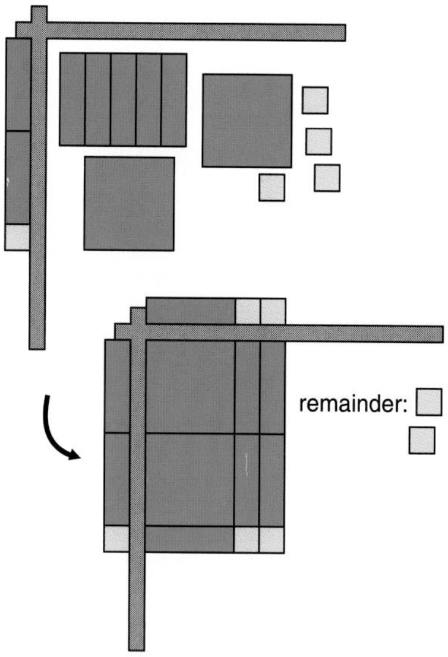

8. What are the numerator, denominator, quotient, and remainder in the above division?

3.6 SOLUTIONS

7. $\frac{x^2 + 3x}{x} = x + 3$

8. numerator: $2x^2 + 5x + 2$
denominator: $2x + 1$
quotient: $x + 2$
remainder: 2

9. Divide.

a. $\frac{6x^2 + 3x}{3x}$ b. $\frac{9x + 3}{3}$

c. $\frac{x^2 + x + xy + y}{x + y}$ d. $\frac{xy + 2x + x^2}{x + y}$

e. $\frac{2x^2 + 6x + 4}{x + 2}$ f. $\frac{3x^2 + 10x + 5}{x + 3}$

10. For each division in problem 9, write the related multiplication equation.

11.

a. Divide. $\frac{y^2x + x^2y + 2xy + x^2 + y^2 + x + y}{x + 1}$

b. Write four multiplications having the product $y^2x + x^2y + 2xy + x^2 + y^2 + x + y$.

MULTIPLICATION WITHOUT THE LAB GEAR

Here is a method for multiplying polynomials without the Lab Gear. To perform the multiplication $(x + 2)(3y - 4x + 5)$, write the terms along the side and the top of a table.

	$3y$	$-4x$	5
x			
2			

Then enter the products of the terms in the corresponding boxes.

	$3y$	$-4x$	5
x	$3xy$	$-4x^2$	$5x$
2	$6y$	$-8x$	10

Then combine like terms, and you are done.

$(x + 2)(3y - 4x + 5) =$
$3xy - 4x^2 - 3x + 6y + 10$

Use this method for the following products.

12. $x(2x + 3xy + y^2)$

13. $(2x - y)(x + 3y)$

14. $(2x - y)(x - 3y)$

15. $(2x + y)(x - 3y)$

16. $(2x + y)(x + 3y)$

17. $(x + xy + 2yx)(y + 2 + x)$

This method for multiplication is a way to apply the distributive law to the multiplication of polynomials. *Every term must be multiplied by every term.*

MULTIPLICATION PUZZLES

Fill in the tables, including the polynomial factors along the side and the top. All coefficients are whole numbers. Is more than one solution possible for either table?

18.

$2x^3$		$-6x$
	$-x$	-3

19.

$12xy$	$15x^2y$	
		x^2y^2

20. Create a puzzle of this type that has a unique solution. Give the solver as few terms as possible.

21. Solve a classmate's puzzle.

REVIEW WHAT'S YOUR SIGN?

22. What is the sign of the missing factor?

a. -123.4 · ____ = 567.89

b. 98.76 · (-54.3) · ____ = -21

c. 98.76 · (-54.3) · ____ = 0

3.6 SOLUTIONS

9. a. $2x + 1$
b. $3x + 1$
c. $x + 1$
d. x remainder $2x$
e. $2x + 2$
f. $3x + 1$ remainder: 2

10. a. $3x(2x + 1) = 6x^2 + 3x$
b. $3(3x + 1) = 9x + 3$
c. $(x + y)(x + 1) = x^2 + x + xy + y$
d. $(x + y)x + 2x = xy + 2x + x^2$
e. $(x + 2)(2x + 2) = 2x^2 + 6x + 4$
f. $(x + 3)(3x + 1) + 2 = 3x^2 + 10x + 5$

11. a. $y^2 + xy + y + x$

12. $2x^2 + 3x^2y + xy^2$

13. $2x^2 + 5xy - 3y^2$

14. $2x^2 - 7xy + 3y^2$

15. $2x^2 - 5xy - 3y^2$

16. $2x^2 + 7xy + 3y^2$

17. $x^2 + 3xy^2 + 3x^2y + 7xy + 2x$

22. a. Negative
b. Positive
c. Zero

▼ 3.7 Reciprocals

Core Sequence: 1-12, 17-27

Suitable for Homework: 8-12, 19-28

Useful for Assessment: 6, 16, 21, 23

What this Lesson is About:

- Understanding and using reciprocals
- Multiplication and division by numbers between 0 and 1
- Preview of solving linear equations
- Review of division by zero

Even though the Lab Gear is mentioned in the lesson the students do not need the blocks.

In spite (or because) of many years of doing arithmetic by rote, many students have a lot of trouble understanding reciprocals, and multiplication and division by numbers between 0 and 1. This can be a major handicap in doing any sort of calculations in any science, or even in daily life.

We will study opposites and reciprocals algebraically, as functions, in **Thinking/Writing 3.B**, after Lesson 8.

This lesson concentrates on number sense. The goal is not to teach any particular algorithm for arithmetic with decimals and fractions. Instead, the focus is on understanding what happens, and developing an intuition for it. Some of the problems specifically discourage the use of calculators, while others encourage it. As always, in those problems that do not specify, calculator use is acceptable.

Even more than usual, the Explorations are crucial in this lesson. They provide challenging problems for students to grapple with and discuss, something they may not be accustomed to doing when dealing with numbers. It is that discussion which will make it possible to make some headway in their understanding.

A MODEL FOR MULTIPLICATION

A MULTIPLICATION SHORTCUT

You may play an estimation game based on problem 2. For example, ask students to give you a number for x, if $3x$ is: between 1 and 2; between 10 and 20; between -1 and -2; between -10 and -20.

LESSON 3.7

Reciprocals

A MODEL FOR MULTIPLICATION

You cannot easily show multiplication by fractions with the Lab Gear, but the Lab Gear can help you think about it. For example, (1/5) · 50 is read *one-fifth of fifty.* This means that we divide 50 into five parts and take one of them.

The diagram shows that (1/5) · 50 = 10.

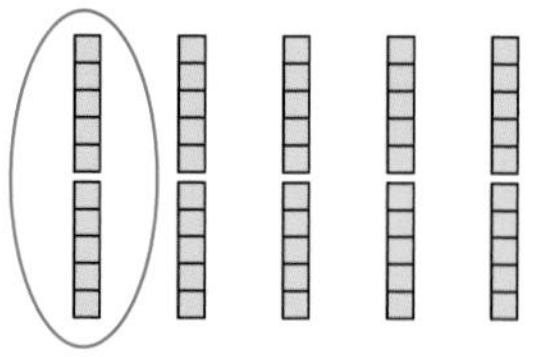

(2/5) is two of five parts, so 2/5 · 50 = 20.

1. Find a number you could multiply by 8 to get a number less than 8.
2. Without finding its value, decide whether x would be more or less than 1. Explain how you know.
   a. $8 \cdot x = 50$ b. $8 \cdot x = 5$
   c. $8 \cdot x = 0.05$
3. Find the value of x for each equation in problem 2. (Hint: Remember that for any multiplication, there are two related divisions. You may use a calculator.)

A MULTIPLICATION SHORTCUT

4. Take 8, 3, and 2. They are three numbers whose product is 48. Another multiplication possibility is 6 · 4 · 2. Find as many ways of writing 48 as a product of three different numbers as you can. Do not use 1 as a factor.

5. **Exploration** *Do not use 1 as a factor.*
   a. Write 2 as a product of two different numbers.
   b. Write 4 as a product of four different numbers.
   c. Write 6 as a product of six different numbers.
   d. Write 12 as a product of twelve different numbers.

Definition: The product of a number and its *reciprocal* is 1. Another way of saying this is, *the reciprocal of a number is the result of dividing 1 by the number.*

Examples: 3 · 1/3 = 1
2/3 · 3/2 = 1
0.31 · 100/31 = 1

6. Explain how the reciprocals of 3, 2/3, and 0.31 may have been found for the examples above. (No calculator was used.)

Guess the value of x, *without using your calculator.* If you think about reciprocals you will have to do very little arithmetic.

7. a. $5 \cdot \frac{1}{5} \cdot x = 6$
   b. $4 \cdot x \cdot 9 \cdot \frac{1}{4} = 45$
   c. $x \cdot 8 \cdot 7 = 8$
   d. $x \cdot 8 \cdot 3 = 3$
   e. $\frac{2}{3} \cdot x \cdot 3 \cdot \frac{1}{2} = 15$
8. a. $2 \cdot x \cdot 3 = 2$
   b. $x \cdot 2 \cdot 2 \cdot 9 \cdot 3 = 6$
   c. $\frac{1}{5} \cdot (5x) \cdot 3 = 1$
   d. $\frac{1}{5} \cdot (5x) = \frac{3}{5}$
9. Make up two more equations like problems 7 and 8 and solve them.

3.7 SOLUTIONS

1. Answers will vary.
2. a. x would be more than 1 since 50 is greater than 8. We must multiply 8 by an integer greater than 1 to get 50.
   b. x would be less than 1 since 5 is smaller than 8, so we must multiply 8 by a fraction to get 5.
   c. x would be less than 1.
3. a. 6.25
   b. 0.625
   c. 0.00625
4. Answers will vary.
   The key is to use fractions, e.g.
   8 · 12 · 1/2
5. Answers will vary. Use fractions. One possible solution for each is given.
   a. (1/2) · 4
   b. (1/2) · 4 · (1/3) · 6
   c. (1/5) · 5 · (1/3) · 6 · (1/4) · 12
   d. (1/2) · 2 · (1/3) · 3 · (1/4) · 4 · (1/5) · 10 · (1/6) · 12 · (1/7) · 21
6. Answers will vary.
   Use the definition.
7. a. 6
   b. 5
   c. 1/7
   d. 1/8
   e. 15
8. a. 1/3
   b. 1/18
   c. 1/3
   d. 3/5
9. Answers will vary.

10. Find two numbers a and b that will satisfy each equation. *Don't use your calculator.* Instead, think about reciprocals. Do not use 1 for a or b.
   a. $a \cdot b \cdot 14 = 28$ b. $a \cdot b \cdot 28 = 14$
   c. $\frac{2}{3} \cdot a \cdot b = 10$ d. $a \cdot b \cdot 10 = \frac{2}{3}$

RECIPROCALS ON THE CALCULATOR

Most scientific calculators have a key for reciprocals: $\boxed{1/x}$, or $\boxed{x^{-1}}$. (On calculators that do not have such a key, you can divide 1 by a number to find the number's reciprocal.)

11. Find the reciprocal of:
   a. 1/23; b. 0.456; c. 7.89.

12. **Report** What is the result when you
   a. multiply a number by its reciprocal?
   b. divide a number by its reciprocal?

   Be sure your results work for all numbers. Explain how you reached your conclusions.

13. 1/82 < 0.0123 < 1/81. Explain.
14. Find two consecutive whole numbers such that 0.00123 is between their reciprocals.
15. Repeat problem 14 for 0.000123
16. Explain your method for solving problems 14 and 15.

A MODEL FOR DIVISION

17. **Exploration** Find a positive number such that when you divide that number by 5, your answer is
   a. a number less than 1;
   b. a number between 10 and 20;
   c. a number greater than 100.

18. Find a positive number such that when you divide 5 by it, your answer is
   a. a number less than 1;
   b. a number between 10 and 20;
   c. a number greater than 100.

Division by numbers between 0 and 1 is hard to show with the Lab Gear.

These diagrams show 10/5, 10/2, and 10/1.

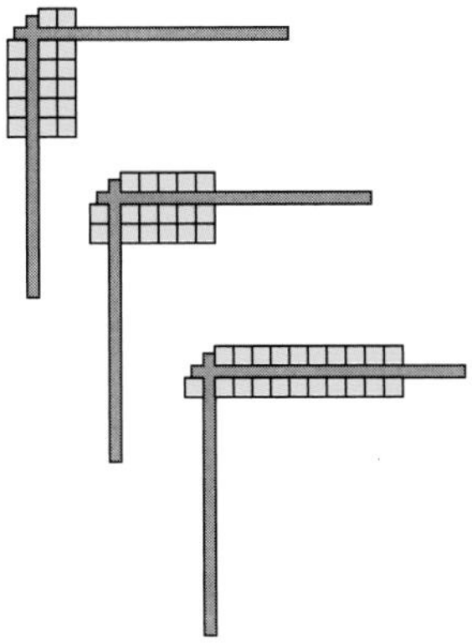

What would 10/(1/2) look like? We cannot actually build this with the Lab Gear, but we could imagine what it would look like if we sliced each block in half.

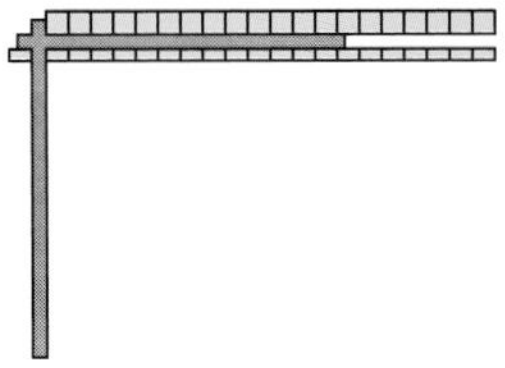

Problem 5 is very important. If necessary, give the hint that the numbers need not be whole numbers. Or you may hold off until a student thinks of the hint and have the student give it to the class.

Problem 6 is a bit of review of arithmetic. It is best to let students help each other with it in their groups, rather than have a class discussion of it, which would be boring for many.

Problems 7-9 preview the use of reciprocals in equation solving.

RECIPROCALS ON THE CALCULATOR

You can precede problem 11 with another estimation game. (What is an approximate value of the reciprocal of...?)

Some students will do problem 12 by trying various numbers. Others may use variables. Make sure to have a class discussion in which those who used variables can explain to the class what they did.

Make sure that students understand the notation in problem 13. Problems 14 and 15 can be done by trial and error, but some students may discover a quicker way (finding the reciprocal of the given number).

3.7 SOLUTIONS

10. Answers will vary.
11. a. 23
   b. about 2.1930
   c. about 0.1267
12. Answers will vary.
   Students should give more than one example and they should also use fractions and negative numbers.
   a. 1
   b. The number squared (x^2)
13. The reciprocal of 0.0123 is 81.3, which means 1/81.3 = 0.0123. So 1/82 < 1/81.3 < 1/81
14. 813 and 814
15. 8130 and 8131
16. Find the reciprocal of the decimal and take the two consecutive whole numbers that are closest in value to the reciprocals. One number should be greater than the reciprocal and the other one less than the reciprocal.
17. a. Any number less than 5
   b. Any number between 50 and 100
   c. Any number greater than 500
18. a. Any number greater than 5
   b. Any number between 1/4 and 1/2
   c. Any number less than 1/20

A MODEL FOR DIVISION

A DIVISION SHORTCUT

Most students do not know that you can divide a number by something, and end up with an answer greater than the original number.

Problem 21 helps prepare students for the next section, and also reviews division by zero. If students insist that $8/0 = \infty$ (infinity), tell them that division by zero is not defined, because infinity is not a real number. For one thing, it would follow that $\infty \cdot 0 = 8$, but also $\infty \cdot 0 = 9$, and so on, so all numbers would be equal. However, it is of course true that 8 divided by a very small number is a very large number.

Do not necessarily expect students to believe that one cannot divide by zero. For some reason some students resist this idea, and no amount of logic seems to convince them. At least they should know how math teachers feel about this.

Problem 23 is phrased in a way parallel to the comparable rule for subtraction, drawing attention to the fact that the rules reflect similar structures.

SMALL NUMBERS

This small optional problem should reinforce students' understanding of the arithmetic of small numbers.

19. a. What is the answer to the division shown in the figure?
b. Dividing by 1/2 is equivalent to multiplying by what number?

20. a. Will the result of the division 8/(1/4) be more or less than 8?
b. Use a sketch to show the division 8/(1/4).
c. What is the answer to the division?
d. Dividing by 1/4 is equivalent to multiplying by what number?

21.
a. What is the result of the division of 8 by 0.1, 0.01, 0.001?
b. What would happen if you divided 8 by a number that is much smaller than 0.001, almost equal to zero?
c. How about dividing 8 by 0?

A DIVISION SHORTCUT

22. a. If you multiplied 5 by a number and got 30, what was the number?
b. If you divided 5 by a number and got 30, what was the number?
c. Compare your answers to parts (a) and (b). How are these numbers related?

23. *Dividing by a number is the same as multiplying by its reciprocal.* Explain, using examples.

Use this fact to perform each of the following divisions without your calculator.

24. 12/(1/4) **25.** 12/(2/3)

26. 10/0.4 **27.** $x^2/(1/x)$

SMALL NUMBERS

28. Find two numbers such that you get a result between 0 and 1 whether you add them, multiply them, subtract one from the other, or divide one by the other.

3.7 SOLUTIONS

19. a. 20
b. 2

20. a. More than 8
b. Similar to picture in text.
c. 32
d. 4

21. a. 80, 800, 8000
b. The result is extremely large. The number would be 8 followed by many, many zeroes.
c. Impossible. Or, if we extend the conclusion of part b, 8/0 is infinity.

22. a. 6
b. 1/6
c. They are reciprocals of each other.

23. See #11.

24. 48

25. 18

26. 25

27. x^3

28. Answers will vary.

LESSON

3.8 A Hot Day

You will need: graph paper

The sign at Algebank near Abe's house gives the time and temperature. The temperature is given two ways, using both the Celsius and Fahrenheit temperature scales. One hot day Abe made a record of the time and temperature at several times during the day. He tried to look at the bank sign exactly on the hour, but usually he was off by a few minutes. His data appear below.

Time	Temp (C)	Temp (F)
11:03	31	87
12:00	32	90
2:00	35	95
3:04	35	95
4:08	34	93
8:03	27	81

1. **Exploration** Abe heard on the radio that the low for the night had been 74 degrees (Fahrenheit) at 4:30 A.M. and the high for the day had been 97 degrees at 3:30 P.M. Using the information in the table, estimate what you think the Celsius readings on the bank sign would have been at those two times. Explain how you got your answers.

TEMPERATURE VARIATION

2. a. Draw a pair of axes on graph paper. Label the horizontal axis *Time* and the vertical axis *Temp*.
   b. Plot the points that show how the Celsius temperature changes with time. Your first point will be (11:03, 31).
3. a. Draw another pair of axes like the first one.
   b. Plot the points that show how the Fahrenheit temperature changes with time. Your first point will be (11:03, 87).
4. Write a short description of what your graphs show. Compare the two graphs.

COMPARING TEMPERATURE SCALES

A graph will help to show how the two temperature scales are related.

5. Draw a pair of axes. Put the Fahrenheit temperature on the vertical axis (label it *F*) and the Celsius temperature on the horizontal axis (label it *C*). Put the axes in the middle of your graph paper and leave plenty of room to extend your graph in all directions. Plot the points in Abe's table. Your first point will be (31, 87).
6. The points of your graph should fall approximately in a straight line. Draw a straight line that seems to go through most of the points.

Use your graph to estimate the answers to these questions. If necessary, extend your graph.

7. Approximately what is the
   a. Fahrenheit temperature when the Celsius temperature is 25°?
   b. Celsius temperature when the Fahrenheit temperature is 50°?
   c. Celsius temperature when the Fahrenheit temperature is -30°?

3.8 SOLUTIONS

1. Answers will vary.
   Students can analyze the data in the table or make a graph.

2.

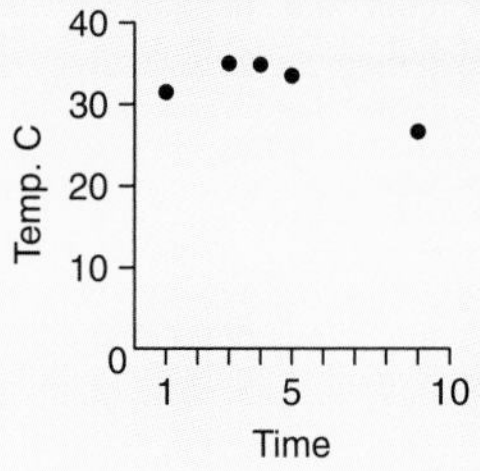

3.

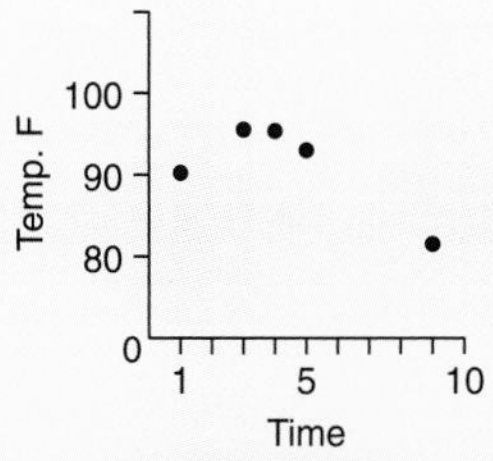

4. Both graphs are curves of similar shape, but the Fahrenheit graph has a greater angle of curvature.

5., 6.

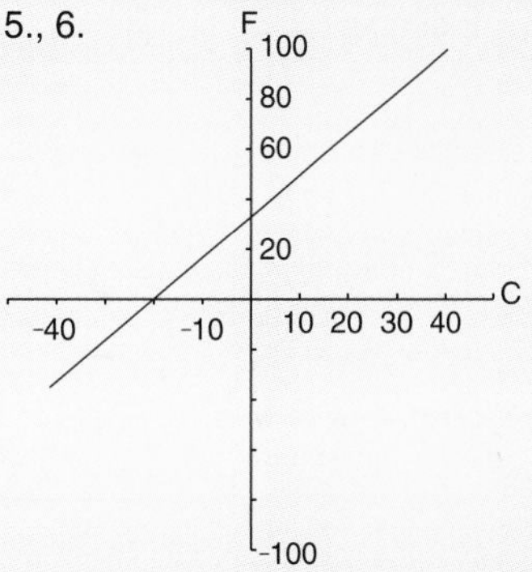

7. Answers will vary. The following are exact.
   a. 77°F
   b. 10°C
   c. -34°C

3.8 A Hot Day

Core Sequence: 1-17

Suitable for Homework: 11-17

Useful for Assessment: 9, 10, 13, 15, 17

What this Lesson is About:

- Graphing data
- Applying linear functions
- Preview of slope
- Preview of inverse functions

This is a real-world application. The big question is the conversion from Fahrenheit to Celsius and back. In the Exploration, students are asked to extrapolate from the limited data in the table. In the course of the lesson, they will be introduced to other ways to solve the problem. The end of the lesson returns to the technique of working backwards.

The first two sections involve graphs. Students may need help sorting out issues of scale for the axes.

TEMPERATURE VARIATION

This section does not appear to be related to the main question of unit conversion, but actually it is. Comparing the two graphs should show the students that the actual changes in temperature are the same, irrespective of the units used.

COMPARING TEMPERATURE SCALES

You may discuss with your students the issue of whether the points should lie exactly on a line. (After all, the points in the previous graphs didn't. These are the temperatures Abe read on a sign on a particular day. Why should they form a straight line?) You could also point out that he did not make the readings exactly on the hour. (This is irrelevant, since the time is not involved in this graph.)

If your students expect the points to lie exactly on a straight line, how do they explain the fact that they do not? (The actual reason is that the bank's thermometer seems to round values to the nearest degree, which will mean a small error in some cases. You do not need to explain this to your students, at least not until the end of the lesson.)

The main point of this section is to use the fact that the data are nearly linear to make predictions by using the graph.

Problems 9-10 are not easy. Students should be encouraged to discuss them in their groups. Do not get into a big formal discussion of slope. This will happen in Chapter 8. The point here is just to raise the question.

CONVERTING CELSIUS TO FAHRENHEIT

CONVERTING FAHRENHEIT TO CELSIUS

The conversion methods in problems 11-12 could be represented with arrows, as in Lessons 1 and 4. This will help enormously when trying to reverse the process in problems 16-17.

Any discussion showing the relationship between the formula and the graph in the previous section should be encouraged. (If you graphed values given by the formula, would you get an exactly straight line?)

If students find a discrepancy between what the formula predicts and what the bank's thermometer indicated, be sure to discuss the causes of the discrepancy. (See above.)

Students will derive the formulas from the definitions of Celsius and Fahrenheit in Chapter 10.

8. Is there a temperature where a Fahrenheit and Celsius thermometer show the same number? If so, what is it?

Abe's sister Bea wanted to estimate the Fahrenheit temperature for 17° Celsius. Someone had told her that the best way to remember the Celsius-Fahrenheit relationship was to memorize the fact that 16° Celsius is 61° Fahrenheit. Abe joked, "So 17° Celsius must be 71° Fahrenheit!" Bea replied, "I'll just add one degree. That means 17° Celsius must be 62° Fahrenheit."

9. Explain what Bea did wrong. Use your graph. Give examples explaining to Bea how to make the conversion correctly.

10. Judging from your graph, if you increase the Celsius temperature by one degree, by about how much does the temperature increase on the Fahrenheit scale?

CONVERTING CELSIUS TO FAHRENHEIT

Bea and Abe's parents, Mr. and Mrs. Gral, were planning a trip to Europe, where temperatures are given in Celsius. They asked their children to help them figure out how to convert from Celsius to Fahrenheit.

Abe asked his science teacher, who gave him the following rule: To get the Fahrenheit temperature, multiply the Celsius temperature by 1.8, then add 32.

11.

a. Write a formula for this rule. Use *F* for the Fahrenheit temperature and *C* for the Celsius temperature.

b. Check your formula by using it to convert one of the Celsius temperatures in Abe's table.

Bea looked up the subject in an almanac, which gave these instructions: To get the Fahrenheit temperature, multiply the Celsius temperature by 9, divide by 5, then add 32.

12.

a. Write a formula for this rule.

b. Check your formula by using it to convert one of the Celsius temperatures in Abe's table.

13. Compare the two formulas you wrote. Do you think they always give the same results? Explain, giving examples.

14. Use either method to convert these two Celsius temperatures to Fahrenheit.

a. 20° Celsius = ___ Fahrenheit

b. 21° Celsius = ___ Fahrenheit

15. According to your calculation in problem 14, when you increase the Celsius temperature by one degree, by about how much does the temperature increase on the Fahrenheit scale? Where does this number appear in the formula? Explain.

CONVERTING FAHRENHEIT TO CELSIUS

A journalist from Spain, G. Balear, is staying with the Grals. She is writing an article for a Spanish newspaper about her experiences in the United States. She wants to convert Fahrenheit temperatures to Celsius for her article.

16. The Fahrenheit temperature dropped to 41°. Bea is trying to help Ms. Balear convert it to Celsius. She has the idea of working backwards using the rule from the almanac. Use this method, or another method you think might work, to convert 41° F to Celsius.

17. Describe the method you devised in problem 16 for converting Fahrenheit to Celsius. Explain why it works. Show that it works for other temperatures by using it to convert some of the temperatures in Abe's table.

3.8 SOLUTIONS

8. Yes. (-40, -40)
9. Answers will vary.
   If Bea is right, then 1°C is the same as 1°F. Examples from the graph will show that this is not true.
10. Exact answer is 1.8.
11. a. $F = 1.8°C + 32$
    b. Answers will vary.
12. a. $F = (9/5)C + 32$
    b. Answers will vary.
13. Yes. 9/5 = 1.8
14. a. 68°F
    b. 69.8°F
15. 1.8. This number is the coefficient of *C* in the formula.
16. 5°C
17. $C = (5/9) \cdot (F - 32)$. This formula works because it is only a rearrangement of the first formula.

°F	°C
87	30.56
90	32.22
95	35
93	33.89
81	27.22

THINKING WRITING

3.B Opposites and Reciprocals

OPPOSITES

The function $y = -x$ can be thought of as the *opposite function,* since y and x are opposites.

1. a. Make a function diagram for the function $y = -x$.

b. Describe the in-out lines. (Are they parallel? Do they meet in a single point? If so, where is that point?)

2. To answer these questions, look at the diagram you made for problem 1.

a. As x increases, what happens to y?

b. Are x and y ever equal? Explain.

c. When x increases by 3, what happens to y?

3. Find the number and its opposite that are described. Use trial and error. Look for patterns. Try to develop a shortcut strategy.

a. a number 16 more than its opposite

b. a number 0.5 more than its opposite

c. a number 21 less than its opposite

d. a number A less than its opposite

e. a number 8 more than twice its opposite.

4. **Report** In a few paragraphs, summarize what you learned about opposites and their function diagrams. Include examples.

RECIPROCALS

The function $y = 1/x$ can be thought of as the *reciprocal function,* since y and x are reciprocals.

5. a. Make an in-out table for the function $y = 1/x$, using the following values for x: -5, -4, -3, -2, -1, -0.8, -0.6, -0.4, -0.2, and the opposites of these numbers (0.2, 0.4, etc.)

b. Make a whole-page function diagram for the function.

6. Use the function diagram you made in problem 5. Follow y with your finger as x goes up its number line. Answer these questions.

a. As x increases, what happens to y?

b. Are x and y ever equal?

7. On your function diagram of $y = 1/x$, as x moves up the number line, answer questions (a-h), describing what happens to y. (Does it move up or down? Fast or slowly? From what to what?)

a. when x is a negative number far from 0

b. when x approaches -1

c. when x passes -1

d. when x approaches 0

e. when x passes 0

f. when x approaches 1

g. when x passes 1

h. when x is a large positive number

8. Use your calculator to look for a number and its reciprocal that satisfy these requirements. If you cannot find an exact number, get as close as you can by trial and error. One is impossible.

a. The number is 9 times its reciprocal.

b. The number is 1/9 of its reciprocal.

c. The number equals the opposite of its reciprocal.

d. The number is 3 times its reciprocal.

e. The number is one more than its reciprocal.

9. **Report** Summarize what you learned about reciprocals and their function diagrams. Include examples. (Do not forget to discuss what happens when $x = 0$.)

3.B SOLUTIONS

1. a.

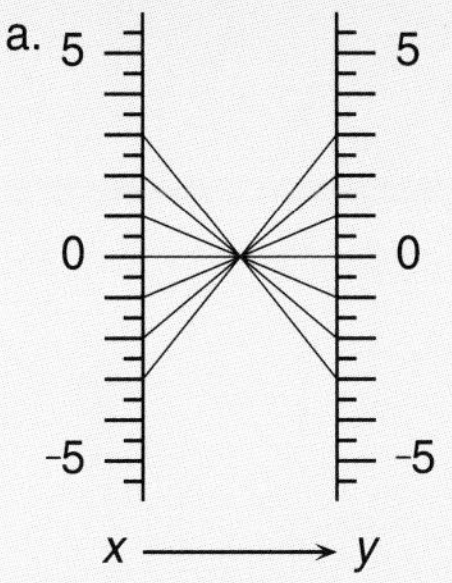

b. The lines all meet at one point on the zero line.

2. a. y decreases.
b. Yes, at zero
c. y decreases by 3.

3. a. 8, -8
b. 1/4, -1/4
c. -21/2, 21/2
d. $-A/2$, $A/2$
e. 8/3, -8/3

4. Answers will vary.

5. a.

x	y
-5	-1/5
-4	-1/4
-3	-1/3
-2	-1/2
-1	-1
-0.8	-1.25
-0.6	-1.67
-0.4	-2.5
-0.2	-5
0.2	5
0.4	2.5
0.6	1.67
0.8	1.25
1	1
2	1/2
3	1/3
4	1/4
5	1/5

(Solutions continued on page 510)

THINKING WRITING

3.B Opposites and Reciprocals

Core Sequence: 1-9

Suitable for Homework: 1-9

Useful for Assessment: 4, 9

What this Assignment is About:

- Relationship between numbers and their opposites
- Relationship between numbers and their reciprocals
- Preview of solving equations

OPPOSITES

This section is considerably easier than the next. If you plan to assign it separately, you can make it more substantial by asking students to attempt to write up a generalized strategy for problems like 3a, b, c. (They may be able to do this even if they cannot answer 3d in formal algebraic notation.)

RECIPROCALS

Neatness and a large scale will pay off in problem 5b.

Problem 7 is important and should be discussed in class before or after the assignments are turned in.

Problem 8c is impossible, as students can see by observing that a (real) number and its reciprocal always have the same sign. Problems 8d and 8e are difficult. Getting within one tenth of the answer is good enough. Point out to your students that scientific calculators allow the user to enter 1.5 [−] 1.5 [x^{-1}] [=], for example, to find the difference between 1.5 and its reciprocal. (Programmable calculators make this even more convenient once you know how to enter a formula and evaluate it for different values of the variable.)

▼ 3.9
Equations and the Cover-Up Method

Core Sequence: 1-8, 10-12

Suitable for Homework: 4-8, 10-15

Useful for Assessment: 10-12

What this Lesson is About:

- Introduction to writing equations
- Introduction to equation solving by symbol manipulation
- Review of division by zero

*W*riting and solving equations will be the focus of the work in Chapters 4, 6, and beyond. In this lesson we apply the idea of working backwards to the solving of linear equations. This work is motivated with a real-world application.

WRITING EQUATIONS

*I*n the long run, it is far more important to learn to write equations than it is to learn how to solve them. This is especially true in the electronic age, as computers and calculators provide many ways of solving equations, but still no way to create them.

LESSON 3.9

Equations and the Cover-Up Method

WRITING EQUATIONS

A seamstress makes dresses for a living. After an illness, she has only \$100 in her business bank account. She takes out a \$1000 loan at Algebank. The interest on the loan is \$15 per month if it gets paid back in the first year. She spends \$720 on dress-making materials, and keeps the rest in her bank account to cover additional costs, such as sewing machine repairs or whatever else may come up. Materials for one dress come to \$20. She makes two dresses a day, four days a week, and spends one day a week selling the dresses and dealing with other matters related to her business.

She sells as many dresses as she can to private customers for \$160 each, and the rest of the dresses to stores, for \$100 each. She needs \$750 a week for living expenses and puts any income over that in her bank account. She hopes to pay back her loan, and to make enough money so that when she needs to buy more materials, she does not have to take out another loan. Can the seamstress meet her goals? How could she improve her financial situation?

One way to think about a problem like this one is to break it down into smaller problems, and to write and solve equations for those. For example, let's write an expression that would tell us how much money the seamstress puts in her bank account every week.

1. **Exploration** Assume the seamstress has x private customers a week. Answer the following questions for one week, in terms of x.

a. How many dresses does she sell to stores?

b. How much money does she receive from private customers?

c. How much money does she receive from stores?

d. What is the total amount of money she receives every week?

e. How much of it is she able to put in her bank account? Simplify your answer.

If you answered the questions correctly, you should have ended up with the expression $60x + 50$ for the amount she deposits every week as a function of x. Let's say that she would like this amount to be \$300. This gives us the equation $60x + 50 = 300$. Remember that x is the number of private customers per week. We can now find out how many private customers she would need to deposit \$300 per week. All we need to do is solve the equation.

SOLVING EQUATIONS

Definition: Finding all the values of a variable that make an equation true is called *solving the equation.*

You have already solved equations by trial and error. The *cover-up method* is another technique for solving equations. It is based on the idea of working backwards.

Example 1: $60x + 50 = 300$

With your finger, cover up the term that has the x in it. The equation looks like

$$\square + 50 = 300.$$

Clearly, what's in the box is 250. So

$$60x = 250.$$

Think of a division that is related to this multiplication, and you will see that

$$x = 250/60$$

or $$\mathbf{x = 4.1666....}$$

So in order to deposit \$300 a week, the seamstress needs to have more than four private customers a week.

3.9 SOLUTIONS

1. a. $8 - x$
   b. $160x$
   c. $100(8 - x)$
   d. $160x + 100(8 - x)$
   e. $160x + 800 - 100x - 750 = 60x + 50$

Example 2: This one is about a more complicated equation.

$$5 + \frac{3x - 1}{4} = 7$$

Cover up the expression $\frac{3x-1}{4}$. You get

$$5 + \square = 7.$$

Whatever is hidden must be equal to 2. So

$$\frac{3x - 1}{4} = 2$$

Now cover up $3x - 1$ with your finger.

$$\frac{\square}{4} = 2$$

What is under your finger must be 8. So

$$3x - 1 = 8.$$

Cover up the term containing x.

$$\square - 1 = 8$$

What's under your finger must equal 9. So

$$3x = 9$$

and $\mathbf{x = 3.}$

2. Check the solutions to examples 1 and 2 by substituting them in the original equations.

Solve each equation. Use the cover-up method, then check each answer by substituting.

3. a. $3(x - 10) = 15$
b. $3(x + 10) = 15$
c. $3 + \frac{x}{10} = 15$
d. $\frac{18}{x} + 12 = 15$

4. a. $34 - \frac{2x + 6}{2} = 4$
b. $34 - \frac{2x + 6}{2} = -4$

5. a. $21 = 12 + \frac{3x}{8}$ b. $12 = 21 + \frac{3x}{8}$

6. a. $5 + \frac{x}{6} = 17$ b. $5 + \frac{6}{x} = 17$
c. $5 - \frac{x}{6} = 17$ d. $5 - \frac{6}{x} = 17$

7. a. $3 = \frac{12}{x + 1}$ b. $3 = \frac{x + 1}{12}$
c. $3 = \frac{12}{x + 7}$ d. $3 = \frac{x + 7}{12}$

8. Make up an equation like the ones above that has as its solution
a. 4; b. -4; c. $\frac{1}{4}$.

Since the cover-up method is based on covering up the part of the equation that includes an x, it can be used only in equations like the ones above, where x appears only once. In other equations, for example

$$160x + 100(8 - x) - 750 = 300,$$

you cannot use the cover-up method, unless you simplify first.

9. Find out how many private customers the seamstress needs every week so that, at the end of four weeks, she has enough money in her bank account to pay back her loan and buy dress-making materials for the next four weeks. Use equations and the cover-up method if you can. Otherwise, use any other method. In either case, explain how you arrive at your answers.

*I*n this lesson, make sure the students can work together on problem 1. The purpose is simply to introduce students to the idea of writing an equation to solve a problem. They will get much more practice with that later, and you should not expect mastery at this early date. If they have trouble doing it, you should help them. Do not let this take too much time, as it is simply a motivator for the main part of the lesson.

SOLVING EQUATIONS

*T*he cover-up method is related to working backwards, to the concepts of inverse operations, and to reciprocals and opposites. Demonstrate some examples and make sure students understand the ones given in the text.

*A*ssign problem 9 if you want your students to analyze the seamstress problem fully. Allow them to use whatever techniques they want. Trial and error and making organized tables are likely to be more widespread techniques than equation solving at this point. This is fine. However, make sure that the various approaches are discussed, so students can learn from each other.

*B*ecause the problem is so complicated, students may forget one or another of the details (for example, the interest on the loan or the fact that for the next four-week period she will need materials for only 28 dresses). Nevertheless, it should not be too difficult to reach the correct answer, particularly if students are allowed to work in groups.

3.9 SOLUTIONS

3. a. 15
b. -5
c. 120
d. 6

4. a. 27
b. 35

5. a. 24
b. -24

6. a. 72
b. 0.5
c. -72
d. -0.5

7. a. 3
b. 35
c. -3
d. 29

8. Answers will vary.

9. To pay back her loan plus interest, she needs to make $1015 after four weeks, or $253.75 a week. Dress-making materials cost $160 a week ($20 per dress, 8 dresses a week). So for one week, she needs to put $413.75 (253.75 + 160) in the bank. Now solve the equation for x, $60x + 50 = 413.75$. We get $x = 6.0625$. She needs more than six private customers a week.

REVIEW DIVIDING BY ZERO

*M*ake sure to discuss the difference between problems 11 and 12. In one case, there is no possible quotient; in the other, there is an infinite number of them. In neither case is there a unique possibility, which is why division by zero is not defined.

DISCOVERY BE PRODUCTIVE

*T*his section does not require having done **Thinking/Writing 3.A**, as it does not rely on functions. (However, your students will need to use the table of letter values.)

REVIEW DIVIDING BY ZERO

10. Explain, using multiplication, why $20/5 = 4$.

11. Explain, using multiplication, why 20/0 is not defined. (Hint: Start by writing $20/0 = q$. Write a related multiplication. What must q be?)

12. Explain, using multiplication, why 0/0 is not defined. (Hint: Start by writing $0/0 = q$. Write a related multiplication. What must q be? Could it be something else?)

DISCOVERY BE PRODUCTIVE

Say that the product of a word is the product of the numbers corresponding to its letters. (For the letter values, see **Thinking/Writing 3.A**.) For example, the word `optic` has value

$$15 \cdot 16 \cdot 20 \cdot 9 \cdot 3 = 129{,}600$$

13. What is the product of the word `ALGEBRA`?

14. Find words whose product is as close to one million as possible.

15. Find words having these products. (Hint: It would help to find the prime factors of the numbers.)

a. 6 b. 8
c. 12 d. 14
e. 15 f. 16
g. 20 h. 24
i. 35 j. 455
k. 715 l. 2185
m. 106,029 n. 4,410,000

3.9 SOLUTIONS

10. Multiply both sides by 5. The equation holds, i.e. 20 = 20.
11. $20/0 = q$. A related multiplication is $q \cdot 0 = 20$. There is no number, q, that multiplies 0 to give 20. Therefore, q is not defined, which means 20/0 is not defined.
12. $0/0 = q$. A related multiplication is $q \cdot 0 = 0$. q can be any real number since any number multiplied by 0 will give 0. Since q has many values, q is not defined.
13. 15, 120
14. The word *beddy-bye*, which is not in any dictionary, has a product of exactly one million. It is not likely that any dictionary word does.
15. Some answers—others may be possible:
    a. FA, CAB
    b. BAD, DAB, AHA
    c. FAB, CAD, LA
    d. BAG, AN, GAB
    e. ACE, O
    f. DAD, PA, BAH
    g. AT, BABE, ADE
    h. FAD, AX, LAB
    i. AGE
    j. MAGE, GAME, GEM
    k. MAKE
    l. AWES, SEW
    m. QUICK
    n. OXYGEN

LESSON

3.10 Combining Functions

You will need:

graph paper

DIAGRAMS OF COMBINED FUNCTIONS

Function diagrams can be used to show the result of combining functions. Here are two simple functions. One function doubles x. The other function adds 1 to x.

$y_1 = 2x$ $y_2 = x + 1$

Notation: The 2 in the name y_2 is called a *subscript*. It is written lower and smaller than the y. It does *not* mean *multiply by 2* or *square*. It is just a way to distinguish two variables that would otherwise have the same name.

1. Draw function diagrams for y_1 and y_2.

This two-step function diagram shows one way of combining y_1 and y_2. First, double x. Then add 1 to the result. The y value of y_1 becomes the new x value for y_2.

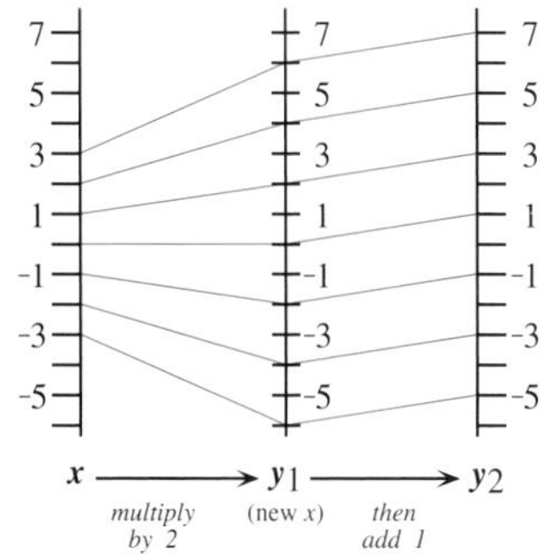

These two steps can be combined as shown in this one-step function diagram.

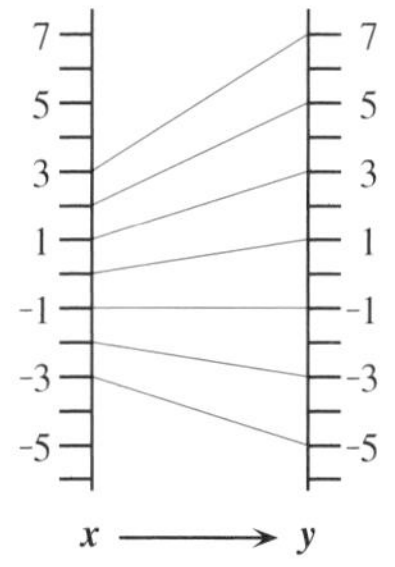

2. Write a rule for this function diagram.

The functions y_1 and y_2 can also be combined in the other order: First, add 1 to x. Then double the result. The y value of y_2 becomes the new x value for y_1.

3. Draw a two-step function diagram showing the combination of the functions in this order.
4. Summarize your two-step function diagram in a one-step function diagram.
5. Write a rule for the one-step function diagram you drew.
6. Does the order in which we combine the functions matter? Explain.

These problems are about the following two functions.

$y_1 = -3x$ $y_2 = x + 2$

7. Show a two-step function diagram, combining the functions by performing y_1 first and then y_2.

▼ 3.10 Combining Functions

Core Sequence: 1-23

Suitable for Homework: 7-14, 19-23

Useful for Assessment: 6, 11, 22

What this Lesson is About:

- Composition of functions
- Preview of inverse functions
- Review of the distributive law
- Review of the commutative law
- Review of inverse operations, reciprocals, and opposites

This lesson wraps up much of the diverse work of this chapter by addressing the underlying mathematics. Do not be intimidated by the title; this chapter has provided plenty of preparation for students to handle the concepts presented here. Their exposure to the arrows tool and function diagrams is one of the main reasons these concepts are accessible to first-year algebra students.

At the same time the lesson provides review of such basic ideas as the commutative and distributive laws.

We do not use functional notation, as it would not be used enough in this course to justify the time and effort needed to learn it. On the other hand, the y_1, y_2 notation is the one used on some graphing calculators, and subscripts will be used in Chapter 5 when discussing sequences.

3.10 SOLUTIONS

1.

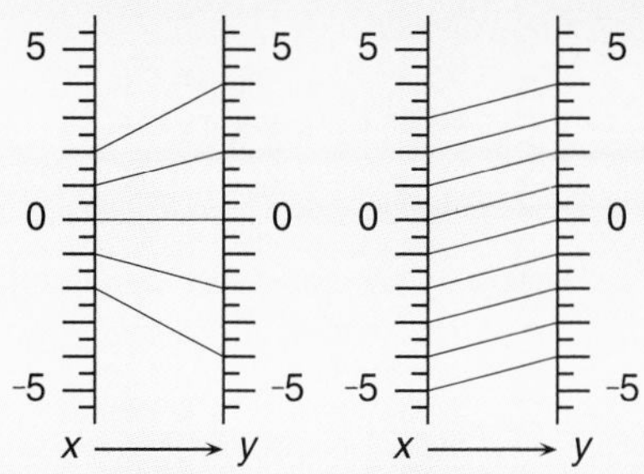

$y_1 = 2x$ $y_2 = x + 1$

2. $y = 2x + 1$

3.

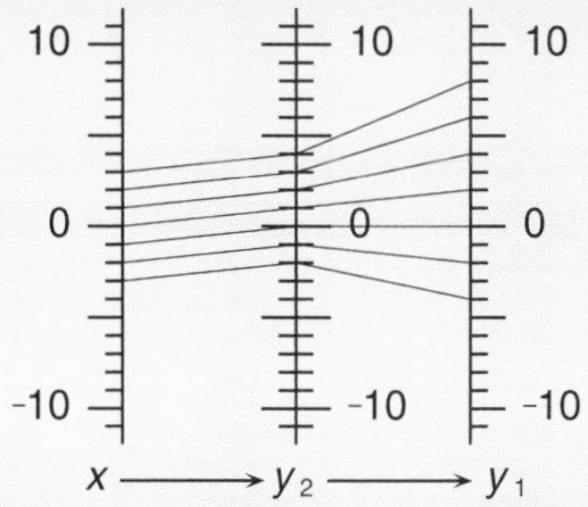

4.

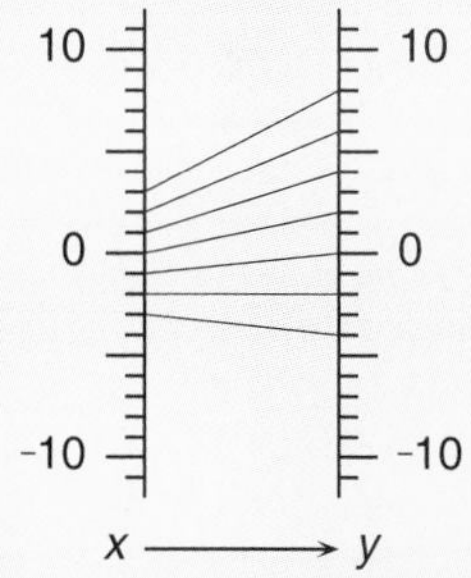

5. $y = 2x + 2$
6. Yes. From #2 and 5, we can see that switching the order in which we combine functions results in two different functions.
7.

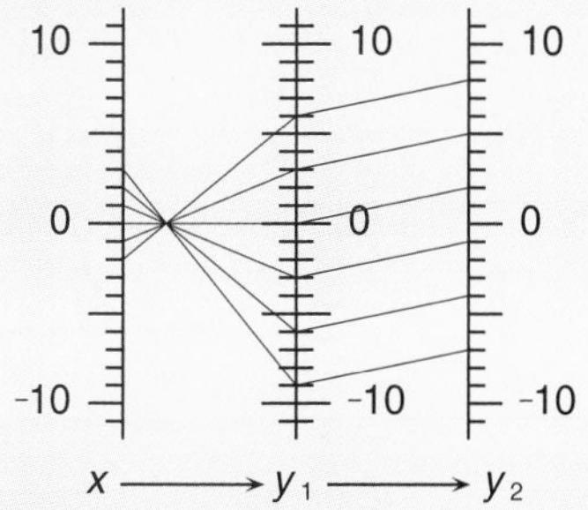

DIAGRAMS OF COMBINED FUNCTIONS

After doing problems 1-10, you may have a class discussion of the same problems with the help of the arrow representation, using variables. For example, for problems 7 and 9:

$$x \xrightarrow{(y_1)} -3x \xrightarrow{(y_2)} -3x + 2$$
$$x \xrightarrow{(y_2)} x + 2 \xrightarrow{(y_1)} -3(x + 2)$$

However, do not start with this. Give students a chance to come up with their own generalization first.

INVERSE ACTIONS

INVERSE FUNCTIONS

Problem 15 can be explored at many levels. At the lowest level it is just a review of inverse operations. Some of your students may be ready to take this further and use more complicated functions (such as linear functions of the form $y = mx + b$). Obviously, some functions would be too difficult for many students to work with at this stage. For example, do not involve the whole class in a discussion of the inverse function for $y = x^2 + 3x$, or of which functions have and do not have inverses. These ideas are beyond what can be expected at this level.

Problem 16 reviews reciprocals and the relationship between multiplication and division.

8. Summarize your two-step diagram in a one-step diagram and write the function that corresponds to your one-step function diagram.

9. Repeat problems 7 and 8, but this time combine the two functions by performing y_2 first, followed by y_1.

10. Did the resulting function change, when you changed the order in which you combined the two functions? Explain.

11. **Exploration** Sometimes you can combine two functions in either order and the resulting function is the same. Find pairs of functions that have this property. You may use function diagrams to verify your answer. Discuss any patterns you notice.

INVERSE ACTIONS

The inverse of an action is the action that undoes it. For example, suppose you were leaving home in the car. You would perform these four actions.

ACTION 1: Open the car door.
ACTION 2: Get into the car.
ACTION 3: Close the door.
ACTION 4: Start the car.

If, before driving away, you suddenly realized that you forgot something, you would have to undo all these actions. You would undo the actions in the reverse order:

First, UNDO ACTION 4: Stop the car.
Second, UNDO ACTION 3: Open the door.
Next, UNDO ACTION 2: Get out of the car.
Last, UNDO ACTION 1: Close the car door.

12. Describe how to undo these actions.
a. In the morning, you put on your socks, then put on your shoes. What do you do in the evening?
b. To take a break from this homework, you close your math book, stand up from your desk, turn on the television, and sit down on the sofa. What do you do to get back to work?

13. Al believes that the way to undo the actions *open the car window; stick your head out* is *close the car window; pull your head in.* Comment on this idea.

14. Create your own example of inverse actions.

INVERSE FUNCTIONS

15. **Exploration** Choose any function and make a function diagram for it. Then draw the mirror image of this function diagram. What is the function associated with the mirror image? How is it related to the original function? Try this with several functions. Write about any patterns you notice.

The inverse of a function is a function that undoes it. For example, look at these two input-output tables.

x	y
2	6
-1	-3
4	12

x	y
6	2
-3	-1
12	4

16. a. What happens when you use an output from the first table as the input for the second table?
b. What two functions do you think are represented by these two tables? How are the functions related?

3.10 SOLUTIONS

8.

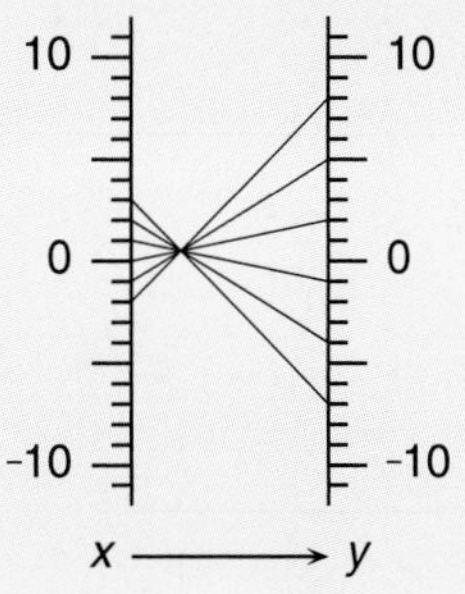

$y = -3x + 2$

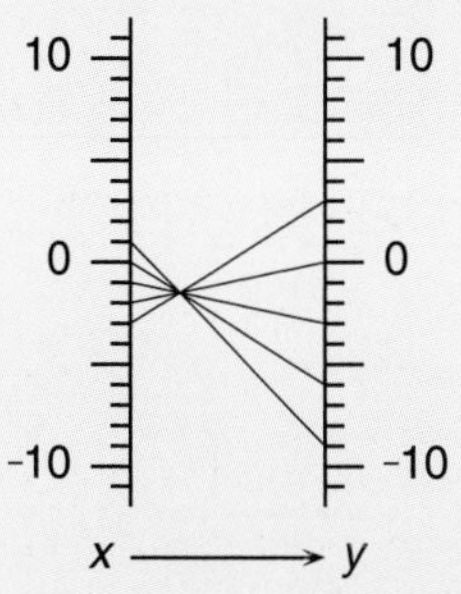

$y = -3(x + 2)$

9.

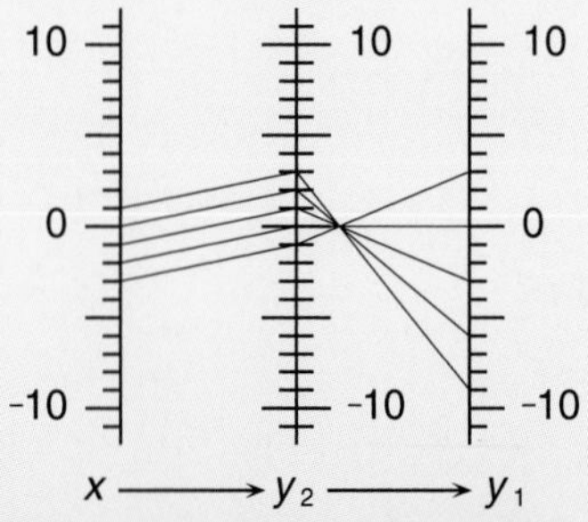

10. Yes. The order of operations is important. Performing y_1 and then y_2 is the same as multiplying a number by -3 and then adding 2. On the other hand, reversing the order is the same as adding 2 to a number and then multiplying by -3. The results are not the same.

11. Answers will vary.
Any pairs of functions of the form $y = x + b$ or $y = mx$ will work.

12. a. Take off your shoes, take off your socks.
b. Get up from the sofa, turn off the TV, sit down at your desk, open your math book.

13. If Al closes the window first, his head would get stuck.

14. Answers will vary.

15. Answers will vary.
The function for the mirror image is the inverse function, i.e. it undoes the effect of the first function. So the final output is the same as the original input.

If $y_1 = 2x$ and $y_2 = (1/2)x$, a two-step function diagram shows that y_2 undoes y_1.

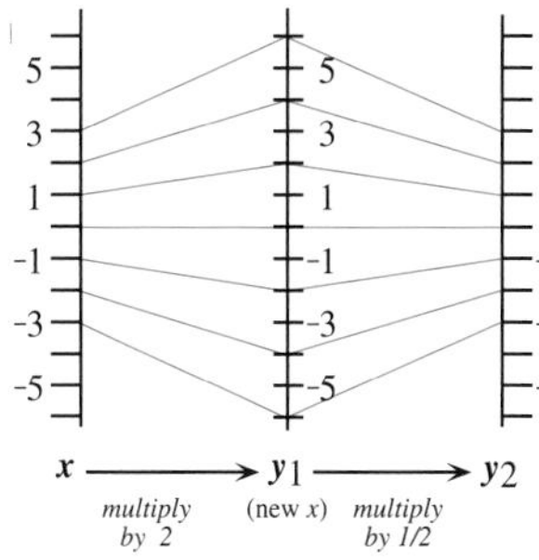

This is shown dramatically when the two-step diagram is summarized in a one-step diagram.

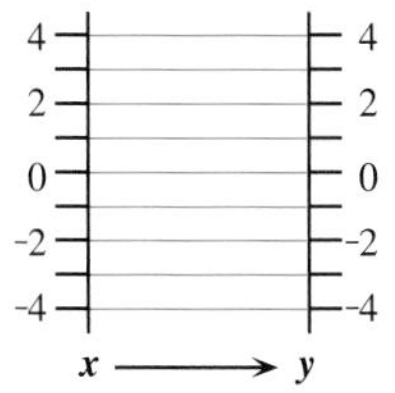

A function y_1 performs the following operations on a number.

Multiply the number by 3, subtract 1.

17. Write in words what the inverse function does. (Call it y_2.)

18. a. Write a rule in the form $y_1 =$ for the original function.

b. Write a rule in the form $y_2 =$ for the inverse function.

19. a. Make separate function diagrams for y_1 and y_2.

b. Describe how the diagrams you made are related.

20. Make a two-step function diagram for the combination of y_1 and y_2.

21. Make a one-step function diagram summarizing your two-step diagram. Would it matter if you combined y_1 and y_2 in the other order?

22. **Summary** Write a summary of what you have learned in this lesson about combining function diagrams, especially those of inverse functions. Use examples.

23. Find functions that are their own inverses. What do you notice about their function diagrams? Explain.

*P*roblems 17-21 explore the inverse function for $y = 3x - 1$. Do not expect all students to be able to generalize from this one example. What students should have mastered and reflect in problem 22 is that: inverse functions have mirror image diagrams; combining inverse functions leads to the function $y = x$ (the identity function, though this vocabulary is not necessary at this stage); and that reciprocals and opposites are useful in finding inverse functions.

MORE INVERSE FUNCTIONS

*T*his is difficult. Some examples can be constructed by working backwards: thinking about what must be true of the function diagram of a function that is its own inverse, creating such a diagram, and finding its function.

*S*tudents who have done **Thinking/Writing 3.A** may remember that functions like $y = b - x$ are their own inverses.

3.10 SOLUTIONS

16. a. We get back the original input.
    b. $y = 3x$ and $y = (1/3)x$. The two functions have coefficients that are reciprocals of each other. One function is the inverse of the other.

17. Add 1 to the number, divide the result by 3. Or, add 1 to the number, multiply the result by 1/3.

18. a. $y_1 = 3x - 1$
    b. $y_2 = (x + 1)/3 = (1/3)(x + 1)$

19. a.

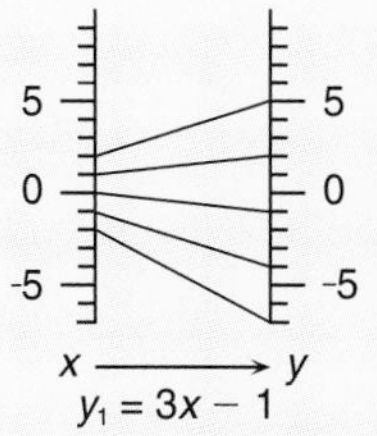

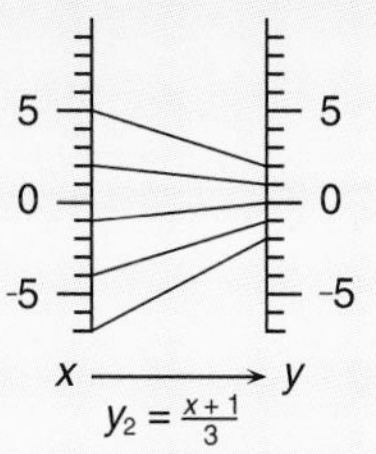

b. The y_1 axis is a line of symmetry. If we fold the paper along the y_1 axis, all the lines will match up. Also, the output of y_2 is the same as the input to y_1.

20.

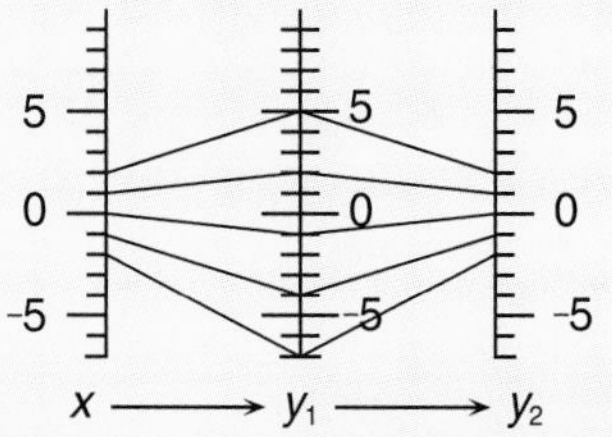

21.

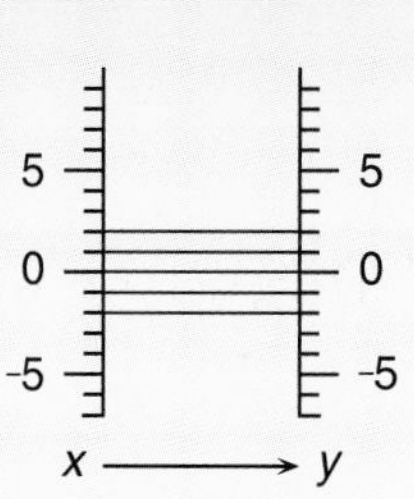

22. Answers will vary.

▼ 3.11
Math on Another Planet

Core Sequence: none of this lesson

Suitable for Homework: 9-17

Useful for Assessment: 17

What this Lesson is About:

- Opposites and reciprocals
- The properties of zero and one
- Modular arithmetic

This lesson should appeal to the students' imagination and show that mathematics can be interesting when it is frivolous, as much or more as when it is serious or useful.

The properties of zero and one in addition and multiplication, respectively, are not very interesting to students (or teachers) in the context of the real numbers. After eight or nine years of exposure to the fact that $2 + 0 = 2$, it loses its appeal. In this lesson, the identity element for mathematical structures other than the real numbers provides a fresh environment in which to think about one and zero. In addition, opposites and reciprocals are approached in an unfamiliar context.

LESSON 3.11

Math on Another Planet

SMALL POCKETS

On the treeless planet of Glosia, the currency consists of florins, ecus, and ducats. *One florin is worth two ecus, and one ecu is worth two ducats.* Since there is no paper, there is no paper money, and the people of Glosia have to carry coins everywhere. King Evariste VII, being immensely rich, must wear bloomers with enormous reinforced pockets to hold his money.

One day the King realizes that there is a new trend in Glosian fashion. Elegant men and women wear only small pockets. Evariste VII, not one to be left behind by the great movements of style, decides to institute a drastic economic reform by enacting a strange law: *One ducat is worth two florins!* (The old rules are not changed.) When you realize trades can be made in either direction, you can see how the King's brilliant legislation will abolish poverty forever.

The people of Glosia are ecstatic. With the new system, one may have a fortune in one's pockets, and yet never carry more than three coins! One can be rich and fashionable at the same time. For example, if you own eight ecus, you can go to the bank, and trade them in for four florins. These can be traded again, for two ducats, which equal one ecu, which will certainly fit in your pocket.

1. **Exploration**
   a. The King trades his coins at the bank, according to their official value, with the object of having as few coins as possible in the tiny pocket of his slinky new pants. He starts with 1000 florins. What does he end up with?
   b. Prince Enbel has one ducat. He buys a toastereo (a popular appliance which, unfortunately, does not make coffee), costing 50 ecus. If he is given the fewest coins possible, how much change does he get?
   c. Princess Lisa has one ecu. She wins the first prize in a contest in *Names* Magazine. The prize is one ducat, one ecu, and one florin. She now has four coins, but they won't fit into her pocket. What does she have after trading them in to get as few coins as possible? (The second prize would have been a T-shirt with the *Names* logo and no pockets at all.)
   d. Sol Grundy has no money. He gets a job at the toastereo store, earning one florin per day, seven days a week. Since his pockets are fashionably small, he trades his money as often as possible in order to have as few coins as possible. If he starts his new job on Monday, how much does he have each day of the week? The next week? (Assume he doesn't spend any money.)

3.11 S O L U T I O N S

1. a. e, d
   b. e, f
   c. e
   d.

Date	Amount
Mo	f
Tu	d
We	d + f
Th	e
Fr	e + f
Sa	e + d
Su	e + f + d

For next week, Sol Grundy has the same amount of money.

2. f, d, e, d + f, d + e, e + f, e + f + d

3.

Sum	f	e	d	d + e	d + f	e + f	e + f + d
f	d	f + e	d + f	e + f + d	e	d + e	f
e	f + e	f	d + e	d + f	e + f + d	d	e
d	d + f	d + e	e	f	e + f	e + f + d	d
d + e	e + f + d	d + f	f	e + f	d	e	d + e
d + f	e	e + f + d	e + f	d	d + e	f	d + f
e + f	e + d	d	e + f + d	e	f	f + d	e + f
e + f + d	f	e	d	d + e	d + f	e + f	e + f + d

2. Make a list of the amounts of money one can have that cannot be reduced to a smaller number of coins. (Hint: There are seven possible amounts.) One of the amounts is $(d + e)$.
3. Make an addition table for Glosian money. It should be a seven-by-seven table, with a row and column for each of the amounts you found in problem 2. For example, your table should show that $(d + e) + d = f$.
4. One of the seven amounts you found in problem 3 can be considered to be the "zero" of Glosian money, since adding it to a collection of coins does not change the collection's value (after trading to get the smallest possible number of coins). Which amount is the zero for Glosian money?
5. The opposite of an amount is the amount you add to it to get the zero. Find the opposite of each of the seven amounts in problem 3.

A LONG MONTH

The King can never remember which month it is and how many days the month has. He decides to start a new calendar, with a single infinite month, the month of *Evary,* named after himself. This is what the calendar looks like.

Evary						
Mo	Tu	We	Th	Fr	Sa	Su
			1	2	3	4
5	6	7	8	9	10	11
12	13	14	15	16	17	18
19	20	21	22	23	24	25
26	27	28	29	30	31	32
33	34	35	36	37	38	...

6. What day of the week will it be on Evary 100th? Explain how you figured it out.

The King is so pleased with the new calendar that he decides to invent a new kind of math. He calls it *Calendar Math.* In Calendar Math, Monday + Tuesday →

$$5 + 6 = 11 \rightarrow \text{Sunday},$$

or, more briefly, Mo + Tu = Su.

7. Check whether, if you picked different numbers for Monday (such as 12, 19, etc.) and Tuesday (13, 20, etc.), you would still get Sunday for the sum.
8. Make an addition table for Calendar Math. It should be a seven-by-seven table, with the days of the week along the left side and across the top and their sums inside the table.

*T*he mathematical content underlying this lesson is not a traditional part of the pre-college curriculum. Yet, the ideas of identity and inverse element and the mathematical structures known as groups and fields are the backbone of arithmetic and algebra. The approach presented here proves that these ideas do not have to be presented in the super-abstract and dull manner that was too often the case with the *New Math* of the sixties and seventies.

SMALL POCKETS

*T*his is the most alien-looking section. It can be skipped if you are uncomfortable with it. It is not needed in order to do the next section which is based on numbers. It would be a good idea for you to work out the problems before attempting them with the class. (They are not difficult, just unusual.)

*T*his section requires a lot of reading. Perhaps students should be encouraged to take turns reading aloud in their groups.

*P*roblem 1 requires a certain amount of careful computation. The computations are almost purely algebraic and involve very little work with numbers. This Exploration previews all of problems 2-5.

3.11 SOLUTIONS

4. e + f + d
5.

Amount	Opposite
f	d + e
d	e + f
d + f	e
e	d + f
e + f	d
e + d	f
e + f + d	e + f + d

6. The 100th day in Evary is a Friday. One way to do this problem is to extend the calendar and fill in the days. Another way is to use modular arithmetic. The cycle starts on Thursday and ends on a Wednesday. If we divide 100 by 7, then a remainder of 1 corresponds to Thursday, 2 to Friday, 3 to Saturday, 4 to Sunday, 5 to Monday, 6 to Tuesday, and 0 to Wednesday. A similar method to this is to subtract 4 from 100. Then divide the result by 7. A remainder of 1 corresponds to Monday, 2 to Tuesday, 3 to Wednesday, 4 to Thursday, 5 to Friday, 6 to Saturday, and 0 to Sunday.
7. Yes, we still get a Sunday.
8.

Sum	Mo	Tu	We	Th	Fr	Sa	Su
Mo	Sa	Su	Mo	Tu	We	Th	Fr
Tu	Su	Mo	Tu	We	Th	Fr	Sa
We	Mo	Tu	We	Th	Fr	Sa	Su
Th	Tu	We	Th	Fr	Sa	Su	Mo
Fr	We	Th	Fr	Sa	Su	Mo	Tu
Sa	Th	Fr	Sa	Su	Mo	Tu	We
Su	Fr	Sa	Su	Mo	Tu	We	Th

A LONG MONTH

*T*here are computational shortcuts possible. For example, in problem 11,

Mo + Mo → 5 + 5 → 10 → Sa.
So, Mo + Mo + Mo = Mo + Sa →
5 + 3 = 8 → Th.

*I*n problem 14 point out that Calendar Zero, just like zero among the real numbers, does not have a reciprocal. Also, zero times any number equals zero.

*B*oth problems 11-12 and also 16 point out the cyclical nature of this mathematical structure. A subtle point, probably too difficult for students to discover or even understand, is that the addition table for Calendar Math has *exactly* the same underlying structure as the addition table of ducats, ecus, and florins, in the previous section.

*Y*ou will find masters for the addition and multiplication tables for problems 3, 8, and 13 in the back of this Teacher's Edition.

*F*or problem 17, you may ask students to investigate whether the commutative, associative, and distributive laws hold in Calendar Math. You can also introduce the term *identity element* to describe 0 for addition and 1 for multiplication and ask that these be included in the summary, along with information on opposites and reciprocals.

9. *Calendar Zero* is a day of the week such that, when you add it to any other day, you get that other day for the answer. What day is Calendar Zero?

10. Find the *Calendar Opposite* for each day of the week. That is the day you add to a given day to get Calendar Zero. If a day does not have an opposite, or is its own opposite, explain.

11. Calculate.

a. Mo + Mo
b. Mo + Mo + Mo
c. Mo + Mo + Mo + Mo, etc.

12. How many times do you add Mo to itself to get back Mo?

13. Make a multiplication table for Calendar Math. Here is an example of a result that would appear in it.
Mo · Tu → 5 · 6 = 30 → Fr,
so, Mo · Tu = Fr.

14. What is special about Calendar Zero in multiplication?

15. *Calendar One* is a day of the week such that when you multiply it by any other day, you get that other day for the answer. What day is Calendar One?

16. The *Calendar Reciprocal* of a day is the day you multiply it by to get Calendar One. Find the Calendar Reciprocal for each day. If a day does not have a reciprocal, or is its own reciprocal, explain.

17. Calculate Su^2, Su^3, etc. What power of Su is equal to Su?

18. **Summary** Summarize Calendar Math.

3.11 SOLUTIONS

9. Calendar Zero is Wednesday.

10.

Day of Week	Calendar Opposite
Mo	Fr
Tu	Th
We	We
Th	Tu
Fr	Mo
Sa	Su
Su	Sa

11. a. Mo + Mo = Sa
b. Mo + Mo + Mo = Th
c. Mo + Mo + Mo + Mo = Tu
d. Mo + Mo + Mo + Mo + Mo = Su
e. Mo + Mo + Mo + Mo + Mo + Mo = Fr
f. Mo + Mo + Mo + Mo + Mo + Mo + Mo = We
g. Mo + Mo + Mo + Mo + Mo + Mo + Mo + Mo = Mo

12. 8 times

13.

Times	Mo	Tu	We	Th	Fr	Sa	Su
Mo	Su	Fr	We	Mo	Sa	Th	Tu
Tu	Fr	Th	We	Tu	Mo	Su	Sa
We	We	We	We	We	We	We	We
Th	Mo	Tu	We	Th	Fr	Sa	Su
Fr	Sa	Mo	We	Fr	Su	Tu	Th
Sa	Th	Su	We	Sa	Tu	Fr	Mo
Su	Tu	Sa	We	Su	Th	Mo	Fr

14. The result of all the multiplications with Calendar Zero is Calendar Zero.

15. Calendar One is Thursday.

16.

Day of Week	Calendar Reciprocal
Mo	Sa
Tu	Tu
We	none
Th	Th
Fr	Su
Sa	Mo
Su	Fr

By definition, Calendar Zero has no reciprocal and Calendar One is its own reciprocal.

17. Su^2 = Fr
Su^3 = Th
Su^4 = Su
Now the cycle repeats.

18. Answers will vary. Students should give and define Calendar Zero, Opposite, One, and Reciprocal.

LESSON 3.12

Similar Figures

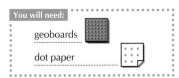

You will need:
- geoboards
- dot paper

EQUIVALENT FRACTIONS

1. Using a rubber band, connect the origin and (6, 9). The line misses most geoboard pegs, but it goes *exactly* over two of them (in addition to the pegs it connects). What are their coordinates?

Problem 1 provides a way to find equivalent fractions on the geoboard. If you think of (6, 9) as representing 6/9, you have found two other fractions equivalent to it, making this a set of three equivalent geoboard fractions.

2. **Exploration** Find as many sets of equivalent geoboard fractions as possible. Do not use zero in the numerator or denominator. There are 56 fractions distributed in 19 sets. Do not include sets that consist of just one fraction.

ENLARGING WITHOUT DISTORTION

3. a. Make the face of an alien with rubber bands on your geoboard. The whole face needs to fit in the bottom left quarter of the board. In other words, none of the coordinates can be greater than 5. Don't make it too complicated.

b. Make a record of the coordinates you used. You will need those in the next problems.

c. Copy the face on dot paper.

4. Doubling the x-coordinates and leaving the y-coordinates the same, make a copy of your alien's face on dot paper. This is called the $(2x, y)$ copy.

5. Repeat problem 4, but this time leave the x-coordinates as in the original and double the y-coordinates only. This is called the $(x, 2y)$ copy.

6. Repeat problem 4 again, with both x- and y-coordinates doubled. This is called the $(2x, 2y)$ copy.

7. **Summary** Write a paragraph answering these questions: Which of the copies looks most like an enlarged version of the original? How are the other copies distorted?

8. Write a story about the alien's adventures, explaining why its face went through these changes.

9. Enlarge the following figures without distortion. Explain how you did it.

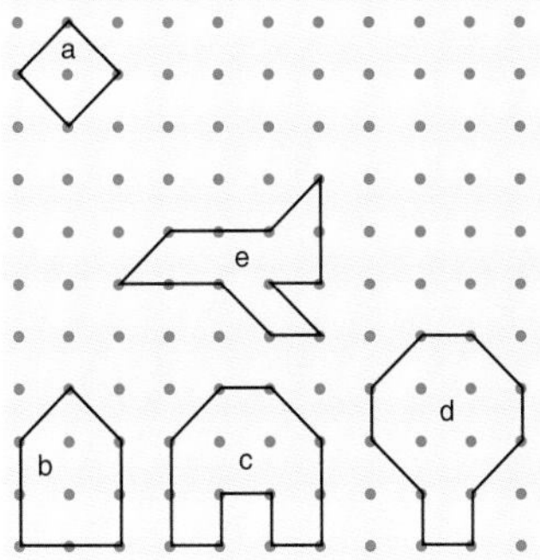

▼ 3.12 Similar Figures

Core Sequence: 1-7, 10-16

Suitable for Homework: 3-9, 15-17, 20

Useful for Assessment: 16

What this Lesson is About:
- Review of equivalent fractions
- Preview of similar figures
- Proportional thinking

This lesson prepares students for several lessons on direct variation in Chapter 4 and on proportional thinking and slope throughout the course.

EQUIVALENT FRACTIONS

Problem 2 will require a lot of work, but it is worth doing, as it provides a review of the key mathematical concept underlying this lesson. It is a good activity for collaboration with a partner or a group.

If students seem to be having trouble with it, remind them to use the method shown in problem 1 to find the sets.

ENLARGING WITHOUT DISTORTION

This section establishes an intuitive foundation for the idea of similar figures and proportionality. Do not expect full mastery of these ideas. We will return to them many times throughout the course.

3.12 SOLUTIONS

1. (2, 3), (4, 6)
2. Answers will vary.
3. Answers will vary.
4. Answers will vary. This will stretch the alien along the x-axis.
5. Answers will vary. This will stretch the alien along the y-axis.
6. Answers will vary. This is an enlargement of the alien without any distortion.
7. See #4-6.
8. Answers will vary.
9. One way to do this is to make a list of the coordinates. Double, triple, etc. each coordinate. This represents an enlargement without distortion.

You may use class discussion of problem 7 to generalize to $(3x, 3y)$ or $(4.5x, 4.5y)$ copies, but do not be heavy-handed about it, as the ideas are still new.

Problem 9 is quite difficult for many students. Their best bet is to use the $(2x, 2y)$ technique. If they want to do it visually, they should make sure every side is enlarged by the same ratio. (Doubling is easiest.)

SIMILAR RECTANGLES

Problems 10-14 analyze one set of three similar rectangles. The ideas are related to the work in the previous two sections. The number hinted at in problem 14 is the ratio of the sides of the rectangles.

You should lead a whole-class discussion of the different methods for determining whether fractions are equivalent, including the ones suggested in the text.

Problem 17 is challenging. Students may be able to solve it by noticing that the long side is twice as long as the short side in each rectangle. They can see this even if they don't know how long the sides are. One way is to divide each rectangle into two squares.

SIMILAR RECTANGLES

Definition: When one figure can be obtained from another by enlarging it or shrinking it without distortion, the figures are said to be *similar.*

10. Make a rectangle having vertices at (0, 0), (4, 0), (4, 6), and (0, 6). Find a smaller rectangle that is similar to it by finding a number you can multiply the given coordinates by to get whole number coordinates that will fit on the geoboard. Sketch both on the same figure.

11. Repeat problem 10, but find a larger rectangle that is similar to the given one. Sketch it on the same figure as in problem 10.

The following questions are about the three rectangles from problems 10 and 11.

12. Connect the origin with the opposite vertex in the largest rectangle. Does your rubber band pass through vertices of the other two rectangles?

13. What are the length and width of each rectangle? How are they related to each other?

14. Can you think of a *single number* that tells what all three rectangles have in common?

Here are two ways to tell whether two rectangles are similar.

Geoboard diagonal method: Make both rectangles in the bottom left of a geoboard, with one vertex on the origin, and sides along the x- and y-axes. Then connect the origin to the opposite vertex of the larger rectangle. If the diagonal you created passes exactly over the vertex of the smaller rectangle, they are similar.

Calculator division method: Check whether the ratio of the dimensions is the same in both the rectangles.

Example:

a. a 2-by-6 rectangle and a 3-by-8 rectangle

b. a 2-by-6 rectangle and a 3-by-9 rectangle

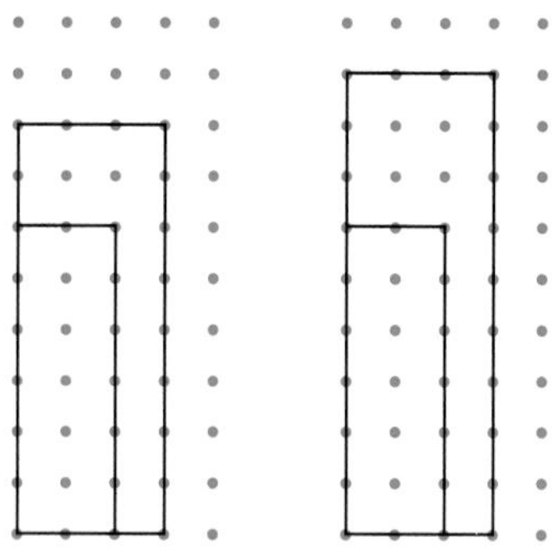

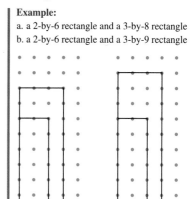

2/6 = 0.3333333...
3/8 = 0.375
3/9 = 0.3333333...

15. Explain the results of the two methods in this example.

You may know other methods for recognizing whether fractions are equivalent. You can use those also, to determine whether rectangles are similar.

16. Summary Explain how the ideas of *similar rectangles* and *equivalent fractions* are related.

17. Are these two rectangles similar? The first one has vertices: (0, 1), (2, 0), (4, 4), and (2, 5). The other one has vertices (7, 3), (9, 6), (3, 10), and (1, 7). Since the methods outlined above will probably not work, explain how you arrive at your answer.

3.12 SOLUTIONS

10. Multiply each coordinate by 1/2.
11. Multiply each coordinate by 3/2.
12. Yes
13. The ratios: width/length or length/width are constant.
14. 2/3 or 3/2
15. The 2-by-6 and 3-by-9 rectangles are similar.
16. Similar rectangles have ratios that will reduce to the same fraction in lowest terms. Equivalent fractions are fractions that will reduce to the same fraction in lowest terms.
17. Yes. The ratio of sides is 2:1 for both rectangles. This may not be easy to see, but students will find creative ways to show this.

REVIEW *THE COMMUTATIVE AND ASSOCIATIVE LAWS*

18. Write an expression using
- the numbers 1, 2, and -3, in any order,
- two subtractions,

in as many ways as possible.

In each case, calculate the value of the expression.

Examples: $2 - 1 - -3 = 4$
$2 - (1 - -3) = -2$
$(-3 - 1) - 2 = -6$

19. Do the commutative and associative laws apply to subtraction? Explain.

DISCOVERY *CLOCKMATH*

Clock Math can be defined by saying that only the numbers on the face of a clock (1, 2, ..., 12) are used. In Clock Math, $5 + 9 = 2$, and $5 \times 9 = 9$. This is because when you pass 12, you keep counting around the clock.

20. **Report** Write a report on Clock Math. You may start with a science fiction or fantasy story to explain an imaginary origin for Clock Math. Your report should include, but not be limited to, answers to the following questions: Is there a *Clock Zero*? What is it? Does every number have a *Clock Opposite*? What is it? Is there a *Clock One*? Does every number have a *Clock Reciprocal*? What is it? Don't forget to make addition and multiplication tables.

REVIEW *THE COMMUTATIVE AND ASSOCIATIVE LAWS*

In addition to the commutative and associative laws (in a negative sort of way) these problems review distributing the minus sign.

DISCOVERY *CLOCK MATH*

This works very much like Calendar Math, with one major difference. In Calendar Math, every day except Wednesday has a reciprocal. In Clock Math, several numbers have no reciprocal. (There is an interesting pattern there.) One consequence is that one could define division (except division by zero) in Calendar Math, but not in Clock Math.

3.12 SOLUTIONS

18. Answers will vary.
19. $2 - 1 - -3 = 4$
    Since $1 - 2 - -3 = 2$, the commutative law does not hold for subtraction.
    Since $1 - (2 - -3) = -4$, the associative law does not hold for subtraction.
20. Answers will vary.
    - Clock Zero = 12.
    - Every Clock number has a Clock Opposite. They are (number, its opposite) 1, 11; 2, 10; 3, 9; 4, 8; 5, 7; 6, 6; and 12, 12.
    - Clock One = 1.
    - Not every number has a Clock Reciprocal. The ones that do are (number, its reciprocal) 1, 1; 5, 5; 7, 7; and 11,11.

THINKING WRITING 3.C More Banking

Core Sequence: 1-11

Suitable for Homework: 1-12

Useful for Assessment: 11-12

What this Assignment is About:

- Combining functions
- Using variables and function diagrams to analyze a real-world problem

In this assignment we go back to the problem that opened this chapter. The difference is that now students should be able to analyze the problem at a somewhat higher level, with the help of variables and function diagrams.

Iterating a function of the type $y = mx + b$ yields a sequence of numbers that is not that easy to analyze with complete generality. Do not expect your students to understand completely all the ramifications of this problem.

For your own information: If the formula was simply of the form $y = x + b$, we would have an arithmetic sequence (these will be studied in Chapter 5); if the formula was of the form $y = mx$, we would have a geometric sequence (these will be studied in Chapter 8); finally, the form $y = mx + b$ with $-1 < m < 1$ yields a sequence that converges towards a limit (these too will be studied in Chapter 8).

THINKING WRITING 3.C More Banking

Reg works for Algebank. He was trying to analyze the investment plan described in the first lesson of this chapter. He decided to use x's and y's in his analysis. He wrote:

x = amount of money the person invests
y = amount of money the person has after one month

Since the bank doubles the investor's money and deducts the $100 fee, the function relating x and y is $y = 2x - 100$.

1. Make a function diagram for this function.
2. Use your function diagram to find out
   a. how much an investor, who had $300 after one month, started with;
   b. how much an investor, who started with $300, had after one month.
3. Use your function diagram to find the amount of money the investor started with, who ended up with the same amount of money after one month. (This is called the *fixed point* of the function.)
4. What happens to an investor who starts out with an amount of money less than the fixed point? With an amount of money greater than the fixed point?

To analyze what happens to an investment over a period of more than one month, Reg connected function diagrams. Since the amount at the end of the first month is the amount at the beginning of the second month, he used the y-number line from the first diagram as the x-number line of the next, doing this many times.

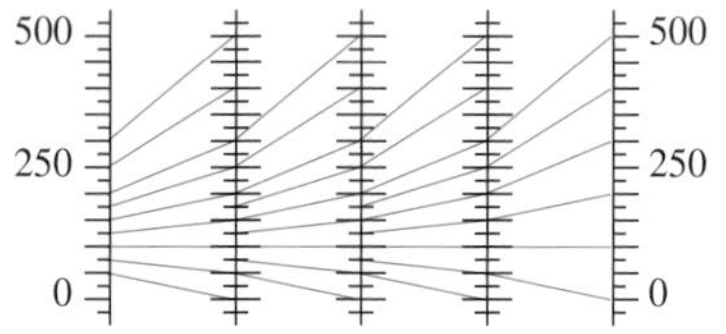

5. Describe what the linked function diagrams show.
6. How could one use a single-function diagram to follow what would happen to an investment over a period of more than one month?
7. Use Reg's method to analyze a plan where the investment is multiplied by 1.5 and the service charge is $50. Describe what your linked diagrams show.
8. Compare the plan in problem 7 with the first plan for someone who invests
   a. $90; b. $100; c. $110.
9. Which do you think has a bigger influence on the amount of money the investor makes, the service charge, or the number by which the investment is multiplied? Write an explanation supporting your opinion. Use several examples.
10. Explain why Al thought it was important to know whether the service charge was deducted before or after the money was doubled. Use some examples. Express each policy with a function.
11. **Report** Write a report on investment plans of the type studied in this assignment and in Lesson 1, plus, optionally, other plans of your design. Use variables. Your report should include, but not be limited to, answers to problems 9 and 10.
12. **Project** Find out what the service charge and interest rate are at three real banks. Figure out what would happen to $100 invested at each service charge and interest rate over a period of three years. Write up what you discover as if it were an article for the school newspaper, and you were giving advice to students.

3.C SOLUTIONS

1.

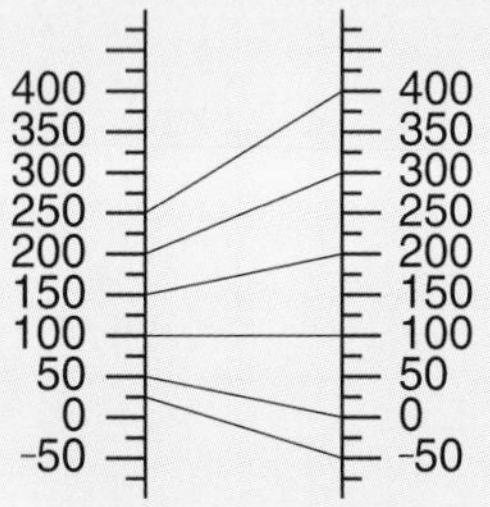

2. a. $200
   b. $500
3. $100
4. An investor who starts out with an amount less than the fixed point will lose money. One who starts out with an amount more than the fixed point will gain money.
5. The linked function diagrams show how one's money grows in a certain number of months. From left to right, the first vertical axis represents one's initial investment. Each vertical axis afterward represents one's balance at the end of one month. The fixed point is still $100, shown by the horizontal line. Any investment below the fixed point will eventually be less than zero dollars, and any investment above the fixed point will gain in value.
6. We can use a single function diagram to show how an investment grows in a certain number of months, but we cannot use one function diagram to show what happens for any number of months.
7. This is similar to #5, and the fixed point is still $100. However, in this plan an investment grows slowly and loses money more slowly than the one in #5.
8. First plan: $y_1 = 2x - 100$
   a. The investor will have a debt of $60 at the end of the 4th month.
   b. Neither gain nor lose money
   c. The investor will have $260 in the 4th month.

   Second plan: $y_2 = 1.5x - 50$
   a. The investor will have a debt of $13.91 at the end of the 6th month.
   b. Neither gain nor lose money
   c. The investor will have $150.63 in the 4th month.

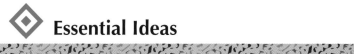

Essential Ideas

(**Thinking/Writing 3.C** continued)

There is a reproducible page of linked function diagrams in the back of this Teacher's Edition.

WORKING BACKWARDS

Abe and Bea had baked a batch of cookies. They told Reg, Al, and Lara that they could each have one-third of the cookies. Later, Reg went into the kitchen and took one-third of the cookies. An hour after that, not knowing that Reg had already taken his share, Lara claimed one-third of the remaining cookies. A few minutes later Al, thinking he was the first to find the cookies, devoured one-third of what was left.

1. If 8 cookies are left, how many must Abe and Bea have baked?

TWO NEGATIVES

2. Find the sign of the result.
a. $3 - 5$ b. $3 - (-5)$
c. $-5 - (3)$ d. $-5 - (-3)$

3. Find the sign of the result.
a. $-(5)(-3)$ b. $-(5 - 3)$
c. $-[-3 - (-5)]$ d. $-(-5)(-3)$

POSITIVE, NEGATIVE, OR ZERO?

4. For each expression, write *P, N,* and/or 0, depending on whether it can possibly be positive, negative, or 0. (Try various values for the variables to help you decide. For example, -2, 0, and 2.) Explain your answers.
a. $5x$ b. $-2x^2$
c. $-9y$ d. $5y^2$
e. z^3 f. $-a^4$

SIMPLIFYING EXPRESSIONS

Simplify each expression.

5. $12x - 6xy - (-3x) - (-2y)$

6. $-3x^2 - (3)2 + x^2 - (2 - x^2)$

7. $x - (x - 5) - (5 - x)$

FROM WORDS TO ALGEBRA

8. a. Translate each step into algebra.
1) Think of a number.
2) Add 4.
3) Multiply the result by 2.
b. If I got 46, what was my original number?

9. a. Translate each step into algebra.
1) Think of a number.
2) Multiply by 2.
3) Add 4.
b. If I got 46, what was my original number?
c. Compare your answer to part (b) with your answer to part (b) in problem 8. Were your answers the same or different? Explain.

COMPARING EXPRESSIONS

10. Find a value of x for which
a. $-8x - 1$ is less than $8x + 3$;
b. $-8x - 1$ is greater than $8x + 3$;
c. $-8x - 1$ is equal to $8x + 3$.

MULTIPLICATION TABLES

Find these products. Combine like terms.

11. $(x + 3)(2x + 4)$

12. $(x + 3)(2x + 4y)$

13. $(x + 3 + y)(2x + 4y)$

Fill in the blanks.

14.

	x	-3	$5y$
___	$2x^2$	$-6x$	$10xy$

15.

	___	___	___
$3y$	$-6x^2y$	$15y^3$	$-3y$

16. ___ $(x - 2) = 2 - x$

SOLUTIONS

(3.C Solutions continued)

9. Answers will vary.
Assuming the service charge is not extremely large, the number by which the investment is multiplied has a bigger influence in the long run.

10. Answers will vary.
Deducting the $100 service charge first and then doubling the amount is the same as doubling the amount and then deducting $200 as a service fee. So doubling first is more beneficial to Al.

11. Answers will vary.

12. Answers will vary.

1. 27

2. a. negative b. positive
c. negative d. negative

3. a. positive b. negative
c. negative d. negative

4. a. P, N, 0
b. 0, N
c. P, N, 0
d. P, 0
e. P, N, 0
f. 0, N

5. $15x - 6xy + 2y$

6. $-x^2 - 8$

7. x

8. a. 1) x
2) $x + 4$
3) $2(x + 4)$
b. 19

9. a. 1) x
2) $2x$
3) $2x + 4$
b. 21
c. The answers are not the same, because the order of operations is important.

10. a. $x > -1/4$
b. $x < -1/4$
c. $x = -1/4$

11. $2x^2 + 10x + 12$

12. $2x^2 + 6x + 4xy + 12y$

13. $2x^2 + 12y + 4y^2 + 6x + 6xy$

14. $2x$

15. $-2x^2$, $5y^2$, -1

16. -1

OPPOSITES AND RECIPROCALS

17. Simplify each expression. Look for shortcuts.

a. $9 \cdot \frac{1}{3} \cdot \frac{2}{3} \cdot 5 \cdot \frac{3}{2}$

b. $[5x - (-5x)] - [5x - (-5x)] - 16x$

c. $0.5 \cdot 25 \cdot 0.02 \cdot 2$

18. Gabe and Abe were arguing about *xy*. Gabe said that the opposite of *xy* is *yx*. Abe said that the opposite of *xy* is -*xy*. Lara overheard them, and said she thought that the opposite of *xy* is -*yx*. Write an explanation that will settle their argument.

19. What numbers are

a. greater than their reciprocal?

b. less than their reciprocal?

c. equal to their reciprocal?

d. less than their opposite?

e. equal to their opposite?

20. a. Which of the following is the reciprocal of 3*x*?

$$\frac{1}{3x}, \frac{3}{x}, \text{ or } \frac{1}{3}$$

b. Check your answer by substituting two different numbers for *x* and showing that the product of 3*x* and its reciprocal is 1 in both cases.

INVERSE FUNCTIONS

Write the inverse of each of the following functions.

21. a. The function adds 2 to *x* and multiplies the result by 4.

b. The function multiplies *x* by 4 and adds 2 to the result.

c. $y = 7x - 4$

22. a. The function takes the opposite of *x*.

b. The function takes the opposite of *x*, adds 5, and divides the result by 2.

c. $y = \frac{3 - x}{6}$

Scientists sometimes use the Kelvin temperature scale. To convert Kelvin temperatures to Celsius, you subtract 273. For example, the melting temperature of iron is 1808° Kelvin, or 1535° Celsius.

23. Lead melts at 600° Kelvin. What temperature is that in Fahrenheit? (Use the information from Lesson 8.)

24. Explain how to convert Kelvin temperatures to Fahrenheit, and how to convert Fahrenheit to Kelvin. (Hint: Use arrows to show each step of the conversion.)

25. a. Make a function diagram for the function $y_1 = (x/2) + 1$.

b. Make the function diagram of its inverse and find the rule.

c. Find the function that results from combining y_1 and its inverse. Does the order in which you combine the functions matter? Explain.

SOLVING EQUATIONS

Use the cover-up method to solve these equations.

26. $\frac{24}{x - 5} + 3 = 9$ **27.** $\frac{x - 5}{24} + 3 = 9$

28. $\frac{5 - x}{24} + 3 = 9$ **29.** $\frac{24}{5 - x} + 3 = 9$

30. Compare the solutions to each pair of equations. (Use related multiplication equations.)

a. $\frac{2}{M} = 6$ and $\frac{6}{M} = 2$

b. $\frac{8}{M} = 4$ and $\frac{4}{M} = 8$

c. $\frac{20}{M} = 5$ and $\frac{5}{M} = 20$

d. Make up another example like this.

31. Describe the pattern you found in problem 30. Explain why it works.

SOLUTIONS

17. a. 15 b. $-16x$ c. 0.5

18. Answers will vary.

19. a. numbers between -1 and 0, numbers greater than 1
  b. numbers less than -1, numbers between 0 and 1
  c. 1, -1
  d. negative numbers
  e. 0

20. a. $\frac{1}{3x}$

21. a. $y^{-1} = \frac{x}{4} - 2$
  b. $y^{-1} = \frac{x - 2}{4}$
  c. $y^{-1} = \frac{x + 4}{7}$

22. a. $y^{-1} = -x$
  b. $y^{-1} = -(2x - 5)$
  c. $y^{-1} = -(6x - 3)$

23. 620.6°*F*

24. First subtract 273 from *K* to get *C*. Then use $F = 1.8C + 32$ to convert *C* to *F*.
To convert *F* to *K*, first convert *F* to *C* by using $C = (5/9)(F - 32)$. Then add 273 to *C* to get *K*.

25. a.

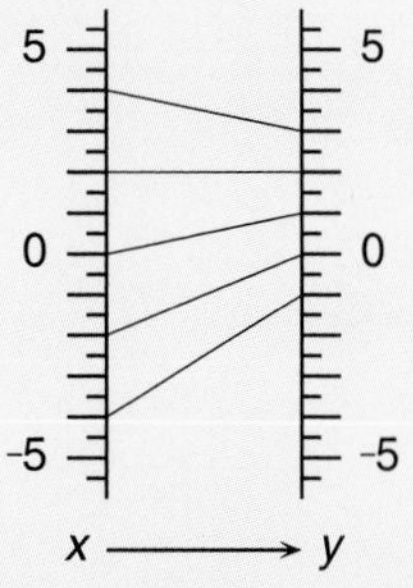

$y_1 = {}^x/_2 + 1$

b.

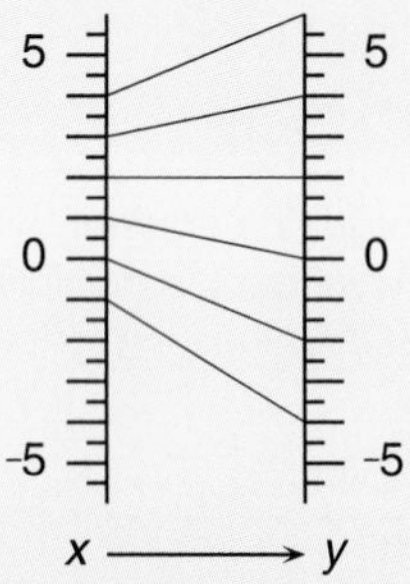

c. $y^0 y^{-1} = x$
No, it doesn't matter in which order

26. 9

27. 149

28. -139

29. 1

PRACTICE

REVIEW/PREVIEW *SIMPLIFY*

1. $x + 0.2x$ **2.** $x - 0.2x$

3. $x + 0.8x$ **4.** $x + (1/4)x$

5. $x - (1/4)x$

PREVIEW *EQUAL RATIOS*

The equations below all involve two equal ratios. Find the value of x that will make the ratios equal. You may want to use trial and error with your calculator.

6. $\frac{x}{4} = \frac{6}{1}$ **7.** $\frac{3}{x} = \frac{5}{7}$

8. $\frac{x}{3} = \frac{5}{7}$ **9.** $\frac{3}{1} = \frac{6}{x+7}$

10. $\frac{4}{5} = \frac{6}{x+7}$

REVIEW/PREVIEW *EQUATIONS*

11. For each equation, use trial and error to find a value of n that makes it true.

a. $3n + 10 = 5n$
b. $5n + 10 = 3n$
c. $7n + 10 = 8n$
d. $8n + 10 = 7n$

12. Use trial and error or the cover-up method to solve these equations.

a. $2(x + 5) = 8$
b. $5 + 2(x + 4) = 19$
c. $3(2x + 4) - 7 = 11$
d. $-4(10x - 3) - 6 = -14$

13. Find a positive integer that satisfies each equation.

a. $3n - 1 = 47$
b. $n^2 - 5 = 59$

14. Find a negative integer and a positive integer that satisfy the equation

$$n^2 - n = 20.$$

SOLUTIONS

30. a. 1/3, 3
    b. 2, 1/2
    c. 4, 1/4
    d. Answers will vary.

31. Answers are reciprocals of each other. Let's look at $\frac{6}{M} = 2$. The related multiplication is $6 = M \cdot 2$. Since 2 times 3 is 6, M must be 3. Now, $\frac{2}{M} = 6$. The related multiplication is $2 = M \cdot 6$ so 6 divided by 3 is 2. But dividing by 3 is the same as multiplying by 1/3.

1. $1.2x$
2. $0.8x$
3. $1.8x$
4. $(1\ 1/4)x$ or $(5/4)x$
5. $(3/4)x$
6. 24
7. 4.2
8. $\frac{15}{7}$
9. -5
10. 0.5
11. a. 5
    b. -5
    c. 10
    d. -10

12. a. -1
    b. 3
    c. 1
    d. 0.5

13. a. 16
    b. 8

14. 5, -4

Chapter 4
Interpreting Graphs

Overview of the Chapter

*T*his chapter concentrates on the meaning of Cartesian graphs. On the one hand, this means thinking about applications and the meaning of different units on the axes. On the other hand, it means understanding the relationship between the coordinates of individual points and the equations of graphs.

A number of numerically-oriented activities offer a change of pace, while addressing issues like rounding, estimation, and the use of calculators.

1. Algebra Concepts Emphasized:

- Three representations of functions: tables, graphs, and equations
- Functions
- Using different units on the x- and y-axes
- Which polynomial graphs are straight lines
- Which polynomial graphs pass through the origin
- Intercepts
- What it means for a point to be on or off the graph of a function
- Horizontal and vertical lines
- Proportional thinking
- Direct variation
- Points on direct variation lines
- Discrete vs. continuous functions
- Step functions
- Writing and graphing simple inequalities
- Discovering a two-variable function from data
- Identity and inverse elements
- Order of operations (exponentiation)
- Algebraic structure

CHAPTER 4

The spiral curve of a West African chameleon's tail

Coming in this chapter:

Exploration

- Find as many functions as possible whose graphs go through the origin.
- Find as many functions as possible whose output is 5 when the input is 2.

INTERPRETING GRAPHS

2. Algebra Concepts Reviewed:

- Subtraction of signed numbers
- Estimation and rounding
- Geoboard area
- Dividing on a calculator
- Review of repeating decimals

3. Algebra Concepts Previewed:

- Inverse variation
- Intersection of graphs
- Slope
- Area under a line

4. Problem-Solving Techniques:

- Trial and error
- Looking for patterns
- Drawing a picture
- Organized searches
- Creating algorithms

5. Connections and Context:

- What information is and is not conveyed by graphs
- Interpreting graphs
- Motion: speed, distance, time
- Density, weight, volume
- Similar rectangles
- Measurement error
- Fitting a line to data
- Dimensions
- π
- Unit conversion
- Traffic safety
- Pick's Formula
- Abstract algebra (finite groups)

▼ 4.1
A 100-Mile Trip

Core Sequence: 1-13, 18-20

Suitable for Homework: 6-17

Useful for Assessment: 5, 11, 13, 15-17

What this Lesson is About:

- What information is and is not conveyed by graphs
- Preview of motion
- Preview of inverse and direct variation
- Using different units on the *x*- and *y*-axes

This lesson uses travel at constant speed as a context to introduce the interpretation of graphs. Secondarily, it serves as a preview of the algebra of motion. (A more complete exploration of motion will take place in Chapter 12.)

Problems 1-2 will start your students thinking about the three variables in a motion problem: distance, time, and speed. You may use them as a springboard for class discussion, but at least make sure there is an opportunity to discuss these questions in groups. Without some sense of the meaning of these three variables students will not get a lot out of the lesson.

Do not teach a formula about the relationship of distance, time, and speed. Students will be guided to one through the building and interpretation of tables.

LESSON 4.1

A 100-Mile Trip

You will need: graph paper

1. By which of these methods do you think a person could travel 100 miles in one day? Explain how you arrive at your guess.
walking / running / bicycling / ice skating / riding a scooter / riding in a car / riding in a helicopter

2. Ophelia and Xavier are traveling along a road. If you could view the road from above and make a sketch of what you saw every ten minutes, your sketches might look something like the figure below.
   a. Which person (O or X) is traveling faster?
   b. If the entire length of the road is six miles, can you figure out approximately how fast each person is traveling? Explain.

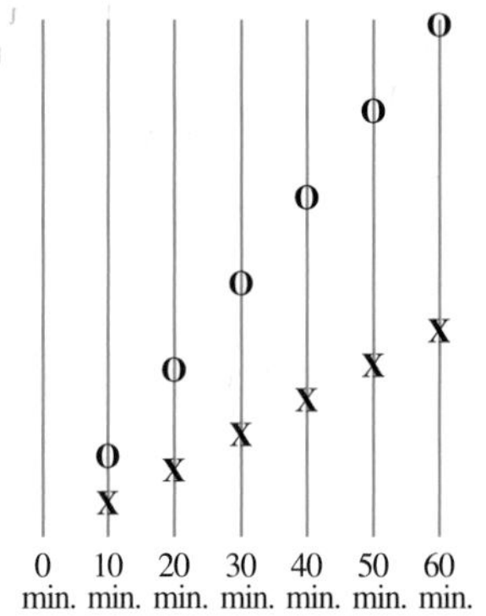

TIME VS. SPEED

3. Copy and complete this table showing how many hours it would take each person to travel 100 miles.

Person	Mode of Travel	Speed (mph)	Time (hours)
Abe	walking	4	25
Al	van	50	
Bea	skating	10	
Gabe	scooter	30	
Lara	helicopter	100	
Lea	bike	25	
Reg	running	8	

4. Copy and complete the graph that shows how long it would take for each person to make the 100-mile trip.

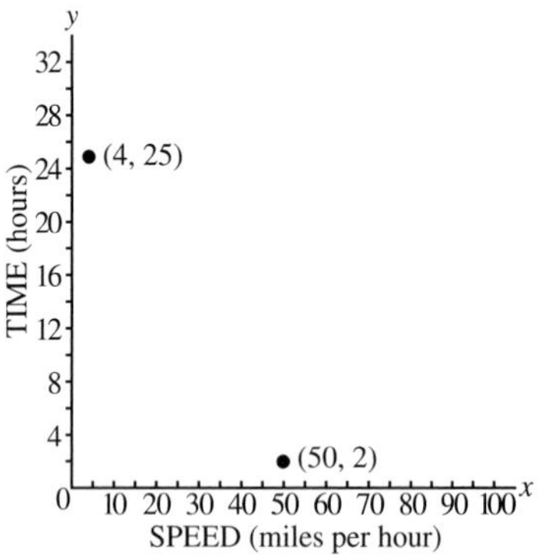

4.1 SOLUTIONS

1. Answers will vary. Some sample examples are as follows:

   bicycling: Yes. Triathletes bicycle 100 miles in one race. The winners take as few as 5 to 6 hours.

   walking: No. An average walking time is about 3 mph on flat ground. 100 miles/3 mph ≈ 33.33 hours, which is more than one day.

   riding a scooter: Yes. A scooter can go 30 mph so 100 miles/30 mph ≈ 3.33 hours.

   riding in a helicopter: Yes. A helicopter can go faster than a car (80-100 mph). 100 miles/80 mph = 1.25 hours.

   running: Yes. There are 100-mile races, one of which is called the Western States Ultra Endurance Race. The fastest runners take between 15 and 16 hours.

   ice skating: Yes. Skating seems to be a more efficient means of travel than running because the skater glides on the ice. If a runner can run 100 miles in a day, a skater should be able to do it also, because she's going faster.

   riding in a car: Yes. One example of a day trip is from San Francisco to Death Valley (550 miles) in 12 hours.

2. a. Ophelia is traveling faster than Xavier.
   b. Yes. A certain number of miles per hour tells how fast an object, such as a car, is traveling. The person with the circle marker is traveling about 6 mph because the entire distance of 6 miles is traveled in the one hour of observation time. The X marker is slightly less than 3 mph, say 2.7 mph. Let the distance between the X marker and 3-mile point (the midpoint of the full 6-mile segment) be one unit. The six miles can be divided into 9 of these units. The dash marker is 4/9 of the entire 6 miles. $4/9 \cdot 6 \approx 2.67$ miles.

3.

Person	Mode of Travel	Speed	Time
Abe	walking	4	25
Al	van	50	2
Bea	skating	10	10
Gabe	scooter	30	3.33
Lara	helicopter	100	1
Lea	bike	25	4
Reg	running	8	12.5

5. **Generalization**

a. What pattern do you notice in the table?

b. How long would it take for someone who travels at a constant speed of S miles per hour to cover 100 miles?

DISTANCE VS. TIME

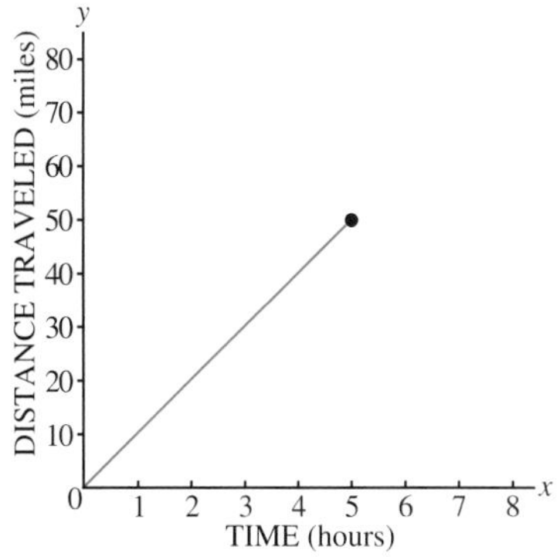

6. The graph shows Bea's progress on the trip. It shows that after 5 hours of roller-skating she had traveled 50 miles.

a. Copy the graph onto graph paper. Use a whole piece of graph paper. You will be adding more to this graph.

b. One of the points on the graph is (5, 50). Mark and label three more points on the graph of Bea's progress.

7. In this lesson we are assuming everyone travels at a constant speed. How valid is this assumption? For each mode of travel what might make it impossible to travel at a constant speed? Explain.

The table shows how long it took for Abe to go certain distances.

Abe's Progress

Time (hours)	Distance (miles)
1	4
2	8

8. a. Copy and complete the table up to 20 miles.

b. For this problem, use the same axes you used for Bea. Plot and label the points from the table in part (a).

c. Connect the points with a straight line. Then find and label a point that is on the line but not in your table. Interpret the coordinates of the point in terms of this problem.

9. Make a table like the one you made for Abe showing Gabe's progress on his scooter and Al's progress in the van. Make graphs of their progress on the same axes you used to show Abe's and Bea's progress. Label the four different lines.

10. Use your graphs to help you answer these questions. If Bea and Abe start out at the same time,

a. how far apart will they be after one hour?

b. how far apart will they be after two hours?

11. **Generalization** Look for a pattern. How far apart will Abe and Bea be after H hours? Explain.

You can use this lesson to introduce the terminology "time versus speed" which means "time as a function of speed."

TIME VS. SPEED

This section previews inverse variation, which will be studied in more detail in Chapter 5. Unless your students bring it up, there is no need to dwell on generalities about this at this time.

However, it is useful to discuss the pattern, which students are likely to see as a *constant product* pattern, and to write an equation relating speed to time, as suggested in problem 5.

DISTANCE VS. TIME

Problem 7 is there to point out the limitations of the mathematical model this lesson is based on. Students may point out that a skater could tire and slow down, that speed may change when going up or down hills, that traffic conditions can affect the speed of a car, or wind that of a helicopter....

A more sophisticated analysis of motion will have to wait for Chapter 12, where the concept of average speed will be discussed and will provide justification for the usefulness of work with constant speed.

Problem 13 should be discussed in class, even if it was assigned as homework.

4.1 SOLUTIONS

4.

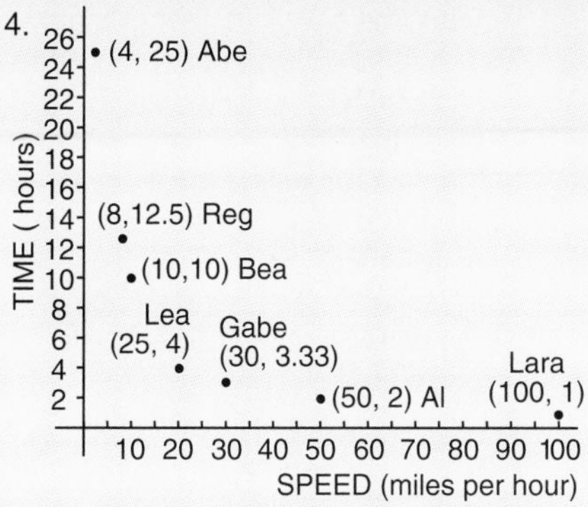

5. a. The product of the speed and time is 100 miles.

b. It would take (100/s) hours

6. a., b.
8. b.
9.
12. a.

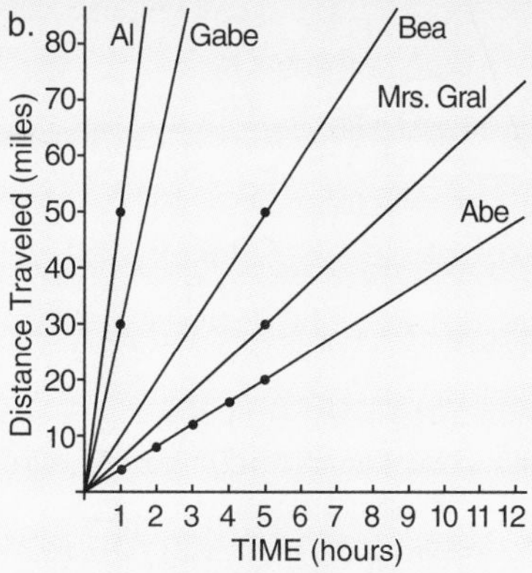

7. Constant speed is an unrealistic assumption.

walking: The person may tire or have steep hills to climb which would slow her down.

van: Heavy traffic may slow down the van. The van must start from 0 mph and accelerate to a speed of 50 mph; this is not a constant speed.

skating: A sudden white-out or fall would slow down the skater.

scooter: Same as the van

helicopter: Wind conditions might slow down the helicopter.

bike: Hills or fatigue would slow down the biker.

running: Same as the bike

8. a.

Time (hrs.)	Distance (mi.)
1	4
2	8
3	12
4	16
5	20

DISTANCE VS. SPEED

Use this section if you want your students to have more practice with the ideas in this lesson.

SPEED BY GRAPHS AND FORMULAS

This section wraps up the lesson. Problem 16 is the main point of the lesson and deserves a full-class discussion.

For problem 17 students should arrive at a formula from looking at the patterns in the data tables. Once the formulas are found, you may point out that speed can be measured in *miles per hour*. In that way, the units reflect what is being done: To get speed, you divide distance by time.

DISCOVERY *FRAMING PHOTOGRAPHS*

This somewhat challenging application reviews similar rectangles, which were introduced in Chapter 3, Lesson 12. It also helps lay the groundwork for the concept of direct variation, to which we will devote much of this chapter.

Even if they are done at home, problems 18-20 should be discussed in class.

12. Mrs. Gral was traveling at a constant speed. She started at the same time as Abe, and was two miles ahead of him after one hour.

a. Add a graph of Mrs. Gral's progress to your axes.

b. How far ahead was Mrs. Gral after two hours?

c. After three hours, how far was Mrs. Gral behind Bea?

d. How fast was Mrs. Gral going? What mode of travel do you think she was using?

13. Summary

a. How does the mode of travel affect the steepness of the line? Explain.

b. What is the meaning of points on two of the graphs that have the same x-coordinate but different y-coordinates?

c. What is the meaning of the vertical distance between two lines for a given value of x?

DISTANCE VS. SPEED

14. Using the same speed data, figure out how far each person could travel in two-and-a-half hours. Make a table and a graph showing speed on the horizontal axis and distance on the vertical axis.

15. How would the graph be changed if the travel time was greater? Less? Explain.

SPEED BY GRAPHS AND FORMULAS

16. Summary Each graph in this lesson gives information on how fast people travel, but it does it in a different way. Explain.

17. Generalization If someone is traveling at a constant speed of S miles per hour, for a distance of D miles, and takes T hours, what is the relationship between S, D, and T? Write this relationship in more than one way.

DISCOVERY *FRAMING PHOTOGRAPHS*

A photograph is mounted on a background which sticks out one inch on each side. The width of the photo is two inches and the height is three inches.

18. a. Sketch the photo and its frame.

b. What are the dimensions of the frame?

c. Are the photo and frame similar rectangles? Explain.

19. The photo needs to be enlarged so it will fit in a frame having a height of 12 inches. Again, the width of the frame is to be one inch. Find the dimensions of the enlarged photo and its frame. Of course the photo cannot be distorted!

20. Is the frame for the enlarged picture similar to the picture? Is it similar to the original frame? Explain.

4.1 SOLUTIONS

8. c. Answers will vary. Take the point (6, 24). This point means in 6 hours Abe walks 24 miles.

9. Gabe's progress:

Time (hrs.)	Distance (mi.)
1	30
2	60
3	90
4	120
5	150

Al's progress:

Time (hrs.)	Distance
1	50
2	100
3	150
4	200
5	250

10. a. 6 miles
b. 12 miles

11. $6H$ miles.

After H hr.	Miles apart
1	6
2	12
3	18
4	24
H	$6H$

The number of miles apart is always six times the number of hours they have traveled.

12. b. 4 miles
c. 12 miles
d. 6 mph. She was probably jogging, since she was going faster than walking and slower than running.

13. a. The faster the speed, the steeper the line. Al's van is faster (50 mph) than Abe's walking feet (4 mph) and Al's line is steeper than Abe's line. Each hour, Al travels more miles than Abe.
b. This means one is traveling a greater distance in the same time as another.
c. This measures the difference in the distance they traveled at a given time.

14.

Person	Mode of Travel	Dist.
Abe	walking	10
Al	van	125
Bea	skating	25
Gabe	scooter	75
Lara	helicopter	250
Lea	bike	62.5
Reg	running	20

(Solutions continued on page 510)

LESSON 4.2

Points, Graphs, and Equations

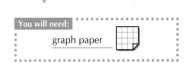

You will need: graph paper

PATTERNS FROM POINTS

1. a. Draw a pair of axes and plot these points.

x	y
0	-1
-2	-3
-5	-6
5	4

b. Study the table and your graph. Describe the relationship between the x-value and y-value of each pair.

c. Use the pattern you found to add more points to your table and graph.

d. Write an equation that tells how to get the y-value from the x-value.

2. Repeat problem 1 for each of these tables.

a.

x	y
4	-8
1	-2
-3	6
0	0

b.

x	y
-3	-3
5	-3
-6	-3
-1	-3

c.

x	y
6	4
12	-2
-1	11
3	7

GRAPHS FROM PATTERNS

3. For each description below, make a table of at least five (x, y) pairs that fit it. Then graph the (x, y) pairs. Use a separate coordinate system for each graph.

a. The y-coordinate is always equal to the x-coordinate.

b. The y-coordinate is always four less than the x-coordinate.

c. The y-coordinate is always one-half of the x-coordinate.

d. The y-coordinate is always the opposite of the x-coordinate.

e. The y-coordinate is always the square of the x-coordinate.

EQUATIONS FROM PATTERNS

4. For each description in problem 3, find an equation that describes the relationship between x and y. Write the equations on your graphs.

5. a. Make a table of four number pairs (x, y) that have this property: The sum of x and y is always 6.

b. Graph these (x, y) pairs.

c. Connect the points with a straight line.

d. Write the relationship between x and y as an equation.

6. a. Using fractions and negative numbers, write two more (x, y) pairs having the property that the sum of x and y is 6. Do these points lie on the line?

b. Choose a point that is not on the line. Do its (x, y) coordinates add up to 6?

c. Write any number pair (x, y) whose sum is not 6. Find this point. Is it on the line you drew?

4.2 Points, Graphs, and Equations

Core Sequence: 1-13

Suitable for Homework: 4-13

Useful for Assessment: 11-13

What this Lesson is About:

- Three representations of functions: tables, graphs, and equations
- Review of similar rectangles
- Preview of direct variation

This is a straightforward but very important lesson that allows students to get experience going from one to another of these three representations of functions.

The key idea this lesson is driving towards is that if a point lies on the graph of an equation, its coordinates must satisfy the equation. Conversely, if the coordinates of a point satisfy an equation, the point must lie on the graph of the equation. This seemingly simple idea is difficult for students to master. We will return to it in Lesson 4.

4.2 SOLUTIONS

1. a.

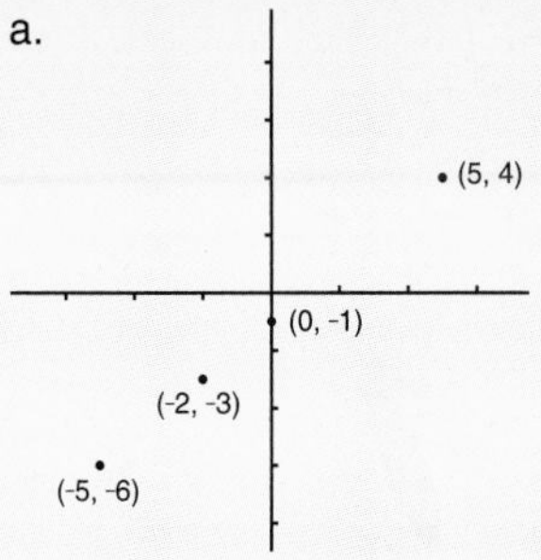

b. The y-value is one less than the x-value.

c. Answers will vary. One possible extension is:

x	y
1	0
2	1
3	2
4	3
-1	-2
-3	-4
-4	-5

d. $y = x - 1$

2. a. i.

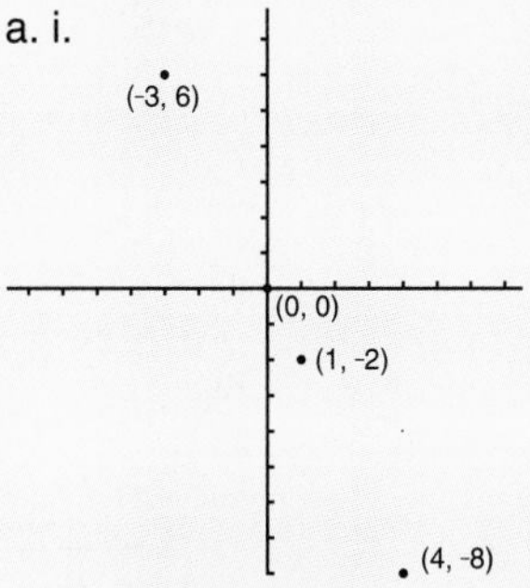

ii. If you multiply each x-value by negative 2, you get the associated y-value.

iii. One possible table of values is:

x	y
-2	4
-1	2
2	-4
3	-6

iv. $y = -2x$

b. i.

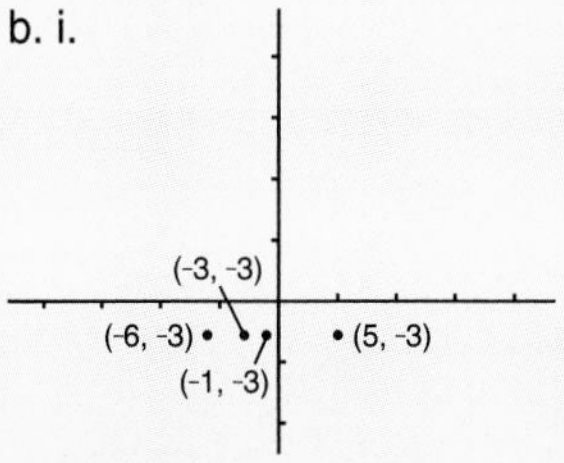

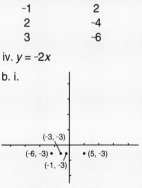

ii. The x-value can be any number and the y-value is always -3.

EQUATIONS FROM GRAPHS

On each graph below, four points are labeled. For each graph:

a. Make a table of the (x, y) pairs and look for a relationship between x and y.
b. Add three more points to the table, making sure each one does belong on the graph.
c. Write an equation describing the relationship between x and y.

7.

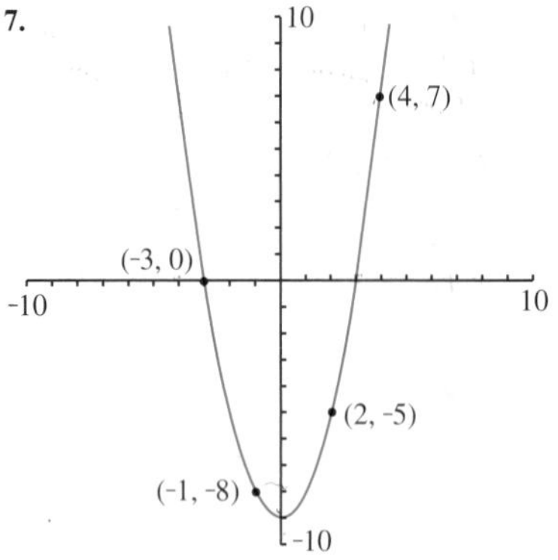

8.

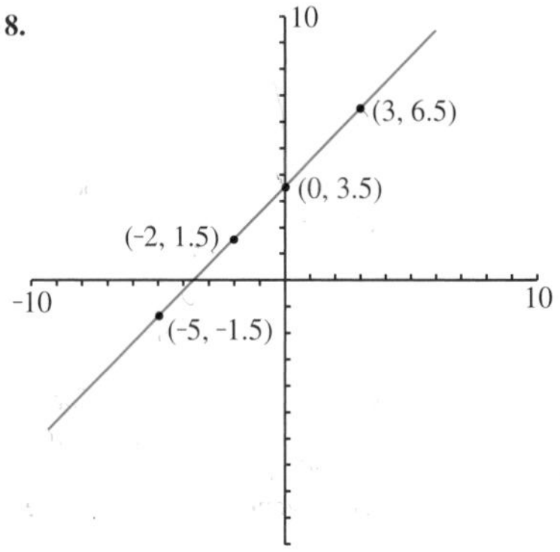

9.

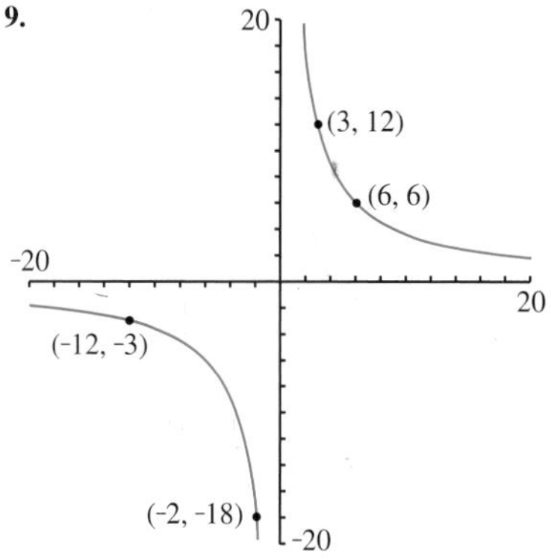

10.

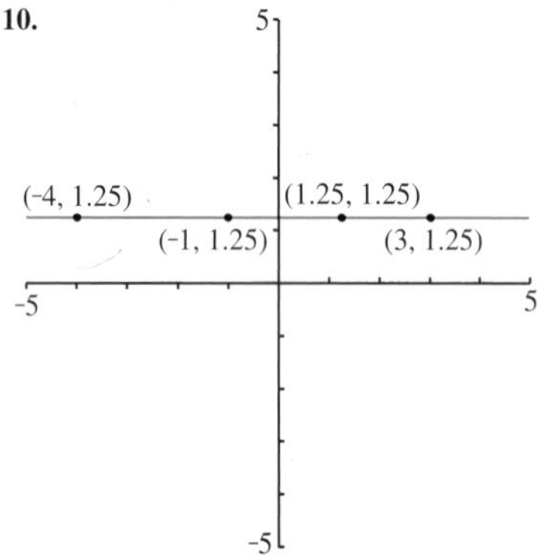

POINTS AND EQUATIONS

The following questions are about the graph of the function $y = 4x + 5$. Try to answer the questions without graphing.

11. Is the point (7, 32) on it? Explain.

12. The point $(3, y)$ is on it. What is y? Explain.

13. The point $(x, 6)$ is on it. What is x? Explain.

iii. One possible table of values is:

x	y
-5	-3
-4	-3
-2	-3
0	-3
1	-3
2	-3
3	-3
4	-3

iv. $y = -3$

c. i.

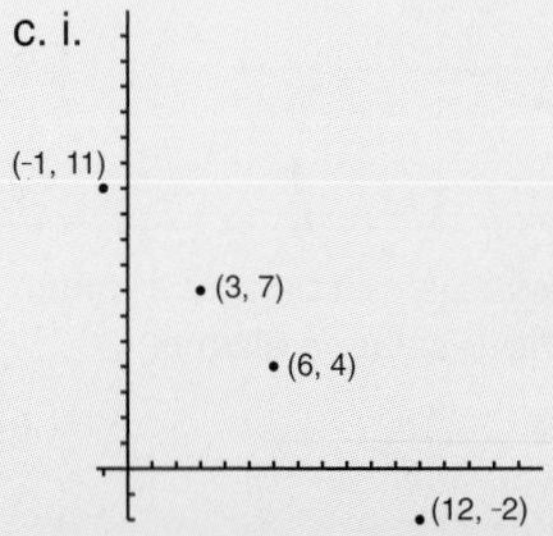

ii. The sum of x and y is 10.

iii. One possible table of values is:

x	y
0	10
1	9
2	8
4	6
5	5
7	3
-2	12
-3	13

iv. $y = 10 - x$

3. a. $y = x$

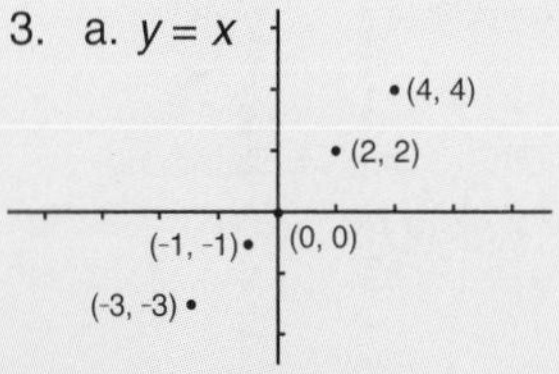

b. $y = x - 4$

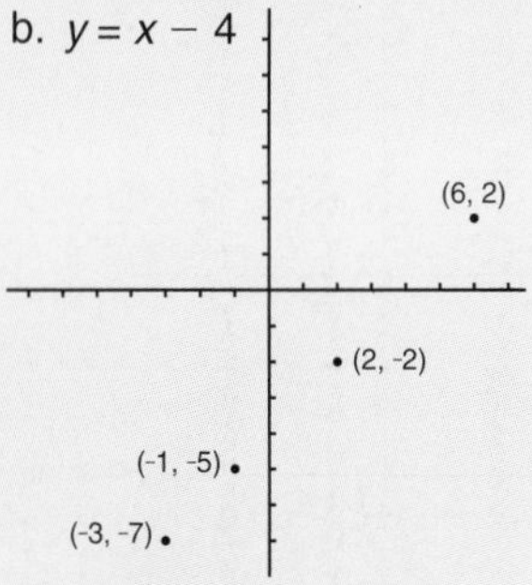

c. $y = 0.5x$

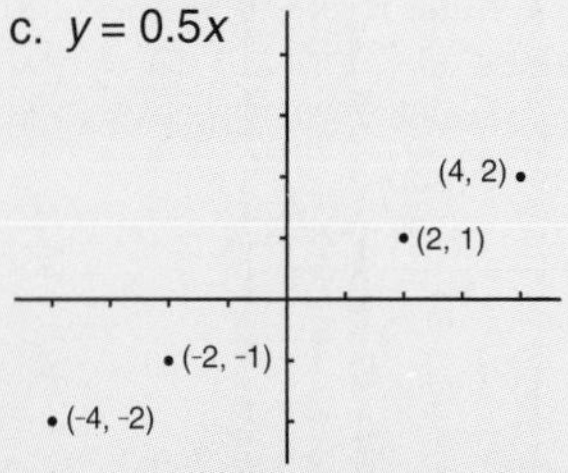

(Solutions continued on page 510)

LESSON 4.3

Polynomial Functions

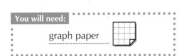

You will need: graph paper

Definition: A *polynomial function* is a function of the form $y =$ a polynomial.

1. **Exploration** Which of these polynomial functions do you think have graphs that are straight lines? Which have curved graphs? Explain why you think so.
   a. $y = x^2$ b. $y = 2x - 1$
   c. $y = 2x^2$ d. $y = x^3$

ORDER OF OPERATIONS

2. Make a table of at least eight (x, y) pairs for each function. Use negative numbers and fractions as well as positive whole numbers in your tables. Then make a graph from each table. Label each graph with its equation. You will need to refer to these graphs later.
   a. $y = x^2$ b. $y = x^3$

To make a table of values for graphing $y = -x^2$, we have to know what the expression $-x^2$ means. Does it mean *square x, then take its opposite* or *take the opposite of x, then square it*? Which operation should be done first?

To avoid this kind of confusion, mathematicians have agreed on the following rule.

Rule: *Exponentiation should be performed before other operations.* To change this order, we have to use parentheses.

Examples:
- $-x^2$ means *square x, then take the opposite.*
- $(-x)^2$ means *take the opposite of x, then square the result.*

3. Make a table of at least eight (x, y) pairs for each function. Use negative numbers and fractions as well as positive whole numbers in your tables. Then make a graph from each table. Label each graph with its equation.
   a. $y = (-x)^2$ b. $y = -x^2$
4. Compare your graphs in problem 3 with the graph of $y = x^2$. Explain what you observe.
5. Graph these polynomial functions.
   a. $y = -x^3$ b. $y = (-x)^3$
6. Compare your graphs in problem 5 with the graph of $y = x^3$. Explain what you observe.

DEGREE

Definition: The degree of a polynomial function in one variable is the highest power of the variable that appears in the polynomial.

Examples: $y = x^3$ and $y = x^2 + 2x^3$ are both third-degree polynomial functions. The equation $y = 2x$ is first-degree, and the equation $y = 1$ is zero-degree.

7. What is the degree of each of these polynomial functions?
   a. $y = 5 + x^2 - x$
   b. $y = 4x^3 - 3x^2 + 5$
   c. $y = 45$
8. Make a table of at least eight values for each third-degree function. Use negative numbers and fractions as well as positive whole numbers in your tables. Then make a graph from each table.
   a. $y = 2x^3$ b. $y = x^3 + 1$
   c. $y = -x^3 - 2$

4.3 Polynomial Functions

Core Sequence: 1-15, 17

Suitable for Homework: 8-17

Useful for Assessment: 4, 6, 12-15

What this Lesson is About:
- Order of operations (exponentiation)
- Which polynomial graphs are straight lines
- Which polynomial graphs pass through the origin
- Review of subtraction of signed numbers

If you have access to graphing calculators, problem 1 provides an opportunity to use them. With that tool students can carry out the Exploration with many more examples than the ones given. Groups can report their findings by making large posters on butcher paper.

ORDER OF OPERATIONS

Here we expand on the rules we learned in Chapter 1, Lesson 9. (Your students probably know them by now, but if necessary you could review them briefly first.)

The next section will provide some practice applying this rule. More practice will come up naturally in the course of the work.

4.3 SOLUTIONS

1. The straight line is *b*. The curved graphs are *a*, *c*, and *d*. Use of a graphing calculator supports this conclusion. Students may see from Lesson 2 that when the pattern between each *x*- and *y*-value in a table of ordered pairs involves only multiplication and addition (rather than exponentiation) the graph is a line (rather than a curve).
2. a. $y = x^2$
   i. One possible table of values is:

x	y
-3	9
-2.5	6.25
-2	4
-1	1
0	0
1	1
1.5	2.25
2	4

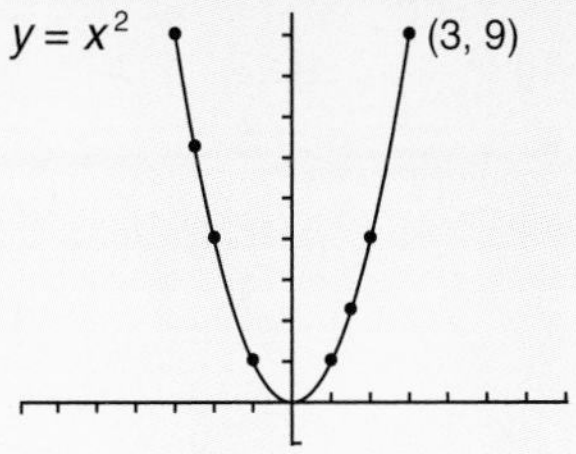

b. $y = x^3$
i. One possible table of values is:

x	y
-3	-27
-2.5	-15.625
-2	-8
-1	-1
0	0
1.8	5.832
1	1
2	8

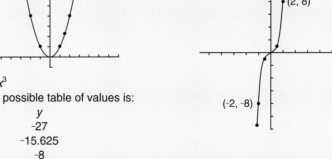

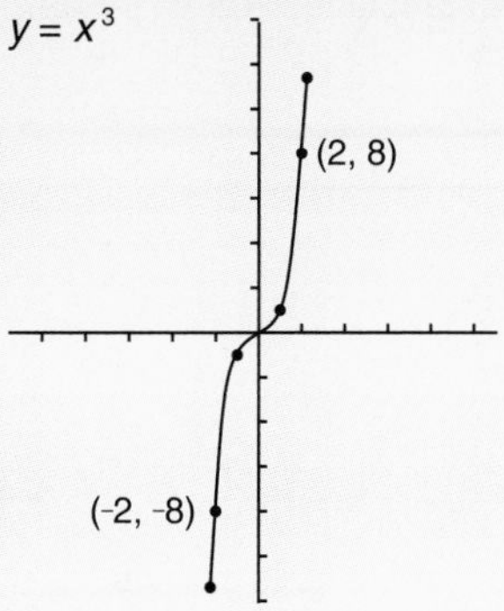

DEGREE

The degree of a polynomial was defined in Chapter 1, Lesson 6, in the Lab Gear model. Here the degree of a polynomial is defined in terms of the powers of the variable. Both definitions are equivalent, though of course this one is more general.

Problems 8-11 could take a long time for students to do as homework. You might have them do the problems in class, in groups. Or, you could assign one-third of the students to do part (a) of those problems, one-third part (b), and one-third part (c). The results could then be shared in class. This is also the perfect opportunity to use the graphing calculator.

THE EFFECT OF DEGREE

Again, the use of graphing calculators could enhance this discussion.

REVIEW POSSIBLE OR IMPOSSIBLE?

More thinking about the arithmetic of signed numbers.

9. Repeat problem 8 for these second-degree functions.
a. $y = x^2 - 1$ b. $y = -3x^2$
c. $y = -x^2 + 2$

10. Graph these first-degree functions.
a. $y = 5x$ b. $y = x$
c. $y = -2x + 1$

11. Graph these zero-degree functions.
a. $y = 4$ b. $y = -3$
c. $y = 0$

THE EFFECT OF DEGREE

12. Tell whether each sentence (a-b) could describe the graph of a zero-degree, first-degree, second-degree, or third-degree polynomial function. More than one answer may be possible for each description.
a. The graph is a straight line.
b. The graph is a curve.

13. Repeat problem 12 for these descriptions.
a. The graph goes through the origin.
b. The graph never crosses the *x*-axis.
c. The graph never crosses the *y*-axis.

14. Repeat problem 12 for these descriptions.
a. The graph passes through quadrants I and III only.
b. The graph passes through quadrants II and IV only.
c. The graph passes through quadrants I and II only.

15. Summary How does the degree of the equation affect its graph? Write a summary explaining everything you know about this.

16.
a. Make a table of values and graph the function $y = 24/x$.
b. Is this a polynomial function? Explain.

REVIEW POSSIBLE OR IMPOSSIBLE?

17. Decide whether each of the following situations is possible or impossible. If it is possible, give an example. If it is impossible, explain *why* it is impossible. Can you subtract
a. a negative number from a negative number to get a positive number?
b. a negative number from a negative number to get a negative number?
c. a negative number from a positive number to get a positive number?
d. a negative number from a positive number to get a negative number?
e. a positive number from a negative number to get a negative number?
f. a positive number from a negative number to get a positive number?

4.3 SOLUTIONS

3a. i. A sample table of values is:

x	*y*
-3	9
-2.5	6.25
-2	4
-1	1
0	0
1	1
1.5	2.25
2	4

ii. The graph is the same as #2a.

3b. i. A sample table of values is:

x	*y*
-3	-9
-2.5	-6.25
-2	-4
-1	-1
0	0
1	-1
1.5	-2.25
2	-4

ii. $y = -x^2$

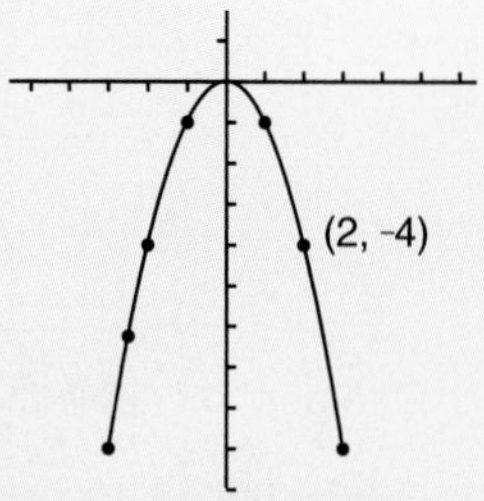

4. The graph of $y = (-x)^2$ is the same as the graph of $y = x^2$. The graph of $y = -x^2$ is the reflection of $y = x^2$ over the horizontal axis.

5. a. and b.

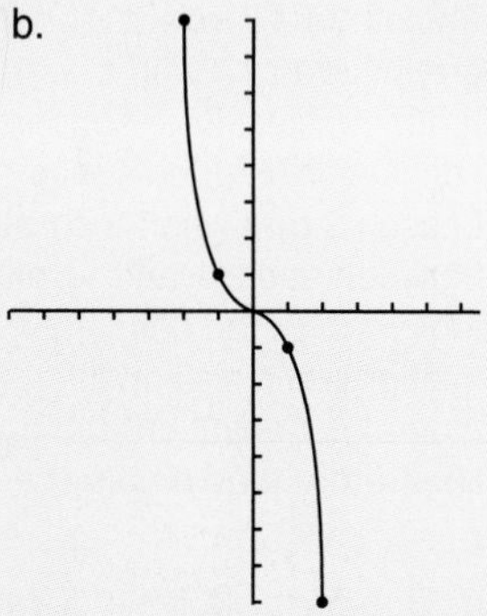

6. $y = -x^3$ and $y = (-x)^3$ are each the reflection of $y = x^3$ over the *y*-axis.

7. a. 2
b. 3
c. 0

(Solutions continued on page 511)

LESSON 4.4

Graphs Through Points

You will need:

graph paper 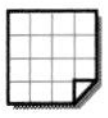

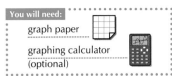

graphing calculator (optional) 

INTERCEPTS

Definitions: The *y-intercept* of a graph is the point where the graph crosses the *y*-axis. The *x-intercept* of a graph is the point where the graph crosses the *x*-axis.

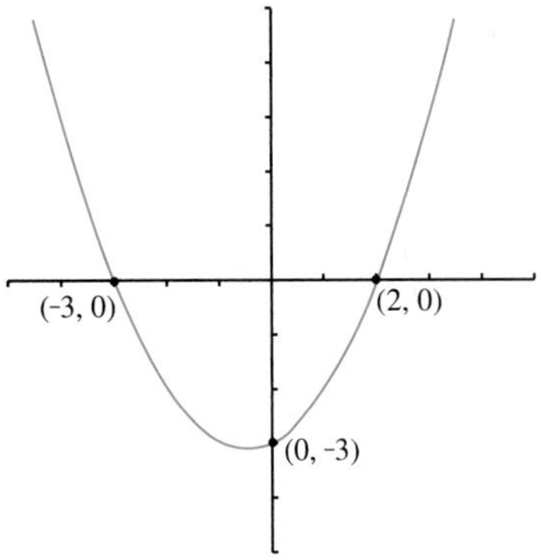

Example: The curve in the figure above has *y*-intercept (0, -3), and *x*-intercepts (-3, 0) and (2, 0).

For problems 1-5:

a. Guess the coordinates of the *x*- and *y*-intercepts (if you think they exist).

b. *On graph paper* draw the graph described.

c. Check the correctness of your guess.

1. A line is parallel to the *y*-axis and passes through the point (2, -3).

2. A line passes through the origin and the point (2, -3).

3. The sum of every (x, y) pair on the line is 8.

4. The line passes through the points (2, -3) and (3, -2).

5. To get the *y*-coordinate, square the *x*-coordinate and add 1.

POINTS ON AND OFF GRAPHS

6. Bea thinks that $8 - 2x$ means *multiply x by 2 and subtract the result from 8.* Lea thinks it means *subtract 2 from 8 and multiply the result by x.* Who is right? Explain.

7. Which of these points do you think will lie on the graph of $y = 8 - 2x$? Explain.

a. (2, 4)	b. (2, -4)
c. (0.5, 6)	d. (0.5, -6)
e. (-1, -10)	f. (-1, 10)

For the remaining problems in this lesson (8-23), use a graphing calculator if you have one. Otherwise, use graph paper.

8. a. Graph $y = 8 - 2x$.

b. Use your graph to check your answers to problem (a).

c. Write both coordinates of the *x*-intercept of $y = 8 - 2x$.

d. Write both coordinates of the *y*-intercept of $y = 8 - 2x$.

Definition: If two graphs share a point, they are said to *intersect* at that point.

9. a. On the same coordinate system, graph $y = 2x - 8$.

b. Do your two graphs intersect at any point? If so, where?

▼ 4.4 Graphs Through Points

Core Sequence: 1-12, 14-23

Suitable for Homework: 19-23

Useful for Assessment: 19, 23

What this Lesson is About:

- Intercepts
- What it means for a point to be on or off the graph of a function
- Preview of intersection of graphs
- Graphs that pass through the origin

INTERCEPTS

Encourage discussion of student guesses for problems 1-5 before proceeding with parts (b) and (c). Do not expect many students at this stage to be able to predict the intercepts in all cases. On the other hand, do not teach any techniques to do it yet. The purpose of these activities is to familiarize students with the definition of intercept and to lay the groundwork for later, more in-depth work.

Problems 10-12 could be divided among three groups of students using large grid paper, if they don't have graphing calculators. Then the groups should share their results with the entire class.

4.4 SOLUTIONS

1. a. *x*-intercept: (2, 0)
   y-intercept: none

   b.

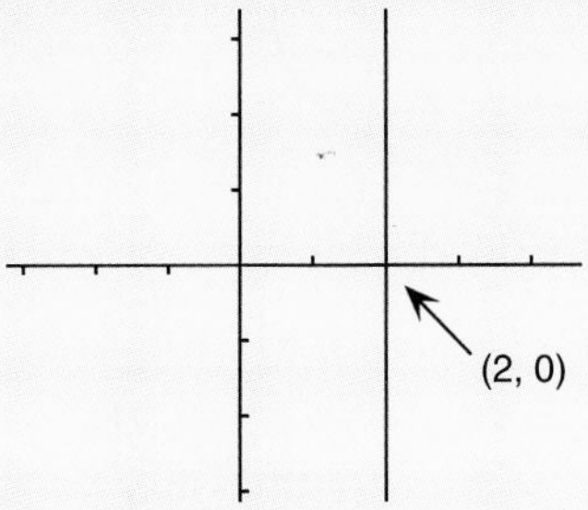

2. a. *x*-intercept: (0, 0)
   y-intercept: (0, 0)

   b.

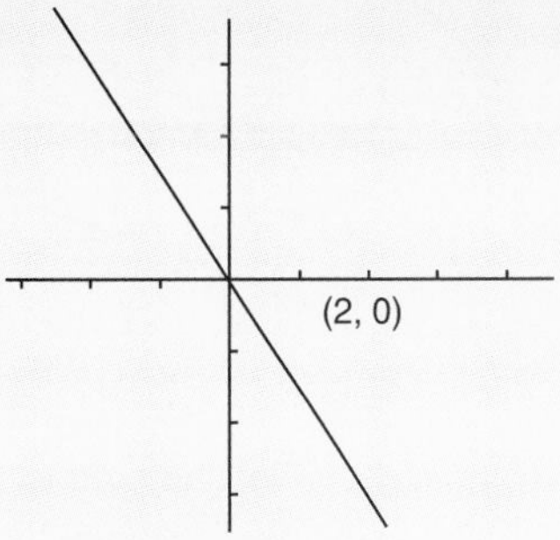

3. a. *x*-intercept: (8, 0)
   y-intercept: (0, 8)

   b.

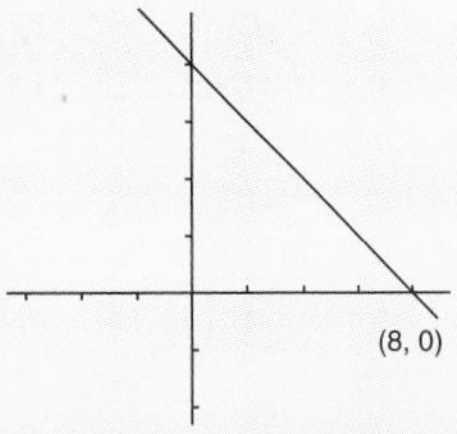

4. a. *x*-intercept: (5, 0)
   y-intercept: (0, -5)

   b.

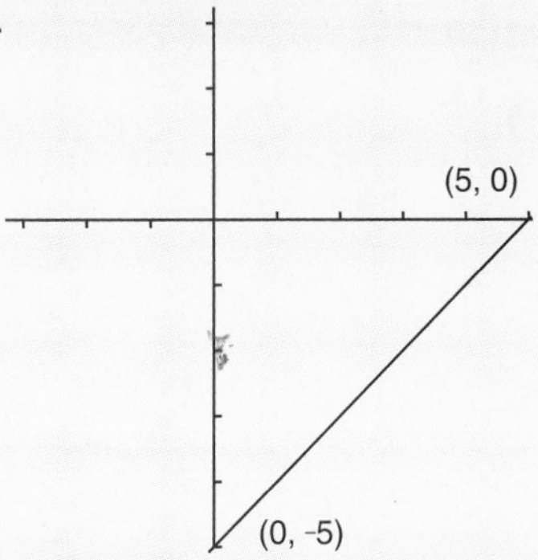

5. a. *x*-intercept: none
   y-intercept: (0, 1)

POINTS ON AND OFF GRAPHS

FIND AN EQUATION

Problem 19 addresses the key concept of this lesson and of the chapter so far. Keep its questions in mind when teaching these sections. You may ask students to read this problem before starting work on these sections, so that they will use the sections well.

For problems 10-13, you should probably discuss what "between the two graphs" means. The best way to determine if a point *P* is between the two graphs is to draw a vertical line through *P*. If *P* is between the points where the vertical line meets the two graphs, it can be said to be between the graphs.

Here is an interesting activity to throw light on the concept of which points are on and which are off the graphs. Use a graphing calculator or computer program to graph a function. Then challenge the students to erase the graph by using the calculator's point-plotting commands. For example, on the TI-81 use the PT-CHG command on the DRAW menu to erase a graph point by point.

Problem 13 previews slope and the idea of translating a graph up and down. With a graphing calculator, it can be extended to ask for many graphs between the given two.

In problems like 14-18 it is important to have a class discussion in order to show students the wide range of possible answers. Students working alone or in a small group are likely to find only a few solutions, and will not get as much out of this section as they could in a teacher-guided discussion.

GRAPHS THROUGH THE ORIGIN

This section gives students an opportunity to apply what they have learned in the previous sections to a specific case: the point (0, 0). Be sure to discuss problem 21 in class.

Lesson 5 will focus on *lines* through the origin.

Follow these instructions for problems 10 through 12 below.

a. Make tables of values for the two functions given. Then graph them on the same pair of axes. Label at least three points on each graph.
b. Find and label a point that is not on either graph.
c. Find and label a point that is on both graphs (if there is one).
d. Find and label a point that is in the region between the two graphs.
e. Find and label a point that is neither on nor between the graphs.

10. $y = 2x$ and $y = 0.5x$

11. $y = x$ and $y = x + 2$

12. $y = x^2$ and $y = x^2 - 3$

13. For problems 10-12, find an equation whose graph is entirely contained between the two given graphs.

FIND AN EQUATION

In problems 14-17, find the equation of any graph that satisfies the characteristics given.

14. A second-degree function whose graph passes through the point (0, 0)

15. A second-degree function whose graph passes through the point (0, 1)

16. A third-degree function whose graph passes through the point (0, -1)

17. A first-degree function whose graph passes through the point (-1, -1)

18. a. Write any equation whose graph contains the point (1, 2).
b. Write any other equation whose graph passes through the point (1, 2).
c. Graph the two equations. Where do they intersect?

19. **Report** Write a report explaining the answers to these questions. Use examples in your explanations.
a. Given an equation, how can you figure out which points lie on its graph?
b. Given a point and an equation, how can you tell whether or not the point lies on the graph of the equation?

GRAPHS THROUGH THE ORIGIN

20. Which of the following equations have graphs that go through the origin? How could one tell without actually graphing them?
a. $y = 2x - 6$ b. $y = x^2 - x$
c. $y = -x^3 - 4$

21. Give three equations (one each of first, second, and third degree) that satisfy each of these two given conditions.
a. The graph will pass through the origin.
b. The graph will not pass through the origin.

22. Write the equation of a graph that lies in quadrants I and III *only* and
a. passes through the origin;
b. does not pass through the origin.

23. **Summary** Explain how you can tell from an equation whether or not its graph goes through the origin. Give some examples.

4.4 SOLUTIONS

5. b.

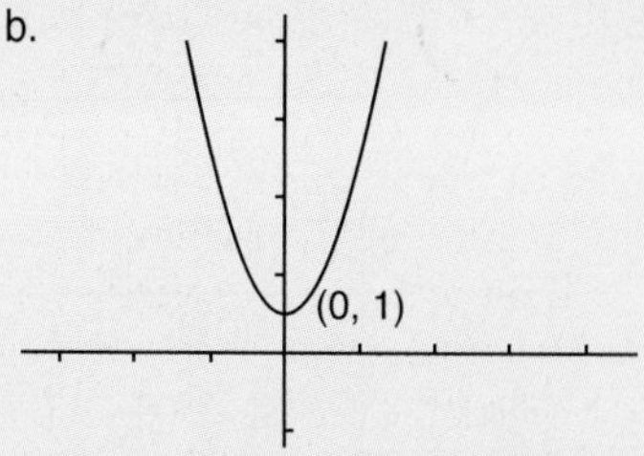

6. Lea is correct. Find the product before the difference, according to the order of operations rules.

7. Analyzing $y = 8 - 2x$
a. Yes: $8 - 2(2) = 8 - 4 = 4$
b. No: -4 is not equal to $8 - 2(2)$ which equals 4.
c. No: 6 is not equal to $8 - 2(0.5)$ which equals 7.
d. No: -6 is not equal to $8 - 2(0.5)$ which equals 7.
e. No: -10 is not equal to $8 - 2(-1)$ which equals 10.
f. Yes: $8 - 2(-1) = 8 + 2 = 10$.
So *a* and *f* lie on the graph.

8. a.

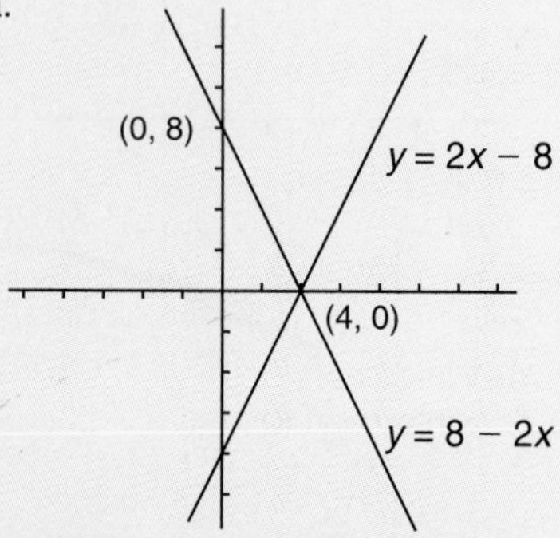

b. Student checks work using the graph
c. (4, 0)

(Solutions continued on page 512)

THINKING WRITING

4.A The Bicycle Trip

Sally is riding her bike on a trip with her bicycle club. She left the staging area in Chapley at 10 A.M. and took a break at a rest area located about halfway to the final destination of Berkhill, 70 miles away. Neil is driving the sweep vehicle, a van with food, water, first aid, and a bicycle rack. The distance-time graph below shows their progress. There are train tracks along the road. The progress of a train is also shown on the graph.

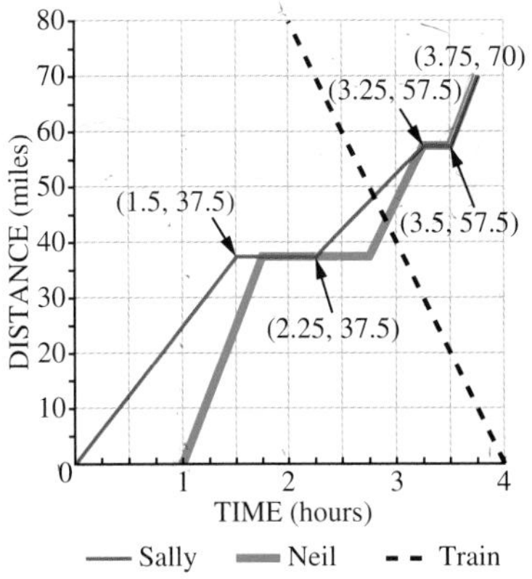

1. Compare Sally's and Neil's progress. Who left first? Where did she or he stop? What happened at the end? What was the total distance covered?
2. Including the origin, the coordinates of six points on Sally's graph are given. Describe her ride between consecutive points.
   a. At what time did each leg of her trip start and end? How far did she ride each time? How long did it take? How long were her breaks?
   b. How fast was she going during each leg of the trip?
3. a. If you were to guess about which part of the trip was downhill or uphill, what would you guess? Why?
   b. How else might one account for the different speeds?
4. How fast did Neil drive in each leg of his trip?
5. Describe the train's progress. Which way was it going? Where and when did it pass Sally and Neil?
6. Where were Sally, Neil, and the train at 12:30 P.M.?
7. At what times were Sally, Neil, and the train 20 miles from the staging area?
8. The equation of the train's motion is $D = 160 - 40t$.
   a. Choose three points on the train's graph and check that their coordinates satisfy the equation.
   b. Do any points in Sally's and Neil's graphs satisfy the train's equation? If so, which ones?
9. **Summary**
   a. In a distance-time graph, what does it mean if two points are on the same horizontal line? On the same vertical line?
   b. As you go from left to right on the graph, what is the meaning of a part that goes up? Down? What is the meaning of a horizontal segment? Why is a vertical segment impossible?
   c. What is the significance of a point that belongs to the motion graphs of two different people?
10. **Report** Tell the story of the bicycle trip. Use information you gathered from the graph. Make guesses about the trip. Include a graph for Irva, another member of the bicycle club. She too left at 10 A.M. and stopped at the rest area.

4.A SOLUTIONS

1. Sally left first. She rode 37.5 miles in 1.5 hours. She rested for 45 min. and then rode 20 miles in one hour. She rested again for 15 min. before her last ride of 12.5 miles in 15 min. Her total time for the 70-mile trip was 3 hours and 45 min.

   Neil started 1 hour after Sally and drove 37.5 miles in 45 min. when he caught up with Sally during her first rest. He stopped for one hour and then drove 20 miles in 30 min. where he caught up again with Sally who was beginning her second rest. They stayed together from then on with Neil stopping for Sally's 15- min. rest and then staying with her on the last 15 min., 12.5-mile leg of the trip. His total time for the 70-mile trip was 2 hours and 45 min.

2. a. Sally's first leg started at 10 A.M. and ended 37.5 miles later at 11:30 A.M. The second leg started at 12:15 P.M. and ended 20 miles later at 1:15 P.M. Her final leg started at 1:30 P.M. and ended 12.5 miles later at 1:45 P.M. She took two breaks: the first from 11:30 A.M. to 12:15 P.M. (45 min.) and the second from 1:15 P.M. to 1:30 P.M. for a total of 1 hour resting time. Her total riding time was 2 hours and 45 min. The entire trip took 3 hours and 45 min.
   b. Sally traveled 23 mph on the first leg, 20 mph on the second leg, and she hustled at 50 mph for the final leg.

(Solutions continued on page 513)

THINKING WRITING **4.A The Bicycle Trip**

Core Sequence: 1-10

Suitable for Homework: 4-10

Useful for Assessment: 9-10

What this Assignment is About:
- Interpreting graphs
- Speed, distance, time

This activity is reminiscent of Chapter 2, **Thinking/Writing 2.B (The Car Trip)**. A Cartesian graph can carry considerably more information than a function diagram, and therefore it is a more powerful tool, but on the other hand it is somewhat harder to interpret.

If problems 1-3 are discussed in class, the rest of the assignment, while challenging, should be accessible to most students. Problem 1 should help establish the general meaning of the graph. Problem 2 should help students learn how to interpret specific data points on it. Some students may need help with problem 2b. Problem 3 is intended to challenge the natural but erroneous assumption that *uphill* on the graph corresponds to *uphill* in the motion represented. In fact, given Sally's speed, one might guess that much of the trip is downhill or flat, except perhaps for the very last stretch.

Note that time on the graph is indicated with Sally's ride starting at time 0, while in fact she started at 10 A.M. You could discuss whether it would be better to label the graph with the actual times, and let students do it either way in their report.

You may have students compare with each other the graphs they created for Irva in problem 10 and discuss their plausibility. The discussion can be continued with the whole class by putting the most interesting graphs on transparencies and discussing them.

▼ 4.5.
Lines Through the Origin

Core Sequence: 1-20

Suitable for Homework: 10-22

Useful for Assessment: 10, 13-14, 20

What this Lesson is About:

- Proportional thinking
- Preview of direct variation
- Preview of slope
- Application to speed, distance, time

Problems 1-2 review the ideas that ended Lesson 4, in the more specific case of linear functions.

This lesson previews direct variation, which is the subject of the next lesson, and slope, which will be studied in depth in Chapter 8.

RATIO

The main point of this section is that points whose x- and y-coordinates are in the same ratio are on a line though the origin. Conversely, the coordinates of points that are on the same line through the origin have the same ratio.

The problems should guide students to this discovery, particularly since they have seen similar rectangles not long ago (Chapter 3, Lesson 12).

LESSON 4.5

Lines Through the Origin

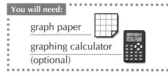

You will need:
- graph paper
- graphing calculator (optional)

Definition: Since the graphs of first-degree equations are straight lines, these equations are also called *linear* equations.

1. Predict whether or not the graph of each linear equation will pass through the origin. Explain how you know, using graphs or calculations.
   a. $y = 4 - 2x$ b. $y = -2x$
   c. $y = 2x$ d. $y = 2x - 4$

2. Write two linear equations which you think will have graphs through the origin. Explain your reasoning.

RATIO

Lara and Lea were arguing about points and graphs. Lea said, "If the point (1, 4) lies on the line, then the point (2, 8) must also lie on the line." Lara showed her that she was wrong by drawing three lines.

3. On graph paper, draw a line that goes
   a. through both points;
   b. through (1, 4) but not through (2, 8);
   c. through (2, 8) but not through (1, 4).

4. Of the three lines you drew in problem 3, which goes through the origin?

5. a. Plot and label at least three more points that are on the line through (1, 4) and (2, 8).
   b. Find the equation of the line through (1, 4) and (2, 8).

6. Plot these eight points on the same axes. Label them with their coordinates.

(1, 2)	(-1, -2)	(1, -2)
(-1, 2)	(3, 6)	(-3, -6)
(6, 3)	(6, -3)	

   a. Draw a line connecting each point with the origin. Which points lie on the same line through the origin?
   b. Explain how to find the equations of the lines you drew.

Definition: The *ratio* of a to b is the result of the division a/b.

Example: The ratio of 6 to 3 is 6/3 or 2, while the ratio of 3 to 6 is 3/6, or 1/2, or 0.5.

7. a. Write two (x, y) pairs for which the ratio of y to x is 1/3.
   b. Plot these two points and graph the straight line through them. Find the equation of the line.
   c. Write two (x, y) pairs for which the ratio of y to x is 3.
   d. Plot these two points and graph the straight line through them. Find the equation of the line.

4.5 SOLUTIONS

1. b and c pass through the origin. We can check 1a by substitution: $y = 4 - 2x$: 0 is not equal to $4 - 2(0) = 4$. So $y = 4 - 2x$ does not pass through the origin.
2. Answers will vary. One possible solution is $y = 6x$: $0 = 6(0) = 0$. The coordinates (0, 0) can be substituted into the equation with valid results.
3.

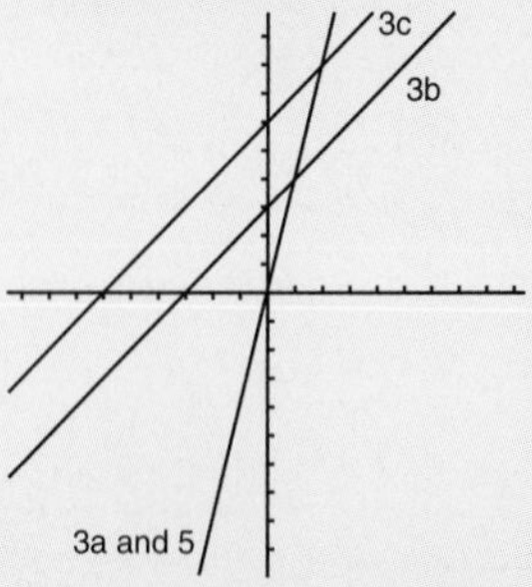

4. The first line through (1, 4) and (2, 8) also goes through the origin.
5. a. See solution #3.
   b. $y = 4x$
6.

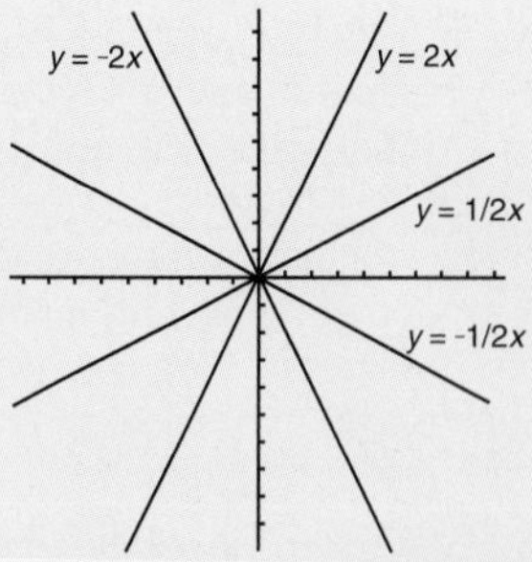

   a. (3, 6), (1, 2), (-1, -2) and (-3, -6) lie on the same line through the origin. (-1, 2) and (1, -2) also lie on the same line through the origin.
   b. To find the equation of the lines, look for a pattern. y is a multiple of x, $y = kx$. To find k divide y by x. (Or find the ratio of y to x.)
7. a. Sample pairs (6, 2) and (-3, -1)
   b.

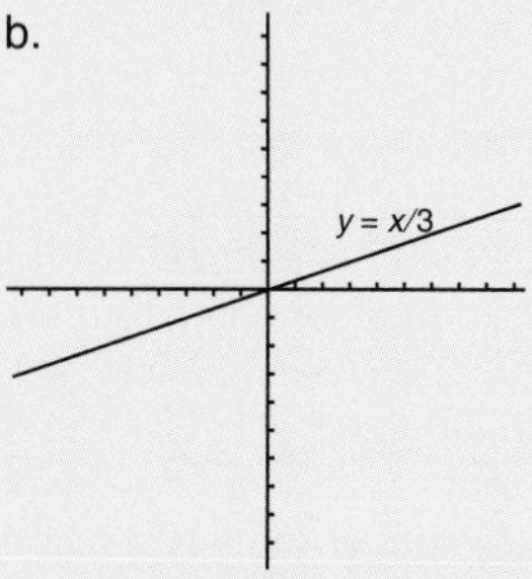

   c. Sample pairs (2, 6) and (-1, -3)

8. For each line in the graph below, find three points on the line. Then find an equation for the line.

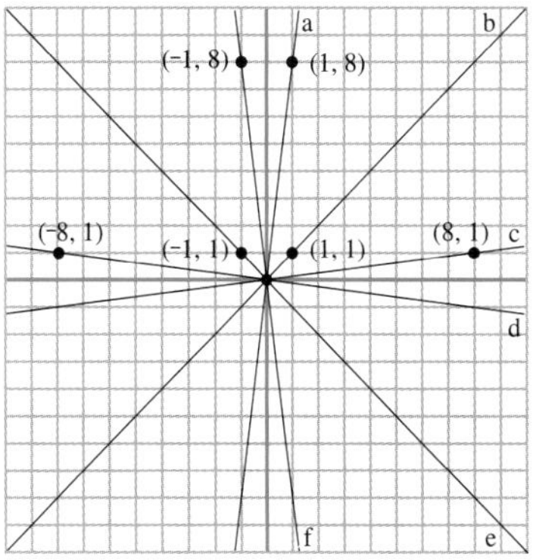

9. Explain how you can find more points on the same line through the origin as (4, 5) without drawing a graph. Then check by graphing the line. Find the equation of the line.

Lea noticed that for the points (1, 4) and (2, 8) the ratio of the *y*-value to the *x*-value was the same. That is, 4/1 = 8/2. She guessed that (100, 400) will lie on the same line through the origin because the ratio of the *y*-value to the *x*-value is also 4.

10. Tell whether or not you agree with Lea, and why.

11. Find a point whose coordinates have the same ratio of *y* to *x* as the point (4, 12). Does this point lie on the same line through the origin as (4, 12)? If so, find the equation of this line.

12. a. Graph the line through (-1, 2) and (3, 4).
b. Is the ratio of 5 to -10 equal to the ratio of -1 to 2?
c. Is the point (5, -10) on the line? Explain why or why not.

13. Generalization
a. What would be the ratio of the coordinates of points on the line through the origin and the point (*a, b*)? Explain.
b. If $b/a = d/c$, what can you say about the line joining (*a, b*) to (*c, d*)? Explain.

14. Summary Explain what ratio has to do with lines through the origin.

SPEED

The table shows the amount of time it took several people to travel the distances given.

Person	Time (hours)	Distance (kilometers)
A	3	80
B	7	140
C	12	320
D	1	30
E	2	30
F	1	20
G	5	150

15. a. Draw a pair of axes and label the vertical axis *distance* and the horizontal axis *time*. Plot and label the points in the table. Draw lines connecting each point with the origin.
b. Which points lie on the same line through the origin?

16. Use the table and your graph to answer these questions.
a. Which people are traveling at the same speed?
b. Who is traveling faster, *A* or *B*?
c. How far will *A* have traveled in four hours?

SPEED

*T*his section connects what was learned in the previous one with the material in Lesson 1 and in **Thinking/Writing 4.A**.

4.5 S O L U T I O N S

d.

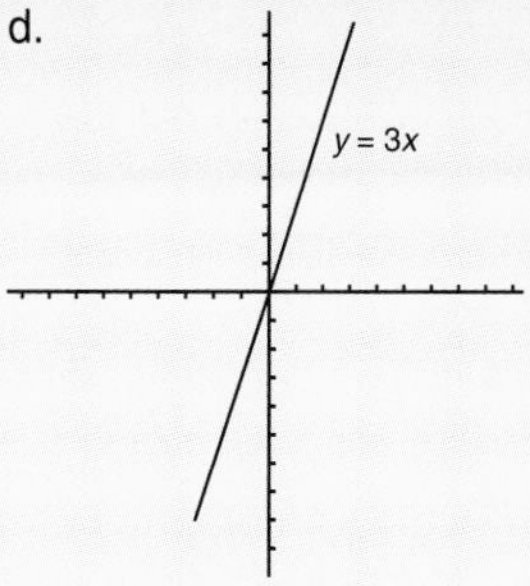

8. The following are sample ordered pairs:
a. (0.5, 4), (0.25, 2), (-1, -8); *y* = 8*x*
b. (2, 2), (-1, -1), (3.5, 3.5); *y* = *x*
c. (4, 0.5), (2, 0.25), (-8, -1); *y* = (1/8)*x*
d. (4, -0.5), (2, -0.25), (8, -1); *y* = -(1/8)*x*
e. (-2, 2), (3, -3), (2.5, -2.5); *y* = -*x*
f. (0.5, -4), (0.25, -2), (1, -8); *y* = -8*x*

9. Find the ratio of *y* to *x* which is 5/4, then find other pairs of coordinates in this ratio by multiplying *y* and *x* by a constant. For example, multiplying 4 and 5 by 2 results in (8, 10) which also has the ratio of 10/8 = 5/4.

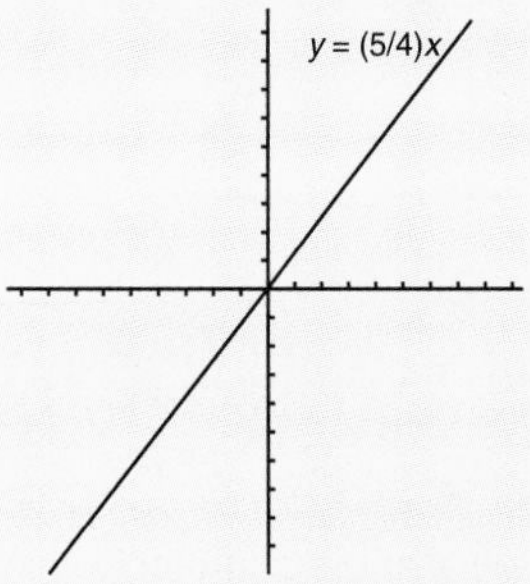

10. I agree with her because the ratio of *y* to *x* in (100, 400) is 400/100 = 4/1. When the *y* to *x* ratio of coordinates remains constant, the points lie on the same line that goes through the origin.

11. Sample point (1, 3). Yes. *y* = 3*x*.

12. a.

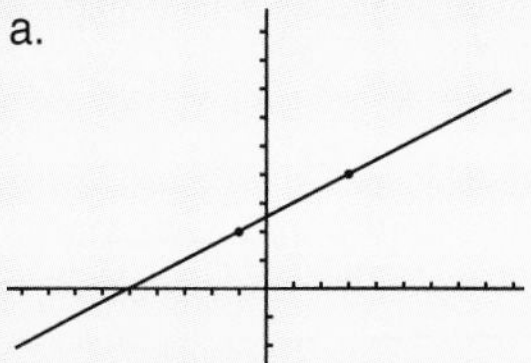

DISCOVERY *HAPPY NUMBERS*

This activity is well suited for group work. It is a good preview of Chapters 5 and 7, where it is useful for students to recognize perfect squares.

For problem 22, students should be able to describe what the final outcome is for "unhappy" numbers.

17. a. *H* has been traveling two hours at the same speed as *G*. Add *H* to your graph.

b. I have been traveling four hours at the same speed as *A*. Add me to your graph.

18. *J* is traveling faster than *B* but more slowly than *D*. Draw one possible distance-time graph showing *J's* progress.

19. Each line you drew has an equation that relates distance to time. Find these equations and add them to your graph.

20. Summary

a. Explain how one can think of speed as a ratio.

b. If you are given time and distance for two travelers, explain how to use calculations or graphs to compare their speeds.

DISCOVERY *HAPPY NUMBERS*

Take the number 23.
Square each digit and add.
$2^2 + 3^2 = 13$
Repeat this process.
$1^2 + 3^2 = 10$
$1^2 + 0^2 = 1$
$1^2 = 1$
The final result is 1.

Whenever the final result of this procedure is 1, the original number is called a *happy* number. So 23 is a happy number.

21. There are 17 two-digit happy numbers. Try to find all of them. It will save you time and help you look for patterns if you keep a neat record of the above process for each number.

22. Describe any patterns you notice.

4.5 SOLUTIONS

12. b. Yes, because both ratios equal -(1/2).

c. No, because the line containing (-1, 2) and (5, -10) passes through the origin. The line containing (-1, 2) and (3, 4) does not.

13. a. $y/x = b/a$. We found in this lesson that if a line passes through the origin, then the coordinates of the points on the line have the same *y* to *x* ratio.

b. The line containing (a, b) and (c, d) passes through the origin because if two points have the same *y* to *x* ratio, then the line containing those points passes through the origin.

14. If a line passes through the origin, then the coordinates of the points on the line have the same *y* to *x* ratio. If the coordinates of a set of points have the same *y* to *x* ratio, then they are on the same line which passes through the origin.

15. a.

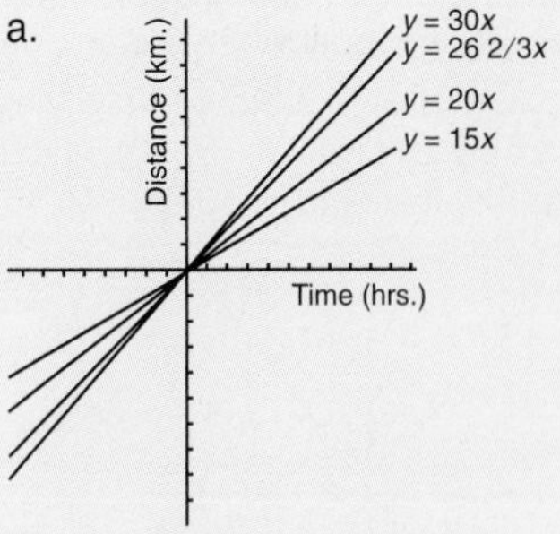

b. (1, 30) and (5, 150)
(1, 20) and (7, 140)
(3, 80) and (12, 320)

16. a. Traveling at the same speed are: *A* and *C*, *B* and *F*, and *D* and *G*

b. *A* (26 and 2/3 km/hr) is traveling faster than *B* (20 km/hr.)

c. *A* will have traveled 106 and 2/3 km.

17. a. Add point (2, 60) to graph in number 15.

b. Add point (4, 106 2/3) to graph in number 15.

18.

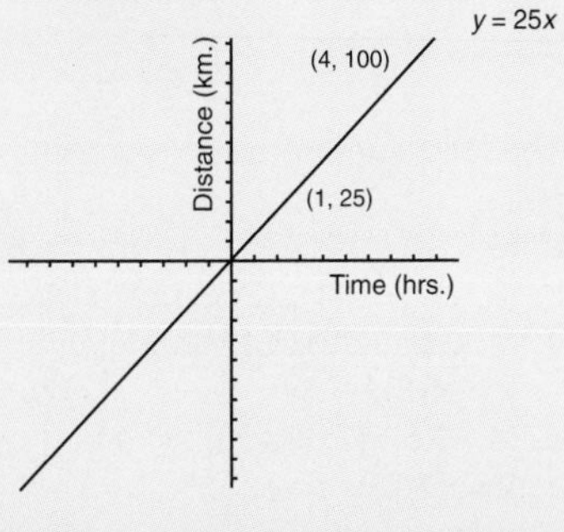

(Solutions continued on page 514)

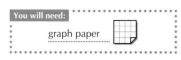

LESSON 4.6 In the Lab

You will need: graph paper

A MYSTERY LIQUID

Reg, Bea, and Gabe were doing an experiment in science class. They had an unknown liquid whose volume they measured in a graduated cylinder. A graduated cylinder is a tall, narrow container that is used for measuring liquid volume accurately. They used a cylinder that weighed 50 grams and measured volume in milliliters. They used a balance to find the weight of the liquid to the nearest gram.

Reg's Data

Volume	Weight
10 ml	16 g
20 ml	32 g
50 ml	80 g
80 ml	128 g

1. Plot Reg's data, with *weight* on the vertical axis and *volume* on the horizontal axis.

2. Does it make sense to connect the points on your graph? Explain.

3. Find an equation relating weight to volume.

4. Estimate the weight of:
a. 60 ml of liquid;
b. 1 ml of liquid.

5. If you add 30 ml to the volume, how much are you adding to the weight? See if you get the same answer in two different cases.

6. If you double the volume, do you double the weight?

Bea's Data

Weight	Volume
16 g	10 ml
32 g	20 ml
48 g	30 ml
64 g	40 ml

7. Plot Bea's data with *volume* on the vertical axis and *weight* on the horizontal axis.

8. Connect the points on your graph with a line and write an equation for the line.

9. Estimate the volume of:
a. 100 g of liquid; b. 1 g of liquid.

10. Compare Bea's graph with Reg's graph. Explain the similarities and differences.

We say that Reg graphed weight versus volume, while Bea graphed volume versus weight.

11. If you add 10 ml to the volume, how much are you adding to the weight? See if you get the same answer in three different cases. Is the answer consistent with what you found in Reg's data?

> **Definition:** *Density* equals weight per unit of volume. This means that to find the density of the mystery liquid, you would find the weight of 1 ml of the liquid. (Actually, scientists use *mass* rather than *weight,* but we will use weight which is equivalent for our purposes.)

4.6 In the Lab

Core Sequence: 1-24

Suitable for Homework: 7-20, 23-27

Useful for Assessment: 24

What this Lesson is About:
- Direct variation
- Application to density, weight, volume
- Preview of slope

The data presented in this lesson involve no measurement error, in order for the mathematical structure to be more apparent. If you have access to a science lab, you may carry out your own experiment similar to the one described in this lesson. You would then have to deal with the issue of measurement error, which will be addressed in Lesson 7.

A MYSTERY LIQUID
THE MYSTERY GROWS

Because the investigation is very guided, students should be able to carry it out without too much trouble. The risk is that they will do it mechanically and not really get a sense of the patterns that unfold. The key point of the lesson is the concept of direct variation, which is discussed in detail in the next section.

4.6 SOLUTIONS

1.

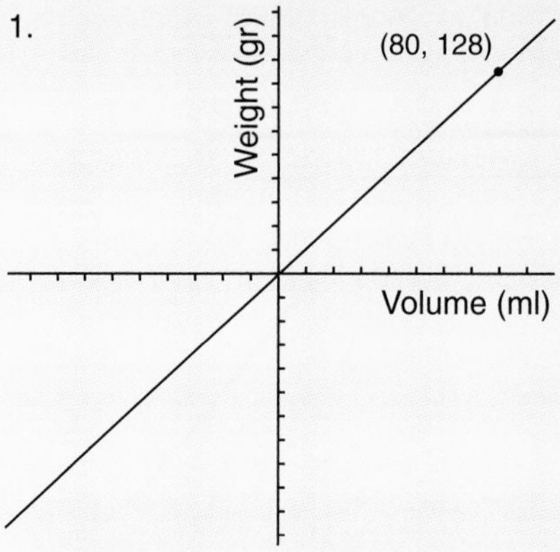

2. Yes. The four points fall on a line. Each unit of volume has a constant weight (1.6 grams). So each change in volume should result in a proportional change in weight.

3. $w = (8/5)v$ where w = weight in grams and v = volume in milliliters.

4. a. $w = (8/5) \cdot 60 = 96$ grams
b. $w = (8/5) \cdot 1 = 1.6$ grams

5. 48 grams. Yes, from (20, 32) to (50, 80) and from (50, 80) to (80, 128)

6. Yes

7.

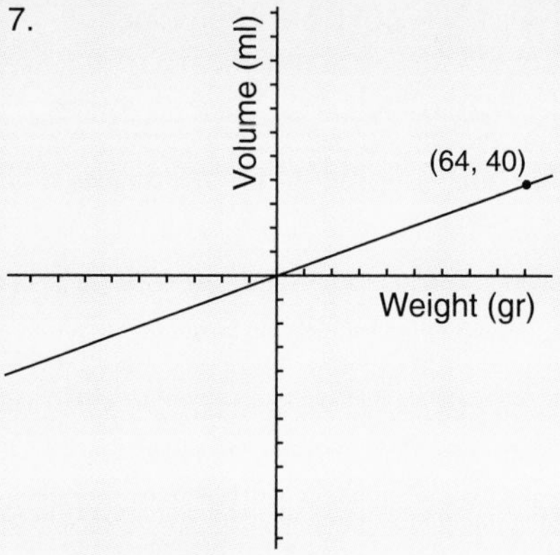

8. $V = (5/8)w$

9. a. $V = (5/8) \cdot 100 = 62.5$ ml
b. $V = (5/8) \cdot 1 = 0.625$ ml

10. Both graphs are lines that contain the origin. The points on Reg's graph have a common weight to volume

Since Reg's and Bea's data switch the role of x and y, the corresponding functions are inverses of each other. However, unless the axes are marked with the same units, the graphs are not symmetric with respect to the $y = x$ line. In fact, if the axes do not have the same scale, the $y = x$ line is *not* at a 45-degree angle. This, not the standard equal scales used in traditional algebra courses, is the most common situation in all applications of mathematics.

Gabe's mistake is that he included the weight of the graduated cylinder in his data. For problem 20, do not teach any algorithms for finding the equation. If students are stuck, suggest that they think of what made up the total weight indicated in Gabe's data. They should see that it is the sum of the weight of the cylinder, which is constant (50 grams), and the weight of the liquid, which was figured out in problem 3.

DIRECT VARIATION

Problems 21-23 should probably be done in class to allow for a full discussion of the ideas that came up in problems 1-20.

The pattern referred to in problem 23a is that for every 10 ml added, the weight increases by 16 grams, or for every milliliter added, the weight increases by 1.6 grams.

12. Find the density of the mystery liquid, using three different pairs of weight/volume values from Reg's and Bea's data. Do all your answers agree? Explain.

13. In problems 4b and 9b, you have found the weight in grams of one ml of liquid, and the volume in ml of one gram. Multiply the two numbers. Explain the result.

THE MYSTERY GROWS

Gabe's Data:

Volume	Weight
10 ml	66 g
20 ml	82 g
40 ml	114 g
60 ml	146 g

14. Draw a pair of axes and label the vertical axis *weight* and the horizontal axis *volume.* Plot Gabe's data.

15. If you double the volume, does the weight double? Check this in two cases.

16. If you add 20 ml, how much weight are you adding? Is this consistent with what you learned from Reg's and Bea's data?

17. *According to Gabe's graph,* what is the weight of 0 ml of the liquid? Does this make sense?

18. What might be the real meaning of the y-intercept on Gabe's graph? Did Gabe make a mistake? Explain.

19. Find the density of the mystery liquid by dividing weight by volume for three different pairs of values from Gabe's data. Do all your answers agree? Explain.

20. Write an equation that expresses weight as a function of volume for Gabe's data.

DIRECT VARIATION

Definition: If the relationship between two variables x and y can be expressed in the form $y = mx$, we call this a *direct variation,* or say that *y varies directly with x.*

21. Which of Reg's, Bea's, and Gabe's data are an example of a direct variation? Explain.

22. Compare Gabe's graph to Reg's. How are they the same and how are they different?

23. There are number patterns in all the data.

a. What pattern is there in all of Reg's, Bea's, and Gabe's data?

b. What patterns are true only of Reg's and Bea's data?

24. **Summary** What do you know about direct variation? Be sure to discuss equation, graph, and number patterns. You may get ideas from this lesson and Lesson 5.

ratio of 8/5 and points on Bea's graph have a common volume to weight ratio of 5/8. The coordinates are reversed, for example (10, 16) on Reg's graph is (16, 10) on Bea's graph.

11. 16 grams. Yes, this is consistent.

12. Three possible ratios are:
16/10 = 1.6 g/ml 32/20 = 1.6 g/ml
48/30 = 1.6 g/ml
All solutions agree since the weight is proportional to the volume.

13. (8/5)(5/8) = 1. The numbers are reciprocals. The product of a pair of reciprocals is 1.

14.
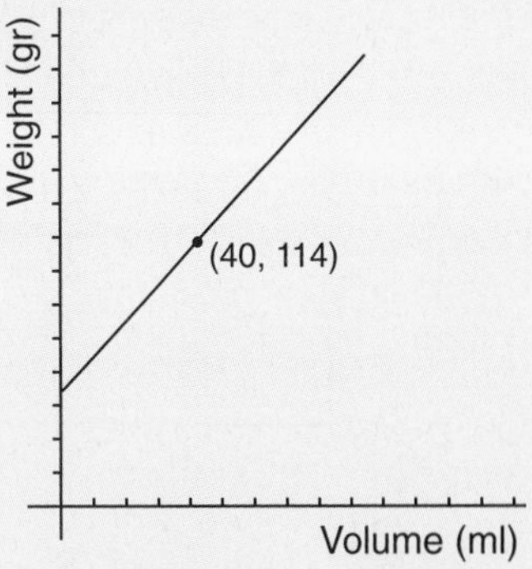

15. No. When volume doubles from 10 ml to 20 ml, the weight of 66g changes to 82g, not 132g. Volume change of 20 ml to 40 ml results in weight change from 82g to 114g, rather than 164g.

16. 32g. Yes, this is consistent with Reg's and Bea's data.

17. 50g. No. 0 ml of liquid should weigh 0 grams.

18. 50g represents the weight of the graduated cylinder when it is empty. Gabe should subtract 50g from each weight so his points will show the weight of the liquid only.

19. 146/60 ≈ 2.433g/ml
114/40 = 2.85g/ml
82/20 = 4.1g/ml
Gabe's points fall on a line that does not contain the origin. The weight to volume ratios of the coordinates are not the same, so the density calculation is not constant.

20. Weight = 1.6 · Volume + 50

21. Reg and Bea's data are examples of direct variation. Reg's equation is $w = (8/5)V$ and Bea's equation is

OTHER SUBSTANCES

25. The graph shows the relationship between weight and volume for some familiar substances. The substances are aluminum, cork, gold, ice, iron, and oak. Which substance do you think is represented by each line? Explain why you think so.

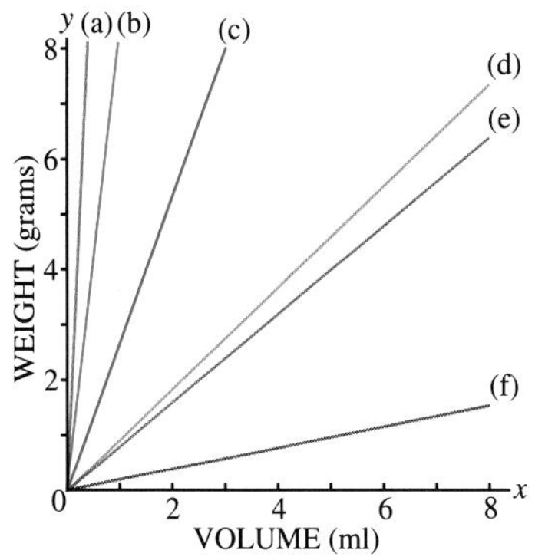

26. Using the graph, estimate the densities of the substances in problem 25.

27. Project

a. Look up the densities of those substances in a science book, almanac, or other reference book. How close were your estimates?

b. Based on your research, what do you think the mystery liquid is? Could it be water? Explain.

OTHER SUBSTANCES

This optional section is straightforward and gives students a chance to apply what they learned in the lesson.

4.6 SOLUTIONS

$V = (5/8)w$. These are both in the form of $y = mx$.

22. Gabe's and Reg's graphs have the same steepness. Each of Reg's points is 50g lower than each corresponding point on Gabe's graph. The weight-intercepts are different, Gabe's at (10, 50) and Reg's at (0, 0).

23. a. For each change of 10 ml of volume in Reg's, Bea's, and Gabe's data, there is a corresponding change of 16g of weight.
    b. Reg's and Bea's data have a constant weight to volume ratio for each pair of coordinates. Gabe's coordinates each have a different ratio.

24. Direct variation can be expressed in the form $y = mx$. The graph of a direct variation equation is a line containing the origin. The coordinates of each point on a direct variation have a constant y to x ratio. For each constant change in x there is a corresponding constant change in y.

25. From densest to least dense, the substances are gold, iron, aluminum, ice, oak, and cork. For each change of one unit of volume, graph (a) has the largest change in weight. Its weight/volume ratio (or density) would be the largest. Graph f is the least steep of all so its weight/volume ratio would be the smallest.

26. a. $8/0.5 = 16$
    b. $8/1 = 8$
    c. $8/3 \approx 2.67$
    d. $7.5/8 = 0.9375$
    e. $6.6/8 = 0.825$
    f. $1.5/7 \approx 0.2$

27. a. Student research
    b. Dishwashing liquid

▼ 4.7
Real Numbers and Estimation

Core Sequence: 1-13

Suitable for Homework: 7-19

Useful for Assessment: 7, 12, 18

What this Lesson is About:

- Measurement error
- Fitting a line to data
- Estimation
- Creating algorithms

In the real world, numbers rarely have the perfection of textbook numbers. In this lesson we try to address this in two ways:

- introducing the idea of measurement error, a crucial concept in statistics and science;
- discussing algorithms for mental calculations leading to estimates.

A graphing calculator could be used, but is not essential.

MEASUREMENT ERROR

Make sure the students do not connect the dots in the graph. The idea of fitting a line is to use it rather than line segments connecting the dots to approximate the relationship between the variables.

Some teachers pass out spaghetti (uncooked!) to place on the graph as a help in finding the line of best fit. At this level, eyeballing the best fit is satisfactory.

If you use a graphing calculator for problem 2, do not use the automatic line-fitting feature. Instead, plot the points and try graphing various lines through the origin until you find one that provides a satisfactory fit.

In problem 6, students may use the average of the four numbers they found in problem 5, or they may pick a number in the middle of the range, so that there would actually be a total of three methods to discuss in problem 7. Class discussion of this would be useful.

LESSON 4.7

Real Numbers and Estimation

You will need:

graph paper

graphing calculator (optional)

MEASUREMENT ERROR

The three tables in Lesson 6 contained data that were invented. You can tell because all the points lie exactly on a line. In real experiments measurements can never be exact. This table contains more realistic data.

Volume	Weight
10 ml	32 g
20 ml	63 g
50 ml	146 g
80 ml	245 g

1. Draw and label a pair of axes and plot these points.
2. You cannot draw a straight line through all the points, but draw one that passes as closely as possible to all of them. Be sure your line goes through the origin. (Explain why it must pass through the origin.)
3. What is the equation of the line you drew? (Hint: Choose a point on the line to help you figure this out.)
4. Based on your answer to problem 3, what would you estimate the density of the substance to be?
5. Find the ratio of weight to volume for each data point in the table.
6. Based on your calculations in problem 5, what do you estimate the density of the substance to be?
7. **Summary** You estimated the density of this substance in two different ways. If you did not get the same answer using both methods, explain any differences. Which method do you like better, and why?

ESTIMATING TEMPERATURE

In Chapter 3, Lesson 8, you learned this rule for converting Celsius to Fahrenheit: *Multiply the Celsius temperature by 1.8. Add 32 to the result.*
If

F = the Fahrenheit temperature and
C = the Celsius temperature,

then this statement can be written as a function:

$$F = 1.8\,C + 32.$$

8. Draw and label a pair of axes with F on the y-axis and C on the x-axis. Make a table of values, using values of C from -10 to 30. Use your table to graph the function $F = 1.8\,C + 32$. Label a few points on your graph.

Abe doesn't like to multiply by 1.8. Since 1.8 is a little less than 2, and 32 is a little more than 30, he made up this rule for estimating: *To estimate the Fahrenheit temperature, multiply the Celsius temperature by 2 and add 30.*

9. Using the letters C and F as was done in problem 8, write a function for Abe's rule.
10. Make a table using values of C from -10 to 30 for the function you wrote for Abe's rule. Use your table to graph the function on the same pair of axes as you used in problem 8.

4.7 SOLUTIONS

1. 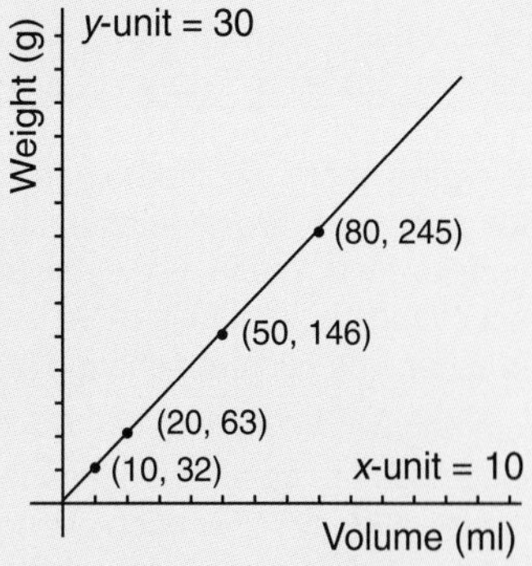

2. The line goes through the origin, because 0 ml of a substance weighs 0g.
3. Answers will vary. One possible solution is $w = 3.0625 \cdot v$.
4. 3.0625
5. 32/10 = 3.2, 63/20 = 3.15, 146/50 = 2.92, 245/80 = 3.0625.
6. Answers will vary: Sample solution is 3.1.
7. Answers will vary. Differences found in the densities will be due to a point taken that is close to but not exactly on the line.
8.

Celsius	Fahrenheit
-10	14
-5	23
0	32
10	50
20	68
30	86

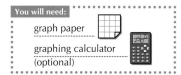

11. Compare the two graphs.
   a. How far off would Abe's estimate be if the Celsius temperature were 0?
   b. Compare the result from Abe's estimation method with the exact values for several other temperatures. Be sure to try some negative Celsius temperatures. Do you think Abe's method is a good one? Why or why not?
   c. There is one temperature for which Abe's estimation method gives the exact value. What is it?

12. For what range of temperatures would you judge Abe's method to be acceptable? Explain.

Sometimes exact answers are important. In everyday life, estimates or *rules of thumb* are often just as good. For example, Mr. and Mrs. Gral, who are planning a trip to Europe, are not really interested in knowing how to make exact temperature conversions. They just want some advice about what to wear.

13. Bea and Abe are making a chart for their parents' reference. Complete it.

Celsius temperature between __ and __	You should wear:
	your coolest clothes
	a sweater
	a coat
	heavy coat, gloves, hat, and scarf
	a space suit

ESTIMATING A TIP

Here is a method to figure out how much tip to leave for the server at a restaurant. Say the bill was for $20.73.

- Round up to the next even whole number of dollars, in this case 22.
- Add half of the number you got to the number, in this case 22 + 11 = 33.
- Round up to the next multiple of five, in this case 35.
- Divide by ten to get the tip, in this case $3.50.

14. What percentage of $20.73 is $3.50? (Round off your answer.)

15. Does this method always give the same percentage of the bill? Try it for several amounts to see whether the percentage varies. If it does, what seem to be the lowest and the highest value it will give?

Here is another method to figure out the tip.

- Divide the amount of the bill by ten. (In this case you would get $2.07.)
- Multiply the result by two. (In this case you would get $4.14.)
- Take the average of the two numbers, rounded to the nearest nickel.

16. a. What is the tip by this calculation?
   b. What percentage of the bill is it?

17. Does the second method always give the same percentage of the bill? Explain.

18. **Summary** Compare the two methods. Explain which one you prefer and why.

19. What percentage of the bill do you think is an appropriate tip? Create your own method to figure it without a calculator.

ESTIMATING TEMPERATURE

This section extends the work from Chapter 3, Lesson 8. Here students are given an alternate method for conversion that lends itself to mental calculation, but is less accurate.

A graphing calculator, including its trace feature, could be useful for this section.

Problem 13 could make for animated discussions. Students may use Abe's method to make conversions for this problem.

ESTIMATING A TIP

There will be more discussion of percent in Chapters 6 and 8. If your students' arithmetic is shaky, you can use this section as an opportunity to review the meaning of percent, but do not get bogged down.

Note that algorithms like these, while perfectly reasonable, are difficult to describe in terms of an equation.

For many students, the methods given would not be that easy to use. A tip of 10% or 20% is easier to estimate than 15%!

Problem 19 deserves group and/or class discussion.

4.7 SOLUTIONS

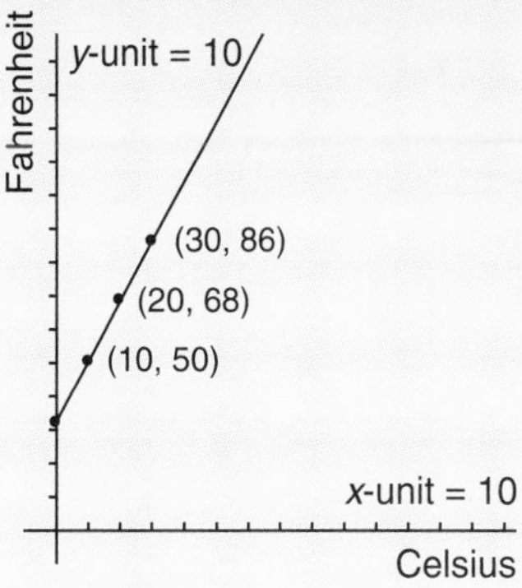

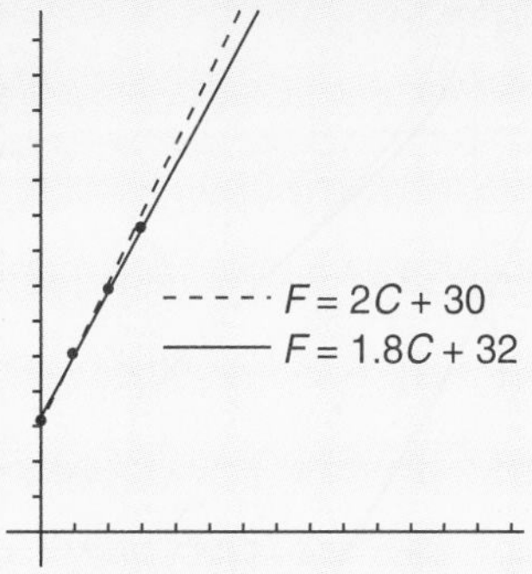

9. $F = 2C + 30$

10.

Celsius	Fahrenheit
-10	10
-5	20
0	30
10	50
20	70
30	90

11. a. At 0 degrees C Abe's estimate is 2 degrees F too low.
   b. Answers will vary. When looking at temperatures for weather, Abe's method is a good one because it is only a few degrees off. His method becomes less accurate as the Celsius temperatures get very large or very small.
   c. (10, 50)

12. Answers will vary. One possible solution is that Abe's method is acceptable for temperatures from -10 degrees C to 30 degrees C. See #11b for an explanation.

13. Answers will vary (higher numbers in warmer climates and lower numbers in colder climates). One possible solution is:

Celsius temperature between __ and __	You should wear:
above 20 degrees C	your coolest clothes
between 13 degrees C and 20 degrees C	a sweater
between 5 and 13 degrees C	a coat
between -20 and 5 degrees C	heavy coat, gloves, hat, and scarf
below -20 degrees C	a space suit

(Solutions continued on page 514)

▼ 4.8
Jarring Discoveries

Core Sequence: 1-10, 12-16, 25-30

Suitable for Homework: 5-11, 18-31

Useful for Assessment: 7-10, 14, 21, 24

What this Lesson is About:

- Application of direct variation to geometric questions
- Preview of slope
- Dimensions
- Preview of π
- Dividing on a calculator

*O*ur approach to direct variation has been very algebraic up to now. The point of this lesson is to give it some geometric meaning.

FLAT SCIENCE

*T*his activity relates our recent work with graphs and direct variation to the work we have been doing on area. What students will discover is that if the sides of the jar are parallel, then the area grows directly with the height. However, if the sides move apart from each other, the area grows faster and faster, and if they move towards each other, the area grows more and more slowly.

LESSON 4.8

Jarring Discoveries

You will need:

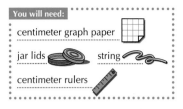

- centimeter graph paper
- jar lids
- string
- centimeter rulers

FLAT SCIENCE

Doctor Dimension is a flat scientist. He stores two-dimensional liquids in two-dimensional jars, like the ones shown in this figure.

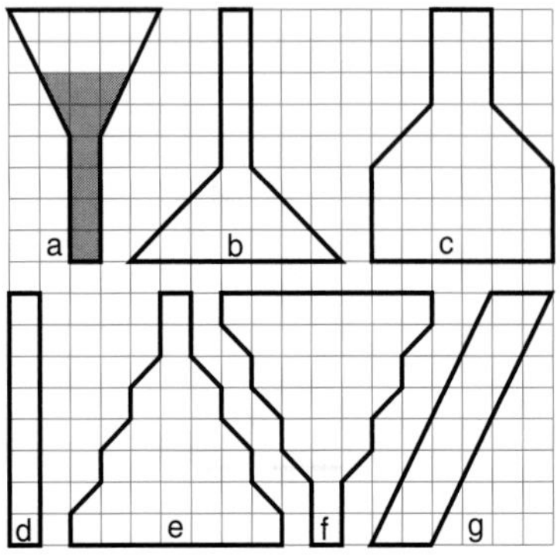

One day, as part of his scientific research, he decides to graph the amount of liquid in a jar as a function of the height of liquid. Since he lives in a two-dimensional world, liquid is measured in square units. For example, jar (a) is filled to a height of six units and contains eight square units of liquid.

The following graph represents jar (a).

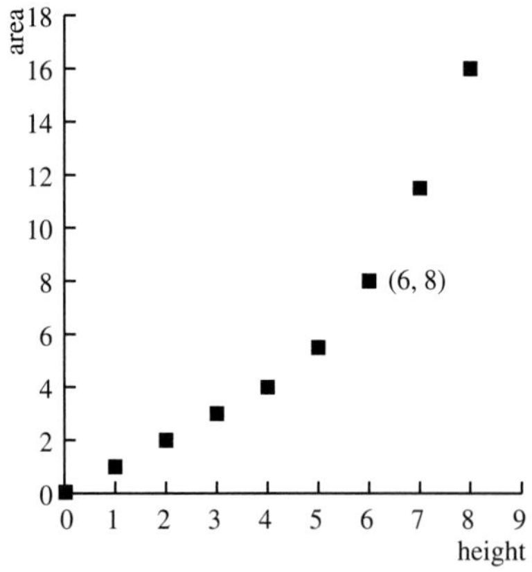

1. Some of the dots lie on one straight line. In which part of the graph does this happen? Explain why this is so.
2. Make a graph for each of the remaining jars.
3. For which jars is the area of liquid a direct variation function of the height? Explain.

4.8 SOLUTIONS

1. Points representing an equal number for height and area lie on a straight line. They are (0, 0), (1, 1), (2, 2), (3, 3), (4, 4).
2. b.

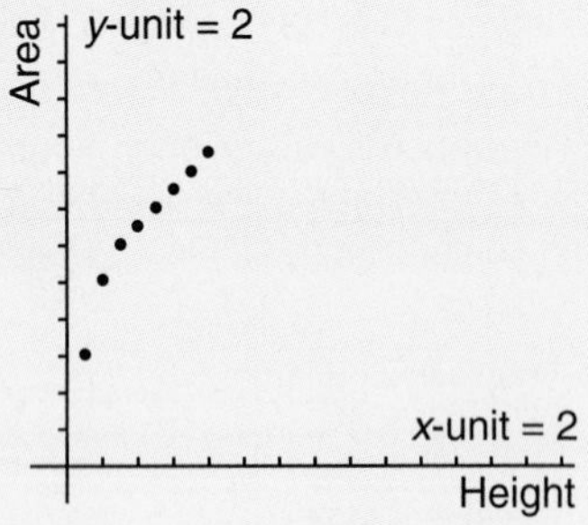

c.

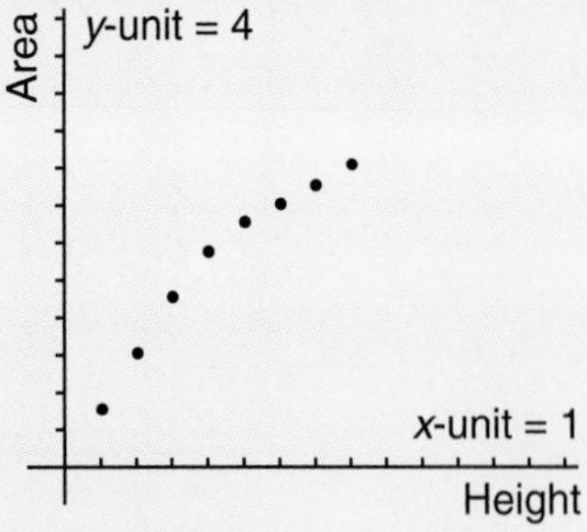

d.

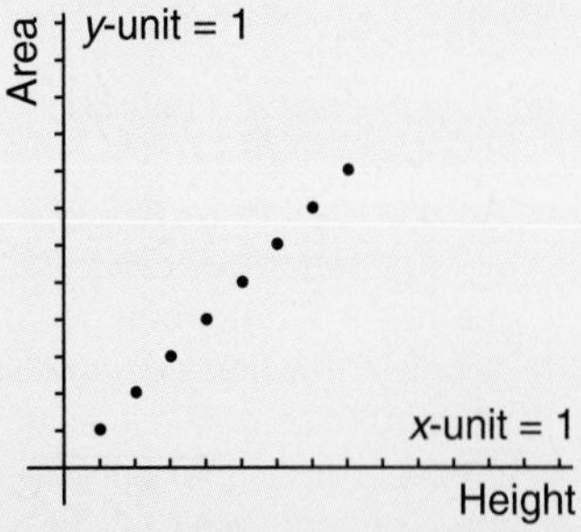

e.

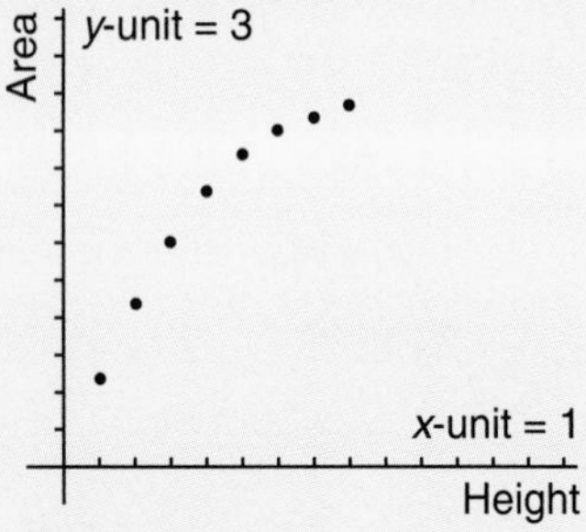

f.

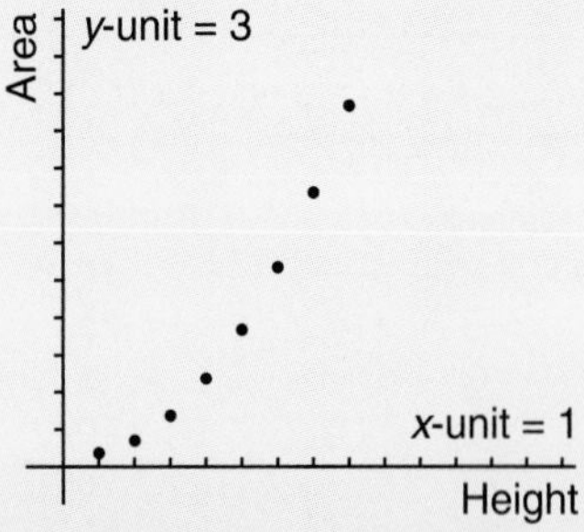

4. Draw two different jars for each graph below.

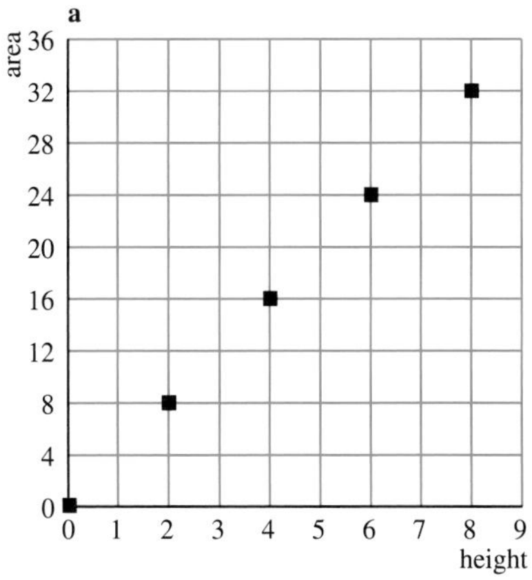

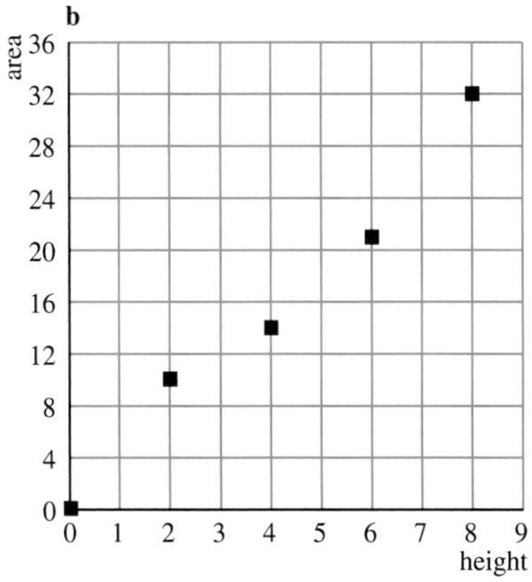

5. Draw a jar for part (a) of problem 4 for which the area of liquid is *not* a direct variation function of the height.

6. Predict the shape of the graph for this jar. Then test your prediction.

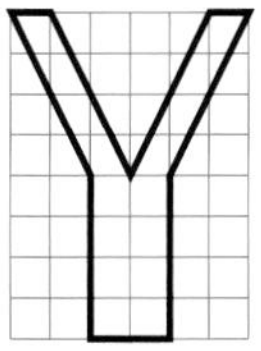

7. **Summary** Explain how the shape of the jar affects the shape of the graph. Explain what it takes for a jar to have a graph that is a straight line through the origin.

8. **Generalization** How do you think the shape of a three-dimensional jar affects the shape of the graph of the volume of liquid as a function of height? What jar shapes correspond to a direct variation function?

A dipstick can be used to measure the amount of liquid in a jar, but the dipstick must be specially designed for the jar. For example, the following dipstick would work for jar (a).

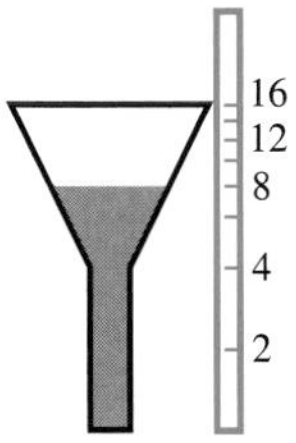

On it, area is marked off with a tick for every two square units.

9. Note that the dipstick ticks are not evenly spaced. Explain why.

*N*ote that in problems 4-5, only a few points are given on the graph. As long as the jars the students create match those, the jars can have many shapes. In particular, for problem 5 it is enough to have one data point off the line of the given points to ruin the direct variation.

*D*o not discuss this as such, but this lesson helps lay the groundwork for understanding slope and rate of change by focusing students' attention on when the rate of change is constant and when it changes. The dipstick questions (problems 9-10) in particular address this.

*P*roblem 11 is quite challenging. One approach is to use the graphs and find *x*-values for regularly spaced *y*-values. In other words, heights for regularly spaced areas. Those heights are where the ticks should be placed.

JAR LIDS: CIRCUMFERENCE

*I*f you want all students to work with the same data, you could make the measurements at the overhead and record them on the chalkboard. However, students will be more interested in the lesson if you can get them to bring jar lids from home and have each group work on its own set of lids. (Students should not work on their own individual data because then they would have no one with whom to check the validity of their answers.)

4.8 SOLUTIONS

2. g.

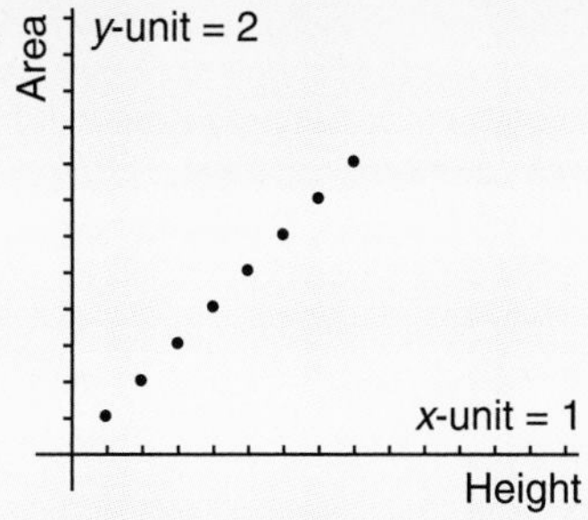

3. d and g have the area as a direct variation function of the height. Direct variation graphs are straight lines through the origin.

4. a. Answers will vary. Sample answers are given.

Jar 1

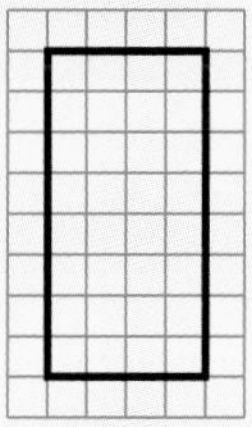

Jar 2

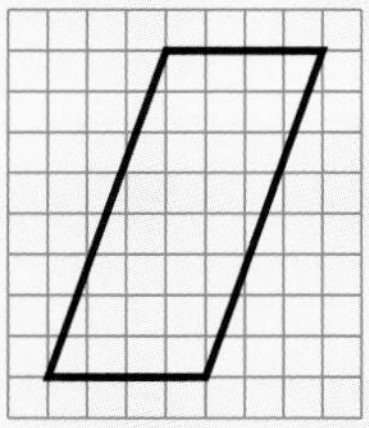

4. b. Answers will vary. Sample answers are given.

Jar 1

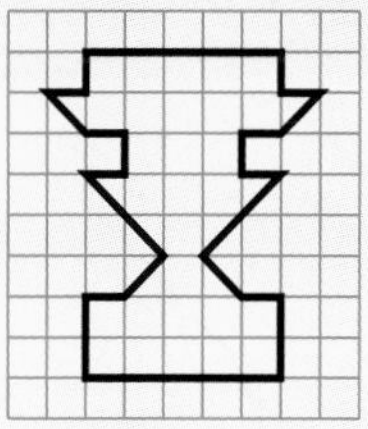

Jar 2

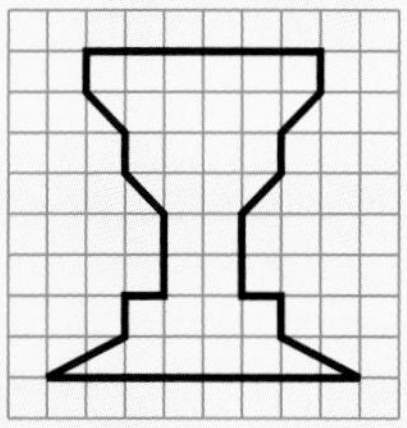

6. Direct variation graph which is a line through the origin.

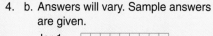

*B*ecause of measurement error, you should remind students of what they learned in Lesson 7: Even if a relationship is a direct variation, the points may not lie *exactly* on a line. The line must be approximated visually or by calculating the average of the ratios.

*I*f students do not bring up π, you should not bring it up either, *until the end of the lesson*. If they do, insist that they base all their answers on their measurements. A comparison of the value obtained that way with the actual value of π will provide a good reminder of the reality of measurement error.

JAR LIDS: AREA

*T*his is more difficult than the previous section; the measurements are more difficult to make accurately, and the relationship is mathematically more difficult to uncover. However the approach outlined in problems 19-23 allows students to use what they know about direct variation to make progress towards discovering the relationship of the area of a circle to its radius.

*A*nother approach, perhaps more accurate, to this investigation is to use a very sensitive scale and make circles and the corresponding squares out of heavy cardboard. Since the weights of the circles and squares are proportional to their areas, the ratio of weights will be the same as the ratio of areas discovered by the method outlined in the text.

10. Which jars would have a dipstick whose ticks are evenly spaced? Explain.

11. **Project** Draw an accurate dipstick for each of several different jars. Write a report showing sketches of the jars and their dipsticks, and explain your method.

JAR LIDS: CIRCUMFERENCE

For this section, use jar lids of at least five different sizes, including one very small one and one very large one.

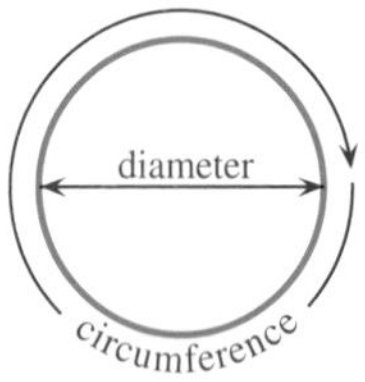

12. Measure the diameter and circumference of each of the jar lids in centimeters, as accurately as possible. (Use the string to help find the circumference.) Make a table showing your data.

13. Make a graph of your data, putting diameter on the *x*-axis and circumference on the *y*-axis. Don't forget to include a point for a lid having diameter 0.

14. What is the relationship of circumference to diameter for each jar lid? Describe it in words and with an equation. Explain how you figured it out.

15. Is the relationship between diameter and circumference an example of direct variation? Explain.

16. According to your data, what is the approximate value of the ratio of circumference to diameter?

JAR LIDS: AREA

17. Estimate the area of the top of each jar lid by tracing around it on centimeter graph paper and estimating the number of square centimeters it covers. Make a table and a graph of the relationship between diameter and area, including a point for a lid having diameter 0.

18. Is the relationship between diameter and area an example of direct variation? Explain.

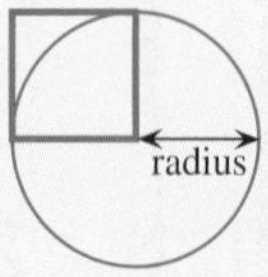

The figure shows a square whose side equals the radius of the circle.

19. For each jar lid, calculate the area of a square like the one shown in the figure. Add a column for these data in your jar-lid area table.

20. Graph the area of the circles as a function of the area of the squares.

4.8 SOLUTIONS

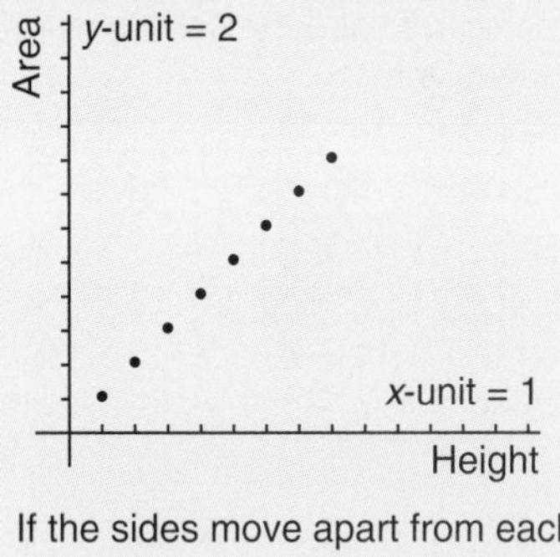

7. If the sides move apart from each other, the area grows faster and faster. If the sides move towards one another then the area grows more and more slowly. If a jar has a wide base and narrow top as in b, c, and e, then moving from left to right on the graph the points climb steeply at first and then less steeply. The opposite is true in a and f which have narrow bases and wide tops. Moving from left to right their graphs begin with a slight climb from one point to the next and then the graph climbs steeply. If a jar has no change in width from bottom to top as in d and g then the graph is a line through the origin because there is a constant change in area for each unit increase in height (direct variation). When the sides of a jar are parallel, then the graph is a straight line through the origin.

8. If a three-dimensional jar changes in narrowness then its graph will curve. If a 3-D jar is a cylinder then it will correspond to a direct variation function.

9. The bottom of the jar is narrow with parallel sides so the amount of a liquid varies directly with the height. Each additional unit of height corresponds to a constant amount of liquid, so the dipstick ticks are evenly spaced. Above 4 units in height, each additional unit of height corresponds to a growing amount of liquid. Ordered pairs of numbers approximating the height and amount of liquid are: (1, 1), (2, 2), (3, 3), (4, 4), (5, 5.75), (6, 8). When height changes from 3 to 4, the liquid changes by one unit also. When height changes from 4 to 5, the liquid changes by 1.75 units of liquid, and when height changes 5 from 5 to 6 the amounts of liquid change 2.25 units. The ticks are more closely spaced to show the larger amounts of liquid for each unit change in height.

21. What is the relationship between the area of the circles and the area of the squares? Describe it in words and with an equation. Explain how you figured it out.

22. Is the relationship between the area of the circles and the area of the squares an example of direct variation? Explain.

23. According to your data, what is the approximate value of the ratio of the area of the circle to the area of the square?

24. **Summary** According to your data, what is the relationship between the area of a circle and its radius? The area of a circle and its diameter? Explain.

REVIEW *DIVIDING ON A CALCULATOR*

Phil used his calculator to find the reciprocal of 7, and got the number 0.1428571429. Lyn's calculator, on the other hand, gave the number 0.1428571428.

25. Explain how two calculators can give different results, even though neither is defective.

Phil's grandfather does not believe in calculators. He said, "Do you really believe either number is the reciprocal of 7? I have news for you. Multiply each one by 7 without a calculator, and you'll see why you should not trust these machines."

26. Work with a classmate. Do the two multiplications on paper to see who was right, Phil, Lyn, or their grandfather. Explain your results.

The grandfather added, "To find the real reciprocal of 7, you have to use good old-fashioned long division."

27. Find the real reciprocal of 7.

28. **Report** Write a letter to Lyn and Phil's grandfather, explaining why students are allowed to use calculators nowadays. Your letter should include, but not be limited to:
- Answers to the grandfather's probable objections;
- A table showing the real reciprocals of the whole numbers from 0 to 10, and the reciprocals as given by Lyn's and Phil's calculators;
- An explanation of how you can find the real reciprocal by using a calculator;
- An argument explaining why Lyn's or Phil's calculator is the better one for the purpose of finding reciprocals.

29. Make a *division table* like this one. Extend it to show whole-number numerators and denominators from 0 to 10. You may use a calculator, but enter only exact answers. Look for patterns and work with a partner. Some answers were entered for you.

Numerators

Denominators	0	1	2	3	...
0					
1					
2	0	0.5	1	1.5	...
3					
...					...

30. What patterns do you notice about the row of your table for denominator 7?

31. Learn how to use the FIX mode on your calculator.

REVIEW *DIVIDING ON A CALCULATOR*

Since dividing on a calculator is a source of potential misunderstandings based on rounding off, it is important to discuss these questions explicitly. This section offers students an opportunity to do some work with numbers and to think of the advantages and limitations of calculators. In addition, it gives them a chance to review repeating decimals.

Lyn's calculator must not be a scientific calculator, since most of them round off correctly. However, some calculators do truncate. It would be a good idea to find one that does, to make the discussion more concrete.

Long division in problem 27 should remind your students about repeating decimals, which is all they need in order to be able to finish the section with the help of their calculators.

You may want to teach the class how to use the FIX mode on the calculator. (See the calculator's instruction manual.)

4.8 SOLUTIONS

10. A cylinder would have a dipstick with evenly-spaced ticks because the amount of liquid and the height would have a direct variation relation.

11. See right-margin notes on page 143.

12. Answers will vary. One possible solution is given:

Diameter (cm)	Circumference (cm)
0	0
1.7	5.4
6.8	21.5
7.8	24.9
9	27.3
10	31.8
11.7	37

13.

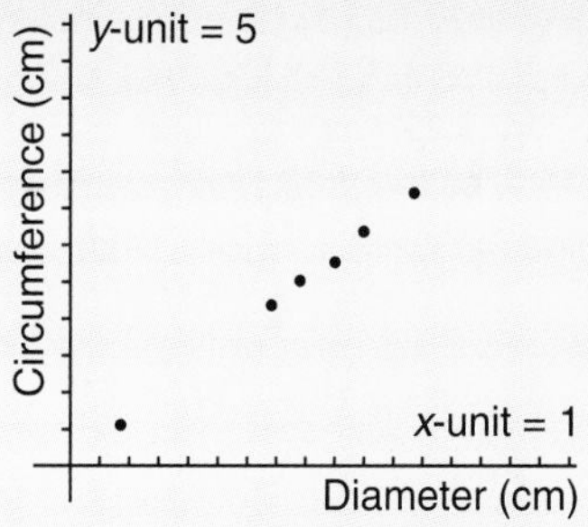

14. The correspondence between diameter and circumference is a direct variation function. The ratio of circumference to diameter is constant (about 3.13 is the average). $C = 3.13\ D$. Because the graph forms a line throught the origin, it must be a direct variation function $y = mx$. To find m find the ratio of y to x or D to C.

15. Yes, the ratio of circumference to diameter is a constant.

16. Answers will vary; however the ratio of circumference to diameter is approximately 3.14.

17. See table under number 19.

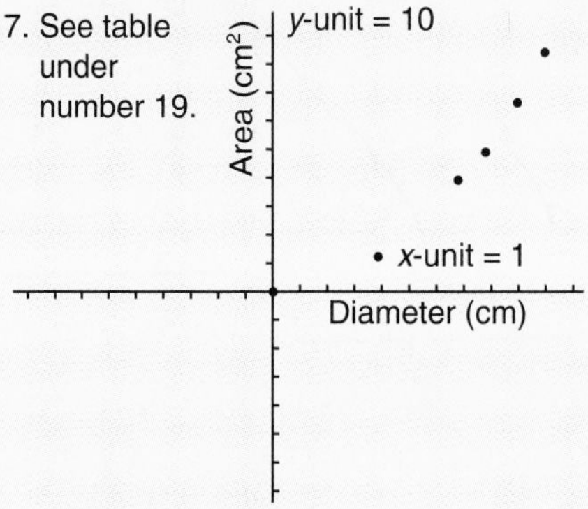

(Solutions continued on page 514)

THINKING WRITING **4.B Direct Variation**

Core Sequence: 1-11

Suitable for Homework: 3-11

Useful for Assessment: 3, 11

What this Assignment is About:

- Properties of direct variation
- Points on direct variation lines
- Preview of area under a line

POINTS ON LINES

This section is somewhat abstract and should be started in class. If students have trouble choosing values for m and (a, b), you may get them started with an example on the overhead or chalkboard, and then have them work in groups or individually.

The Report will require students to make some generalizations based on their experiments. *After they have done that*, it may be worthwhile to discuss their generalizations by operating directly on the variables. For example, if (a, b) is on the line $y = mx$, then we know that $b = ma$. But if that is true, we can multiply both sides by k, and find that $bk = mak$, so the point (ak, bk) must also be on the line. (Do not expect most students to follow this argument this early in the course.)

THINKING WRITING

4.B Direct Variation

You will need: graph paper

POINTS ON LINES

1. Choose a number m, and draw the graph of the equation $y = mx$. Choose any point (a, b) on the line.
   a. Is the point $(2a, 2b)$ on the line?
   b. Is the point $(3a, 3b)$ on the line?
   c. Is the point (ka, kb) on the line for any value of k?
2. Refer to the line you drew in problem 1.
   a. Is the point $(a + 1, b + 1)$ on it?
   b. Is the point $(a + k, b + k)$ on the line for any value of k?
3. **Report** Repeat problems 1 and 2 for several graphs of the form $y = mx$, $y = x + b$, and $y = mx + b$. If a point (a, b) is on the line, in what case is (ka, kb) on the line? What about $(a + k, b + k)$?

AREA FUNCTIONS

4. The graph shows $y = 2x$. The region between the line and the x-axis from $x = 0$ to $x = 6$ is shaded.
   a. What is the area of the shaded region?
   b. What is the area of the region between the line and the x-axis from $x = 0$ to $x = 4$?

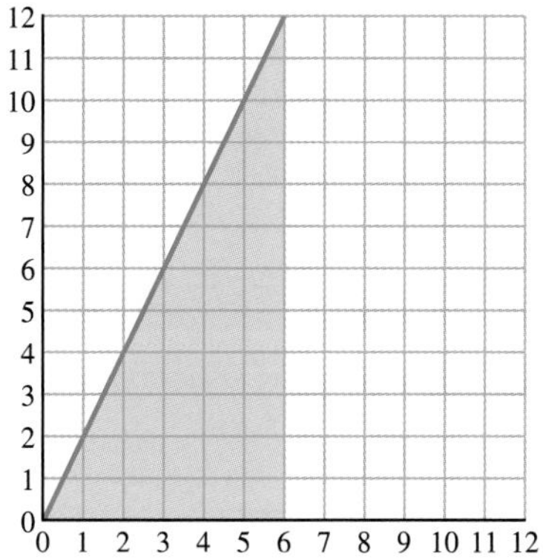

Endpoint	Area
$x = 1$	
$x = 2$	
$x = 3$	
$x = 5$	
$x = a$	

5. Copy and complete the table giving the area between the line and the x-axis from $x = 0$ to the given endpoint value of x.
6. Find a function relating the area to the endpoint value of x.

4.B SOLUTIONS

1. a. Yes. $(2a, 2b)$ is on the line.
   b. Yes. $(3a, 3b)$ is on the line.
   c. Yes, (ka, kb) is on the line.

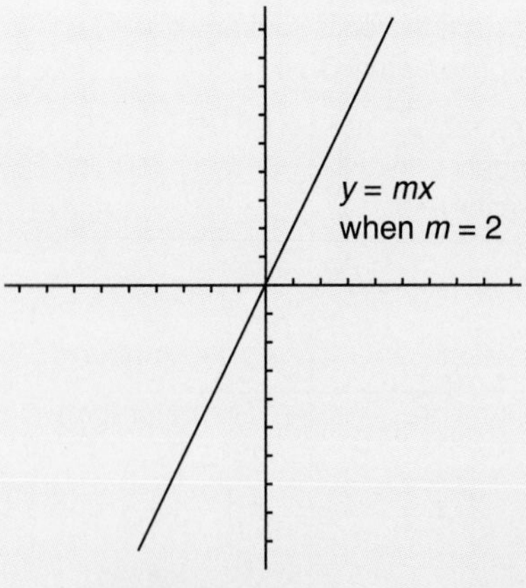

2. a. Answers will vary. If $m = 1$ then the answer is yes. For m not equal to 1, the answer is no.
   b. Yes, if $m = 1$. No, if m is not equal to 1 and $k \neq 0$, then $(a + k, b + k)$ is not on the line.
3. If $y = mx$, then point (ka, kb) is on the line. When $m = 1$ $(y = x)$ then $(a + k, b + k)$ is on the line. For m not equal to 1, $y = xm$ does not have $(a + k, b + k)$ on the line.
4. a. 36 sq. units
5.

Endpoint	Area
$x = 1$	1
$x = 2$	4
$x = 3$	9
$x = 5$	25
$x = a$	a^2

   b. 16 sq. units
6. Area = x^2

7. Is the area function you wrote an example of direct variation? Explain.

Endpoint	Area
$x = 1$	
$x = 2$	
$x = 3$	
$x = 5$	
$x = a$	

8. The graph shows the line $y = 3$. Copy and complete the table giving the area between the line and the x-axis from $x = 0$ to the given endpoint value of x.

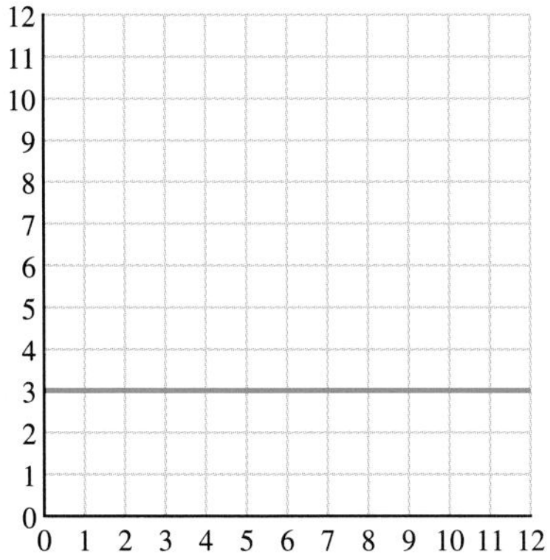

9. Find a function relating the area to the endpoint value of x.

10. Is the area function you wrote an example of direct variation? Explain.

11. **Report** Repeat problems 4 through 7 for several other lines. For which lines did you find area functions that are examples of direct variation? What generalizations can you make? Write an illustrated report about your results.

AREA FUNCTIONS

This section echoes the work we did with two-dimensional jars in Lesson 8. However, since the shapes are simpler, it should be possible for students to get equations for the area as a function of the x-coordinate of the endpoint.

This is a very rich problem with a wide range of possible generalizations. For example, students can compare: horizontal lines with lines through the origin, different values of m in $y = mx$, different values of b for the same m in the form $y = mx + b$. Each of these comparisons yields interesting results.

The reports may span a very broad range of thoroughness. You may want to post the best ones or have the authors present their findings to the class.

It is not likely that any student will reach the generalization that the area function is equal to $(m/2)x^2 + bx + c$, nor is it important that students do so. However, if there is a lot of interest in this topic, you may want to pursue it all the way to that generalization, step by step. Start with the case where $m = 0$, then the case where $b = 0$, and finally see if what you discovered still works when neither parameter is 0.

4.B SOLUTIONS

7. Since the area to endpoint ratio should be a constant, it is not direct variation. Another way to say this is that the function is not in the form of $y = mx$.

8.

Endpoint	Area
$x = 1$	3
$x = 2$	6
$x = 3$	9
$x = 5$	15
$x = a$	$3a$

9. $y = 3x$

10. Yes, an equation of the form $y = mx$ is an example of direct variation. When $m = 3$, $y = 3x$ is a direct variation function.

11. Reports should include that any horizontal line produces a direct variation relation between the area and the endpoints. See Teacher's Notes for a further discussion of this lesson.

▼ 4.9
Rules of the Road

Core Sequence: 1-16

Suitable for Homework: 10-16

Useful for Assessment: 12-14

What this Lesson is About:

- Unit conversion
- Applications of direct variation
- Traffic safety

UNIT CONVERSION

You may introduce this lesson with a discussion of why 100 mph is about 147 fps. The conversion could be done by first finding out how many feet per hour correspond to 100 mph, and then figuring out how many fps that is. Another approach is to write

$$100\ \frac{1\text{ mile}}{1\text{ hour}} = 100\ \frac{5280\text{ ft}}{3600\text{ seconds}} = 146.67\text{ fps.}$$

In almost every case, unit conversion is a case of direct variation. (An exception is Fahrenheit to Celsius conversion.) We will return to unit conversion in Chapters 12 and 14.

LESSON 4.9

Rules of the Road

You will need: graph paper

UNIT CONVERSION

When you talk about the speed you are traveling, you usually give the speed in *miles per hour.* In this lesson it will be useful to give speed in *feet per second.* Use the fact that 100 miles per hour (mph) is about 147 feet per second (fps).

1. How many fps is 50 mph?

2. Complete the table to show the relationship of miles per hour to feet per second. Extend the table up to 80 miles per hour.

mph	fps
10	14.7
20	

3. If you made a graph from your table with *mph* on the *x*-axis and *fps* on the *y*-axis, what would the graph look like? (If you are not sure, draw it.)

4. If you were traveling at 1 mph, how fast would you be going in fps?

STOPPING DISTANCE

To stop a car in an emergency, you first react and then put on the brakes.

stopping distance =
reaction distance + braking distance

5. What kinds of things do you think would affect reaction time and distance? Braking time and distance?

Reaction time is often considered to be about 3/4 of a second, but how far you travel during this time depends on how fast you are going.

6. Reaction distance:

a. Figure out how many feet you would travel in 3/4 of a second if you were going at various speeds (10 mph, 20 mph, etc.). Make a table to display your data.

b. Graph your data. Put *reaction distance in feet* on the *y*-axis and *speed in miles per hour* on the *x*-axis.

c. Describe the relationship between the two variables on your graph.

7. Braking distance: A formula for finding braking distance in feet is to take the speed in miles per hour, square it, and divide the result by 20. For example, if the speed were 10 mph, the braking distance would be $(10)^2/20 = 100/20 = 5$ feet.

a. The graph on the next page shows the relationship between the braking distance (in feet) and the speed (in miles per hour). All the points on the graph were found by using the formula. Make a table showing the coordinates of at least five points on the graph.

b. According to the table and graph, if you double your speed, will you double your braking distance? Explain, giving examples.

4.9 SOLUTIONS

1. 73.5 fps

2.

mph	fps
10	14.7
20	29.4
30	44.1
40	58.8
50	73.5
60	88.2
70	102.9
80	117.6

3. It would be a straight line through the origin.

4. 1.47 fps

5. Weather conditions, alertness of the driver, distraction level from other passengers in the car, drinking or substance abuse, etc. are all factors that would affect reaction time and breaking time.

6. a.

Traveling Speed (mph)	Traveling Speed (fps)	Reaction Distance (feet)
10	14.7	11.025
20	29.4	22.05
30	44.1	33.075
40	58.8	44.1
50	73.5	55.125
60	88.2	66.15
70	102.9	77.175
80	117.6	88.2

b.

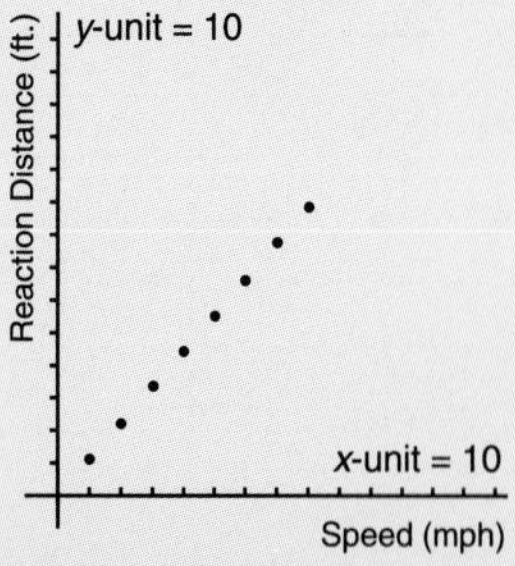

c. Speed and reaction distance have a direct variation relation.

7. a.

Speed (mph)	Braking distance (ft)
0	0
10	5
20	20
30	45
40	80

b. No. When speed doubles from 10 mph to 20 mph, braking distance quadruples from 5 to 20 ft. When speed doubles from 20 to 40 ft, braking distance quadruples from 20 to 80 ft.

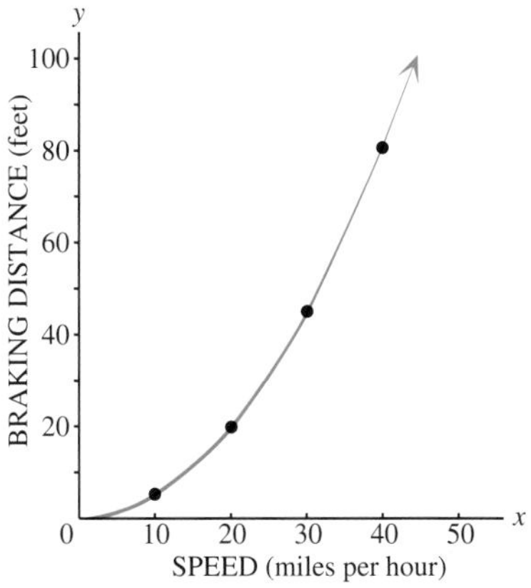

8. Total stopping distance: Use your tables and graphs from problems 6 and 7 to make a table with the headings shown. Use at least five different speeds.

Speed (mph)	Reaction distance (feet)	Braking distance (feet)	Total stopping distance (feet)

SAFE DISTANCE

It is estimated that about 30 percent of all automobile accidents are caused by following too closely. Two rules of thumb for avoiding accidents follow.

Rule 1: The 3-Second Rule. Notice when the vehicle in front of you passes some object, such as a road sign. Then time approximately three seconds by counting, "One-thousand-one, one-thousand-two, one-thousand-three." If you pass the same object before you get to one-thousand-three, you are following too closely.

Rule 2: The 1-for-10 Rule. Leave one car length between you and the car in front of you for every 10 mph of driving speed.

9. **Exploration** Which rule do you think is safer? Taking into account what you found out about stopping distance, what do you think would make a good rule of thumb?

To compare the two rules, it helps to convert miles per hour to feet per second, so that all units are in feet and seconds.

10. a. Copy and complete the table to show the distance traveled in three seconds at the speeds given. Extend the table up to 100 miles per hour.

Speed (mph)	Speed (fps)	Distance (ft)
10	14.7	44.1
20		

b. According to the table, how many feet would a car traveling at 50 mph cover in three seconds?

c. If you were instructed to stay three seconds behind the car in front of you, how many feet would that be, if you were traveling at 70 mph?

d. If you slowed down to 35 mph, could you cut your following distance in half? Explain.

e. If you drew a graph with speed on the *y*-axis and *distance traveled in three seconds* on the *x*-axis, what would it look like? Explain. If you are not sure, sketch the graph.

STOPPING DISTANCE

SAFE DISTANCE

This investigation is straightforward. You may have an interesting discussion about problem 5.

To answer problem 9 thoroughly, students would have to do a fair number of calculations. Use your judgment to decide how complete an answer you want. They will be guided through an analysis of the question in problems 10-13.

A full answer to problem 14 could include a graph showing both rules (and perhaps a student-created rule) as well as *total* stopping distance displayed on the same axes.

4.9 SOLUTIONS

8.

Speed (mph)	Reaction Distance (ft)	Breaking Distance (ft)	Total Stopping Distance (ft)
10	11.025	5	16.025
20	22.05	20	42.05
30	33.075	45	78.075
40	44.1	80	124.1
50	55.125	125	180.125
60	66.15	180	246.15
70	77.175	245	322.175
80	88.2	320	408.2

9. Rule #1 is safer because it allows for greater distances between cars at greater speeds. For example, suppose you were going 50 mph or 73.5 fps. By Rule #1 you would allow for about 73.5 fps · 3 sec = 220.5 feet between the cars. At 50 mph the total stopping distance is 180.125 feet. Rule #1 allows enough stopping distance to avoid a collision. Suppose a car is about 18 feet long. At 50 mph, Rule #2 would allow 18 ft · 5 = 90 feet between cars. The total stopping distance of 180.125 ft would mean a likely collision, because only 90 ft braking distance was allowed when 180.125 was required. A good rule of thumb would be to use Rule #1.

10. a.

Speed (mph)	Speed (fps)	Distance (ft)
10	14.7	44.1
20	29.4	88.2
30	44.1	132.3
40	58.8	176.4
50	73.5	220.5
60	88.2	264.6
70	102.9	308.7
80	117.6	352.8
90	132.3	396.9
100	147	441

b. 220.5 ft
c. 308.7 ft
d. Yes, at 35 mph your 3-second following distance would be 154.35 ft which is one half of 308.7 ft.
e. The graph of speed vs. distance traveled in 3 seconds is a direct variation line through the origin. The speed to distance ratio always equals 4.41, so Distance = 4.41 · Speed.

DISCOVERY ROUNDING

*E*ven if these problems are done at home, make sure they get discussed in class. They require careful reasoning. Do not teach any algebraic methods to deal with percent. It would be a distraction from the main point of this activity, which is rounding. Students should use trial and error and their calculators to work on these problems.

*W*e will do more work with percent in Chapters 6 and 8.

11. Most cars are about 14 to 18 feet in length. Choose a car length in this interval and make a table showing safe following distances at certain speeds according to Rule 2.

Speed (mph)	Speed (fps)	Safe distance (car lengths)	Safe distance (feet)
10	14.7	1	
20		2	

12. Use your tables to compare Rule 1 and Rule 2. How are they different? Which one suggests greater caution? Explain.

13. Should one evaluate Rule 2 based on its implementation using a small-car length or a large-car length? Explain.

14. Report Use the information about total stopping distance to decide whether you agree with the advice given by Rule 1 or by Rule 2, or whether you would suggest a different rule. Write a paragraph explaining your opinion.

DISCOVERY ROUNDING

Because of measurement error, it is meaningless to say that someone weighs 157.2490368 pounds. No scale is that accurate, and even if it were, one does not need that level of accuracy. For most purposes, it is satisfactory to talk of someone's weight to the nearest pound, so this number should be rounded off to 157.

When dealing with amounts of money, one usually rounds off to the nearest cent. In some cases, one rounds up, or down. When doing work with *real* numbers, make sure you do not copy answers from your calculator without thinking of whether you should round off, round up, or round down.

15. If you buy one 95-cent pastry at the Columbia Street Bakery, you will be charged $1.00 even. But if you buy two pastries, you will be charged $2.01.

a. What is the sales tax in this town?

b. Does the cash register round off to the nearest cent, or does it round up or down? Explain.

16. In the same town, if you buy a 94-cent soda at Eddie's, you will be charged $1.00. If you buy two sodas, you will be charged $1.99. Does this cash register round off to the nearest cent? Does it round up or down? Explain.

4.9 SOLUTIONS

11.

Speed (mph)	Speed (fps)	Safe distance (car lengths)	Safe distance (feet)
10	14.7	1	18
20	29.4	2	36
30	44.1	3	54
40	58.8	4	72
50	73.5	5	90
60	88.2	6	108
70	102.9	7	126
80	117.6	8	144
90	132.3	9	162
100	147	10	180

12. Rule #1 allows for more space between cars than Rule #2, and as a result Rule #1 suggests greater caution. For example, at 60 mph Rule #1 allows for 264.6 feet, whereas Rule #2 allows for 108 feet.

13. The safe distance speeds are greater when a larger car length is used. For example, if the car is 14 feet long then at 60 mph Rule #2 would allow for a safe distance of $6 \cdot 14$ ft = 84 feet. Using a longer car of 18 feet in length, one gets a greater safe distance of $6 \cdot 18$ ft = 108 feet.

14. Rule #1 gives greater distances for its total braking distance calculations. See answers to numbers 9 and 12.

15. a. Answers will vary. 5.8%, 5.9%, or 6% will satisfy this question. At 6%:

b. The cash register rounds down to the nearest cent.
1 loaf: $0.95 \cdot 0.06 + 0.95 = 1.007$ rounds down to $1.00
2 loaves: $1.90 \cdot 0.06 + 1.9 = 2.014$ rounds down to $2.01

16. The cash register rounds off to the nearest cent. If the decimal is greater or equal to 0.005 then you round up, otherwise you round down.

Sample at 6%:
1 soda: $0.94 \cdot 1.06 = 0.9964$; round up to $1.00
2 sodas: $1.88 \cdot 1.06 = 1.9928$; round down to $1.99

LESSON 4.10

Up in the Air

You will need:
graph paper

People rarely travel at constant speeds. Almost all travel involves speeding up and slowing down. However, sometimes to simplify a problem it is useful to use the average speed over a given period of time. In this lesson we will use the average speed.

MULTIPLE MEANINGS

The graph below shows the relationship between the altitude of the airplane and the time after take-off.

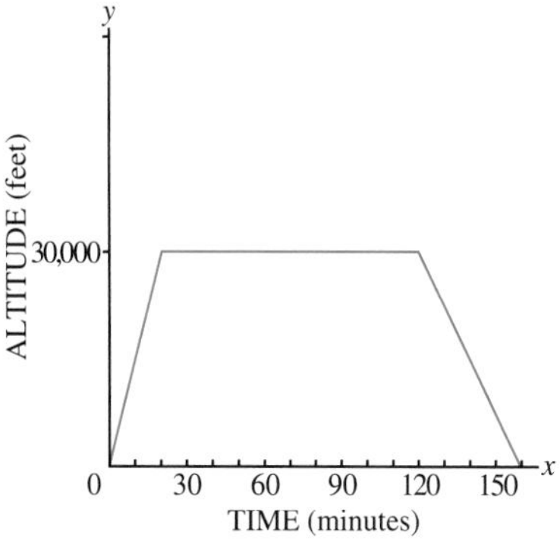

1. How high was the airplane 20 minutes after take-off?
2. How long after take-off did the airplane reach its cruising altitude?
3. How long did the plane cruise at a constant altitude before descending?
4. Can you figure out the speed of the airplane from this graph? Explain.

The graph below shows that Flight 101 left its home airport at 8 A.M. and flew to the town of Alaberg. It stayed in Alaberg for several hours and then returned to its home airport.

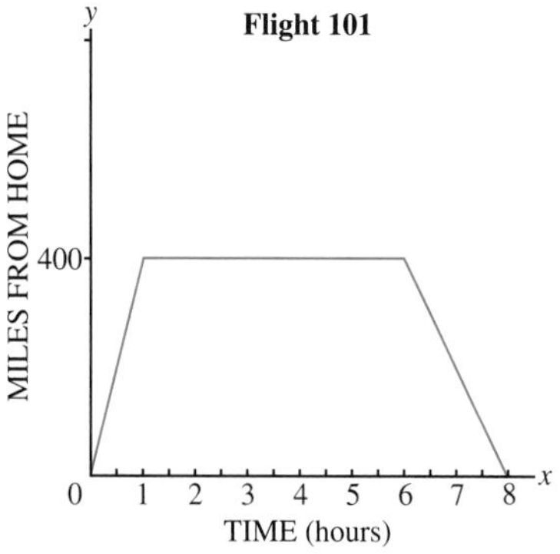

5. According to the graph, how far away is Alaberg?
6. How long did it take Flight 101 to get to Alaberg?
7. How long did the plane stay in Alaberg?
8. Can you figure out the speed of the airplane from this graph? Explain.

Someone made this graph about Flight 202, but accidentally left off the labels and the scale for the axes.

4.10 Up in the Air

Core Sequence: 1-23

Suitable for Homework: 9-23

Useful for Assessment: 20-23

What this Lesson is About:

- Interpreting graphs
- Discrete vs. continuous functions
- Estimation and rounding

MULTIPLE MEANINGS

This section is intended to help students see how the same mathematical structure may correspond to several different real-world situations. This is a profound and important idea.

Even if they do it as homework, make sure students have a chance to discuss problem 11 with their groups. The most interesting graphs can be shared with the class.

4.10 SOLUTIONS

1. 30,000 feet
2. 20 min.
3. 100 min.
4. No. Speed would be calculated by dividing the distance traveled by the amount of time taken to travel that distance. We don't know the distance traveled to attain the cruising altitude. It might have been a very steep ascent or a more gradual ascent to reach the altitude.
5. 400 miles
6. 1 hour
7. 5 hours
8. Yes. The speed going to Alaberg was 400 mph. The return speed was 200 mph.

DISCRETE AND CONTINUOUS GRAPHS

We have repeatedly discussed when it is appropriate to connect the dots in a graph. Here we give a name to the two different types of graphs: when there are no intermediate values, the graph is *discrete*; otherwise, it is *continuous*.

Problems 13-14 are tricky, because all we are given is the number of passengers between terminals. We have no information about what happened *at* the terminal. For example, it is possible (though unlikely) that everyone got off the train somewhere, and a whole other group got on before the train left the station.

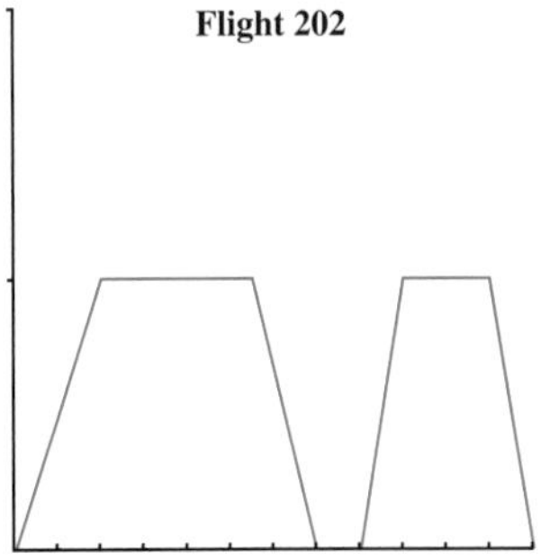

9. Copy the graph and label the axes like those in the figure just before problem 1. Write a description of what the graph conveys.

10. Make another copy of the graph and label the axes like those in the figure preceding problem 5. Write a description of what that graph conveys.

11. What else might the axes and scale be for the graph about Flight 202? Make up another possibility and write a description of what your graph shows.

DISCRETE AND CONTINUOUS GRAPHS

Alaberg has a large airport with several terminals. A small train runs through the airport, carrying passengers between the terminals. Passengers use this train when they have to transfer from one plane to another. The graph shows the relationship between the location of the train between the terminals and the number of passengers in the train.

12. Write a description of what is conveyed by this graph.

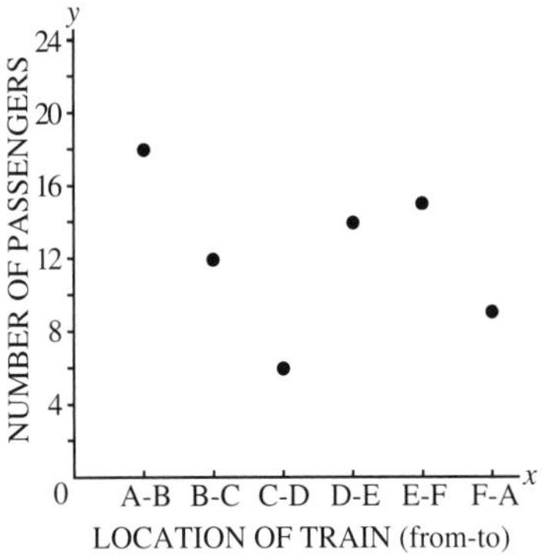

13. Can you tell how many passengers got on and off at each terminal? Explain.

14. Can you tell if the train was ever empty?

15. Can you tell from this graph how fast the train was traveling?

The Alaberg Airport Express is a van service that carries passengers between the city and Alaberg Airport. A group of math teachers is holding a convention in Alaberg, and 1024 people have arrived at the airport. They all need to get into the city.

16. If the Alaberg Airport Express van holds 20 people, how many trips will be needed to take all the people into the city?

4.10 SOLUTIONS

9. Descriptions will vary but should include these points: Flight 202 reached its highest altitude of 30,000 feet 20 min. after take off and flew at that altitude for 40 min. Its descent took 10 minutes. It stayed on the ground for 10 min. and then took off a second time taking 10 min. to reach the same cruising altitude of 30,000 ft, where it stayed for 20 minutes. Its final descent took 10 min.

10. Descriptions will vary but should include these points: Flight 202 took off and flew for one hour to a town 400 miles away where it stayed for two hours. It then returned to the home airport covering the 400 miles in 30 min. It remained on the ground for 30 min. and then flew for 30 min. to the same or another destination also 400 miles away. It stayed on the ground at this destination for one hour and then returned the 400 miles to the home airport. This final trip took 30 min.

11. Answers will vary. If we label the *x*-axis *time* and the *y*-axis *amount of fuel remaining* we could have the following description: It took 20 min. to fill up the fuel tanks of Flight 202. The tanks remained full for 40 min. Because of a malfunction in the fuel system, the tanks were emptied in 10 min. Mechanics found and repaired the problem and in 10 min. refueled the plane. The tank remained full for 20 min. while a supervisor inspected the plane. Unhappy with the repair job, he ordered the tank emptied again, which took 10 min.

12. The train carried 18 passengers from terminal A to B. At each terminal some passengers got on the train. The train left terminal B with 12 people and proceeded to terminal C. It left terminal C with 6 people and went to terminal D. It carried 14 people from terminal D to E, 15 from E to F, and 9 people from F to A.

13. No. Explanations will vary. Sample: The train carried 18 people from terminal A to B. It left terminal B with 12 people and proceeded to terminal C. Perhaps all 18 passengers disembarked at terminal B and 12 new passengers boarded the train. Perhaps six of the 18 passengers got off at B and no new passengers boarded, leaving the same 12 passengers who traveled from terminal A to B and then to C. Many combinations are possible.

17. If more vans were available, fewer trips would be needed per van. If 15 vans were available, and the trips were divided as evenly as possible among the vans, what would be the maximum number of trips that any van would need to take?

18. Copy and complete the table to show the relationship between vans available and maximum number of trips per van necessary. (Once again, assume that the trips would be divided as evenly as possible among the vans.)

Number of vans	Max number of trips per van necessary
1 ⋮ 15	

19. a. Make a graph from your table.
    b. What is the rule for finding the maximum number of trips per van necessary, given the number of vans?

20. The graphs you used in problems 12 and 19 involved points instead of lines. Explain why it does not make sense to connect these points.

Definition: If the points are not connected on a graph, it is called *discrete.* If the points are connected, it is called *continuous.*

YOUR OWN GRAPHS

21. The meaning of this graph is still up in the air until you add some things to it. Copy the graph, label the axes, and show the scale. If it makes sense, connect the points. Tell what the graph conveys.

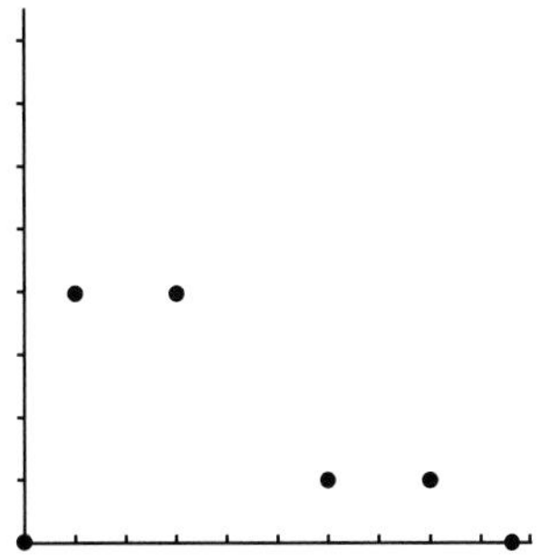

22. Make up a discrete graph. Label the axes and indicate the scale. Write a description of what the graph conveys.

23. Repeat problem 22 for a continuous graph.

YOUR OWN GRAPHS

*Y*ou may use this section as a writing assignment or have students present their graphs as bulletin board displays. This may work well as an activity to do with a partner.

*I*n any case, class discussion of open-ended questions like these is essential.

4.10 SOLUTIONS

14. You can tell if the train was empty while traveling from one terminal to another, but you cannot tell if it was empty at a terminal while passengers disembarked and boarded.

15. No. There is no indication of distance or time.

16. 52 trips will be needed. (1024/20 = 51.2, so round up to 52.)

17. In problem 16, we found that 52 trips would be necessary. Each van would take 3 trips. There would be 7 remaining trips to be made, so 7 vans would have to make an additional fourth trip. The answer is 4.

18.

# of Vans	Maximum # of trips per van necessary
1	52
2	26
3	18
4	13
5	11
6	9
7	8
8	7
9	6
10	6
11	5
12	5
13	4
14	4
15	4

19. b. 52 trips will always be necessary. Divide 52 by the number of vans, then round your answer up to the next integer.

20. In many cases, only whole number values are possible.

21. Answers will vary. (Some answers will be discrete, some continuous.) Sample: Al was 5 miles away from home. At 4:01 he got into his car, and it took him two minutes to get it started. Because he was late, he sped for the next 3 minutes, covering 3 miles, when he stopped at a red light for 2 minutes.

22. Answers will vary.

23. Answers will vary. Be sure graph is reasonable for intermediate values.

▼ 4.11 Horizontal and Vertical Lines

Core Sequence: 1-12

Suitable for Homework: 6-15

Useful for Assessment: 11

What this Lesson is About:

- Horizontal and vertical lines
- Step functions
- Writing and graphing simple inequalities

STEP FUNCTIONS

*T*his is not the first step function we have encountered, but it is the first time we use the words. The open and closed circle convention for the graphs is also introduced.

HORIZONTAL AND VERTICAL LINES

*S*tudents often have trouble with these, perhaps because insufficient attention is paid to them in the traditional course. This lesson should be sufficient to get these ideas across.

LESSON 4.11

Horizontal and Vertical Lines

You will need: graph paper

STEP FUNCTIONS

1. This graph shows how the number of passengers in the Alaberg Airport Express van changes over time. The graph shows a trip between the city and the airport.
   a. Write a description of what is shown by this graph.
   b. Why is there a long horizontal line on the graph?

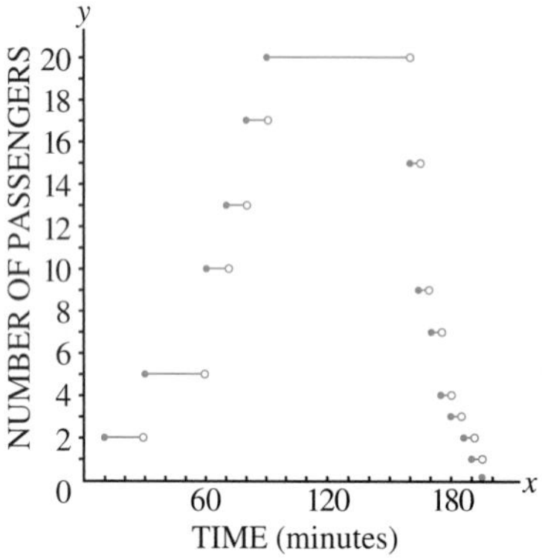

Definitions: This graph is an example of a *step function.* Note that the endpoints of the steps are either filled-in (this is called a *closed circle*), or hollow (this is called an *open circle*).

For a given value of x, the value of y can be found by looking for the corresponding point on the graph. Only points on the steps and closed circles are considered to be on the graph. The open circles are there to show where the step ends, but that point is not considered to be on the graph. This way a given x-value has only one corresponding y-value.

2. After 60 minutes, how many people were in the van?

HORIZONTAL AND VERTICAL LINES

3. a. Graph the vertical line through the point (1, -2).
   b. Label four more points on this line.
   c. Which coordinate is the same for all the points on the line, the x-coordinate or the y-coordinate?
4. a. Graph the horizontal line through the point (1, -2).
   b. Label four more points on this line.
   c. Which coordinate is the same for all the points on the line, the x-coordinate or the y-coordinate?
5. a. The equation of a line is $y = -3$. There is no x in the equation because the value of y does not depend on the value of x. Graph this equation.
   b. Did you graph a horizontal or a vertical line?

4.11 SOLUTIONS

1. a. The van carried 2 passengers for 20 min. when it stopped to pick up 3 additional passengers. The 5 passengers traveled for 30 min. until 5 more passengers were picked up. The 10 passengers traveled for 10 min. when 3 people boarded the bus. The 13 passengers continued for 10 min. until 4 new passengers boarded. The 17 passengers traveled for 10 min. until the last three passengers boarded, to fill the bus. The full bus of 20 passengers traveled for 70 min., then 5 passengers got off. Five min. later 2 got off, 5 min. later 3 got off. Then the van made a series of five-minute rides, stopping to let off one passenger at a time until the bus was empty.
   b. The full bus of passengers traveled for 70 min. with no boarding or unboarding of passengers.
2. 10 people were in the van after 60 min.
3. a. b.

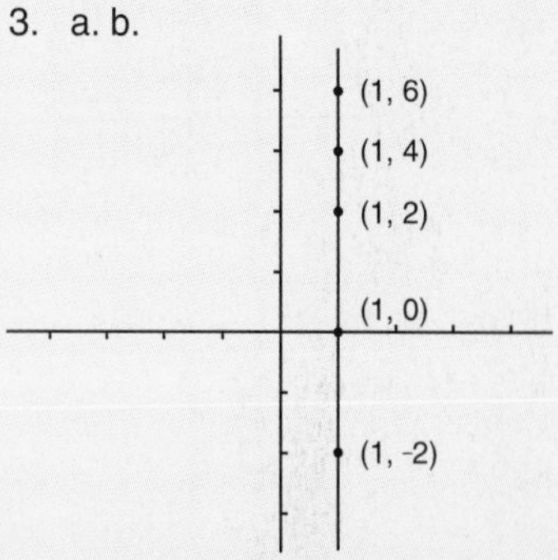

   c. The x-coordinates are the same for all the points on the line.

4. a. b.

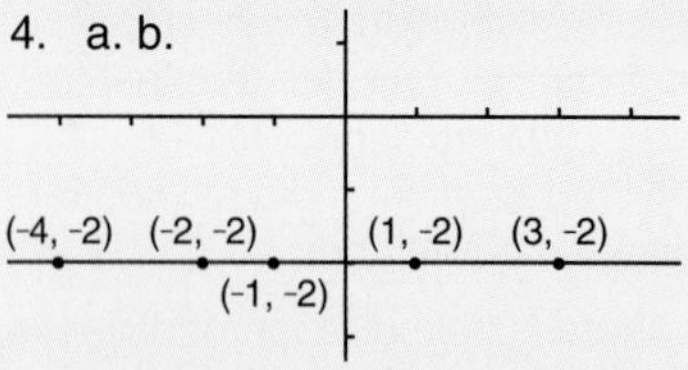

   c. The y-coordinates are all the same.

5. a.

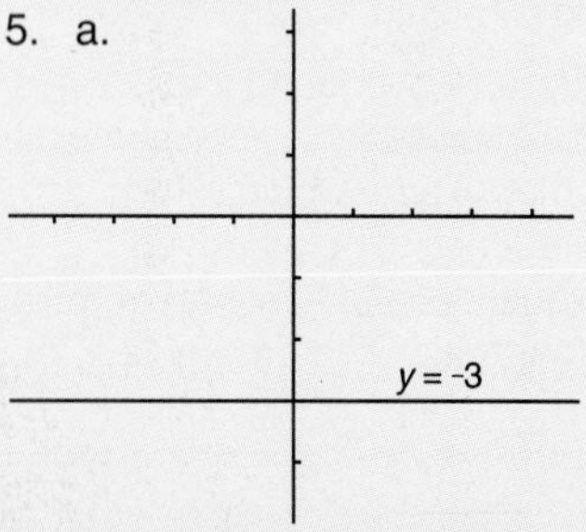

   b. Horizontal line

6. a. The equation of a line is $x = 6$. There is no y in the equation because the value of x does not depend on the value of y. Graph this equation.
   b. Did you graph a horizontal or a vertical line?

7. a. Graph the vertical line through (2, -5). Write its equation.
   b. Find the coordinates of any point on the line.
   c. Find the coordinates of any point to the right of the line.
   d. Find the coordinates of any point to the left of the line.
   e. For each part (b), (c), and (d), answer this question: What do you think all the points chosen by students in your class have in common?

8. The equation of a line is $y = 5$. If possible, answer these questions without graphing the line.
   a. Is the line vertical or horizontal?
   b. Where does the point (4, -2) lie in relation to the line? Explain.
   c. Write the coordinates of one point on the line and one point not on the line.
   d. What can you say about the y-coordinate of any point that lies on the line? Below the line? Above the line?

INEQUALITIES

The x-coordinate of any point that lies to the left of the vertical line $x = 6$ must be a number less than 6. For example (2, 7) is such a point, since $2 < 6$. The expressions $2 < 6$ and $x < 4$ are examples of *inequalities.*

9. The mathematical shorthand for *less than* is <. What are the mathematical symbols for *greater than, less than or equal to,* and *greater than or equal to*?

Inequalities can be used to describe sets of points on a graph. For example, all the points that lie on or to the right of the line $x = 7$ can be described by the inequality $x \geq 7$.

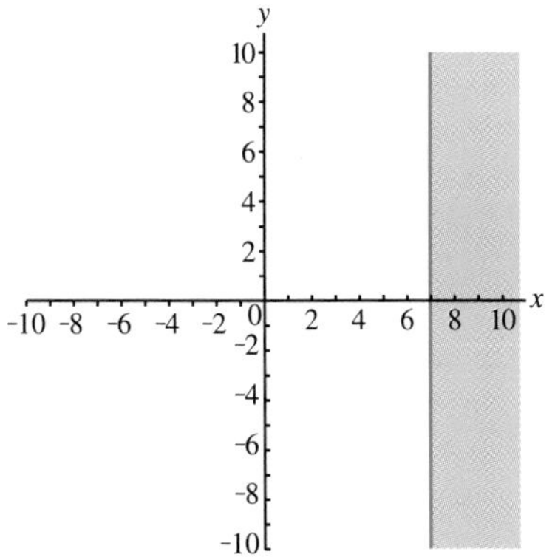

10. Graph each set of points given. Use one or more inequalities to describe it.
   a. All points that lie on or below the line $y = -1$
   b. All points that lie on or above the x-axis
   c. All points that lie on or between the vertical lines $x = 3$ and $x = 6$

11. **Report** Write an illustrated report on horizontal lines, vertical lines, and inequalities.

INEQUALITIES

This section reminds students of the notation for inequalities and previews the use of Cartesian graphs for representing them. It also helps students get practice with the equations of horizontal and vertical lines.

We do not graph inequalities on the number line because the same ideas and insights are conveyed just as well with the Cartesian graph, with the added bonus of increasing familiarity with this difficult and profound representation.

4.11 SOLUTIONS

6. a.

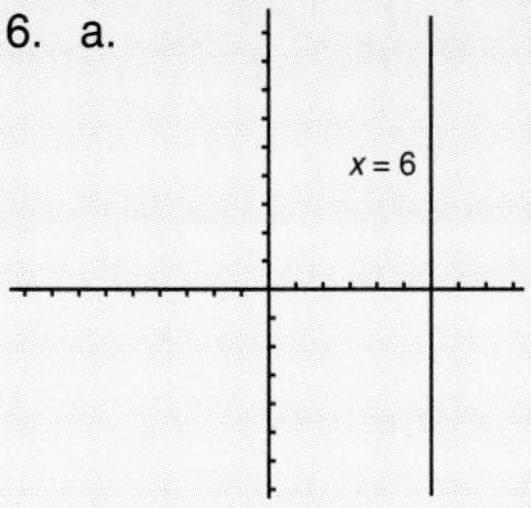

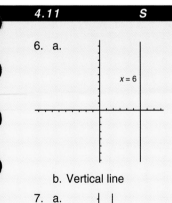

   b. Vertical line

7. a.

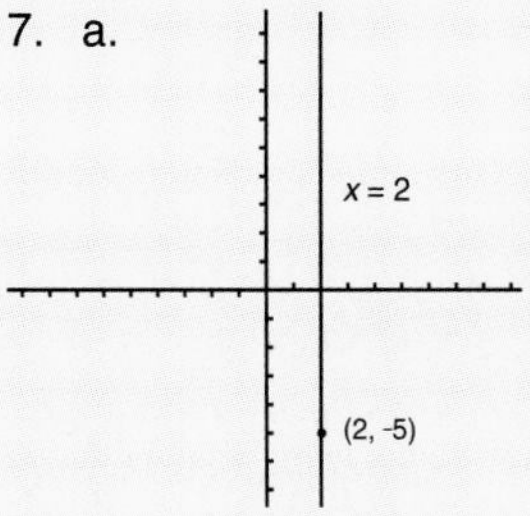

   b. Answers will vary. Sample: (2, 3)
   c. Answers will vary. Sample: (3, 0)
   d. Answers will vary: Sample: (0, 0)
   e. For part (b) the x-coordinate is 2.
      For part (c) the x-coordinate is greater than 2.
      For part (d) the x-coordinate is less than 2.

8. a. Horizontal
   b. (4, -2) lies below the line $y = 5$
   c. Answers will vary. Sample: (0, 5) is on the line and (0, 4) is not on the line.

9. Greater than is >.
   Less than or equal to is ≤
   Greater than or equal to is ≥

10. a.

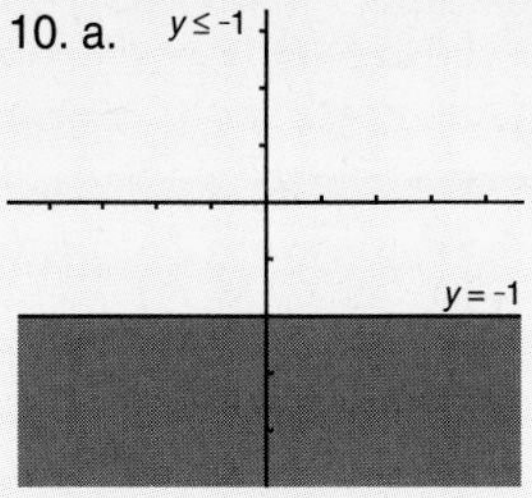

   b.

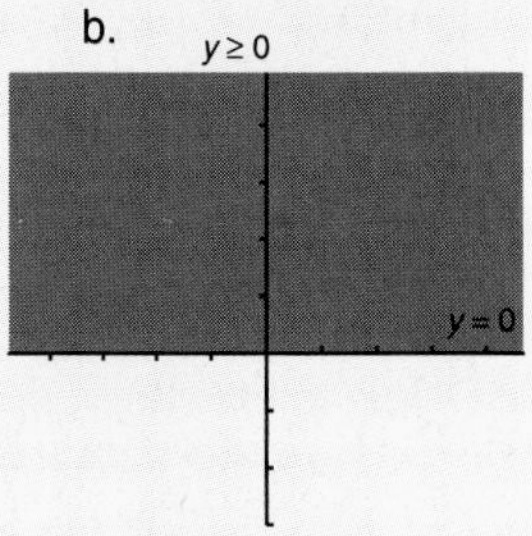

DISTANCE VS. TIME, AGAIN

This problem reviews the work on speed, distance, and time, and previews slope. In addition it allows students to think about the meaning of horizontal and vertical lines in a particular application.

Problem 12e is impossible, since it implies Paul was in many places at the same time. A distance versus time graph cannot include a vertical line. Contrast this with the fuel versus distance graph in the **Essential Ideas,** where the vertical segments are meaningful.

COST OF MAILING A LETTER

This section gives students a chance to use a step function with a real-world application.

DISTANCE VS. TIME, AGAIN

These graphs represent the motion of Paul's car. The vertical axis shows distance from his house, and the horizontal axis shows time.

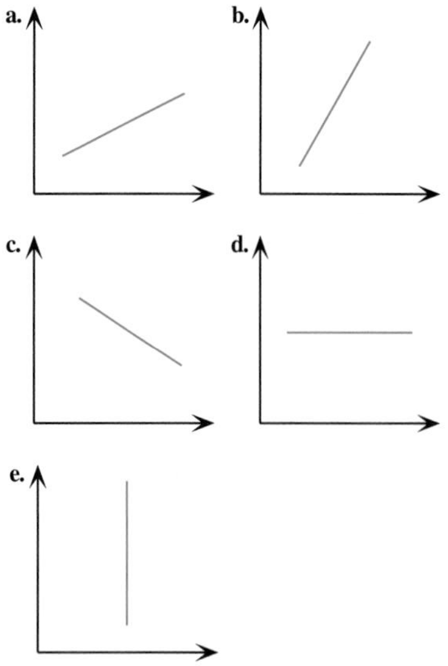

12. Describe the trips shown in each graph. Are all of them possible?

COST OF MAILING A LETTER

In January of 1991 the United States Postal Service raised its rates for first-class mail. It printed the following table in a flyer for postal customers.

13. Answer questions (a-c) using the information in the following table.

Single-Piece Letter Rates:

Pieces not exceeding (oz)	The rate is	Pieces not exceeding (oz)	The rate is
1	$0.29	7	$1.67
2	$0.52	8	$1.90
3	$0.75	9	$2.13
4	$0.98	10	$2.36
5	$1.21	11	$2.59
6	$1.44		

a. How much does it cost to mail a letter weighing 7 and 1/2 ounces?

b. How much does it cost to mail a letter weighing exactly 3 ounces?

c. Would it be possible for a letter to cost 45 cents to mail? If so, how much would it weigh? If not, explain why not.

14. Use the data in the table to graph the relationship of cost to weight. It is a step function. Copy and complete this graph.

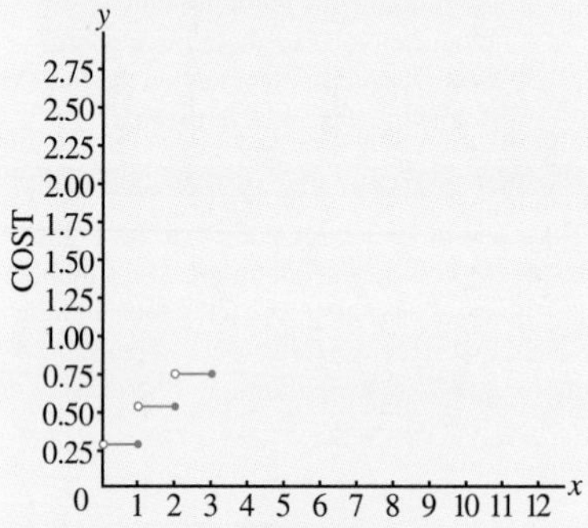

15. Study the table. What is the rule being used to determine these rates?

4.11 SOLUTIONS

c. $3 \le x \le 6$

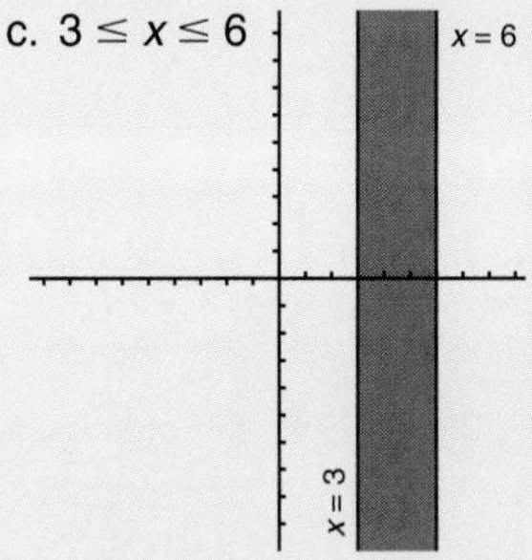

11. Report should include the fact that $y = k$ is a horizontal line and $x = k$ is a vertical line. $Y \ge k$ is the shaded region on and above the line $y = k$. $Y \le k$ is the shaded region on and below the line $y = k$. $X \ge k$ is the shaded region on and to the right of $x = k$. $X \le k$ is the shaded region on and to the left of $x = k$.

12. a. Paul was not at home when he got in his car and drove farther away from his home.
   b. Paul was not at home when he got in his car and drove away from his home. He drove faster than in 12a.
   c. Paul was away from home when he got in his car and drove toward home.
   d. Paul was not at home when he got in his car and either stood still or drove in a circle around his home. The distance away from home doesn't change.
   e. Impossible. This graph means Paul traveled without any elapsed time.

13. a. $1.90 b. $0.75
   c. Impossible. Such a letter would weigh between 1 and 2 ounces, but such a letter would cost 52 cents to send.

14.

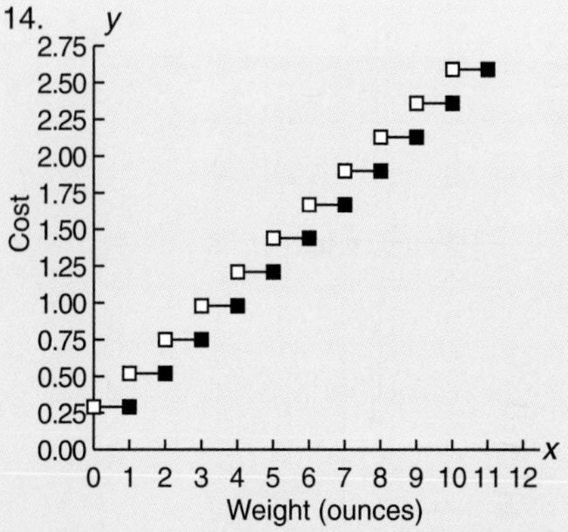

15. Up to and including one ounce is 29 cents. Each additional ounce, or fraction of an ounce, is an additional 23 cents.

LESSON 4.12

Complicated Areas

You will need:

geoboards

dot paper

DISCOVERING AN AREA FORMULA

1. a. Find the area of this figure.
   b. Explain how you did it, with the help of illustrations on dot paper.
   c. Compare your approach with other students' work.

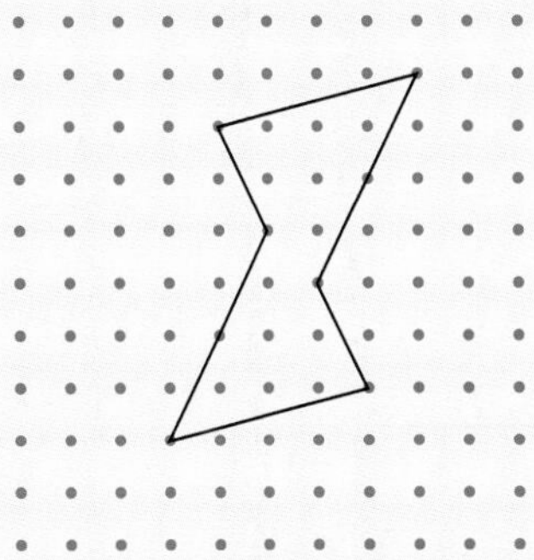

In the figure above, the rubber band is in contact with 8 geoboard pegs (which we will call *boundary dots*). The figure encloses 12 inside pegs, which we will call *inside dots.*

2. For each figure, give the number of boundary dots, the number of inside dots, and the area.

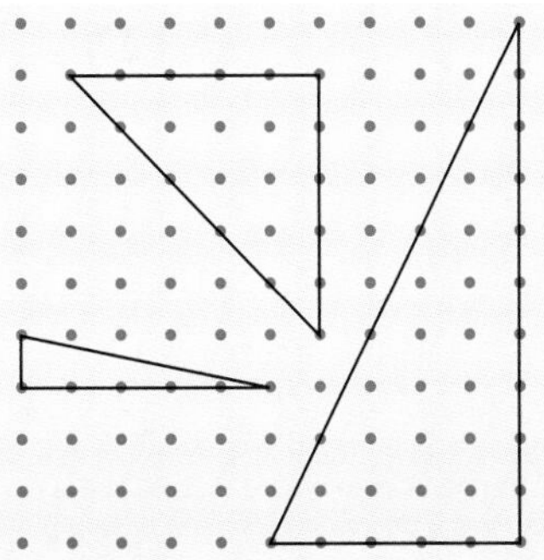

3. **Exploration** Try to figure out the relationship between boundary dots, inside dots, and area. (Hints: Sketch many simple figures, count their dots, and find their areas. Keep detailed and clear records. Start by working on the problem for figures having zero inside dots, then one inside dot, and so on.) Keep records of your work in a table like this one.

Boundary Dots	Inside Dots	Area
...	...	...

4. Make three figures having 3 boundary dots and 0 inside dots. Find the area of each figure.

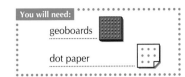

4.12 Complicated Areas

Core Sequence: 15-16

Suitable for Homework: 15-17

Useful for Assessment: 7, 9, 11, 13

What this Lesson is About:

- Review of geoboard area
- Discovering a two-variable function from data
- Review of repeating decimals
- Patterns and functions

DISCOVERING AN AREA FORMULA

This section is not essential to the development of area that is needed for later lessons on square roots. However, it is useful in that it keeps students' geoboard area skills in practice.

This section also gives students another chance to discover a function of two variables by analyzing data. They have already done this in Chapter 1, Lesson 8, and Chapter 2, **Thinking/Writing 2.C**. In fact, the formula is a more general version of Pick's Formula, which has already been seen in Chapter 2, Lesson 11. By now, we can hope that students need less guidance.

4.12 SOLUTIONS

1. a. 15 sq. units
   b. Answers will vary. Put a rectangle around the given figure. Between the given figure and the rectangle, draw segments to form small rectangles and right triangles. Find the area of the surrounding rectangle and subtract the sum of the areas of the small rectangles and right triangles. This difference is the desired area.
   c. Class discussion

2.

Boundary	Inside Dots	Area (sq.units)
15	6	12.5
7	0	2.5
20	16	25

3.

Boundary Dots	Inside Dots	Area
4	0	1
5	0	1.5
6	0	2
7	0	2.5
8	0	3
9	0	3.5
10	0	4
11	0	4.5
12	0	5
n	0	$0.5n - 1$
n	1	$0.5n$
n	2	$0.5n + 1$
n	3	$0.5n + 2$
n	x	$0.5n + (x - 1)$

Area = one half · boundary dots + (inside dots − 1)

4. Area = 0.5

DISCOVERY ***ASSORTED PROBLEMS***

Problem 15 could lead to a good class discussion. If you do discuss it, be sure to talk about the graphic interpretation of the question. In fact, a graphing calculator could provide an immediate check on the correctness of the suggested functions.

Do not give any hints on problem 16!

For problem 17 there are several ways to represent the terms in the sums graphically, as parts of a square array of dots. Probably the clearest is to use the diagonals.

5. Make three figures having 4 boundary dots and 0 inside dots. Find the area of each figure.

6. Make three figures having 5 boundary dots and 0 inside dots. Find the area of each figure.

7.
a. If two figures have no inside dots and the same number of boundary dots, what can you say about their areas?
b. What happens to the area if the number of boundary dots increases by 1?

8. a. Predict the area of a figure having 10 boundary dots and 0 inside dots.
b. Check your prediction by making three such shapes and finding their areas.
c. What would the area of a figure having 99 boundary dots and 0 inside dots be?

9. Generalization Explain how one could find the area of a figure having *b* boundary dots and 0 inside dots, without making or drawing the figure.

10. Make figures having 10 boundary dots and 1, 2, 3, etc. inside dots. For each one, find its area. Keep your work organized in a table.

11. What happens to the area when the number of inside dots increases by 1?

12. a. Predict the area of a figure having 10 boundary dots and 10 inside dots.
b. Check your prediction by making three such shapes and finding their areas.
c. What would the area of a figure having 99 boundary dots and 101 inside dots be?

13. Generalization Explain how one could find the area of a shape having *b* boundary dots and *i* inside dots, without making or drawing the figure. You have discovered *Pick's Formula*.

14. Use the result from problem 13 to check your answers to problems 1 and 2.

DISCOVERY ***PATTERNS AND FUNCTIONS***

15. Find as many functions of x as possible whose value is 5 when x is 2.

16. Multiply.

$$\left(1-\frac{1}{7}\right)\cdot\left(1-\frac{2}{7}\right)\cdot\left(1-\frac{3}{7}\right)\cdot\ldots\cdot\left(1-\frac{9}{7}\right)$$

17. 1
1+2+1
1+2+3+2+1
1+2+3+4+3+2+1

What do you notice about these sums? Explain the pattern, using a figure if you can.

4.12 SOLUTIONS

5. Area = 1
6. Area = 1.5
7. a. Figures with no inside dots and the same number of boundary dots have the same areas.
   b. When the number of boundary dots increases by 1, the area increases by 0.5 square units.
8. a. Area = 4
   b. Students graphs will vary. All areas = 4.
   c. 48.5, since (99/2) − 1 = 48.5
9. To find the area of a shape having *b* boundary dots and 0 inside dots take one half of *b* and then subtract one.

10.

Inside dots	Area
0	4
1	5
2	6
3	7
n	$5 + (n - 1) = n + 4$

11. The area increases by one when the number of inside dots increases by one.
12. a. 14 sq. units
    b. Student graphs will vary. All areas are 14 sq. units.
    c. 149.5 because 0.5(99) + (101 − 1) = 149.5
13. The area equals one half the number of boundary points plus one less than the number of inside points, or Area = 0.5 · Boundary dots + Inside dots − 1.
14. Students should now use Pick's Formula to check their solutions to problems 1 and 2.
15. Answers will vary. Following are a few possible solutions: $y = x + 3$, $y = x^3 - 3$, $y = 7x - 9$
16. 0. 6/7 · 5/7 · 4/7 · 3/7 · 2/7 · 1/7 · 0/7 · ... = 0
17. The sum is the square of the largest number in the series.

THINKING WRITING

4.C Letter Strings

In abstract algebra, letters do not stand for numbers. Abstract algebra has many applications, for example, to particle physics or to the analysis of the Rubik's cube. Here is a simple example.

THE YZ GAME

In this game, starting with a string of Y's and Z's, the object is to simplify the string by following strict rules. The rules are:

YYY can be erased.
ZZ can be erased.
the commutative law: YZ = ZY.
E is the empty string (a string with no Y's or Z's).

Examples:

a. YZZYYZYZYYZ (erase ZZ)
Y YYZYZYYZ (erase YYY)
ZYZYYZ (commute YZ)
ZZYYYZ (erase ZZ and YYY)
Z (can't be simplified)

b. ZYYYZ (erase YYY)
Z Z (erase ZZ)
E (the empty string is left)

1. Simplify the strings.
a. YZYZZYYZ b. YYYYZZZYZY
c. YZYZYZYZYZYZYZYZYZZZYZYZYYZY

Including the empty string E, there are six essentially different strings that cannot be simplified. They are called the *elements of the YZ group.*

2. Find all the elements of the YZ group.

The symbol ↔ represents the operation *put together and simplify.* For example:

Y ↔ YY = E
YZ ↔ YZ = YY
Y ↔ E = Y

3. Compute.
a. E ↔ YZ b. YZ ↔ YY
c. Z ↔ YZ

4. Find the missing term.
a. YZ ↔ ___ = E
b. Z ↔ ___ = YZ
c. YY ↔ ___ = Z

For the YZ group, ↔ works a little bit like multiplication. Another way to write the first two rules is

$$Y^3 = E \text{ and } Z^2 = E.$$

5. The only powers of Y are: Y, Y^2, and E. Explain.

6. Find *all* the powers of each element of the YZ group.

7. Simplify. (Show your work.)
a. Y^{1000} b. $(YZ)^{1001}$

8. Make a ↔ table.

9. What element of the group works like 1 for multiplication?

10. What is the reciprocal of each element? (In other words, for each element, what element can be put together with it to get the 1?)

THE yz GAME

For this group, the rules are:

yyy can be erased.
zz can be erased.
yzy = z.
The empty string is called e.
There is no commutative law.

11. Do problems 1-10 for the yz group. (Hint: zyy and yyz *can* be simplified.)

12. Report Write a report on the yz group.

4.C SOLUTIONS

1. a. Y
b. Z
c. YZ or ZY

2. E, Y, YY, Z, YZ or ZY, YYZ

3. a. YZ
b. Z
c. Y

4. a. ZYY
b. ZYZ or Y
c. YZ

5. Any power of Y greater than 3 can be rewritten in terms of Y, Y^2, or E.

6. E is the only power of E. The powers of Y are Y, Y^2, and E. The powers of YY are Y^2, Y, and E. The powers of Z are Z and E. The powers of YZ are YZ, Y^2, Z, Y, YYZ, and E. The powers of YYZ are YYZ, Y, Z, Y^2, YZ, and E.

7. a. Y
b. YYZ

8.

	E	Y	YY	Z	YZ	YYZ
E	E	Y	YY	Z	YZ	YYZ
Y	Y	YY	E	YZ	YYZ	Z
YY	YY	E	Y	YYZ	Z	YZ
Z	Z	YZ	YYZ	E	Y	YY
YZ	YZ	YYZ	Z	Y	YY	E
YYZ	YYZ	Z	YZ	YY	E	Y

9. E works like 1 for multiplication because E combined with any element equals that element and 1 times any number equals that number.

10. The reciprocal of E is E; of Y is YY; of YY is Y; of Z is Z; of YZ is YYZ; of YYZ is YZ.

(Solutions continued on page 515)

THINKING WRITING 4.C

Letter Strings

Core Sequence: none of the assignment

Suitable for Homework: 11-12

What this Assignment is About:

- Algebraic structure
- Abstract algebra (finite groups)
- Identity and inverse elements

This activity, while not particularly difficult, will feel unfamiliar. It works best as a group activity in class.

Our last experience with abstract algebra was **Math on Another Planet** in Chapter 3, Lesson 11.

A master for the tables for problems 8 and 11 may be found on page 569.

THE YZ GAME

You can introduce the game by writing a very long string of Y's and Z's on the board and having students suggest ways to simplify it according to the rules. With the next string, you can ask them to predict the outcome of simplifying.

Problem 2: The six elements are E, Y, YY, Z, YZ, YYZ.

Problem 6: It is interesting that the powers of YZ and YYZ span all six elements in the group.

THE yz GAME

This is quite a bit more challenging, because of the absence of the commutative law. It would be best to have the students prepare group reports for problem 12.

Note that yyz = yyyzy = zy, and zyy = yzyyy = yz.

The elements of the group are e, y, yy, z, yz, and zy. Note: yz and zy are not equal! A consequence of this is that it is quite difficult to predict correctly what a long string will simplify to.

Another difference with the commutative case is that no element's powers span the whole group.

Essential Ideas

FUEL VS. DISTANCE

Gabe's scooter gets good mileage, but it has a small tank. The graph below shows how much gas was in his tank during one trip he took.

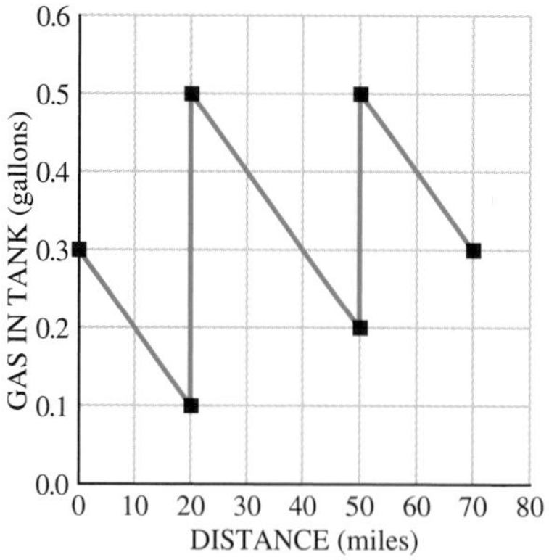

1. Write a paragraph describing Gabe's trip. Include the answers to these questions: How much gas did Gabe start with? How much did he end with? How many times did he stop for gas? How much gas did he use for the whole trip? How far did he travel before stopping each time? What is probably the capacity of his gas tank? How many miles did he get per gallon?

2. The gas station stops took ten minutes each. Gabe left home at 9 A.M. and arrived at his destination at 11:05 A.M. How fast does the scooter go?

3. In what ways might this graph be unrealistic?

EQUATIONS AND GRAPHS

4. Make a graph of several (x, y) pairs having the property that the sum of x and y is 16. Connect the points on your graph. Write the equation of your graph.

5. Write the equation of:
   a. a line through the origin containing the point (2, 5);
   b. another first-degree polynomial containing the point (2 ,5);
   c. a second-degree polynomial containing the point (2, 5).

These questions are about the graph of the equation $y = -x^2 + 2$.

6. Which of these points are on it?
   (3, -11) (-3, 11) (3, -7) (-3, -7)

7. The point $(-6, y)$ is on it. What is y?

8. The point $(x, -14)$ is on it. What are the two possible values of x?

For each of the equations below, if possible, find an (x, y) pair for which
   a. x is negative and y is positive;
   b. x is positive and y is negative;
   c. x and y are both negative.

9. $y = 4x$ 10. $y = x^2 - 2$

11. $y = x(x - 1)$ 12. $y = -2x + 6$

13. Which of the above four equations' graphs
   a. are straight lines?
   b. pass through the origin?

14. If possible, sketch the graph of a zero-degree, first-degree, second-degree, and third-degree polynomial function which passes through all quadrants but the first.

SOLUTIONS

1. Gabe started his trip with 0.3 gallons in his scooter's tank. He drove 20 miles using up 0.2 gallons of gas. He refueled putting 0.4 gallons of gas in his tank and then drove 30 miles using 0.3 gallons of gas. He refueled again, putting 0.3 gallons of gas in his tank. He then drove 20 miles using 0.2 gallons of gas. He began the trip with 0.3 gal. of gas and ended with 0.3 gal. in his tank. He stopped twice for gas. Gabe used 0.7 gal. of gas to go a total of 70 miles. So he averaged 100 miles per gallon of gas. His scooter's tank probably has a capacity of 0.5 gal. of gas, which means he can go 50 miles on each tank of gas.

2. 40 mph. (70 miles/1.75 hr. = 40mph)

3. Answers will vary. Gabe averages a constant number of miles per gallon for each leg of his trip. Miles per gallon usually fluctuate depending on different speeds. That is, one gets higher miles per gallon at higher speeds and lower miles per gallon at lower speeds. The number of times Gabe must stop and go for stop signs or lights would also affect the miles per gallon.

4.

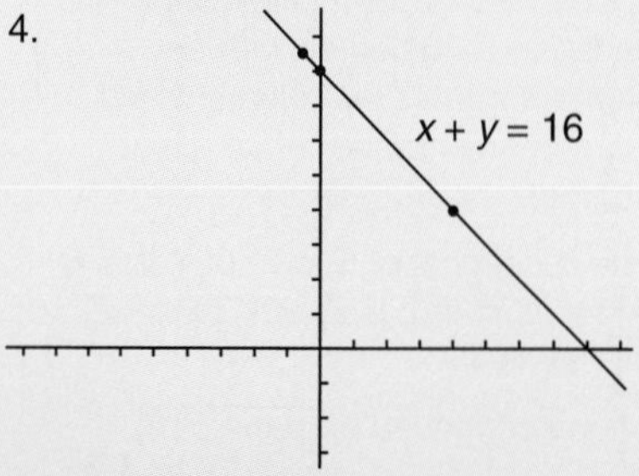

5. a. $y = 2.5x$
   b. Answers will vary, but equations will take the following form: $y - 5 = m(x - 2)$ for any m.
   c. Answers will vary. One possible solution is $y = x^2 + 1$.

6. (3, -7) and (-3, -7) are on the graph of $y = -x^2 + 2$

7. y is -34.

8. x could be 4 or -4.

For problems 9-12, the answers will vary when they exist.

9. a. impossible b. impossible
   c. Sample (-1, -4)

10. a. Sample (-2, 2) b. Sample (1, -1)
    c. Sample (-1, -1)

11. a. Sample (-2, 6)
    b. Sample (0.5, -0.25)
    c. Impossible

For problems 15 through 17:

a. Plot the points given in the table.
b. Study the table and your graph. Describe the relationship between the x-value and y-value of each pair.
c. Use the pattern you found to add more points to your table and graph.
d. Write an equation that tells how to get the y-value from the x-value.

15.

x	y
0	1
1	3
-1	-1
3	7

16.

x	y
2	9
3	6
-3	-6
4.5	4
4	4.5

17.

x	y
3	8
-2	3
-1	0
0	-1
1/2	-3/4
2	3

DISTANCE VS. TIME

18. These graphs represent the motion of Paul's car. The vertical axis shows distance from his house, and the horizontal axis shows time. Write a short paragraph describing the trip summarized by each graph.

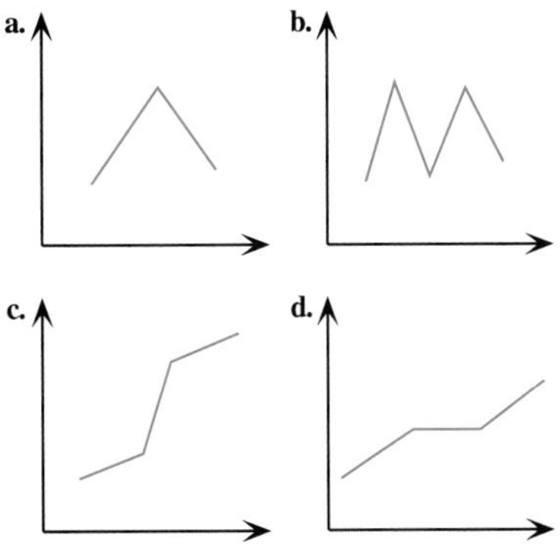

POSTAL PROBLEM

The post office puts size restrictions on first-class mail. Standard letters that are 1/4 inch thick or less must meet these requirements for width and height.

- The height is at least 3 and 1/2 in. and cannot exceed 6 and 1/8 in.
- The width is at least 5 in. and not more than 11 and 1/2 in.

19. The first condition can be written $3.5 \le \text{height} \le 6.125$. (This is called a *compound inequality*.) How would you write the second condition?

◆ S O L U T I O N S

12. a. Sample (-1, 8)
    b. Sample (4, -2)
    c. Impossible

13. a. The graphs of equations in #9 and #12 are straight lines.
    b. The graphs of equations in #9 and #11 pass through the origin.

14. First degree: $y = -2x - 3$

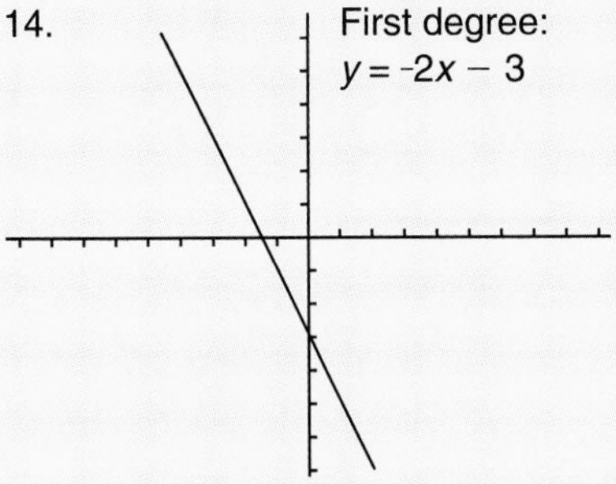

Second degree: $y = -(x + 2)^2 + 1$

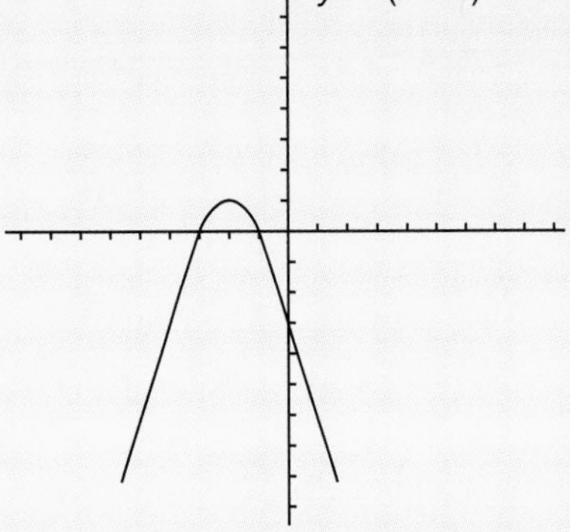

Third degree: $y = -(x + 1)^3 - 1$

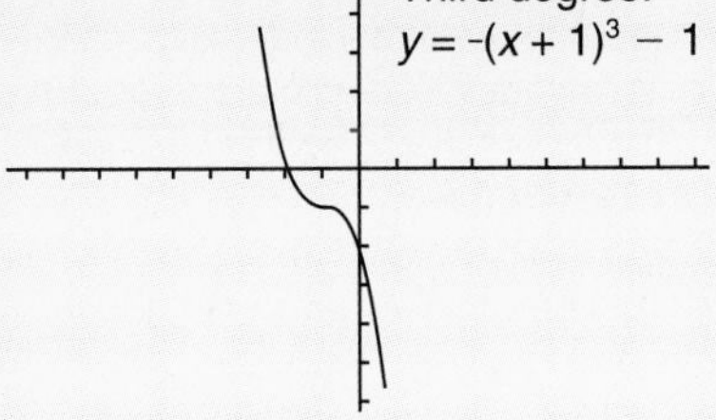

15. a. $y = 2x + 1$

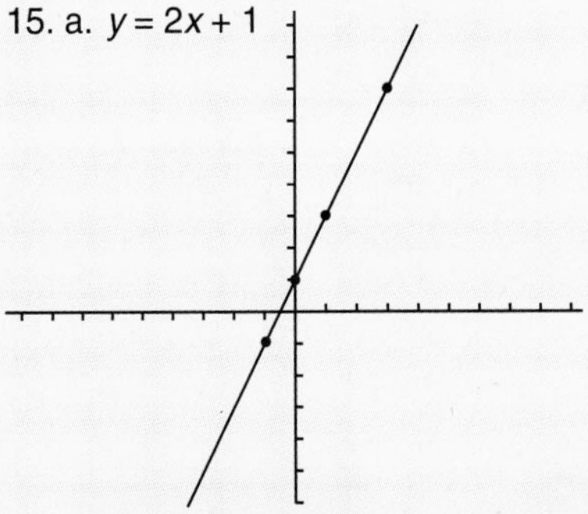

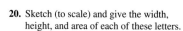

20. Sketch (to scale) and give the width, height, and area of each of these letters.

a. The letter having the least possible area

b. The letter having the greatest possible area

c. The tallest, thinnest letter

d. The shortest, widest letter

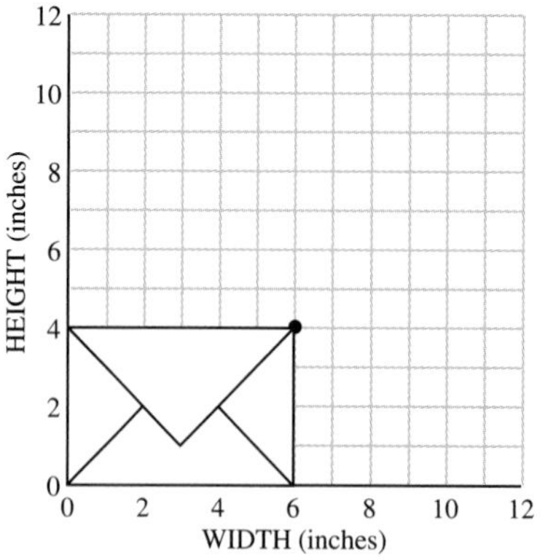

You can use a graph to show allowable dimensions of a letter. In the graph above, the point (6, 4) represents the dimensions of a letter that is 4 in. high and 6 in. wide.

21. Plot four points for the four envelopes you listed in problem 20. (Don't draw the envelopes!)

22. Write the equations of two horizontal and two vertical lines through those points.

23. The four points should form a rectangle. Find some points inside the rectangle, outside the rectangle, and on the rectangle. Which points represent allowable dimensions of letters? Explain, using examples.

In order to avoid extra fees, your letter must satisfy the following restriction.

- The width divided by the height must be between 1.3 and 2.5, inclusive.

24. Write a compound inequality for this restriction.

25. Find the ratio of the width to the height of each letter you listed in problem 20. Which ones meet the new requirement?

26. a. Experiment with your calculator until you find an allowable width and height that have a ratio of 1.3. On your graph, plot these dimensions. Draw a line through this point and the origin.

b. Find other points on the line. What is the ratio for each one? Explain.

c. Repeat (a) and (b) for the ratio 2.5.

27. Check the ratio for points between the two lines, above the upper line, and below the lower line.

28. Explain how to use the graph to find

a. dimensions that satisfy all the rules;

b. dimensions that satisfy the first two rules, but not the ratio rule;

c. dimensions that satisfy the ratio rule, but not the first two rules.

29. If the ratio of the width to the height is 1.3, what is the ratio of the height to the width?

30. Find the equation of the lines through the origin in your graph. Explain how they are examples of direct variation.

SOLUTIONS

b. Double the x-value and add 1 to get the y-value

c. Answers will vary. Sample (2, 5), $(x, 2x + 1)$

d. $y = 2x + 1$

16. a. $y = 18/x$

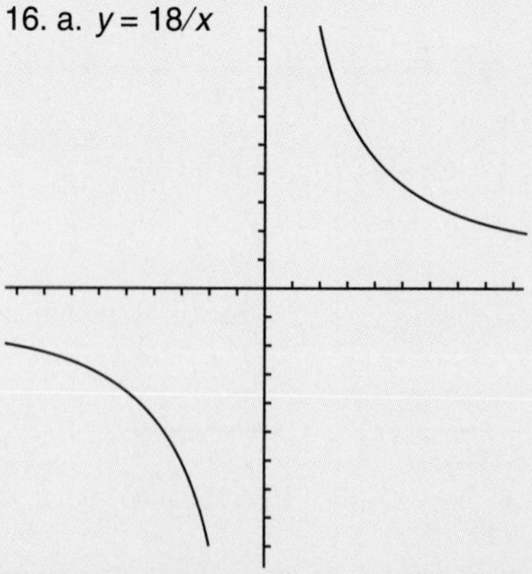

b. The product of the x-value and y-value is 18.

c. Sample (-2, -9), (1, 18)

d. $y = 18/x$

17. a. $y = x^2 - 1$

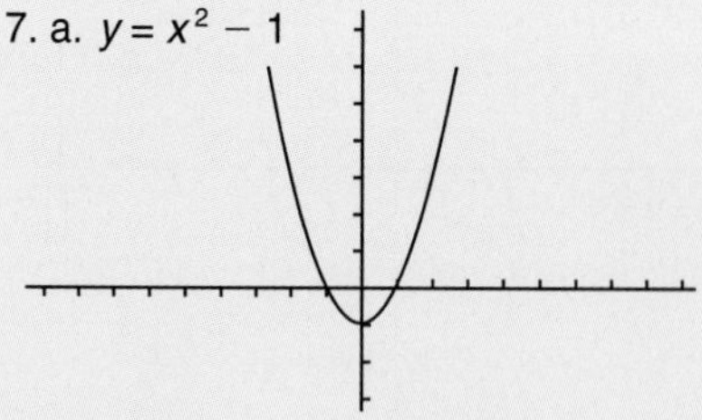

b. Square the x-value and subtract one to get the y-value

c. Sample (1, 0), (-3, 8)

d. $y = x^2 - 1$

18. a. Answers will vary. Paul does not start or end any of the trips at home. Paul got in his car and drove to a destination away from his home. When he arrived at his destination he may have returned immediately on the same road to a place that was farther away from home than his original point of departure. The road may have made a loop so that Paul continued driving on the same road which at first took him farther away from home, and then brought him back closer and closer to home.

(Solutions continued on page 515)

PRACTICE

REVIEW

DIRECT VARIATION

1. Without graphing, tell which of the following lines pass through the origin. Explain. The line containing points
   a. (2, 6) and (4, 12);
   b. (3, 8) and (4, 9);
   c. (6, 5) and (18, 15).

2. A line contains the points (0, 1) and (2, 4). Does it also contain the point (4, 8)? Explain.

3. A line contains the points (2, 5) and (4, 10). Does it also contain the point (200, 500)? Explain.

CREATE AN EQUATION

4. Create an equation that has $x = 3$ as a solution.

5. Create an equation that has $y = -3$ as a solution.

6. Create an equation where x appears on both sides of the equation and
   a. the solution is $x = 0$;
   b. the solution is $x = -1/2$.

■ SOLUTIONS

1. a. Yes
   b. No
   c. Yes
2. No
3. Yes

4.-6. Answers will vary.

Chapter 5
SUMS AND PRODUCTS

Overview of the Chapter

*T*his chapter deals with algebraic sums and products in several different ways. The first two lessons and the first **Thinking/ Writing** assignment involve analysis of graphs of the form $x + y = S$ and $x \cdot y = P$, which we call *constant sum* and *constant product* graphs. This is followed by work on the distributive law and an introduction to factoring trinomials. This is related (through the zero product property) to graphing parabolas, a topic which we preview. A lesson with a number-theoretic flavor investigates a puzzle based on sums and products of natural numbers. The chapter ends with an introduction to arithmetic sequences and their sums.

*T*his chapter has an unusual number of *problem of the week*-sized problems. You do not have to do all of them as you encounter them. If you wish, you can make a note of them, and save them for future assignments, as you forge ahead into future chapters.

1. New Uses for Tools:

- Multiplying binomials (minus in both factors) in the corner piece
- Inverse variation in function diagrams

2. Algebra Concepts Emphasized:

- Variables and operations
- Function diagrams and graphs for equations of the form $x + y = S$
- Function diagrams and graphs for equations of the form $x \cdot y = P$
- Interpolating and extrapolating in Cartesian graphs
- Division and the distributive law
- Minus and the distributive law
- Multiplying binomials
- Factoring trinomials, with $a = 1$
- Common factors
- Sequences
- Arithmetic sequences
- Sums of arithmetic sequences
- Even and odd numbers

CHAPTER 5

The colorful spiral of a lollipop

Coming in this chapter:

Exploration Build as many rectangles as you can with one x^2, ten x-blocks, and any number of yellow blocks.

Build as many rectangles as you can with x^2, 18, and any number of x-blocks.

Sums and Products

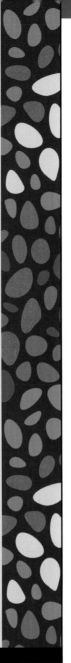

3. Algebra Concepts Reviewed:

- Operations with signed numbers
- The distributive law
- Order of operations
- Terms and degree of polynomials
- Interpreting graphs
- Equation solving (cover-up method)
- Equation solving (by trial and error)
- Identity and inverse elements

4. Algebra Concepts Previewed:

- Inverse variation
- Intersections of graphs
- Square roots
- The zero product property
- Factoring trinomials ($a \neq 1$)
- Graphing $y = x^2 + bx + c$ and $y = (x - p)(x - q)$
- Intercepts of a parabola
- Vertex of a parabola
- *Smile* and *frown* parabolas
- Perfect square trinomials
- Equation solving
- Mean and median
- Geometric sequences
- Slope

5. Problem-Solving Techniques:

- Recognizing patterns
- Systematic search
- Using algebraic notation
- Problem posing

6. Connections and Context:

- The *stamps* problem from number theory
- Symmetry and symmetry groups
- Abstract algebra

▼ 5.1
Constant Sums

Core Sequence: 1-20

Suitable for Homework: 10-20

Useful for Assessment: 12, 17-20

What this Lesson is About:

- Function diagrams for $x + y = S$
- Cartesian graphs for $x + y = S$
- Review of addition of signed numbers

Starting with an application, we look at equations of the form $x + y = S$ in several different ways. Function diagrams and Cartesian graphs each give insight into interesting attributes of equations of this type. Thinking about what quadrants the Cartesian graphs lie in provides a good review of addition of signed numbers.

AT THE GAS STATION

Problems 4-5 require the students to use algebraic notation. Group or class discussion may be needed.

LESSON 5.1

Constant Sums

You will need: graph paper

AT THE GAS STATION

When Oliver and Alice pulled up to the self-serve island at Jacob's gas station, they noticed a new sign:

Buy Gas Card in Office

They went into the office, which was decorated with photographs and cartoons. The attendant Harold explained to them that he could sell them a gas card for any amount from 5 to 100 dollars. They would put it in the special slot in the pump, and pump gas as usual. The value of the card would automatically go down, and a display on the pump would indicate the value left in the card. After getting gas, there would be no need to go back to the office, unless they wanted to trade the card back for cash. (This could be done only if the card had less than \$5 left on it.) Or they could use the remaining money left on the card the next time they stopped at Jacob's.

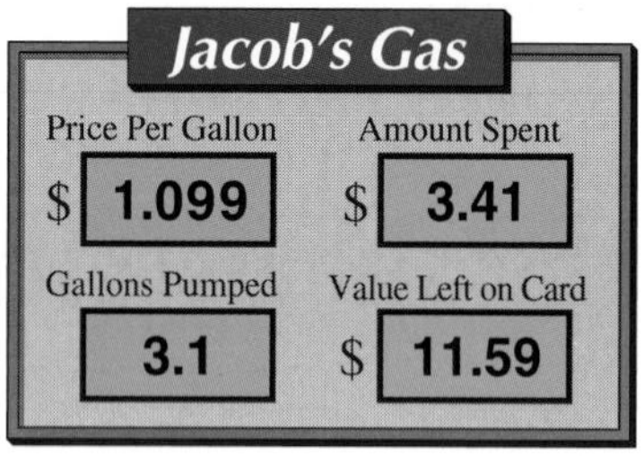

1. Look at the dials in the figure. How much did Oliver and Alice pay for their gas card?
2. Oliver and Alice plan to buy about \$10.00 worth of gas. List at least five other pairs of numbers that will appear on the last two dials while they are pumping gas.
3. When exactly 11 gallons have been pumped, what numbers will appear on the four dials?
4. **Generalization** When D dollars have been spent, what is the value left on the card?
5. When G gallons have been pumped,
   a. how many dollars have been spent?
   b. what is the value left on the card?

FUNCTION DIAGRAMS FROM RULERS

Alice wanted to know how long her ruler was. Oliver suggested she measure it with a longer ruler, as in this figure.

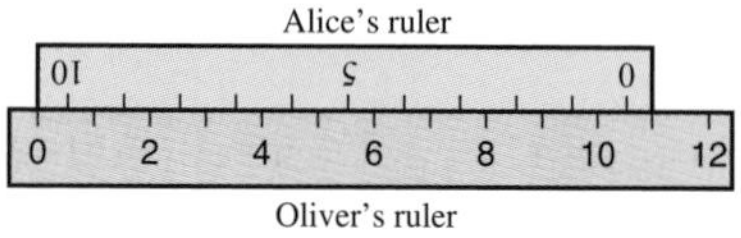

6. How long is her ruler?

5.1 SOLUTIONS

1. \$15.00
2. Answers will vary. Sample answers: (3.50, 11.50), (4.00, 11.00), (9.05, 5.95)
3. price per gallon: \$1.099, gallons pumped: 11.0, amount spent: 12.09, value left on card: 2.91
4. 15-D
5. a. 1.099 G dollars spent
   b. 15.00-1.099 G dollars left on card
6. 11 inches
7. The sum of x and y is always 10.5. The pattern will be the same regardless of which ruler you use for x and which for y. The units are the same on both rulers; the same pairs of numbers would be obtained from calling either one x.
8. $y = 10.5 - x$
9. 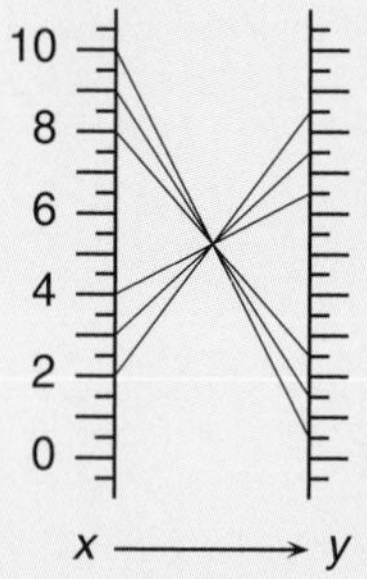

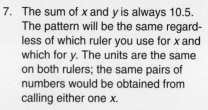

$y = 10.5 - x$

Oliver had to write about function diagrams for algebra. (His class was using this textbook, and in a curious coincidence, they were doing exactly this page!) He decided to use the rulers as a way to get tables of x- and y-values and build a function diagram from them. He used the rulers setup to create a table that started this way.

x	y
1	9.5
2	8.5
3	7.5

7. Describe the pattern for the numbers in the table. Does it matter which ruler you use for x and which for y? Explain.

8. Write a function of the type $y =$ *an expression in terms of* x for Oliver's table.

9. Make a function diagram for Oliver's table. (Use at least five in-out lines.)

10. Use rulers to create two more tables, and for each, write a function and make a function diagram. At least one of them should match 0 with a number other than a whole number.

11. How could you set up rulers to get this function diagram? Explain.

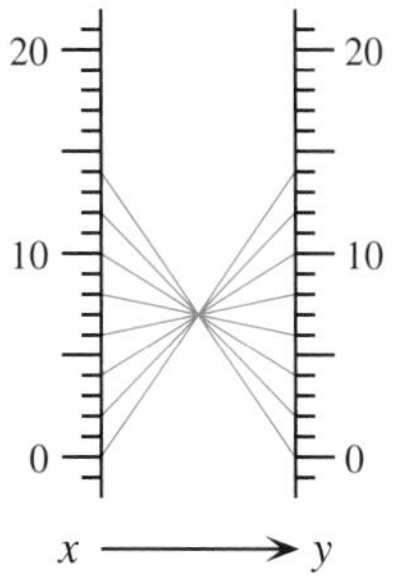

All the function diagrams you just drew have something in common. For each one, the sum of all the (x, y) pairs is a constant. We could call them *constant sum* functions.

12. **Summary** Write an illustrated summary describing what you noticed about diagrams of constant sum functions. It should include, but not be limited to, examples and answers to the following questions:

- Do the in-out lines meet in one point?
- If they do, could you predict the position of this point if you knew the value of the constant sum?

GRAPHS OF CONSTANT SUMS

13. a. On a pair of axes, plot these (x, y) pairs.
$(2, 4)$ $(4, 2)$ $(-1, 7)$ $(8, -2)$

b. In words, we could describe the pattern of the (x, y) pairs by saying that the sum of x and y is always six. How would you write this using algebra?

c. Find three more (x, y) pairs that fit this pattern, and add the points to your graph.

d. Connect all the points with a line or curve. Describe the graph.

14. a. Find points such that $x + y < 6$. Where are they in relation to the graph in problem 13?

b. Repeat for $x + y = 6$.

c. Repeat for $x + y > 6$.

15. Find a point (x, y) such that $x = y$ and $x + y = 6$. Label it on the graph.

16. Choose a positive value for S and make a table of (x, y) pairs that satisfy the equation $x + y = S$. Use your table to make a graph.

FUNCTION DIAGRAMS FROM RULERS

Of course, for problem 10, use rulers with the same units! We will do a problem with rulers in different units (inches and centimeters), in Chapter 13.

The point where all the in-out lines of a linear function meet is called the *focus*. We will study it in more detail in Chapter 8. In the case of the constant sum relationship, it is always half-way between the x- and y-number lines, and half-way between 0 and the constant sum.

Use the Function Diagrams and In-Out Tables on page 570 for some of these problems.

5.1 SOLUTIONS

10. Answers will vary. Two possible answers are given.

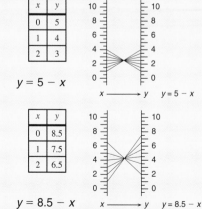

x	y
0	5
1	4
2	3

$y = 5 - x$

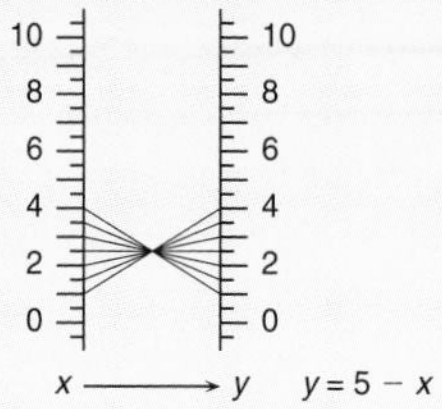

x	y
0	8.5
1	7.5
2	6.5

$y = 8.5 - x$

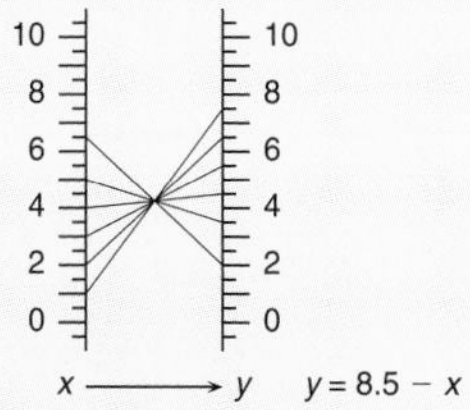

11. The sum of x and y is always 14. I would slide the rulers so that 10 on one matched up with 4 on the other. Then I would know that each pair would add to 14.

12. All functions will be of the form $y = S - x$. The in-out lines will meet in a point, halfway between the two number lines, and located on the in-out line $(S/2, S/2)$.

13. $x + y = 6$

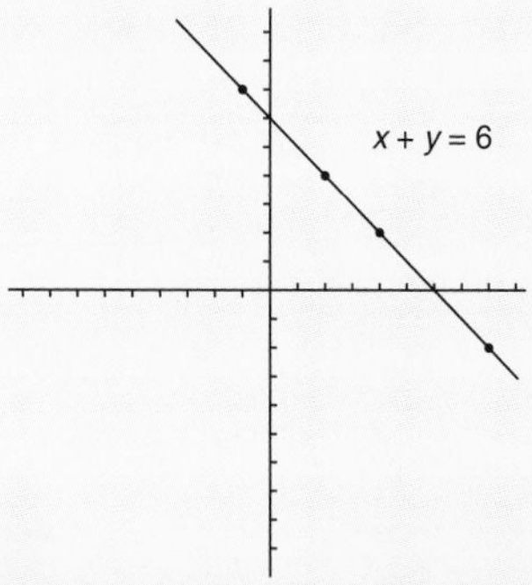

14. a. below the line
b. on the line
c. above the line

15. (3, 3)

16. Answers will vary. One possible answer is $x + y = 10$.

16., 17.

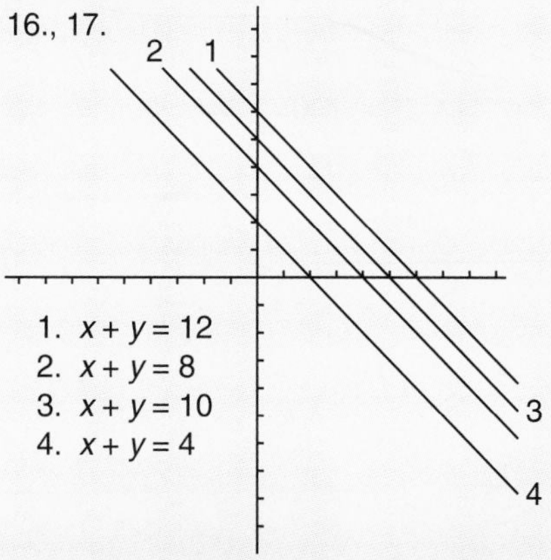

GRAPHS OF CONSTANT SUMS

If you assign problems 16 and 17 as homework, be sure that students understand the idea of choosing various values of *S*.

If you assign problem 20 as homework, you should precede it with a class discussion of problems 13-19. If you assign problem 20 as classwork, you may assign group reports on these problems, asking each group to display their findings on chart paper or transparencies and explain them to the class orally.

17. Experiment with some other constant sum graphs. Try several different positive values for *S*. For each one, make a table of at least five (x, y) pairs having the sum *S*. Then draw a graph. Draw all your graphs on the same pair of axes.

18. Do any of the lines go through the origin? If not, do you think you could pick a number for your sum so that the line would go through the origin? Explain.

19. Repeat your investigations for equations of the form $x + y = S$, where *S* is negative. Keep a record of what you try, using tables and graphs.

20. Report Write an illustrated report summarizing your findings about constant sum graphs. Your report should include neatly labeled graphs with accompanying explanations. Include answers to the following questions:

- Were the graphs straight lines or curved, or were there some of each?
- Without drawing the graph, could you now predict which quadrants the graph would be in, if you knew the value of *S*? Explain.
- Without drawing the graph, could you predict the *x*-intercepts and *y*-intercepts of the graph, if you knew the value of *S*? Explain.
- What determines whether the graph slopes up or down as it goes from left to right? Could you predict this without graphing if you knew the value of *S*? Explain.
- Do any of your graphs intersect each other? If so, which ones? If not, why not?

5.1 SOLUTIONS

17. Answers will vary. See graph on preceding page for sample answers.

18. The line will go through the origin if $S = 0$.

19. Answers will vary. See graph for sample answers.

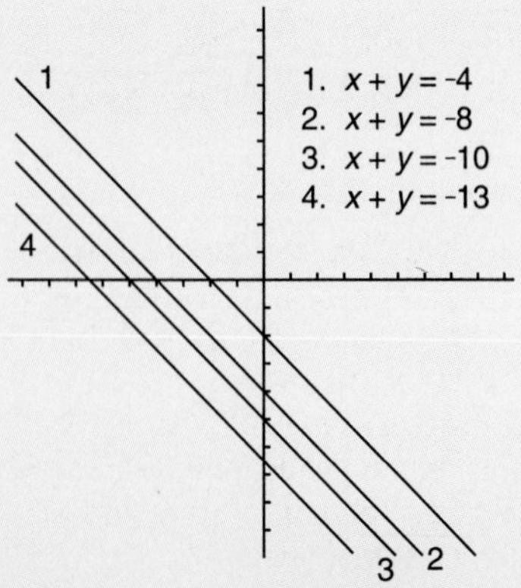

20. Answers will vary. Some key points are given:

The graphs will be straight lines. They will all be parallel. They can't intersect one another because the sum of *x* and *y* cannot simultaneously take on two different values. The *x*-intercept is $(S, 0)$ and the *y*-intercept is $(0, S)$. All graphs slope down from left to right. If *S* is positive, the graph passes through quadrants I, II, and IV. It does not pass through quadrant III, since you can't add two negative numbers and get a positive number. If *S* is negative it passes through II, III, and IV. It does not pass through quadrant I, since you can't add two positive numbers and get a negative number. If $S = 0$, the graph will go through the origin and lie in quadrants II and IV. For every point on the graph, *y* will be the opposite of *x*, so this graph can lie only in quadrants in which *x* and *y* have opposite signs.

LESSON 5.2

Constant Products

MILES PER GALLON

If you plan to take a trip of 100 miles, the amount of gas you need depends on how many miles per gallon your vehicle gets. Some very large recreational vehicles get only about 5 miles per gallon, while a scooter can get 100 miles per gallon.

1. Copy and complete the table to show how many gallons of gasoline you should buy if your vehicle gets the mileage indicated. Continue the table up to 100 miles per gallon.

Mileage (miles per gallon)	Gasoline needed (gallons)	Total trip distance (miles)
5	—	100
10.5	—	100
20	—	100

2. Graph the (x, y) pairs in the first two columns of the table.

3. Describe your graph in words. If you were to extend your graph, would it go through the origin? Would it touch or cross the axes? Explain.

CONNECTING THE DOTS

4. Make a table containing these points and plot the (x, y) pairs on a Cartesian graph.

(2, 12) (3, 8) (4, 6) (8, 3)

5. Describe the pattern of the (x, y) pairs in problem 4

a. in words; b. using algebra.

6. a. Find five more (x, y) pairs that fit this pattern and add the points to your table and graph. Use positive values for x. Include some fractional values.

b. Add five more (x, y) pairs to your table and graph. This time use negative values for x, including some fractional values.

7. Study the points on your graph. If necessary, add more points so that you can answer the following questions.

a. Which quadrants do your points lie in? Why?

b. Can you find a point on the y-axis that fits the pattern? Can you find a point on the x-axis? Explain.

c. If you were to connect the points with a smooth curve, would the curve go through the origin? Explain.

8. Add to your graph a point that fits the pattern and

a. has an x-value less than 1/2;

b. has a y-value less than 1/2;

c. has an x-value greater than 24;

d. has a y-value less than -24.

9. Study your answers to problems 4-8. Then very carefully connect the points with a curve. Your curve should have two parts *that are not connected* to one another.

a. Describe the graph.

b. Explain why the two parts are not connected.

5.2 Constant Products

Core Sequence: 1-10, 12-14

Suitable for Homework: 1-3, 13-14

Useful for Assessment: 13-14

What this Lesson is About:

- Cartesian graphs for $x \cdot y = P$
- Review of multiplication of signed numbers
- Preview of inverse variation
- Preview of square roots and of intersection of graphs
- Interpolating and extrapolating in Cartesian graphs

MILES PER GALLON

CONNECTING THE DOTS

Be sure to discuss the issues raised in problems 7 and 9. When to connect the dots and when not to is often a source of confusion to students. (They will have an opportunity to think more about this, and to write about it, in the following section.)

Use problem 10 to discuss the broader question of how to locate *all* the points that satisfy the given properties. This will help reinforce the understanding of the fact that the points on the graph satisfy the equation, and the points off the graph do not, which is almost certainly the most important idea about graphing students should learn in a first-year algebra course.

5.2 SOLUTIONS

1.

Mileage (miles per gallon)	Gasoline needed (gallons)	Total trip distance (miles)
5	20	100
10.5	9.52	100
20	5	100
25	4	100
40	2.5	100
100	1	100

2.

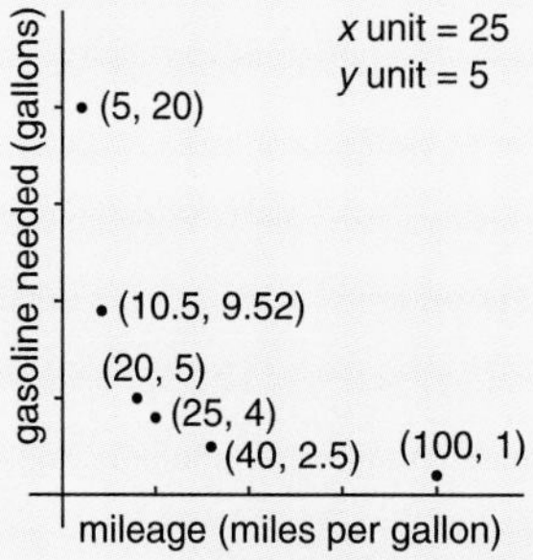

3. The graph is curved. It does not go through the origin, and it will never touch either axis. Since the product of x and y is always 100, neither coordinate can ever be 0. (If either coordinate were 0, the product would be 0.) However, as you extend the curve farther and farther in either direction, it gets closer and closer to the x-axis or y-axis.

4., 6.

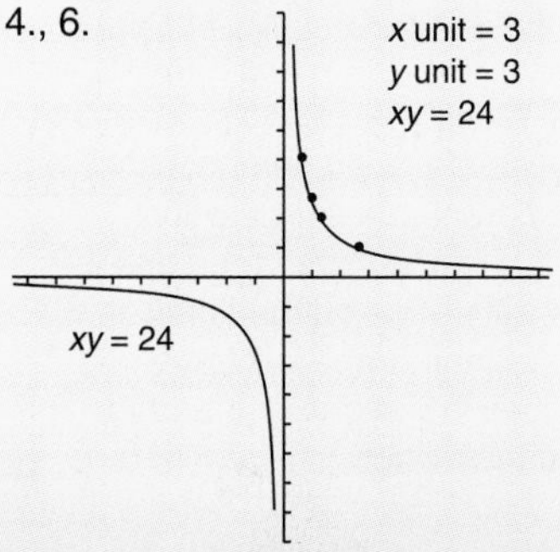

5. a. The product of each (x, y) pair is 24.

b. $xy = 24$

6. Answers will vary. Two possible answers are (1/2, 48) and (-4, -6).

7. a. quadrants I and III

b. No. The product is 24; neither of the factors could be 0.

c. No. The product of 0 and 0 is not 24.

8. Answers will vary.

9. a. The two parts are curved. Each one gets closer and closer to one of the axes as you move farther to the left or the right.

b. In order for the two parts to be connected, it would be necessary to cross the axes. This is impossible, as explained in #7.

Although this fact seems obvious, it certainly is not always apparent to students. This discussion also serves as preparation for the following section.

*P*roblem 11 previews the work on intersections of graphs and on square roots. Do not expect all students to master all the ideas that are raised by the problem. Instead, use it as a way to start thinking about a couple of big ideas. We will return to square roots in Chapter 9, and to the intersection of graphs in Chapter 10. Students who are starting to get insights into either concept may try to address it in their report.

*T*he Report (problem 13) can be assigned as homework or used for a group report as a way of focusing the discussion of the main points of this lesson. There is often lively discussion among students about whether or not the graphs touch the axes or pass through the origin.

*B*y the way, making generalizations about quadrants in which the graphs lie is a good review of multiplication rules for signed numbers.

*O*f course, an equation of the form $xy = P$ can also be written as the inverse variation function $y = P/x$. We will return to this in the next section, and again in Chapter 12.

10. For (a-d), find several pairs of numbers (x, y) that satisfy the description. Plot these points on your graph.

a. x is positive and xy is more than 24.

b. x is positive and xy is less than 24.

c. x is negative and xy is more than 24.

d. x is negative and xy is less than 24.

11. Plot a point (x, y) such that $xy = 24$ and $x = y$.

We could call the curve you drew in problem 9 a *constant product* graph, since the product of the coordinates of every point is the same number. We could graph many other *constant product* graphs of the form $xy = P$, where P could be any number we choose.

12. Experiment with the graphs of some equations of the form $xy = P$. Try several different positive values for P. Then try several different negative values for P. For each one, make a table of at least eight (x, y) pairs having the same product. Then draw a graph. Draw all your graphs on the same pair of axes.

13. Report Write a report summarizing your findings about constant product graphs. Your report should include neatly labeled graphs with accompanying explanations. Include answers to the following questions:

- What is the shape of the graph?
- Without drawing the graph, could you now predict which quadrants the graph would be in, if you knew the value of P? Explain.
- Do any of the graphs go through the origin? If not, do you think you could find a value of P so that the graph would go through the origin? Explain.
- Where can you find points whose product is not P?
- Comment on anything you notice about the x-intercepts and y-intercepts.
- Do any of your graphs intersect? Explain why or why not.

OTHER GRAPHS

In order to graph some functions, Tomas made tables of values, plotted the points, and connected the dots. (For one of the equations, he tried two different ways.) He asked his teacher if he had done it right. Mr. Stephens answered that the individual points had been plotted correctly, but he asked Tomas to think about how he had connected them. He said, *"Every point on the graph, even the ones obtained by connecting the dots, must satisfy the equation."* Tomas didn't understand. Mr. Stephens added, "Check whether you connected the dots correctly, by substituting a few more values of x into the equation. Use your calculator to see if the y-value you get is on the graph you drew." Tomas still didn't understand.

5.2 SOLUTIONS

10. Answers will vary.

11. $(\sqrt{24}, \sqrt{24})$

12. Answers will vary. The figure shows some sample answers.

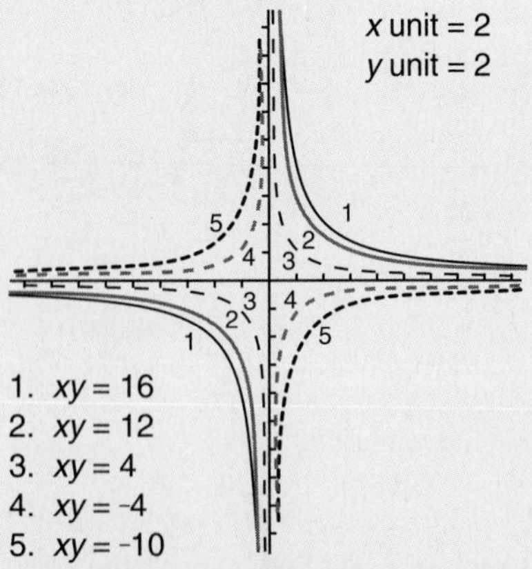

1. $xy = 16$
2. $xy = 12$
3. $xy = 4$
4. $xy = -4$
5. $xy = -10$

13. Answers will vary. Some key points are given:

The graphs will be curved, with two branches that are not connected. The two branches of each graph will not be connected because that would require crossing the axes, and points on either of the axes will satisfy a constant product equation only if the product is zero. None of the graphs will intersect each other, since the product of two numbers cannot simultanously have two different values. Therefore, no point could lie on two different constant product curves. Points whose products are not P will not be on the curve $xy = P$. If $P < 0$, the graph will have branches in quadrants II and IV. This is because x and y have different signs in these quadrants and hence xy is negative. If $P > 0$, the graph will have branches in quadrants I and III, where x and y have the same sign and hence a positive product. The only graph which is not curved would be $xy = 0$, which consists of the two axes. This graph is the limiting case. (Notice that as P gets smaller, the graphs get closer and closer to the axes.)

Name: Tomas

$y = x - 2$		$y = x^2$		$y = -6/x$	
x	y	x	y	x	y
-2	-4	-2	4	-2	3
-1	-3	-1	1	-1	6
0	-2	0	0	0	imp.
1	-1	1	1	1	-6
2	0	2	4	2	-3

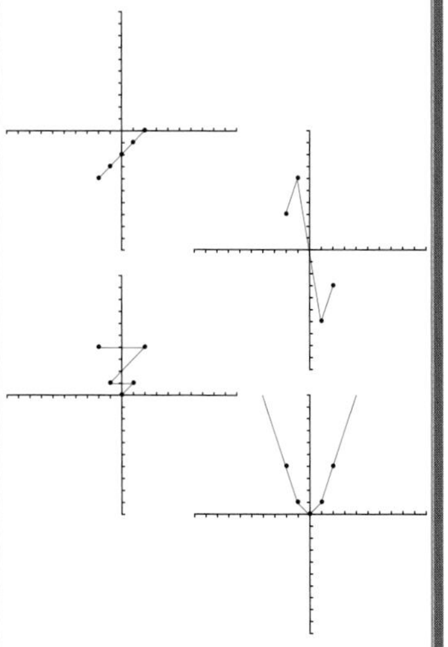

14. **Report** Explain how Tomas can improve his graphs. Show your calculations. Give Tomas advice he can understand, on:

- how to label axes, points, and graphs;
- how to connect the dots correctly;
- how to extend the graph to the left and right;
- how a calculator can help.

OTHER GRAPHS

Problem 14 must be preceded with class discussion of the graphs and of Mr. Stephens's comments. The mistakes made by Tomas are standard mistakes and might as well be discussed specifically, but they are difficult to root out if students do not understand the basic ideas underlying Cartesian graphing.

Do not expect mastery of this. See problem 14 as an opportunity for you to see how students understand graphing at this point in the course. There will be time to pursue the discussion, and deepen their understanding, but it is important to start now!

$y = x - 2$: The graph could be extended to the left and right, because it is a straight line. Additional points could be tried for confirmation if students are not sure it will remain a straight line.

$y = x^2$: In the first attempt, the points are connected from top to bottom, giving three values for y when $x = 0$. Only one ($y = 0$) is valid. The other attempt is better, but not perfect. Trying values such as $x = 0.5$, $x = 3$, and $x = 4$ could help students see that straight line segments do not accurately represent this curve.

$y = -6/x$. This reviews the work in problems 1-13 in a different format. Getting additional points is essential.

5.2 SOLUTIONS

14. Answers will vary. Some key points are given:

Tomas graphed $y = x^2$ correctly once and incorrectly once. He needs to use his calculator to find points between those whose values are easy to find by mental calculation. He also needs to connect the dots in order, as x goes from left to right. His one attempt at graphing $y = -6/x$ was not successful because he connected points by drawing a line through points that could not possibly be on the graph. He probably needs to include more points in his table in order to see the pattern. He graphed $y = x - 2$ correctly, but he could have thought about the pattern, realized that it should be a straight line (from what he learned in Chapter 4), and extended the graph. He needs to label axes and indicate the scale on his graphs.

▼ 5.3
The Distributive Law

Core Sequence: 1-36

Suitable for Homework: 10, 15-36

Useful for Assessment: 10, 35-36

What this Lesson is About:

- Terms and degree of polynomials
- Recognizing patterns
- Division and the distributive law
- Multiplying binomials

At this point in the course, some students should start developing facility with the distributive law, and will need the Lab Gear less and less. This lesson is part of that transition, since students are encouraged to use the blocks initially, but to look for patterns and generalize.

If students can work accurately without the Lab Gear (for example with the multiplication table model introduced in Chapter 3, Lesson 6), do not insist on their using it, as they will probably resent it. If on the other hand they are making many mistakes, remind them that the blocks are there to help correct and prevent errors.

HOW MANY TERMS?

Problems 1-9 may not be sufficient for students to be able to make generalizations. If needed, encourage them to set up their own multiplications to check their conjectures. (In addition, there are more practice problems later in the lesson.) You should assign problem 10 as homework, but make sure the students are ready for it.

DIVISION AND THE DISTRIBUTIVE LAW

Students often make mistakes by simplifying algebraic fractions incorrectly. The Lab Gear image of division (which was introduced in Chapter 3, Lesson 6) can help them understand what they do wrong when they make these types of mistakes. In the case of division by a whole number, it is sometimes possible to represent the division by showing sets of blocks instead of using the corner piece.

Again, students should gradually move away from the Lab Gear. In problems like 15-19, where the common factor is in plain view, some students should see the benefits of working on paper.

LESSON 5.3

The Distributive Law

You will need:

the Lab Gear 

HOW MANY TERMS?

For each multiplication, write an equation of the form *length · width equals area.* (You may use the Lab Gear and the corner piece to model the multiplication by making a rectangle.) In your expression for the area, combine like terms.

1. $x(2x + 5)$
2. $2x(y - 2)$
3. $y(2y + 2 - x)$
4. $(2x + 2)(3x - 5)$
5. $(x + 2)(3y + 1)$
6. $(x + 2)(y - 3x + 1)$

For each multiplication, write an equation of the form *length · width · height equals volume.* (You may want to use the Lab Gear and the corner piece to model the multiplication by making a box.) In your expression for the volume, combine like terms.

7. $x(x + 2)(x + 5)$
8. $y(x + 2)(y + 1)$
9. $x(x + 5)(x + y + 1)$

Definitions: A polynomial having two terms is called a *binomial;* one having three terms is called a *trinomial.* A polynomial having one term is called a *monomial.*

10. **Report** In problems 1-9, you multiplied two or three polynomials of degree 1. In each case, the product was also a polynomial. Write a report describing the patterns you saw in the products. You should use the words *monomial, binomial,* and *trinomial.* Give examples and illustrate your work with drawings of the Lab Gear. Your report should address the points listed below, but should also include any other observations you made.
    - What determines the degree of the product?
    - What determines the number of terms in the product?
    - Compare problems having one variable to problems having two variables.

DIVISION AND THE DISTRIBUTIVE LAW

As you probably remember, you can use the corner piece to model division.

Example: Simplify $\frac{4x + 6 + 2y}{2}$

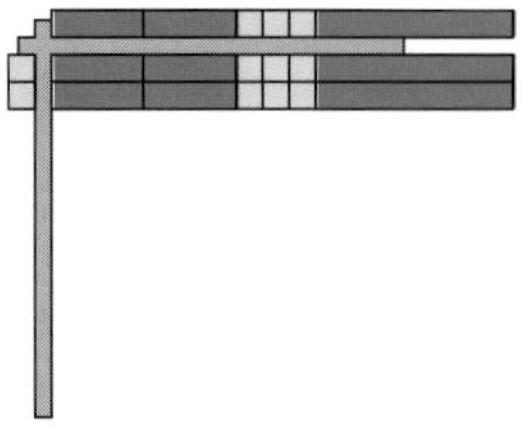

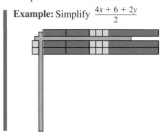

In some cases, you can use the Lab Gear in another way to show that a division like this one can be thought of as three divisions.

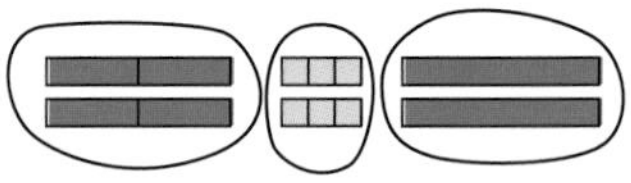

11. What is the result of the division?

Simplify these expressions, using the Lab Gear if you wish.

12. $\frac{10x + 5y + 15}{5}$
13. $\frac{2x + 4}{x + 2}$

5.3 SOLUTIONS

1. $2x^2 + 5x$
2. $2xy - 4x$
3. $2y^2 + 2y - xy$
4. $6x^2 - 4x - 10$
5. $3xy + 6y + x + 2$
6. $xy + 2y - 3x^2 - 5x + 2$
7. $x^3 + 7x^2 + 10x$
8. $xy^2 + 2y^2 + xy + 2y$
9. $x^3 + x^2y + 6x^2 + 5xy + 5x$
10. Answers will vary. A few key points follow:

    If you are multiplying polynomials of degree 1, then the degree of the product will be the same as the number of polynomials being multiplied (i.e. the number of factors). In general, the degree of the product is the sum of the degrees of the factors. The product of a monomial and a binomial or a trinomial will have two or three terms, respectively. The product of a binomial and a binomial will have four terms, but sometimes two of these are like terms and can be combined. The product of a binomial and a trinomial will have six terms before combining like terms. In general, the number of terms in the product (before combining like terms) is the product of the number of terms in the factors. This can be illustrated by comparing $(x + 2)(x + 5)$ with $x(x + 2)(x + 5)$. Multiplying by x did not increase the number of terms in the product, but it did increase the degree. Comparing these two expressions modeled with the Lab Gear illustrates this point well.

14. $\frac{x^2 + 4x + 4}{x + 2}$

15. $\frac{3(y - x) + 6(x - 2)}{3}$

Another way to simplify some fractions is to rewrite the division into a multiplication and use the distributive law.

Example: To simplify $\frac{6x + 4 + 2y}{2}$:

- Rewrite the problem as a multiplication.
  $$\frac{1}{2}(6x + 4 + 2y)$$
- Apply the distributive law.
  $$\frac{1}{2} \cdot 6x + \frac{1}{2} \cdot 4 + \frac{1}{2} \cdot 2y$$
- Simplify.
  $$3x + 2 + y$$

You can see that we could have divided every term in the numerator by 2. That is:
$$\frac{6x + 4 + 2y}{2} = \frac{6x}{2} + \frac{4}{2} + \frac{2y}{2}.$$

The single division problem was equivalent to three divisions. This example illustrates *the distributive law of division over addition and subtraction.*

Divide.

16. $\frac{9x + 6y + 6}{3}$

17. $\frac{3x^2 + 2x}{2x}$

18. $\frac{6x^2 + 4x}{2x}$

19. $\frac{2(x + 3) + 5(x + 3)}{x + 3}$

DISTRIBUTIVE LAW PRACTICE

Find these products, using the Lab Gear or any other method.

20. $2x(x - 1)$ 21. $y(y + 4)$

22. $3x(x + y - 5)$ 23. $(x + 5)(3x - 2)$

24. $(2x + 4)(x + y + 2)$

25. $(2y - x - 3)(y + x)$

Write equivalent expressions without the parentheses. Combine like terms.

26. $z(x + y) + z(x - y)$

27. $z(x + y) + z(x + y)$

28. $z(x + y) + x(z + y)$

29. $z(x + y) - x(z + y)$

MULTIPLYING BINOMIALS

The following problems involve multiplying two binomials of the form $ax + b$ or $ax - b$. Multiplications like this arise often in math. As you do them, look for patterns and shortcuts.

30. $(3x + 2)(5x + 6)$

31. $(3x - 2)(5x + 6)$

32. $(3x + 2)(5x - 6)$

33. $(ax + 2)(3x + d)$

34. $(2x + b)(cx - 3)$

35. When you multiply two binomials of the form $ax + b$ or $ax - b$,
   a. what is the degree of the product?
   b. how many terms are in the product?

36. When multiplying two binomials of the form $ax + b$ or $ax - b$, how do you find
   a. the coefficient of x^2?
   b. the coefficient of x?
   c. the constant term?

You may have a class discussion of how one could use the multiplication table format to do problems 11-19 correctly. This is quite tricky in some cases, but quite straightforward in others. For example, for problem 11, it could be set up this way.

	?	?	?
2	$4x$	6	$2y$

We return to problems of this type in Chapter 6, Lesson 5.

For problem 13, it could be set up this way.

	?
x	$2x$
2	4

DISTRIBUTIVE LAW PRACTICE
MULTIPLYING BINOMIALS

Use the practice problems only if your students need them. If you assign them for homework, students who want to use the Lab Gear approach for problems 20-25 will have to use sketches.

A class discussion of problems 35-36 should help students consolidate their strategies. It is likely FOIL (first/outer/inner/last) will be proposed as a method. Students (or you) may suggest other techniques. In any case, make sure they see that techniques used for multiplying binomials may not work in the more general case of multiplying polynomials that have more or fewer terms.

5.3 SOLUTIONS

11. $2x + y + 3$
12. $2x + y + 3$
13. 2
14. $x + 2$
15. $y - x + 2(x - 2) = y + x - 4$
16. $3x + 2y + 2$
17. $(3/2)x + 1$
18. $3x + 2$
19. 7
20. $2x^2 - 2x$
21. $y^2 + 4y$
22. $3x^2 + 3xy - 15x$
23. $3x^2 + 13x - 10$
24. $2x^2 + 2xy + 8x + 4y + 8$
25. $2y^2 + xy - 3y - x^2 - 3x$
26. $xz + yz + xz - yz = 2xz$
27. $2xz + 2yz$
28. $2xz + zy + xy$
29. $zy - xy$
30. $15x^2 + 28x + 12$
31. $15x^2 + 8x - 12$
32. $15x^2 - 8x - 12$
33. $3ax^2 + 6x + dax + 2d$
34. $2cx^2 + bcx - 6x - 3b$
35. a. second degree
    b. There are four, but two are like terms and can be combined.
36. a. Multiply the coefficients of the two x terms.
    b. Multiply the constant term of each binomial by the coefficient of x in the other binomial. Add the two results.
    c. Multiply the two constant terms.

▼ 5.4
Factoring Trinomials

Core Sequence: 1-24

Suitable for Homework: 15-24

Useful for Assessment: 6, 8, 10, 19

What this Lesson is About:

- Factoring trinomials of the form $x^2 + bx + c$
- Preview of greatest common factor
- Recognizing factorable trinomials

*I*nstead of trying to develop skill in rapid factoring, we try to get students to notice patterns so that they recognize factorable trinomials.

*T*he National Council of Teachers of Mathematics recommends that factoring receive less emphasis in the algebra curriculum. We support this recommendation, and so we do not provide endless drill in factoring trinomials. As a skill, factoring is no longer important; within a few years hand-held calculators will be able to factor polynomials. Actually, if you understand the relationship between the factors of $ax^2 + bx + c$, the zeroes of $ax^2 + bx + c = 0$, and the x-intercepts of $y = ax^2 + bx + c$, you can factor any trinomial with the graphing calculators currently available.

*H*owever, understanding factoring, *as a concept*, is a very important part of understanding the distributive law and multiplication. This lesson is important as a part of developing students' understanding of algebraic *structure*.

*T*he pattern underlying this lesson and the subsequent writing assignment can be seen in the following calculation.

$$(x + m)(x + n) = x^2 + mx + nx + mn$$
$$= x^2 + (m + n)x + mn$$

*S*o the coefficient of the x-term is the sum of m and n, and the constant term is their product. This explanation is not understandable by most students before this lesson, but you may want to present it to the class afterwards. We will return to a similar argument in Lesson 5, problem 13, after the students have had substantially more experience with this pattern.

LESSON 5.4

Factoring Trinomials

You will need:

the Lab Gear 

LAB GEAR RECTANGLES

1. **Exploration**
   a. Use the Lab Gear to make as many different rectangles as you can with one x^2-block, ten x-blocks, and any number of yellow blocks. For each one, write a multiplication equation to show that *area = length times width.* Look for patterns.
   b. Use the Lab Gear to make as many different rectangles as you can with one x^2-block, 18 yellow blocks, and any number of x-blocks. For each one, write a multiplication equation to show that *area = length times width.* Look for patterns.

2. Use the Lab Gear to help you find the other side of the rectangle having the given area. Look for patterns. One is impossible.

	Side	Area
a.	$x + 4$	$x^2 + 9x + 20$
b.	$x + 3$	$x^2 + 4x + 3$
c.	$x + 6$	$x^2 + 6x + 8$
d.	$x + 1$	$x^2 + 3x + 2$
e.	$x + 4$	$x^2 + 7x + 12$

FACTORS AND PRODUCTS

Definition: To factor means to write as a product.

For example, two ways of factoring 12 are to write it as $6 \cdot 2$ or as $4 \cdot 3$. Some polynomials can be factored. With the Lab Gear we model this by making a rectangle or a box.

3. By making a Lab Gear rectangle and writing a related multiplication equation, show that $5y + y^2$ can be written as the product of a monomial and a binomial.

You have factored the polynomial $5y + y^2$.

4. By making a rectangle with the Lab Gear and writing a related multiplication equation, show that the trinomial $x^2 + 3x + 2$ can be written as a product of two binomials.

As this problem showed, some trinomials of the form $x^2 + bx + c$ can be factored.

5. Factor each trinomial into the product of two binomials. It may help to use the Lab Gear to make rectangles.
   a. $x^2 + 8x + 7$
   b. $x^2 + 8x + 12$
   c. $x^2 + 8x + 15$

6. Are there any more trinomials of the form $x^2 + 8x +$ ___ that can be factored into two binomials? If so, write and factor them. If not, explain.

7. Factor each trinomial into the product of two binomials. It may help to use the Lab Gear to make rectangles.
   a. $x^2 + 13x + 12$
   b. $x^2 + 8x + 12$
   c. $x^2 + 7x + 12$

8. Are there any more trinomials of the form $x^2 +$ __$x + 12$ that can be factored into two binomials? If so, write and factor them. If not, explain.

LAB GEAR RECTANGLES

*T*his section reviews familiar material, but the way the problems are posed should help students start to see the patterns that will help them with the rest of the lesson.

FACTORS AND PRODUCTS

*E*ven though we have done much work on this topic, this is the first time we use the word *factoring*. Make sure students associate it with examples such as the one in problem 3, as well as with the trinomials that constitute the main topic of this lesson.

*F*or problems 6 and 8, the discussion is mostly intended to focus on whole numbers, but note the following examples.

$$(x + 4.5)(x + 3.5) = x^2 + 8x + 15.75$$
$$(x + 5)\left(x + \frac{12}{5}\right) = x^2 + \frac{37}{5}x + 12$$

*I*f you think your students, or some of them, are ready for this, you may bring these examples up now; or wait until after **Thinking/Writing 5.A**.

THE THIRD DEGREE

*U*se these problems primarily to review the idea of factoring out the common factor.

*V*ery few students are likely to factor the polynomial in problem 11 successfully without the Lab Gear. If any do, encourage them to describe their strategy to the class.

THE THIRD DEGREE

9. Factor these third-degree polynomials into a product of three first-degree polynomials. Making a box with the Lab Gear may help.
a. $x^2y + 5xy + 6y$
b. $x^3 + 5x^2 + 6x$
c. $y^3 + 5y^2 + 6y$
d. $xy^2 + 5xy + 6x$

10. Describe a strategy to factor the polynomials above without the Lab Gear.

11. Factor, using the Lab Gear if you need to, $x^2y + x^2 + 5xy + 5x + 6y + 6$.

PLUS AND MINUS

12. a. Use the corner piece and the Lab Gear to show the multiplication
$$(y + 4)(y + 3).$$
Write the product.
b. How many blocks of each type were needed to show the product?

13. a. Use the corner piece and the Lab Gear to show the multiplication
$$(y - 4)(y + 3).$$
Write the product.
b. Compare the number of blocks of each type used to show this product with the number of blocks used in problem 12.

14. Write another multiplication that requires one y^2-block, seven y-blocks, and twelve 1-blocks to show the product. Model it with the blocks and write the product. Compare work with your classmates. Is there more than one possibility?

MISSING TERMS

Supply the missing terms. Then compare your answers with your classmates' answers.

15. $x^2 + 15x + \_\_ = (x + \_\_)(x + \_\_)$

16. $x^2 - 7x + \_\_ = (x - \_\_)(x - \_\_)$

17. $x^2 + \_\_x + 15 = (x + \_\_)(x + \_\_)$

18. $x^2 - \_\_x + 7 = (x - \_\_)(x - \_\_)$

19. Which problems, 15-18, have more than one answer? Explain.

FACTORING BY TRIAL AND ERROR

20. If possible, factor each trinomial into a product of binomials. Try to do it without using the Lab Gear.
a. $x^2 + 5x + 6$
b. $a^2 + 11a + 30$
c. $m^2 + 20m + 100$
d. $p^2 + 2p + 1$

21. Factor.
a. $x^2 - 5x + 6$
b. $x^2 - 13x + 12$
c. $x^2 - 8x + 15$
d. $x^2 - 9$

22. Factor.
a. $6x^2 + 5x + 1$
c. $6x^2 + x - 1$
d. $6x^2 - x - 1$

23. Factor.
a. $x^4 - 8x^2 + 15$
b. $x^4 - 8x^2 + 16$

WHAT'S YOUR PROBLEM?

24. Make up six trinomials of the form $x^2 + bx + c$. Four should be factorable, and two should be impossible to factor. Exchange with another student, and try to factor each other's trinomials.

5.4 SOLUTIONS

1. a. $x(x + 10) = x^2 + 10x$
$(x + 1)(x + 9) = x^2 + 10x + 9$
$(x + 2)(x + 8) = x^2 + 10x + 16$
$(x + 3)(x + 7) = x^2 + 10x + 21$
$(x + 4)(x + 6) = x^2 + 10x + 24$
$(x + 5)(x + 5) = x^2 + 10x + 25$
b. $(x + 1)(x + 18) = x^2 + 19x + 18$
$(x + 2)(x + 9) = x^2 + 11x + 18$
$(x + 3)(x + 6) = x^2 + 9x + 18$

2. a. $x + 5$
b. $x + 1$
c. impossible
d. $x + 2$
e. $x + 3$

3.
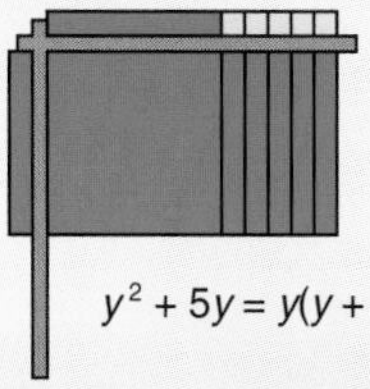

4.
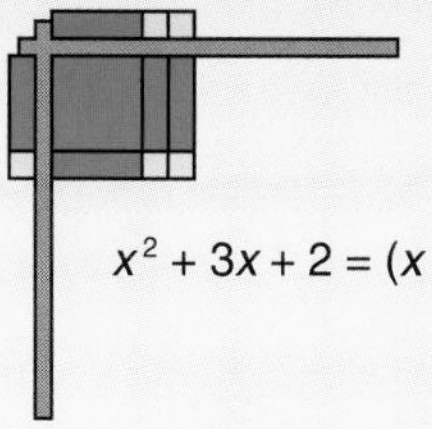

5. a. $(x + 1)(x + 7)$
b. $(x + 2)(x + 6)$
c. $(x + 3)(x + 5)$

6. Only $x^2 + 8x + 16$, which equals $(x + 4)(x + 4)$. There are no more trinomials if we consider only whole numbers, since we have used all the whole number pairs that add to 8. However, there is an infinite number of possibilities if we allow other numbers. Example:
$(x + 3.5)(x + 4.5) = x^2 + 8x + 15.75$

(Solutions continued on page 516)

Additional problems of this type can be created by working backwards: multiply a binomial (in y) by a trinomial (in x and y). You may suggest to your strongest students that they create a challenge of this type for each other.

PLUS AND MINUS

This section continues the work to develop students' familiarity with the product of binomials. It is the last section in this lesson that relies on the Lab Gear.

In problem 14, students may want to use the product $(y - 4)(y - 3)$. This is correct, but they have not yet been introduced to the Lab Gear model of this kind of multiplication. Encourage them to make some guesses about this question, but do not spend too much class time on it. We will return to this in Lesson 6.

MISSING TERMS

FACTORING BY TRIAL AND ERROR

WHAT'S YOUR PROBLEM?

These sections allow students to see how well they have internalized the pattern from the previous sections. The case with minus in both factors is approached for the first time.

Problems 22-23 are more difficult. It is not essential all students be able to do them, though they can be offered the challenge. The Lab Gear helps for problem 22, but for problem 23, the best way is to rewrite the expression with $X = x^2$: $X^2 - 8X + 15$. They know how to factor that. Then replace X with x^2 in the factored expression.

If you want more practice with factoring, make up a practice sheet from students' suggested trinomials for problem 24.

If students are not sure how to begin problem 24, discussion may help. The best way to create trinomials that can be factored is to multiply two binomials. As for impossible ones, it is a good bet that most randomly selected trinomials cannot be factored! (Which is why factoring is not important as a skill in applied mathematics.) Naturally, understanding the sum-product pattern also helps find trinomials that are possible or impossible to factor.

THINKING WRITING 5.A Analyzing Graphs

Core Sequence: 1-12

Suitable for Homework: 4-12

Useful for Assessment: 12

What this Assignment is About:

- Intersections of constant sum and constant product graphs
- Factoring $x^2 + bx + c$

As your students probably figured out over the course of the past two lessons, in order to factor a trinomial of the form $x^2 + bx + c$, we search for two numbers that have the sum b and the product c. This lesson presents a graphical interpretation of this idea, by looking at intersections of constant sum and constant product graphs. If the graphs of $x + y = b$ and $xy = c$ intersect, the coordinates (p, q) of one of the points of intersection are the same values p and q in $(x - p)(x - q)$, the factored form of the trinomial.

It may be a good idea to have students work on problems 1-3 in class before attempting the rest as homework.

While working on this lesson, some of your students may wonder about the case where the graphs meet at a point with coordinates that are not whole numbers. Since some students may find this discussion intimidating, you may choose to hold off until the students have had a chance to write their reports. However it is an important discussion for the stronger students, as it helps generalize the ideas of this lesson beyond the limited case of whole-number solutions.

You may start the discussion with the examples given in the Teacher's Guide for Lesson 4. Or you may initiate an exploration of the same examples with the help of the tracing function in a graphing calculator. Specifically, look for the intersection of the graphs for:

$xy = 15.75$ and $x + y = 8$
$xy = 12$ and $x + y = 37/5$.

THINKING WRITING 5.A Analyzing Graphs

You will need: graph paper

CONSTANT PRODUCTS

1. a. On the same pair of axes, graph the constant product function $xy = 24$ and the constant sum function $x + y = 10$.
b. Find and label the points where these two graphs intersect.
c. Add the graph of $x + y = 4$ to the same pair of axes. Does it intersect either graph?

2. If possible, factor each trinomial.
a. $x^2 + 10x + 24$
b. $x^2 + 4x + 24$

3. Explain the relationship between problem 1 and problem 2.

4. Make a large graph of the constant product equation $xy = 36$. Show both branches on your graph.

5. On the graph of $xy = 36$, find two (x, y) pairs whose sum is 13. Plot and label these points, and connect them with a straight line. What is the equation of the line connecting these two points?

6. Add to your graph several lines of the form $x + y = S$, where S is an integer, as described below. Draw at least three lines
a. that intersect the graph of $xy = 36$ in the first quadrant. (Label the graphs and the points of intersection.)
b. that intersect the graph of $xy = 36$ in the third quadrant. (Label the graphs and the points of intersection.)
c. that never intersect the graph of $xy = 36$.

7. Consider the expression $x^2 +$ ___$x + 36$. What numbers could you put in the blank to get a trinomial that can be factored? Explain your answer, giving examples.

CONSTANT SUMS

8. Make a large graph of the constant sum $x + y = 12$.

9. a. Find many (x, y) pairs whose product is 20.
b. Plot these points and connect them with a smooth curve.
c. What is the equation of the curve?
d. Where does it meet the graph of $x + y = 12$?

10. Add to your graph several curves with equations of the form $x \cdot y = P$, where P is an integer, as described below. Draw at least three curves
a. that intersect the graph of $x + y = 12$ in the first quadrant;
b. that intersect the graph of $x + y = 12$ in the second and fourth quadrants;
c. that never intersect the graph of $x + y = 12$.

11. Consider the expression $x^2 + 12x +$ ___. What numbers could you put in the blank to get a trinomial that can be factored? Explain your answer, giving examples.

12. Report Summarize what you discovered in this lesson. Concentrate on the question: *How are the points of intersection of constant sum and constant product graphs related to factoring trinomials?* Use examples and illustrate your report with graphs. (The examples given in this lesson involved only positive whole numbers for the sums and products. In your report, you may use negative numbers or zero.)

5.A SOLUTIONS

1.

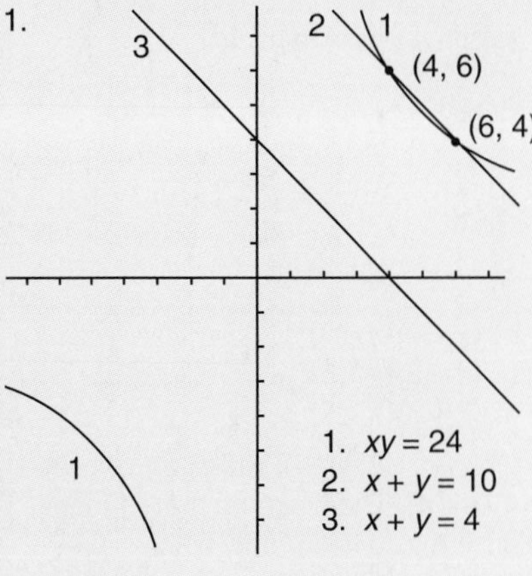

c. No

2. a. $(x + 6)(x + 4)$
b. impossible

3. Answers will vary. The main idea is that a trinomial of the form $x^2 + Sx + P$ will factor if the graph of $xy = P$ intersects the graph of $x + y = S$.

4.

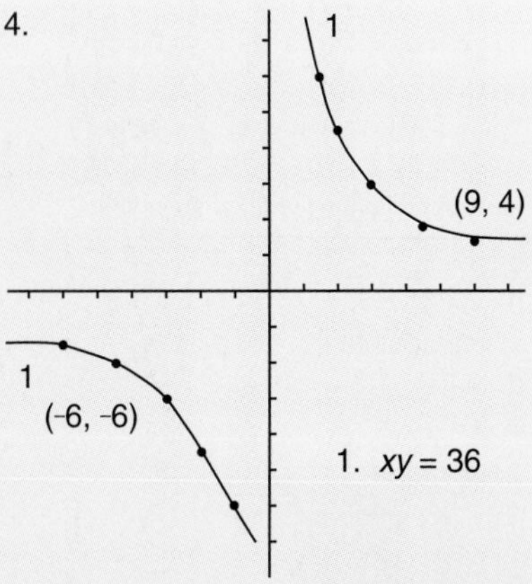

(Solutions continued on page 516)

LESSON 5.5

Graphing Parabolas

You will need: graph paper

Definitions:

- Second-degree polynomial functions are also called *quadratic* functions.
- Graphs of quadratic functions have a special shape called a *parabola.*
- The lowest or highest point on a parabola is called its *vertex.*

Here are two quadratic functions and their graphs. Each one has two x-intercepts and one vertex.

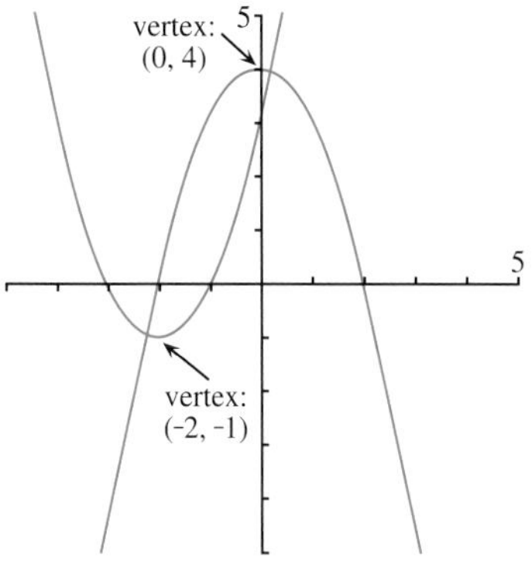

1. What is the y-coordinate of the x-intercepts? What is the x-coordinate of the y-intercept?

2. For each parabola in the figure,
a. what are the x- and y-intercepts?
b. which x-intercept is the vertex closer to?

FINDING INTERCEPTS AND THE VERTEX

3. a. Copy and complete the table of values for the quadratic function $y = x^2 + 2x - 8$. Use at least six values from -5 to 5. Using the format shown will help you avoid making mistakes in computation.

x	$x^2 + 2x - 8$	y
-5	$(-5)^2 + 2(-5) - 8$	7
-4	______	—
...	______	—
4	______	—
5	______	—

b. Use your table to make a graph of the function.
c. Label the intercepts and the vertex.

4. Repeat problem 3 for the function $y = (x + 4)(x - 2)$.

5.
a. Compare your graphs in problems 3 and 4. Explain what you observe.
b. How are the x-intercepts related to the expression $(x + 4)(x - 2)$?

6. The quadratic function $y = x^2 - 6x + 8$ can be written in factored form as $y = (x - 4)(x - 2)$.
a. Make a table of values for this function, including the intercepts and the vertex.
b. Graph the function. Label the intercepts and the vertex.
c. How are the x-intercepts related to the expression $(x - 4)(x - 2)$?
d. How is the y-intercept related to the expression $x^2 - 6x + 8$?

5.5 SOLUTIONS

1. The y-coordinate of the x-intercepts is 0. The x-coordinate of the y-intercepts is 0.
2. a. The "smile" parabola has x-intercepts at (-3, 0) and (-1, 0) and y-intercept at (0, 3). The "frown" parabola has x-intercepts at (-2, 0) and (2, 0) and y-intercept at (0, 4).
   b. In each case, the vertex is halfway between the x-intercepts.
3. a. Completing the table as shown gives the points (-4, 0), (4, 16) and (5, 27). Other table entries will vary.

   b.

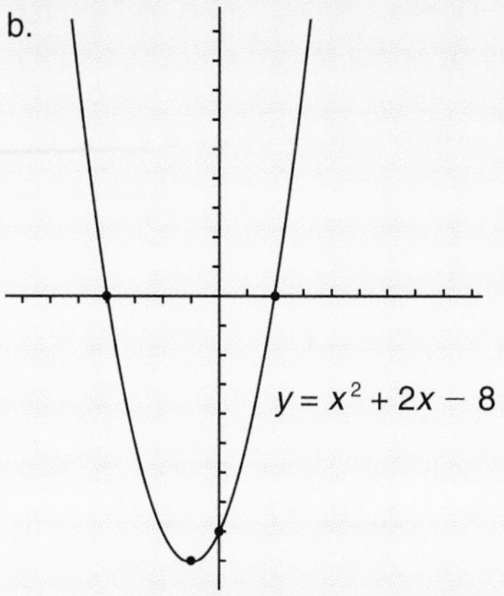

   c. x-intercepts: (-4, 0) and (2, 0); y-intercept: (0, -8); vertex: (-1, -9)
4. a. Tables will vary.
   b. Graph is the same as in #3.
5. a. The graphs are the same because

5.5 Graphing Parabolas

Core Sequence: 1-24, 27-28

Suitable for Homework: 14-29

Useful for Assessment: 5, 11-13, 18-19, 22

What this Lesson is About:

- Graphing $y = x^2 + bx + c$ and $y = (x - p)(x - q)$
- Intercepts of a parabola
- Vertex of a parabola
- *Smile* and *frown* parabolas
- Preview of zero product property
- Preview of perfect square trinomials
- Preview of building-block numbers
- Systematic search

The purpose of this lesson is not to develop students' skills in graphing parabolas by hand. With the advent of graphing calculators and software, rapid graphing by hand is no longer a priority. At any rate, it is too early in the course to expect students to have a full understanding of graphing parabolas. The main point at this stage is to give students some *graph sense*: a general understanding of the parabola and its most significant points, the vertex and the intercepts.

The relationship between factors and roots is a fundamental result in algebra, perhaps among the most fundamental. Discuss this, but do not expect mastery. The idea is difficult for some students. The zero product property will be covered in more detail in Chapter 13. This lesson is intended as a preview.

Note that problems 1-2 serve as a reminder of the definition of intercepts. Problem 2b previews the important idea that the x-coordinate of the vertex is the average of the x-coordinates of the x-intercepts.

FINDING INTERCEPTS AND THE VERTEX

If students are making computational mistakes, insist on the format shown in problem 3. Computational errors are easy to spot, because they yield a graph that does not look like a parabola.

You may allow students to use a graphing calculator for some of problems 6-10 and 14-20, or perhaps share the work within their group. In any case, make sure that they keep a record of their work to refer back to.

The generalizations requested in problems 11-13 are not easy. It is essential that this work be done in class, with a chance for students to discuss the patterns that they uncover. A graphing calculator is a convenient way to test conjectures by graphing additional parabolas quickly.

Note that problem 13a is also a generalization of the work in Lessons 3, 4, and **Thinking/Writing 5.A**.

One of the main patterns we want students to notice is that the factored form reveals the x-intercepts most clearly (the values of p and q), while the other form reveals the y-intercept most clearly (the value of c). The x-coordinate of the vertex is easily obtained from either form. (Since it is halfway between p and q, it can be found by taking their average, which is $(p + q)/2$. From previous work we know this is $-b/2$.)

Some students may not see these patterns without help. Others may see a relationship between the expressions and the coordinates of the points, but not understand the reasons for it. Only a few will spontaneously see the reason for the connection. This is why discussion, in small groups and whole-class, is essential. Again don't expect immediate mastery by all students.

Pay special attention to issues of sign. The x-intercepts in problem 4 are -4 and 2, not 4 and -2. In problem 13, b is *the opposite of* $p + q$. The x-coordinate of the vertex is $-b/2$, not $b/2$.

SMILES AND FROWNS

The only values of a we will consider in this lesson in the expressions $y = ax^2 + bx + c$ and $y = a(x - p)(x - q)$ are 1 and -1. (The only exception to this is problem 20, which previews later work.) These two values are enough to give us both *smile* and *frown* parabolas.

Problems 17-20 will check how well the students understand the ideas of this lesson.

It is not necessary to use the *concave up* and *concave down* terminology at this level, but you could mention it if you wish.

For each problem, 7-10:

a. Write the function in factored form.
b. Make a table of values, including the intercepts and the vertex.
c. Graph the function, labeling the intercepts and the vertex.

7. $y = x^2 - 2x - 3$

8. $y = x^2 + 4x + 3$

9. $y = x^2 - 4x + 3$

10. $y = x^2 + 2x - 3$

11. Write the equation of a quadratic function whose graph would cross the x-axis at (2, 0) and (-3, 0). Explain how you know it will work.

12. Write the equation of a parabola having y-intercept -4. Explain how you know it will work.

13. **Generalization** Consider functions of the form $y = x^2 + bx + c$ that can be factored into $y = (x - p)(x - q)$.

a. How are b, c, p, and q related?
b. How would you find the coordinates of the intercepts?
c. How would you find the coordinates of the vertex?

SMILES AND FROWNS

14. Make a table of values for the quadratic function $y = (x - 4)(x - 1)$ and graph it.

15. Repeat for $y = -(x - 4)(x - 1)$.

16. Compare your graphs from problems 14-15. What is alike about the graphs and what is different? How do their x-intercepts and vertices compare?

17. Write an equation of a quadratic function whose graph satisfies these given conditions.

a. a *smile* parabola having x-intercepts (3, 0) and (-2, 0)
b. a *frown* parabola having x-intercepts (3, 0) and (-2, 0)
c. a *smile* parabola having x-intercepts (-3, 0) and (-2, 0)
d. a *frown* parabola having x-intercepts (-3, 0) and (-2, 0)

18. Explain how you know that your answers to problem 17 are correct. You may check your answers by making a table of values, and graphing.

19. Write the equation of a quadratic function that passes through the origin and (5, 0). Explain.

20. Write an equation of a quadratic function whose graph satisfies the given conditions.

a. a parabola having one x-intercept at (1, 0) and the vertex with x-coordinate 2
b. a parabola having one x-intercept at (1, 0) and the vertex at (2, 1)
c. a parabola having one x-intercept at (1, 0) and the vertex at (2, 2)

HOW MANY x-INTERCEPTS?

21. Graph each of these four quadratic functions on the same axes.

a. $y = x^2 + 6x + 5$
b. $y = x^2 + 6x + 8$
c. $y = x^2 + 6x + 9$
d. $y = x^2 + 6x + 12$

5.5 SOLUTIONS

the equation in #4 is just the factored form of the equation in #3.

b. They are the values of x that, when substituted into the expression, make it equal to 0.

6. a. Tables will vary.

b.

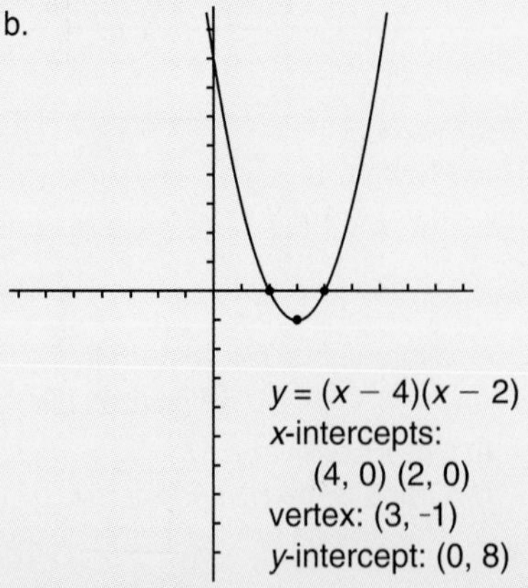

c. They are the values of x that, when substituted into the expression, make it equal to 0.

d. It is the constant term.

7. a. $y = (x - 3)(x + 1)$

b. x-intercepts: 3 and -1, y-intercept: -3, vertex (1, -4)

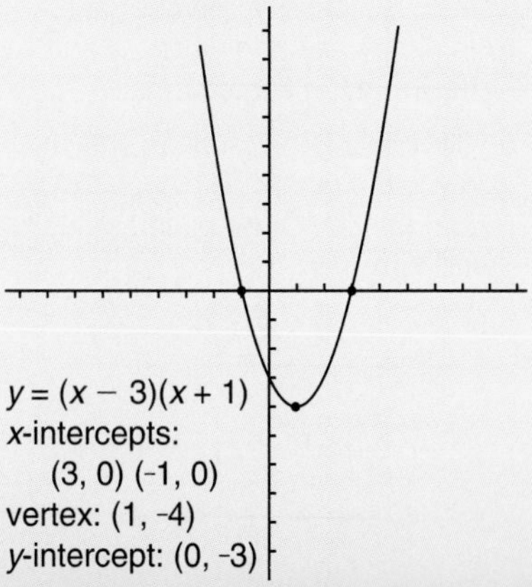

22. Write a paragraph describing and comparing the graphs you drew in problem 21. Which graph or graphs have two x-intercepts? Which have one? Which have none? Could you have predicted this before graphing? Explain.

23. Consider the quadratic function $y = x^2 + 4x +$ ___. Fill in the blank with a number that will give a function whose graph is

a. a parabola having one x-intercept;
b. a parabola having two x-intercepts;
c. a parabola having no x-intercepts.

24. Check your answers to problem 23 by graphing, or explain why you are sure you are correct.

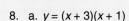

PUZZLES *MAKING CHANGE*

25. Find the largest number of pennies, nickels, and dimes that you can have and still not be able to make change for a quarter. Explain your answer.

26. Find the largest number of coins you can have and still not be able to make change for a dollar. (Assume that you can have any coins except a silver dollar.) Explain this answer.

PREVIEW *ZEROING IN*

27. If $ab = 0$, $bc = 0$, and $ac = 1$, what is b?

28. If $abc = 0$ and $bcd = 1$, what conclusion can you draw? Explain.

PUZZLE *SQUARE SUMS*

29. Arrange the whole numbers from 1 to 18 into nine pairs, so that the sum of the numbers in each pair is a perfect square.

HOW MANY x-INTERCEPTS?

This section uses factoring as a way to count the x-intercepts. This ties in well with the previous lessons. More powerful techniques will be introduced in Chapter 12.

Problems 22-24 will need class discussion.

PUZZLES *MAKING CHANGE*

This previews the optional Lesson 8. The puzzles are accessible to all students.

PREVIEW *ZEROING IN*

These problems preview the zero product property. They are small, but extremely important as a preparation for Chapter 13.

PUZZLE *SQUARE SUMS*

This is a bit of work, and would make a good *problem of the week*. Students who find it difficult should be encouraged to be systematic in their search for solutions. (What perfect squares are possible? For each one, which pairs of numbers could be used?) Students may want to work in pairs.

A challenging generalization: For what numbers other than 18 is this problem solvable?

5.5 S O L U T I O N S

8. a. $y = (x + 3)(x + 1)$
 b. x-intercepts: -3 and -1, y-intercept: 3, vertex (-2, -1)

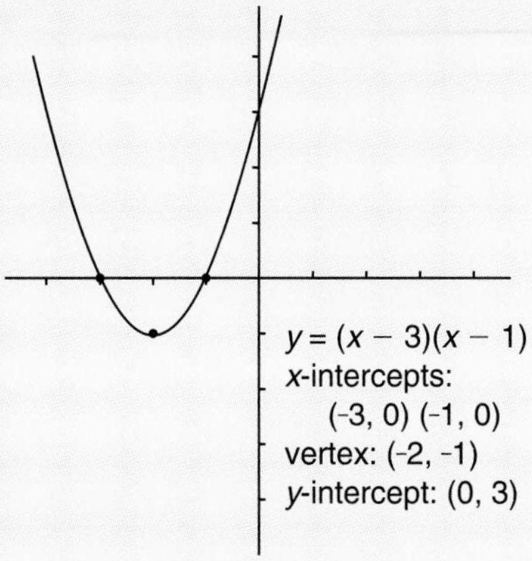

9. a. $y = (x - 3)(x - 1)$
 b. x-intercepts: 3 and 1, y-intercept: 3, vertex (2, -1)

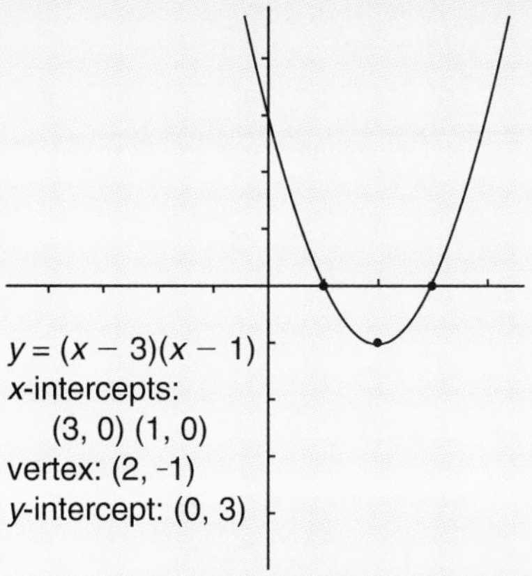

10. a. $y = (x + 3)(x - 1)$
 b. x-intercepts: -3 and 1, y-intercept: -3, vertex (-1, -4)

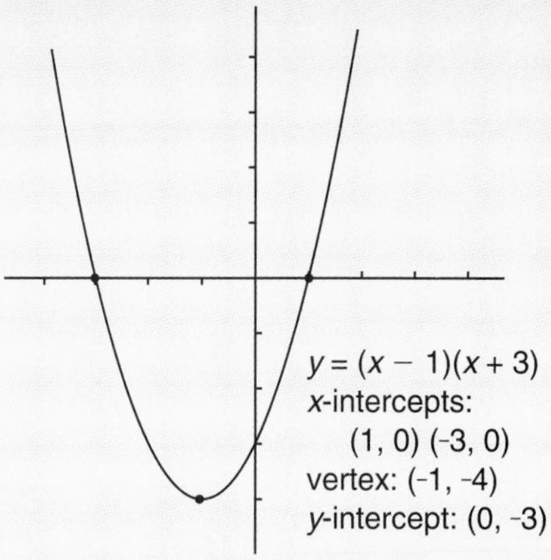

11. Answers will vary. One possibility is = $(x - 2)(x + 3)$. If I substitute either 2 or -3 for x, the resulting value of y is 0.

(Solutions continued on page 517)

▼ 5.6
Factors

Core Sequence: 1-25

Suitable for Homework: 10-25

What this Lesson is About:

- Recognizing factors of monomials
- Factoring by *taking out* the greatest common factor

This lesson concentrates on symbol manipulation skill and involves no writing.

Problem 1 can be generalized by using algebraic notation, though this may be too difficult to understand for most students at this level. You may return to this generalization at the end of the lesson.

Problem 1a: $(2n)(2n + 2) = (4n)(n + 1)$
Problem 1b: $(2n + 1)(2n + 3)$
Problem 1c: $(3n)(3n + 3) = (9n)(n + 1)$

SAME AREA, DIFFERENT PERIMETER

RECOGNIZING FACTORS

These sections help prepare students to recognize the factors of monomials, a necessary skill when factoring out common factors.

Allow the students to work without physically manipulating the Lab Gear, if they can do that successfully. In fact, starting with problem 7, work without the blocks should be the norm, though students should be allowed to use them if they want.

LESSON 5.6 Factors

You will need:

the Lab Gear 

1. Exploration

a. Draw a rectangle whose sides are any two consecutive even numbers, like 4 and 6. Find its area. If the side lengths have to be whole numbers, is it possible to draw a rectangle having the *same area but different sides*? Try this with another pair of consecutive even numbers. Is it possible this time? Do you think it is always, sometimes, or never possible?

b. Does your result change if you use two consecutive odd numbers, like 3 and 5?

c. What about consecutive multiples of 3, like 6 and 9?

SAME AREA, DIFFERENT PERIMETER

Example: Use the Lab Gear to build a rectangle having a width of $2x$ and a length of $x + 1$.

a. Sketch the rectangle. Label it with an equation of the form *length times width equals area.*

b. Find the perimeter of the rectangle.

c. Rearrange your rectangle into a rectangle having the *same area* but a *different perimeter.*

d. Write another equation of the form *length times width equals area.*

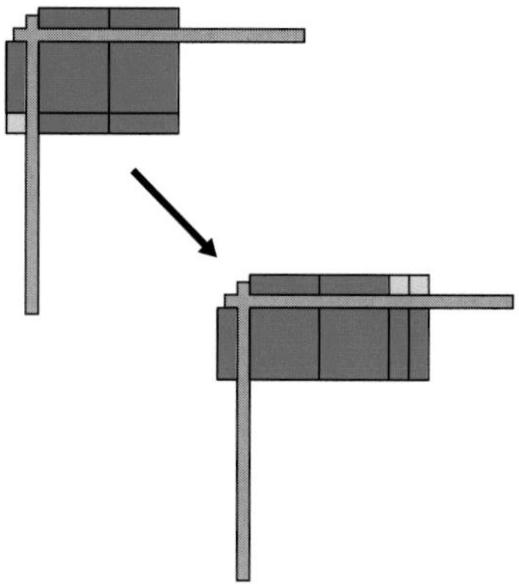

For problems 2-4 below, build a Lab Gear rectangle of the given width and length. Then follow the instructions in parts (a) through (d) in the example.

2. width: $2x$ length: $2x + 2$

3. width: $3x$ length: $3 + x$

4. width: x length: $4 + 4x$

For problems 5-6 follow the instructions in the example, but build at least two rectangles, and three if possible.

5. width: $4 + 2x$ length: $2 + 4x$

6. width: $2 + 2x$ length: $3 + 2x$

5.6 S O L U T I O N S

1. For even numbers, it is always possible to find two different ways, since the sides can be $2n$ and $2n + 2$ or $4n$ and $n + 1$. This can be seen by noting that $2n(2n + 2) = 4n(n + 1)$. If two consecutive odd numbers are used, the area is $(2n + 1)(2n + 3)$, so the sides can only be $(2n + 1)$ and $2n + 3$, unless you include the possibility of the dimensions 1-by-$(2n + 1)(2n + 3)$. For consecutive multiples of 3, note that $3n(3n + 3) = 9(n + 1)$, so there will always be two possibilities.

   Solution to example:
   a. The sketch should be labeled with the equation $2x(x + 1) = 2x^2 + 2x$.
   b. The perimeter of the rectangle is $6x + 2$.
   c. The rectangle in the second sketch has perimeter $6x + 4$.
   d. The second sketch illustrates that $x(2x + 2) = 2x^2 + 2x$.

2. 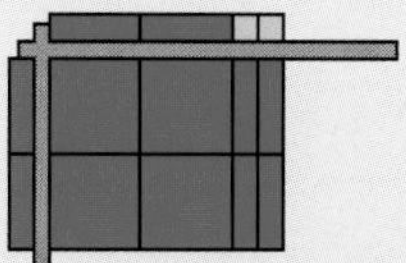

   $2x(2x + 2) = 4x^2 + 4x$
   Perimeter: $8x + 4$

   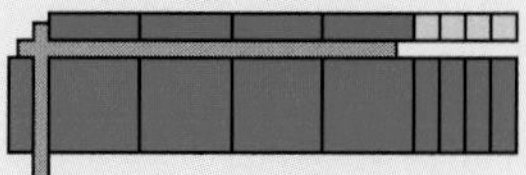

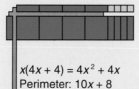

   $x(4x + 4) = 4x^2 + 4x$
   Perimeter: $10x + 8$

3. 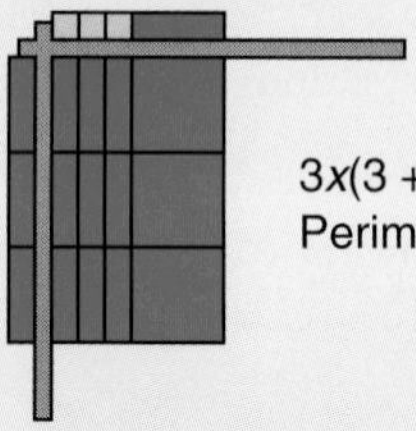

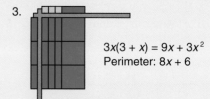

   $3x(3 + x) = 9x + 3x^2$
   Perimeter: $8x + 6$

   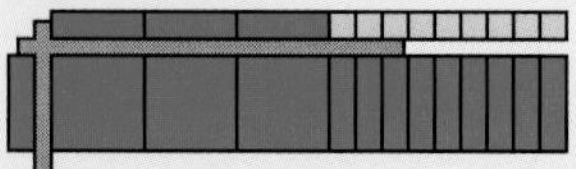

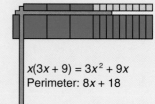

   $x(3x + 9) = 3x^2 + 9x$
   Perimeter: $8x + 18$

RECOGNIZING FACTORS

For each expression, 7-12, write as many different products equal to it as you can. Use only whole numbers. (In some cases, it may be helpful to use the Lab Gear to build rectangles and/or boxes.)

7. 24

8. $6y^2$

9. $(2x + 4)(3x + 6)$

10. $12x^3$

11. $12x^2 + 4x$

12. $2x(6x + 18)$

COMMON FACTORS

Example: As you know, factoring a polynomial can sometimes be modeled by making a Lab Gear rectangle.

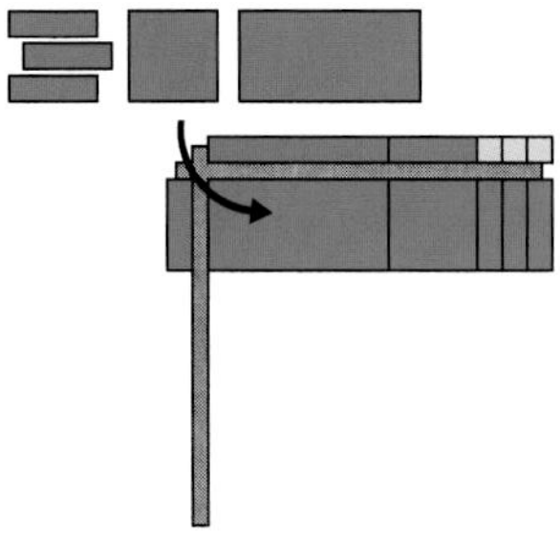

$$xy + x^2 + 3x = x(y + x + 3)$$

By multiplying the factors, you get the original polynomial back. Factoring is using the distributive law in reverse.

In this example, we say that x is a *common factor* of all three terms in the original polynomial, because it divides each term evenly. In the case of $2x^3 + 8x^2 + 2x^2y$, the common factors are 2, x, and x^2. In factoring such a polynomial, it is usually best to *take out* the *greatest common factor,* which is $2x^2$.

In the following problems, factor the polynomials by taking out the greatest common factor. Not all are possible.

13. $2x^3 + 8x^2 + 2x^2y$

14. $2x^2 - 6x$

15. $2x^2 + 6x + 1$

16. $3x^2 + 2x + 4xy$

17. $3x^2y - 3xy + 6xy^2$

18. $3y^2 + 9y - 6y^3 + 3x^2y + 6xy^2 + 9xy$

FACTORING COMPLETELY

As you have seen in this lesson, there are often many ways to factor a polynomial. However, there is only one way to factor it *completely.* For example, $(4x + 8)(3x + 9)$ is factored, but to factor it completely you would have to factor 4 out of $(4x + 8)$ and 3 out of $(3x + 9)$.

Factor completely.

19. $(2x + 6)(3x + 6)$

20. $4(x^2 + 5x + 6)$

21. $4x^2 + 40x + 64$

22. $2x^2 + 8x + 8$

23. $3x^2 + 21x + 30$

24. $2x^2 + 26x + 72$

25. $x^3 + 5x^2 + 6x$

COMMON FACTORS

FACTORING COMPLETELY

The best strategy for problems 16-25 is to take out the common factor first, and then factor the resulting trinomial.

5.6 SOLUTIONS

4.

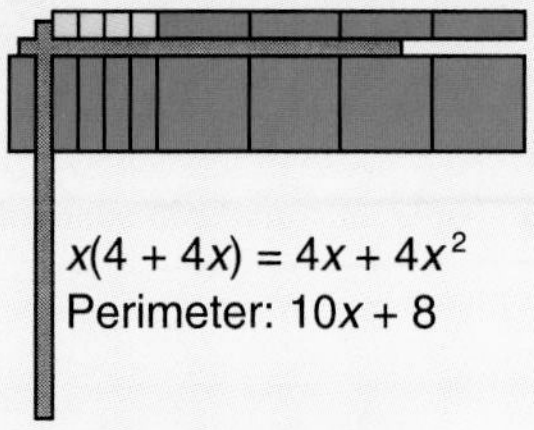

$x(4 + 4x) = 4x + 4x^2$
Perimeter: $10x + 8$

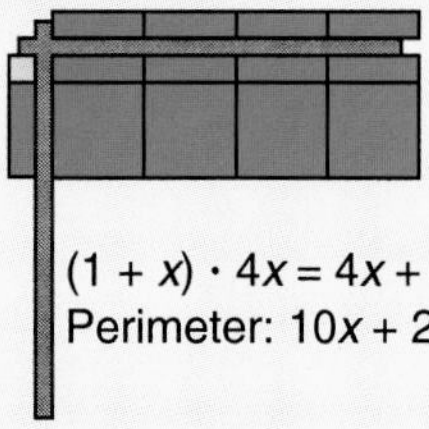

$(1 + x) \cdot 4x = 4x + 4x^2$
Perimeter: $10x + 2$

5.

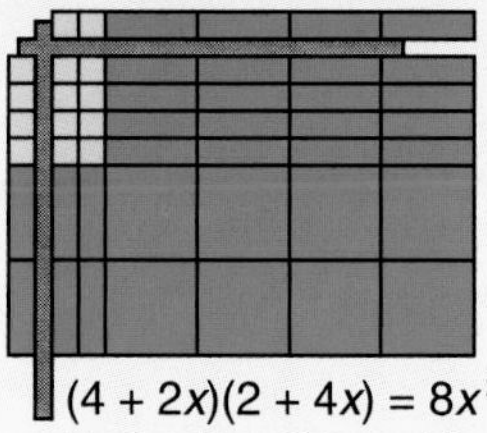

$(4 + 2x)(2 + 4x) = 8x^2 + 20x + 8$
Perimeter: $12x + 12$

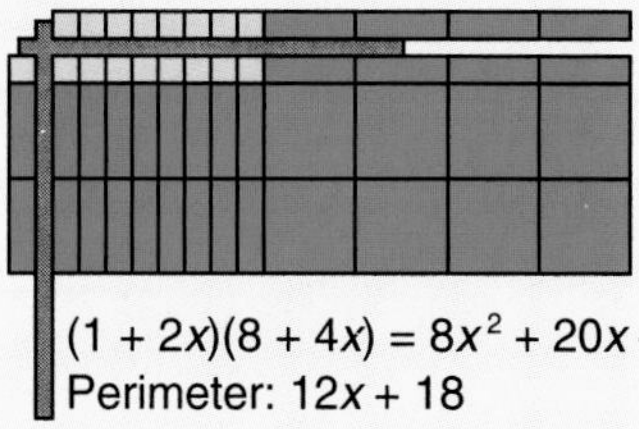

$(1 + 2x)(8 + 4x) = 8x^2 + 20x + 8$
Perimeter: $12x + 18$

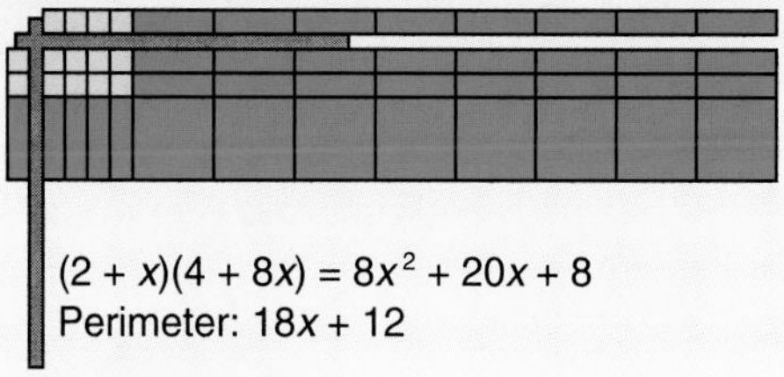

$(2 + x)(4 + 8x) = 8x^2 + 20x + 8$
Perimeter: $18x + 12$

6.

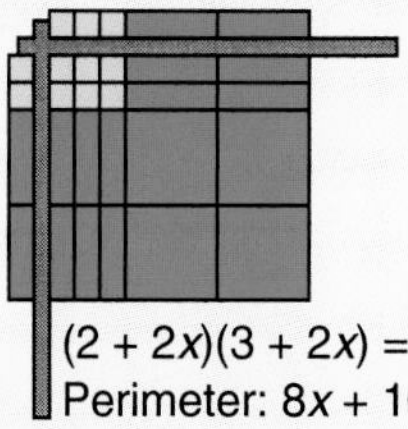

$(2 + 2x)(3 + 2x) = 4x^2 + 10x + 6$
Perimeter: $8x + 10$

(Solutions continued on page 518)

▼ 5.7 Minus and the Distributive Law

Core Sequence: 1-28

Suitable for Homework: 1-8, 24-28

Useful for Assessment: 12

What this Lesson is About:

- Review of order of operations
- Multiplying binomials (minus in both factors) in the corner piece
- Preview of square of a binomial
- Review of equation-solving (cover-up method)
- Function diagrams of constant products
- Preview of inverse variation
- Preview of square roots

REVIEW *ORDER OF OPERATIONS*

Distinguishing between expressions like $(5 - 3)(x - 2)$ and $5 - 3(x - 2)$ is a source of confusion to students, even many who have dutifully memorized the order of operations. This section should help.

If your students have trouble with these problems, you may want to assign extra practice along these lines. If you do, get student volunteers to make up pairs of related problems like problems 4-5 or 6-7 for the class to work on.

LESSON 5.7

Minus and the Distributive Law

You will need:

the Lab Gear 

REVIEW *ORDER OF OPERATIONS*

1. Compare these two expressions, and these two figures.

$(5 - 3)(x - 2)$

$5 - 3(x - 2)$

(i)

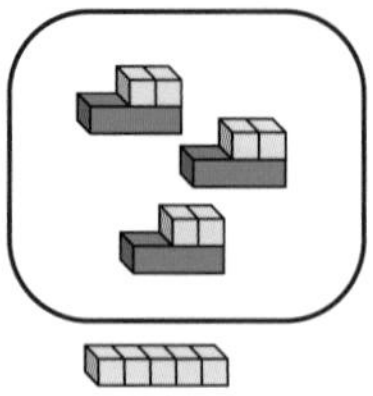

(ii)

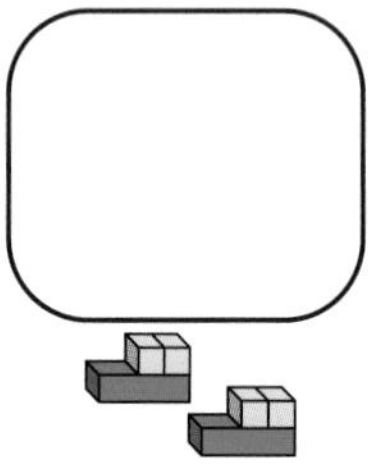

a. Which expression means *multiply $(x - 2)$ by 3 and subtract the result from 5*? (Remember order of operations.)

b. Which figure shows that expression with the Lab Gear?

c. Which expression means *subtract 3 from 5 and multiply the result by $(x - 2)$*?

d. Which figure shows that expression with the Lab Gear?

e. Here are the same expressions, rewritten without parentheses. Which is which?

$11 - 3x$ $\qquad$ $2x - 4$

Write without parentheses.

2. $7 - 3(y - 4)$ $\qquad$ **3.** $(7 - 3)(y - 4)$

4. $(4 - 2)x + 1$ $\qquad$ **5.** $(4 - 2)(x + 1)$

6. $x - 2(x + 1)$ $\qquad$ **7.** $(x - 2)(x + 1)$

8. $(x - 2)x - 1$

If you added another set of parentheses to the expression in problem 8, you would get $(x - 2)(x - 1)$. One way to multiply these binomials is to use the multiplication table format.

	x	-2
x	____	____
-1	____	____

9. What is the product?

USING THE CORNER PIECE

In this lesson, you will learn how to model a product like this with the Lab Gear. You will practice it with numbers before using variables.

Example: In the case of $(6 - 2)(5 - 3)$ set up the problem as shown in the figure. The method you will follow is to *multiply all the blocks on the left side by all the blocks across the top.*

5.7 SOLUTIONS

1. a. $5 - 3(x - 2)$
   b. figure i
   c. $(5 - 3)(x - 2)$
   d. figure ii
   e. $11 - 3x = 5 - 3(x - 2)$
   $2x - 4 = (5 - 3)(x - 2)$
2. $7 - 3(y - 4) = 7 - 3y + 12 = 19 - 3y$
3. $(7 - 3)(y - 4) = 4y - 16$
4. $(4 - 2)x + 1 = 2x + 1$
5. $(4 - 2)(x + 1) = 2x + 2$
6. $x - 2(x + 1) = x - 2x - 2 = -x - 2$
7. $(x - 2)(x + 1) = x^2 - x - 2$
8. $(x - 2)x - 1 = x^2 - 2x - 1$
9. $x^2 - 3x + 2$
10. 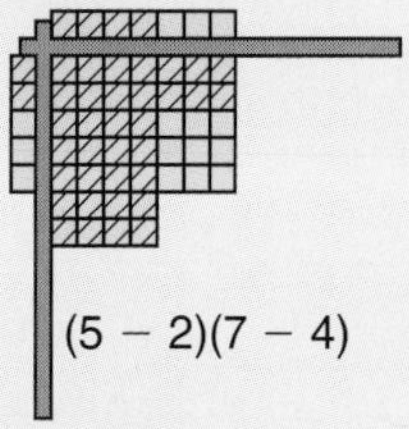
    $(5 - 2)(7 - 4)$
11. $(y - 2)(y - 1)$
12. The process described below follows the order that is described in the text:
    i. $y \cdot y = y^2$
    ii. $-1 \cdot -2 = 2$
    iii. $-2 \cdot y = -2y$
    iv. $y \cdot -1 = -y$
13. $(6 - 2) \cdot (5 - 3) = 4 \cdot 2 = 8$
14. a. 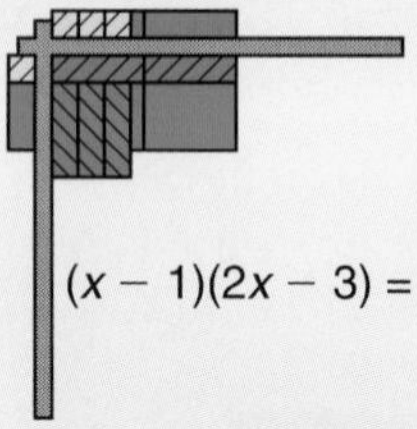
    $(x - 1)(2x - 3) = 2x^2 - 5x + 3$

    b. 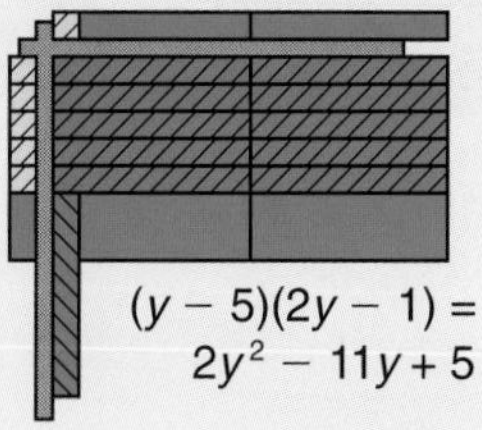
    $(y - 5)(2y - 1) = 2y^2 - 11y + 5$

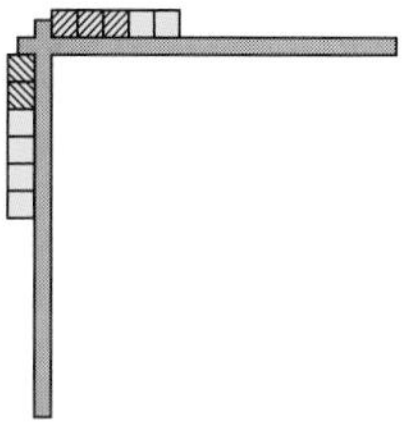

Put the upstairs blocks at the corner of the corner piece.

First, multiply the downstairs blocks. Then multiply the upstairs blocks by each other. Since $-2(-3) = 6$, a positive number, these blocks must appear *downstairs* somewhere. They will be arranged in a 2-by-3 rectangle. It would be nice to line up the rectangle with its factors, but then it would have to be upstairs, making it -6, which would be wrong. So we can *line it up with only one of the two factors*. Let's choose the -3.

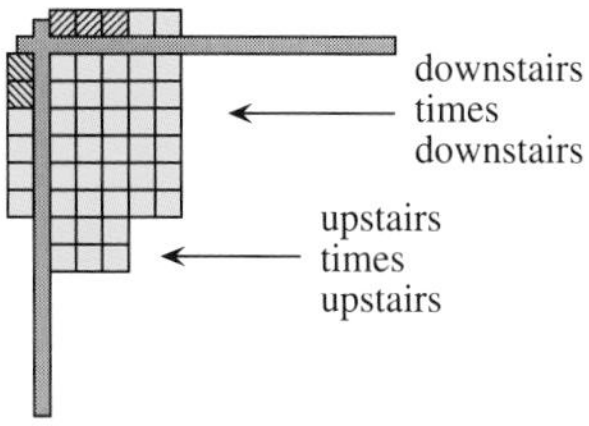

Finally, multiply upstairs blocks on the left with downstairs blocks at the top, and vice versa, placing them as shown.

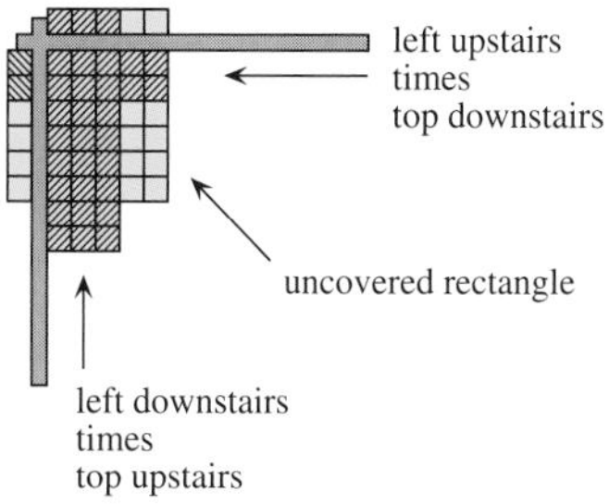

You can now see that the answer (4 times 2 = 8) is shown by *the uncovered rectangle.*

10. Use the corner piece to show the product $(5 - 2)(7 - 4)$.

USING VARIABLES

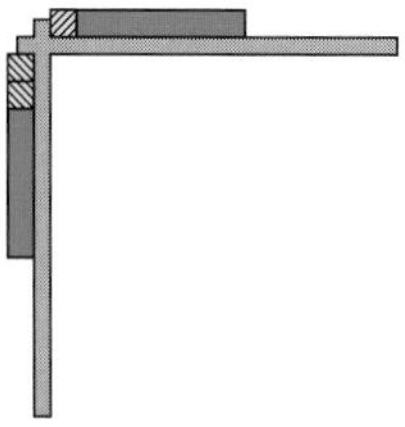

11. Write the polynomials being multiplied.

12. Follow the process shown in the following figures with your blocks. Write a brief explanation of each step.

USING THE CORNER PIECE

USING VARIABLES

So far, students have not multiplied binomials in the corner piece when there is a minus in both factors. The reason we have delayed this technique is that it is fairly tricky, and it is definitely easier to use than the multiplication table method.

However, the technique is interesting and very popular with some students. If you are pressed for time, show the technique as a demonstration only. However, students need to understand the model for work in Chapter 7, but they need not be proficient at it.

You may demonstrate the example, or other problems like it, on the overhead. If students have trouble with the technique, a good hint is to remind them that they need to end up with an uncovered rectangle of the right dimensions. Paying attention to where that rectangle needs to be will help place the blocks correctly. You may challenge students to explain why the "perfect fit" always occurs.

Problem 15 combines review of previous techniques with practice of the new one. By presenting related problems, students' attention to the patterns is heightened. Problem 16 serves as a preview of three important identities. (We will return to them in Chapter 7.)

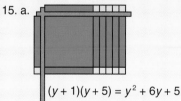

5.7 SOLUTIONS

15. a.

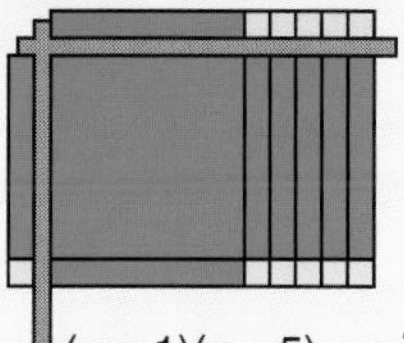

$(y + 1)(y + 5) = y^2 + 6y + 5$

b.

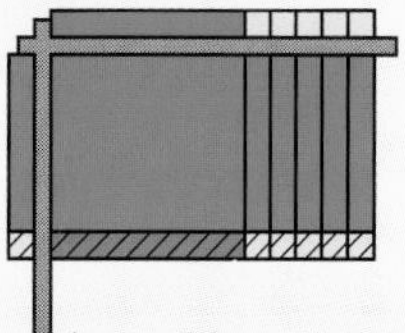

$(y - 1)(y + 5) = y^2 + 4y - 5$

c.

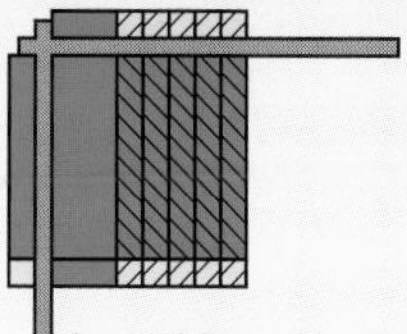

$(y + 1)(y - 5) = y^2 - 4y - 5$

d.

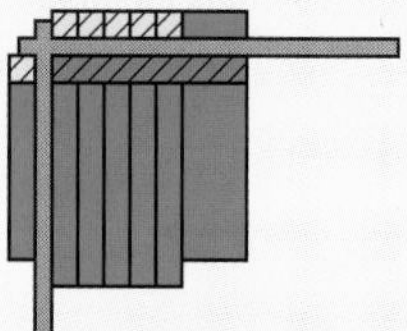

$(y - 1)(y - 5) = y^2 - 6y + 5$

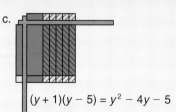

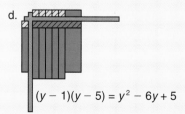

16. a. $4x^2 + 12x + 9$
b. $4x^2 - 12x + 9$
c. $4x^2 - 9$

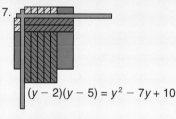

17.

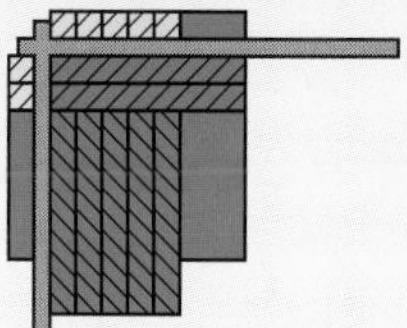

$(y - 2)(y - 5) = y^2 - 7y + 10$

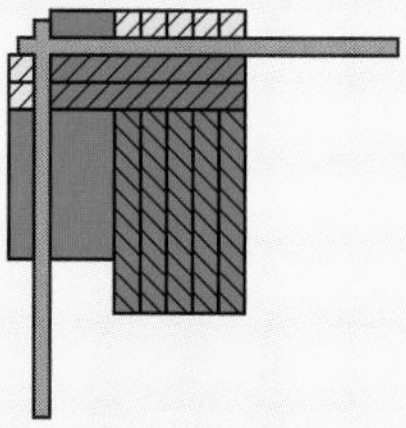

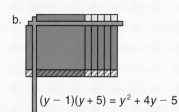

DISCOVERY MAKE A SQUARE

*T*his is related to the work in Lessons 3-6, including especially **How Many *x*-Intercepts?** in Lesson 5. It also previews the identity for the square of a binomial (Chapter 7), and completing the square (Chapter 13).

REVIEW SOLVING EQUATIONS

*T*hese problems look like the ones in problems 2-6. They illustrate the wisdom of the popular maxim, "Think before you distribute." Since students do not learn formal equation-solving methods until Chapter 6, they will have to solve these using trial and error or the cover-up method. Distributing makes these problems harder; they are easily solved using the cover-up method.

*I*f necessary, remind students of the cover-up method by doing an example at the board. Mastery of that method is not absolutely essential, but these problems are a good way to review order of operations and inverse operations.

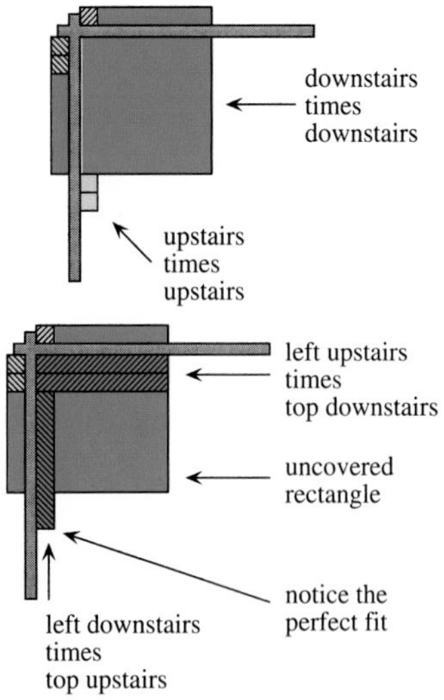

13. Write the dimensions of the uncovered rectangle and the product.

14. Use the Lab Gear to multiply.
   a. $(x - 1)(2x - 3)$
   b. $(y - 5)(2y - 1)$

15. Use the Lab Gear to multiply.
   a. $(y + 1)(y + 5)$
   b. $(y - 1)(y + 5)$
   c. $(y + 1)(y - 5)$
   d. $(y - 1)(y - 5)$

16. Use the Lab Gear to multiply.
   a. $(2x + 3)^2$ b. $(2x - 3)^2$
   c. $(2x + 3)(2x - 3)$

17. This figure shows four ways to set up the multiplication $(y - 2)(y - 5)$. Of those, three will work. Experiment to find out which three. Sketch your solutions.

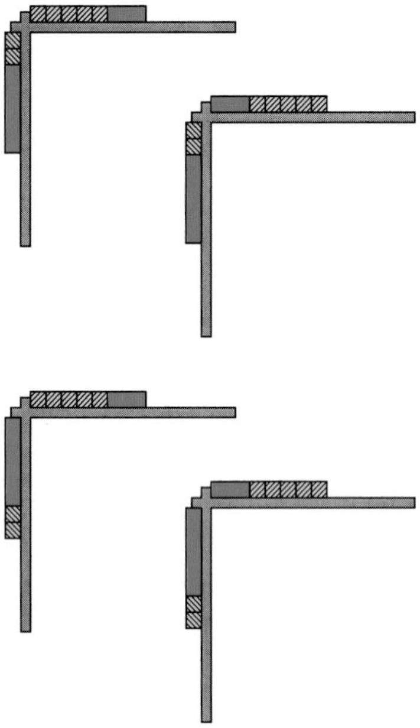

5.7 SOLUTIONS

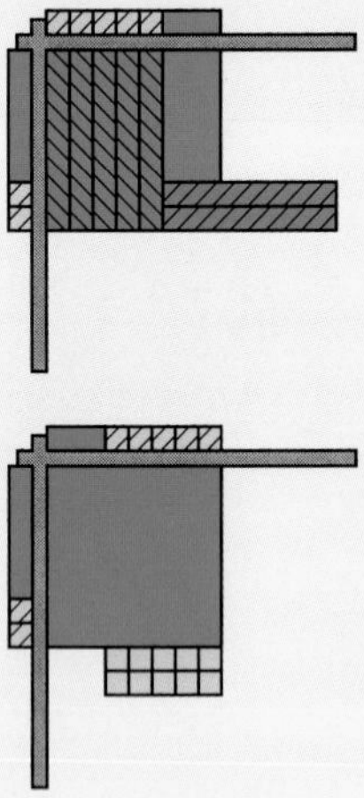

18. $(x + 3)^2 = x^2 + 6x + 9$
19. $(2x + 1)^2 = 4x^2 + 4x + 1$
20. Not possible
21. Not possible
22. $(3x + 2)^2 = 9x^2 + 12x + 4$
23. $(x + y)^2 = x^2 + 2xy + y^2$
24. a. $x = 3$
   b. $x = 4$
   c. $x = 2$
   d. $x = -3$
   e. $x = 7$

25. a.

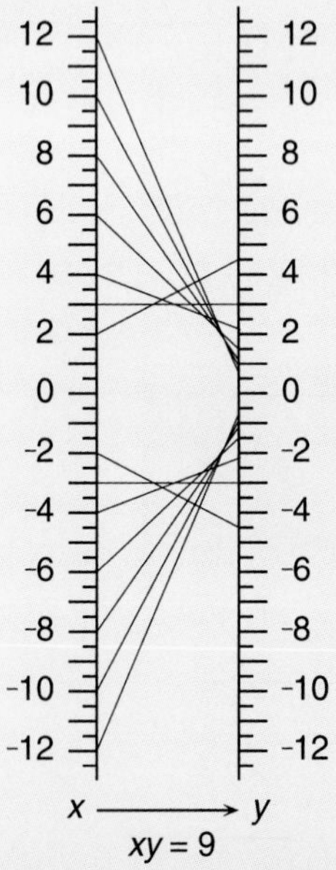

DISCOVERY *MAKE A SQUARE*

For each problem, arrange the blocks into a square. Not all are possible. Write an equation relating the side length and area of the square.

18. $x^2 + 6x + 9$

19. $4x^2 + 4x + 1$

20. $x^2 + 8x + 4$

21. $x^2 + 4x + 16$

22. $9x^2 + 12x + 4$

23. $x^2 + 2xy + y^2$

REVIEW *SOLVING EQUATIONS*

24. Use the cover-up method to solve these equations.

a. $30 - 3(2x + 1) = 9$

b. $19 - 2(x + 5) = 1$

c. $(5 - 3x) - 2 = -3$

d. $5 - 3(x - 2) = 20$

e. $(5 - 3)(x - 2) = 10$

REVIEW *FUNCTION DIAGRAMS FOR CONSTANT PRODUCTS*

For each equation, 25-27:

a. Make a large function diagram (with number lines ranging from at least -12 to 12), using your calculator to help you find values if needed.

b. Do all the in-out lines meet in a single point?

c. Are there any horizontal in-out lines? (In other words, in-out lines where $x = y$.) For what values of x and y?

d. Follow the y-value with your finger as x changes from -12 to 12. Describe y's motion. (Does it move up or down? Does it ever *jump*? For what values of x does it move fast? Slowly?)

25. $xy = 9$

26. $xy = 8$

27. $xy = -9$

28. x is greater than 1, and $6/x$ is a whole number. What could x be? (Hint: There are more than three solutions.)

REVIEW *FUNCTION DIAGRAMS FOR CONSTANT PRODUCTS*

Problem 25 is visually interesting, yielding a beautiful symmetric design. The questions help students think of the function $y = 9/x$ and how it changes. Because this may be difficult for some students, if you assign this problem for homework, make sure to save some class time to discuss it. The question about the horizontal lines previews the concept of square roots. (See Lesson 2, problem 11.)

Problem 28 generalizes problem 27 to the case where the product is not a perfect square, or is negative.

Problem 28 is surprisingly difficult. You should encourage a discussion in groups, and hold off as much as possible on giving away the answer. One hint you can give students is to use a function diagram or Cartesian graph to help investigate the question. Another hint is to point out x need not be a whole number. Or you can lead a discussion, starting with the question, *What whole numbers could 6/x be*?

5.7 SOLUTIONS

b. No

c. Yes. $x = y = 3$ or $x = y = -3$

d. As x moves from -12 to 12, y moves downward. y jumps at zero. y moves fast for values of x close to zero.

26. a.

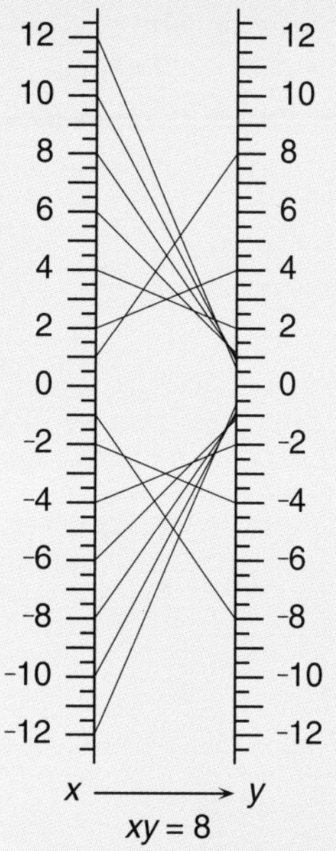

b. No, the lines do not meet at a single point.

c. Yes, there is a pair of horizontal lines at $x = y \approx 2.83$ and $x = y \approx -2.83$.

d. As x changes from -12 to 12, y moves down and jumps at zero. y moves fast when x values are close to zero.

(Solutions continued on page 518)

▼ 5.8 Building-Block Numbers

Core Sequence: none of the lesson

Suitable for Homework: 5-28

Useful for Assessment: 11, 17

What this Lesson is About:

- Searching for patterns in a number-based problem
- Generalizations using algebraic notation
- An application of common factors
- Problem-posing and constraints
- Preview of sums of arithmetic sequences

In number theory, the problem addressed in this lesson is called *the stamps problem.*

FOOD FOR THOUGHT

Problem 1 poses a version of the problem that originates in the reality of fast food marketing and leads to an interesting puzzle.

TWO BUILDING BLOCKS

A STRATEGY

The problem is limited to a simpler version, which students may be able to solve by generalization from experiments with specific cases. The main discovery we expect here is that two building blocks with no common factors other than one can generate all but a finite number of the natural numbers.

LESSON 5.8

Building-Block Numbers

In this lesson, use just whole numbers.

FOOD FOR THOUGHT

1. **Exploration** Eric tried to order 13 chicken nuggets at the fast food store. The employee informed him that he could order only 6, 9, or 20 nuggets. Eric realized he had to decide between ordering 6 + 6 = 12, or 6 + 9 = 15. What numbers of nuggets can be ordered by combining 6, 9, and 20? What numbers cannot be ordered? What is the greatest number that cannot be ordered? Explain.

TWO BUILDING BLOCKS

2. You have an unlimited supply of coins. What amounts can be obtained, and what amounts cannot be obtained using only dimes and quarters? Explain.
3. At Albert's Kitchen Supply, cabinets are available in two lengths: 3 feet and 5 feet. By putting cabinets end to end, walls of different lengths can be accommodated. Imagine that kitchens can be any size. What length walls are possible to line exactly with cabinets? What lengths are impossible?
4. In 1958 it cost 4 cents to mail a letter. In 1963 it cost 5 cents. Imagine you have an unlimited supply of 4- and 5-cent stamps. What amounts can you make? What is the largest amount you cannot make?

For each problem, 5-10, using only addition and the building-block numbers given, what numbers can you reach? What numbers can't you reach? If there is one, what is the greatest number you cannot reach?

5. 2, 5 **6.** 7, 11 **7.** 4, 6

8. 5, 12 **9.** 5, 15 **10.** 8, 1

Given the two numbers 7 and 11 and the operation of addition, it is possible to build every number beyond 59. However, with the numbers 4 and 6 there is no limit to the size of numbers that cannot be built.

11. **Generalizations** Suppose you find that for two numbers, *a* and *b,* and the operation of addition, you can build every number beyond a certain number. What can you say about *a* and *b*? Explain, using examples. (Hint: You may need to use the idea of common factors. For example: 4 and 6 have the common factor 2; 5 and 15 have the common factor 5.)
12. Given two numbers, *a* and *b,* such that their greatest common factor is 1, how can you calculate the greatest number that *cannot* be written as a sum of multiples of *a* and *b*? Explain, using examples.

A STRATEGY

In problems 13 and 14 you will investigate the numbers 5 and 6 as building blocks.

13. Write the numbers from 1 to 40 in an array like this.

0	1	2	3	4
5	6	7	8	9
10	11	12	13	14...

a. Circle the multiples of 5. (0 is a multiple of 5.)

b. Circle the numbers that are equal to 6 plus a multiple of 5.

c. Circle the numbers that are equal to 12 plus a multiple of 5.

5.8 SOLUTIONS

1. If *a*, *b*, *c* are whole numbers, then the number of nuggets that can be ordered is in the form of $6a + 9b + 20c$. The greatest number that cannot be ordered is 43. We can easily see this if we set up an array of numbers from 1 to 50 in the following manner:

1	7	13	19	25	31	37	43	49
2	8	14	20	26	32	38	44	50
3	9	15	21	27	33	39	45	
4	10	16	22	28	34	40	46	
5	11	17	23	29	35	41	47	
6	12	18	24	30	36	42	48	

Cross out numbers that you can order, soon you will see a few patterns, and 43 will be the greatest number that cannot be ordered.

2. If *d* and *q* are whole numbers, then the various amounts in cents we can obtain are in the form of $10d + 25q$. If *p* and *n* are whole numbers, then the amounts that cannot be made are in the form of $1p + 5n$, where *p* is not a multiple of 10 and *n* is not a multiple of 5.
3. All lengths are possible except 1, 2, 4, and 7 feet.
4. Any amount is possible except 1, 2, 3, 6, 7, and 11 cents, with 11 being the largest amount you cannot make.
5. All numbers can be reached except 1 and 3.
6. All numbers after 59 can be reached. 59 is the largest number that cannot be reached. The following numbers below 59 can be reached: 7, 11, 14, 18, 21, 22, 25, 28, 29, 32, 33, 35, 36, 39, 40, 42, 43, 44, 46, 47, 49, 50, 51, 53, 54, 55, 56, 57, 58. All the numbers below 59 not in this list cannot be reached.
7. All even numbers can be reached, except 2. All other numbers are impossible to be reached. Hence there is no greatest number that is impossible to reach.
8. All numbers after 43 are possible to be reached. 43 is the largest number that cannot be reached. The following numbers below 43 cannot be reached: 1, 2, 3, 4, 6, 7, 8, 9, 11, 13, 14, 16, 18, 19, 21, 23, 26, 28, 31, 33, 38, 43. The omitted numbers below 43 in this list can be reached.
9. All multiples of 5 are possible to be reached; all others are impossible. Hence, there is no greatest number that cannot be reached.

d. Circle the numbers that are equal to 18 plus a multiple of 5.

e. Circle the numbers that are equal to 24 plus a multiple of 5.

14. What is the largest number that **cannot** be built from 5 and 7? Explain how you know for sure that every number greater than this number can be built.

15. Repeat the same strategy to analyze 5 and 6 as building blocks.

16. Repeat the same strategy to analyze 4 and 7 as building blocks. (This time set up your array with only four columns.)

17. Generalization If you were to use the same strategy for numbers a and b, with $a < b$:

a. How many columns should you have in your array?

b. What numbers should you circle first?

c. What numbers should you circle next?

d. What is the smallest number in the last column you circled? (Write this number in terms of a and b.)

e. If you were not able to solve problem 12, try again with the help of this strategy.

DISCOVERY *HOLIDAY MATH*

18. Candles are lit every night for the eight nights of Hanukah. Two candles are lit on the first night, three on the second night, and so on, adding one candle each night. How many candles should be in the boxes of candles sold especially for Hanukah? Explain.

19. Find the words to the song "The Twelve Days of Christmas."

a. Make a sketch or drawing to show what is happening in the song. How many gifts did the singer receive on the twelfth day of Christmas? Explain.

b. The singer received six gifts on the 3rd day. How many gifts did the singer receive on the 4th day? The 5th day? The nth day? Explain.

c. The singer received 22 turtledoves. Find the total number of each other kind of gift that the singer received.

d. Suppose there were n days of Christmas. How many gifts would the singer receive in all? Explain.

PREVIEW *COIN PROBLEMS*

20. You have ten coins. Their total value is \$1.10. How many of each coin do you have? The problem has several solutions. Find as many as you can.

21. Add extra information that makes problem 20 have a unique solution. Explain how you know the solution is unique.

22. Create your own coin problem that has several solutions. Solve your problem.

23. Solve someone else's coin problem.

Problem 12 poses a question that students may be able to answer from the work they have already done. The following section leads them to a solution, or to a confirmation of their conjecture.

DISCOVERY *HOLIDAY MATH*

You may want to do these problems before winter vacation. There is no reason not to, irrespective of where you are in the book at that time. This section can serve as preview of Lessons 9-11. Or, it can be used as an interesting *problem of the week*.

PREVIEW *COIN PROBLEMS*

Here students make up their own word problems. Adding constraints to make the problems have a unique solution is an interesting challenge, that previews the work with simultaneous equations in Chapter 10.

5.8 S O L U T I O N S

10. All numbers can be reached.

11. If a and b are relatively prime (their greatest common factor is 1), then you can build every number beyond a certain number.

12. The greatest number that cannot be written as a sum of multiples of a and b if they are relatively prime is $a \cdot b - (a + b)$.

13.

~~0~~	1	2	3	4
~~5~~	~~6~~	7	8	9
~~10~~	~~11~~	~~12~~	13	14
~~15~~	~~16~~	~~17~~	~~18~~	19
~~20~~	~~21~~	~~22~~	~~23~~	~~24~~
~~25~~	~~26~~	~~27~~	~~28~~	~~29~~
~~30~~	~~31~~	~~32~~	~~33~~	~~34~~
~~35~~	~~36~~	~~37~~	~~38~~	~~39~~
~~40~~				

a. The answers are in the first column above.

b. The answers are in the second column.

c. The answers are in the third column.

d. The answers are in the fourth column.

e. The answers are in the fifth column.

14.

~~0~~	1	2	3	4
~~5~~	6	~~7~~	8	9
~~10~~	11	~~12~~	13	~~14~~
~~15~~	16	~~17~~	18	~~19~~
~~20~~	~~21~~	~~22~~	23	~~24~~
~~25~~	~~26~~	~~27~~	~~28~~	~~29~~
~~30~~	~~31~~	~~32~~	~~33~~	~~34~~
~~35~~	~~36~~	~~37~~	~~38~~	~~39~~
~~40~~	~~41~~	~~42~~	~~43~~	~~44~~
~~45~~	~~46~~	~~47~~	~~48~~	~~49~~

23 is the largest number that cannot be built from 5 and 7 because if we continued the array, all the numbers after 23 would be crossed out, since they are composed of the sum of multiples of 5 and 7.

15. 19 is the largest number that cannot be built by 5 and 6.

16.

~~0~~	1	2	3
~~4~~	5	6	7
~~8~~	9	10	~~11~~
~~12~~	13	~~14~~	~~15~~
~~16~~	17	~~18~~	~~19~~
~~20~~	~~21~~	~~22~~	~~23~~

17 is the largest number that cannot be built by 5 and 6.

17. a. a columns

b. multiples of a

c. b plus a multiple of a

d. $a + b$

e. $ab - (a + b)$

DISCOVERY NEGATIVE STAMPS

This is a silly idea which would have a disastrous effect on the federal deficit.

DISCOVERY PAGE NUMBERS

These problems can be used to preview arithmetic sequences. The problems are not easy, and would make good *problems of the week*, that students could work on in conjunction with the next two lessons.

24. Add extra information to your problem so it will have a unique solution.

DISCOVERY NEGATIVE STAMPS

25. You want to mail a letter. It needs 52 cents postage, but all you have are 29-cent stamps: 29 + 29 = 58. What would be convenient would be to have negative stamps. Then you could put two 29-cent stamps and a minus 6-cent stamp on your envelope, and it would solve your problem. Write a paragraph about this idea. How would the post office "sell" negative stamps? Why do you think they don't do it?

DISCOVERY PAGE NUMBERS

26. How many *digits* are used in numbering the pages of this book? Explain how you figured it out.

27. It took 1992 digits to number the pages of a book. Every page was numbered, starting with page 1. How many pages does the book have?

28. Explain how to find out how many digits are needed to number the pages of a book that has n pages, if n is

a. more than 9, but less than 100;

b. more than 99, but less than 1000.

5.8 SOLUTIONS

18. (9 + 2) · 8/2 = 44 candles. This is using Gauss's formula for adding consecutive sums.
19. a. (12 + 1) · 12/2 = 78 gifts. This is using Gauss's formula for adding consecutive sums.
    b. For the fourth day, the series would look like:
    1 + 2 + 3 + 4 = 5 · 4/2 = 10 gifts.
    For the fifth day:
    1 + 2 + 3 + 4 + 5 = 6 · 5/2 = 15 gifts
    For the nth day: $(n + 1) \cdot n/2$
    c. The number of other kinds of gifts, not counting turtledoves, is 364 − 22 = 342 gifts.
20. Some of the possible solutions are:
    4 quarters, 0 dimes, 1 nickel, 5 pennies
    3 quarters, 0 dimes, 7 nickels
    2 quarters, 4 dimes, 4 nickels
    1 quarter, 8 dimes, 1 nickel
21. If one added the condition "using only quarters, nickels, and pennies" or "using only quarters and nickels," it would give a unique solution.
22. Students' problems will vary.
23. Answers will vary.
24. Answers will vary.
25. Answers will vary.

THINKING WRITING 5.B Distributing

INSIDE AND OUTSIDE PRODUCTS

Look at this sequence of consecutive integers.

8, 9, 10, 11

- The product of the outside pair is 88.
- The product of the inside pair is 90.
- The difference between the inside product and the outside product is 2.

1. Find the difference between the inside and outside product for each of these sequences.

a. 4, 5, 6, 7
b. 10, 11, 12, 13
c. $10, 10 + 1, 10 + 2, 10 + 3$
d. $y, y + 1, y + 2, y + 3$

2. What pattern did you notice in problem 1?

3. Look at some sequences of four integers that differ by three. For example, you could try 4, 7, 10, 13. What pattern do you notice in the difference between their inside and outside products?

4. What pattern would you expect to see in the difference of inside and outside products for sequences of numbers that differ by two? What about sequences of numbers that differ by four? Experiment.

5. Find the difference between the inside and outside product for each of these sequences.

a. $y, y + 2, y + 4, y + 6$
b. $y, y + 3, y + 6, y + 9$
c. $y, y + 5, y + 10, y + 15$
d. $y, y + 5, y + 2 \cdot 5, y + 3 \cdot 5$
e. $y, y + x, y + 2x, y + 3x$

6. Report Write a detailed report describing the patterns you discovered in this lesson. Give examples and show all your calculations. Your report should include, but not be limited to, the answers to the following questions:

- How is the difference between the inside and outside products related to the difference between numbers in the sequence?
- How can you use algebra (and/or the Lab Gear) to show that your answer is correct?
- Does your generalization work for all kinds of numbers? For example, could you choose a sequence made up entirely of negative numbers? What about fractions?

MORE DISTRIBUTIVE LAWS?

You might wonder if there are more distributive laws.

7. Is there a distributive law of exponentiation over addition? If there were, it would mean that $(x + y)^2$ would always be equal to $x^2 + y^2$. It would also mean that $(x + y)^3$ would equal $x^3 + y^3$. Do you think such a law exists? Explain why or why not.

8. Is there a distributive law of multiplication over multiplication? If there were, it would mean that $a(xy)$ would always be equal to $ax \cdot ay$. For example, $2(xy)$ would have to equal $2x \cdot 2y$. Do you think such a law exists? Explain why or why not.

9. Report Write a report about distributive laws. Use numerical examples and/or sketches of the Lab Gear. Your report should include a discussion of which of the following laws exist, and why.

The distributive law of:

- multiplication over addition and subtraction
- division over addition and subtraction
- exponentiation over addition and subtraction
- multiplication over multiplication

5.B SOLUTIONS

1. a. 2 b. 2 c. 2
 d. $(y + 1)(y + 2) - y(y + 3)$
2. The products differ by 2.
3. The products differ by 18.
4. The difference of inside and outside products for sequences of numbers that differ by 2 is 8, and for sequences of numbers that differ by 4 is 32.
5. a. 8 b. 18 c. 50 d. 50 e. $2x^2$
6. Suppose the sequence were x, $x + a$, $x + 2a$, $x + 3a$, where a is any real number. $(x + a)(x + 2a) - x(x + 3a) = x^2 + 3ax + 2a^2 - (x^2 + 3ax) = 2a^2$. This proves that the difference of the products is always $2a^2$ regardless of the value of a, be it a fraction, a negative number, etc.
7. No, there is not a distributive law of exponentiation. We can see that $(x + y)^2 = (x + y)(x + y) = x^2 + 2xy + y^2$. There is a middle term, $2xy$, that is added to $x^2 + y^2$.
8. No, there is not a distributive law of multiplication over multiplication. $2(xy) \neq 2x \cdot 2y = 4xy$. $2xy$ cannot equal $4xy$.
9. The distributive law is applicable to multiplication over addition and subtraction and division over addition and subtraction. Since division is multiplying by the reciprocal, we can say that division over addition and subtraction is the same as multiplication over addition and subtraction. Exponentiation over addition and subtraction and multiplication over multiplication does not work as shown in problems 7 and 8.

THINKING WRITING 5.B Distributing

Core Sequence: 1-9

Suitable for Homework: 1-9

Useful for Assessment: 6, 9

What this Assignment is About:

- Using variables to generalize and understand number patterns
- Applying the distributive law
- Preview of notation for arithmetic sequences
- Review of order of operations and the distributive law

The two sections are unrelated and need not be done consecutively.

INSIDE AND OUTSIDE PRODUCTS

This section applies the work on the distributive law to the dissection of an interesting number pattern in arithmetic sequences.

The use of algebraic notation helps gain insight into numerical patterns and helps prepare students for the work in the next three lessons.

Building the problem with the Lab Gear provides dramatic confirmation of the pattern for problems 1d, 5a, and 5e. If that does not occur to your students, you may suggest it.

MORE DISTRIBUTIVE LAWS?

Students often over-generalize the distributive law because they are not aware that it applies only to certain operations. This section should help them think about this, but of course it may not be sufficient to eliminate this type of mistake forever.

▼ 5.9
Staircase Sums

Core Sequence: 1-3, 7-16

Suitable for Homework: 4-6, 9-16

Useful for Assessment: 6, 11-12, 16

What this Lesson is About:

- A geometric approach to arithmetic sequences
- Review of addition of signed numbers

This is the first of three lessons about sequences. Sequences are not a traditional Algebra 1 topic. We teach them primarily to give students a better understanding of concepts that are more central to the course, such as variables, operations, and functions. They also provide an interesting environment for problem solving, and a preview of future courses. If you are going to cover Chapter 11 later, you will need to teach these lessons, otherwise you may skip the rest of this chapter, or perhaps just do Lesson 12 as a change of pace.

This lesson previews arithmetic sequences using a geometric approach: students build *staircases* to explore sums of consecutive numbers. Graph paper may be sufficient for most students, but if some want to build the staircases with Lab Gear blocks, allow them to.

ONE STEP AT A TIME

Problem 2b may be very difficult for some students. You may want to pose the question and come back to it after students have done problem 3.

Problem 3 is often assigned as a *problem of the week*. It is a rich problem, which can be solved at many levels. Most students should be able to see that odd numbers can be made into two-step staircases, and that powers of two cannot be made into staircases. You can leave it at that and skip problems 4-6.

But there is more to find out, and if you wish, you can take a whole class period or more to lead the research into this problem.

For one thing, the problem can be generalized by including negative numbers and 0, as is suggested in problems 4-6. The number of different ways to write a number as a sum of consecutive integers is equal to the number of its odd factors (which

LESSON 5.9

Staircase Sums

ONE STEP AT A TIME

Here is an example of a kind of arrangement that we'll call a *staircase*. It has 4 steps and the first step is of height 2.

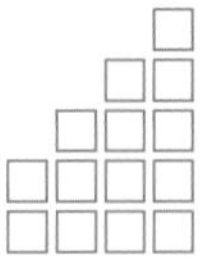

Definition: For this lesson, we will define a *staircase* as a sequence of stacks of tiles in which each stack is one tile higher than the previous stack. *There must be two or more steps in the staircase,* and the first step can be of any height.

1. How many tiles would you need to build each of these staircases?
   a. First step: 7 Number of steps: 8
   b. First step: 8 Number of steps: 7
   c. First step: 6 Number of steps: 9

2. There are two different nine-tile staircases: 2 + 3 + 4 and 4 + 5.
   a. Find three different 15-tile staircases.
   b. Find four different 105-tile staircases.

3. **Exploration** Find every possible staircase with each number of tiles from 2 to 34. Hints:
   - Work with other students.
   - Keep organized records of your work.
   - It is not necessary to draw the staircases.
   - Look for strategies: What numbers can be made into two-step staircases? Three-step?
   - Look for patterns: What numbers are easiest? What numbers are impossible?

4. The number 10 can be written as the sum of four consecutive numbers.
   a. What are these four numbers?
   b. If negative integers and zero are allowed, can the number 10 be written as the sum of consecutive numbers in any other way? If so, show how.

5. Show how the number 4 can be written as a sum of consecutive integers if negative numbers and zero can be used.

6. **Generalization** What is the maximum number of consecutive integers that can be used to write the number 17 as a sum? What is the maximum number of consecutive integers that can be used to write the number N as a sum? (Assume N is an integer.) Explain your answer, giving examples.

SUMS FROM RECTANGLES

7. a. On graph paper, sketch the staircase illustrated at the beginning of the lesson. Then make a rectangle by sketching a copy of the staircase *upside down* on the first staircase. (You can also do this by building the staircases with tiles.)
   b. What are the length, width, and area of the rectangle?

8. Imagine a staircase having 100 steps, and a first step of height 17.
   a. It would be half of what rectangle? (Give the length and width.)
   b. How many tiles would you need to build the staircase? Explain how you know.

5.9 SOLUTIONS

1. a. 84
   b. 77
   c. 90
2. a. 7 + 8, 4 + 5 + 6, 1 + 2 + 3 + 4 + 5
   b. 52 + 53, 34 + 35 + 36, 12 + 13 + 14 + 15 + 16 + 17 + 18, 6 + 7 + 8 + 9 + 10 + 11 + 12 + 13 + 15 + 15
3. The following table is a list of staircases with numbers of tiles from 2 to 34:

Number	Staircase
2	impossible
3	1 + 2
4	impossible
5	2 + 3
6	1 + 2 + 3
7	3 + 4
8	impossible
9	2 + 3 + 4; 4 + 5
10	1 + 2 + 3 + 4
11	5 + 6
12	3 + 4 + 5
13	6 + 7
14	2 + 3 + 4 + 5
15	7 + 8, 4 + 5 + 6, 1 + 2 + 3 + 4 + 5
16	impossible
17	8 + 9
18	3 + 4 + 5 + 6, 5 + 6 + 7
19	9 + 10

9. Show how you could find the sum of:
   a. the integers from 5 to 55, inclusive;
   b. the integers from 0 to 100, inclusive.

GAUSS'S METHOD

Math teachers like to tell a story about Carl Friedrich Gauss. One day in elementary school he was punished by his teacher who asked him to add up all the whole numbers from 0 to 100. Carl immediately gave the answer, to his teacher's amazement. He grew up to be one of the greatest mathematicians of all time.

Gauss's method was to imagine all the numbers from 0 to 100 written from left to right, and directly beneath that, all the numbers written from right to left. It would look like this:

0	1	2	3	4	5	6	7	8	9...
100	99	98	97	96	95	94	93	92	91...

He mentally added each column, getting 100 each time. He multiplied 100 by the number of columns, and did one more thing to get the correct answer.

10. Finish Gauss's calculation. Be sure to use the correct number of columns, and to carry out the final step. Did you get the same answer as in problem 9b?

11. What would happen if the numbers to be added started at 1 instead of 0? Obviously, the sum should be the same. Would Gauss's method still give the same answer? Explain.

12. **Summary** You now know two methods for calculating staircase sums: one involves making a rectangle; the other is Gauss's method. Both methods work well, but it is easy to make mistakes when using them. Write a paragraph explaining how you would use each method to calculate the sum, $5 + 6 + 7 + ... + 89$. Use sketches as part of your explanation. Both methods should give the same answer.

VARIABLE STAIRCASES

You can build staircases with the Lab Gear. This diagram shows $(x) + (x + 1) + (x + 2) + (x + 3)$.

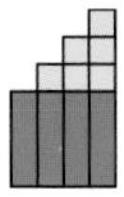

13. In terms of x, what is the sum of $(x) + (x + 1) + (x + 2) + (x + 3)$?

14. Find the sum of $(x) + (x + 1) + (x + 2) + (x + 3)$ if:
   a. $x = 4$; b. $x = 99$.

15. Find each sum. Explain how you got your answer.
   a. $(x) + (x + 1) + (x + 2) + ... + (x + 26)$
   b. $(x + 1) + (x + 5) + ... + (x + 84)$

16. **Generalization** What is the sum of each staircase?
   a. $1 + 2 + 3 + ... + n$
   b. $(x) + (x + 1) + ... + (x + n)$
   c. $(x + 1) + ... + (x + n)$

throws light on the difficulty with powers of two). Students are not likely to discover this on their own, but you can point them in that direction.

Finally, one can think about staircases as the sum of a triangular number, and a multiple of the number of steps. For example, the staircase pictured at the beginning of the lesson is the sum of the fourth triangular number ($10 = 1 + 2 + 3 + 4$) and the number $4(= 4 \cdot 1)$. This geometric insight allows us to test whether a number can be written as a sum of n consecutive positive integers by subtracting the nth triangular number from the original number and seeing if the result is a multiple of n. This is a very sophisticated insight, which you cannot expect to originate among the students.

You could ask students to write a full report on problem 3, or perhaps to present group oral reports. Don't expect students to come up with all the patterns described above, but do encourage students to look for more patterns than those that are most immediately obvious.

SUMS FROM RECTANGLES
GAUSS'S METHOD

A geometric and a numerical approach to sums of arithmetic sequences. *It is very important that you do not teach a formula.* The two methods presented here constitute the mathematical foundation of the formula, and using them deepens the students' understanding of the problem. Students do not have the mathematical maturity to really understand how the formula is a generalization of the process presented here. The unfortunate result of teaching a formula at this level is that students turn off their brains.

VARIABLE STAIRCASES

Actually, this section does lead students to discover a formula. But do not encourage them to memorize it. Formulas are difficult to remember, while the two methods presented in this lesson, once understood, are difficult to forget.

In any case, the formula students discover does not have enough generality to deserve memorization, since it deals only with arithmetic sequences having common difference 1.

5.9 SOLUTIONS

20	2 + 3 + 4 + 5 + 6
21	10 + 11, 6 + 7 + 8, 1 + 2 + 3 + 4 + 5 + 6
22	4 + 5 + 6 + 7
23	11 + 12
24	7 + 8 + 9
25	12 + 13, 3 + 4 + 5 + 6 + 7
26	5 + 6 + 7 + 8
27	13 + 14, 8 + 9 + 10, 2 + 3 + 4 + 5 + 6 + 7
28	1 + 2 + 3 + 4 + 5 + 6 + 7
29	14 + 15
30	9 + 10 + 11, 6 + 7 + 8 + 9, 4 + 5 + 6 + 7 + 8
31	15 + 16
32	impossible
33	16 + 17, 10 + 11 + 12, 3 + 4 + 5 + 6 + 7 + 8
34	7 + 8 + 9 + 10

The easiest numbers to do are prime numbers. Numbers that are a power of 2 are impossible.

4. a. 1 + 2 + 3 + 4
   b. Yes. -9 + -8 + -7 + -6 + -5 + -4 + -3 + -2 + -1 + 0 + 1 + 2 + 3 + 4 + 5 + 6 + 7 + 8 + 9 + 10
5. -3 + -2 + -1 + 0 + 1 + 2 + 3 + 4
6. Answers will vary. Sample: The maximum number of consecutive integers that can be used to write the number 17 is 34. The maximum for N consecutive integers is $2|N|$. Number 5 is a good example for the number 4. 4 can be expressed as the sum of 8 consecutive integers.

(Solutions continued on page 518)

▼ 5.10
Sequences

Core Sequence: 1-21

Suitable for Homework: 6-13, 18-24

Useful for Assessment: 18

What this Lesson is About:

- Looking for patterns
- Using symbolic notation
- Definition of a sequence
- Even and odd numbers
- Definition of arithmetic sequence

GRAPHS OF SEQUENCES

This section previews **Thinking/Writing 5.C**, which will pursue sequences as functions in greater depth.

Problem 3 shows the sequence of triangular numbers, which students may remember from Chapter 1, Lessons 5 and 11. If students have trouble with problem 3b, you may hint that this sequence can be seen as a sequence of staircase sums, so the methods from Lesson 9 can be used. (In fact, problem 17a in Lesson 9 was the same problem, presented differently.)

GETTING EVEN
THAT'S ODD!

The main point of these sections is once again to give students a chance to recognize numerical patterns and to generalize them with the help of algebraic notation.

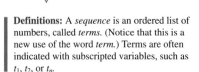

LESSON 5.10

Sequences

Definitions: A *sequence* is an ordered list of numbers, called *terms.* (Notice that this is a new use of the word *term.*) Terms are often indicated with subscripted variables, such as t_1, t_2, or t_n.

GRAPHS OF SEQUENCES

Definition: The *natural numbers* are the numbers we count with: 1, 2, 3, 4, ...

The natural numbers are the easiest sequence of numbers to write using a variable. The first natural number is 1, the second natural number is 2, and so on; $t_1 = 1$, $t_2 = 2$, ... The nth natural number is n, so $t_n = n$. The graph shows the sequence of natural numbers.

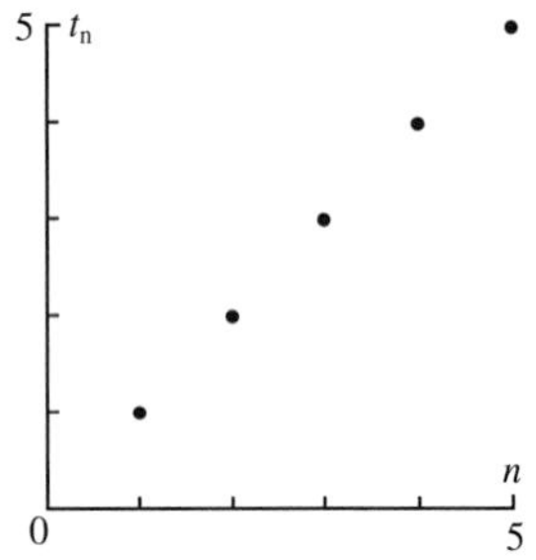

1. Graph the first few terms of the sequence below. Does it make sense to connect the dots? Explain.

n	1	2	3	4	...	n
t_n	2	5	8	11	...	$3n - 1$

2. Make a table, and graph the first few terms of the sequence whose n^{th} term is $t_n = 3n + 1$. Compare your graph with the one you drew in problem 1. How are they the same? How are they different?

3. You may remember this sequence.

n	1	2	3	4	...	n
t_n	1	3	6	10	...	?

   a. What is the 6th term?
   b. What is the nth term?
   c. Graph the first few terms. Is your graph a straight line?

GETTING EVEN

4. If 2 is the first even number, 4 the second, and so on, what is the millionth even number? In terms of n, what is the nth even number?

5. Graph the first few terms of the sequence of even numbers. Is your graph a straight line?

n	1	2	3	...	?	n
t_n	2	6	?	...	42	?

6. The nth term in the above sequence is the *sum of the first n even numbers.*
   a. What is t_5?
   b. Which term has a value of 42?
   c. Graph the first few terms. Is your graph a straight line?
   d. In terms of n, what is the nth term of this sequence?

THAT'S ODD!

7. If 1 is the first odd number, 3 the second, 5 the third, what is the one-hundredth odd number?

5.10 SOLUTIONS

1.

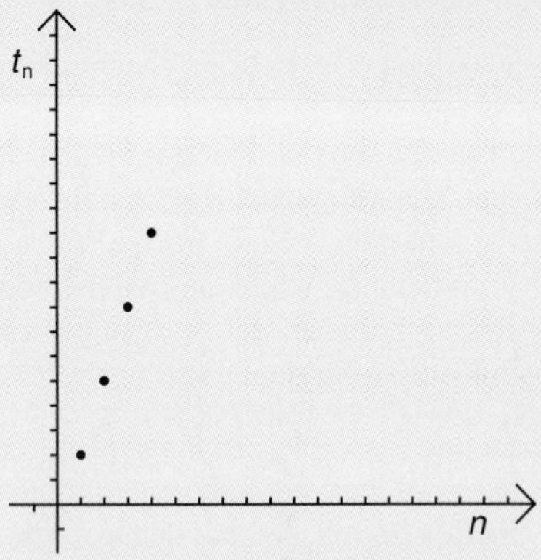

It does not make sense to connect the dots, since n takes on only the values of the natural numbers.

2.

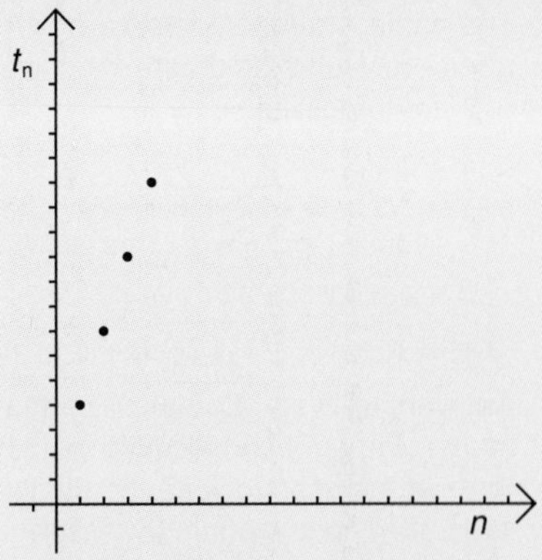

They have the same steepness, but the points in the second graph are above the points in the first.

3. a. 21
   b. $n(n + 1)/2$
   c. No, it is a parabola.
4. 2 million. The nth even number is $2n$
5.

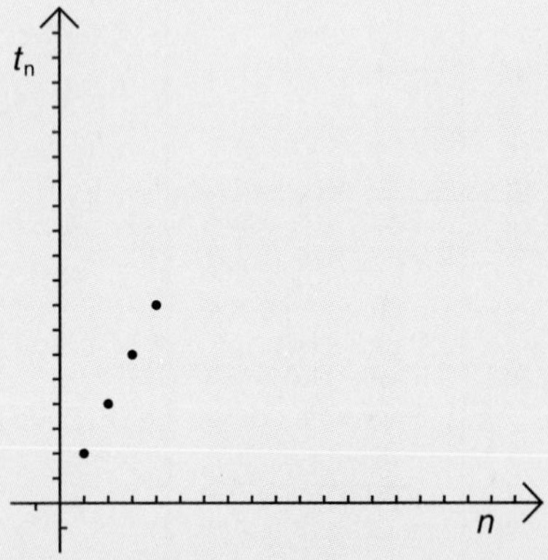

Yes, the points lie in a straight line.

8. a. In terms of n, what is the nth odd number?
b. Graph the first few terms in the sequence of odd numbers.

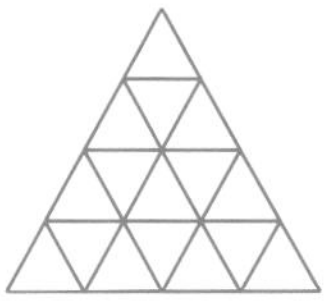

9. a. Look at the figure. How many unit triangles are in the first row? The second? The third? (Count triangles whether they point up or down.)
b. If the triangle were extended indefinitely, how many unit triangles would there be in the nth row?

10. a. How many unit triangles are there altogether in the first two rows? The first three rows?
b. How many unit triangles are in the first n rows?

11. What is the sum of the first two odd numbers? The first three?

12. a. What is the sum of the first n odd numbers?
b. Graph the first few terms in the sequence of sums of odd numbers.

ARITHMETIC SEQUENCES

Definition: In an *arithmetic sequence,* the difference between consecutive terms is always the same. It is called the *common difference.*

Examples: These are arithmetic sequences.
2, 7, 12, 17, 22 (The common difference is 5.)
5, 8, 11, 14, 17, 20, 23, 26, 29, 32 (The common difference is 3.)

These are not arithmetic sequences.
3, 9, 27, 81
1, -1, 1, -1, 1, -1
4, 9, 16, 25, 49

13. Which of these are arithmetic sequences? For those that are, what is the common difference?
a. 2, 6, 8, 12, 16, 20
b. 3, 6, 3, 7, 3, 8
c. 19, 13, 7, 1, -5, ...
d. the sequence of even numbers
e. the sequence of odd numbers
f. $2, 2 + 9, 2 + 2 \cdot 9, 2 + 3 \cdot 9, 2 + 4 \cdot 9$

14. Make up an arithmetic sequence for another student.

15. Answer these questions about a classmate's sequence.
a. Is it really an arithmetic sequence?
b. What is the common difference?
c. In terms of n, what is the nth term?

16. For each arithmetic sequence, find the common difference, and write the nth term in terms of n.
a. 2, 7, 12, 22, ...
b. $2 + 1 \cdot 5, 2 + 2 \cdot 5, 2 + 3 \cdot 5, ...$
c. $2, 2 + 1 \cdot 5, 2 + 2 \cdot 5, 2 + 3 \cdot 5, ...$

17. Answer the same questions as in problem 15 for:
a. $y, y + 1 \cdot 5, y + 2 \cdot 5, y + 3 \cdot 5, ...$
b. $2 + 1 \cdot x, 2 + 2 \cdot x, 2 + 3 \cdot x, ...$
c. $y + 1 \cdot x, y + 2 \cdot x, y + 3 \cdot x, ...$
d. $y, y + 1 \cdot x, y + 2 \cdot x, y + 3 \cdot x, ...$

18. **Summary** Explain how to calculate the nth term of an arithmetic sequence, if you know the first term and the common difference. Test your method on several arithmetic sequences.

Problem 6d may be difficult for some students. As a hint, you may suggest they compare this table to the one for problem 3. The other patterns are straightforward.

ARITHMETIC SEQUENCES

You may explain that arithmetic sequences are a generalization of the staircases studied in the previous lesson. Staircases are arithmetic sequences having common difference 1.

Problems 14-17 should be done in class. Problem 15c in particular would make for a good class discussion. Collect, on the chalkboard or overhead, student-created sequences for which they did find a formula for the nth term. Check that the formulas do work, and ask the students who discovered them to share their method with the class. If that is insufficient help for everyone to see the pattern, you may point out that in all cases, the formula is of the form $t_n = a + n \cdot d$, where d is the common difference, and a depends on the problem. Finding a is the challenge.

In the course of the discussion, you may discuss the merits of calling the initial term of the sequence t_0 instead of t_1. (Calling it t_0 has the advantage that it is easier to find a formula for t_n.)

5.10 SOLUTIONS

6. a. 30
b. The 6th term.

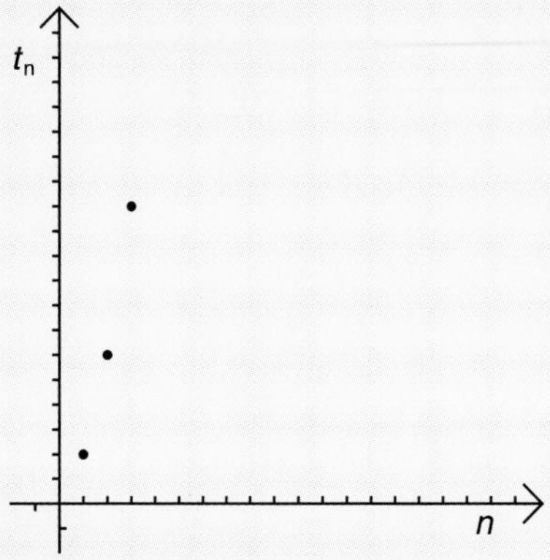

c. not a straight line
d. $n(n + 1)$

7. 199

8. a. $2n - 1$
b.

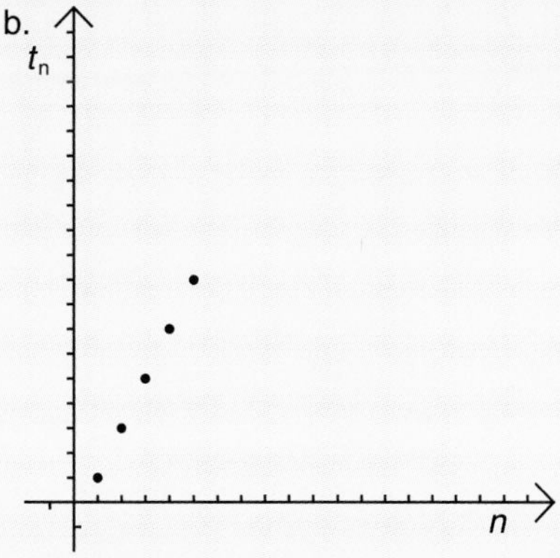

9. a. 1, 3, 5
b. $2n - 1$

10. a. 4, 9
b. n^2

11. 4, 9

12. a. n^2
b.

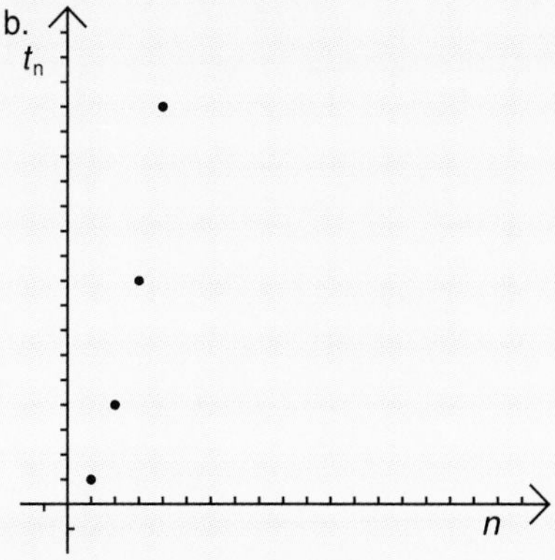

13. a. no
b. no
c. yes, -6
d. yes, 2
e. yes, 2
f. yes, 9

PREVIEW ***EQUATIONS***

Even though the word is not mentioned, these problems give students an opportunity to think about the *mean*.

PREVIEW ***ANOTHER ODD TRIANGLE***

This is an interesting pattern, which touches on many of the ideas in this lesson, and previews the next lesson. Another candidate for *problem of the week*.

PREVIEW ***EQUATIONS***

19. For each equation, find values of x_1, x_2, and x_3, that make it true.

a. $(x_1 + x_2 + x_3)/3 = 100$

b. $(x_1 + x_2 + x_3)/3 = 50$

c. $(x_1 + x_2 + x_3)/3 = 20$

d. $(x_1 + x_2 + x_3)/3 = 10$

20. For each equation in problem 19, find another set of values for x_1, x_2, and x_3 that will work.

21. If possible, find a value of x_3 to satisfy each equation.

a. $(15 + 20 + x_3)/3 = 100$

b. $(15 + 20 + x_3)/3 = 50$

c. $(15 + 20 + x_3)/3 = 20$

d. $(15 + 20 + x_3)/3 = 10$

PREVIEW ***ANOTHER ODD TRIANGLE***

1
3 5
7 9 11
13 15 17 19
21 23 25 27 29

22. Look at the array of numbers above.

a. Write the next two rows.

b. Describe how the array is made.

23. a. Look at the middle number in rows that have a middle number. What is the pattern?

b. In rows that do not have a middle number, think of the number between the middle two numbers. What is the pattern?

c. Find the sum of the numbers in each row. What is the pattern?

24.

a. What is the first number in the nth row?

b. What is the last number in the nth row?

c. What is the sum of all the numbers in the first n rows?

5.10 SOLUTIONS

14. Answers will vary.

15. Answers will vary.

16. a. Difference: 5; n^{th} term: $2 + 5(n - 1)$
    b. Difference: 5; n^{th} term: $2 + 5n$
    c. Difference: 5; n^{th} term: $2 + 5(n - 1)$

17. a. Difference: 5; n^{th} term: $y + 5(n - 1)$
    a. Difference: x; n^{th} term: $2 + nx$
    a. Difference: x; n^{th} term: $y + nx$
    a. Difference: x; n^{th} term: $y + (n - 1)x$

18. To find the nth term, take the first term and add the common difference $(n - 1)$ times.

19. Answers will vary.

20. Answers will vary.

21. a. 265
    b. 115
    c. 25
    d. -5

22. a. Fifth row: 31, 33, 35, 37, 39, 41
    Sixth row: 43, 45, 47, 49, 51, 53, 55
    b. The nth row contains the next n odd numbers.

23. a. The middle number is n^2 in row n.
    b. The number halfway between the two middle numbers is n^2 in row n.
    c. The sum of the numbers in row n is n^3.

24. a. $n^2 - (n - 1)$
    b. $n^2 + (n - 1)$
    c. $[n(n + 1)/2]^2$

LESSON 5.11

Averages and Sums

MEANS AND MEDIANS

You probably know how to find the average of a set of numbers. For example, the ages of the people in Tina's family are 10, 48, 20, 22, and 57. You would find the average age by adding the numbers and dividing by 5.

$$\frac{10 + 48 + 20 + 22 + 57}{5} = 31.4$$

We call this average the *mean*. Another kind of average is the *median*.

Definition: The *median* is the middle of a set of numbers that are in order from least to greatest. To find the median of an even number of numbers, find the two middle numbers and find their mean.

Examples: To find the median age in Tina's family, first write the numbers in ascending or descending order.

10 20 **22** 48 57

The median is **22.**

These are the ages of people in Lana's family: 52, 20, 15, and 53. To find the median, first write the numbers in ascending or descending order.

53 **52 20** 15

Compute the mean of the middle two numbers: $\frac{52 + 20}{2}$ = **36**, so the median is 36.

1. Find the mean of the ages in Lana's family. Compare it with the median.
2. Make up a sequence of seven numbers in which
   a. the mean is less than the median;
   b. the median is less than the mean;
   c. the mean and the median are equal.
3. Repeat problem 2 for a sequence of eight numbers.
4. **Exploration** Find some sequences of numbers in which the mean and the median are equal. Work with your classmates and compare your answers. What can you conclude about these sequences? Write a summary of your conclusions, including examples. (At least one example should be an arithmetic sequence, and at least one should not be.)
5. For each example below, make up two sequences that fit the given description.
   a. The greatest term is 19, and both mean and median equal 10.
   b. There are six terms. The greatest is 25, the mean is 10, and the median is less than 10.
   c. There are seven terms. The least is -60, the median is 18, and the mean is less than 18.
   d. The mean and the median are both -4. There are nine terms.
6. 🔑 If possible, make up an arithmetic sequence that fits each description in problem 5. If it's not possible, explain why not.

MEANS AND SUMS

7. Find the mean and the sum of each arithmetic sequence.
   a. -2, -14, -26, -38, -50, -62, -74
   b. -5, -1.8, 1.4, 4.6, 7.8, 11, 14.2, 17.4
   c. 31, 29, 27, 25, 23, 21
   d. 17, 20, 23, 26, 29, 32
8. 🔑 Study your answers to problem 7.
   a. In which cases was the mean one of the terms in the sequence?
   b. When the mean was not one of the terms in the sequence, how was it related to those terms?

5.11 Averages and Sums

Core Sequence: 1-16

Suitable for Homework: 7-16

Useful for Assessment: 6, 8-9, 12

What this Lesson is About:

- Mean and median
- Sums of arithmetic sequences

MEANS AND MEDIANS

In an arithmetic sequence, the mean equals the median. This is also true of any sequence of numbers where the terms are distributed symmetrically around the median.

The main emphasis of the lesson is not on the statistical analysis of data, but on gaining more familiarity with arithmetic sequences.

MEANS AND SUMS

The relationship: **number of terms *times* mean *equals* sum** is true of any set of numbers. In the particular case of arithmetic sequences, the mean is easy to find: It is the average of the least and greatest terms. This leads to a shortcut in figuring out the sum of an arithmetic sequence.

5.11 SOLUTIONS

1. The mean age is 35, which is slightly less than the median.
2. Answers will vary. One possibility is given for each problem.
   a. 10, 20, 30, 36, 40, 50, 60 (mean: 35.1, median: 36)
   b. 5, 6, 7, 8, 10, 20, 30 (mean: 12.286, median: 8)
   c. 1, 2, 3, 4, 5, 6, 7 (mean: 4, median: 4)
3. Answers will vary. One possibility is given for each problem.
   a. 1, 2, 3, 8, 9, 10, 11, 12 (mean: 7, median: 8.5)
   b. 1, 2, 3, 4, 5, 10, 20, 30 (mean: 9.375, median: 4.5)
   c. 1, 2, 3, 4, 5, 6, 7, 8 (mean: 4.5, median: 4.5)
4. Answers will vary. Students should notice that all arithmetic sequences have this property. They should be able to give examples of nonarithmetic sequences that also have this property. (These sequences will be symmetric with respect to the mean and median.)
5. Answers will vary. Sample answers are given.
   a. 1, 10, 19 and 1, 2, 18, 19
   b. 1, 4, 8, 10, 12, 25 (mean: 10, median: 9) and 1, 4, 6, 9, 15, 25 (mean: 10, median: 7.5)
   c. -60, 10, 15, 18, 20, 21, 22 (mean: 6.57, median: 18) and -60, 5, 10, 18, 19, 20, 60 (mean: 10.286, median 18)
   d. -9, -7, -6, -5, -4, -3, -2, -1, 1 and -14, -12, -10, -6, -4, -2, 2, 4, 6
6. a. Answers will vary. One possibility is 1, 4, 7, 10, 13, 16, 19.
   b. Not possible. The mean and the median of an arithmetic sequence are always equal.
   c. Same answer as (b).
   d. Answers will vary. One possibility is -8, -7, -6, -5, -4, -3, -2, -1, 0
7. a. sum: -266 mean: -38
   b. sum: 49.6 mean: 6.2
   c. sum: 156 mean: 26
   d. sum: 147 mean: 24.5
8. a. 7 (a)
   b. It was halfway between the two middle terms.
   c. The sum divided by the number of terms is the mean.

Again, we avoid emphasizing a formula, and instead encourage students to use reasoning. In some cases, they will need to be able to find the value of the last term, using the technique learned in Lesson 10.

THEATER SEATS

This is a practical application of sums of arithmetic sequences. It should not present any difficulties.

c. How are the number of terms, the mean, and the sum related?

Suppose we wanted to find the sum and the mean of this arithmetic sequence:

3, 9, 15, 21, 27, 33, 39, 45, 51.

Using Gauss's method, write the sequence twice, once from left to right, and then from right to left.

3	9	15	21	27	33	39	45	51
51	45	39	33	27	21	15	9	3

9.
a. Add each column above.
b. Find the mean and the sum of the sequence.
c. How are your answers to (b) related to the sum of each column?

10. Using your results from problem 9, find a shortcut for calculating the sum and the mean of an arithmetic sequence. Try it on the examples in problem 7, comparing your results with your previous answers.

11. Find the sum and the mean of each arithmetic sequence described.
a. The sequence has 15 terms. The first term is 12, and the last term is 110.
b. The first term is -11, and the last term is -33. Each term is obtained by adding -2 to the previous term.
c. The first term is -14, and the difference between consecutive terms is 5. There are 41 terms in the sequence.
d. The first term is 7, and each term is obtained by adding -1.4 to the previous term. There are eight terms in the sequence.

12. **Generalization** Find the sum and the mean of each arithmetic sequence.
a. The first term is *b,* and the final term is 5. There are six terms in the sequence.
b. The first term is *b,* and the final term is *f.* There are 10 terms in the sequence.
c. The first term is *b,* and the final term is *f.* There are *n* terms in the sequence.
d. The first term is *b,* and each successive term is obtained by adding *d.* There are *n* terms in the sequence.

THEATER SEATS

Seats in a theater are arranged so that there are 35 seats in the front (first) row, 38 in the next row, 41 in the row behind that, and so on, adding three seats each time.

13. How many seats are in the
a. 10th row? b. the nth row?

14. How many total seats are needed if the theater has
a. 26 rows? b. *n* rows?

15. How would your answers to questions 13-14 be different if there were 34 seats in the first row?

16. Suppose there were 35 seats in the first row, 37 in the next, and so on, adding two seats each time. How would your answers to questions 13-14 be different?

5.11 SOLUTIONS

9. a. The sum of each column is 54.
b. The mean is 27; the sum is 243.
c. The mean is half the sum of each column.

10. Answers will vary, but all methods should confirm the answers in #7. One possible way of stating the shortcuts follows: The shortcut to find the mean is to average the first term and the last term. The shortcut to find the sum is to average the first and last terms and multiply the result by the number of terms.

11. a. (12 + 110)/2 = 61 (mean)
61 · 15 = 915 (sum)
b. Knowing that the common difference is -2 makes it possible to figure out that there are 12 terms.
(-11 + -33)/2 = -22 (mean)
-22 · 12 = -264 (sum)
c. Knowing that the difference between consecutive terms is 5 makes it possible to find the last term by adding 5 to -14 forty times, i.e. -14 + 5(40) = 186. Then find the mean (86) and the sum (3526) as above.
d. Find the last term: 7 + (-1.4)7 = -2.8. Then find the mean (2.1) and the sum (16.8) using the method above.

12. a. mean: $(b + 5)/2$
sum: $[(b + 5) \cdot 6]/2$
b. mean: $(b + f)/2$
sum: $[(b + f) \cdot 10]/2$
c. mean: $(b + f)/2$
sum: $[(b + f) \cdot n]/2$
d. mean: $[b + b + (n - 1)d]/2$
sum: $[b + b + (n - 1)d] \cdot n/2$
Simplifying:
mean: $[2b + (n - 1)d]/2$
sum: $[2b + (n - 1)d] \cdot n/2$

13. a. 62 b. $35 + (n - 1) \cdot 3$

14. a. There are 35 seats in the first row. The 26th row has 35 + (26 − 1) · 3 seats, or 110 seats. The total is [(35 + 110) · 26]/2 , or 1885 seats.
b. $[35 + 35 + (n - 1) \cdot 3] \cdot n/2 = [70 + (n - 1) \cdot 3] \cdot n/2$ seats

15. The answers to 13 (a) and (b) would be 1 seat less. The answer to 14 (a) would be 26 seats less and to 14 (b) would be *n* seats less.

16. 13(a) would be 9 seats less. 13 (b) would be $n - 1$ seats less. 14 (a) would be (1 + 2 + 3 + 4 + 5 + ... 25) = 325 seats less. 14(b) would be $(1 + 2 + 3 + (n - 1)) = n(n - 1)/2$ seats less.

LESSON

5.12 Smooth Moves

You will need:

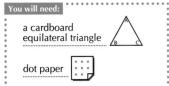

a cardboard equilateral triangle 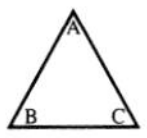

dot paper 

FLIPS AND TURNS

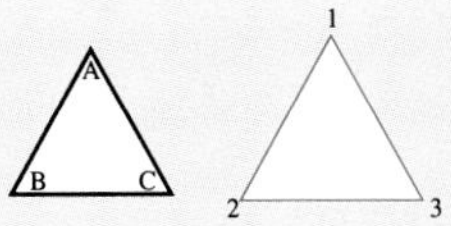

1. a. Write the letters A, B, and C on your triangle, near the vertices. Make sure the same letter appears on both sides of the cardboard at each vertex.

b. Outline the triangle on a piece of paper, and write the numbers 1, 2, and 3 outside the outline, as in the figure.

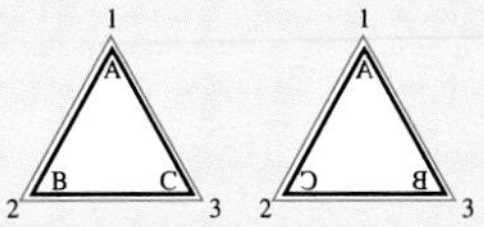

There are several different ways you can place the triangle on its outline. The two ways shown in the figure can be written ABC and ACB. ABC is called the *home position.*

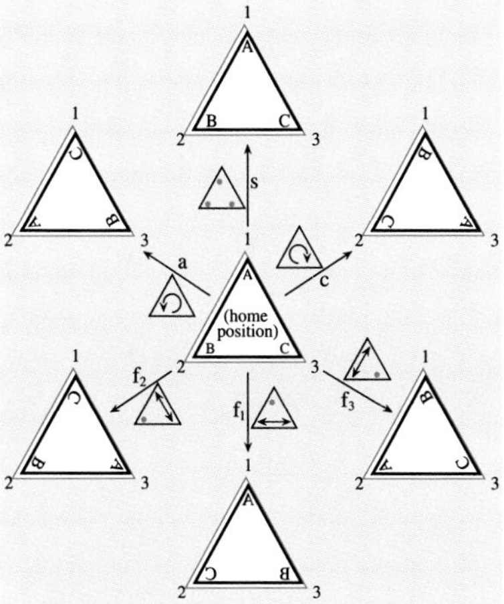

• means *this corner does not move.*

As you can see on the figure, you can get from the home position to each other position by using one of the following moves.

Turns:

- the clockwise turn (abbreviation: *c*)
- the counterclockwise turn (abbreviation: *a* — short for *anticlockwise*)

To do the turns (also called *rotations*), you do not lift the triangle off the page. You turn it until the triangle fits into the outline again.

5.12 Smooth Moves

Core Sequence: none of the lesson

Suitable for Homework: 5-15

Useful for Assessment: 8-9, 11-14

What this Lesson is About:

- Symmetry
- Abstract algebra
- Identity and inverse elements
- Using algebraic notation to represent varied mathematical structures

This lesson provides the geometry connection for this chapter, taking the place of the usual geoboard lesson.

The **Magic Carpets** section is shorter and requires less in the way of materials, so you may want to do it even if you skip the work on triangle symmetry.

5.12 SOLUTIONS

1. No answer is needed.

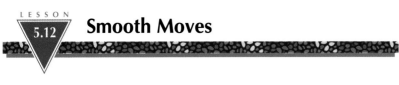

FLIPS AND TURNS

THE ALGEBRA OF MOVES

It is important for the triangles to be made of some kind of stiff cardboard. Paper will not work nearly as well. Having a class set of ready-made triangles will save some fussing. If you plan to assign homework from these sections, students will have to make their own triangles.

Patterns for the triangles can be found in the back of this book.

To make sure everyone understands how to do moves in succession, you may want to have all students do the example, and perhaps other problems like it at the same time. Make sure everyone gets to the same endpoint. The most common mistake is in executing f_2 and f_3, which students often confuse with f_1.

In problem 8, you may want to demonstrate how to fill one or two cells of the table, taking care to emphasize which move is done first and which is done next. To yield a correct table, this must be done consistently throughout.

Flips:

There are three flips. To do a flip you keep one corner in place and have the other two switch positions. For example, for flip 2 (f_2), you keep corner 2 fixed, and corners 1 and 3 switch positions. (Flips are also called *reflections.*)

Stay:

the *move* that does not move (abbreviation: s)

2. Which corner stays fixed and which changes position
 a. for flip 3 (f_3)?
 b. for flip 1 (f_1)?

Practice the turns and flips, making sure you know what each one does. In this lesson, you will have to execute turns and flips in succession, without going back to the home position in between.

> **Example:** Do f_1, then a. (Such a sequence is simply written f_1a.) If you start at the home position, and do these moves in order, you will end up in the position BAC. (Try it.) But since you could have ended up there *in one move* (f_3), you can write: $f_1a = f_3$.

3. Find out whether $af_1 = f_3$

4. Simplify. That is, give the one move that has the same result as the given sequence of moves.
 a. aa b. f_1f_3 c. f_3f_1
 d. sf_2 e. ac f. ca

5. Simplify.
 a. $f_1f_2f_3$ b. $af_1af_2af_3$
 c. $f_1af_2af_3a$ d. $cf_1cf_2cf_3$

6. Figure out a way to write each of the six moves in terms of only f_1 and c.

7. Fill in the blanks.
 a. a ___ $= f_1$ b. ___ $a = f_1$
 c. f_1 ___ $= f_2$ d. ___ $f_1 = c$

THE ALGEBRA OF MOVES

Executing moves in order is an *operation* on triangle moves, just as multiplication is an operation on numbers. The set of six moves, together with this operation, is called the *symmetry group* for the triangle.

8. Make a *multiplication table* for triangle moves. That is, figure out the one move that has the same result as doing the two given moves. Describe any interesting patterns you find in the finished table.

Then...

First...	s	a	c	f_1	f_2	f_3
s	—	—	—	—	—	—
a	—	—	—	f_3	—	—
c	—	—	—	—	—	—
f_1	—	—	—	—	—	—
f_2	—	—	—	—	—	—
f_3	—	—	—	—	—	—

9. For each of the six moves, what move *undoes* it?

Executing one move (or sequence) repeatedly can be written with *power notation.* For example, f_2^7 means *execute f_2 seven times.*

10. Simplify.
 a. a^{999} b. c^{1000}
 c. f_2^{1000} d. $(af_2)^{1001}$

11. **Project** What flips and turns are possible for another figure, like a rectangle or a square? Write a report on the symmetry group for that figure.

5.12 SOLUTIONS

2. a. Corner C stays fixed while A and B change positions.
 b. Corner A stays fixed while B and C change positions.

3. $f_1 \neq f_3$

4. a. $aa = c$
 b. $f_1f_3 = a$
 c. $f_3f_1 = c$
 d. $sf_2 = f_2$
 e. $ac = s$
 f. $ca = s$

5. a. $f_1f_2f_3 = f_2$
 b. $af_1af_2af_3 = f_3$
 c. $f_1af_2af_3a = f_1$
 d. $cf_1cf_2cf_3 = f_1$

6. $s = f_1f_1$ or ccc or f_1cccf_1
 $a = cc$
 $c = c$
 $f_1 = f_1$
 $f_2 = f_1c$
 $f_3 = cf_1$

7. a. af_3 ___ $= f_1$ b. _f_2_ $a = f_1$
 c. f_1 _c_ $= f_2$ d. _f_3_ $f_1 = c$

8.

	s	a	c	f_1	f_2	f_3
s	s	a	c	f_1	f_2	f_3
a	a	c	s	f_2	f_3	f_1
c	c	s	a	f_3	f_1	f_2
f_1	f_1	f_3	f_2	s	c	a
f_2	f_2	f_1	f_3	a	s	c
f_3	f_3	f_2	f_1	c	a	s

9. s undoes s
 c undoes a
 a undoes c
 f_1 undoes f_1
 f_2 undoes f_2
 f_3 undoes f_3

10. a. $a^{999} = s$
 b. $c^{1000} = c$
 c. $f_2^{1000} = s$
 d. $(af_2)^{1001} = f_3$

11. Answers will vary. A rectangle has four symmetries: s, half turn, f_1, and f_3. A square has four line symmetries (f_1, f_2, f_3, f_4), three rotational symmetries (90, 180, and 270-degree turns around the center of the figure), and the s symmetry.

DISCOVERY MAGIC CARPETS

Imagine that you can travel from dot to dot on dot paper, using magic carpets such as the ones illustrated in this figure. Carpets cost only $1, plus $1000 per arrow.

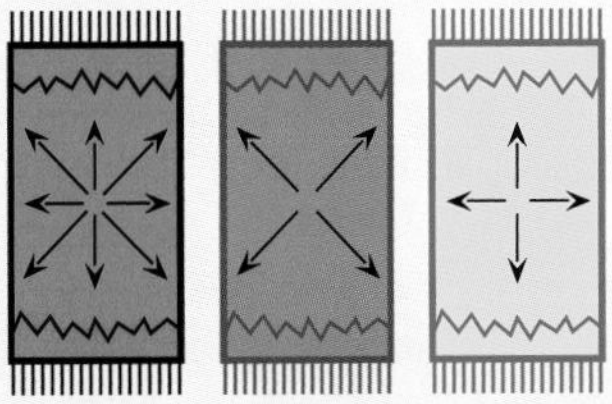

De Luxe	Model X	Carpet Plus
$8001	$4001	$4001

Magic carpets move in carpet steps. Each step takes the carpet and its riders to the next dot in the direction of one of the carpet's arrows. Each step takes one second. Carpets do not turn, so that the Carpet Plus cannot move diagonally, and the Model X cannot move horizontally or vertically.

Say you want to go from the origin to (6, 4). Here is a way to get there on each of the three carpets shown.

De Luxe: → → ↗ ↗ ↗ ↗

Model X: ↗ ↗ ↗ ↗ ↗ ↘

Carpet Plus: → → → → → → ↑ ↑ ↑ ↑

12. Find another way to get to (6, 4) on each of the three carpets.

13. Compare the advantages and shortcomings of the three carpets. Keep in mind cost, speed, and ability to reach any dot.

14. Project

a. Experiment with various $3001 carpets. What are the advantages and shortcomings of each design? Again, keep in mind cost, speed, and ability to reach any dot. Give a full explanation of your findings.

b. Repeat part (a) for $5001 carpets.

Using the directions North, East, West, and South instead of the arrows, the three examples given above could be written:

De Luxe — E E (NE) (NE) (NE) (NE)
Model X — (NE) (NE) (NE) (NE) (NE) (SE)
Carpet Plus — E E E E E E N N N N,

or even:

De Luxe — $E^2\,(NE)^4$
Model X — $(NE)^5\,(SE)$
Carpet Plus — $E^6\,N^4$.

Since all three paths lead to the same place, we can write:

$$E^2\,(NE)^4 = (NE)^5\,(SE) = E^6\,N^4.$$

In a sense, the last expression is the simplest.

15. What are the rules that allow you to simplify expressions using the N, E, W, S notation? Explain.

DISCOVERY MAGIC CARPETS

Model X is faster than Carpet Plus, but it can reach only half of the dots. It is interesting that there is a 3-arrow carpet that will get to all the dots. (However, it is slow in certain directions.)

In problem 15, the rules can be expressed in a way similar to the rules for the Letter String groups of Chapter 4, **Thinking/ Writing 4.C**.

Parentheses can be removed.
The commutative law
NS or SN can be removed.
EW or WE can be removed.

5.12 SOLUTIONS

12. Answers will vary. Sample:

De Luxe: ↗ ↘ ↗ ↗ ↗ ↗

Model X: ↘ ↗ ↗ ↗ ↗ ↗

Carpet Plus: → ↑ → ↑ → ↑ → ↑ → →

13. De Luxe: Advantage: It can reach every dot. It's the fastest of all three models.
Disadvantage: It's the most expensive.

Model X: Advantage: It is cheaper than the De Luxe. The dots it can reach take the same amount of time as the De Luxe model, so it is faster than the Carpet Plus.
Disadvantage: It cannot reach all the dots.

Carpet Plus: Advantage: It can reach every dot and is cheaper than the De Luxe.
Disadvantage: It is the slowest of all three carpets.

14. Answers will vary.

15. Moving North one space is the same as moving the opposite of South one space, thus we can write the equality $N = S^{-1}$ which indicates this relationship. So for example, if we want to simplify the following relationship, we can use this inverse relationship: $N^2S = N^2N^{-1} = NNN^{-1} = N$.

THINKING WRITING 5.C Sequences as Functions

Core Sequence: 1-13

Suitable for Homework: 5-13

Useful for Assessment: 13

What this Assignment is About:

- Preview of geometric sequences
- Review of arithmetic sequences
- Linear, quadratic, and exponential functions and their graphs
- Preview of slope

This assignment is intended to focus students' attention on a functional interpretation of sequences. In particular, students should see that arithmetic sequences correspond to linear functions.

You can demonstrate how to graph sequences by putting n on the x-axis and t_n on the y-axis, as was done in Lesson 10.

The mystery sequences in problem 11 are quadratic. Other examples can be found in Lesson 10, problems 3, 5, and 12. The numerical pattern that relates consecutive terms in such sequences can be expressed in various ways. One way is to state that the differences between consecutive terms form an arithmetic sequence.

The common difference is visible in the graphs of arithmetic sequences as the *rise* between consecutive points. This previews slope, which is covered formally in Chapter 8.

THINKING WRITING 5.C Sequences as Functions

A sequence can be thought of as a function. The input numbers are the natural numbers, and the output numbers are the terms. In this assignment, we will study sequences as functions.

Definition: In a *geometric sequence,* each term is obtained from the previous term by multiplying by a constant amount, the *common ratio.*

Examples: These are geometric sequences.
2, 10, 50, 250, 1250
3, 1, 1/3, 1/9, 1/27

For each of the following:

a. Tell whether the sequence is geometric, arithmetic, or neither.

b. If it is arithmetic, find the common difference. If it is geometric, find the common ratio.

1. 5, 1, -3, -7, -11 **2.** -7, 2, 11, 20, 29

3. 1, 1, 2, 3, 5, 8 **4.** 6, 3, 3/2, 3/4, 3/8

5. 25, 5, 1, 1/5, 1/25

6. 1/2, 3/4, 7/8, 5/16, 31/32, 63/64

7. Find the final term of each sequence.

a. a geometric sequence having five terms, common ratio 2, and first term 6

b. an arithmetic sequence having six terms, common difference 9, and first term -4

8. Find the first term of each sequence.

a. an arithmetic sequence having 10 terms, common difference 7, and last term -3

b. a geometric sequence having eight terms, common ratio 1/2, and last term 1/4

9. Graph these arithmetic sequences by graphing the term number (n) on the horizontal axis and the term (t_n) on the vertical axis.

a. 2, -4, -10, -16, -22

b. 2, 8, 14, 20, 26

c. -5, -11, -17, -23, -29

10. Graph these geometric sequences.

a. 2, 6, 12, 24, 48

b. 3, 3/2, 3/4, 3/8, 3/16

c. 1/8, 1/4, 1/2, 1, 2

11. These *mystery sequences* are neither geometric nor arithmetic. Graph them.

a. 5, 8, 13, 20, 29, 40, 53, 68

b. 7, 13, 23, 37, 55

c. -2, 7, 22, 43, 70

12. By looking at the graphs in problem 11, one might think that the sequences are geometric, but it is clear from looking at the numbers that there is no common ratio. However, the numbers do have a special pattern. Find the pattern and describe it.

13. Report Write a report about what you discovered about graphs of arithmetic sequences, geometric sequences, and the mystery sequences in problem 11. Illustrate your report with examples. Your report should include, but not be limited to, answers to the following questions:

- Which sequences have graphs that are straight lines? Which have graphs that are curved? How are the two kinds of curved graphs different?
- For arithmetic sequences, how does the common difference show up in each graph?
- For geometric sequences, what difference does it make in the graph if the common ratio is greater or less than 1?
- What are the graphs of the mystery sequences called?

5.C SOLUTIONS

1. arithmetic sequence, common difference -4
2. arithmetic sequence, common difference 9
3. neither
4. geometric sequence, common ratio 1/2
5. geometric sequence, common ratio 1/5
6. neither
7. a. Multiplying each term by 2 to get the next term gives the sequence 6, 12, 24, 48, 96, so the final term is 96.
   b. Adding 9 to each term to get the next term gives the sequence -4, 5, 14, 23, 32, 41, so the final term is 41.
8. a. -66
   b. 32
9. a.

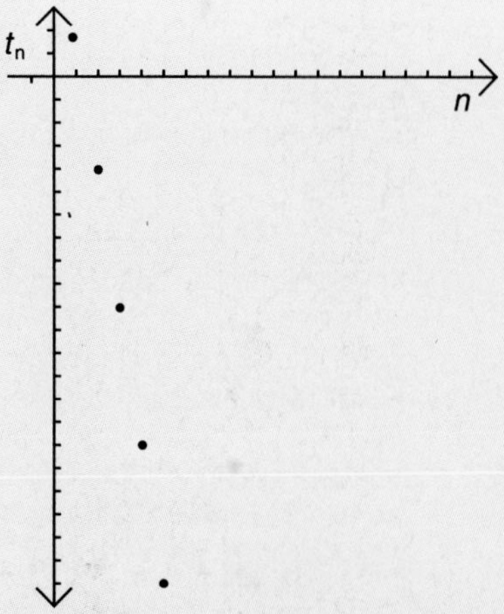

b.

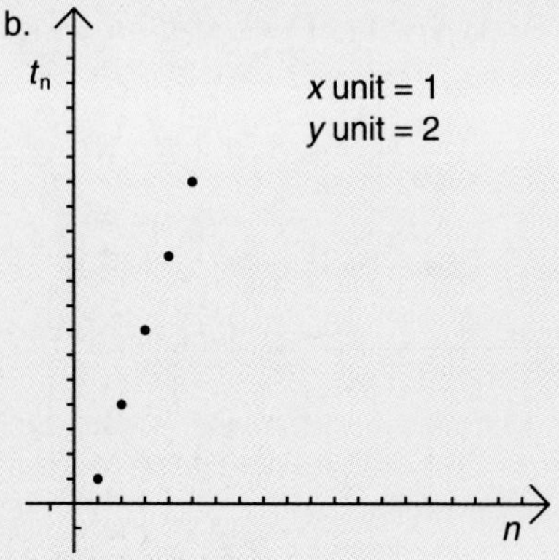

(Solutions continued on page 518)

Essential Ideas

CONSTANT SUMS AND PRODUCTS

1. If possible, write an equation of the form $x + y = S$ such that the graph of the equation
a. lies in the 2nd, 3rd, and 4th quadrants;
b. lies in the 1st, 2nd, and 3rd quadrants;
c. passes through the origin;
d. intersects the x-axis at (-7, 0);
e. contains the point (12, -3.25).

2. A graph has an equation of the form $x + y = S$. Find two more points on the graph if:
a. the point (-3, -5.8) is on the graph;
b. the graph has x-intercept (1/2, 0);
c. the graph has y-intercept (0, -6.5).

3. If possible, write an equation of the form $x \cdot y = P$ such that the graph of the equation
a. lies in the 2nd and 4th quadrants;
b. contains the point (-9, 1/2);
c. passes through (-2.5, -3.5);
d. intersects the graph of $x + y = 16$ at the point (10, 6);
e. passes through the origin.

4. Write one equation of the form $x + y = S$ and one of the form $x \cdot y = P$ such that
a. neither graph passes through the first quadrant;
b. the two graphs intersect at (8, 4) and (4, 8).

THE DISTRIBUTIVE LAW

5. Write an equivalent expression without parentheses. Combine like terms.
a. $2 \cdot (3 + x)$
b. $2 \cdot (3x)$
c. $(6x + 3)(2x - 4)$
d. $(6x \cdot 3)(2x - 4)$
e. $(6x \cdot 3)(2x \cdot 4)$

6. In which part of problem 5 did you use the distributive law to remove parentheses? Explain.

7. Write equivalent expressions without the parentheses. Combine like terms.
a. $-2(9 + x) - x(2 - x)$
b. $-2(9) + x - x(2 - x)$
c. $-2(9 + x) - 2x - x$
d. $-2(9) + x(-2x) - x$

8. In which parts of problem 7 did you use the distributive law to remove parentheses? Explain.

9. Write without parentheses. Combine like terms.
a. $(x + 3)(x + 5)$
b. $(x + 3)(x - 5)$
c. $(x - 3)(x - 5)$
d. $(x - 3)(x + 5)$

10. Divide.
a. $\frac{6y^2 + 4xy}{2y}$
b. $\frac{4x + 4}{4}$

FACTORING

11. Multiply $(2x - 7)(3x + 5)$.

12. Factor $6x^2 - 11x - 35$.

13. a. Fill in the blank with a whole number so that the trinomial $x^2 + 9x +$ __ can be factored as a product of binomials. Write the factored form.
b. How many different integer answers are there for part (a)? Find all of them. (Don't forget negative integers.)

14. a. Fill in the blank with an integer so that the trinomial $x^2 +$ __$x + 18$ can be factored as a product of binomials. Write the factored form.

SOLUTIONS

1. a. Answers will vary. The value of S must be negative.
   b. Answers will vary. The value of S must be positive.
   c. $x + y = 0$.
   d. $x + y = -7$
   e. $x + y = 8.75$
2. Answers will vary. One possibility for each is given.
   a. (-8, -0.8) (-4.4, -4.4)
   b. (1/4, 1/4), (0, 1/2)
   c. (-6.5, 0), (-6, -0.5)
3. a. Answers will vary. P must be negative.
   b. $xy = -4.5$
   c. $xy = 8.75$
   d. $xy = 60$
   e. $xy = 0$
4. a. Answers will vary. P and S must both be negative.
   b. $x + y = 12$ and $xy = 32$
5. a. $6 + 2x$
   b. $6x$
   c. $12x^2 - 18x - 12$
   d. $36x^2 - 72x$
   e. $144x^2$
6. It was used in parts (a), (c), and (d). The distributive law requires two operations, so it was not used in the problems containing only multiplication. In (c), it was used twice.
7. a. $-18 - 4x + x^2$
   b. $-18 - x + x^2$
   c. $-18 - 5x$
   d. $-18 - 2x^2 - x$
8. It is used in all except (d). The distributive law is not required to remove the parentheses in (d) because only multiplication is involved.
9. a. $x^2 + 8x + 15$
   b. $x^2 - 2x - 15$
   c. $x^2 - 8x + 15$
   d. $x^2 + 2x - 15$
10. a. $3y + 2x$
    b. $x + 1$
11. $6x^2 - 11x - 35$
12. $(2x - 7)(3x + 5)$
13. a. Answers will vary.
    b. There is an infinite number of possibilities, so it is not possible to find all of them.
14. a. Answers will vary.
    b. The following integer answers are possible: 19, 11, 9, -9, -11, -19.

b. How many different integer answers are there for part (a)? Find all of them. (Don't forget negative integers.)

15. Factor completely.

a. $(2x + 8)(x^2 + 2x)$

b. $2yx^2 + 12yx + 16y$

c. $x^3 + 6x^2 + 8x$

16. How many x-intercepts does each parabola have? Explain.

a. $y = x^2 + 12x + 20$

b. $y = x^2 + 12x + 36$

c. $y = x^2 + 12x + 49$

d. $y = x^2 - 12x + 36$

17. In problem 16, find the coordinates of:

a. the y-intercept;

b. the x-intercept(s), if any;

c. the vertex.

SEQUENCES

18. If you were to plot these sequences (with n on one axis and t_n on the other axis), for which one(s) would the points lie in a straight line? Explain how you know.

a. 3, 3.5, 4.5, 5.5, 6.5

b. -1, -10, -19, -28, -37, -46

c. 1/2, 1/4, 1/8, 1/16, 1/32

d. 4, 7, 11, 16, 22, 29

PYRAMIDS

A pyramid is made by stacking rows of blue, red, and yellow blocks. There are 100 blocks in the bottom (first) row, 98 in the next row, and so on, with 2 fewer blocks in each successive row. The bottom row is blue, the next row is red, the third row is yellow, and so on, continuing the pattern.

19. Make a sketch or schematic drawing of what you think the pyramid might look like. Write about any patterns you notice.

20. How many rows of blocks are there?

21. How many rows of each color are there?

22. How many blocks are in the 10th row? 11th row? n^{th} row? Top row?

23. What color is the 10th row? What color is the top row?

24. There are 30 blocks in a row. Which row is it?

25. Given the number of a row (5th, 10th, 20th, etc.) can you give its color? Explain the pattern.

26. Given the number of blocks in a row, can you give its color? Explain the pattern.

27. How many blocks in all are needed to build the pyramid?

28. How would your answers to questions 19-27 be different if there were 50 blocks in the bottom row?

29. Suppose four colors were used instead of three. Would any of your answers to problems 19-27 be different? Explain.

30. Report Summarize and explain the patterns you noticed in the above problems. What generalizations can you make?

SOLUTIONS

15. a. $2x(x + 4)(x + 2)$
b. $2y(x + 2)(x + 4)$
c. $x(x + 4)(x + 2)$

16. a. two, because there are two distinct factors, $(x + 10)$ and $(x + 2)$
b. one, because the two factors are the same, $(x + 6)$ and $(x + 6)$
c. none, because $49 > 36$
d. one, because the two factors are the same, $(x - 6)$ and $(x - 6)$

17. a. x-intercepts: -10 and -2; y-intercept: 20; vertex: (-6, -16)
b. x-intercept: -6; y-intercept: 36; vertex: (-6, 0)
c. x-intercepts: none; y-intercept: 49; vertex: (-6, 13)
d. x-intercept: 6; y-intercept: 36; vertex: (6, 0)

18. The only one is (b). It is an arithmetic sequence with a common difference of -9.

19. Answers will vary.

20. 50

21. 17 red, 16 yellow, and 17 blue

22. 82 in the tenth row, 80 in the eleventh row, $100 - 2(n - 1)$ in the nth row, and 2 in the top row

23. The 10th row is blue and the top row is red.

24. There are 30 blocks in the 36th row. This can be found by solving the equation $100 - 2(n - 1) = 30$.

25. Write down the row numbers of the blue rows, the red rows, and the yellow rows and look for patterns in the numbers. By looking at patterns, we can see that if the number is a term in the sequence 1, 4, 7, 10...(that is, $3n + 1$), it will be blue. Likewise, red rows will be those in the sequence $3n + 2$, and yellow rows will be in the sequence $3n$ (that is, multiples of 3).

26. Yes. Use the number of blocks in a row to find its row number, as in #24. Then use the row number to find the color, using the patterns found in #25.

27. $100 + 98 + 96 + ... + 2 = (102 \cdot 50)/2 = 2550$

28. If there were 50 blocks in the bottom row, there would be 25 rows total. The relationship of color to row number described in #25-#27 would be the same, so using this we could figure out that the top row would be blue. This means that blue occurs

PRACTICE

REVIEW

THE DISTRIBUTIVE LAW

Simplify each pair of expressions.

1. a. $4 + 2[s - 6s - 1)]$
b. $(4 + 2)[s - 6(s - 1)]$

2. a. $4x - 2x[x - 6(x + 1)]$
b. $4x - x[x - 6(x + 2)]$

EQUATIONS

3. The solution to this equation is 6:
$5x - 1 = 29.$
a. Change one number in the equation so that the solution will be 5.
b. Change the coefficient of x so that the solution to the equation will be 15.

PARENTHESES

4. Simplify. Compare your answers for (a) and (b).
a. $10 - 5 - 3 + 2$
b. $10 - (5 - 3 + 2)$

5. What is the smallest number you can get by inserting parentheses in the first expression? The largest number? Explain, showing your work.

6. a. Make up an expression containing three terms whose value depends upon where the parentheses are placed. Find all the possible values.
b. Make up an expression containing three terms whose value does not depend upon where the parentheses are placed.

SOLUTIONS

(5.E.I. Solutions continued)

one more time than the other colors, so there are 8 yellow, 8 red, and 9 blue rows. To figure out the number of blocks in the nth row, we would use the expression $50 - 2(n - 1)$ instead of $100 - 2(n - 1)$. Likewise, given the number of blocks in a row, say 30, we would solve the equation $50 - 2(n - 1) = 30$. There are almost 4 times as many blocks in the first pyramid. The number of blocks in this pyramid is $(50 + 48 + ... + 2) = (52 \cdot 25)/2 = 650$.

29. This would not affect the answers to #20, #22, #24, or #27. However, the color pattern would obviously change. Let's assume the fourth color is purple. Blue rows would be those in the sequence $4n + 1$, red rows would be those in the sequence $4n + 2$, yellow rows in the sequence $4n + 3$, and purple rows in the sequence $4n$. For example, the 36th row would be purple because 36 is a multiple of 4. The top (50th) row would be red, since it is two more than a multiple of 4. Hence blue and red would appear one more time than yellow and purple, so there would be 12 yellow, 12 purple, 13 red, and 13 blue rows.

30. Reports will vary.

1. a. $2 - 10s$
   b. $-30s + 36$
2. a. $10x^2 + 16x$
   b. $5x^2 + 16x$
3. a. Answers may vary. Possible answer: $5x - 1 = 24$
   b. $2x - 1 = 29$
4. a. 4
   b. 6
5. $10 - 5 - (3 + 2) = 0$
   $10 - (5 - 3) + 2 = 10$
6. a. Answers will vary.
   b. Answers will vary.

Chapter 6
Making Comparisons

Overview of the Chapter

In the context of making comparisons, students solve linear equations, work with rational expressions, and explore some ideas about similarity. The theme of comparisons is explored in several real-world contexts, and the difference between comparing by differences and comparing by ratios is introduced.

Equations are contrasted with identities. The main algebraic focus is on developing skill in equation solving, using several substantially different approaches; tables, graphs, and symbol manipulation are developed as methods for solving equations and inequalities. Through work with the Lab Gear, standard techniques are developed for solving equations by symbol manipulation.

In previous chapters, students have learned how to solve equations using trial and error and the cover-up method. They will begin to see the limitations of these methods as their skill with more effective techniques improves, but you should not discourage them from using these methods. There are many opportunities in this chapter for comparing methods of solving equations, and you should encourage discussion of this.

1. New Uses for Tools:

- The Lab Gear for solving equations
- Graphs and tables for solving equations and inequalities
- The multiplication table format to divide by a monomial

2. Algebra Concepts Emphasized:

- Expressing numerical relationships with variables
- Writing equations
- Solving linear equations
- Equations and identities
- Equations with no solutions
- Adding and subtracting the same amount to both sides of an equation
- Two ways of comparing quantities: ratio and differences
- Proportional thinking
- Multiplying and dividing both sides of an equation by the same amount
- Solving for one variable in terms of another
- Chunking
- Equivalent equations in two variables
- The use of parameters

3. Algebra Concepts Reviewed:

- Order of operations
- Applying linear functions, equations, and inequalities
- Using tables and graphs
- The meaning of inequalities
- The distributive law
- Substitution
- Division by a monomial
- Direct variation
- Signed number arithmetic
- Averages, ratios, percents
- Geoboard area

4. Algebra Concepts Previewed:

- Solving inequalities
- Solving quadratic equations
- Graphing linear equations
- Slope
- Square roots
- Rules for solving inequalities
- Completing the square

5. Problem-Solving Techniques:

- Using variables, equations, and graphs
- Using tables
- Systematic search
- Reducing a problem to an easier version

CHAPTER 6

The outward spiral path of a spider web

Coming in this chapter:

Exploration A movie discount card, valid for three months, costs $\$T$. With the card, it costs only $\$D$ to attend a movie, instead of \$5. How many movies would you have to see in three months in order to save money with the discount card? Does your answer depend on T, D, or on both?

Making Comparisons

6. Connections and Context:

- Applications of linear functions and equations
- Mathematics as a tool for decision-making
- Equations with whole number solutions
- Visualizing quantitative information
- Mathematics in literature
- Preview of the Pythagorean theorem

Equation Solving with the Lab Gear

Most of Lessons 2-9 involves the Lab Gear, though none of them for the entire lesson. You can follow the lessons in the order they are given, emphasizing Lab Gear work in class and other work at home, or you can combine the Lab Gear work of consecutive lessons in order to reduce the number of times you take out the blocks.

In any case, the work on inequality and equation solving using the workmat should follow this general scheme.

A. Use the blocks to solve the problem.Record the answer.

B. Write the original equation (translated from the picture). Record the answer.

C. Write the original equation. At several points in the process, record what is on the mat. (One student can manipulate the blocks, and another one can take a "snapshot" of the workmat when there is a pause. For the next problem, the roles are switched.) Record the final answer.

D. Write the original equation. Record what you do at each step. (Again, working in pairs is helpful. To demonstrate, have one student work with the blocks on the overhead while another records each step on the chalkboard.) Record the final answer.

E. Analyze the record of what you did at each step. (At this point, some students will begin to generalize, and will rely much less on the blocks.)

F. Have one student work with the blocks, and the other without. Compare answers. Switch roles for the next problem.

These instructions are more or less the ones given in the Lab Gear problems in this chapter, but you should use your judgment in deciding where in this progression your class is at any particular time and modify the instructions accordingly. Remember that the point of the work with the Lab Gear is to help the students get to the point eventually where they understand algebra well enough to be able to manage without the blocks.

Educational research shows that it is the process of translating work with manipulatives into work without them which is the most productive in helping students learn mathematics. Completely disembodied, abstract work is not effective with most students. On the other hand, work with manipulatives will usually engage students, but discussion to help facilitate transfer to a more abstract level is essential.

One way to facilitate this transfer is to keep track of shortcuts and rules the students discover when simplifying expressions and solving equations on the workmat. These Lab Gear Rules can be named after the students who discover them and written on a large piece of butcher paper on the bulletin board. Later you can discuss with the class what the corresponding Algebra Rules are and write those on another piece of paper.

▼ 6.1 Comparing Car Rentals

Core Sequence: 1-15

Suitable for Homework: 5-18

Useful for Assessment: 7, 11-12, 14

What this Lesson is About:

- Applying linear functions, equations, and inequalities
- Using tables and graphs
- Mathematics as a tool for decision-making

While an individual is not likely to do all the work in this lesson before deciding on a car rental company, this sort of analysis would be very important to a large organization before making a decision about making purchases or signing a contract with one or another supplier. The concepts needed would be similar to what's outlined here, though the scale of the expense, the complexity of the data, and the tools used would differ.

You may discuss with your students how the problem has been simplified for inclusion in an algebra text. For example, what about differences among cars? The cost of gasoline? Insurance? It is as important to know the limitations of one's mathematical analysis, and to acknowledge its assumptions, as to do the analysis correctly.

LESSON 6.1

Comparing Car Rentals

You will need: graph paper

This table gives the results of a phone survey of the cost of renting a mid-size car in a large city.

Company	Daily rate	"Free" miles	Cost per additional mile
A	$34.99	150 miles	24 cents
B	$26.95	100 miles	30 cents
C	$39.95	100 miles	30 cents
D	$41.95	unlimited mileage	—
E	$27.99	unlimited mileage	—

1. **Exploration** Suppose you wanted to rent a car for a short trip and you had the information in the table. There is one car that is clearly the "best deal" in most cases. Which car is this? If this car were not available, how would you decide which car to rent? Write a paragraph explaining how you would decide. Include the following:
   - What things would you consider?
   - Show any calculations you would need to do to make your decision.
   - Is there any additional information not included in the table that you think you would need to know?

USING TABLES

2. Which car do you think would be the best deal if you planned to drive a short distance? Which car would you rent to drive several hundred miles? Explain.

This table gives the cost of renting each car for one day to drive the indicated number of miles.

3. Copy and complete the table, indicating how much it would cost to rent each car for the given miles.

Total Cost of Car Rental

Company	Miles driven				
	50	100	150	200	250
A	34.99	34.99	34.99	46.99	58.99
B	26.95	26.95	41.95	56.95	—
C	—	—	—	—	—
D	—	—	—	—	—
E	—	—	—	—	—

4. Copy and complete the next table. It ranks each car according to the amount it would cost to rent it to drive the given number of miles. The code is **1** for least expensive and **5** for most expensive.

6.1 SOLUTIONS

1. Company E is clearly the "best deal." Student solutions will vary and should include the number of days the car is to be rented. Renters may need to know if there are any costs for dropping the car off in a place other than the city of origin, the minimum age requirements for drivers, and any required insurance coverage.
2. Company B is best for a one-day trip of 100 miles or less. Company E is best for a one-day trip of 150 miles, and Company E is best for a one-day trip of 300 miles. Company B has a lower rate than all the other companies, but it becomes more expensive if you drive over 100 miles, whereas Company E has a relatively low daily rate and unlimited mileage.
3.

TOTAL COST OF CAR RENTAL

Company	Miles Driven				
	50	100	150	200	250
A	34.99	34.99	34.99	46.99	58.99
B	26.95	26.95	41.95	56.95	71.95
C	39.95	39.95	54.95	69.95	84.95
D	41.95	41.95	41.95	41.95	41.95
E	27.99	27.99	27.99	27.99	27.99

4.

COMPANY RANKINGS

Company	Miles Driven				
	50	100	150	200	250
A	3	3	2	3	3
B	1	1	3	4	4
C	4	4	4	5	5
D	5	5	3	2	2
E	2	2	1	1	1

Company Rankings

Company	Miles driven				
	50	100	150	200	250
A	3	—	—	—	—
B	1	—	—	—	—
C	4	—	—	—	—
D	5	—	—	—	—
E	2	—	—	—	—

5. In the table you just completed, you can see that B is less expensive than A for 50 miles and 100 miles of travel, but this is reversed for 150 miles of travel.
   a. Which is less expensive for 125 miles of travel?
   b. Show that the costs of A and B are almost exactly the same for 130 miles of travel.

USING GRAPHS

6. The graph above problem 7 shows, for a single day of rental, how the cost of renting a car from Company A varies as a function of the number of miles driven.
   a. Make an enlarged copy of the graph on your own paper.
   b. Add to the same grid a similar graph for each of the other four companies. Your graphs must be accurate.

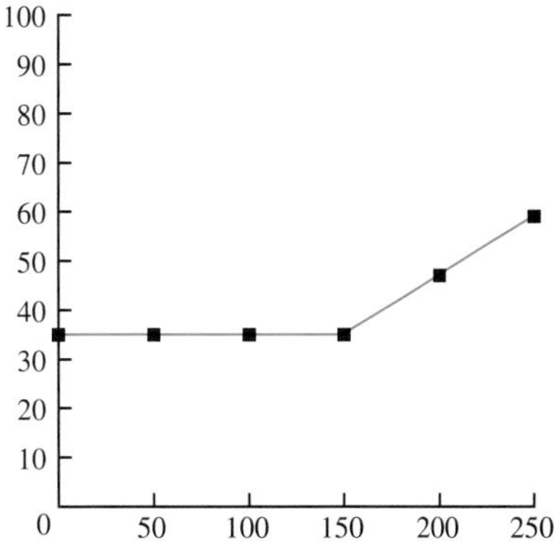

7. Two of the graphs should be horizontal lines. Which ones, and why?

8. According to your graphs, if you plan to drive 100 miles or less,
   a. which company is the most expensive?
   b. which company is the least expensive?

9. Company A has a higher daily rate and lower mileage costs than Company B.
   a. Which of the two is more expensive for someone who travels 100 miles?
   b. Which is more expensive for someone who travels 150 miles?
   c. For what length trip is the cost of the two the same?

10. Company D has a slightly higher daily rate than Company C, but its mileage costs are zero.
   a. For what length trip is D cheaper?
   b. For what length trip are they the same?

USING TABLES

*T*his should not present any major intellectual obstacles at this point, but since the work can be tedious, students should team up.

USING GRAPHS

USING EQUATIONS

*L*ooking at functions that have different parts actually helps throw light on the relationship between points in tables and points on graphs.

*P*roblems 14-15 deserve a full discussion in class, even if you assign them as homework. In the discussion, talk about the role of each symbol in the equation.

*I*n a way this is the most important part of the lesson. Being able to write an equation like these will allow someone to use a graphing calculator or spreadsheet to investigate questions like the ones discussed in this lesson. However, it is only after doing lessons like this one that students develop enough feel for what is going on to be able to write the equations. The goal, of course, is to get to the point where the student can write the equation without having to make tables and graphs. For most students that is not possible at the beginning of first-year algebra, but by the end of the year, they should be much closer to that level of understanding.

6.1 SOLUTIONS

5. a. For 125 miles, Company B is less expensive than Company A.
   b. For 130 miles Company A costs \$34.99. Company B costs 26.95 + 0.3(30) = \$35.95

6. a., b.
11. a., b.

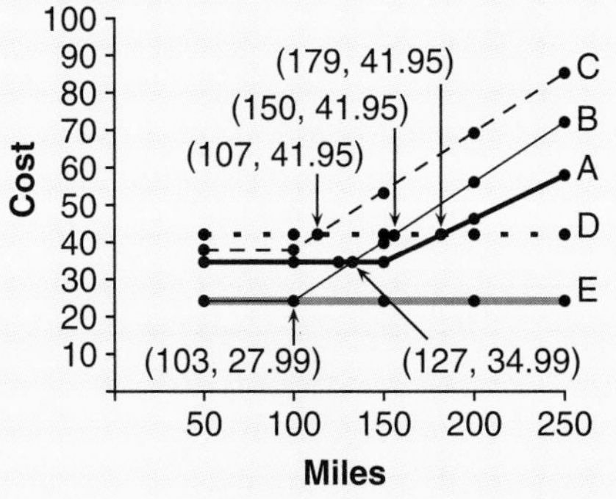

7. The graphs for companies D and E are horizontal because the cost for each does not change when the mileage changes from 50 to 250.

8. a. For 100 miles or less Company D is most expensive.
   b. For 100 miles or less Company B is least expensive.

9. a. Company A is more expensive than Company B for a 100-mile trip.
   b. Company B is more expensive than Company A for a 150-mile trip.
   c. The cost for Company A equals the cost of Company B for a 127-mile trip.

10. a. Company D is cheaper than C for a trip of more than 107 miles.
   b. Company D and Company C are the same for a 107-mile trip.

DISCOVERY GRADE AVERAGES

*T*his is the first in a series of optional sections on averages. Students are interested in how grades are computed, and these sections give you a chance to capitalize on that interest. You can make the problems even more relevant by adding similar problems based on your own grading policy.

*T*o be continued in **Grading Policies**, after Lesson 3.

11. The graphs for B and D intersect at the point (150, 41.95).

a. Label this point of intersection on your graph.

b. Label other points of intersection on any of the other graphs.

c. How would you interpret these points of intersection in terms of cost comparisons?

12. In what ways are tables better than graphs in helping you make a decision of this type? In what ways are graphs better?

USING EQUATIONS

Equations are useful if you want to use a computer or a programmable calculator to help you analyze a problem like this one. You can write an equation for the cost of renting a car from Company A for one day as a function of the number of miles traveled. Notice that the graph has two parts: a horizontal part, and a part that slopes upward. The equation also has two parts.

If y is the cost in dollars and x is the number of miles driven, then:

$y = 34.99$ if $x \leq 150$

$y = 34.99 + 0.24(x - 150)$ if $x > 150$

13. Which part of the equation represents the horizontal part of the graph?

14. Explain every part of the second equation. (Why is 150 subtracted from x? Why are parentheses necessary? What is the meaning of the quantity in the parentheses? Why is it multiplied by 0.24? Why is the result added to 34.99? What is the meaning of the sum?)

15. Write equations for the costs of renting the other cars as a function of miles driven.

DISCOVERY GRADE AVERAGES

Mrs. Washman gives a quiz every Thursday. A student's current average at the end of any week can be computed by finding the ratio of *total correct points* to *total possible points* to date. The table shows Caden's scores.

	Q1	Q2	Q3	Q4	Q5
Correct	8	9	10	13	—
Possible	12	20	10	15	—

16. Find Caden's current average at the end of week 1, week 2, week 3, and week 4.

17. Caden found his current average by doing this computation:

$$\frac{8}{12} + \frac{9}{20} + \frac{10}{10} + \frac{13}{15} = \frac{40}{57}$$

Amiko said this was wrong because you don't add fractions by adding the numerators and adding the denominators. Who was right? Were they both right? Were they both wrong? Explain.

18. What would Caden's average be at the end of week 5 if Quiz 5 had

a. 20 points, and he got 12 correct?

b. 40 points, and he got 80% correct?

c. 25 points, and he got N correct?

6.1 SOLUTIONS

11. a. See the figure for problem #6.
 b. See the figure for problem #6.
 c. These points of intersection show the mileage for which two companies charge the same amount.

12. Answers will vary. Consider that the exact costs are easier to read on tables. Graphs show least and most expensive companies at a particular mileage other than the ones calculated on the table. Graphs also show where two or more companies charge the same amount.

13. For $x \leq 150$, \$34.99 shows the horizontal part of the graph.

14. Because \$0.24 is charged for every mile over 150, one must first calculate the number of miles in excess of 150, which is $x - 150$. This expression must be multiplied by \$0.24 to get the cost for each mile over 150. This is written $0.24(x - 150)$. Without parentheses, $0.24x - 150$, each mile travelled would cost \$0.24 and then a deduction of \$150 would be given. (This is not what the company wants to charge. For example if x were 350, $0.24(350) - 150$ would be $84 - 150 = -66$ which means the company would owe you \$66 for this part of the equation. Whereas, $0.24(350 - 150)$ is $0.24(200)$ which is a more reasonable charge of \$48 for the 200 miles in excess of 150. The daily rate of \$34.99 is added to the charge for miles in excess of 150, $0.24(x - 150)$ for the total cost, y, of driving x miles.

15. Company B: $y = \$26.95$ for $x \leq 100$.
 $y = \$26.95 + \$0.30(x - 100)$ for $x > 100$.
 Company C: $y = \$39.95$ for $x \leq 100$.
 $y = \$39.95 + \$0.30(x - 100)$ for $x > 100$.
 Company D: $y = \$41.95$
 Company E: $y = \$27.99$

16. Week 1: 0.67
 Week 2: 0.53
 Week 3: 0.64
 Week 4: 0.70

17. Amiko was correct.

18. a. 0.68
 b. 0.74
 c. $\frac{40 + N}{57 + 25}$

LESSON 6.2

Which is Greater?

You will need:

the Lab Gear 

Exploration For each problem, if possible, give one value of x that

a. makes the right side greater;
b. makes the left side greater;
c. makes the two sides equal.

Describe the method you used for each problem.

1. x ? $2x + 3$
2. $y - 2$? $-y - 2$
3. $6x$? $7x^2 + 6x - 7$

USING THE LAB GEAR

For each problem:

a. Simplify each expression.
b. Compare the two expressions. It may help to build them with the Lab Gear, one on each side of the workmat.
c. Is one side greater, or are they equal? Write the correct symbol: $>$, $<$, or $=$. If it is impossible to tell, write **?**. Remember that x is not necessarily a positive integer.

4. $x(x + 2) - 4$ $\quad$ $(x + 1)(x + 1)$
5. $(x + 1)(x + 2)$ $\quad$ $2 + 3x - x^2$
6. $3x^2 + 9 - (x^2 + 2)$ $\quad$ $3x^2 + 9 - x^2 + 2$
7. $3x^2 + 9 - (x^2 + 2x)$ $\quad$ $3x^2 + 9 - x^2 + 2x$
8. If you did not get at least one **?** as an answer in problems 4-7, check your work.

USING TABLES

For which values of x is $14x - [4x - (2 - 3x)]$ greater than $5x - 2[x - (3x + 2)]$?

These two expressions are too complicated to build with the Lab Gear. It is easier to compare them if they are simplified first. Both expressions have two sets of grouping symbols, *parentheses* and *brackets.* Brackets mean exactly the same thing as parentheses.

Rule: Simplify from the inside out, removing the parentheses first.

9. Removing parentheses, the first expression is $14x - [4x - 2 + 3x]$. Continue simplifying.
10. Removing parentheses, the second expression is $5x - 2[x - 3x - 2]$. Continue simplifying.

The table below compares the expressions $9x + 4$ and $7x + 2$ for some values of x.

x	$9x + 4$	$7x + 2$
10	94	72
5	49	37
0.1	4.9	2.7

11. Copy and extend the table.
    a. Find some values of x for which $9x + 4$ is less than $7x + 2$.
    b. Try to find a value of x for which the two expressions are equal.
    c. Describe any patterns you see in your table.

Lea and Earl were trying to compare these expressions:

Expression A: $5 - [x - (3x + 1)]$

Expression B: $5 - 3[x - (3x + 1)]$

They got different results when they simplified Expression B.

6.2 Which is Greater?

Core Sequence: 1-15, 18-27

Suitable for Homework: 9-15, 18-28

Useful for Assessment: 15, 27

What this Lesson is About:

- Review of the meaning of inequalities
- Preview of the solving of inequalities
- Systematic search

Most of this chapter concentrates on equations. Starting with inequalities helps students put equations in context. However, do not expect most students to master the algebraic solving of inequalities in this course, let alone in this lesson.

USING THE LAB GEAR

This section continues the preview of equation solving and inequalities that was begun in Chapter 3, Lesson 5, with the **Which is Greater?** Lab Gear problems.

Students will probably need some review, so you will probably want to do one of these problems, or a problem like it, as an example on the overhead.

USING TABLES

This section introduces one method of solving equations and inequalities. Work with tables will make later work on solving equations and inequalities using graphs much easier to understand. In the age of

6.2 SOLUTIONS

Answers will vary for #1-3:

1. a. Sample: $x = 0$ (any $x > -3$)
   b. Sample: $x = -4$ (any $x < -3$)
   c. $x = -3$
2. a. Sample: $y = -1$ (any $y < 0$)
   b. Sample: $y = 1$ (any $y > 0$)
   c. $y = 0$
3. a. Sample: $x = 3$ (any $x < -1$ or $x > 1$)
   b. Sample: 0 (any x: $-1 < x < 1$)
   c. $x = -1$ or $x = 1$
4. a. $x^2 + 2x - 4$, $x^2 + 2x + 1$
   b & c. $x^2 + 2x - 4 < x^2 + 2x + 1$
5. a. $x^2 + 3x + 2$, $2 + 3x - x^2$
   b & c. $2 + 3x - x^2 < x^2 + 3x + 2$
6. a. $2x^2 + 7$, $2x^2 + 11$
   b & c. $2x^2 + 7 < 2x^2 + 11$
7. a. $2x^2 - 2x + 9$, $2x^2 + 2x + 9$
   b & c. ? It is impossible to tell which is greater or smaller. When $x = 0$ they are equal. When $x > 0$, $2x^2 - 2x + 9 < 2x^2 + 2x + 9$. When $x < 0$, $2x^2 - 2x + 9 > 2x^2 + 2x + 9$.
8. #7c was a ?.
9. $14x - [4x - 2 + 3x]$
   $= 14x - [7x - 2]$
   $= 14x - 7x + 2$
   $= 7x + 2$
10. $5x - 2[x - 3x - 2]$
    $= 5x - 2[-2x - 2]$
    $= 5x + 4x + 4$
    $= 9x + 4$
11. a. Tables will vary.

x	$9x + 4$	$7x + 2$
10	94	72
5	49	37
0.1	4.9	2.7
0	4	2
-0.1	3.1	1.3
-1	-5	-5
-2	-14	-12
-3	-23	-19
-5	-41	-33
-10	-86	-68

b. $x = -1$ makes the two expressions equal.

c. Answers may vary. If $x > -1$, then $9x + 4 > 7x + 2$; if $x < -1$, then $9x + 4 < 7x + 2$.

electronic graphing, graphical solutions are of essential importance, and tables provide a necessary conceptual building block.

Comparing expressions provides a context for work on simplifying expressions in which there is more than one grouping symbol. It gives a motivation for simplifying, since it is much easier to compare expressions in simplified form.

Problems 16-17 could get tedious. If you choose to assign them, do them in class, so students can work with a partner in order to expedite the computations.

SOLVING INEQUALITIES

This section introduces what it means to "solve" an inequality formally. Students are asked to solve some simple ones. The purpose at this stage is not to learn solving techniques, though discussion of those should not be discouraged.

The main point is to introduce the concept of solving an inequality. Problems 25-27 are intended to warn students that a purely symbolic approach can be confusing if one loses sight of the meaning of the problem. A full algebraic technique for solving inequalities will be postponed until a future course.

DISCOVERY *SQUARES ON A CHESSBOARD*

This is a challenging counting problem, which can be used as a *problem of the week* or as a topic for group investigation.

Simplifying Expression B

	Lea's work	Earl's work
Step 1	$5 - 3[x - 3x - 1]$	$5 - 3[x - 3x - 1]$
Step 2	$5 - 3[-2x - 1]$	$5 - 3[-2x - 1]$
Step 3	$5 + 6x - 3$	$2[-2x - 1]$
Step 4	$2 + 6x$	$-4x - 2$

Lea and Earl wanted to know which one of them had made a mistake. They asked their teacher, Mr. Martin. "You can't both be right," he said, "but you could both be wrong."

12. Are Lea and Earl both wrong, or is only one of them wrong? Is Mr. Martin wrong? Look for mistakes in their work. When you find a mistake, explain what the student did wrong.

13. Look at Expressions A and B again. Simplify both expressions correctly.

14. Using the simplified form of each expression, compare Expressions A and B by making a table of values.

15. Summarize the information in your table by telling when Expression A is greater, when Expression B is greater, and when the two expressions are equal.

16. Simplify each pair of expressions.

a. $4x - 2x[3 - 6(x + 1)]$
$4 - x[x - 6(2x + 1)]$

b. $4 - 2[y - 6(y + 1)]$
$4 - [y - 6(y + 1)]$

17. Compare each pair of expressions in problem 16. Make a table of values and summarize your findings in each case, telling when the first expression is greater, when the second expression is greater, and when they are equal.

SOLVING INEQUALITIES

18. Use a table of values to show that $2x + 6 > 8$ for all values of x greater than 1.

We say that the *solution* to the inequality $2x + 6 > 8$ is "all numbers greater than 1" because this describes *all* the values for which the inequality is true. Using mathematical symbols, we say that the solution is $x > 1$.

Find the solution of each inequality. That is, describe all the numbers for which the inequality is true.

19. $x + 5 > 1$ **20.** $n - 5 > 1$

21. $y + 5 > 0$ **22.** $r - 5 > 0$

23. $x - 5 > -1$ **24.** $x + 5 > -1$

25. $-x > 6$ **26.** $-x > -6$

27. Many students get problems 25 and 26 wrong. Check your answers to them by substituting specific values of x. What makes them more difficult than the other ones?

DISCOVERY *SQUARES ON A CHESSBOARD*

28. How many squares of any size are there on an 8-by-8 chessboard? Explain how you get your answer. (Hint: First analyze smaller boards.)

6.2 SOLUTIONS

12. Both Lea and Earl are wrong.
Lea's work: In step 3 Lea made a mistake when she multiplied -3 and -1 from step 2. Rather than $5 + 6x - 3$, she should have $5 + 6x + 3$.

Earl's work: In step 3 Earl made a mistake when he added 5 and -3 from step 2 rather than multiplying the expression in brackets by -3. He should multiply before adding. Rather than $2[-2x - 1]$ he too should have $5 + 6x + 3$.

13. a. $5 - [x - (3x + 1)]$
$= 5 - [x - 3x - 1]$
$= 5 - [-2x - 1]$
$= 5 + 2x + 1$
$= 2x + 6$

b. $5 - 3[x - (3x + 1)]$
$= 5 - 3[x - 3x - 1]$
$= 5 - 3[-2x - 1]$
$= 5 + 6x + 3$
$= 6x + 8$

14.

x	$2x + 6$	$6x + 8$
4	14	32
2	10	20
0.5	7	11
0	6	8
-0.5	5	5
-1	4	2
-5	-4	-22

15. $2x + 6$ equals $6x + 8$ when $x = -0.5$. $2x + 6 > 6x + 8$ for $x < -0.5$ and $6x + 8 > 2x + 6$ for $x > -0.5$.

16. a. $12x^2 + 10x$, $11x^2 + 6x + 4$
b. $10y + 16$, $5y + 10$

17. Tables will vary.

x	$12x^2 + 10x$	$11x^2 + 6x + 4$
10	1300	1164
5	350	309
2	68	60
0.5	8	9.75
0	0	4
-0.5	-2	3.75
-2	28	36
-5	250	249
-10	1100	1044

Answers may vary. $12x^2 + 10x > 11x^2 + 6x + 4$ for $x < -4.83$ or $x > 0.83$. $12x^2 + 10x = 11x^2 + 6x + 4$ for $x \approx -4.83$ or $x \approx 0.83$. $11x^2 + 6x + 4 > 12x^2 + 10x$ for $-4.83 < x < 0.83$

LESSON 6.3

Solving Linear Equations

You will need: the Lab Gear 

1. **Exploration** Find a value of x that makes each equation true. Describe the method you used.
   a. $3(x + 2) = x + 5$
   b. $3x + 2 = x + 5$
   c. $3x + 2 = x - 5$
   d. $3(x + 2) = x - 5$

USING THE LAB GEAR

The easiest equations to solve are linear, or first-degree equations in one variable. All four of the equations above are linear. The equation $x^2 = 2x - 1$ is not linear, because it contains an x^2 term.

You have already learned to solve equations by trial and error and the cover-up method. Some kinds of equations can also be solved using the Lab Gear.

This figure represents an equation. We want to find out what value of x will make the quantity on the left side of the workmat equal to the quantity on the right side.

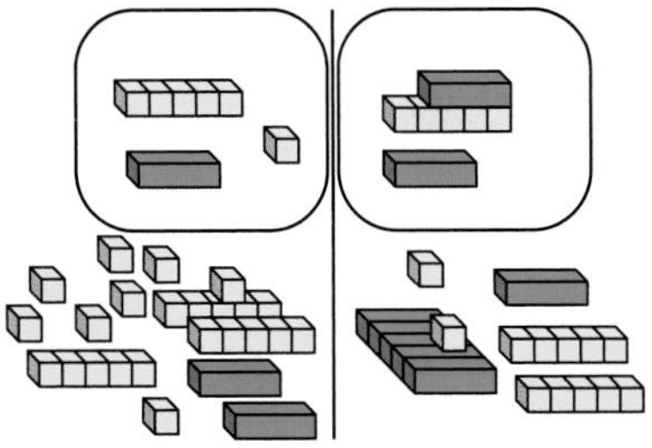

2. Copy the figure with your Lab Gear.

3. Simplify each side. If you did it correctly, your blocks should match this figure.

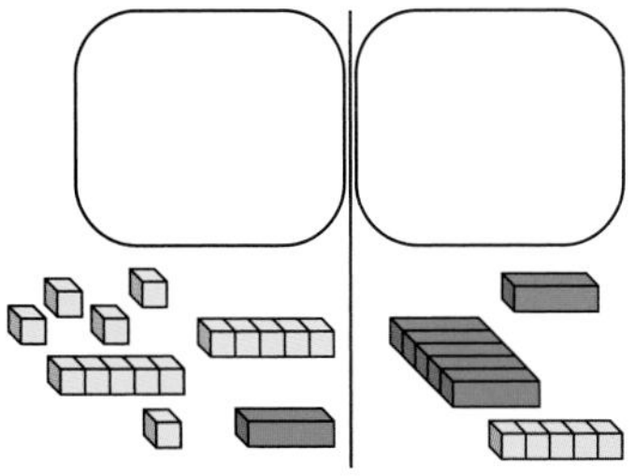

4. Rearrange the blocks to match this figure. Which blocks on the right side can be matched with identical blocks on the left side?

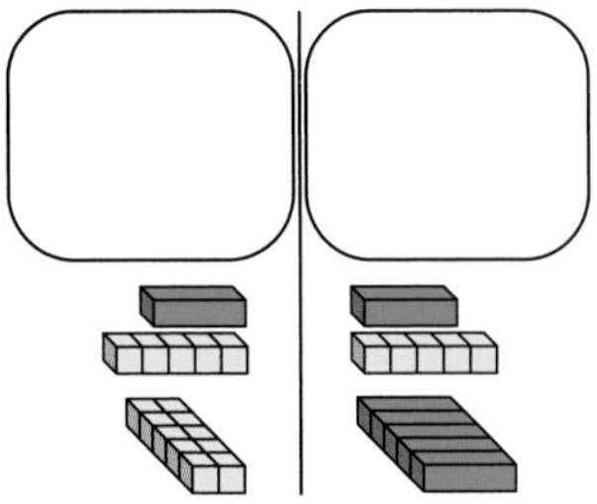

There are some blocks that cannot be matched with blocks on the other side. The figure shows a two-dimensional view of these blocks.

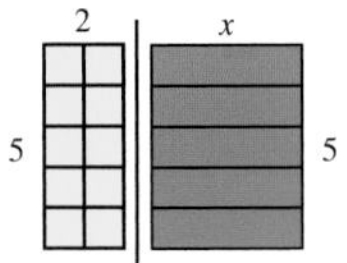

▼ 6.3 Solving Linear Equations

Core Sequence: 1-23

Suitable for Homework: 14-29

What this Lesson is About:

- Solving linear equations with the Lab Gear
- Review of linear equation solving techniques
- Expressing numerical relationships with variables
- Using trial and error to solve puzzles
- Review of averages

USING THE LAB GEAR

The goal of this section is for students to begin to recognize some general strategies for solving linear equations. These strategies will be discussed in Lessons 6 and 8, so you should not teach them here. However, be alert to generalizations that students make, and allow them to teach anything they understand to members of their group, or even to the whole class. You may want to lead a class discussion in the end, in which students share their "shortcuts."

6.3 SOLUTIONS

(6.2 Solutions continued)

y	$10y + 16$	$5y + 10$
10	116	60
5	66	35
0.5	21	12.5
0	16	10
-1	6	5
-1.2	4	4
-2	-4	0
-5	-34	-15
-10	-84	-40

$10y + 16 > 5y + 10$ for $x > -1.2$
$10y + 16 = 5y + 10$ for $x = -1.2$
$10y + 16 < 5y + 10$ for $x < -1.2$

18. Tables will vary.

x	$2x + 6$
1.2	8.4
2	10
3	12
30	66
100	206
1.02	8.04

19. $x > -4$
20. $n > 6$
21. $x > -5$
22. $r > 5$
23. $x > 4$
24. $x > -6$
25. $x > -6$
26. $x > 6$
27. The previous two problems are more difficult because of the negative sign before x. If students are solving problems 25 and 26 algebraically, they may want to add x to both sides so they can work with x and not $-x$.
28. 204 squares.

6.3 Solutions

1. Explanations may vary.
   a. $x = -0.5$
   b. $x = 1.5$
   c. $x = -3.5$
   d. $x = -5.5$
2. No solution is necessary.
3. No solution is necessary.
4. The x- and 5-blocks on the right can be matched with identical blocks on the left.

The Lab Gear example stops short of suggesting that students remove matching blocks from the two sides of the workmat. This is to give them the opportunity to discover this technique themselves.

Look at these remaining blocks. Remember that the two sides are equal. This is true even though they don't *look* equal. Remember x can have any value.

5. What must x be in order for the two sides to be equal?

This figure shows how you would set out the blocks to solve the equation $2x + 1 = 4x - 5$.

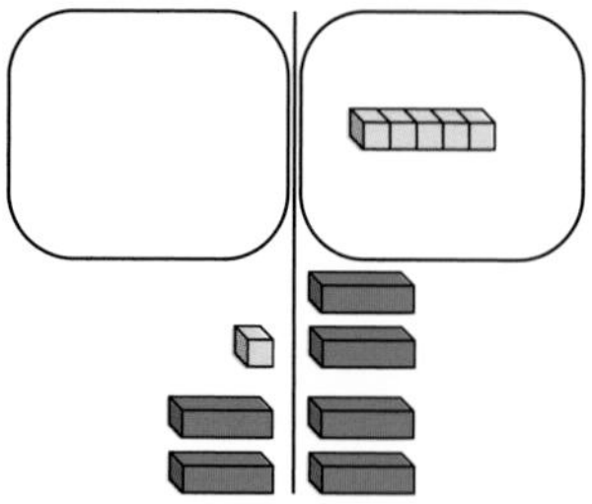

Each side is simplified. The blocks have been arranged to show which blocks can be matched with blocks on the other side. Even so, it is not easy to tell what the solution is.

It helps to add zero.

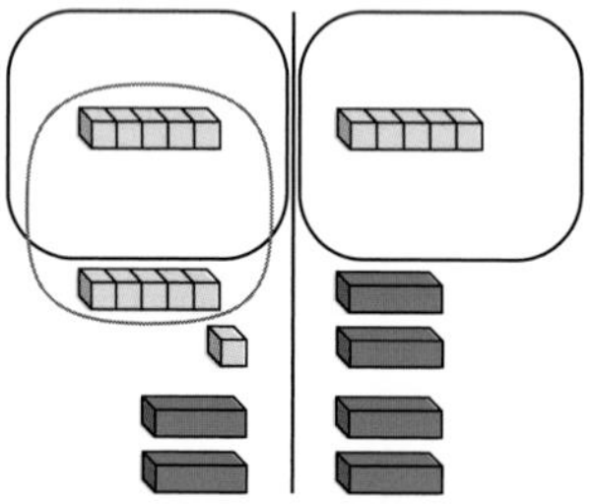

Notice that the blocks on one side are rearranged to show which ones can be matched with blocks on the other side.

The remaining blocks (those that cannot be matched with blocks on the other side) can then be rearranged to make it easy to see the solution to the equation.

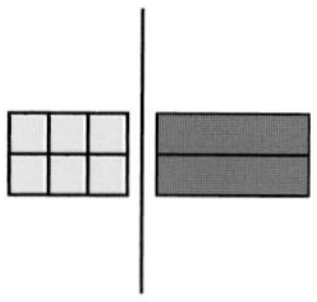

6. What is the solution to this equation?

For problems 7-11:

a. Write the original equation.

b. Use the Lab Gear to find the solution. Write equations to show some of the steps as you move your blocks.

c. Write the solution.

7.

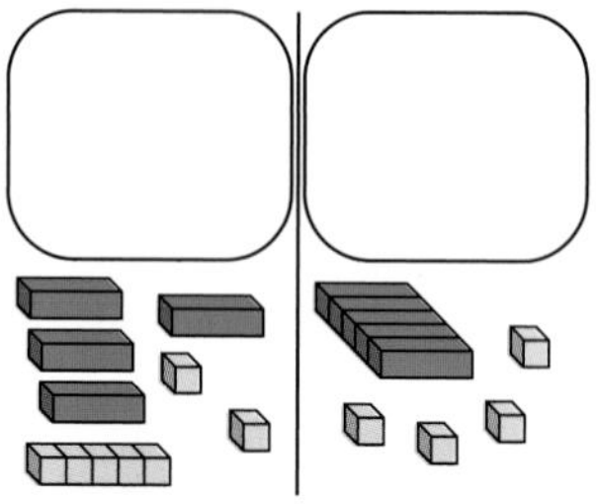

8.

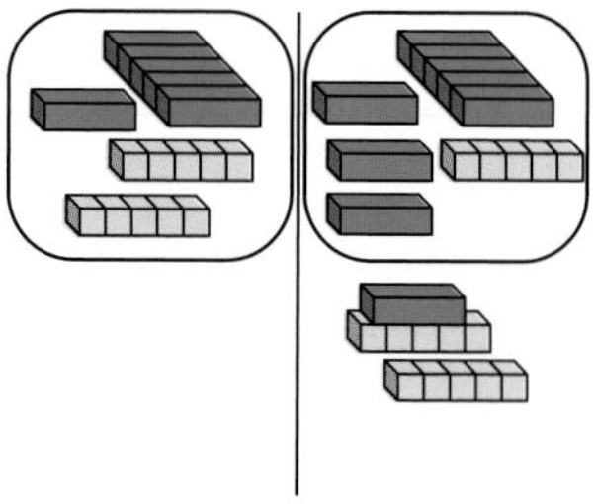

6.3 SOLUTIONS

5. x must equal 3.

6. $x = 3$ is the solution to the equation.

Answers to part b will vary for #7-11.

7. a. $4x + 7 = 5x + 4$
   c. $x = 3$

8. a. $-(6x + 10) = 10 - x - (8x + 5)$
   c. $x = 5$

9.

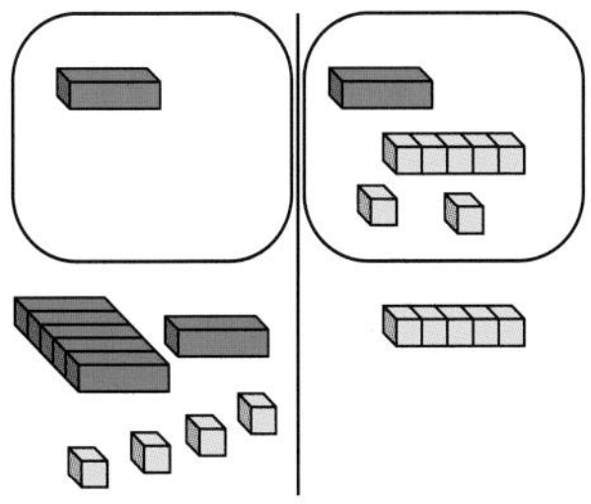

10.

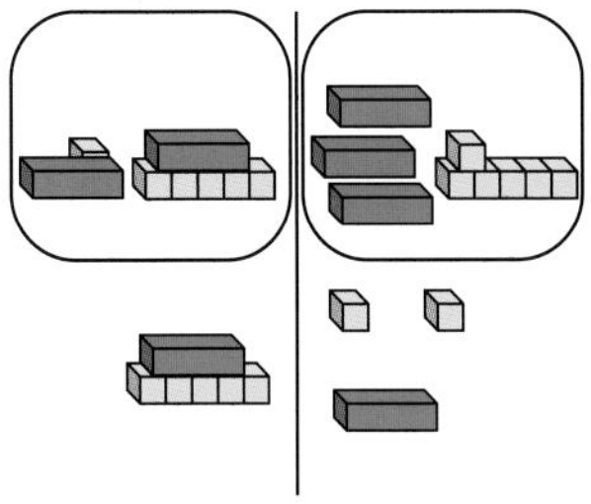

11.

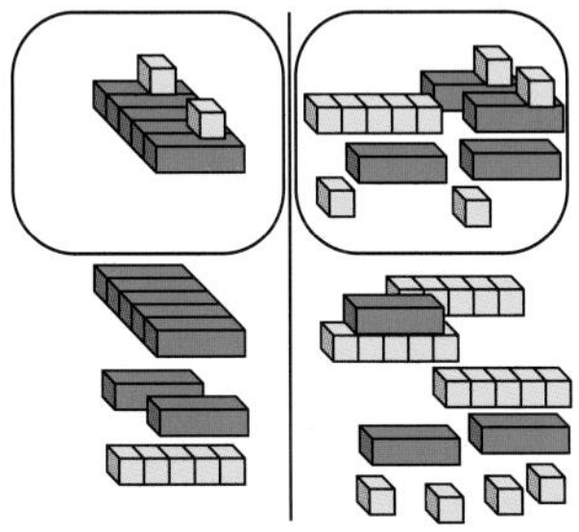

MORE EQUATIONS

You have learned to solve equations using tables, trial and error, the cover-up method, and the Lab Gear. Solve these equations in whatever way you want, but *show your work.*

12. $3x + 5 = 6$

13. $3x + 5 = -2x - 10$

14. $2y - 6 = 5y + 3$

15. $\frac{6x - 6}{4} = 3$

16. $\frac{6x - 6}{4} + 15 = 3$

Make up an equation satisfying each of the following descriptions. Try to make up one that would be challenging for another student to solve, but not so challenging that you can't solve it.

17. An equation whose solution is $x = 4$

18. An equation whose solution is $y = -1/2$

19. An equation that has variables on both sides of the equation and the solution $m = 2$

20. An equation that has more than one solution

MORE EQUATIONS

Again, do not teach students new techniques for solving linear equations. These are discussed later in this chapter. Instead, use this as an opportunity to review trial and error, the cover-up method, the use of tables, and/or any techniques discovered by students for solving equations. Because such a review may be important, start this section in class, and assign the rest as homework. (When in class, allow the students to use the Lab Gear if they want to.)

Problems 17-20 are especially good for homework, since students will need to think independently. The next day the initial activity could center around solving one another's equations. Particularly interesting equations (not necessarily the hardest ones) should be discussed by the whole class.

DISCOVERY USING VARIABLES

Because of the fact that it will soon be possible to solve equations by calculator, skill in solving equations is not as important as skill in setting up equations. These problems help students get some practice with writing expressions having variables, starting with data in story form.

6.3 SOLUTIONS

9. a. $6x + 4 - x = 5 - (x + 7)$
   c. $x = -1$

10. a. $5 - x - (x + 6 - x) = x + 2 - (3x + 5 - 1)$
   b. $x = -1$

11. a. $7x + 5 - (5x - 2) = 2x + 15 - x + 4 - (4x + 7 - 2)$
   c. $x = 1.4$

12. $x = 1/3$

13. $x = -3$

14. $y = -3$

15. $x = 3$

16. $y = -7$

Answers will vary for #17-20. Samples:

17. $2x + 5 = 13$

18. $2y + 3 = 2$

19. $2m + 7 = m + 9$

20. $x^2 + 3 = 7$

If students find these problems difficult, you may encourage them to set up tables as an intermediate step. For example, for problem 21, filling in values in a table like the following may help students find the formula.

Months	Age
0 to 11	0
12 to 23	1
24 to 35	2
etc.	

In a way, this is a review of step functions, which were seen in Chapter 2, Lesson 6, and Chapter 4, Lesson 11.

PUZZLES *MAGIC SQUARES*

If students are frustrated, you can help by leading an investigation of what the magic sum might be. Once it is known, the puzzle is much easier. Moreover, this approach will help review averages.

Starting with any arrangement, you can inspect the sums of the rows and take their average. The average of the sums of the columns should be the same number, which is the magic sum. Try to move numbers around until each row adds up to this sum. Then move numbers around *within the rows* until the columns add up to the magic sum.

DISCOVERY *GRADING POLICIES*

This is a continuation of **Grade Averages**, after Lesson 1. To be continued in **Weighted Averages**, after Lesson 5.

DISCOVERY *USING VARIABLES*

21. A student is x years old. How many months old is he? (Are you sure?)

22. Another student is y years old.
a. How many years until she can vote?
b. How many months?

23. I start with 99 peanuts. It takes me x seconds to eat one.
a. How long will it take to eat them all?
b. After eating n peanuts, how many are left?
c. After z seconds, how many peanuts are left?

PUZZLES *MAGIC SQUARES*

These puzzles will be easier to solve if you make yourself little squares of paper with numbers written on them. To solve the puzzles, move the papers around, until you find a satisfactory arrangement.

24. Arrange all the numbers from 1 to 9 into a 3-by-3 square, so that the sum of all the numbers in any row or column is always the same.

25. Repeat problem 24, but make sure the *diagonals* also add up to the same amount.

26. Arrange all the numbers from 1 to 16 into a 4-by-4 square, so that the sum of the numbers in any row or column is always the same.

DISCOVERY *GRADING POLICIES*

At the Shell School, math teachers give a six weeks grade based on six quizzes and two writing assignments. The math department policy requires that quizzes and writing assignments be counted equally.

For each student in her class, Mrs. Washman averages the quizzes, averages the writing assignments, and then adds those two numbers and divides by two.

For each student in his class, Mr. Pitcher adds all the grades together and divides by eight.

27. Make up a list of grades of a student who would have a higher grade with Mrs. Washman's method.

28. Make up a list of grades of a student who would have a higher grade with Mr. Pitcher's method.

29. Is it possible for a student to have the same grade using either method? Explain.

6.3 SOLUTIONS

21. The student is at least $12x$ months old but the exact number of months cannot be determined without more information. For example, on the student's x^{th} birthday he is $12x$ months old.

22. Assume the student is younger than 18 years.
a. There are $18 - y$ years until she can vote.
b. If today is her y^{th} birthday then she has $216 - 12y$ months to vote. If it is not her y^{th} birthday yet she has fewer than $216 - 12y$ months, but more information is needed to be exact.

23. a. $99x$ seconds
b. $99 - n$
c. $99 - (z/x)$

24. Answers may vary. Sample:

4	8	3
2	6	7
9	1	5

26.

1	15	16	2
12	6	9	7
8	10	5	11
13	3	4	14

LESSON 6.4

Equations and Identities

You will need:

the Lab Gear

Definition: An *identity* is an equation that is true for all values of the variables.

1. Which of these equations are identities? Explain your answers.
   a. $3x + 9 - 2(x + 2) = 3x + 9 - 2x + 2$
   b. $3x + 9 - 2(x + 2) = 3x + 7(x + 2)$
   c. $3x + 9 - 2(x + 2) = x + 5$
   d. $3x + 9 - 2(x + 2) = x + 7$

USING THE LAB GEAR

To solve the equation $5(x + 1) = 25$ you can model both the left side and the right side as rectangles. In this case, you can match the rectangles, and it is easy to see what the value of x must be.

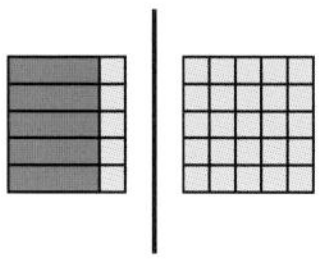

2. What is the value of x that makes both sides equal?

Use the Lab Gear to solve these equations. If the equation is an identity, explain how you know, using sketches if necessary.

3. $3(x + 2) = 15$
4. $3(x + 2) = 3x + 6$
5. $4(2x + 1) = 4(x + 5)$
6. $4(2x - 1) = 4(x - 1)$
7. $4(2x - 1) = 4(2x + 1)$
8. $2(2x + 2) = 4(x + 1)$
9. $4(2x - 2) = 2(4x - 4)$

USING GRAPHS AND TABLES

10. Make a table of (x, y) pairs and graph each linear function.
    a. $y = -2(x - 1) + 2$
    b. $y = -2x + 4$
11. By simplifying the left side, show that $-2(x - 1) + 2 = -2x + 4$ is an identity.
12. For each pair of functions, decide whether or not both members of the pair would have the same graph. Explain.
    a. $y = 3 - 4x$ and $y = 4x - 3$
    b. $y = -6 - 8x$ and $y = 8x - 6$
    c. $y = 2x^2$ and $y = 2x(x + 2) - 4x$
    d. $y = 5 - x$ and $y = -x - 5$
    e. $y = -x + 5$ and $y = 5 - x$
13. Look at your answers to problem 12. For each pair that would not have the same graph, graph both functions on the same axes. Find the point where the two graphs intersect and label it on the graph.
14. Which of the pairs of graphs that you drew in problem 13 do not have a point of intersection? Can you explain why this is so?
15. When graphing two linear functions, there are three possibilities: You may get the same line, two parallel lines, or two lines that intersect. Explain what the tables of (x, y) values look like in each case.

ALWAYS, SOMETIMES, NEVER

While an identity is true for all values of x, an equation may be true for only some values of x, or for no values of x.

6.4 SOLUTIONS

1. a. This is not an identity. The equation simplifies to $x + 5 = x + 11$. There is no x for which this is true.
   b. This is not an identity. The equation simplifies to $x + 5 = 10x + 14$. There is only one value of x that satisfies this equation, $x = -1$.
   c. This is an identity. The equation simplifies to $x + 5 = x + 5$ which is true for all x.
   d. This is not an identity. The equation simplifies to $x + 5 = x + 7$, which is not true for any value of x.
2. $x = 4$
3. $x = 3$
4. This is an identity. It simplifies down to $3x + 6 = 3x + 6$, which is true for all values of x.
5. $x = 4$
6. $x = 0$
7. No solution. This equation simplifies to $0 = 8$, which is never true.
8. This is an identity. The equation simplifies to $4x + 4 = 4x + 4$, which is true for all values of x.
9. This is an identity. The equation simplifies to $8x - 8 = 8x - 8$, which is true for all values of x.
10. a.

x	y
-2	8
-1	6
0	4
1	2
2	0
3	-2

b.

x	y
-2	8
-1	6
0	4
1	2
2	0
3	-2

6.4 Equations and Identities

Core Sequence: 1-36

Suitable for Homework: 10-23, 36

Useful for Assessment: 14-15, 22, 29, 35-36

What this Lesson is About:

- Equations and identities
- Equations with no solutions
- Solving equations with the Lab Gear
- Preview of solving equations with tables and graphs
- Review of the distributive law
- Preview of the square of a binomial
- Preview of completing the square

The concept of identity was previewed in Chapter 1, Lesson 4, but this is the first formal introduction to it. This lesson gives students two ways of visualizing, with graphs and with the Lab Gear, why some equations are identities and why some have no solution.

USING THE LAB GEAR

These equations require students to understand multiplication well enough to model both sides. This should not be a problem at this point. After multiplying, the problems are similar to the Lab Gear problems in Lesson 3.

If students want to solve these equations without the Lab Gear, suggest they compare their answers with those obtained by other students using the blocks. (Or, they can take turns, with one student using the Lab Gear and the other one solving the equation on paper.)

USING GRAPHS AND TABLES

ALWAYS, SOMETIMES, NEVER

These are very important sections. In addition to the comparison of equations and identities, their purpose is to help students start seeing how graphs can be used to solve equations. If they are done at home, make sure that at least problems 15 and 18-21 are discussed in class the following day.

If students simplify the expression in problem 10a, it will be obvious that the tables and graphs are identical. But if they don't, do not hint at it; let them find out through their calculations.

We will return to graphical solutions in Lesson 5, and again in Chapter 10.

REVIEW ***WHICH IS GREATER?***

This problem reviews the basic operations and how to use parentheses, as well as inequalities. If your students have trouble with it, suggest they substitute values for x and make tables. They can also make graphs of the form $y =$ *the first expression*, and $y =$ *the second expression* and use those.

REVIEW/PREVIEW ***MAKE A SQUARE***

This section reviews the distributive law. In addition, it is an important preview of the square of a binomial, to which we will return in Chapter 7, and of completing the square, which we will see in Chapter 12.

Examples: $2x + 6 = 4$ is true when $x = -1$, but not when $x = 0$. The equation $x + 5 = x$ is never true, because a number is never equal to five more than itself. We say this equation has *no solution.*

16. For each equation, state whether it is *always, sometimes,* or *never* true. If it is always or never true, explain how you know. It may help to simplify and to use tables, graphs, or sketches of the Lab Gear.

a. $2x + 5 = 2x + 1$

b. $3(x - 4) - 4(x - 3) = 0$

c. $(x + 5)^2 = x^2 + 25$

d. $6x - (7 - x) + 8 = 7x + 1$

17. Look at the equations in problem 16 that you decided were *sometimes* true. For each one, find a value of x that makes it true and one that makes it false. Show your work.

For each equation 18-21:

State whether the equation is always, sometimes, or never true. Explain.

18. $0.5x - 2 = 0.5(x - 2)$

19. $0.5x - 2 = 0.5(x - 4)$

20. $0.5x - 2 = x - 4$

21. $0.5(x - 2) = x - 4$

22. **Report** Write a report about equations that are always, sometimes, or never true. Use one example of each type. Illustrate each example with a graph and a Lab Gear sketch. Be sure to include the definition of *identity* and full explanations.

REVIEW ***WHICH IS GREATER?***

23. Which is greater, or does it depend on the value of x? Explain.

a.	$-2x$	$-2x + 7$
b.	$6x - 4$	$6x + 4$
c.	$-x^2$	x^2
d.	$(-x)^2$	$-x^2$

REVIEW/PREVIEW ***MAKE A SQUARE***

Make a square with these blocks, adding as many yellow blocks as you want, but nothing else. For each square, write an equation relating the side length to the area.

24. $x^2 + 10x +$ __ **25.** $4x^2 + 8x +$ __

26. $9x^2 + 6x +$ __ **27.** $x^2 + 2x +$ __

28. $4x^2 + 12 +$ __

29. 🔑 Is it possible to get a different square by adding a different number of yellow blocks? Explain your answer.

Make a square with these blocks, adding as many x-blocks as you want, but nothing else. For each square, write an equation relating the side length to the area.

30. $x^2 +$ __ $+ 25$ **31.** $4x^2 +$ __ $+ 25$

32. $x^2 +$ __ $+ 36$ **33.** $9x^2 +$ __ $+ 1$

34. $x^2 +$ __ $+ 9$

35. 🔑 Is it possible to get a different square by adding a different number of x-blocks? Explain your answer.

36. **Summary** Describe the pattern for the square of a binomial, in terms of the Lab Gear, and in terms of the algebraic symbols.

6.4 SOLUTIONS

10. a., b.

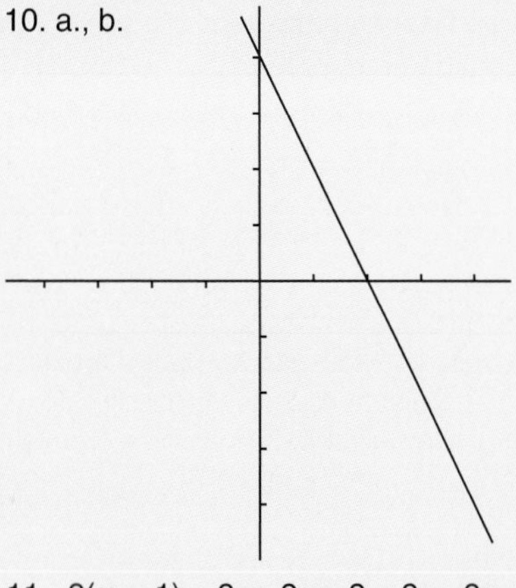

11. $-2(x - 1) + 2 = -2x + 2 + 2 = -2x + 4$

12. a. These would not have the same graph because $3 - 4x \neq 4x - 3$ for all values of x, only for $x = 3/4$.

b. They do not have the same graph because $-6 - 8x \neq 8x - 6$ for all values of x, only for $x = 0$.

c. These would have the same graph since the second equation simplifies to $y = 2x^2$, so that we have $y = 2x^2$ for both graphs.

d. These do not have the same graph because $5 - x$ is never equal to $-x - 5$.

e. These have the same graph because $-x + 5 = 5 - x$ for all values of x.

13. a.

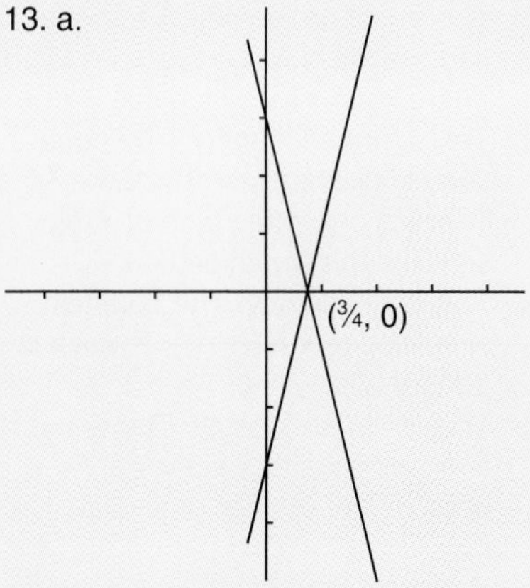

(Solutions continued on page 519)

THINKING WRITING

6.A Money Matters

DISCOUNTS

A discount card at a movie theater costs $10. With that card, it costs only $3 to attend a movie, instead of $5. The card is valid for three months.

1. Use the same pair of axes for both of the graphs in this problem. Make a graph of the *total cost* (including the cost of the discount card if you got one) as a function of the *number of movies* you see

a. if you have the discount card;

b. if you do not have the discount card.

2. What is the total cost of seeing n movies in three months

a. with the discount card?

b. without the discount card?

3. a. If you saw 12 movies in three months, how much would you save by buying the discount card?

b. If you saw only two movies in three months, how much would you save by *not* buying the discount card?

4. Report Write a report explaining how you would decide whether or not to buy the card. Do a complete analysis of the situation, using graphs, tables, and equations. Your discussion should include, but not be limited to, answers to the following questions:

- What is the break-even point; that is, how many movies would you have to see in order to spend exactly the same amount with and without the discount card?
- How would your decision be affected if the cost of the discount card were raised to $12?
- How would your decision be affected if the cost of the discount card were changed to $$K$?

PAYMENTS

Today Lara opened a bank account and deposited $700. She has just started a part-time job and will get a paycheck of $130 every two weeks, on the 1st and the 15th of the month. She plans to take $40 out of each paycheck for cash expenses and deposit the rest in her bank account. On the 15th of every month, when her car payment is due, she will write a check for $220.

5. Make a table showing how much money Lara will have in her account on the 1st and 15th of every month over the next five months. It may help to show deposits and withdrawals. Look for a pattern.

6. How much money will Lara have in her account on the 1st and the 15th of the month

a. eight months after receiving her first paycheck?

b. n months after receiving her first paycheck?

7. Report Imagine that you are Lara's older sister or brother. Write a letter to her showing why she will run out of money, and when. Give her some suggestions for what she might do to avoid this.

THINKING WRITING

6.A Money Matters

Core Sequence: 1-4

Suitable for Homework: 1-7

Useful for Assessment: 4, 7

What this Assignment is About:

- Applying linear functions, equations, and inequalities
- Using tables and graphs
- Mathematics as a tool for decision-making

These problems are somewhat like the chapter introductory problem on car rental, but not as difficult. They can be solved without equations, but they are written in such a way that students are encouraged to write equations and use their budding equation-solving techniques.

Some students may not be able to answer the part of problem 4 that asks for an analysis of the case where the discount card costs $$K$.

6.A SOLUTIONS

1.

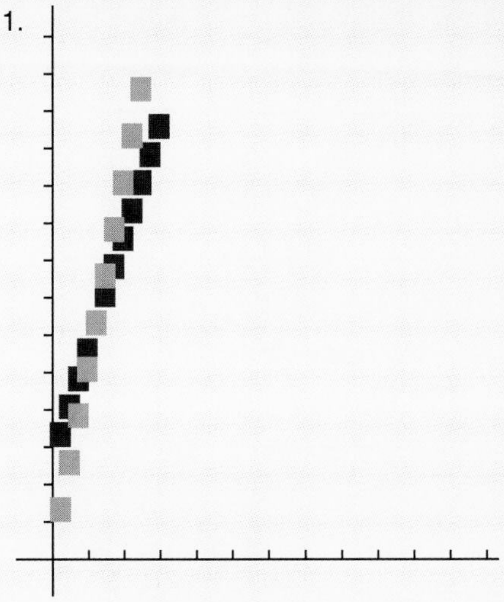

a. With discount card

x	y
1	13
2	16
3	19
4	22
5	25
6	28
7	31
8	34
n	$10 + 3n$

b. Without discount card

x	y
1	5
2	10
3	15
4	20
5	25
6	30
7	35
8	40
n	$5n$

2. a. $3n + 10$

b. $5n$

3. a. $5(12) - [3(12) + 10] = \$14$ saved

b. $16 - 10 = \$6$ saved

4. Reports should include: The break-even point of 5 movies for $25.00; if the discount card's cost were raised to $12, the new break-even point would be 6 movies for $30; if the cost of the discount card were raised to $$K$, the new break-even point would be $0.5K$ movies for $$2.5K$.

(Solutions continued on page 521)

▼ 6.5 Graphical Solutions

Core Sequence: 1-17, 21-31

Suitable for Homework: 10-34

Useful for Assessment: 12

What this Lesson is About:

- Graphical solution of equations and inequalities
- Preview of solving quadratics
- Review of equation-solving methods
- Review of substitution
- Review of division by a monomial

*T*his lesson takes the "table" method, introduced earlier in the chapter, a step further. Emphasis is on solving linear equations, but since the method is completely general, a few simple quadratics are included. The hardest part of this method for students is to realize that they are solving for *x*, even though the graph shows both *x* and *y*.

A GRAPHICAL ANALYSIS

FINDING SOLUTIONS

*I*f students have trouble using graphs to analyze the inequalities and equations, or can use them but do not fully understand this technique, they should use tables of values. For example, for problems 1-7, a large table for each function can be generated by the class and displayed on the chalkboard or overhead projector. Such a

LESSON 6.5

Graphical Solutions

You will need:

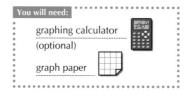

graphing calculator (optional)

graph paper

A GRAPHICAL ANALYSIS

1. On the same axes, graph $y = x - 1$ and $y = 0.25x + 2$.

Your graph should look like the one below. The three points that are marked and labeled with their coordinates are all on the part of the graph of $y = x - 1$ that is *below* the graph of $y = 0.25x + 2$.

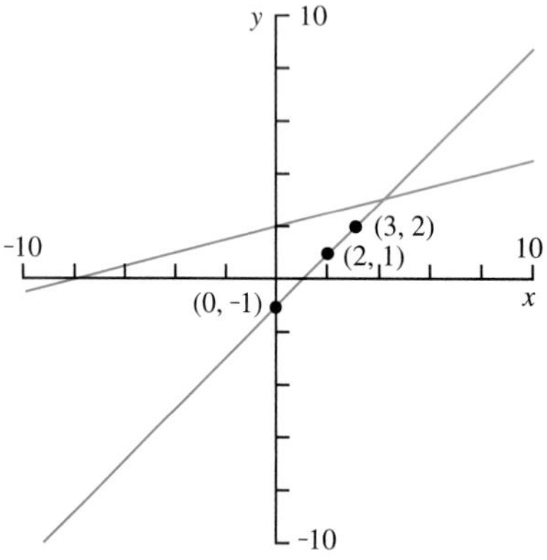

2. Find the coordinates of three points on the part of the line $y = x - 1$ that is *above* the graph of $y = 0.25x + 2$.

3. Find the coordinates of the point where the two lines cross.

4. If $x = 100$,
  a. which graph is above, $y = x - 1$ or $y = 0.25x + 2$?
  b. what is the value of $0.25x + 2$?
  c. what is the value of $x - 1$?

5. If $x = -100$,
  a. which graph is above, $y = x - 1$ or $y = 0.25x + 2$?
  b. what is the value of $0.25x + 2$?
  c. what is the value of $x - 1$?

6. Describe all the values of *x* for which the graph of $y = x - 1$
  a. is above the graph of $y = 0.25x + 2$.
  b. is below the graph of $y = 0.25x + 2$.

7. Describe all the values of *x* that satisfy each equation or inequality.
  a. $0.25x + 2 = x - 1$
  b. $0.25x + 2 > x - 1$
  c. $0.25x + 2 < x - 1$

FINDING SOLUTIONS

8. Using trial and error, find three values of *x* that satisfy each inequality.
  a. $2x < 3x + 1$
  b. $2x > 3x + 1$

It is often easy to find a few values of *x* that satisfy an inequality. It is harder to find *all* the values, that is, to *solve* the inequality. You have solved equations and inequalities using trial and error, the cover-up method, tables, and the Lab Gear. Another method is to use graphs.

6.5 SOLUTIONS

1. No solution needed.
2. Answers will vary. Sample: (5, 4), (6, 5), (7, 6), any $(x, x - 1)$ for $x > 4$
3. (4, 3)
4. a. When $x = 100$, $y = x - 1$ is above.
   b. $0.25(100) + 2 = 27$
   c. $100 - 1 = 99$
5. a. When $x = -100$, $y = 0.25x + 2$ is above.
   b. $0.25(-100) + 2 = -23$
   c. $-100 - 1 = -101$
6. a. $y = x - 1$ is above $y = 0.25x + 2$ for all values of *x* greater than 4.
   b. $y = x - 1$ is below $y = 0.25x + 2$ for all values of *x* less than 4.
7. a. $x = 4$
   b. For all *x*-values less than 4
   c. For all *x*-values greater than 4
8. Answers will vary.
   a. Samples: $x = 0$, $x = 1$, $x = 1.5$ (any $x > -1$)
   b. Samples: $x = -2$, $x = -3$, $x = -4$ (any $x < -1$)
9. a. $x > -1$
   b. $x < -1$

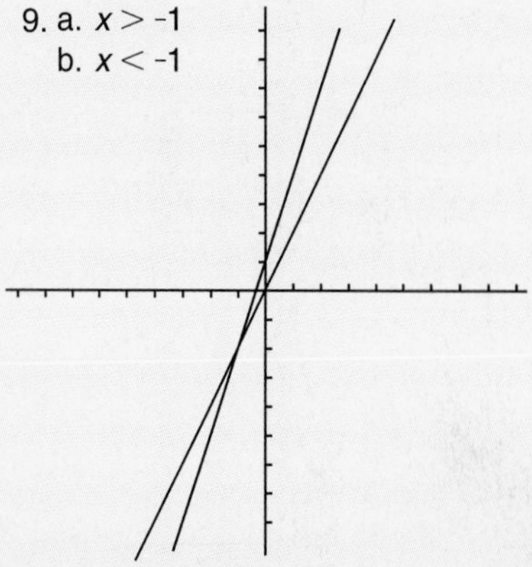

10. a.

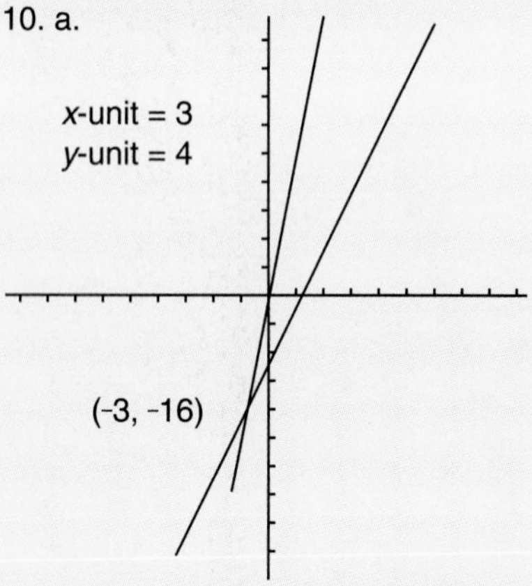

9. Graph $y = 2x$ and $y = 3x + 1$ on the same pair of axes. Use the graphs to solve the two inequalities in problem 8. Remember that even though the graph shows values of both x and y, the original inequalities involved only the variable x. Your answers should involve only x.

10. Graph each pair of functions on graph paper. Use a separate grid for each pair.
   a. $y = 2x - 10$ and $y = 5x - 1$
   b. $y = 2x + 10$ and $y = 5x - 2$
   c. $y = 2x - 10$ and $y = 5x - 2$
   d. $y = x^2$ and $y = 4x - 4$

11. Use your graphs from problem 10 to find the values of x that make these equations true.
   a. $2x - 10 = 5x - 1$
   b. $2x + 10 = 5x - 2$
   c. $2x - 10 = 5x - 2$
   d. $x^2 = 4x - 4$

12. **Summary** Write a paragraph explaining how you can use graphs to help solve equations and inequalities. Illustrate by showing how you would use your method to solve these equations and inequalities.
   a. $-2x + 1 > 3x - 4$
   b. $2x - 1 > -3x + 4$
   c. $3x + 4 = -2x - 6$
   d. $x^2 = x + 2$

MORE EQUATIONS AND INEQUALITIES

Use the techniques you have learned to solve these equations and inequalities. You can use trial and error, the cover-up method, tables, graphs, or the Lab Gear. Show your work.

13. $6x + 1 \leq -3x + 7$
14. $2x + 32 = 6x + 28$
15. $4(x + 5) = 4x + 20$
16. $-3 + m < -m - 3$
17. $\frac{5x + 3}{4} - 6 = 1$
18. $x^2 = 6 - x$
19. $\frac{x}{x + 1} = 1$
20. $\frac{x + 5}{2} + x = 19$

REVIEW SUBSTITUTION

For each problem, write a simple expression that shows the relationship between Δ and ◊. (Hint: If you cannot find the relationship by using algebra, make a table of values of Δ and ◊ that make the expressions true, and find a pattern in the table.) Show your work.

21. Δ − ◊ = Δ
22. ◊ + 2 = ◊ + Δ + Δ
23. ◊ + Δ + Δ + ◊ = ◊
24. ◊ − Δ + ◊ − Δ = ◊
25. Δ + Δ = ◊ + ◊
26. ◊ + Δ + Δ + ◊ = 4

reference could make the graphs much easier to interpret.

Some computer software and graphing calculators make it easy to generate tables of values. This feature should be used.

MORE EQUATIONS AND INEQUALITIES

This section provides an opportunity for review and practice of all equation-solving methods. For most classes, it is probably not a good idea to assign the whole section for homework, since students who have trouble with symbol manipulation will probably still not feel confident with equation-solving methods. One approach is to assign these for group work. You can move around the room, observing the methods used by the different groups. Then you can choose some problems for discussion, having students present different approaches so that the class can compare methods. Students often enjoy arguing about which method is "best" for a particular problem.

REVIEW SUBSTITUTION

These problems resemble the ones in Chapter 1, Lesson 4. However, by now students should be more sophisticated, and should be able to use algebraic shortcuts to analyze the relationships between the two variables. If not, substitution is still a valid approach.

6.5 SOLUTIONS

b.

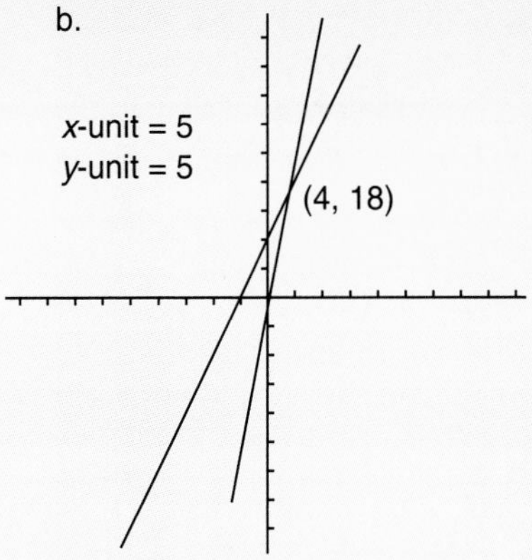

c.

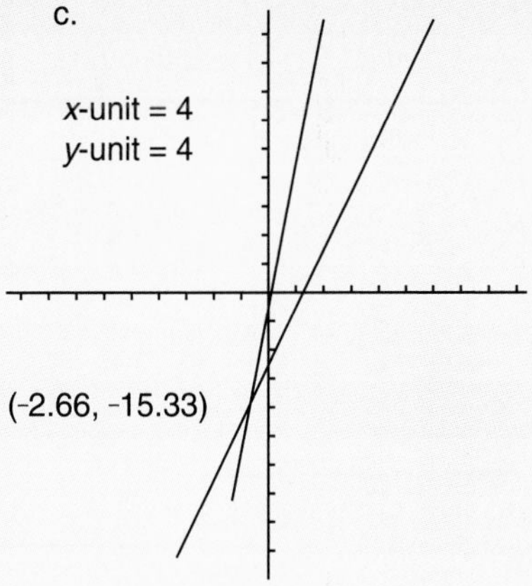

d.

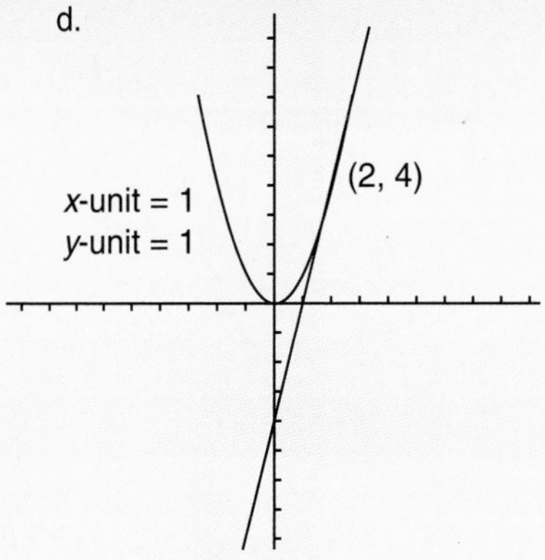

11. a. $x = -3$
   b. $x = 4$
   c. Answers will vary because of difficulty of reading the graph. Exact answer is $x = -8/3$
   d. $x = 2$

REVIEW/PREVIEW **DIVISION AND THE DISTRIBUTIVE LAW**

This serves to review the division of a polynomial by a monomial, with a different format. At the same time, it helps preview Lesson 9.

DISCOVERY **WEIGHTED AVERAGES**

More on grading. See **Grading Policies**, after Lesson 3. To be continued after Lesson 12, with **Can Tara Make a *B*?**

REVIEW/PREVIEW *DIVISION AND THE DISTRIBUTIVE LAW*

To divide a polynomial by a monomial, you can use the multiplication table format. For example, here is the setup to divide $10x^2 - 5x$ by 5.

	?	?
5	$10x^2$	$-5x$

Ask yourself: *What times* $5 = 10x^2$*?* and *what times* $5 = -5x$*?* Write the answers across the top of the table: $2x^2 - x$.

Divide.

27. $\frac{10x^2 - 5x}{x}$ **28.** $\frac{10x^2 - 5x}{5x}$

If the denominator does not divide every term of the numerator, you will still have fractions in the answer. For example:

$$\frac{10x^2 - 5x}{2} = 5x^2 - \frac{5x}{2}$$

Divide.

29. $\frac{10x^2 - 5x}{10}$ **30.** $\frac{10x^2 - 5x}{x^2}$

31. $\frac{10x^2 - 5x}{3}$

DISCOVERY *WEIGHTED AVERAGES*

Mr. Cody counts the quiz average (Q) in his class three times as much as the test average (T). That is, he uses the formula:

$$\frac{3Q + T}{4}$$

(This is called a *weighted* average, because he weights the quizzes three times as much.)

Mr. Fletcher counts the test average twice as much as the quiz average. He uses the formula:

$$\frac{Q + 2T}{3}$$

Oliver's grades:
Quizzes: 75 80 85 95 70
Tests: 95 100 80

Connie's grades:
Quizzes: 95 98 94 88 90
Tests: 80 80 95

32. Which teacher would Oliver prefer to have?

33. Which teacher would Connie prefer to have?

34. Oliver and Connie are both in Mr. Dodge's class. He gives students an A who have an average of 90 or better. If possible, show how Mr. Dodge can weight the tests and quizzes so that

a. Oliver has an A average;

b. Connie has an A average;

c. both Connie and Oliver have an A average.

6.5 SOLUTIONS

12. a. $x < 1$ b. $x > 1$
c. $x = -2$ d. $x = -1$ and $x = 2$

13. $x \le 2/3$ 14. $x = 1$

15. True for all values of x

16. $m < 0$

17. $x = 5$ 18. $x = 2$

19. No solution. For the fraction to equal 1, the numerator must equal the denominator.

20. $x = 11$

21. Δ can equal any number. $\lozenge$ equals zero.

22. $\Delta = 1$. $\lozenge$ can equal any number.

23. $\Delta = (-1/2)\lozenge$ or $\lozenge = -2\Delta$

24. $\lozenge = 2\Delta$ or $\Delta = (1/2)\lozenge$

25. $\Delta = \lozenge$

26. $\lozenge = 2 - \Delta$ or $\Delta = 2 - \lozenge$

27. $10x - 5$ 28. $2x - 1$

29. $x^2 - x/2$ 30. $10 - 5/x$

31. $(10x^2)/3 - (5x)/3$

32. For Oliver, $Q = 81$ and $T = 91.67 \approx 92$

$$\frac{3Q+T}{4} = \frac{3(81)+92}{4} = \frac{335}{4} = 83.75 \approx 84$$

$$\frac{Q+2T}{3} = \frac{81+2(92)}{3} = \frac{81+184}{3} = \frac{265}{3} \approx 88.33 \approx 88$$

Oliver would prefer Mr. Fletcher.

33. For Connie, $Q = 93$ and $T = 85$

$$\frac{3Q+T}{4} = \frac{3(93)+85}{4} = 91$$

$$\frac{Q+2T}{3} = \frac{93+2(85)}{3} \approx 87.67 \approx 88$$

Connie would prefer Mr. Cody.

34. a. For Oliver to get an A, the tests would need to be counted more heavily. One way is to find n such that $\frac{81 + n(92)}{n+1} \ge 90$.

b. For Connie to get an A, the quizzes would need to be counted more heavily. One possibility is to find n such that $\frac{n(93) + 88}{n+1} \ge 90$.

c. By trial and error find n and m such that $\frac{n(93) + m(85)}{n+m} \ge 90$ and $\frac{n(81) + m(92)}{n+m} \ge 90$.

This is impossible, since for Oliver to get an A, m must be greater than n, but the reverse must be true for Connie to get an A.

LESSON 6.6

Solving Techniques: Addition and Subtraction

You will need:

the Lab Gear 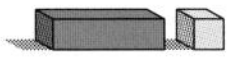

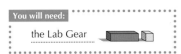

One key to solving linear equations is a technique based on this fact: If two quantities are equal, and you **add or subtract the same quantity from both**, you end up with equal quantities. This provides you with a method for simplifying equations.

USING THE LAB GEAR

1. Write the equation shown by this figure.

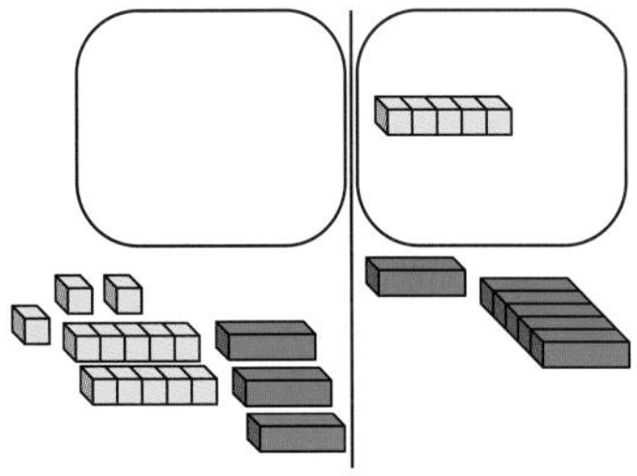

2. Remove three x-blocks from each side. Add 5 to each side and simplify. Finally, form rectangles on both sides, setting them up to show a common side.

3. Write the solution to the equation. Explain.

For each figure in problems 4-7, write the equation, then solve for x. Use the method shown in problem 2.

4.

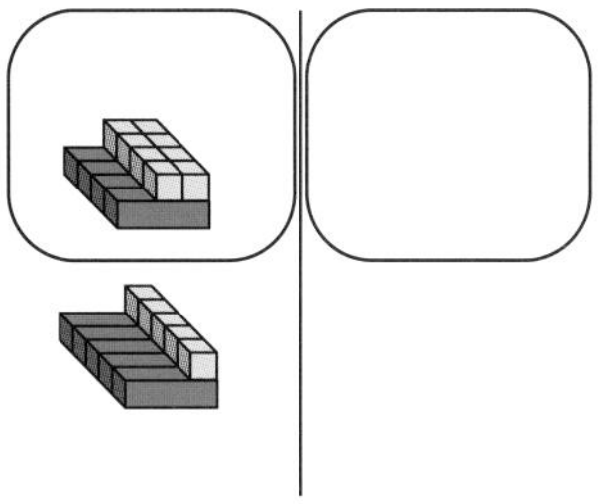

5.

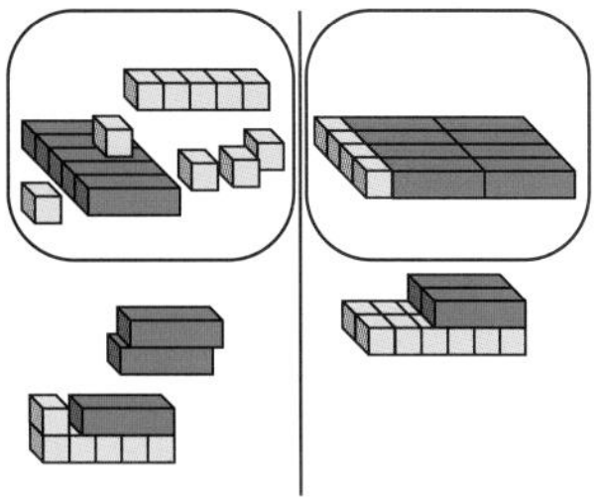

6.

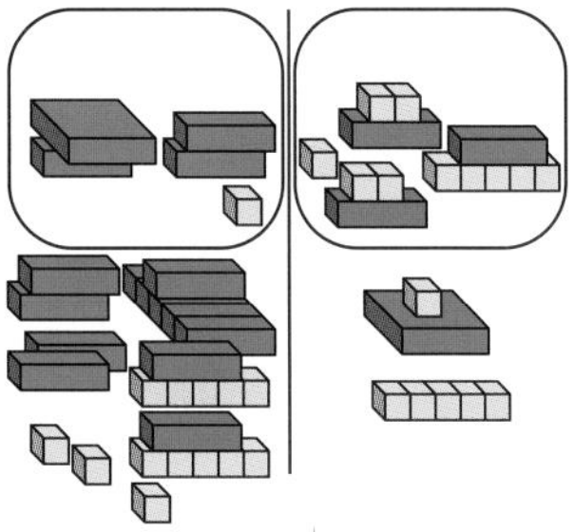

▼ 6.6 Solving Techniques: Addition and Subtraction

Core Sequence: 1-21

Suitable for Homework: 14-33

Useful for Assessment: 20-21

What this Lesson is About:

- Adding and subtracting the same amount to both sides of an equation
- An application of linear functions and equations
- Mathematics as a tool for decision-making
- Preview of more difficult trinomial factoring

*I*n this lesson we start to discuss algebraic equation-solving techniques explicitly. However, do not teach the "division-multiplication" technique at this point. If necessary, you can hint at it, using the blocks, or better, ask students who know this technique to share what they know. However, there is no need to do this yet, as a full discussion will happen in Lesson 8.

USING THE LAB GEAR

*M*onitor the students' work, being alert to any techniques or shortcuts they may have discovered. Challenge them to explain and defend the most interesting techniques, by presenting them to the class on the overhead projector.

6.6 SOLUTIONS

1. $3x + 13 = 6x - 5$
2. $18 = 3x$

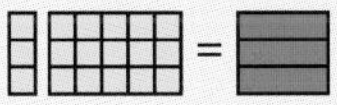

3. $x = 6$
4. $5x - 5 - (4x - 8) = 0$
$5x - 5 + 5 - (4x - 8 + 8) = 5 - 8$
$5x - 4x = -3$
$x = -3$
5. $x - x + 5 - 1 - x - (5x + 9 - 1) = 12 - 2x - (8x + 4)$
$x = 3$
6. $2x + x - x + 5x - x + 5 - x + 5 - x + 3 - (2x - x^2 - x + 1) = 5 + x^2 - 1 - (2x + 6 - x - 4)$
$x = -5/2$
7. $3(x + 2) - [2(2x + 1) + 5] = 2(x + 6) - [3(x + 1) + 2x + 1]$
$x = 9/2$
8. a.

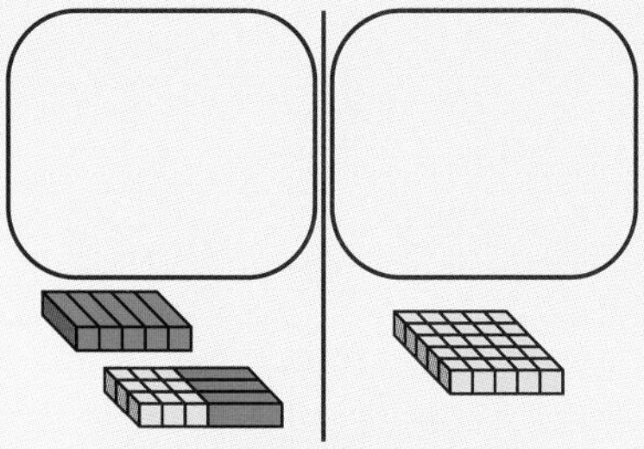

b. Answers will vary.
c. $x = 2$

9. a.

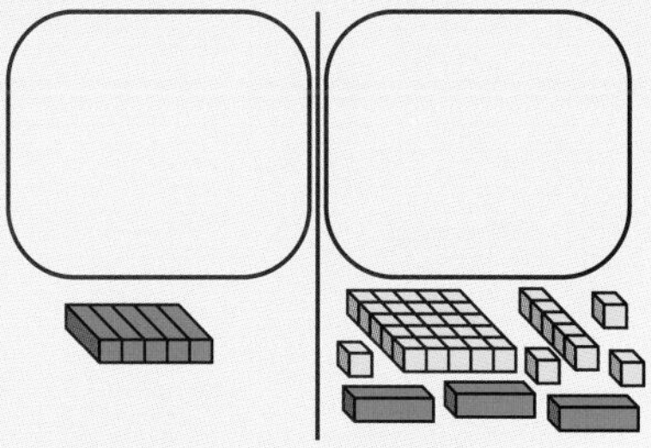

b. Answers will vary.
c. $x = 17$

10. a.

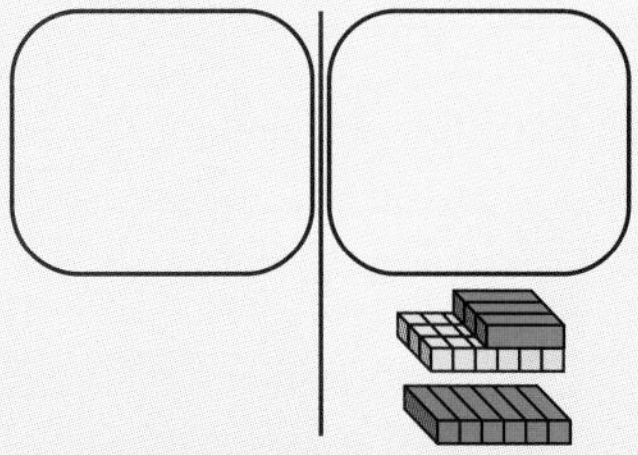

At the end, you may discuss how some of these problems could be solved without the blocks, using the technique of adding and subtracting the same amount from both sides.

SAVINGS PLANS

Students once again use tables to solve a real-life problem. The difference is that writing and solving equations is emphasized and perhaps being seen as a shortcut.

7.

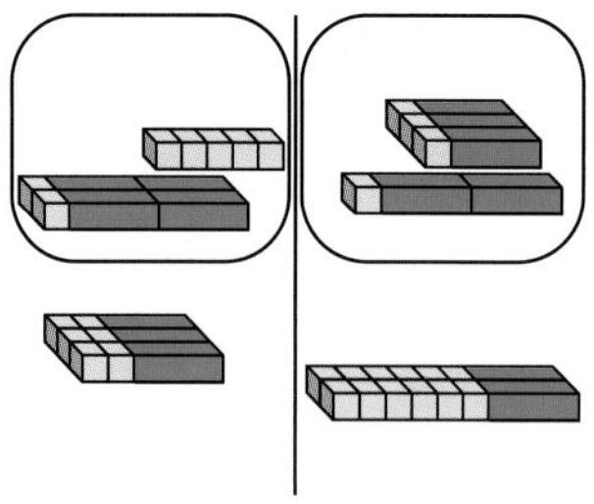

For each problem, 8-11,

a. Model the equation with the Lab Gear.
b. Solve it using the techniques you have learned with the blocks. Record algebraically at least two of the intermediate steps.
c. Write the final answer.

8. $5x + 3(x + 3) = 25$

9. $5x = 25 + 3(x + 3)$

10. $0 = 3(6 - x) + 6x$

11. $15 - 4(x - 2) + 2x = 3$

12. Start with the equation $x = 3$.

a. Add and/or subtract the same amount from both sides repeatedly, getting the equation to be more and more complicated. (The quantities you add and subtract may include x. You may use the Lab Gear. If you do, record some of the steps.) Write the final equation on paper and give it to a classmate.
b. Solve a classmate's equation. If you both do your work correctly, the solution should be $x = 3$. (Again, you may use the Lab Gear.)

SAVINGS PLANS

In this section, you can apply equation solving to real-life problems.

13. Exploration Tania Rhine had \$123. For her birthday, she received \$175 from her grandparents, and her allowance was raised to \$11 a week. What is the largest amount she can spend every week, if

a. she wants to have a total of \$600 by her next birthday?
b. she wants to have \$100 left by her next birthday?

Beatrice had \$321 in her savings account on September 1. She planned to save \$14 a week.

14. Make a table or graph showing how her total savings change as a function of the number of weeks that have passed.

15. Look for a pattern in your table or graph. How much would Bea have at the end of:

a. 4 weeks? b. 52 weeks?
c. n weeks? d. 2 years?
e. n years?

16. Beatrice is considering another possible savings plan. She wants to go to a movie every week, which means she would spend \$5 out of the \$14. She would deposit the rest in her savings account. Make a table or graph of this savings plan to compare with your first one.

17. With the second savings plan, how much would Beatrice have at the end of:

a. 4 weeks?
b. n weeks?

18. Beatrice is saving for a stereo that costs \$549. How long will it take to reach her goal under each savings plan? Try to answer this question without extending your tables or graphs. Instead, try to write and solve equations.

6.6 SOLUTIONS

b. Answers will vary.
c. $x = -6$

11. a.

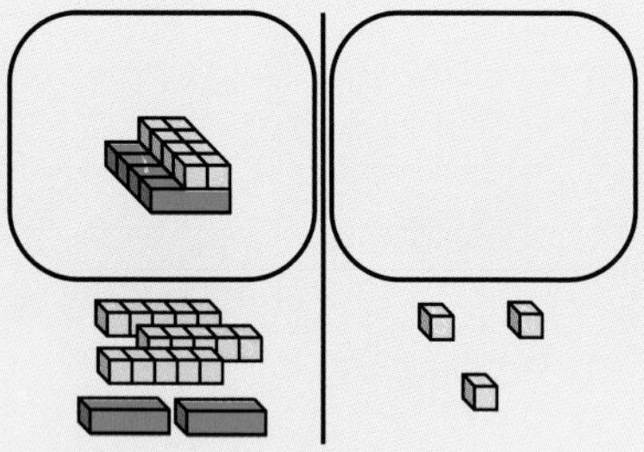

b. Answers will vary.
c. $x = 10$

12. Equations will vary.

13. a. $123 + 175 + 11(52) - 52x = 600$
x is approximately \$5.19
b. $870 - 52x = 100$
x is approximately \$14.80

14.

No. of Weeks	Savings
1	335
2	349
3	363
4	377
5	391
n	$14n + 321$

15. a. \$377
b. \$1049
c. $14n + 321$ dollars
d. \$1777
e. $14(52)n + 321 = 728n + 321$ dollars

16.

No. of Weeks	Savings
1	330
2	339
3	348
4	357
5	366
n	$9n + 321$

17. a. \$357
b. $9n + 321$ dollars

18. First Savings Plan: $14n + 321 = 549$
$n = 16.3$. Beatrice would have enough money for her stereo after saving for 17 weeks when she will have saved \$559.00.
Second savings plan: $9n + 321 = 549$
$n = 25.3$. Beatrice would have enough money for her stereo after saving for 26 weeks, when she will have saved \$555.

19. $21n + 235$

20. $21n + 235 = 549$. $n = 14.95$. Abraham will have enough money for the stereo after saving for 15 weeks when he will have saved \$550.
a. Abraham will have \$550 in 15 weeks. Because Beatrice's first

19. Abraham is also saving for the stereo. He has \$235 in his savings account on October 1 and deposits \$21 per week. Write an expression that gives the amount of money that Abraham has after n weeks.

20. Use tables, graphs, or equations to answer these questions. Show your work. Who will have enough to buy the stereo first, Abraham or Beatrice,
    a. if Beatrice has been following her first plan?
    b. if Beatrice has been following her second plan?

21. On January 15, Bea and Abe see an advertisement about the stereo. For two weeks, it will be on sale for \$499. Will either one of them have enough money to buy the stereo then? Do you think one of them will already have bought the stereo? Will your answer depend on what savings plan Bea was following? Explain, showing all your work.

MORE EQUATION SOLVING

Use any of the methods you have learned to solve these equations. Show your work.

22. $3x + 3 - 5x + 6 = 9x - 3x + 23$
23. $5x - 6 = 13x - 5 - 9x$
24. $10x + 23 = 6x + 27$
25. $2 - 3x + 5 = 7x - 4 - 8x$
26. $4x + 5 = 4x + 7$
27. $3x + 4x = 8 + 7x - 8$

DISCOVERY HARDER FACTORING

Factor these trinomials by making a rectangle with the Lab Gear and writing a multiplication equation relating length, width, and area.

28. $x^2 + xy + x + y$
29. $3x^2 + 5x + 2$
30. $6x^2 + 7x + 2$
31. $6x^2 + 19x + 10$
32. $3x^2 + 16x + 5$
33. $4x^2 + 20x + 25$

MORE EQUATION SOLVING

More practice. You may save these problems for later review. If they are being done in class, allow the use of the Lab Gear.

DISCOVERY HARDER FACTORING

The section is optional because it is not important for students to learn to factor trinomials where the leading coefficient is not 1. However, since it is relatively easy with the help of the Lab Gear, you may assign this section and discuss the patterns that emerge.

6.6 SOLUTIONS

plan will accumulate \$559 in 17 weeks and she started saving 4 weeks before Abraham, she will have the money to buy the stereo first.
   b. Abraham will have the money first. In 19 weeks Beatrice's second plan accumulates only \$492.00.

21. Using a calendar, one finds that there are 19 savings weeks from Sept. 1 to Jan. 15, and 15 savings weeks from Oct. 1 to Jan. 15.
    Abe: 21(15) + 235 = \$550
    Bea (1): 14(19) + 321 = \$587
    Bea (2): 9(19) + 321 = \$492
    Abe started saving on Oct. 1 and could not afford the stereo until Jan. 15 except for the sale price. On Jan. 15 Abe and Bea (1) will be able to buy the stereo on sale. If Bea follows savings plan (2), she will be able to buy the stereo one week after the sale starts.

22. $x = -1.75$
23. $x = 1$
24. $x = 1$
25. $x = 5.5$
26. No solution
27. True for all values of x.
28. $(x + 1)(x + y) = x^2 + xy + x + y$
29. $(3x + 2)(x + 1) = 3x^2 + 5x + 2$
30. $(3x + 2)(2x + 1) = 6x^2 + 7x + 2$
31. $(3x + 2)(2x + 5) = 6x^2 + 19x + 10$
32. $(3x + 1)(x + 5) = 3x^2 + 16x + 5$
33. $(2x + 5)(2x + 5) = 4x^2 + 20x + 25$

▼ 6.7 How Much More Than? How Many Times as Much?

Core Sequence: 1-21

Suitable for Homework: 1-22, but see below

Useful for Assessment: 5-7, 19-21

What this Lesson is About:

- Two ways of comparing quantities
- Visualizing quantitative information
- Proportional thinking

Almost all of this lesson could be assigned for homework. The sections that involve the Lab Gear could really be done without it, by using the Lab Gear as a mental model, and sketching if necessary. However, almost every part of the lesson could provide a great springboard for class discussion, and you may want to do much of it in class, or at least make sure to allot sufficient time for an extended discussion of the homework.

This lesson focuses on the difference between comparing by division and comparing by subtraction. There are two things going on here.

- One is, in a subtle way, the link between Lessons 6 and 8 on equation-solving techniques. While both of those involve operations, this lesson highlights the difference between them.

LESSON 6.7

How Much More Than? How Many Times as Much?

You will need:

graph paper 

the Lab Gear 

COMPARING AGES

On Mark's 12th birthday, he said to his little brother Gordon, "You'd better do what I say. Now I'm twice as old as you are."

The six-year-old math whiz wasn't scared. "That's nothing," he laughed. "A few years ago, you were four times as old as I was. And not long after I was born, you were *thirty-seven* times as old as I was."

1. How old were the two brothers when
  a. Mark was four times as old as Gordon?
  b. Mark was 37 times as old?

2. a. As Mark and Gordon get older, does the *difference* between their ages increase, decrease, or stay the same? Explain.
  b. Does the *ratio* of their ages increase, decrease, or stay the same? Explain.

3. Mark was born in 1980. On the same axes, make two graphs, one showing Mark's age as a function of time and the other showing Gordon's age as a function of time. Label the *x*-axis *years after 1980* and the *y*-axis *age.* Compare the two graphs.

4. a. Make a graph showing the *difference* between the two boys' ages as a function of time. Label the *x*-axis *years after 1980* and the *y*-axis *difference in ages.* Describe your graph.
  b. Make a graph showing the *ratio* of Mark's age to Gordon's age as a function of time. Label the *x*-axis *years after 1980* and the *y*-axis *ratio of ages.* Describe your graph.
  c. Compare the two graphs.

5.
  a. Why do we usually compare people's ages using differences instead of ratios?
  b. What do you think is the smallest possible value for this ratio of Mark's age to Gordon's age? Explain.

6. Beau and Bea said, "The ratio of our ages will always be the same!" How could this be? Discuss.

7. On Mark's 12th birthday, his mother was three times as old as Mark. Was she ever twice as old? Was she ever four times as old? Explain.

COMPARING NUMBERS

When comparing the size of two positive numbers, for example 5 and 15, you can ask two different questions.

- 15 is *how much more than* 5?
- 15 is *how many times as much* as 5?

The question *How much more than...?* is answered using subtraction, as shown in this figure. Since $15 - 5 = 10$, you can say that 15 is 10 more than 5, (or 10 is the difference of 15 and 5).

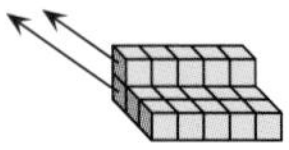

6.7 SOLUTIONS

1. a. Mark was 8 and Gordon was 2.
   b. Mark was 74 months old and Gordon was 2 months old.
2. a. The difference between their ages is always 6 years.
   b. The ratio of their age changes.

Mark's Age in Years	Gordon's Age in Years	Ratio of Mark's to Gordon's Age
12	6	2
11	5	2.2
10	4	2.5
9	3	3
8	2	4
7	1	7
6.167	0.167	37

The ratio decreases as the boys grow older.

3.

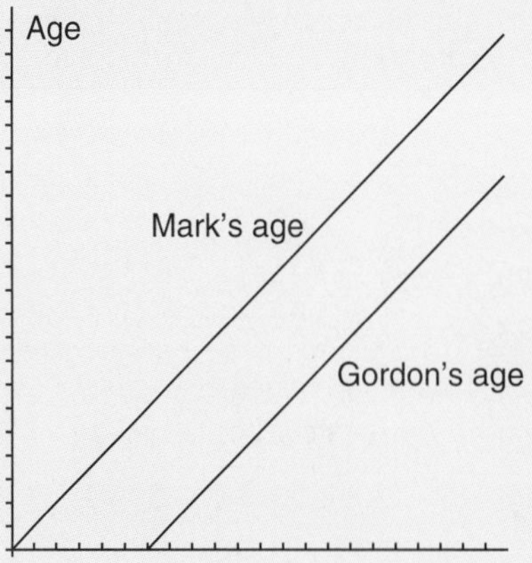

a.

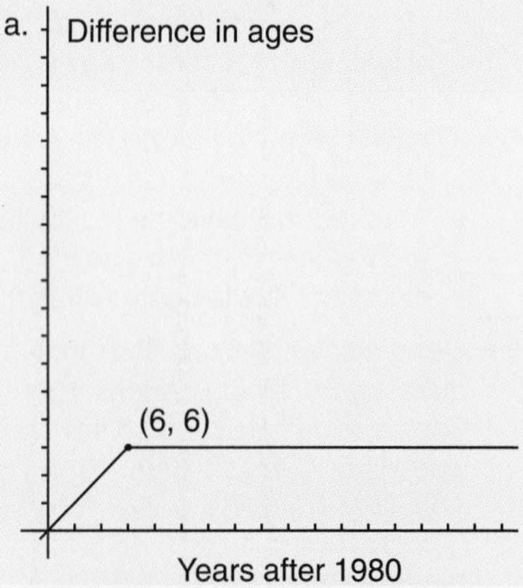

The graph is a line at a 45-degree angle with the *x*-axis until it reaches (6, 6). It is then a horizontal line, 6 units above the *x*-axis.

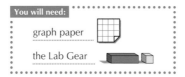

The question *How many times as much...?* is answered using division, as shown with the Lab Gear. Since $15/5 = 3$, 15 is 3 times as much as 5, (or 3 is the ratio of 15 and 5).

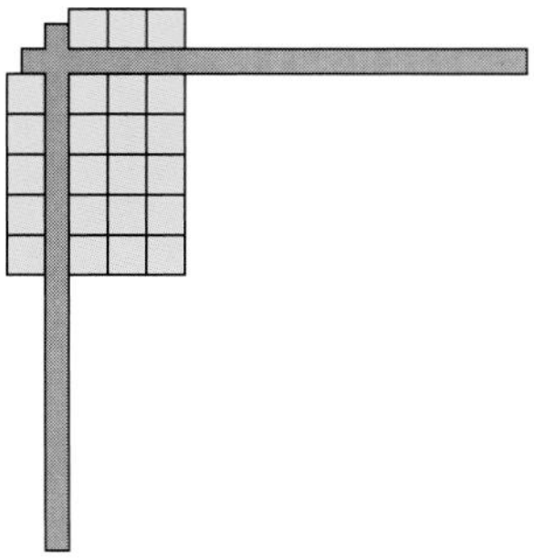

Answer both questions about these pairs of numbers in problems 8-13. Show how you got your answers. In some cases, you may want to use the Lab Gear.

a. The first number is *how much more than* the second?

b. The first number is *how many times as much* as the second?

8. 35 and 5

9. 10 and 10

10. 9 and 8

11. 16 and 4

12. 16 and $\frac{1}{4}$

13. 4 and 16

COMPARING ALGEBRAIC EXPRESSIONS

Sometimes you need to compare quantities given by formulas that involve variables. The same methods can be used as when comparing numbers.

To find out *how much more* $5x$ is than x, subtract $5x - x$, as shown.

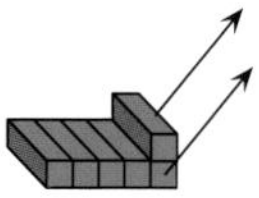

To find out *how many times as much* $5x$ is than x, divide as shown.

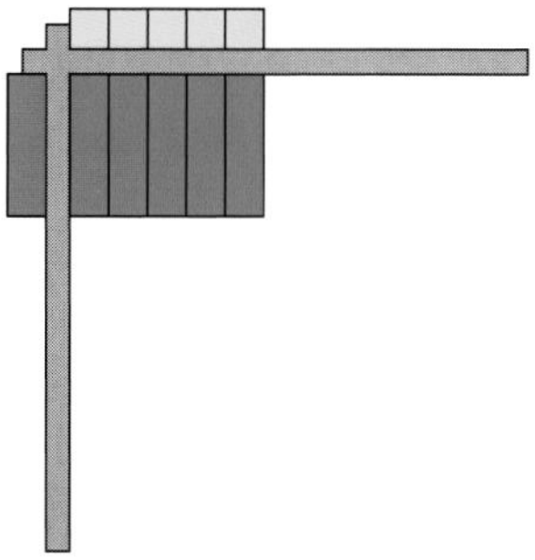

For each pair of expressions in problems 14-18:

a. The first expression is *how much more than* the second?

b. The first expression is *how many times as much* as the second?

14. $5x$ and x

15. $10x$ and 5

16. $10x$ and $5x$

17. $8xy$ and $2x$

18. $2x + 2y$ and $x + y$

APPLICATIONS

19. The Statue of Liberty, which guards the entrance to New York harbor, was given to the United States by the people of France in honor of the centennial of American independence. The statue measures 111 feet 1 inch, from her heel to the top of her head. She was designed by Frederic Auguste Bartholdi. Suppose Mr. Bartholdi had used as a model for the statue a woman who was 5 feet 1 inch tall.

a. How much taller is the statue than the model?

b. How many times as tall is the statue?

c. Which of these two numbers would have been useful to Mr. Bartholdi when designing the statue? Explain.

• More important, this lesson continues the work in proportional reasoning, with the immediate goal of making it easier for students to deal with equations involving rational expressions.

COMPARING AGES

This section is an introduction to the key idea of the lesson, the comparison between difference and ratio.

Age problems are not really "real-world applications" since the only context in which they are ever explored is school mathematics (plus, occasionally, recreational mathematics).

Students would probably enjoy guessing your age. Let them guess only at the ratio between your age and the most common age among the students. Then tell them if their guesses are high or low. Tell them they will have only three guesses, and must plan their strategies carefully.

You can find some age riddles at the end of Lesson 8.

COMPARING NUMBERS

Discuss these problems and perhaps supplement them with examples orally. Students will have no trouble finding the answers once they realize that all they have to do is divide the first number by the second, but it's worth dwelling on the cases where the answer is 1, less than 1, or fractional for the ratios, and 0 or negative for the differences.

6.7 SOLUTIONS

4. b.

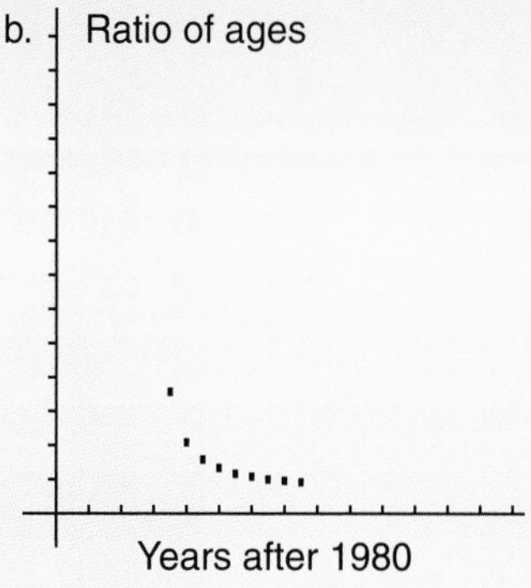

The graph is a curve that decends quickly at first and then more and more gradually as x increases. There are no points for values of x less than 6.

c. The first graph is a line and the second is a curve. The first has y-values for all x-values greater than or equal to zero, and the second has y-values for x-values greater than 6. The first has a constant y-value for x-values greater than or equal to 6, the second has different y-values for each x-value greater than 6.

5. a. We usually compare people's ages using differences instead of ratios because the difference remains constant whereas the ratio changes over time. Using the difference one can tell if two people are or are not about the same age. Using ratios one cannot tell if two peoples' ages are close or not. If the ratio is three, the two people could be 2 yrs and 6 yrs old or 30 yrs and 90 yrs old.

b. The smallest possible ratio of Mark's age to Gordon's age is slightly more than one. When Mark is 90, the ratio is $90/84 = 1.07$.

6. If Beau and Bea are the same age the ratio of their ages will always be 1.

7. Mark's mother will be twice as old as Mark on his 24th birthday when she will be 48. She was 4 times as old when Mark was 8 and she was 32.

8. a. 35 is 30 more than 5.
b. 35 is 7 times as much as 5.

9. a. 10 is 0 more than 10.
b. 10 is 1 time as much as 10.

10. a. 9 is 1 more than 8.
b. 9 is 9/8 times as much as 8.

COMPARING ALGEBRAIC EXPRESSIONS

*T*his is a straightforward generalization of the previous section.

APPLICATIONS

*T*hese would work well as group exercises, followed by whole-class discussion.

DISCOVERY ***TOURNAMENTS***

*T*his is another application of triangular numbers.

20. If Reg takes the bus to work, it takes him about an hour and 15 minutes. If he drives, it takes him about 45 minutes.

a. How much longer does it take on the bus?

b. How many times as long does it take?

c. Which number would be more important to Reg in deciding which method of transportation to use? Why?

21. The A.R. Bagel Company charged 30 cents for a bagel in 1973 and 60 cents in 1983. During the same period of time, the hourly wage of a bagel deliverer increased from $2.50 per hour to $5.00 per hour. The company president said, "We try to pay our employees the highest possible wages and charge our customers the lowest possible prices. In a period of high inflation, our prices have risen only 30 cents in ten years. Yet, during the same time, we doubled hourly wages." How might the president of the Bagel Workers' Union describe this situation? Discuss.

DISCOVERY ***TOURNAMENTS***

22. Twelve teams are playing in a tournament.

a. Each team must be scheduled to play three games with each other team. How many games must be scheduled? (Hint: Start by thinking of a smaller tournament.)

b. The teams play "best out of three" games. In other words, the third game of the three may not get played. What is the smallest number of games that might be played?

6.7 SOLUTIONS

11. a. 16 is 12 more than 4.
 b. 16 is 4 times as much as 4.

12. a. 16 is 15.75 more than 1/4.
 b. 16 is 64 times as much as 1/4.

13. a. 4 is -12 more than 16.
 b. 4 is 1/4 times as much as 16.

14. a. $5x$ is $4x$ more than x.
 b. $5x$ is 5 times as much as x.

15. a. $10x$ is $10x - 5$ more than 5.
 b. $10x$ is $2x$ times as much as 5.

16. a. $10x$ is $5x$ more than $5x$.
 b. $10x$ is 2 times as much as $5x$.

17. a. $8xy$ is $8xy - 2x$ more than $2x$.
 b. $8xy$ is $4y$ times as much as $2x$.

18. a. $2x + 2y$ is $x + y$ more than $x + y$.
 b. $2x + 2y$ is 2 times as much as $x + y$.

19. a. The statue is 106 ft. taller than the model.
 b. The statue is 21.85 times as tall as the model.
 c. By knowing that the whole statue is 21.85 times as tall as the model, Mr. Bartholdi would also know how many times longer were parts of the body such as the arms, legs, or face.

20. a. The bus takes 30 minutes longer than the car.
 b. The bus takes 5/3 times as much time as the car.
 c. The difference would be more important, because he could use it to figure out what time to leave for work.

21. The president of the Bagel Workers' Union would point out that the price of the bagel went up twice the amount, like the wages in the 10-year period. The president of the A.R. Bagel Company is being deceptive when he uses the difference in the prices of the bagels, when he should be using a ratio as he did when he compared the wage increase.

22. a. 198 games
 b. 132 games

LESSON 6.8

Solving Techniques: Multiplication and Division

You will need:

the Lab Gear 

graph paper 

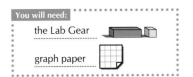

Another key to solving equations is the fact that you can *multiply* or *divide both sides by the same number* (as long as it's not zero).

For example, if $3x = 15$, then divide both sides by 3, and you find that $x = 5$.

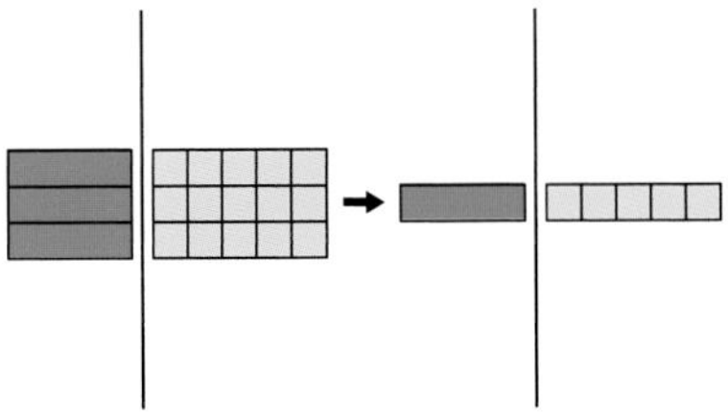

Of course, some divisions cannot be shown easily with the blocks. If you end up with $4y = 7$, then dividing both sides by 4 will reveal that $y = 7/4$. This is impossible to show with the Lab Gear.

USING THE LAB GEAR

Write and solve these equations.

1. 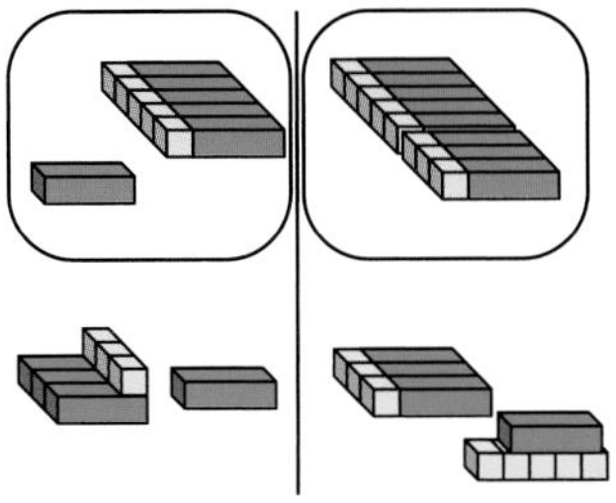

2. 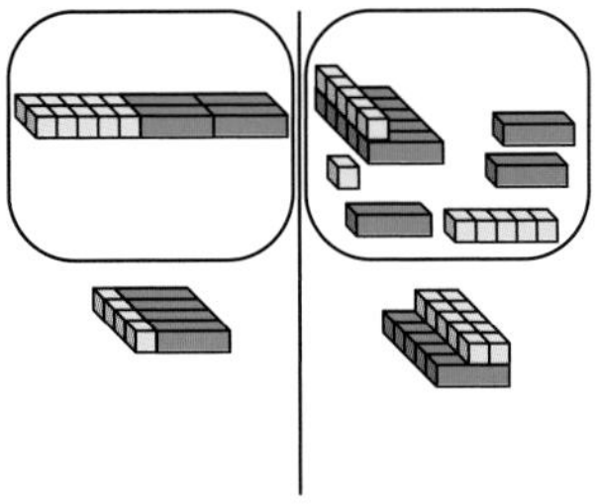

3. 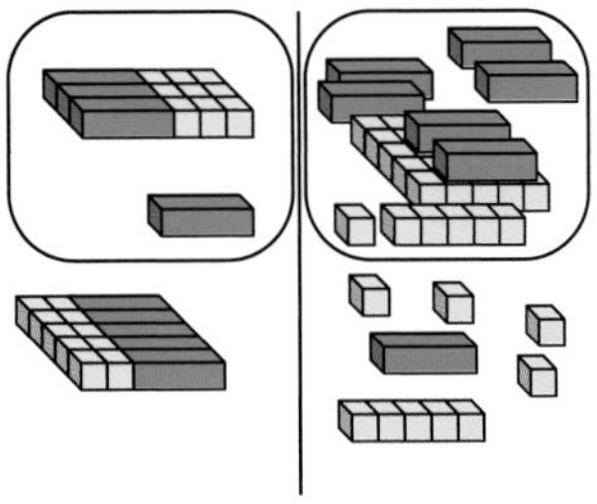

4. 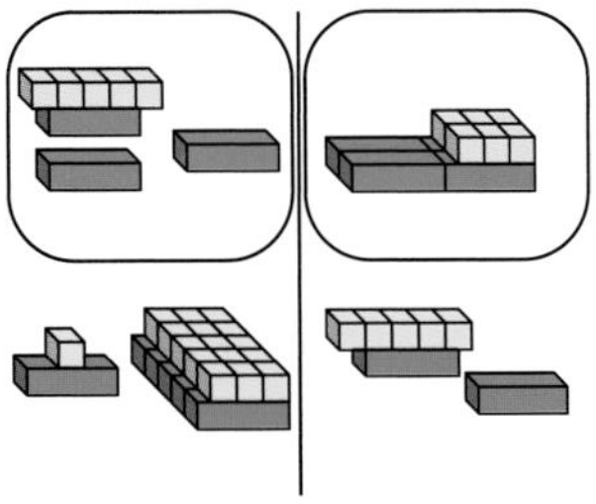

6.8 Solving Techniques: Multiplication and Division

Core Sequence: 1-27

Suitable for Homework: 15-31, 33

Useful for Assessment: 13

What this Lesson is About:

- Multiplying and dividing by the same amount on both sides of an equation
- Solving for one variable in terms of another
- Equivalent equations in two variables
- Equations with whole number solutions

By this time, through using the Lab Gear, many students will probably have come up with the strategy of dividing or multiplying both sides by the same number. We state it for the first time here. In addition, the idea is applied in two situations: solving for y in terms of x, and recognizing equivalent equations.

6.8 SOLUTIONS

1. $4x - 3 - (6x + 5) = 3x + 3 + 5 - x - (8x + 8)$
   $x = 2$
2. $4(x + 1) - 2(2x + 5) = 5x - 10 - (5x - 5 + 3x + 6)$
   $x = -5/3$
3. $5(x + 2) - (3(x + 3) + x) = x + 9 - (31 + 4x - 2x)$
   $x = -23/2$
4. $6x - 16 - (3x - 5) = 2x - 5 - (4x - 3)$
   $x = 9/5$

USING THE LAB GEAR
USING RECIPROCALS

There is no one way that is best for solving linear equations. It is perfectly legitimate for students to have differences of opinion. Of course, getting the right solution is the goal.

*U***sing Reciprocals** does not explicitly mention the strategy of multiplying by the reciprocal of the coefficient of x or the number outside the parentheses, but the title provides a rather obvious hint. Observe how students approach these problems, then discuss the summary.

If you prefer the method of "clearing fractions first," you may introduce it in the context of that discussion.

SOLVING FOR *y*
EQUIVALENT EQUATIONS

This material previews work in Chapter 10, where we will work on simultaneous equations.

USING RECIPROCALS

Solve these without the Lab Gear.

5. $\frac{2}{3}x = 18$ **6.** $\frac{1}{5}x = 99$

Solve these by multiplying or dividing first, and then again by first distributing the number in front of the parentheses. You should get the same answers by both methods.

7. $7(x - 2) = 30$ **8.** $12(x + 6) = 48$

9. $\frac{1}{3}(2x - 4) = 5$ **10.** $\frac{4}{5}(2 - 8x) = 16$

11. $\frac{1}{2}(2x - 4) = 5$ **12.** $\frac{5}{4}(2 - 8x) = 16$

13. Summary Use examples.

a. Explain how to decide which of the two methods (distributing first or later) one should use in problems 7-12.

b. Explain how to decide what number to multiply or divide both sides by when solving an equation.

14. Start with $x = -3$.

a. Create an equation by adding and/or subtracting the same amount from both sides repeatedly, and by multiplying and/or dividing both sides by the same amount repeatedly. Write the final equation on paper and give it to a classmate.

b. Solve a classmate's equation. If you both do your work correctly, the solution should be -3.

SOLVING FOR *y*

You have learned to multiply or divide by a number when solving an equation containing one variable. This is also a useful technique when working with equations containing two variables, such as this one, $4y - 8x = 0$.

In a two-variable equation, it is often useful to solve for one variable *in terms of* another. This means that one variable is alone on one side of the equation.

By adding $8x$ to both sides, it is easy to rewrite this equation so that the y's are on one side and the x's are on the other:

$$4y = 8x.$$

Dividing both sides by 4 gives

$$y = 2x.$$

Transform each equation below so that y is in terms of x. You may use the Lab Gear.

15. $3y - 6x = 9$ **16.** $6x - 3y = 12$

17. $x - y = 1$ **18.** $6x - 5y = 0$

EQUIVALENT EQUATIONS

19. Draw axes and plot three (x, y) pairs that satisfy the graph of $4y - 8x = 0$. Describe the graph.

20. Find three (x, y) pairs that satisfy $y = 2x$ and draw the graph. Compare it with the graph in problem 19. What do you notice? Explain.

If equations in two variables have the same graph on the Cartesian coordinate system, they are called *equivalent equations.*

6.8 SOLUTIONS

5. $x = 27$
6. $x = 495$
7. $x = 44/7$
8. $x = -2$
9. $x = 19/2$
10. $x = -9/4$
11. $x = 7$
12. $x = -27/20$
13. a. When distributing results in integers and not in fractions, it is easier to distribute first. Otherwise, when distributing results in fractions, it is easier to multiply or divide both sides of the equation first.
    b. One multiplies by the reciprocal of the number before the parentheses in equations similar to #7-12. For equations like #5 or 6, one multiplies by the reciprocal of the coefficient of x.
14. Answers will vary.
15. $y = 3 + 2x$
16. $y = 2x - 4$
17. $y = x - 1$
18. $y = (6/5)x$
19. The graph is a direct variation graph with a y to x ratio of 2.

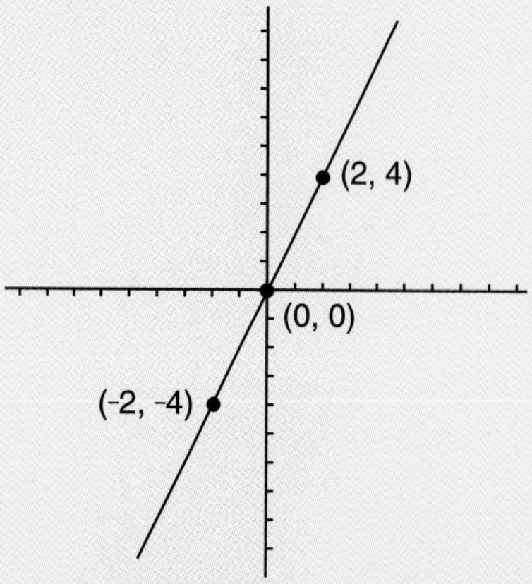

20. The graph of $y = 2x$ is the same as the graph of $4y - 8x = 0$.

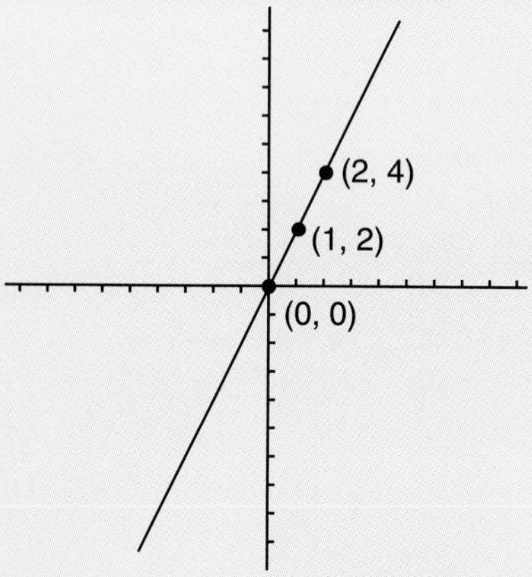

21. Explain how you could have determined *without graphing* that the equation $4y - 8x = 0$ is equivalent to $y = 2x$.

22. a. Write an equation that is equivalent to $6y = 12x$, but looks different.
    b. Describe what the graphs of both equations would look like.

For each group of equations decide which ones, if any, are equivalent equations. If you are unsure, you might want to solve the equations for y, make some tables, or draw some graphs.

23. $x + y = 2$
    $2x + 2y = 2$
    $2x + 2y = 4$

24. $x/y = 12$
    $y/x = 12$
    $y = 12x$

25. $3x - y = 6$
    $2y = 6x - 12$
    $y - 3x = 6$

26. $0.8x = y$
    $x - 0.2x = y$
    $y - 4/5x = 0$

27. $1.2\,x = y$
    $x + 0.2x - y = 0$
    $2.4x - 2y - x = 0$

PUZZLES *AGE RIDDLES*

28. At age 3, Henry could count to 12. How far could he count by age 21?

29. Augustus De Morgan lived in the nineteenth century. He said, "I was x years old in the year x^2." In what year was he born?

30. Diophantus spent one-sixth of his life in childhood and one-twelfth of his life in youth. He spent one-seventh more of his life as a bachelor. Five years after he was married, his son was born. His son lived half as long as his father and died four years before his father. How many years did Diophantus live? How old was he when he got married?

31. Make up an age riddle.

32. Solve a classmate's riddle.

RESEARCH *FAMOUS MATHEMATICIANS*

33. Prepare a report about Diophantus or Augustus De Morgan. What were their contributions to mathematics?

PUZZLES ***AGE RIDDLES***

Problem 28 is a joke. A student who answers 84 has mastered proportions, but not when to use them!

As a follow-up to problem 29, you may ask students to find out if the same question can be asked about anyone in the 20th century.

You may collect the best student-created age riddles, and make a take-home quiz out of them. Do not teach any "canned" methods for solving age problems. Let students find their own solutions, supporting them with hints and suggestions.

RESEARCH ***FAMOUS MATHEMATICIANS***

Do not assign this to the whole class. A pair of students in need of extra credit could collaborate on each of the two mathematicians. They could produce an oral report to present to the class or an illustrated bulletin board display.

6.8 SOLUTIONS

21. When $4y - 8x = 0$ is solved for y in terms of x, the resulting equation is $y = 2x$. This means they are equivalent equations.

22. a. Answers will vary. Sample: $y = 2x$
    b. Both graphs are the same direct variation graph of a line through the origin with a y to x ratio of 2.

23. $x + y = 2$ and $2x + 2y = 4$ are equivalent equations.

24. $y/x = 12$ and $y = 12x$ are equivalent equations.

25. $3x - y = 6$ and $2y = 6x - 12$ are equivalent equations.

26. All three equations are equivalent.

27. $1.2x = y$ and $x + 0.2x - y = 0$ are equivalent equations.

28. There is not enough information to determine solution. (See Teacher's Notes.)

29. Augustus was born in 1806.

30. Diophantus lived for 84 years. He got married when he was 33 years old.

31. Riddles will vary.

32. Solutions will vary.

33. Reports will vary.

THINKING WRITING 6.B Constant Differences, Constant Ratios

Core Sequence: 1-10

Suitable for Homework: 1-10

Useful for Assessment: 10

What this Assignment is About:

- Review of direct variation
- Review of signed number arithmetic
- Graphing linear functions
- The concept of parameter
- Preview of slope

This is also a preview of work in Chapter 10 with linear combinations of the form $ax - by = c$. (Students see these as a variation on constant differences, just as they see $ax + by = c$ as a variation on constant sums.)

This is a much richer assignment than might appear at first sight. The concept of parameter is used for the first time (though it was used informally before, for example when discussing constant sum and product graphs). The concept of slope is previewed. Issues of symmetry and inverse functions are also hinted at.

Students will probably have some trouble understanding the idea of a parameter, without some introduction. Discuss this and give examples in class before assigning the Report.

THINKING WRITING 6.B Constant Differences, Constant Ratios

You will need: graph paper

CONSTANT DIFFERENCE GRAPHS

These three (x, y) pairs follow a pattern: (6, 0), (7, 1), (-4, -10). The difference between y and x always equals 6. The equation $y - x = -6$ describes the relationship between x and y.

Use the same pair of axes for all the graphs in problems 1-5.

1. Graph $y - x = -6$.
2. Choose any other integer D and graph the function $y - x = D$. (For example, if you chose the integer 10, you would graph the equation $y - x = 10$.) Label the graph with its equation.
3. Graph several other functions of the form $y - x = D$. For each graph, you will need to choose a different number for D. Remember to try negative numbers and fractions as well as positive integers.
4. Compare your *constant difference* graphs with the *constant sum* graphs that you investigated in Chapter 5, Lesson 1.
5. Graph some constant difference graphs of the form $x - y = D$. Explain any differences or similarities with graphs of the form $y - x = D$.

CONSTANT RATIO GRAPHS

These three (x, y) pairs follow a pattern: (3, 6), (4, 8), (-4, -8). The ratio of y to x is always equal to 2. The equation $y/x = 2$ describes the relationship between x and y.

Use the same pair of axes for the graphs in problems 6-9.

6. Graph $y/x = 2$.
7. Choose any other number R and graph the function $y/x = R$. (For example, if you chose R to be 3, you would graph the equation $y/x = 3$.) Label the graph with its equation.
8. Graph several other functions of the form $y/x = R$. For each graph, you will need to choose a different number for R. Be sure to try some negative and fractional values as well as positive integers.
9. Now graph some *constant ratio* graphs of the form $x/y = R$. Explain any differences and similarities with graphs of the form $y/x=R$.

PARAMETERS

Note: D and R in problems 2-9 are called *parameters.*

10. **Report** Write a report describing and analyzing any patterns you noticed in the graphs you just drew. Your report should be divided into two parts, one on constant differences, and the other on constant ratios. It should include, but not be limited to, answers to these questions:
    - Can you tell from the value of the parameter which quadrants the lines will pass through? Whether the lines slope up or down?
    - Do any lines go through the origin? If not, do you think you could find a value for the parameter so that the line would go through the origin? Explain.
    - For the constant ratio graphs, why is there a "hole" in the graph when $x = 0$?
    - Comment on anything you notice about the x-intercepts and y-intercepts.
    - There is one constant difference graph that is also a constant ratio graph. What are the values of D and R?

6.B SOLUTIONS

1.

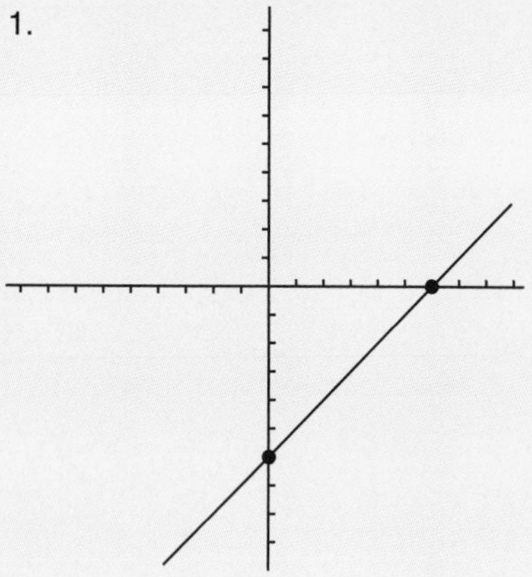

2. Answers will vary.

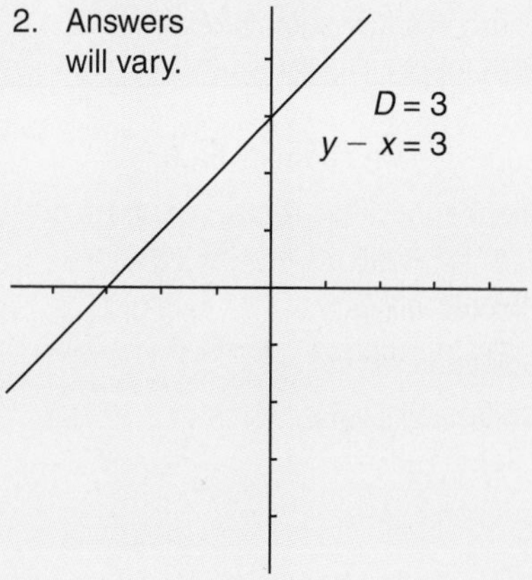

3. Answers will vary.

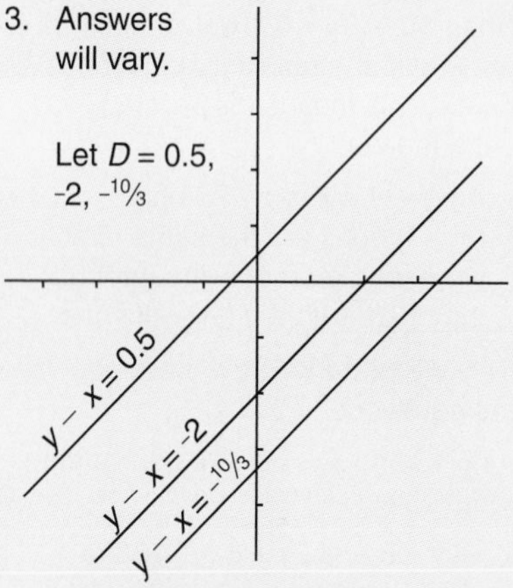

4. Constant difference graphs slope up from left to right whereas constant sum graphs slope down. In both $x + y = D$ and $y - x = D$, the graphs cross the y-axis at $(0, D)$.

(Solutions continued on page 521)

LESSON 6.9

Rational Expressions

You will need:

the Lab Gear 

COMPARING RATIONAL EXPRESSIONS

To add, subtract, multiply, and divide fractions involving variables, use the same rules you use for numerical fractions.

1. 🔑 Review the rules for adding, subtracting, multiplying, and dividing fractions, using an example of each kind.

2. For each expression, substitute 1, 2, and 9 for x and perform the indicated operation. In which problem is the answer the same, regardless of the value of x?

   a. $\frac{5}{x} \cdot \frac{x}{5}$ b. $\left(\frac{5}{x}\right) / \left(\frac{x}{5}\right)$

   c. $\frac{5}{x} + \frac{x}{5}$ d. $\frac{5}{x} - \frac{x}{5}$

A *rational number* is any number that can be written as a ratio of integers. A *rational expression* is an expression that involves a *ratio.* A very simple rational expression is the rational number 1/2, which is the ratio of 1 to 2. A more complicated rational expression is $(x^2 + 3x + 4)/(x^3 - 99)$, which is the ratio of two polynomials.

3. With the numbers 3 and 4, you can write the ratio 3/4 or the ratio 4/3.
   a. Which is greater, 3/4 or 4/3?
   b. Which is greater, 3/4 of 4/3 or 4/3 of 3/4? Explain.

4. 🔑 For each pair of expressions below, write:

   A if the expression in the first column is greater

   B if the expression in the second column is greater

   ? if the value of x determines which one is greater

   Explain your answers.

a.	$\frac{x}{5}$	$\frac{x-2}{5}$
b.	$x - \frac{2}{5}$	$\frac{x-2}{5}$
c.	$\frac{5}{x}$	$\frac{5}{x-2}$

EQUIVALENT RATIONAL EXPRESSIONS

By dividing, you can show that two fractions represent the same ratio. For example, as the figure shows, 10/5 equals 2/1.

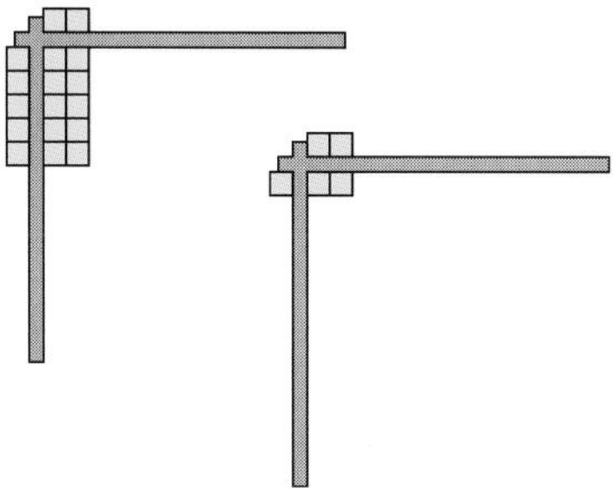

The same thing sometimes works with polynomials. As shown in the figure, the rational expression $(x^2 + 3x + 2)/(x + 1)$ is equal to $(x^2 + 5x + 6)/(x + 3)$ because the result of both divisions is the same.

▼ 6.9 Rational Expressions

Core Sequence: 1-15

Suitable for Homework: 9-27, (1-7 if your students' fraction skills are solid)

Useful for Assessment: 1, 4, 15

What this Lesson is About:

- Review of fraction arithmetic
- Preview of algebraic fractions
- Solving linear equations that involve rational expressions
- Review of equation-solving techniques
- Review of order of operations

This lesson continues the ideas about ratios previewed in Lesson 7.

COMPARING RATIONAL EXPRESSIONS

In this section the focus is mostly on the arithmetic of fractions. The problems may be difficult for some of your students and should probably be done in class.

Problem 2 is a preview of later work with algebraic fractions. Do not get bogged down introducing techniques for operations with algebraic fractions. Let students help each other use whatever arithmetic techniques they know, including the use of calculators. Different techniques should be compared.

Problems 3-4 test students' understanding of fractions as numbers.

6.9 SOLUTIONS

1. Answers will vary.
2. a. $5/x \cdot x/5 = 1$ for all values of x
   b. $x = 1$: $(5/1) \cdot (1/5) = 25$
   $x = 2$: $(5/2) \cdot (5/2) = 25/4$
   $x = 9$: $(5/9) \cdot (5/9) = 25/81$
   c. $x = 1$: $(5/1) + (1/5) = 26/5$
   $x = 2$: $(5/2) + (2/5) = 29/10$
   $x = 9$: $(5/9) + (9/5) = 106/45$
   d. $x = 1$: $(5/1) - (1/5) = 24/5$
   $x = 2$: $(5/2) - (2/5) = 21/10$
   $x = 9$: $(5/9) - (9/5) = -56/45$
3. a. $4/3 > 3/4$
   b. They are both equal to 12/12 or 1.
4. a. A. $x/5$ is 2/5 greater than $(x - 2)/5$.
   b. ? $x - 2/5$ is greater when $x > 0$. $(x - 2)/5$ is greater when $x < 0$. $x - 2/5$ equals $(x - 2)/5$ when $x = 0$
   c. ? $5/(x - 2)$ is greater than $5/x$ if $x < 0$ or $x > 2$. $5/x$ is greater if $0 < x < 2$. The expressions cannot be compared if $x = 0$ or $x = 2$.

EQUIVALENT RATIONAL EXPRESSIONS

Essentially, this reviews dividing by a common factor. The Lab Gear is used as a visual support, but by now your students should already know how to perform such divisions without the Lab Gear, perhaps using the "multiplication table" representation.

The note after problem 5 is intended to remind students that zero cannot be in the denominator. Students at this level are not likely to grasp or remember this fact fully. Do not dwell on it.

SOLVING EQUATIONS INVOLVING RATIOS

The purpose of this section is to help students see how to solve equations that involve rational expressions (but that can be transformed into linear equations). The problems were deliberately chosen to be more complicated than simple proportions of the form $a/b = c/d$ so that students would not be tempted to use "cross multiplying" techniques that they may have learned in a previous class. Resist the temptation to teach this method, since it is very often misunderstood and misused by students at this level. The approach taught in this lesson is more general, and incorporates the same methods already introduced for work with linear equations. (This is what should be reflected in problem 15.)

(There will be opportunities to solve simple proportions in Lesson 11, in an applied context.)

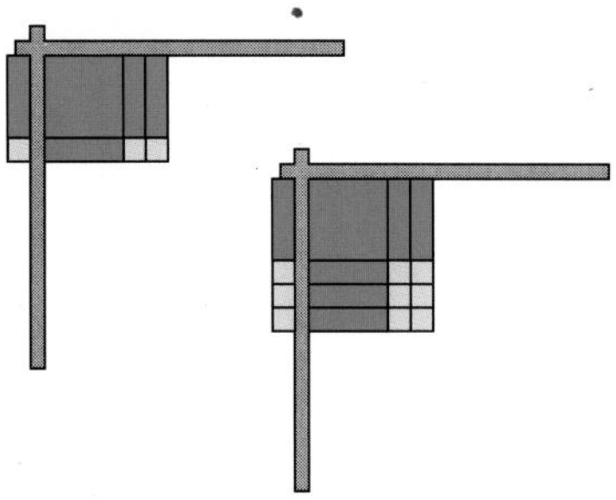

5. What is the result of both divisions?

(**Note:** These two rational expressions are **not** equal when $x = -1$ or $x = -3$. Can you see why? Try substituting these numbers for x and see what happens.)

6. Are these rational expressions equal? Explain. You may use a sketch.
   $(xy + 2x)/x \qquad (y^2 + 2y)/y$

7. For each problem, find a number or expression you could put in the box that would make the two rational expressions equal. Explain each part, perhaps using a sketch.
   a. $\frac{3x}{x}$ $\qquad \frac{3x + 6}{\square}$
   b. $\frac{18}{6}$ $\qquad \frac{15}{\square}$
   c. $\frac{\square}{x + y}$ $\qquad \frac{2x + 2y}{2}$
   d. $\frac{x^2 + 8x + 12}{\square}$ $\qquad \frac{2x + 12}{2}$

SOLVING EQUATIONS INVOLVING RATIOS

8. **Exploration** The equation
$$\frac{x - 3}{5} = x + 1$$
cannot easily be modeled with the Lab Gear. Try to solve it using any technique you have learned. Compare your method and your answers with other students' work.

Lea and Earl both tried to solve this equation. They got different answers.

Lea's work	Earl's work
$5\left(\frac{x-3}{5}\right) = (x + 1) \cdot 5$	$5\left(\frac{x-3}{5}\right) = (x + 1) \cdot 5$
$x - 3 = 5x + 5$	$5(x - 3) = 5(x + 1)$
$-3 = 4x + 5$	$\frac{1}{5} \cdot 5(x - 3) = \frac{1}{5} \cdot 5(x + 1)$
$-2 = 4x$	$x - 3 = x + 1$
$-0.5 = x$	impossible

9. Who is right, or are they both wrong? Copy each student's work and write an explanation beside each step telling what was done. If a step is incorrect, explain why and make a correction.

Solve these equations. Show your work and write a brief explanation of each step.

10. $\frac{6 - x}{8} = \frac{x}{2}$
11. $\frac{6 - x}{8} = \frac{x}{5}$
12. $\frac{x + 5}{x + 7} = 3$
13. $\frac{6 + 2x}{x + 7} = \frac{4}{5}$
14. $\frac{x - 3}{2} = x + 5$

15. **Summary** Describe a general method for solving equations like those in problems 10-14. Include the solution of an example you made up.

6.9 SOLUTIONS

5. $x + 2$
6. Yes they are equal when $x \neq 0$ and $y \neq 0$.
7. a. $x + 2$ when $x \neq 0$
   b. 5
   c. $x^2 + 2xy + y^2$
   d. $x + 2$
8. $x = -2$
9. They are both wrong.
   Lea's work:
   Step 1: Lea multiplied both sides by 5.
   Step 2: On the left, the 5 in the numerator and 5 in the denominator equal 1 and 1 times $(x - 3)$ is $x - 3$. On the right, Lea distributed the 5.
   Step 3: Lea subtracted x from both sides.
   Step 4: This line is incorrect. Lea meant to subtract 5 from both sides to get $-8 = 4x$. The left side has -2 which results from adding 5 to -3. So she added 5 to the left and subtracted 5 from the right.
   Step 5: Lea divided both sides by 4.
   Earl's work:
   Step 1: Earl multiplied both sides by 5.
   Step 2: This line is incorrect. Earl dropped the 5 from the denominator on the left. The right side is correct. He commuted the expression $(x + 1)$ and 5.
   Step 3: Earl multiplied both sides by 1/5
   Step 4: $(1/5) \cdot 5 = 1.1 \cdot (x - 3) = x - 3$ and $1 \cdot (x + 1) = x + 1$
   Step 5: No correction
10. $x = 6/5$
11. $x = 30/13$
12. $x = -8$
13. $x = -1/3$
14. $x = -13$
15. Summaries will vary. Multiply both sides of the equation by the denominator(s) or lowest common denominator and then solve the equation.

REVIEW *EQUATION SOLVING*

Write the equation shown by the blocks, then solve it. If you use the Lab Gear, write equations to show some of the steps as you move your blocks. If you don't, show all your work.

16.

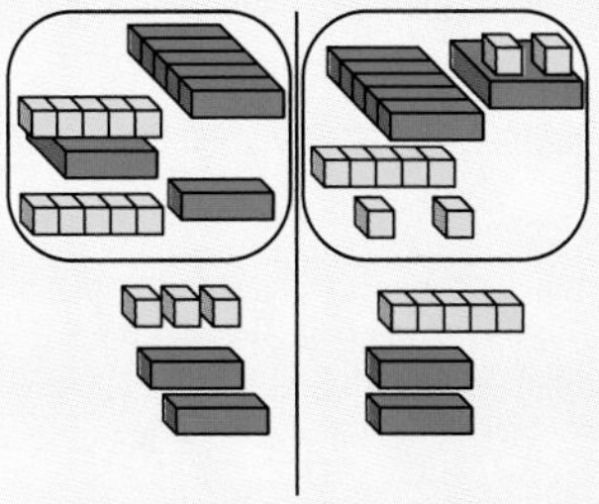

17.

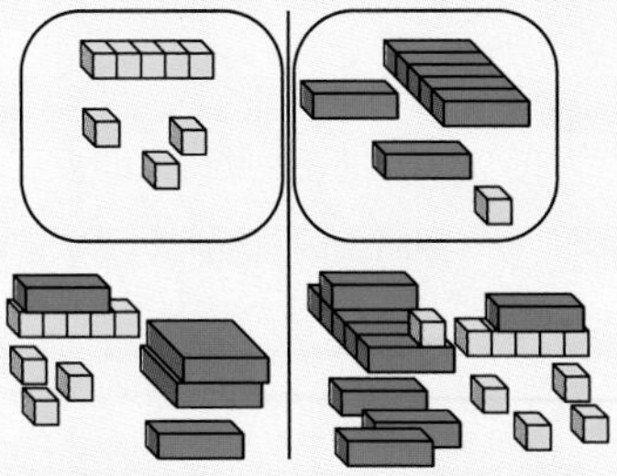

18.

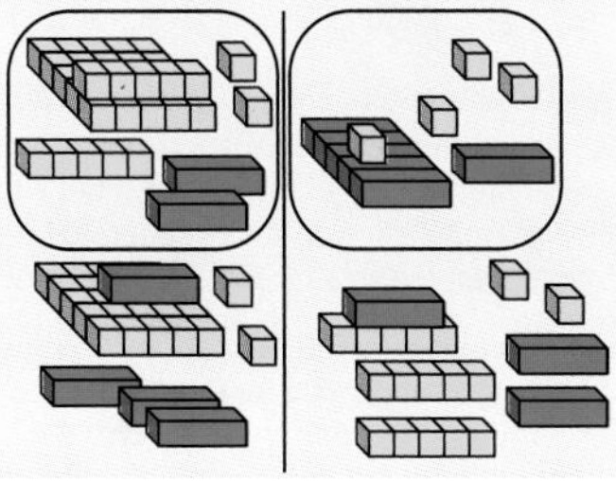

19.

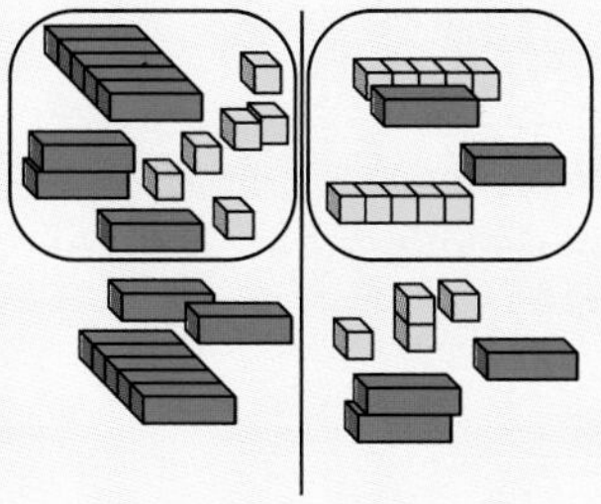

Solve.

20. $(x + 3)^2 = (x - 3)(x + 4)$

21. $(x - 1)^2 = (x + 2)(x - 6)$

PUZZLES *ORDER OF OPERATIONS*

Keeping in mind order of operations, insert as many pairs of parentheses as needed, to make these equations true.

22. $4 \cdot 2 + 3 = 20$

23. $\frac{1}{4} + \frac{1}{2} \cdot \frac{1}{2} = \frac{1}{2}$

24. $5 \cdot 3 - 2 + 6 = 35$

25. $3^2 + 2 \cdot 7 - 4 = 33$

26. $\frac{1}{3} \cdot 6 + 4 \cdot \frac{2}{6} + \frac{1}{3} = \frac{7}{3}$

27. $1 - 2 \cdot 2 + 5 \cdot 6 = -42$

REVIEW EQUATION SOLVING

Extra practice, if you feel your students need it.

Most students should not need the Lab Gear by now, but translating the figures into symbols is still a worthwhile exercise.

Problems 20 and 21 review multiplication of binomials. The equations are easily solved since the x^2 terms cancel. If you think your students need more practice with multiplication of binomials, you can have students make up more problems of this type.

PUZZLES ORDER OF OPERATIONS

Review in puzzle form. Problem 23 is a trick question, since it requires no parentheses. The problems get harder and harder.

6.9 SOLUTIONS

16. $2x + 3 - (6x + x^2 + 5 - 5) = 2x + 5 - (5x + x^2 + 5 + 2 - 2)$
    $x = 3$
17. $x + 3 + 5 - x + x^2 - x^2 - 8 = 8x + 9 - 2x - 1 - (7x + 1)$
    $x = 7$
18. $3x + 27 - x - (2x + 25 + 5 - 5 + 2) = 17 + 2x - x - (6x + 3 - 1)$
    $x = 3$
19. $7x - (7x - x + 6) = x - x + x + 1 - 1 + 2 - (10 + 2x)$
    $x = -1$
20. $x = -21/5$
21. $x = -13/2$
22. $4(2 + 3) = 20$
23. $1/4 + (1/2 \cdot 1/2) = 1/2$
24. $5(3 - 2 + 6) = 35$
25. $(3^2 + 2)(7 - 4) = 33$
26. $(1/3 \cdot 6 + 4)2/6 + 1/3 = 7/3$
27. $(1 - 2)(2 + 5)6 = -42$

▼ 6.10
Improving Your Average

Core Sequence: 1-9

Suitable for Homework: 5-18

Useful for Assessment: 9

What this Lesson is About:

- Review of averages, ratio, and percent
- Writing equations
- Solving equations

Students can apply the equation-solving methods they learned in Lesson 9 to these problems.

FREE THROWS

The answer to problem 1 is debatable, in that LiAnn contributed more points, but Bea had a better average.

For problem 2 let students experiment with their calculators, but insist on thorough record-keeping. Students may be surprised by their answers. Of course (f) is impossible.

The key idea of the lesson is that the average is obtained by dividing free throws made by free throws attempted. In writing equations in problems 3-9 it is necessary to understand how to express the numerator (free throws made) and the denominator (free throws attempted) using the right numbers, variables, and operations.

LESSON 6.10

Improving Your Average

FREE THROWS

Alaberg High School has a girls' basketball team nicknamed "the Gals." Ms. Ball, the coach, is studying these statistics.

Mid-Season Free-Throw Data

	FT-A	Average
Bea	15-20	75%
Gale	3-18	___
Lara	___-8	25%
Lea	5-___	20%
Li Ann	16-24	___

FT-A means *free throws made - free throws attempted.* The average is shown as a percent, but it could be shown as a ratio or decimal. (For example, Bea's average is 15/20 or 0.75.)

1. Copy and complete the table. Who has the best record so far this season?

2. **Exploration** Bea wants to have a season record of 90%. She thinks she can make every free throw that she attempts for the rest of the season. Tell how many she would have to make in a row in order for her season average to be:
   a. 80% b. 85% c. 90%
   d. 95% e. 99% f. 100%
   Discuss.

3. If Bea has had 20 free throw attempts and has made 15 of them, her average is 15/20. If she has x more attempts and makes all of them, her average is $\frac{15 + x}{20 + x}$.
   a. What is the value of this ratio when $x = 40$? (That is, what is her average if she has 40 more attempts and makes all of them?)
   b. What is her average if $x = 25$?

4. Suppose Li Ann had x free throw attempts during the rest of the season and *missed* every one.
   a. What would her season average be, in terms of x? (Hint: The expression will be different from the one in problem 3.)
   b. If she had a season average of 40%, how many more free throws after mid-season must she have attempted?
   c. If she attempted ten more free throws, what would her season average be?

5. Suppose Li Ann *made* every attempted free throw.
   a. What would her season average be, in terms of x?
   b. What would her season average be if she attempted eight more free throws?
   c. If she had a season average of 0.85, how many more free throws must she have attempted?

These problems are not very realistic. Usually people do not make all their attempted free throws, but they don't miss all of them either. Lea hopes that she will make about 40% of her attempted free throws for the rest of the season.

6. If Lea attempts x more free throws, and makes 40% of them, she knows that her average for the season would be
   $$\frac{5 + 0.40x}{25 + x}.$$

6.10 SOLUTIONS

1. **Mid-Season Free-Throw Data**

	FT-A	Average
Bea	15-20	75%
Gale	3-18	17%
Lara	2-8	25%
Lea	5-25	20%
Li Ann	16-24	67%

2. a. 5
   b. 14
   c. 30
   d. 80
   e. 480
   f. impossible
   It is impossible for Bea to get 100% because she already missed 5 free throw attempts. The more she throws accurately, the closer her average gets to 100%, but it will never equal exactly 100%.

3. a. 92%
   b. 89%

4. a. $16/(24 + x)$
   b. 16 attempts
   c. 47%

5. a. $(16 + x)/(24 + x)$
   b. 75%
   c. 30 free throws

a. Explain the meaning of the numerator and denominator of this expression, and how it was figured out.
b. How would the expression change if Lea made 60% of her remaining free throws?
c. How would the expression change if Lea made 20% of her remaining free throws?

7. Assume Lea makes 40% of her remaining free throws and wants to raise her season average to at least 30%. What is the minimum number of free throws she needs?

8. By the end of the season Gale had doubled both her attempts and her successes. What happened to her average?

9. **Generalization** Assume a student has made M out of T free throws. Assume she attempts x more shots and makes N of them. What will her season average be in terms of M, T, x, and N? Explain.

GRADES

Alaberg High School has a "no pass, no play" rule for all sports. Students must have an average of 65% in all their classes in order to qualify to play any sport the following quarter.

Some members of the boys' basketball team (the Bears) are worrying about their averages for algebra. (See the table.)

Their grades in algebra are based on 12 ten-point assignments per quarter. Students who have been absent because of illness (like Hal and Zal) can complete the assignments late.

Mid-Quarter Algebra Scores

	Possible points	Points earned	Average
Al	80	35	—
Hal	70	52	—
Cal	80	63	—
Zal	60	59	—
Sid	80	74	—

10. Copy and complete the table.

Use the table to answer the following questions. Assume that *passing* means having an average of 65% or better, and *failing* means having an average below 65%.

11. Who has the lowest average so far?

12. Answer the following questions for each student.
a. What is the worst conceivable average he could get by the end of the course?
b. What is the best conceivable average he could get?
c. What is the smallest number of points he needs to earn in the remaining assignments in order to pass?

REVIEW EQUATION SOLVING

Solve for the variable.

13. $\frac{y+5}{2} = \frac{19-y}{1}$

14. $\frac{y+5}{4} = \frac{19-y}{2}$

15. $2(y + 5) = 19 - y$

16. $4(y + 5) = 2(19 - y)$

17. $y + 5 = 2(19 - y)$

18. $\frac{-15 + 3x}{5 + 4x} = 7$

Free throw data is readily available in daily newspapers, so you can easily extend this activity with discussion and analysis of real-world basketball data.

GRADES

The mathematics is essentially the same as in the previous section, but this time the number of remaining tests is known.

Trial and error may well be the most popular approach used by your students for problem 12c, in spite of the work expended in the previous section in presenting an equation-solving approach. If so, you may want to follow these problems with a discussion of how they could be done with equations and a discussion of which method students prefer. Do not criticize trial and error. For one thing, the students who use that method probably need that kind of involvement with the numbers. For those students, discussion of writing an equation is much more likely to be meaningful after having used trial and error, than before.

REVIEW EQUATION SOLVING

More practice. Many students should begin to master equation solving by now. This section makes a good in-class group activity, followed by comparison and discussion of several methods for solving the same problem.

6.10 SOLUTIONS

6. a. The numerator is the total number of free throws made. Lea made 5 free throws and then 40% of the remaining x free throws for a total of $5 + 0.40x$. The denominator is the total number of attempted free throws. Lea attempted 25 free throws and then attempted x more for a total of $25 + x$.
b. $0.40x$ would change to $0.60x$. The new expression would be $(5 + 0.60x)/(25 + x)$.
c. $0.40x$ would change to $0.20x$. The new expression would be $(5 + 0.20x)/(25 + x)$.

7. Lea needs a minimum of 25 free throws to raise her average to 30%.

8. Her average remains the same.

9. Season average = $(M + N)/(T + x)$. The numerator is the total number of free throws made. The student made M free throws and then N more, for a total of $M + N$. The denominator is the total number of attempted free throws. She attempted T free throws and then x more, for a total of $T + x$.

10. **Mid-Quarter Algebra Scores**

	possible points	points earned	average
Al	80	35	44
Hal	70	52	74
Cal	80	63	79
Zal	60	59	98
Sid	80	74	93

11. Al has the lowest average so far.

12.

	a. worst possible average	b. best possible average	c. smallest number of points needed to pass
Al	29	63	43
Hal	43	85	26
Cal	53	86	15
Zal	49	99	19
Sid	62	95	4

13. $y = 11$

14. $y = 11$

15. $y = 3$

16. $y = 3$

17. $y = 11$

18. $x = -2$

▼ 6.11
Stuart Little and Alice

Core Sequence: 1-11, 15-17

Suitable for Homework: 8-17

Useful for Assessment: 4, 12-14, 17

What this Lesson is About:

- Proportional thinking
- Mathematics in literature
- Measurement in inches
- Review of equation solving

*B*ecause the measurements mentioned in the quotations are in inches, we ask the students to make their measurements in inches.

*M*ake sure the students actually make the measurements, instead of merely guessing or estimating. This is important in order to make the connection between textbook math, literature, and reality.

*T*o solve problems 4, 8, 9, and 11, students will need to set up and solve proportions like this one.

$$\frac{\text{Stuart's height}}{\text{boy's height}} = \frac{\text{length of Stuart's pants}}{\text{length of boy's pants}}$$

*A*lternately, if they find the ratio of the heights, they can just multiply by the factor. Instead of suggesting a method as "the best one," help the students compare and discuss the methods they discover.

LESSON 6.11

Stuart Little and Alice

You will need:

rulers

measuring tape

and/or yardsticks

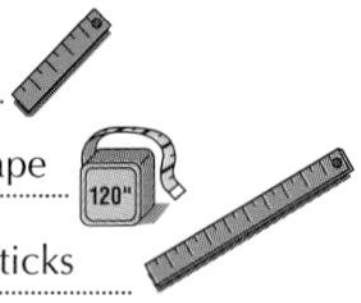

STUART LITTLE

Here is the beginning of *Stuart Little,* a children's book by E.B. White.

> When Mrs. Frederick C. Little's second son arrived, everybody noticed that he was not much bigger than a mouse. The truth of the matter was, the baby looked very much like a mouse in every way. He was only about two inches high; and he had a mouse's sharp nose, a mouse's tail, a mouse's whiskers, and the pleasant, shy manner of a mouse. Before he was many days old he was not only looking like a mouse but acting like one, too — wearing a gray hat and carrying a small cane. Mr. and Mrs. Little named him Stuart, and Mr. Little made him a tiny bed out of four clothespins and a cigarette box.

1. Measure, in inches, the height of several boys in your class. To do the following exercises, choose someone whose height is near the average of the heights you measured.
2. Measure, in inches, the length and width of the average boy's
   a. pants; b. shirt or coat.
3. Measure, in inches, the length and width of:
   a. a book or binder;
   b. a chair or desk.
4. Calculate the size of each item in problems 2-3, if it were to be made for Stuart Little. Explain your work.
5. Draw each item in the size that you calculated in problem 4.

ALICE

Here is an excerpt from *Alice in Wonderland*, a book by the English mathematician Lewis Carroll.

> ...this bottle was not marked "poison," so Alice ventured to taste it, and finding it very nice, (it had, in fact, a sort of mixed flavour of cherry-tart, custard, pine-apple, roast turkey, toffy, and hot buttered toast), she very soon finished it off.
>
> • • • • •
>
> "What a curious feeling!" said Alice, "I must be shutting up like a telescope!"
>
> And so it was indeed: she was now only ten inches high, and her face brightened up at the thought that she was now the right size for going through the little door into that lovely garden.

6. Measure, in inches, the height of several girls in your class. To do the following exercises, choose someone whose height is near the average of the heights you measured.
7. Assuming that before she drank from the bottle, Alice was the size of the average girl in your class, how many times as tall was she after shrinking?
8. a. Measure a real pencil or pen.
   b. Calculate the correct size for a pencil or pen of the same kind for Alice. Explain.

6.11 SOLUTIONS

Answers will vary for # 1-10

Samples:

1. Average boy's height equals 68 inches.
2. a. length 32 inches, width 14 inches
   b. length 28 inches, width at shoulder 18 inches
3. a. length 11.5 inches, width 10 inches
   b. height 33 inches, width 18 inches
4. 2/68 ≈ 0.029. So Stuart's height is 2.9% of the average boy's height. The dimensions of his pants, coat, book, and chair should also be 2.9% of the ones measured.

	length (in.)	width (in.)
pants	0.9	0.4
coat	0.8	0.5
book	0.3	0.3
chair	1	0.5

5. Students' drawings will vary.
6. Sample: 66 inches
7. 10/66 ≈ 0.15. Alice was 0.15 times as tall after shrinking.
8. a. 7 in.
   b. 0.15 · 7 = 1.05 in.
   c. Student drawings will vary.

c. Draw it in the size you calculated in part (b).

9. Measure a real door, and calculate the dimensions of "the little door into that lovely garden."

> "Curiouser and curiouser!" cried Alice (she was so much surprised, that for the moment she quite forgot how to speak good English). "Now I'm opening out like the largest telescope that ever was! Goodbye, feet!"...
>
> ...Just at this moment, her head struck against the roof of the hall: in fact she was now rather more than nine feet high...

10. How many times as tall as an average girl in your class is Alice now?

11. What would be the size of a pencil if it were the right size for giant Alice? Show your calculations.

THE BIG FRIENDLY GIANT

The following are quotations about the Big Friendly Giant, a character in Roald Dahl's book *The BFG*.

a. It was four times as tall as the tallest human.

b. It actually had to bend down to peer into the upstairs windows. That's how tall it was.

c. ...an arm as thick as a tree trunk...

d. The Giant was sprinting down the High Street... Each stride he took was as long as a tennis court.

e. In the middle of the floor there was a table twelve feet high...

f. He had truly enormous ears. Each one was as big as the wheel of a truck...

12. **Project** Estimate the height of the Giant using the information given in each quotation. Explain your work.

- What real-world numbers did you use?
- How did you find them?
- What calculations did you do?
- Did the results of your calculations agree with each other?
- Based on all the calculations, what is your final estimate of the Giant's height?

YOUR OWN STORY

13. **Project**

a. Write and illustrate a story for a young child featuring little people or giants. Make sure the dimensions of all objects are sized correctly.

b. On a separate piece of paper, explain your calculations.

OTHER STORIES

14. **Project** Ask a librarian or an elementary school teacher to suggest a book that involves little people or giants. Make up math problems based on the book. Use specific quotations from the book as much as possible. On a separate piece of paper, solve the problems you make up.

REVIEW SOLVING EQUATIONS

15. Solve the equation,

$$2.5x + 18 + 1.5x - 11 = 19.$$

16. If $x = 3$, calculate, $2.5x + 18 + 1.5x - 11$.

17. Explain how problems 15 and 16 are related.

You may let the students choose one of the projects. Or you may choose for them, but do not assign all three projects, as that would be too much work for any one student. The projects would make good bulletin board exhibits. One way or another, make sure that the work students do is shared, at least as bulletin board exhibits. Problem 12 would make for excellent discussions. Stories created for problem 13 should be read to the class. Problems created for 14 can be assigned as homework.

REVIEW SOLVING EQUATIONS

This section is easy, but makes an important point that some students miss as they drown in the technicalities of equation solving: Problem 16 is the check on the correctness of the solution to problem 15. Students who understand that connection and trust they did 15 correctly need not make any calculations for 16.

6.11 SOLUTIONS

9. 80 in. tall by 30 in. wide. So $0.15 \cdot 80 = 12$ in. wide. $0.15 \cdot 30 = 4.5$ in. wide
10. $9 \cdot 12 = 108$. $108/66 \approx 1.6$. Alice was 1.6 times as tall after stretching.
11. $1.6 \cdot 7 = 11.2$. The pencil would be 11.2 in. long.
12. Student projects will vary.
13. Student projects will vary.
14. Student projects will vary.
15. $x = 3$
16. 19
17. #15 is the solution to the equation and #16 is the check to the solution.

▼ 6.12
Geoboard Squares

Core Sequence: 1-19

Suitable for Homework: 11-18, 20, 29

Useful for Assessment: 10-11

What this Lesson is About:

- Review of geoboard area
- Preview of the Pythagorean theorem
- Preview of square roots
- Preview of rules for inequalities
- Review of solving inequalities

Problem 1 is a big project and quite suitable for group work. Of course, some kind of systematic search is more efficient than random attempts. The crucial thing is for students to be able to recognize a right angle, even when the sides are not horizontal or vertical. Have students use the corner of a piece of paper to measure the angle.

One technique for finding right angles is to count how far across and down one moves from one vertex to the next. Then by switching those numbers, and reversing one direction, one can find the next vertex. (This is easier to do than to explain, and it constitutes a preview of the slope of perpendicular lines.)

FIND THE AREA

There are no new techniques here, but old ones are applied with very interesting results. Since there was no geoboard lesson in Chapter 5, you may ask students to remind each other of the basic area-finding techniques: by addition, by subtraction, by division by two.

Problem 2 yields the perfect squares.

Problems 5 and 8 refer to the limits of the geoboard. Of course on an infinite plane there is an infinite number of squares of the type considered.

Problem 9 reviews the subtraction technique, which is likely the one students have been using in the previous problems. Problem 10 repeats the same problem, but using variables. If students simplify the answer to problem 10d, they will get a very simple answer.

LESSON 6.12

Geoboard Squares

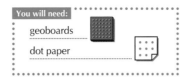

You will need:
- geoboards
- dot paper

1. **Exploration** There are 33 different geoboard squares. Find as many of them as you can. (For this exercise, squares that have the same size are considered the same.) Sketch each square on dot paper.

FIND THE AREA

2. There are 10 geoboard squares having horizontal and vertical sides. What are their areas?

3. Make a 1-by-1 square in the bottom left of your geoboard. Make a square that has this square's diagonal — (0, 1) to (1, 0) — for a side. What is the area of the new square?

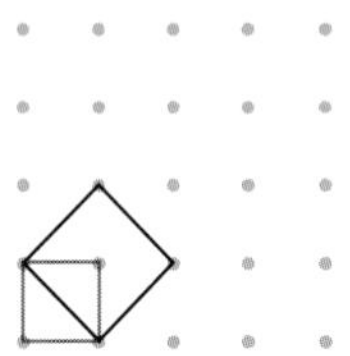

4. Repeat problem 3, starting with larger and larger squares in the bottom left. What is the area of each new square?

5. Explain why only five squares can be found this way.

6. 🔑 Make a square having (0, 1) to (2, 0) as a side.
   a. Explain how you found the other vertices of the square.
   b. Find the area. Explain how you did it.

7. Make squares having (0, 1) to (*x*, 0) as a side. Use $x = 3, 4, \ldots 9$. Find the area of each one.

8. 🔑 Explain why you cannot find a geoboard square having (0, 1) to (10, 0) as one side.

9. Make a square having (0, 2) to (3, 0) as one side.
   a. Sketch the square.
   b. Make and sketch the smallest square having horizontal and vertical sides that entirely covers the original square. What is the area of this square?
   c. What is the total area of the four triangles that surround the original square?
   d. What is the area of the original square?

10. **Generalization** On dot paper, sketch a pair of *x*- and *y*-axes.

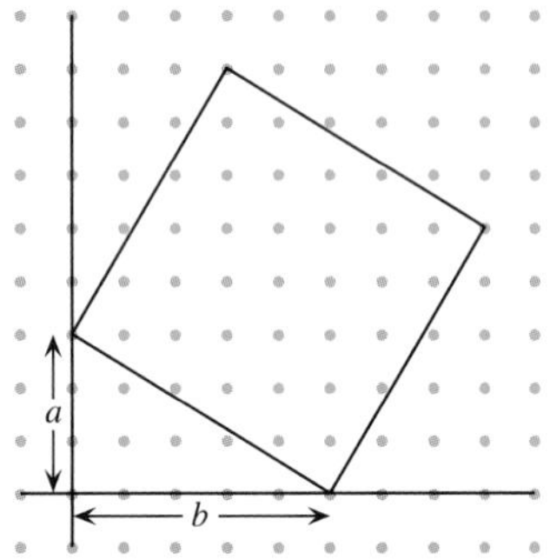

   a. Copy the above figure.
   b. Sketch the smallest square having horizontal and vertical sides that entirely covers the original square. What are its sides in terms of *a* and *b*? What is its area in terms of *a* and *b*?

6.12 SOLUTIONS

2. The areas from smallest to largest are: 1, 4, 9, 16, 25, 36, 49, 64, 81, and 100 square units.
3. The area of the new square is 2 square units.
4. 8, 18, 32, 50
5. The geoboard is too small to make more squares.
6. a. Answers will vary. One approach is to count to the right 1 and up 2 from (0, 1) and (2, 0).
   b. The area is 5 square units. The area of the 3-by-3 square is 9 square units. Four triangles, each with area of 1 unit, can be subtracted to result in the square whose area is wanted. That is, $9 - 4(1) = 9 - 4 = 5$ in^2.
7. 10 square units if $x = 3$
   17 square units if $x = 4$
   26 square units if $x = 5$
   37 square units if $x = 6$
   50 square units if $x = 7$
   65 square units if $x = 8$
   82 square units if $x = 9$
8. The geoboard is too small. Using this method, one would need an 11-by-11 geoboard to find the area of a square with (0, 1) and (10, 0) as vertices.
9. a. No solution is needed.
   b. 25 square units
   c. 12 square units
   d. 13 square units
10. a. See figure in text.
    b. Each side of the square is $\sqrt{a^2 + b^2}$. The area is $a^2 + b^2$.
    c. The area of one triangle is $(1/2)(ab)$ square units. The total area of the four triangles is $4(1/2)(ab)$ or $2ab$

c. What is the area of one of the triangles that surround the original square in terms of a and b? What is the total area of the four triangles in terms of a and b?

d. What is the area of the original square in terms of a and b?

11. **Summary** How does one find the area of a geoboard square? For examples, use the squares having the following as one side.

a. (0, 3) to (4, 0)

b. (2, 4) to (7, 1)

FIND THE SIDE

12. How long is the side of a square if the area is

a. 64? b. 81?

c. 289? d. 0.0121?

13. How long is the side of a square if the area is 70? Give an approximate answer. (Hint: You may be able to use some of the results from problem 12.)

14. Use trial and error on a calculator to answer problem 13 to the closest one-thousandth.

15. **Summary** Use examples to explain.

a. How does one find the area of a square, if given the side?

b. How does one find the side of a square, if given the area?

DISCOVERY CHUNKING

16. Solve: $3(x + 3) + 5 = 4(x + 3)$

It is easier to solve this equation by first solving for $(x + 3)$, and then finding x, instead of distributing. This is called *chunking*, since in this method the quantity $(x + 3)$ is thought of as one chunk.

17. Solve $3y + 5 = 4y$, then use the fact that $y = x + 3$ to solve for x. Explain what you did, and how this problem is related to problem 16.

18. Create an equation that would be easier to solve by chunking than by distributing. Solve it.

19. Solve a classmate's chunking equation.

DISCOVERY INEQUALITY RULES

Like most students, Mary and Martin enjoy discussing inequalities during their lunch period.

20. Martin said, "I noticed something cool. If $5/x$ is less than 5, then $x/5$ is more than 1/5." Mary said, "I don't understand. In the first place, I can't think of a value of x that would make $5/x$ greater than 5."

a. Give Mary at least two values of x that will make $5/x$ greater than 5.

b. Is Martin's statement correct? Give examples to explain your answer.

21. Martin said, "If $a < b$, then by taking the reciprocals of both sides, I get $1/a > 1/b$. Notice that I changed the direction of the inequality." Mary answered, "Sorry, but you're wrong." Who is right? Explain, with examples.

22. Martin said, "If $a < b$, then by taking the opposites of both sides, I get $-a > -b$. Notice that I changed the direction of the inequality." Mary answered, "When will you give up making up rules off the top of your head! You're wrong again!" Who is right? Explain, with examples.

6.12 SOLUTIONS

square units.

d. $a^2 + 2ab + b^2 - 2ab = a^2 + b^2$, so the area of the original square is $a^2 + b^2$.

11. a. $3^2 + 4^2 = 9 + 16 = 25$

b. To find side a, we subtract 1 from 4 to get 3. To find side b we subtract 2 from 7 to get 5. Hence the area of the square would be $3^2 + 5^2 = 34$.

12. a. 8 b. 9

c. 17 d. 0.11

13. 8.37 because (8.37)(8.37) = 70.057

14. 8.367

15. a. To find the area of a square if given a side, square the length of the side. The resulting number is the area $A = s^2$.

b. To find the length of a side from the given area, take the square root of the area, or find the number which when squared equals the area.

16. $x = 2$

17. $y = 5$, and since $y = x + 3$, x must equal 2 as we found in #16.

18. Answers will vary. Sample: $7(x - 4) + 2(x - 4) = 9 - 8(x - 4)$

19. Answers will vary. Solving the sample in #18: Let $y = x - 4$

$7y + 2y = 9 - 8y$

$9y + 8y = 9$

$17y = 9$

$y = 9/17$

20. a. Any value of x between 0 and 1 will satisfy this. For example, if $x = 1/2$, $5/x$ is 10. If $x = 1/3$, $5/x$ is 15.

Problem 11 should be discussed in class. Part (b) cannot be solved by a simple application of the formula discovered in problem 10, because the given vertices are not on the x- and y-axes. The meaning of a and b in this figure is not simply an x- and a y-coordinate. Let students express it in their own words. One way to think of it is to make a copy of the square with a vertex on each axis. Another is to think of a as the difference in the x-coordinates, and b as the difference in the y-coordinates between the two given vertices.

Students should not be required to memorize this result. In Chapter 9 when this is approached again in terms of arbitrary geoboard right triangles, the Pythagorean theorem will be explicitly stated and may be memorized then.

FIND THE SIDE

This section serves as a preview of the concept of square root, which we will continue developing in Chapters 7 and 9.

For problems 13-14, if students know how to find the answer with the square root key of their calculator, it is still worthwhile to discuss how one could find the square root on a calculator without using the key. Such discussion helps clarify the meaning of square root.

DISCOVERY CHUNKING

Many students will distribute first, and think later, which makes an equation like that in problem 16 harder to solve. This is an important idea, to which we will return.

DISCOVERY INEQUALITY RULES

This section is optional because mastery of rules for solving inequalities is not important to achieve in first-year algebra. If you choose to do it, expect some vigorous discussion.

Problem 21 should help prepare the ground for problem 22, by expressing it in terms of a specific value for a and b. There is no consistent pattern for *taking the reciprocal of both sides* of an inequality. For example, if $5/x$ is less than 5, then $x/5$ could be either greater or less than 1/5. (Try $x = 2$, and then try $x = -2$.)

In problem 22, however, Martin is right, as students can readily verify by trying many examples.

REVIEW SOLVING INEQUALITIES

*Y*our students may have trouble solving these by straight algebraic manipulation, because all the methods developed for equations cannot be used when solving inequalities. *Specifically, one cannot multiply or divide both sides by a non-positive number.* If you did the previous section, encourage students to use the rule discovered in problem 23, when needed.

*I*f your students have diverging answers, it would be best to recommend they consider the two expressions:

$y =$ the left side and $y =$ the right side.

*T*hen by making tables of values and/or graphs they will have a better grasp of what's going on, and it will be clearer whose answer is right. This is definitely the easiest approach if your students have access to, and know how to use, a graphing calculator.

DISCOVERY CAN TARA MAKE A B?

*T*his is the last of the series on averages and grading. It follows **Weighted Averages**, Lesson 5.

REVIEW SOLVING INEQUALITIES

Solve these inequalities. Remember that you must find *all the values* of x that make the inequality true. Show your work, and check your answers.

23. $x - 1 > 5$

24. $x + 1 > 5$

25. $2x - 6 > 5x + 3$

26. $2x - 6 < 5x + 3$

27. $3(x + 1) > 6$

28. $2 - 3(x + 1) > 6$

DISCOVERY CAN TARA MAKE A B?

Some auto insurance policies have a "good student" policy for high school students. If a student maintains a *B* average, he or she can qualify for a discount on insurance rates.

Tara doesn't like writing assignments because they take time outside of school, when she would rather be driving her car. However, she does well on quizzes. She needs a *B* in algebra. Her scores are:

Writing Assignments: 45 55
Quizzes: 100 50 90 85 90 95

Tara hopes that the teacher will count quizzes heavily in the average so that she can make a *B*.

29. Is it possible for Tara to make a *B*? If so, how much would the teacher have to weight her quizzes? If not, explain why not.

6.12 SOLUTIONS

b. Martin's statement is not always true. If $x < 0$, it is false. For example, if $x = -2$, 5/-2 is less than 5 but -2/5 is not greater than 1/5.

21. Not always true. For example, if $a = -3$ and $b = 2$, then $-3 < 2$ but $-1/3$ is not greater than 1/2.

22. This time Martin is right! To visualize this, you could draw a number line showing that $-a$ is the reflection of a (over the 0 point) and $-b$ is the reflection of b, so the order of a and b on the number line will be reversed if you take their opposites.

23. $x > 6$

24. $x > 4$

25. $x < -3$

26. $x > -3$

27. $x > 1$

28. $x < -7/3$

29. Quiz average (Q) = 85
Writing average (W) = 50
Solutions will vary. One possible approach is $\frac{n(85) + 50}{n+1} \geq 80$.

THINKING WRITING 6.C Group Theory

MOD CLOCKS

The figure shows a mod clock, which is a special function machine. For any positive whole number input, it will output a number between 0 and 4. For example:

Input	Output
1	1
9	4
13	3
25	0
77	2

Input	Output
5	0
12	2
17	2
26	1
100	0

1. What would be the output of the mod clock for the following inputs? Explain.
   a. 1998 b. 1899 c. 9981

Definition: $a \oplus b$ is the output from the mod clock for the input $a + b$. $a \otimes b$ is the output for the input ab.

Example: $3 \oplus 2 = 0$, and $3 \otimes 2 = 1$

2. Make a table for each of $\oplus$ and $\otimes$.

3. **Generalization** The clock above is a mod 5 clock. Find ways to predict the output of mod 10, mod 2, mod 9, and mod 3 clocks.

GROUPS

Definition: A *group* is a set of elements, together with an operation that satisfies the following rules.

- *closure:* using the operation on two elements of the group yields an element of the group.
- *associative law:* $(ab)c = a(bc)$.
- *identity element:* one of the elements, e, is such that $ae = ea = a$, for any element a in the group.
- *inverse element:* every element a has an inverse a' such that $a a' = a'a = e$

Some groups are *commutative* ($ab = ba$) and some are not.

For 4-7 assume the associative law holds.

4. a. Show that the set {0, 1, 2, 3, 4} together with the operation $\oplus$ is a group.
   b. Show that {0, 1, 2, 3, 4} with $\otimes$ is not a group.
   c. Show that {1, 2, 3, 4} with $\otimes$ is a group.
5. Is the set of the integers a group with the following operations?
   a. addition b. multiplication
6. Show that the set of rational numbers (positive and negative fractions and zero) together with multiplication is not a group. By removing one element, it can be made into a group. Which element? Explain.
7. Think about a mod 4 clock, with the numbers {0, 1, 2, 3}. Is it a group for $\oplus$? For $\otimes$? Can it be made into one by removing an element?
8. **Report** Give examples of groups. For each, give the set and operation. Explain how they satisfy the rules. Include finite, infinite, commutative, and noncommutative groups.

6.C SOLUTIONS

1. a. 3 b. 4 c. 1
2.

⊕	0	1	2	3	4
0	0	1	2	3	4
1	1	2	3	4	0
2	2	3	4	0	1
3	3	4	0	1	2
4	4	0	1	2	3

⊗	0	1	2	3	4
0	0	0	0	0	0
1	0	1	2	3	4
2	0	2	4	1	3
3	0	3	1	4	2
4	0	4	3	2	1

3. For mod 10, the last digit gives the output. For mod 2, divide the last digit by 2. The remainder will be the output. For mod 9, the output is determined by summing up the digits of the input and dividing by 9. The remainder is the output. Mod 3 works the same way. Sum up the digits, divide by 3, and the remainder will be the output.
4. a. closure: It is evident from the table in #2 that this property holds.
   identity element: The identity element is 0.
   inverse element: As can be seen from the table, every element has an inverse under this operation. The inverse of 0 is 0. 4 and 1 are inverses. 2 and 3 are inverses.
   b. closure: It is evident from the table in #2 that the set is closed under this operation.
   identity element: The identity element is 1.

(Solutions continued on page 521)

THINKING WRITING 6.C Group Theory

Core Sequence: none of the lesson

Suitable for Homework: 8

Useful for Assessment: 8

What this Assignment is About:

- Looking for patterns
- Modular arithmetic
- Abstract algebra
- Identity and inverse elements
- Finite and infinite groups
- Preview of number systems

This is the last lesson of the optional strand on group theory and abstract algebra. It represents the culmination of the work of Chapter 3, Lesson 11; Chapter 4, **Thinking/Writing 4.C**; and Chapter 5, Lesson 12. This lesson adds groups of numbers that have the same structure as the quite varied groups seen in the previous lessons. The idea that apparently different things can share a common structure may be the most fundamental concept in mathematics, and certainly in algebra.

Because it is so abstract and number-based, most of the lesson needs to be done in class. If you are not comfortable with the second section, **Groups**, you may still teach the first one, which is essentially a lesson in number patterns and arithmetic.

MOD CLOCKS

The mod clock provides an example of a function from number theory. It behaves quite differently from most of the functions students see in algebra, and therefore it helps broaden their horizons. Another benefit of this section is the review of divisibility patterns.

A good way to introduce this lesson is to play *What's my function?* (see Teacher's Notes for Chapter 2, Lesson 7). This can be played for problems 1 and 3. Mod 5, 10, and 2 outputs can easily be predicted from the last digit of the input. Mod 9 and 3 inputs depend on the sum of the digits, though you should let students discover this for themselves if they can. (The mod 9 pattern is easier to see than the mod 3 pattern.)

The connection with the remainder of a division by the mod number can also be discussed. The "addition" and "multiplica-

(continued on page 242)

(6.C continued)

tion" tables will be reminiscent of the tables made in the previous group theory lessons. Students will need help in getting started. (See the blank tables on page 572.) A comparison of the tables may lead to the discovery of interesting patterns.

- If the operation is commutative, the table is symmetric around its main diagonal.
- The identity element's row and column look like the elements outside the table.
- In some cases, no elements are repeated in any row or column.

GROUPS

This is where we give the formal definition of a group. Merely combining a set with an operation does not guarantee a group. For example, the natural numbers do not constitute a group with any operation, because of the lack of inverse elements. (For addition you need negative numbers, and for multiplication you need fractions.)

Because the definition is abstract, it is best to discuss it in the context of an example, such as the one given in problem 4. A discussion of problems 4-7 can be supplemented with a look back at the groups studied in previous chapters in the light of the new terminology.

(continued on page 243)

Essential Ideas

EQUATIONS, IDENTITIES, INEQUALITIES

1. Always, sometimes, or never true?
a. $2x + 6 = 2x - 6$
b. $2x + 6 = 2(x + 6)$
c. $2x + 6 = x + 6$
d. $2x + 6 = 2(x + 3)$

2. For each equation above, decide which of the two expressions is greater, if they are equal, or if the answer depends on the value of x.

3. Solve the inequalities. You may want to use a graph.
a. $3x < 5$ b. $x + 3 < 5$
c. $3x + 3 < 5$ d. $2x + 6 < x + 6$

SOLVING EQUATIONS

Solve these equations.

4. a. $4x + 8 = 9$
b. $-4x + 8 = 9$
c. $4x - 8 = 9$
d. $-4x + 8 = -9$

5. a. $x - 6 = 2(x - 5)$
b. $2x - 12 = 4(x - 5)$
c. $2.5(x - 5) = 2.5x - 12$

6. a. $\frac{1}{3}(4x - 2) = 5$
b. $\frac{4}{5}(8 - 2x) = 16$
c. $\frac{x - 3}{2} = x - 4.3$

7. a. $6 - 3(m - 4) = 3m$
b. $(6 - 3)(n - 4) = 3n$
c. $6 - 2(p + 4) = (8 - p)(2 + 3)$
d. $(6 - x)(x + 4) = (8 - x)(x + 2)$

8. a. $\frac{d + 9}{5} - 3 = 15$ b. $\frac{f - 2}{4} = f + 3$
c. $\frac{2d + 6}{5} = \frac{3d - 7}{5}$

9. Solve for y in terms of x.
a. $-6x + y = 4$
b. $2y + x = 8$

GRAPHS

10. Graph these equations on the same axes.
$y - x = -6$ $y = 2(x - 5)$
$y = 2x - 12$ $y = 4(x - 5)$

11. Explain how one can use this graph to check the solutions to problem 5.

12. Use your graph to solve the compound inequality, $2x - 12 < x - 6 < 2x - 10$. Explain.

WRITING EQUATIONS

13. Write an expression telling how much money Bea will have if she
a. starts with \$321 and saves \$9 a week for n weeks;
b. starts with \$321 and saves \$$d$ a week for n weeks;
c. starts with \$$m$ and saves \$$d$ a week for n weeks.

14. If Bea starts with \$321, how much must she save each week to reach \$456 in 28 weeks? Write an equation and solve it.

DIFFERENCES AND RATIOS

According to author Glen Rounds, Johnny Inkslinger was Paul Bunyan's accountant. He used a pencil that was "over three feet in diameter and seventy-six feet long — the first one ever used." A typical pencil is a quarter inch in diameter and seven and a half inches long. Most men in those days were probably between 5 feet 6 in. and 6 feet tall.

S O L U T I O N S

1. a. never true b. never true
c. sometimes true d. always true
2. a. $2x + 6$ is always greater than $2x - 6$
b. $2(x + 6)$ is always greater than $2x + 6$
c. $2x + 6 > x + 6$ when $x > 0$
$2x + 6 = x + 6$ when $x = 0$
$x + 6 > 2x + 6$ when $x < 0$
d. $2x + 6$ always equals $2(x + 3)$
3. a. $x < 5/3$ b. $x < 2$
c. $x < 2/3$ d. $x < 0$
4. a. 1/4 b. -1/4
c. 4.25 d. 4.25
5. a. 4 b. 4 c. no solution
6. a. 4.25 b. -6 c. 5.6
7. a. $m = 3$ b. no solution
c. $p = 14$ d. $x = 2$
8. a. $d = 81$ b. $f = -14/3$
c. $d = 13$
9. a. $y = 6x + 4$ b. $y = 4 - x/2$
10.

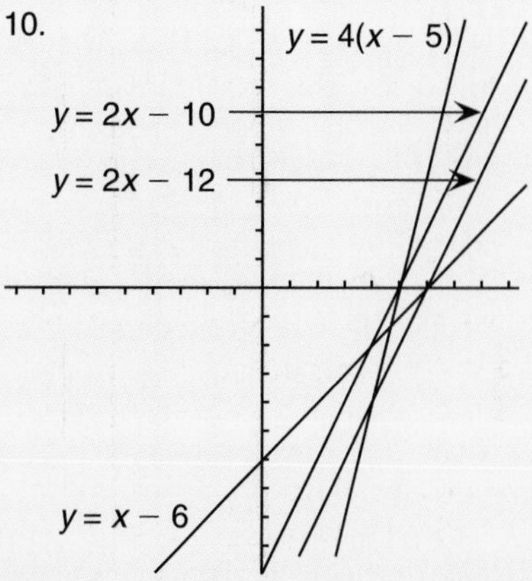

11. The graph of $y - x = -6$ is the same as the graph of $y = x - 6$. The x-coordinate of the intersection of this graph with the graph of $y = 2(x - 5)$ is 4, which gives the solution to 5(a). Similarly, 5(b) can be solved by finding that the intersection of $y = 2x - 12$ and $y = 4(x - 5)$ also occurs at $x = 4$. For 5(c), one could notice that $y = 2(x - 5)$ is parallel to $y = 2x - 12$, so $y = 2.5(x - 5)$ will be parallel to $y = 2.5x - 12$. Hence there is no solution.
12. The graph of $y = x - 6$ is between the graphs of $y = 2x - 12$ and $y = 2x - 10$ for values of x between 4 and 6. Therefore, the solution to the compound inequality is $4 < x < 6$.

15. Compared to a normal pencil, Johnny Inkslinger's was
   a. how much wider?
   b. how many times as wide?
   c. how much longer?
   d. how many times as long?

16. Based on this information, how tall do you think Johnny was? Explain. (Give your answer as a range of probable heights.)

TABLES, GRAPHS, AND EQUATIONS

A telephone company offers two different billing plans. The Community Plan costs \$10.77 a month and allows unlimited local calls. The Thrifty Plan costs \$5.50 a month, but the cost of local calls is 5.5 cents for the first minute, plus 3.5 cents for each additional minute. Both plans cost the same for long distance calls. Which plan should different callers use?

17. Assume that your phone calls last an average of five minutes.
   a. How much does an average call cost under the Thrifty Plan?
   b. Write a formula for the Thrifty Plan. Use y for the cost, x for the number of phone calls.
   c. If you make exactly one five-minute call a day, should you use the Thrifty Plan or the Community Plan?

18. Write a formula for the Thrifty Plan. Use y for the cost and x for the number of phone calls. Assume your calls last an average of:
   a. 1 minute; b. 3 minutes;
   c. 5 minutes; d. 7 minutes.

19. Make tables to show how many calls a month make it preferable to use the Community Plan, for a customer whose calls last an average of:
   a. 1 minute; b. 3 minutes;
   c. 5 minutes; d. 7 minutes.

20. Use a graph to show the costs of both plans for each customer listed in problem 19 as a function of the number of calls made. (Your graph should include five lines.)

A consumer advocate gives advice to people about which plan to choose. In order to do that, he needs to generalize the information revealed in problems 17-20.

21. He would like to have a formula for the Thrifty Plan in terms of two variables: x for the number of local calls, and t for the average duration of each call. Find such a formula.

22. He would like to know the number of local calls at the "break even" point, where both plans cost roughly the same amount, in terms of t. To figure this out, he sets up an equation, with the formula for the Thrifty Plan on the left, and the cost of the Community Plan (10.77) on the right.
   a. Solve the equation for x.
   b. Check your answers to problem 17 with the formula you found in part (a).

23. In trying to use the formula from problem 22 he finds that people don't usually know the average duration of their phone calls. To help them figure it out, he asks them for an estimate of the numbers of local calls they make every week that last approximately: one minute, five minutes, ten minutes, and thirty minutes. Given these four numbers, how can he find the average duration of the phone calls?

24. **Project** Keep track of the duration of your phone calls for a week. Figure out which plan would be more suitable for you if you had your own phone.

(6.C continued)

Problem 8: For examples, students can look back at the lessons listed previously especially for the noncommutative case, of which there are no cases in this lesson. (Instead, see **Letter Strings**, Chapter 5, Lesson 12, and **Smooth Moves**, Chapter 4, Lesson 4.C.) You can help get students started by discussing an example in class, and pointing out where others can be found.

Since this is the last lesson on abstract algebra, if you want to do more, one possible investigation is to explore which of the mod clocks yield groups. It turns out that any number yields a group for $\oplus$, but only prime numbers yield groups for $\otimes$ (and this only once zero has been removed from the set).

At a more advanced level, 11th or 12th grade, you may use Richard Brown's book on *Transformational Geometry*, (Silver, Burdett, and Ginn, Inc. 1973), reissued by Dale Seymour Publications, to explore groups with your pre-calculus students.

◆ SOLUTIONS

13. a. $321 + 9n$ dollars
   b. $321 + dn$ dollars
   c. $m + dn$ dollars

14. The equation is $321 + 28d = 456$, which gives an approximate solution of $d = 4.82$. If Bea saves \$4.82 per week for 28 weeks, she will have \$455.96. (If she cannot borrow the 4 cents, she will have to save for another week.) An alternative plan would be to save \$4.83 per week for 28 weeks, to end up with \$456.24.

15. a. over 35.75 inches wider
   b. over 144 times as wide
   c. over 904.5 inches longer
   d. over 121.6 times as long

16. Using the width of the pencil as a guide, Johnny would be 144 times as tall as most men, who are 66″ to 72″ tall.
   66(144) = 9504 inches = 792 feet
   72(144) = 10368 inches = 864 feet
   Johnny was between 792 and 864 feet tall. Using the length of the pencil as a guide, Johnny would be 121.6 times as tall as most men.
   66(121.6) = 8025.6 inches = 668.8 feet
   72(121.6) = 8755.2 inches = 729.6 feet
   Johnny was between 668.8 feet and 729.6 feet tall.

17. a. A five-minute call costs [0.055 + 0.035(4)] = 0.195 or approximately 20 cents.
   b. $y = 5.50 + 0.195x$
   c. 5.50 + 0.195(30) = \$11.35 or 5.50 + 0.195(31) = 11.55 This means that if the month has 30 days, the Thrifty Plan costs \$11.35, and if the month has 31 days it costs \$11.55. The Community Plan is a better deal.

18. a. $y = 5.50 + 0.055x$
   b. $y = 5.50 + [0.055 + 0.035(2)]$
      $y = 5.50 + 0.125x$
   c. $y = 5.50 + 0.195x$
   d. $y = 5.50 + [0.055 + 0.035(6)]$
      $y = 5.50 + 0.265x$

(Solutions continued on page 522)

Chapter 7
Products and Powers

Overview of the Chapter

*T*he first eight lessons do not offer strikingly new material. Rather, they constitute a return to areas that have been introduced, and in some cases fairly well covered, in Chapters 1, 3, 5, and 6. The difference is the focus on the main identities and the expectation that by now students should have reached a certain level of mastery of the distributive law. By the end of this chapter, they should be able to multiply binomials and trinomials accurately without the help of the Lab Gear, and they should be ready for the factoring lessons of Chapters 13 and 14.

*Y*ou will have to decide how much emphasis to put on the Lab Gear in this chapter. Some students will be ready to work almost entirely without it, and you shouldn't insist that they use it. Other students will need the Lab Gear, and it should be available to them.

*I*f your students already have a solid understanding of the distributive law, you may do Lesson 1 and Lessons 3-5 quickly, and with a light touch. However most classes will benefit from fairly thorough coverage of this material.

*P*roducts and powers are the key ideas behind scientific notation, which is the focus of Lessons 9-11. This part of the chapter helps prepare students for Chapter 8.

*F*inally, squares play an important part in this chapter, which ends with a geoboard lesson on squares and square roots, which previews Chapter 9.

CHAPTER 7

A spiral galaxy, having arms made of gas, dust, and stars

Coming in this chapter:

Exploration The expression $1^3 + 2^3 + 3^3 + 4^3 + 5^3 + \ldots + n^3$ can be modeled by building n cubes out of blocks. Could you rearrange these blocks into a square? If so, what are its dimensions? Experiment with different values of n. Look for a pattern.

PRODUCTS AND POWERS

1. Introduction of New Tools:

- Tree diagrams for counting
- Exponentiation and scientific notation on the calculator
- Squares and square roots on the calculator

2. Algebra Concepts Emphasized:

- Squares and square roots
- Square of a sum
- Square of a difference
- Factoring differences of squares
- Factoring perfect squares
- Factoring multiples of perfect squares
- Large numbers
- Scientific notation
- Operations with numbers in scientific notation
- Compound inequalities
- The exponent 0
- Distance on the Cartesian plane

3. Algebra Concepts Reviewed:

- Order of operations
- The distributive law
- Factoring
- Combining like terms
- Solving equations by graphing
- Equivalent equations
- Exponentiation

4. Algebra Concepts Previewed:

- Linear versus quadratic growth
- Exponential growth
- Optimization
- Completing the square
- Quadratic equations
- Cube of a binomial
- Square of a trinomial
- Simultaneous equations
- Solving inequalities by graphing
- The laws of exponents
- Geometric sequences and their sums
- The Pythagorean theorem
- The distance formula

5. Problem-Solving Techniques:

- Using tables, graphs, variables, and functions
- Using diagrams and geometric models
- Reducing a problem to previously solved problems

6. Connections and Context:

- Three-dimensional visualization
- Astronomy
- Infinity

▼ 7.1
Squares and Cubes

Core Sequence: 1-14, 19

Suitable for Homework: 7, 12-14, 16-19

What this Lesson is About:

- Review of order of operations
- Review of the distributive law
- Preparation for work with squares

*I*n this lesson students have an opportunity to think of the square of a quantity, as opposed to the square of a number. This requires understanding at a more sophisticated level, but again the Lab Gear provides concrete visual support.

*T*he Exploration previews the first lessons of the chapter, by directly addressing a standard student mistake. Experimenting with numbers is an important part of understanding what's wrong with "distributing the square," but for most students it is not sufficient, which is why we will return to this question in many ways in the course of the chapter.

HOW MANY SQUARES?

*I*n some cases the answers may surprise your students. For example, in problems 4a and 5a, it is not immediately clear that there is a way to model the expression with a single square. (In fact problem 5a could lead to a search for other Pythagorean triples. But do not bring this up if your students don't, since the Pythagorean theorem

LESSON 7.1

Squares and Cubes

You will need:

the Lab Gear 

1. **Exploration** Which is greater, $2^2 + 3^2$ or $(2 + 3)^2$? By how much? Which is greater, $5^2 + 8^2$ or $(5 + 8)^2$? By how much? Is it ever true that

$$x^2 + y^2 = (x + y)^2 ?$$

How far apart are they? Experiment and write a paragraph summarizing your work and your conclusions. It may help to use the Lab Gear.

HOW MANY SQUARES?

The square $(x + 2)^2$ can be written as the product $(x + 2)(x + 2)$. It can be represented by *a single square* with side $(x + 2)$, as shown in the figure.

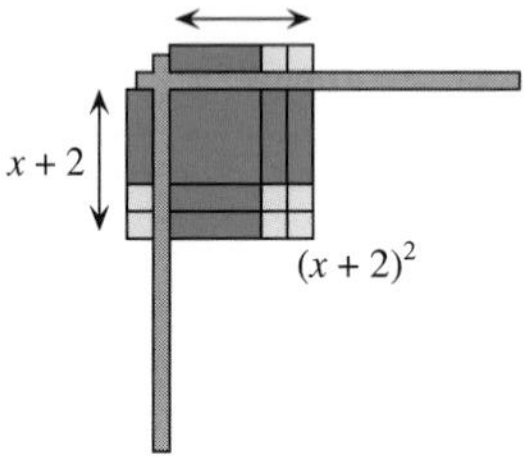

The sum of the squares $x^2 + 2^2$ cannot be written as a product or represented with a single square. It must be represented by *two individual squares.*

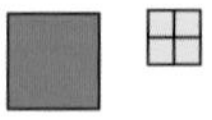

$x^2 + 2^2$

Compare these two expressions.

(i) $2 \cdot 3^2$
(ii) $(2 \cdot 3)^2$

Because the rules for order of operations tell us to perform exponentiation first, expression (i) means *square 3 and then multiply by 2.* This can be modeled by building two squares with the Lab Gear.

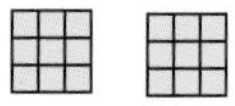

$2 \cdot 3^2$

Expression (ii) means *multiply 2 by 3 and square the result.* Since $2 \cdot 3 = 6$, this can be written more simply as 6^2. This can be modeled by building *one* square with the Lab Gear.

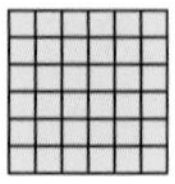

6^2

Make a rough sketch representing each expression, 2-6, with as few squares as possible. Which of these expressions can be modeled as a single square? Which require more than one square? (Be careful!)

2. a. $(x + 1)^2$ b. $x^2 + 1$
3. a. $4x^2 + 4$ b. $(2x + 2)^2$
4. a. $5^2 + 3 \cdot 5^2$ b. $2^2 + 5 \cdot 2^2$
5. a. $3^2 + 4^2$ b. $(3 + 4)^2$
6. a. $(3 \cdot 4)^2$ b. $3^2 \cdot 4^2$
7. Give the value of each expression.
   a. $3^2 + 4^2$ b. $(3 \cdot 4)^2$
   c. $(3 + 4)^2$ d. $3^2 \cdot 4^2$
   e. $5^2 + 3 \cdot 5^2$ f. $2^2 + 5 \cdot 2^2$

7.1 SOLUTIONS

1. $2^2 + 3^2 = 13$ and $(2 + 3)^2 = 25$, so $(2 + 3)^2$ is greater. Also $(5 + 8)^2$ is greater than $5^2 + 8^2$. Using the Lab Gear, it can be seen that the difference between $(x + y)^2$ and $x^2 + y^2$ is $2xy$. The two expressions are equal only if x and/or y is 0.

2. through 6. The following can be modeled as a single square: 2a, 3b, 4a, 5a, 5b, 6a, 6b.

7. a. 25
   b. 144
   c. 49
   d. 144
   e. 100
   f. 24

HOW MANY CUBES?

The cube $(x + 2)^3$ can be written as the product $(x + 2)(x + 2)(x + 2)$. It can be represented by *a single cube* with sides $(x + 2)$, as shown.

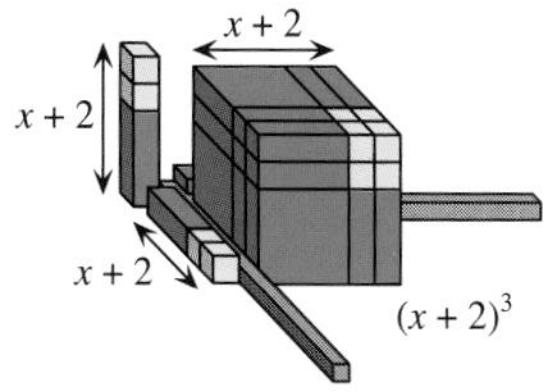

The sum of the cubes $x^3 + 2^3$ cannot be written as a product. It cannot be represented with a single cube. It must be represented by *two individual cubes.*

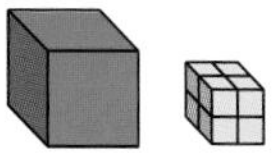

$x^3 + 2^3$

Compare these two expressions.

(i) $3 \cdot 2^3$

(ii) $(3 \cdot 2)^3$

Because the order of operations tells us to perform exponentiation first, expression (i) means *cube 2 and then multiply by 3.* This can be modeled by building three cubes with the Lab Gear.

$3 \cdot 2^3$

Expression (ii) means *multiply 2 by 3 and cube the result.* Since $3 \cdot 2 = 6$, this can be written more simply as 6^3. This can be modeled by building one cube with the Lab Gear.

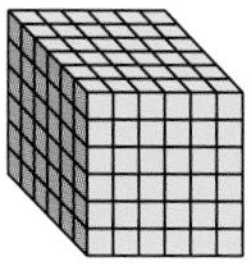

6^3

8. What number does each expression equal?
a. $3 \cdot 2^3$ b. $(3 \cdot 2)^3$

How would you represent each expression with as few cubes as possible? It may help to use the Lab Gear. Make a sketch, giving the dimensions of each cube.

9. a. $(x + 1)^3$ b. $x^3 + 1$

10. a. $x^3 + 8$ b. $(x + 2)^3$

11. a. $x^3 + y^3$ b. $(x + y)^3$

Which of these expressions could be modeled using only one cube? Which require more than one cube? Tell how you would represent each expression with as few cubes as possible. Give the dimensions of each cube.

12. a. $6 \cdot 2^3$ b. $(6 \cdot 2)^3$

13. a. $6^3 + 2^3$ b. $(6 + 2)^3$

14. What is the value of each expression?
a. $6 \cdot 2^3$ b. $(6 \cdot 2)^3$
c. $6^3 + 2^3$ d. $(6 + 2)^3$

will be addressed more fully in Chapter 9, and there is plenty of pressing work in this chapter.) In problem 5b, it is possible to model the expression with three squares.

A fuller investigation of writing whole numbers as sums of squares is presented as an optional Discovery at the end of Lesson 12.

HOW MANY CUBES?

This is the same activity, using cubes. It is not important at this stage that the students memorize an identity for the cube of a binomial. However it is useful for them to actually build the cubes in problems 9-11.

7.1 SOLUTIONS

8. a. 24
   b. 216
9. a. one cube with sides of length $x + 1$
   b. two cubes: one with sides of length x, the other with sides of length 1
10. a. two cubes: one of side x, the other of side 2
    b. one cube of side $x + 2$
11. a. two cubes: one of side x, the other of side y
    b. one cube of side $x + y$
12. a. six cubes, each with side 2
    b. one cube of side 12
13. a. two cubes, one of side 6 and the other of side 2
    b. one cube of side 8
14. a. 48
    b. 1728
    c. 224
    d. 512

MAKING SQUARES FROM CUBES

This is a surprising number pattern, once again involving triangular numbers, which is particularly pleasing to discover by working with actual blocks. Of course, this becomes difficult with large numbers, but it is really worth it to actually make squares from cubes for small numbers. Problem 15 should be done in class, even if problems 16-18 are assigned as homework.

Of course you cannot expect a proof of this result at this level, but in problem 18 students should be able to write an expression in terms of n. You should accept an expression with "..." in it. However it is conceivable that some students or groups will find a formula in closed form (with no dots), especially if they did the problems in Chapter 1, Lesson 11.

REVIEW CUBING WITH A TABLE

Distributive law practice without the blocks. This also previews an activity at the end of Lesson 7, where students will be asked to go one step further and multiply polynomials without using the table format.

MAKING SQUARES FROM CUBES

15. a. Use the Lab Gear to show how the expression $1^3 + 2^3 + 3^3$ can be modeled by building three cubes.

b. What was the total number of blocks needed for part (a)?

c. Make a square by rearranging the blocks you used to make the three cubes. What are the dimensions of the square?

16. a. The expression $1^3 + 2^3 + 3^3 + 4^3$ could be modeled by building four cubes. What is the total number of blocks used?

b. How would one make a square by rearranging these blocks? Give the square's dimensions.

17. Compare your answers to problems 15 and 16. Look for a pattern. Check it for $1^3 + 2^3$. Predict the value of the sum,

$$1^3 + 2^3 + 3^3 + 4^3 + 5^3.$$

Check your prediction.

18. **Generalization** The expression

$$1^3 + 2^3 + 3^3 + 4^3 + 5^3 + \ldots + n^3$$

can be modeled by building n cubes out of blocks. Could you rearrange these blocks into a square? If so, what would its dimensions be? Explain your answer.

REVIEW *CUBING WITH A TABLE*

To find the cube of a polynomial, first find its square, then multiply the result by the polynomial. For example, to calculate $(x + 2y)^3$, first square $x + 2y$.

	x	$2y$
x	x^2	$2xy$
$2y$	$2xy$	$4y^2$

Combine like terms in the body of the table. Multiply this result by $x + 2y$.

	x^2	$4xy$	$4y^2$
x	x^3	$4x^2y$	$4xy^2$
$2y$	$2x^2y$	$8xy^2$	$8y^3$

So $(x + 2y)^3 = x^3 + 6x^2y + 12xy^2 + 8y^3$.

19. Find the cube.

a. $(x + 1)^3$ b. $(2x + 2)^3$

c. $(x + y)^3$ d. $(2x - y)^3$

e. $(3x + 2y - 5)^3$

7.1 SOLUTIONS

15. a. 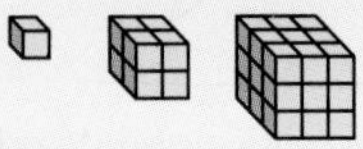

$1^3 + 2^3 + 3^3$

b. 36

c. 6 by 6

16. a. 100

b. 10 by 10

17. $1^3 + 2^3 = 3^2$

$1^3 + 2^3 + 3^3 + 4^3 + 5^3 = 15^2$

The pattern is to add all the bases and take the square of the sum.

18. Using the pattern discovered above:

$1^3 + 2^3 + 3^3 + \ldots n^3 = (1 + 2 + 3 + \ldots + n)^2$

The dimensions are $(1 + 2 + 3 + \ldots + n)$ by $(1 + 2 + 3 + \ldots + n)$.

19. a. $x^3 + 3x^2 + 3x + 1$

b. $8x^3 + 24x^2 + 24x + 8$

c. $x^3 + 3x^2y + 3xy^2 + y^3$

d. $8x^3 - 12x^2y + 6xy^2 - y^3$

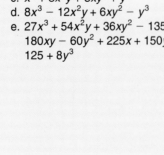

e. $27x^3 + 54x^2y + 36xy^2 - 135x^2 - 180xy - 60y^2 + 225x + 150y - 125 + 8y^3$

LESSON 7.2

Square Windows

You will need:

graph paper

THREE TYPES OF PANES

The A.B. Glare window store has started selling a new kind of window. These windows can be made to order by combining three types of square window panes. Each pane measures one foot on each side. The three types of panes are shown below: corner panes, edge panes, and inside panes.

A 3-foot-by-3-foot window is shown below. It was made by putting together 4 corner panes, 4 edge panes, and 1 inside pane.

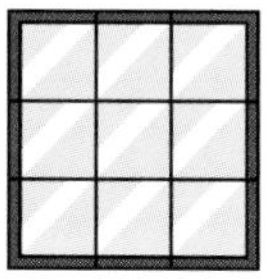

1. Sketch a 4-foot-by-5-foot rectangular window. How many panes of each type were used to make it?

SQUARE WINDOWS

2. **Exploration** An architect was asked to design a recreation hall. He was going to use the A.B. Glare window panes described above. The building code imposes a limit of 72 square feet for the total area of all windows in the main part of the hall. The architect decides to consider various combinations of square windows such that their total area is exactly 72. Find several such configurations, and for each one, find the total number of each type of pane the architect will need.

The architect is not the only one to like square windows. To save time when customers ask for them, Lara is assembling kits with the correct number of corner panes, edge panes, and inside panes to make square windows of various sizes.

3. Make a table to show how many panes of each type are needed for a 2-by-2 window, a 3-by-3 window, and so on, up to a 10-by-10 window.

4. Study the table from problem 3. Which increases the fastest: the number of corner, edge, or inside panes? Which increases the most slowly? Why?

5. Make three graphs of the data in your table, on the same set of axes.
   a. Graph the number of corner panes as a function of the length of the side of the window. For example, since a 3-by-3 window uses four corner panes, the point (3, 4) would be on your graph.
   b. Graph the number of edge panes as a function of the side length.
   c. Graph the number of inside panes as a function of the side length.

6. Study your graphs. Which is the steepest? Explain why.

7.2 Square Windows

Core Sequence: 1-13, 17

Suitable for Homework: 3-17

Useful for Assessment: 4, 7, 12

What this Lesson is About:

- Comparing linear and quadratic growth
- Using tables, graphs, variables, and functions
- Preview of the identity for the square of a sum
- Optimization

THREE TYPES OF PANES
SQUARE WINDOWS

Problems 1-2 will acquaint students with the basic assumptions of the problem. Note that the Exploration has many solutions, and it is not necessary to find all of them. Note that 1-by-1 windows are not possible with the panes we are given. Nevertheless, there are many ways to combine squares of side 2 to 8 for a total area of 72.

When you are sure that all students understand how to find the number for each type of pane for different sizes of square windows, you can let the class move on to the more guided discovery in problems 3-9. By now, this sort of work with tables, graphs, variables, and functions should be routine.

7.2 SOLUTIONS

1. 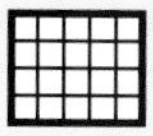
   4 corner panes, 10 edge panes, 6 inside panes

2. Answers will vary. Sample answers:
   Two 6-by-6 windows: 8 corner panes, 32 edge panes, 32 inside panes
   Eight 3-by-3 windows: 32 corner panes, 32 edge panes, 8 inside panes
   Eighteen 2-by-2 windows: 72 corner panes

3.

Dimensions of window	Corner	Edge	Inside	Total
2 by 2	4	0	0	4
3 by 3	4	4	1	9
4 by 4	4	8	4	16
5 by 5	4	12	9	25
6 by 6	4	16	16	36
7 by 7	4	20	25	49
8 by 8	4	24	36	64
9 by 9	4	28	49	81
10 by 10	4	32	64	100

4. The number of inside panes increases fastest. The number of corner panes remains constant as each window has exactly 4 corner panes.

5. 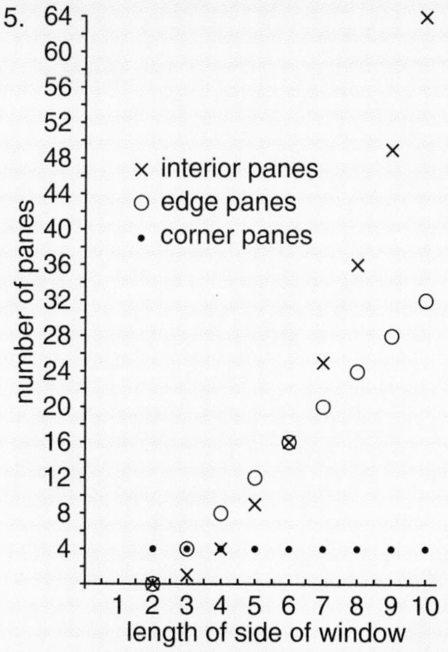

*A*n alternate strategy is to spend more time on the Exploration, then answer problems 7a, 8, and 9 before doing 3-6.

*S*tudents may arrive at a correct equation by inspection of the table developed in problem 3. That's fine, but make sure they understand the relationship between the geometry of the problem and the equations. Recognizing a number pattern is an important skill, but in and of itself it does not throw light on the content of the problem. This is why problem 7 is important.

COMPARING SIZES

*Y*ou may use the Lab Gear on the overhead projector to lead a discussion of problems 12-13. Let students suggest how one could use the Lab Gear to model the problem. At one level, one can use the 1-blocks as window panes, and vary the numbers for different-sized windows. A more sophisticated solution could involve a set-up with y^2 in the center, a 1-block at each corner, and four y-blocks for the edge panes. Other arrangements are possible, for example using y for the side length, and not explicitly showing the difference between the various types of panes.

*O*f course, problems 12-13 preview Lesson 3 on squares of sums.

MAKING THE MOST OF INVENTORY

*P*roblem 16 is an interesting optimization puzzle. Many solutions lead to three panes left over, but none that the authors could find improve on that result.

*I*f your students enjoy the problem, have them explore whether they can improve their results by allowing nonsquare rectangular windows.

PREVIEW *BIGGER WINDOWS*

*P*roblem 17 previews the question of area of similar figures.

7. **Generalization**
   a. Write a formula for the number of panes of each type in an x-by-x window. Explain each formula in reference to a sketch of such a window.
   b. How are the formulas related to the graphs in problem 5?

8. Add up the algebraic expressions for the numbers of each type of pane. If you did your work correctly, the sum should be very simple.

9. Find the number of corner, edge, and inside panes needed for a 100-by-100 window.

COMPARING SIZES

10. Lara has too many window kits of some types and not enough of other types. She has too many kits for 2-by-2 windows and not enough for 3-by-3 windows. How many panes of each type would she have to add to a 2-by-2 kit to convert it to a 3-by-3 kit?

11. Answer question 10 if Lara wanted to convert
    a. a 5-by-5 kit to a 6-by-6 kit;
    b. an 8-by-8 kit to a 9-by-9 kit.

12. **Generalization** How many panes of each type would Lara have to add if she wanted to convert an N-by-N-foot kit to an $N+1$-by-$N+1$-foot kit. Explain, using a sketch of an $N+1$-by-$N+1$ window.

13. How many panes of each type would Lara have to add if she wanted to convert an N-by-N-foot kit to an $N+M$-by-$N+M$-foot kit. Explain, using a sketch of an $N+M$-by-$N+M$ window.

MAKING THE MOST OF INVENTORY

14. Suppose you have 12 panes of each type in inventory.
    a. What is the largest square window you could make? Give the size of the window and tell how many panes of each type you would have left over.
    b. What is the largest square window you could make with the remaining panes? Continue until no more windows can be made. Give the size of all the windows and the number of each type of pane left at the end.

15. Repeat problem 14 for:
    a. 20 panes of each type;
    b. 100 panes of each type.

16. Now assume that instead of trying for the largest possible square window, you try to make any number of square windows, with the goal of having *as few panes as possible left over.*
    a. If you start with 100 panes of each type, what size windows should you make? What will be left over?
    b. Compare your answers with other students' answers.

PREVIEW *BIGGER WINDOWS*

17. Suppose each pane, regardless of the type, costs $1.00.
    a. Make a table and a graph showing the cost of the window as a function of the side length.
    b. Al knows that an 8-by-8 window costs $64.00. He thinks that a 16-by-16 window should cost twice as much, but he isn't sure. What do you think? Explain your opinion.
    c. A 16-by-16 window costs how many times as much as an 8-by-8 window?

7.2 SOLUTIONS

6. The graph of the number of inside panes as a function of side length is the steepest. The center of the window grows faster than the edges because two dimensions are growing. The edges are growing in one dimension only.

7. a. As shown in the figure, there are four corner panes. There are four edge regions, each of length $(x-2)$. There is one center region of dimensions $(x-2)$ by $(x-2)$. Hence for an x-by-x window, there are 4 corner panes, $4(x-2)$ edge panes, and $(x-2)^2$ inside panes.

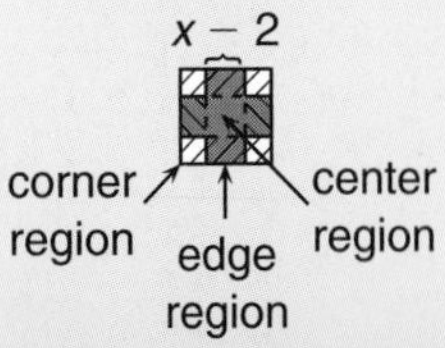

   b. The corner regions do not grow, hence the graph is a horizontal line. The edge regions grow along one dimension; hence the graph is linear. The center panes grow in two dimensions (length and width), and so the graph is quadratic.

8. $4 + 4(x-2) + (x-2)^2 = 4 + 4x - 8 + x^2 - 4x + 4 = x^2$
   This makes sense, since an x-by-x window will have x^2 panes, total.

9. 4 corner panes, 392 edge panes, 9604 inside panes (and 10,000 panes in all)

(Solutions continued on page 522)

LESSON 7.3

Squares of Sums

You will need:

the Lab Gear 

1. Exploration

a. Model the square $(x + 1)^2$ with the Lab Gear. Then add blocks to create the square $(x + 2)^2$. What blocks did you need to add to the first square to get the second? Now add blocks to create the square $(x + 3)^2$. What blocks did you add this time? Continue to make the square grow, keeping an organized record of what blocks you add each time. Write a paragraph about any patterns you notice.

b. If a and b are whole numbers, what blocks would you need to add to $(x + a)^2$ to get $(x + a + 1)^2$? To get $(x + a + b)^2$?

MISSING TERMS

2. a. Use the Lab Gear to build a square using 10 x-blocks and any other blocks that you want (except more x-blocks). Sketch the square.

b. What is the area of the square?

c. What are its dimensions?

d. Is this the only such square you could build? (That is, is your answer *unique*?) If it isn't, try to find another possibility. If you can't build another square, explain why.

3. Repeat problem 2, using 16 one-blocks and any other blocks that you want (except more yellow blocks).

4. Repeat problem 2, using 8 xy-blocks and any other blocks that you want (except more xy-blocks).

5. Can you build a square starting with 3 x^2-blocks, if you can use any other blocks except more x^2-blocks? Explain.

6. Can you build a square starting with 15 one-blocks, if you can use any other blocks except more one-blocks? Explain.

7. Build two different squares starting with 4 x^2-blocks, using any other blocks except more x^2-blocks. Are there more solutions? Explain.

TERMS AND COEFFICIENTS

8. a. Use the Lab Gear to build three squares of the form $(x + b)^2$, using a different value of b each time. Sketch the squares.

b. Write the area of the square next to each sketch, combining like terms.

c. Notice how many terms are in each expression for area. Notice the coefficient of each term. Describe what you notice.

In each expression below, a binomial is squared. Distribute and combine like terms.

9. $(2y + 3)^2$ **10.** $(3x + 2)^2$

11. $(2x + 3y)^2$ **12.** $(3x + 2y)^2$

7.3

Squares of Sums

Core Sequence: 1-20, 22, 27-28

Suitable for Homework: 9-21, 27-28

Useful for Assessment: 13-15, 20

What this Lesson is About:

- The square of a sum
- Preview of completing the square
- Preview of difference of squares and square of a difference
- Review of quotient and remainder

The Exploration is somewhat reminiscent of the work with square windows in the previous lesson.

MISSING TERMS

TERMS AND COEFFICIENTS

The Lab Gear exercises bring in sharp focus the structure of the square of a binomial. Starting with problem 9, students do not need to use the blocks, though you should allow them to if they want.

7.3 SOLUTIONS

1. a. $2x + 3$ blocks are needed to convert $(x + 1)^2$ to $(x + 2)^2$.
$2x + 5$ blocks are needed to convert $(x + 2)^2$ to $(x + 3)^2$.
$2x + 7$ blocks are needed to convert $(x + 3)^2$ to $(x + 4)^2$.
$2x + 2n + 1$ blocks are needed to convert $(x + n)^2$ to $(x + n + 1)^2$.
b. Two x-blocks and $2a + 1$ one-blocks are needed to change $(x + a)^2$ to $(x + a + 1)^2$. To change $(x + a)^2$ to $(x + a + b)^2$ we must add $2b$ x-blocks and $2ab + b^2$ one-blocks.
2. a. Build a square by adding one x^2 and 25 ones.
b. $x^2 + 10x + 25$
c. $x + 5$ by $x + 5$
d. Yes, it is unique.
3. a. You can make a square with the original 16 blocks. Another square can be made by adding one x^2-block and eight x-blocks.
b. One square has area 16. The other square has area $x^2 + 8x + 16$.
c. 4 by 4, or $(x + 4)$ by $(x + 4)$
d. There are two squares, so the answer is not unique.
4. a. Two squares are possible, one requiring the addition of one y^2 and 16 x^2, the other requiring the addition of one x^2 and 16 y^2.
b. $y^2 + 8xy + 16x^2$ or $x^2 + 8xy + 16y^2$
c. $y + 4x$ by $y + 4x$, or $x + 4y$ by $x + 4y$
d. not unique
5. No. The number of x^2-blocks needs to be a perfect square.
6. No. The number of one-blocks needs to be a perfect square.
7. There are several possible solutions:
$(2x + 5)^2 = 4x^2 + 20x + 25$
$(2x + 4)^2 = 4x^2 + 16x + 16$
$(2x + 3)^2 = 4x^2 + 12x + 9$
$(2x + 2)^2 = 4x^2 + 8x + 4$
$(2x + 1)^2 = 4x^2 + 4x + 1$
8. Answers will vary. A sample is given.

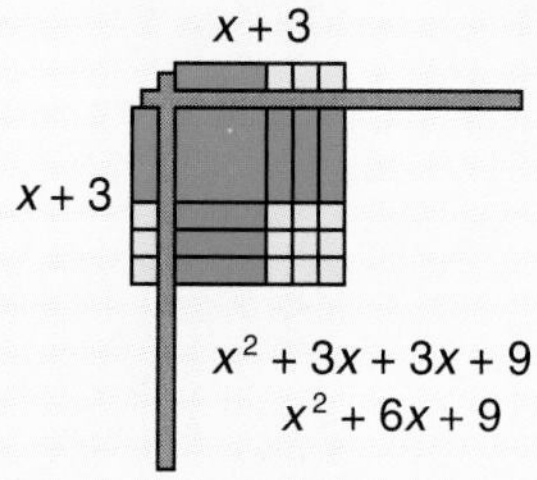

$x^2 + 3x + 3x + 9 =$
$x^2 + 6x + 9$

RECOGNIZING PERFECT SQUARES

*I*f students want to use the Lab Gear, let them, though it will not work for problem 19 or for problems that use large or fractional coefficients. Encourage the use of the table representation, as the breaking up of the middle term into equal halves for inclusion in the table is an important step towards understanding completing the square (which we do in Chapter 13).

*O*ne way to understand the pattern in problem 22 is to substitute 1 for x and y. Then the expression that is being squared is simply a number. In the case of a whole number, its square is a perfect square.

13. Refer to problems 9-12 to answer these questions.

a. How many terms are in each product, after combining like terms?

b. For each binomial, notice the coefficients of each of the terms. Then notice the coefficients in the related expression for area. Describe any relationships you notice.

c. For each binomial, notice the degree of each of the terms. Then notice the degree of each term in the related expression for area. Describe any relationships you notice.

14. **Summary** Summarize the patterns for the square of a binomial.

15. **Generalization** The patterns you found can be generalized by using letters instead of numbers for coefficients. Show how you would find the area of a square having side

a. $a + b$; b. $ax + b$;
c. $a + by$; d. $ax + by$.

16. In each expression below, a binomial is squared. Distribute and combine like terms.

a. $(m + n)^2$ b. $(11m + 2)^2$
c. $(5y + 6x)^2$ d. $(1 + 9y)^2$

RECOGNIZING PERFECT SQUARES

$x^2 + 14x + 49$ is called a *perfect square trinomial.* It is the square of the binomial $(x + 7)$, as you can see by writing it in a multiplication table.

	x	7
x	x^2	$7x$
7	$7x$	49

17. Which of the following are perfect square trinomials? For each one, write the binomial it is the square of.

a. $x^2 + 16x + 16$
b. $x^2 + 4x + 4$
c. $x^2 + 10x + 25$
d. $x^2 + 10xy + 25y^2$

18. All of these are perfect square trinomials. Write each one as the square of a binomial. Sketches may help.

a. $4x^2 + 20xy + 25y^2$
b. $36y^2 + 12xy + x^2$
c. $y^2 + 18y + 81$
d. $25x^2 + 10xy + y^2$

19. None of these expressions is a perfect square trinomial. In each one, change just one of the terms to convert the whole expression into the square of a binomial.

a. $4x^2 + 12x + 10$
b. $2x^2 + 8x + 16$
c. $36x^2 + 30x + 25$
d. $1.44x^2 + 1.6x + 2.25$

20. **Summary** Explain how to recognize a perfect square trinomial. You may use sketches, but be sure to discuss *coefficients, terms,* and *degree.*

21. Look at each perfect square trinomial in this lesson. For each one, find the sum of the coefficients. What do you notice? Explain.

7.3 SOLUTIONS

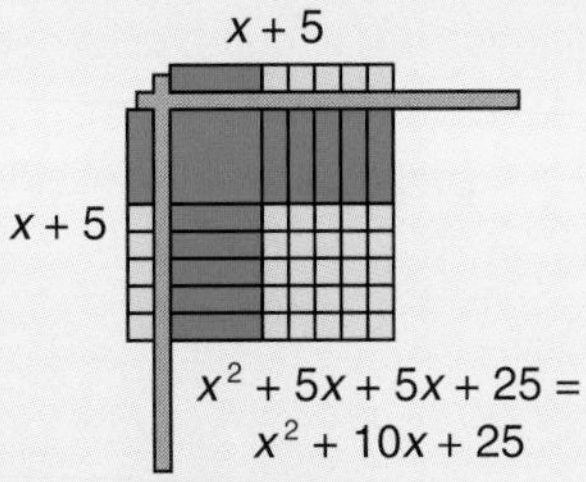

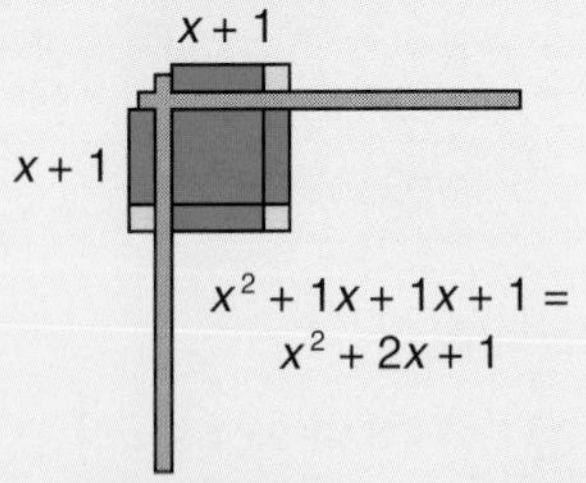

c. Each expression for area has three terms. The constant term is the square of b. The middle term is twice bx. The coefficient of x^2 is 1.

9. $(2y + 3)^2 = 4y^2 + 12y + 9$
10. $(3x + 2)^2 = 9x^2 + 12x + 4$
11. $(2x + 3y)^2 = 4x^2 + 12xy + 9y^2$
12. $(3x + 2y)^2 = 9x^2 + 12xy + 4y^2$
13. a. three terms
 b. The coefficients of the first and last terms are the squares of the coefficients of the terms of the binomials. The coefficient of the middle term is twice the product of the coefficients of the terms of the binomials. Algebraically: $(ax + by)^2 = a^2x^2 + 2abxy + b^2y^2$
 c. Answers will vary. One thing to notice is that the term of lowest degree has degree twice that of the term of lowest degree in the binomial. Likewise, the term of highest degree has degree twice that of the term of highest degree in the binomial.
14. Answers will vary. Main ideas: $(ax + b)^2 = a^2x^2 + 2abx + b^2$ and $(ax + by) = a^2x^2 + 2abxy + b^2y^2$.
15. a. $(a + b)^2 = a^2 + 2ab + b^2$
 b. $(ax + b)^2 = a^2x^2 + 2abx + b^2$
 c. $(a + by)^2 = a^2 + 2aby + b^2y^2$
 d. $(ax + by)^2 = a^2x^2 + 2abxy + b^2y^2$

 To find the area of each square whose side is a binomial, square the first term of the binomial, add twice the product of the terms of the binomial, and finally add the square of the second term of the binomial.
16. a. $(m + n)^2 = m^2 + 2mn + n^2$
 b. $(11m + 2)^2 = 121m^2 + 44m + 4$
 c. $(5y + 6x)^2 = 25y^2 + 60xy + 36x^2$
 d. $(1 + 9y)^2 = 1 + 18y + 81y^2$

PREVIEW ***HOW MANY TERMS?***

22. **Exploration** Two of the following problems are impossible. Solve the other three. Find a pair of binomials such that their product has:

a. three terms
b. four terms
c. five terms
d. one term
e. two terms

REVIEW ***LAB GEAR MULTIPLICATION***

For each of these problems, 23-25:

a. Use the corner piece to show the multiplication.
b. Check that the resulting figure includes an *uncovered rectangle* of the required dimensions.
c. Write a *length times width equals area* equation.

23. $(y + 2)(y + 2)$ **24.** $(y + 2)(y - 2)$

25. $(y - 2)(y - 2)$

26. Which of the uncovered rectangles in problems 23, 24, and 25 are squares?

DISCOVERY ***CONSTRAINED NUMBERS***

27. What are m and n if they are whole numbers and

a. $89 = 12m + n$, with $n < 12$;
b. $123 = 45m + n$, with $n < 45$;
c. $2345 = 67m + n$, with $n < 67$.

28. If N and m are whole numbers, and $N = 7m + n$, find several values of N such that $n = 2$.

PREVIEW ***HOW MANY TERMS?***

This Exploration is a very important preview of the difference of squares (which we tackle formally in the next lesson), as well as a problem-solving opportunity to practice the distributive law. Do not skip it!

It should be done in class, so that students can work in groups. Do not give hints. Let students struggle with this, using trial and error with the help of the Lab Gear and/or the table representation.

REVIEW ***LAB GEAR MULTIPLICATION***

This section offers a transition to the identities that involve minus, as well as a review of multiplication in the corner piece. If you are pressed for time, you may skip it, but only if your students are very much on top of Lab Gear multiplication.

DISCOVERY ***CONSTRAINED NUMBERS***

Ordinary equation-solving techniques will not help here. Make sure students check that their final answer satisfies all three constraints: the equation, the fact that m and n are whole numbers, and the inequality. m and n are the quotient and remainder of the corresponding division.

7.3 SOLUTIONS

17. b, c, and d are perfect squares.
 b. $x + 2$ c. $x + 5$ d. $x + 5y$

18. a. $(2x + 5y)^2$ b. $(6y + x)^2$
 c. $(y + 9)^2$ d. $(5x + y)^2$

19. a. change the constant term to 9
 b. change the first term to x^2
 c. change the middle term to $60x$
 d. change the middle term to $3.6x$

20. Answers will vary. The key ideas are that the first and last terms are perfect squares. The middle term is twice the product of the square roots of the perfect-square terms. Squares of binomials of the form $ax + b$ have three terms: one second-degree, one first-degree, and one zero-degree. Squares of binomials of the form $ax + by$ have three second-degree terms.

21. The sum of the coefficients is a perfect square.

22. Answers will vary. Sample answers are given.
 a. $(x + 1)(2x + 3) = 2x^2 + 5x + 3$
 b. $(x + 1)(y + a) = xy + ax + y + a$
 c. impossible
 d. impossible
 e. $(x + 1)(x - 1) = x^2 - 1$

23.
$y + 2$
$y + 2$
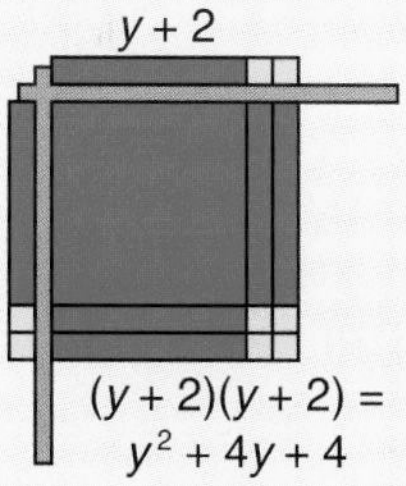
$(y + 2)(y + 2) = y^2 + 4y + 4$

24.
$y + 2$
$y - 2$
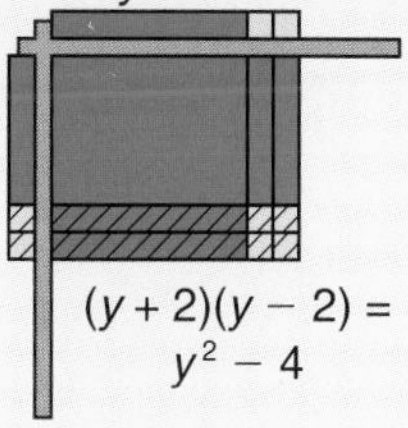
$(y + 2)(y - 2) = y^2 - 4$

25.
$y - 2$
$y - 2$
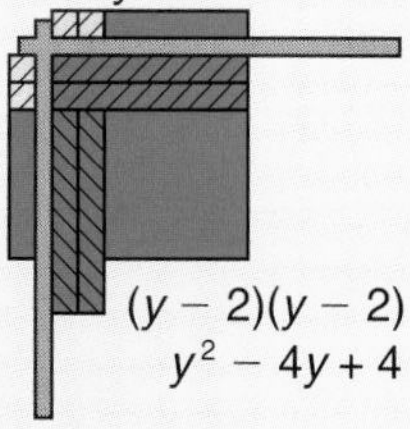
$(y - 2)(y - 2) = y^2 - 4y + 4$

26. the two that are squares of binomials (#23 and #25)

(Solutions continued on page 523)

▼ 7.4
Differences of Squares

Core Sequence: 1-17, 21-32

Suitable for Homework: 1-5, 10-13, 21-32

Useful for Assessment: 5, 9, 13, 17

What this Lesson is About:

- Factoring a difference of squares
- Using different models for the same mathematical structure
- Review of equation solving

*T*he Exploration sets the stage in the context of numbers, as did the Exploration that opened Lesson 1.

CUTTING A SQUARE OUT OF A SQUARE

USING VARIABLES

*I*f you do not have access to scissors, students can fold and tear the graph paper. Or, assign problems 1-5 as homework.

*I*n problem 4, the simplest solutions involve straight cuts, but the geometrically inclined may explore the question of what other shapes are possible for the cut.

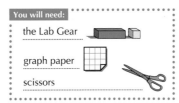

LESSON 7.4

Differences of Squares

You will need:

the Lab Gear 

graph paper 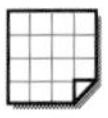

scissors 

1. **Exploration** Which is greater, $3^2 - 2^2$ or $(3 - 2)^2$? Which is greater, $8^2 - 5^2$ or $(8 - 5)^2$? Is it ever true that
$$y^2 - x^2 = (y - x)^2 \text{ ?}$$
Is it ever true that
$$y^2 - x^2 < (y - x)^2 \text{ ?}$$
Experiment, and write a paragraph summarizing your work and your conclusions.

CUTTING A SQUARE OUT OF A SQUARE

Problems 2-4 show how to model the difference of two squares geometrically.

2. Cut a 10-by-10 square out of graph paper. Then, out of the corner of this square, cut a 4-by-4 square. The remaining paper should look like this.

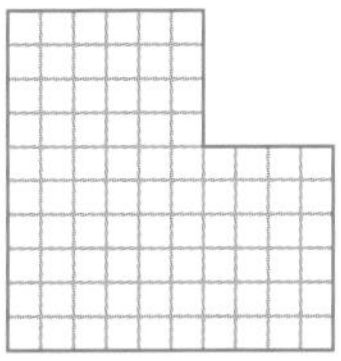

3. The size of the remaining paper represents the *difference* of the 10-by-10 square and the 4-by-4 square. Its area is $10^2 - 4^2$ square centimeters. How many square centimeters is this?

4. The odd-shaped figure you have left after cutting out the 4-by-4 square can be rearranged into a rectangle. You can do this by making a single cut in the paper. Try it. Sketch the resulting rectangle and label its length and width.

5. **Generalization** Repeat problems 2-4 for some other differences of squares. (For example, try cutting a 3-by-3 square out of a 7-by-7 square. Try several others.) Can the resulting shape always be rearranged into a rectangle, no matter what two numbers you use? Can you use fractions? What are the dimensions of the rectangle? If it can always be arranged into a rectangle, explain why. If not, explain when it is possible and when it is not possible. Give examples, using sketches.

USING VARIABLES

Use the Lab Gear to do problems 6-9.

6. Trace the x^2-block on a piece of paper and cut out the square. Then trace a 1-by-1 square in the corner of the x^2-paper and cut it out. What difference is represented by the remaining paper?

7. Show how you can rearrange the remaining paper into a rectangle. Make a sketch showing the dimensions of the rectangle.

7.4 S O L U T I O N S

1. $3^2 - 2^2$ is greater
$8^2 - 5^2$ is greater
$y^2 - x^2 = (y - x)^2$ if $x = 0$ or if $x = y$
$y^2 - x^2 < (y - x)^2$ when $x > 0$ and $x > y$, or when $x < 0$ and $x < y$

3. 84

4. 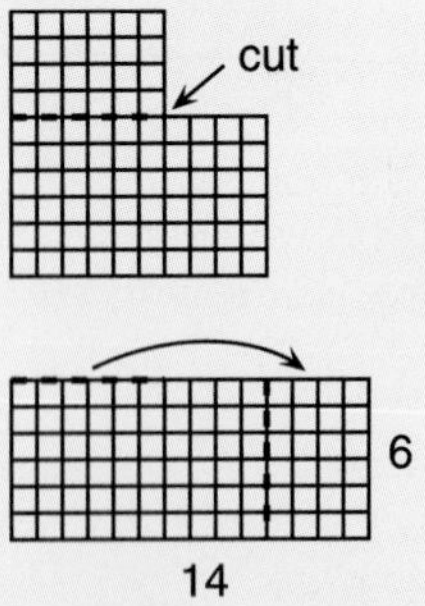

5. Answers will vary. The key idea is that a rectangle is always possible if an n-by-n square is cut out of an m-by-m square (as long as $n < m$). The rectangle will have dimensions $m - n$ by $m + n$. See the figure.

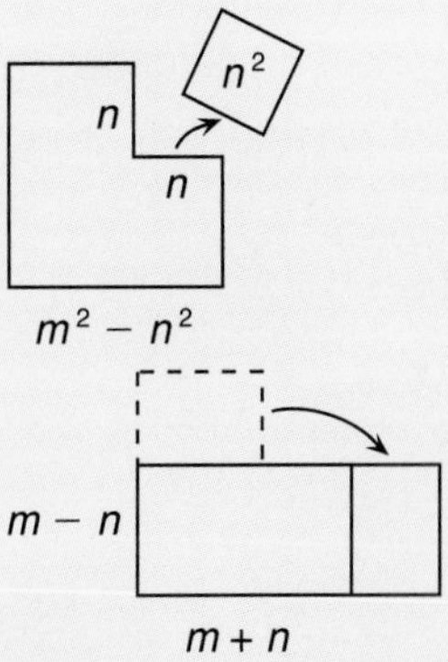

6. $x^2 - 1$

7. dimensions $x - 1$ by $x + 1$

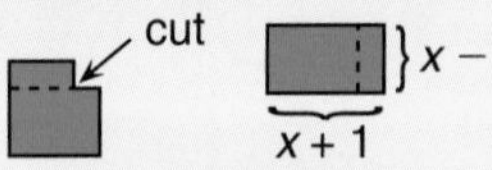

8. a. dimensions are $x - 2$ by $x + 2$
b. dimensions are $y - x$ by $y + x$
c. dimensions are $y - 3$ by $y + 3$
d. dimensions are $y - 5$ by $y + 5$

9. dimensions are $b - a$ by $b + a$

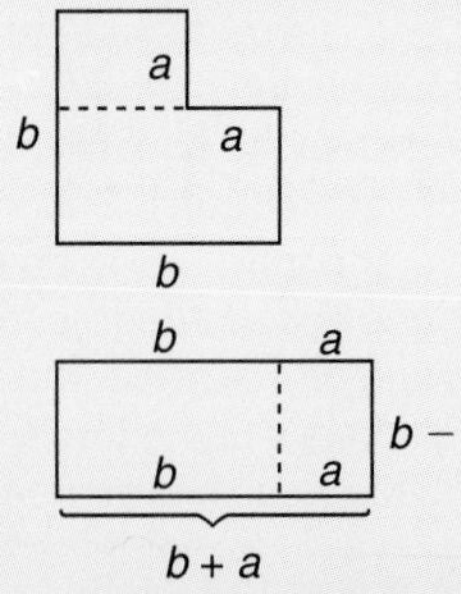

$b^2 - a^2 = (b - a)(b + a)$

8. Repeat problems 6 and 7 for the following squares. You do not have to do the actual cutting unless you want to, but your sketches should be traced in the correct sizes.
   a. Cut a square having area 4 out of a square having area x^2.
   b. Cut a square having area x^2 out of a square having area y^2.
   c. Cut a square having area 9 out of a square having area y^2.
   d. Cut a square having area 25 out of a y-by-y square.

9. **Generalization** Make a sketch showing what remains after a square having area a^2 has been cut out of a square having area b^2. Then show by sketching how this can be rearranged into a rectangle. What are the dimensions of this rectangle?

FACTORING A DIFFERENCE OF SQUARES

When you cut a square out of a square, the area of the remaining paper is the *difference* of the two squares. When you rearrange this paper into a rectangle and write the area as *length · width,* you are writing this difference as a *product,* or factoring. Later in this course you will find this factoring technique helpful in solving equations.

10. Which of these is a difference of two squares?
    a. $4x^2 - 16y^2$
    b. $4x^2 + 16y^2$
    c. $(x - y)(x - y)$
    d. $(a - b)^2$

11. Write these differences as the product of two factors.
    a. $x^2 - 9$ b. $y^2 - 25$
    c. $25 - x^2$ d. $4x^2 - 16$

12. Factor.
    a. $9y^2 - 25$ b. $9 - 25x^2$
    c. $9y^2 - 25x^2$

13. **Generalization** In this lesson you found a technique for factoring a difference of two squares. However, in all the examples you have done, you have assumed that the first square was larger than the second. Does the pattern work if the first square is smaller than the second? That is, if a is less than b, is it still true that
$$a^2 - b^2 = (a - b)(a + b)?$$
Experiment, using some numbers, and explain your conclusions.

REVIEW *THE LAB GEAR MODEL*

14. Use the corner piece to multiply $(y + 5)(y - 5)$. Remember to simplify.

15. Show $y^2 - 25$ with the Lab Gear. Show how you can add zero and rearrange the blocks so that the uncovered part forms a rectangle. What are the dimensions of the rectangle?

16. Explain how one can use the Lab Gear to factor
    a. $x^2 - 1$; b. $y^2 - x^2$.

17. **Summary** Write a paragraph summarizing what you learned in this lesson about differences of squares. Use sketches and examples.

FACTORING A DIFFERENCE OF SQUARES

Students' ability to factor these depends on their understanding of the pattern revealed in the first part of the lesson (and in the Preview at the end of Lesson 3). If they are having trouble, have them check their solutions by distributing with the table representation.

7.4 SOLUTIONS

10. (a) only
11. a. $(x - 3)(x + 3)$
    b. $(y + 5)(y - 5)$
    c. $(5 - x)(5 + x)$
    d. $(2x - 4)(2x + 4)$
12. a. $(3y - 5)(3y + 5)$
    b. $(3 - 5x)(3 + 5x)$
    c. $(3y - 5x)(3y + 5x)$
13. Yes, the pattern works if the first square is smaller than the second. $a^2 - b^2$ is a negative number because a^2 is less than b^2. In the case where a and b are both positive, the expression $a - b$ is negative, so the product of $a + b$ and $a - b$ will be negative. (The cases where a and b are both negative, or a is negative and b is positive, can be considered separately. Similar arguments will work.)
14. $y^2 - 25$

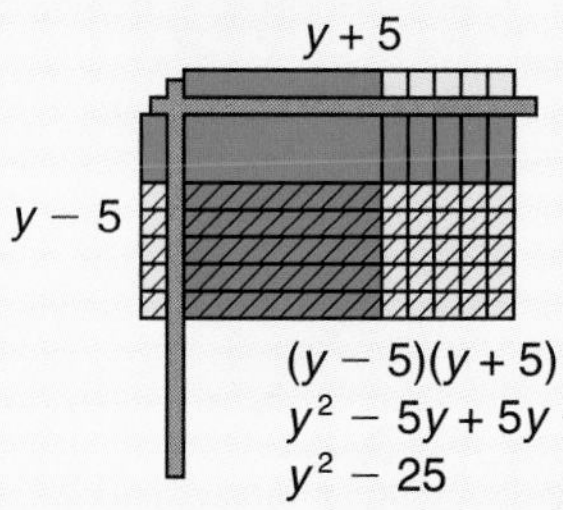

$(y - 5)(y + 5) =$
$y^2 - 5y + 5y - 25 =$
$y^2 - 25$

15. You can add zero in the form $5y - 5y$. Move -25 on top of the $5y$ and the upstairs $5y$ on top of the y^2.

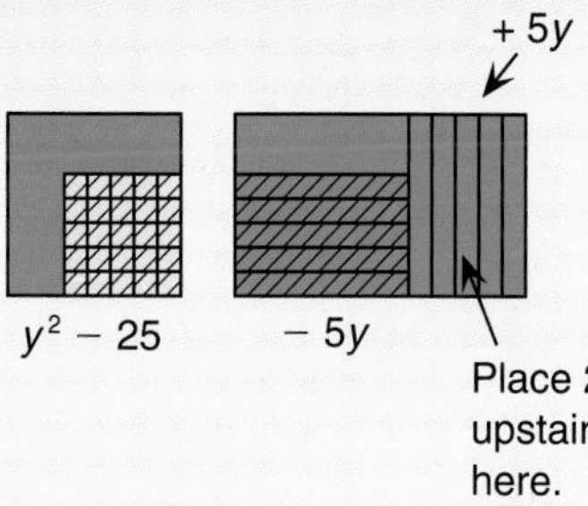

16. a. Add zero in the form $x - x$. Rearrange the upstairs 1- and x-block to show an uncovered rectangle with dimensions $x + 1$ by $x - 1$.
    b. Add zero in the form $xy - xy$ and rearrange upstairs x^2 and xy to show an uncovered rectangle with dimensions $y + x$ by $y - x$.
17. Summaries will vary.

REVIEW THE LAB GEAR MODEL

Problems 14-16 can serve as a review of the whole lesson from a different point of view. It is somewhat less concrete than the paper and scissors activity, since minus is shown according to the Lab Gear *upstairs* convention, instead of through physical removal of the part that is being subtracted.

If some students have forgotten how to do problem 14, group or class discussion should help. Problem 18 bridges the gap between the two representations, since it involves physically removing the square in a Lab Gear layout.

18. Arrange Lab Gear blocks to show a square having area $(x + 5)^2$.

a. Using the blocks, remove a square having area x^2 out of the square having area $(x + 5)^2$, and rearrange the remaining blocks as a rectangle. Write its dimensions.

b. Repeat part (a) and remove a square having area 25.

c. What other squares can you remove from $(x + 5)^2$? Remove one, and rearrange the remaining blocks into a rectangle.

d. Explain how parts (a), (b), and (c) are examples of the pattern you learned about earlier in this lesson.

19. Write each difference as a product of two factors.

a. $(y + 4)^2 - y^2$

b. $(y + 4)^2 - (y + 3)^2$

c. $(y + 4)^2 - (y + 1)^2$

20. Factor. $(y + 2)^2 - (x + 5)^2$

REVIEW SOLVING EQUATIONS

Solve these equations using the cover-up method.

21. $\frac{5 - x}{7} = \frac{8}{14}$

22. $2 - \frac{x - 2}{3} = \frac{2}{3}$

23. $3 + \frac{2 + x}{5} = \frac{19}{5}$

24. $\frac{-7}{6} = \frac{x}{4}$

25. $6 - \frac{14}{x} = \frac{5}{2}$

26. $\frac{2 + x}{8} = \frac{5}{3}$

27. $\frac{1}{x} = 2$

28. $\frac{1 + x}{3} = \frac{2}{9}$

29. $\frac{4}{x} = 5$

30. $\frac{4}{x - 1} = 5$

31. $\frac{4}{3x - 1} = 5$

32. $\frac{4}{x + 4} = \frac{5}{6}$

7.4 SOLUTIONS

18. 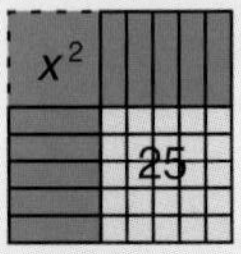

$(x + 5)^2$

Remove x^2:

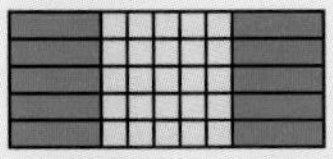
$5(2x + 5)$

Remove 25:

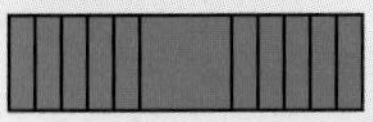
$x(x + 10)$

d. In part (a), we found $(x + 5)^2 - x^2$. Using the pattern of $a^2 - b^2 = (a - b)(a + b)$, this would be $(x + 5 - x)(x + 5 + x)$ which simplifies to $5(2x + 5)$. In part (b), we found $(x + 5)^2 - 5^2$, which is $(x + 5 - 5)(x + 5 + 5) = x(x + 10)$. Part (c) showed a similar pattern. This shows that the pattern $a^2 - b^2 = (a - b)(a + b)$ applies even if a and b are expressions containing more than one term.

19. a. $(y + 4)^2 - y^2 = (y + 4 - y)(y + 4 + y) = 4(2y + 4)$

b. $(y + 4)^2 - (y + 3)^2 = (y + 4 + y + 3)(y + 4 - y - 3) = (2y + 7)(1)$

c. $(y + 4)^2 - (y + 1)^2 = (y + 4 - y - 1)(y + 4 + y + 1) = 3(2y + 5)$

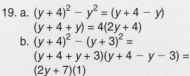

20. $[y + 2 - (x + 5)][y + 2 + x + 5] = (y - x - 3)(y + x + 7)$

21. $x = 1$

22. $x = 6$

23. $x = 2$

24. $x = -14/3$

25. $x = 4$

26. $x = 34/3$

27. $x = 1/2$

28. $x = -1/3$

29. $x = 4/5$

30. $x = 9/5$

31. $x = 3/5$

32. $x = 4/5$

THINKING WRITING

7.A Cube Problems

THE PAINTED CUBE

Lea made a cube by gluing together 27 Lab Gear 1-blocks.

1. Make a sketch of what this cube would look like. What are its dimensions?

Lea painted the cube red on all six sides. Later, Mary and Martin were annoyed when they discovered what Lea had done. They needed the 27 one-blocks to do a hard factoring problem. Besides, they didn't think she should have been gluing and painting Lab Gear blocks.

2. a. When Mary and Martin broke Lea's cube apart into the 27 original small cubes, how many of the 1-blocks did they find to be painted red on three sides?
   b. How many were painted red on only one side?
   c. How many were painted red on two sides?
   d. How many had no red paint on them?
3. Repeat problem 2 for a 4-by-4-by-4 cube.
4. **Report** Write a report about problems 2 and 3. It should include, but need not be limited to, the following:
   - Show how you solved problems 2 and 3. Include sketches.
   - Look for patterns in your answers. Use them to guess the answers for a cube of side 5 and a cube of side 6. How can you check whether or not you are right?
   - Make a generalization to an n-by-n-by-n cube. Write expressions in terms of n for the number of cubes with 0 sides painted, 1 side painted, 2 sides painted, and 3 sides painted. (Explain why the four expressions should add up to n^3, and check that they do.)

CUBES IN CUBES

It is easy to see that there are 27 different 1-by-1-by-1 cubes in this 3-by-3-by-3 cube. It is harder to see how many different 2-by-2-by-2 cubes there are, because they overlap.

5. Figure out how many different 2-by-2-by-2 cubes there are in a 3-by-3-by-3 cube.
6. Think about a 4-by-4-by-4 cube. It contains how many
   a. 1-by-1-by-1 cubes?
   b. 2-by-2-by-2 cubes?
   c. 3-by-3-by-3 cubes?
   d. 4-by-4-by-4 cubes?
   e. cubes altogether?
7. Find how many cubes of each size there are in a 5-by-5-by-5 cube. Try to figure out a systematic way for counting the cubes.
8. **Report** Write a report about these cube problems. It should include, but not be limited to, the following:
   - Describe the strategy you used to answer problems 5, 6, and 7. Use sketches and explain your reasoning.
   - Make a generalization. In an n-by-n-by-n cube, how many cubes of each size (1-by-1-by-1, 2-by-2-by-2, 3-by-3-by-3, and so on) would there be? Write expressions in terms of n.
   - Test your generalization by trying it for a 7-by-7-by-7 cube. How many smaller cubes of each size should there be, according to your generalization? If you add all these numbers, do you get the correct total of 784? Show your work.

THINKING WRITING

7.A Cube Problems

Core Sequence: 1-4

Suitable for Homework: 1-8

Useful for Assessment: 4, 8

What this Assignment is About:

- Three-dimensional visualization
- Review of the distributive law, including preview of square of a difference
- Review of combining like terms

THE PAINTED CUBE

This is an extension of the square window problem into three dimensions. You may discuss with your class a comparison of the rate of growth of the numbers of the different types of cubes as n increases.

CUBES IN CUBES

This problem generalizes the question of the number of squares in a chessboard, which was addressed in Chapter 6, Lesson 2, to three dimensions. However, while it is difficult at this level to come up with a formula for the two-dimensional problem, it is possible to find a formula for the number of cubes in a cube. In fact this was done in the section **Making Squares from Cubes** in Lesson 1. In working on this assignment, students have an opportunity to reduce a tough problem to two previously solved simpler problems.

7.A SOLUTIONS

1. 
2. a. 8 (one at each vertex)
   b. 6 (the central block of each face)
   c. 12 (the middle block along each edge)
   d. 1 (the block at the very center of the cube)
3. a. 8 (one at each vertex)
   b. 24 (the 4 central blocks of each face)
   c. 24 (the 2 middle blocks along each edge)
   d. 8 (the 2-by-2-by-2 cube at the center of the 4-by-4-by-4 cube)
4. Reports will vary. Some main points follow:

	total # of blocks in the cube				
	$3^3 = 27$	$4^3 = 64$	$5^3 = 125$	$6^3 = 216$	n^3
# of blocks painted on 3 sides	8	8	8	8	8
# of blocks painted on 2 sides	12	24	36	48	$12(n-2)$
# of blocks painted on 1 side	6	24	54	96	$6(n-2)^2$
# of blocks painted on 0 sides	1	8	27	64	$(n-2)^3$
sum of painted blocks	27	64	125	216	n^3

The sum of blocks with 0 sides painted, 1 side painted, 2 sides painted, and 3 sides painted is the total number of blocks in the cube.
$(n-2)^3 = n^3 - 6n^2 + 12n - 8$ (no paint)
$12(n-2) = 12n - 24$ (two sides)
$6(n-2)^2 = 6n^2 - 24n + 24$ (one side)
$8 = 8$ (three sides)
Add these expressions: $n^3 - 6n^2 + 12n - 8 + 12n - 24 + 6n^2 - 24n + 24 + 8 = n^3$
The blocks painted on one side are the inside blocks on each of the 6 faces, or $6(n-2)^2$. The blocks painted on two sides are the blocks along each of the 12 edges with the exception of the vertex blocks on each end of an edge (which are

(Solutions continued on page 523)

▼ 7.5
Remarkable Identities

Core Sequence: 1-18, 25-27

Suitable for Homework: 1-14, 19-22, 25-27

Useful for Assessment: 2, 5, 8, 10, 13, 21-24

What this Lesson is About:

- The three main identities
- Factoring when there is a common factor times the square of a sum
- Preview of other identities: cube of a binomial, square of a trinomial
- Review of solving inequalities graphically

By now your students should be more than ready for this lesson, which should not present any major difficulties. Start by using the Lab Gear, but hope that your students will not need it after problem 13.

LESSON 7.5

Remarkable Identities

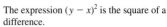

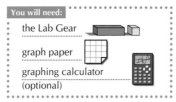

You will need:
- the Lab Gear
- graph paper
- graphing calculator (optional)

REVIEW *MULTIPLYING PATTERNS*

1. Find these products.
a. $(y - 3)(y + 3)$
b. $(y + 5)(y - 5)$

2. What is the pattern in problem 1?

3. Does the pattern still hold for $(2x - 1)(2x + 1)$? Explain.

4. Find these squares.
a. $(y - 3)^2$ b. $(y - 5)^2$
c. $(y + 3)^2$ d. $(y + 5)^2$

5. What is the pattern in problem 4?

6. Does the pattern still hold for $(2x - 1)^2$ and $(2x + 1)^2$? Explain.

THREE IDENTITIES

7. True or False? The square of a sum is equal to the sum of the squares. Explain, using a sketch.

8. Describe a shortcut for finding the square of a sum.

The expression $y^2 - x^2$ is the difference of squares. (Remember that shaded blocks are *upstairs.*)

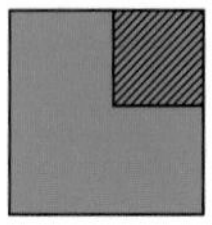

The expression $(y - x)^2$ is the square of a difference.

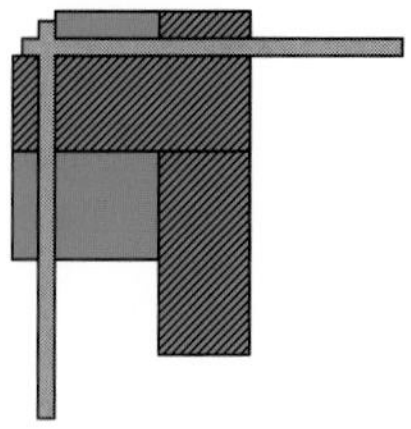

9. True or False? The square of a difference is equal to the difference of the squares. Explain.

10. Describe a shortcut for finding the square of a difference.

11. Find the products.
a. $(y + x)^2$
b. $(y - x)^2$
c. $(y - x)(y + x)$

As you know, identities are algebraic statements that are always true. The three that are shown in problem 11 are especially important and useful. You should memorize them. For example, using the second one,

$$(2x - 5)^2 = (2x)^2 - 2(2x)(5) + 5^2$$
$$= 4x^2 - 20x + 25.$$

12. Multiply by using one of the identities. You may check your answers with the Lab Gear or by setting up the multiplication as a table.
a. $(3x - 2)^2$
b. $(3x + 2)^2$
c. $(3x - 2)(3x + 2)$

7.5 SOLUTIONS

1. a. $y^2 - 9$
b. $y^2 - 25$

2. $(a - b)(a + b) = a^2 - b^2$

3. Yes. $(2x - 1)(2x + 1) = 4x^2 - 1$
The middle terms are $-2x$ and $2x$. They are opposites, so their sum is zero.

4. a. $y^2 - 6y + 9$
b. $y^2 - 10y + 25$
c. $y^2 + 6y + 9$
d. $y^2 + 10y + 25$

5. $(y + a) = y^2 + 2ay + a^2$
$(y - a) = y^2 - 2ay + a^2$

6. Yes. Let $2x = y$ and $1 = a$ in the formula.

7. False

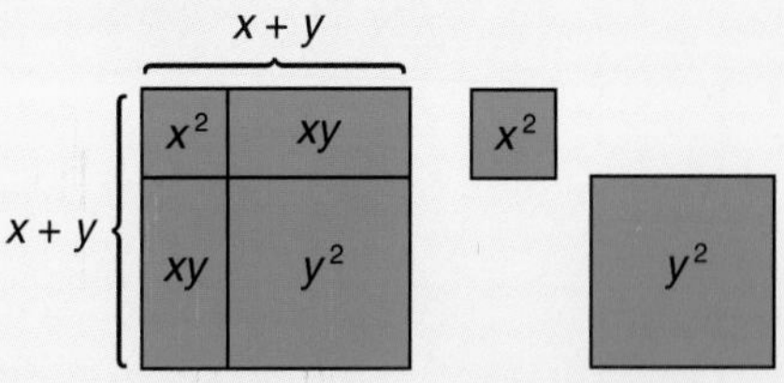

$(x + y)^2$ square of a sum $x^2 + y^2$ sum of squares

8. If there are two terms, square each number. Then double the product of the two terms. That is, $(a + b)^2 = a^2 + 2ab + b^2$.

9. False. $(y - x)^2$ is the square of a difference. $y^2 - x^2$ is the difference of squares. These are equal only if $x = 0$ or $x = y$.

10. Square the first term of the binomial, subtract twice the product of the two terms, and add the square of the second term of the binomial.
$(a - b)^2 = a^2 - 2ab + b^2$

11. a. $(y + x)^2 = y^2 + 2xy + x^2$
b. $(y - x)^2 = y^2 - 2xy + x^2$
c. $(y - x)(y + x) = y^2 - x^2$

12. a. $(3x - 2)^2 = 9x^2 - 12x + 4$
b. $(3x + 2)^2 = 9x^2 + 12x + 4$
c. $(3x - 2)(3x + 2) = 9x^2 - 4$

Even if you don't use the identities for multiplying, it is useful to memorize them in order to recognize them quickly when trying to factor a trinomial. Knowing them is also useful for understanding the solution of quadratic equations.

A CASE OF MISTAKEN IDENTITY

Some of the most common mistakes of math students concern the identities you have learned about in this chapter. Even after having learned the identities, students often forget and write $(x + y)^2 = x^2 + y^2$ or $(x - y)^2 = x^2 - y^2$. This mistake causes math teachers to tear their hair in desperation.

13. Report Write an article or create a poster that you think would help other students avoid these mistakes. (Math teachers all over the world would greatly appreciate your help.) Include explanations, sketches, and examples. Make your article or poster appealing, eye-catching, or humorous so that other students will want to read it.

FACTORING

14. Factor these trinomials.

a. $9x^2 + 6x + 1$
b. $x^2 - 6xy + 9y^2$
c. $4x^2 + 4xy + y^2$
d. $9x^2 - 25$
e. $4x^2 - 4y^2$
f. $a^2x^2 + 2acx + c^2$

15. Use the Lab Gear to make as many different rectangles as you can with $3x^2 + 12x + 12$. Write a product corresponding to each rectangle.

16. The figure below shows a box with a square base.

a. Write an expression for the volume of the box in the form
Height · Area of Base.
b. Write an expression for the volume of the box in the form *Height* · $(Side)^2$.

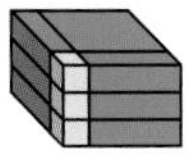

17. Each of these expressions gives the volume of a box that has a square base. For each one, write an expression of the form *Height* · $(Side)^2$. You may want to use the Lab Gear.

a. $3x^2 + 12x + 12$
b. $8x^2 + 8x + 2$
c. $3x^2 + 6xy + 3y^2$
d. $2y^2 + 12y + 18$
e. $xy^2 + 2xy + x$

18. Each of these polynomials gives the volume of a box that has a square base. For each one, write an expression of the form *Height* · $(Side)^2$, without using the blocks. (Hint: The height of the blocks is the factor that is common to all three terms.)

a. $27x^2 + 54x + 27$
b. $60y^2 + 60y + 15$
c. $50x^2 + 100xy + 50y^2$
d. $16y^2 + 96y + 144$
e. $6x^2y + 24xy + 24y$

REVIEW ***MULTIPLYING PATTERNS***

THREE IDENTITIES

A CASE OF MISTAKEN IDENTITY

These sections wrap up the work on the squares of sums and differences of squares that has been done earlier in the chapter. In addition, a little introductory work is done with the square of a difference, but this is close enough to the square of a sum.

If the work is being done in class, you should allow use of the Lab Gear, but encourage anyone who can to do the work on paper.

The three identities are so important that students should be encouraged to create posters or articles about them; see Problem 13, Report.

FACTORING

Problem 14 applies the identities to factoring. The remainder of the lesson extends the work in a challenging direction.

Problems 15-18 focus on the more difficult case of the square of a sum times a common factor.

7.5 SOLUTIONS

14. a. $(3x + 1)^2$
b. $(x - 3y)^2$
c. $(2x + y)^2$
d. $(3x - 5)(3x + 5)$
e. $(2x - 2y)(2x + 2y)$
f. $(ax + c)^2$

15. $3x^2 + 12x + 12 = (x + 2)(3x + 6)$

16. a. $3(x^2 + 2x + 1)$
b. $3(x + 1)^2$

17. a. $3(x + 2)^2$
b. $2(2x + 1)^2$
c. $3(x + y)^2$
d. $2(y + 3)^2$
e. $x(y + 1)^2$

18. a. $27(x + 1)^2$
b. $15(2y + 1)^2$
c. $50(x + y)^2$
d. $16(y + 3)^2$
e. $6y(x + 2)^2$

SQUARING TRINOMIALS

CUBES OF SUMS

Challenge students who are comfortable with the basic three to discover these trickier identities. These do not need to be memorized.

REVIEW/PREVIEW *ALWAYS, SOMETIMES, OR NEVER TRUE?*

This section helps preview **Thinking/ Writing 7.B.** A graphing calculator could be used for problem 27.

SQUARING TRINOMIALS

Do you think there is a pattern for the square of trinomials? Experiment with these problems.

19. $(x + y + 2)^2$

20. $(x + y - 5)^2$

21. Describe the pattern you discovered in problems 19 and 20.

22. What is $(a - b + c)^2$ equal to? Use the pattern you discovered, then check your answer by using the distributive law very carefully.

CUBES OF SUMS

23. Find an identity for the cube of a sum. Lab Gear models using 3-D blocks may help. Explain why the cube of a sum is not the sum of the cubes.

PUZZLE *SUM OF SQUARES*

24. $5x^2 + 20x + 25$

Think of the Lab Gear blocks representing this polynomial. The polynomial is not a perfect square, so you cannot rearrange it into a single square. However, it can be arranged into a *sum of squares.* Figure out how you would do it.

REVIEW/PREVIEW *ALWAYS, SOMETIMES, OR NEVER TRUE?*

25. On the same axes, graph $y = 12 - x$ and $y = 8 - x$.

26. Always, sometimes, or never true? (Explain your reasoning in each case.)

a. $12 - x > 8 - x$

b. $12 - x > 13$

c. $8 - x > 12 - x$

d. $4 > 8 - x$

e. $-4 > 8 - x$

27. Always, sometimes, or never true? (If sometimes true, give the values of x that make it true.)

a. $x > 2x - 8$

b. $2x - 5 > 2x - 8$

c. $x < 2x - 5$

7.5 SOLUTIONS

19. $(x + y + 2)^2 = x^2 + y^2 + 4 + 2xy + 4x + 4y$

20. $(x + y - 5)^2 = x^2 + y^2 + 25 + 2xy - 10x - 10y$

21. The square of the trinomial is the sum of the squares of each term and twice the product of each pair of terms. $(a + b + c)^2 = a^2 + b^2 + c^2 + 2ab + 2ac + 2bc$

22. $(a - b + c)^2 = a^2 + b^2 + c^2 - 2ab + 2ac - 2bc$

23. The cube $(x + y)^3$ can be built with the 3-D blocks. By looking at the components of the cube, we can see that $(x + y)^3 = x^3 + 3x^2y + 3xy^2 + y^3$. It is not equal to $x^3 + y^3$ unless $x = 0$ or $y = 0$ or $x = -y$.

24. (It helps to use the blocks.) $5x^2 + 20x + 25 = x^2 + (2x + 5)^2$

25.

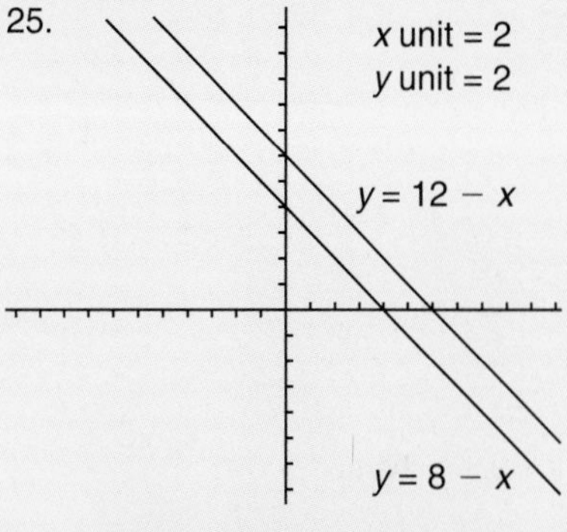

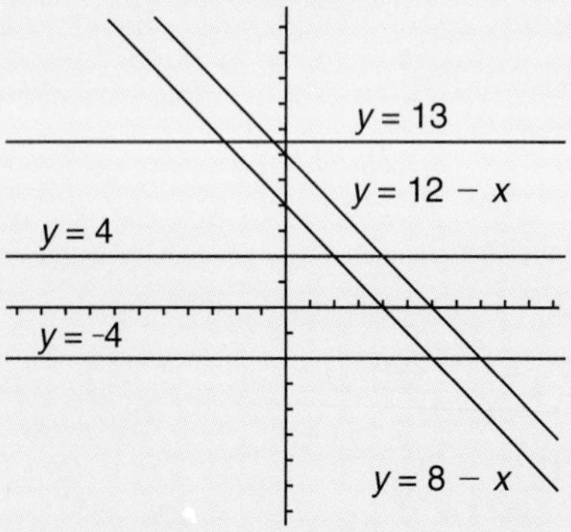

26. a. Always. The graph of $y = 12 - x$ is always above the graph of $y = 8 - x$.

b. Sometimes. The graph of $y = 12 - x$ is above the horizontal line $y = 13$ when x is less than -1.

c. Never. The graph of $y = 8 - x$ is never above $y = 12 - x$.

d. Sometimes. When $x > 4$, the graph of $y = 4$ is above $y = 8 - x$.

e. Sometimes. When $x > 12$, the graph of $y = -4$ is above $y = 8 - x$.

27. a. Sometimes, when $x < 8$

b. Always. The line $y = 2x - 5$ is parallel to the line $y = 2x - 8$.

c. Sometimes; when $x > 5$

LESSON 7.6

How Many Solutions?

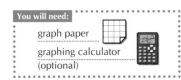

You will need:
- graph paper
- graphing calculator (optional)

LINEAR EQUATIONS

As you learned in Chapter 6, graphing is one way to find solutions to equations. For example, consider the equation $2x - 6 = -x$. This equation can be solved by graphing the lines $y = 2x - 6$ and $y = -x$ on the same axes.

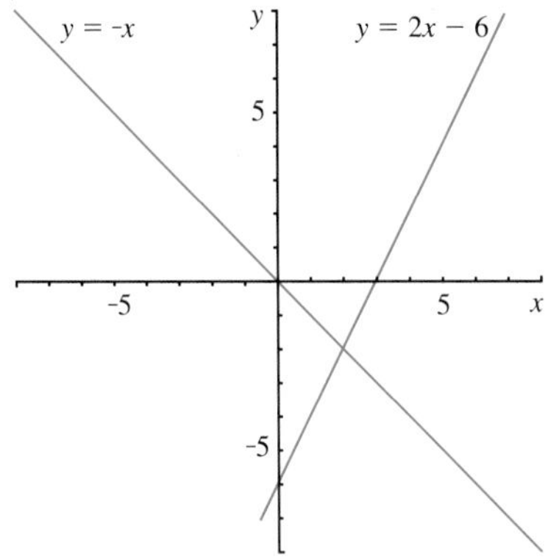

1. a. From the graph above, estimate the point of intersection of the lines $y = 2x - 6$ and $y = -x$.
b. Use algebra to solve the equation $2x - 6 = -x$.

2. The linear equation $2x - 6 = 2x$ has *no solution*. Show that this is true by graphing the lines $y = 2x - 6$ and $y = 2x$. Explain how your graph shows that the equation has no solution.

3. Tell how many solutions each equation has. Use graphs if necessary.
a. $5x - 6 = 5x - 7$
b. $5x - 6 = 0.5(10x - 12)$
c. $5x - 6 = x$

4. For all the equations in problem 3 that have one solution, find the solution.

5.
a. Write and solve a linear equation that has only one solution.
b. Write a linear equation that has an infinite number of solutions.
c. Write a linear equation that has no solution.

6. Is it possible for a linear equation to have two solutions? Three solutions? Explain your answers, using graphs if possible.

QUADRATIC EQUATIONS

Definition: Second-degree equations are called *quadratic equations.*

Example: These are all quadratic equations.
$x^2 = 45$
$3x^2 - 15 = 6x + 2$
$6x^2 + 5x + 8 = 0$

You will learn several methods for solving quadratic equations. In this lesson, we will use graphing. Use a whole piece of graph paper for problems 7-11.

7. Draw a pair of axes on a full page of graph paper. Show all four quadrants. Graph $y = x^2$ very carefully.

8. On the same pair of axes, graph these lines and label them with their equations.
a. $y = 6x - 12$
b. $y = 6x - 9$
c. $y = 6x - 5$

7.6 How Many Solutions?

Core Sequence: 1-19

Suitable for Homework: 1-11, 26

Useful for Assessment: 5, 6, 15, 24

What this Lesson is About:
- Graphing to solve equations
- Equivalent equations
- Preview of simultaneous equations
- Preview of quadratic equations

LINEAR EQUATIONS

This section reviews the material in Chapter 6, Lesson 5, and previews simultaneous equations which will be addressed in Chapter 10.

QUADRATIC EQUATIONS

By observing the number of intersections between a line and a parabola, students will find out that a quadratic equation can have 0, 1, or 2 solutions. A full treatment of quadratic equations will occur in Chapter 13.

7.6 SOLUTIONS

1. a. (2, -2)
   b. $2x - 6 = -x$
   $3x = 6$
   $x = 2$
2. The lines are parallel, so they never intersect.

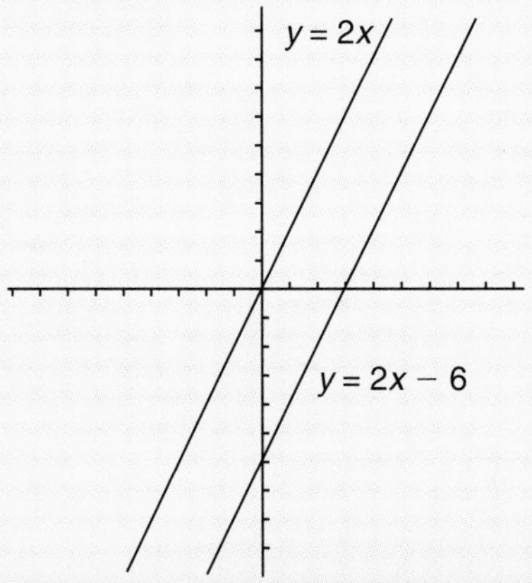

3. a. no solution. (The graph of $y = 5x - 6$ does not intersect the graph of $y = 5x - 7$.)
   b. There is an infinite number of solutions. $y = 5x - 6$ and $y = 0.5(10x - 12)$ are the same line when graphed.
   c. One solution, which can be found by graphing $y = x$ and $y = 5x - 6$ or by solving algebraically.
4. $x = 1.5$ is the solution to 3(c)
5. a. Answers will vary.
   b. Any linear identity will work, for example: $6x + 12 = 6(x + 2)$
   c. Anything of the form $mx + b = mx + c$, where $b \neq c$, will work; for example $6x + 12 = 6x - 10$
6. The solution of linear equations can be modeled by graphing lines. Since two lines intersect in at most one point, it is not possible to have more than one solution unless the equation is an identity.
7.

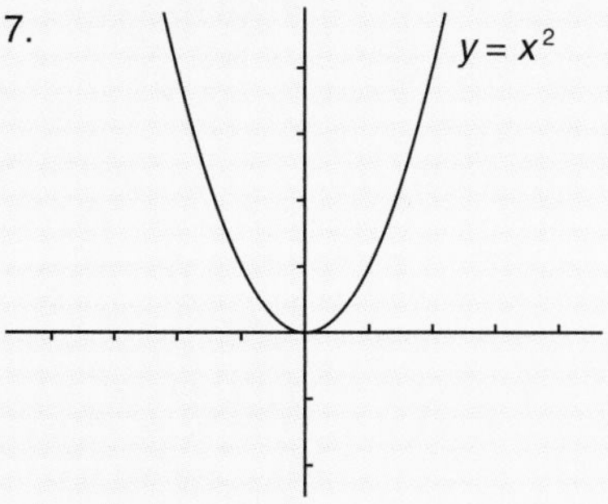

HOW MANY INTERSECTIONS?

*I*n the previous section, students looked at specific examples of quadratics. In this section, they create their own. This would most effectively be done in class, so students can compare answers and help each other out.

WHICH GRAPH SHOULD YOU USE?

*I*t is probably best to do this section with the help of an electronic graphing calculator. If you don't have access to them, you may lead a discussion at the overhead projector.

9. Label the point or points of intersection of each line with the graph of $y = x^2$.

One of the lines you drew touches the graph of $y = x^2$ at only one point.

Definition: A line that touches a graph at only one point is *tangent* to the graph.

10. Which of the lines you drew is tangent to the graph of $y = x^2$?

11. Use the graphs to solve these equations.
a. $x^2 = 6x - 12$
b. $x^2 = 6x - 9$
c. $x^2 = 6x - 5$

HOW MANY INTERSECTIONS?

12. a. Draw a graph of $y = x^2$.
b. On the same axes, draw a line that does not intersect $y = x^2$. Write the equation of the line.
c. Repeat part (b) for another line that does not intersect $y = x^2$.

13. a. Draw a graph of $y = x^2$.
b. On the same axes, draw a line that intersects $y = x^2$ at only one point. Write the equation of the line and label the point of intersection.
c. Repeat part (b) for another line that intersects $y = x^2$ at only one point.

14. a. Draw a graph of $y = x^2$.
b. On the same axes, draw a line that intersects $y = x^2$ at two points. Write the equation of the line and label the points of intersection.
c. Repeat part (b) for another line that intersects $y = x^2$ at two points.

15. Refer to your answers to problems 12-14. Use them to write and solve a quadratic equation that has
a. one solution;
b. two solutions;
c. no solutions.

16. Use graphs to estimate the solutions to these equations.
a. $x^2 = -6x - 11$
b. $x^2 = -6x + 11$
c. $-x^2 = 6x + 11$

17. Write the equation of a line that is tangent to $y = x^2$ at the point (-4, 16).

WHICH GRAPH SHOULD YOU USE?

The solution of the equation $x^2 = 4$ can be found by graphing $y = x^2$ and $y = 4$ on the same pair of axes.

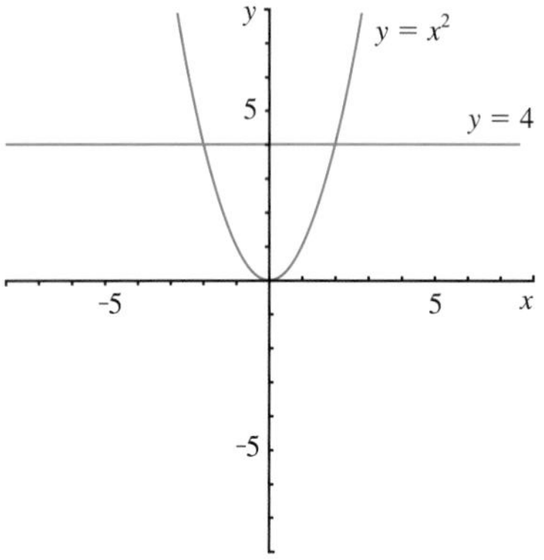

The equation $x^2 = 4$ can also be written as $x^2 - 4 = 0$. It can be solved by graphing $y = x^2 - 4$ and $y = 0$ on the same axes.

18. What is another name for the line $y = 0$?

7.6 SOLUTIONS

8., 9.

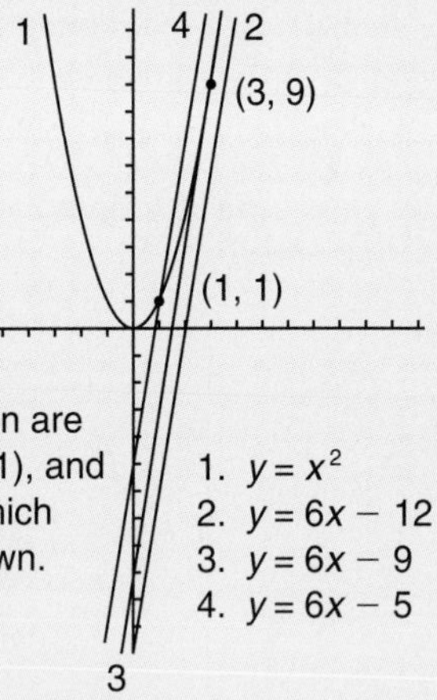

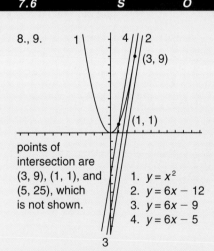

points of intersection are (3, 9), (1, 1), and (5, 25), which is not shown.

10. $y = 6x - 9$

11. a. The line $y = 6x - 12$ does not intersect the parabola, so there is no solution.

b. $y = x^2$ and $y = 6x - 9$ intersect at (3, 9), so the solution is $x = 3$.

c. $y = x^2$ and $y = 6x - 5$ intersect for $x = 1$ and $x = 5$.

12.-14. Answers will vary. Sample answers are given in the figures.

12.

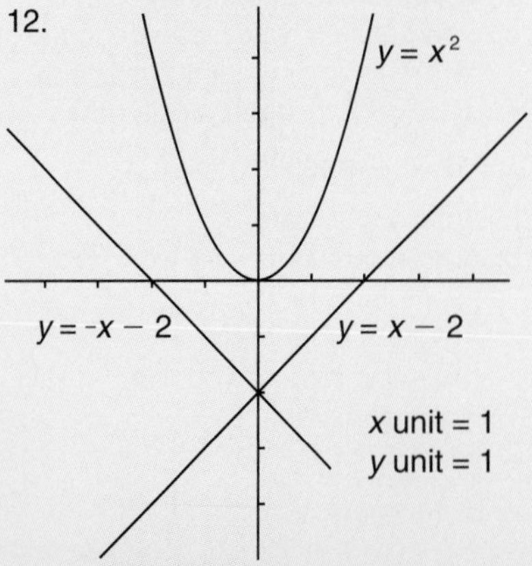

13.

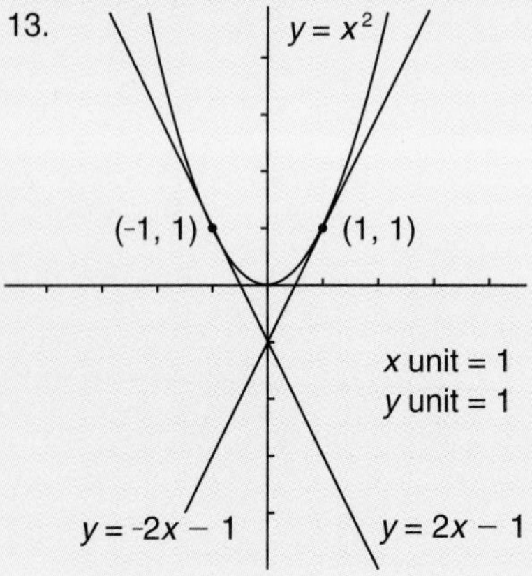

As shown in the figure, the graphs intersect in two points. This means that the quadratic equation $x^2 = 4$ has two solutions.

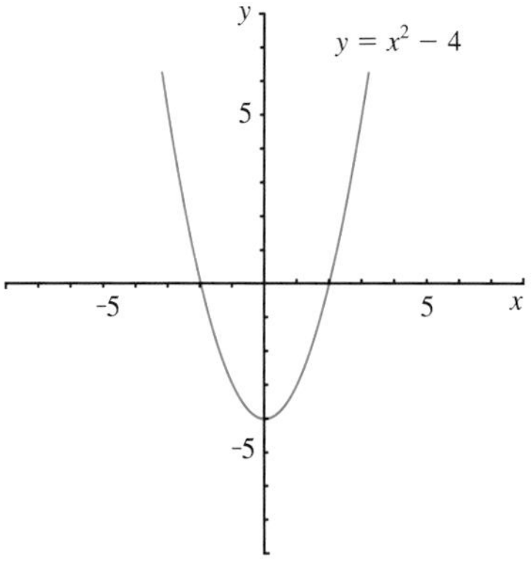

19. What are the two values of x that satisfy the equation $x^2 = 4$? Where do they appear in each of the two graphs above?

20. Explain why all of these quadratic equations are equivalent.
$x^2 = x + 6$
$x^2 - x = 6$
$x^2 - x - 6 = 0$

21. Graph the parabola $y = x^2$ and the line $y = x + 6$ on the same pair of axes. Label the points of intersection.

22. Graph the parabola $y = x^2 - x$ and the line $y = 6$ on the same pair of axes. Label the points of intersection.

23. Graph the parabola $y = x^2 - x - 6$ and $y = 0$ on the same pair of axes. Label the points of intersection.

24. Compare your answers to problems 21-23.
a. What is the solution to the quadratic equation $x^2 - x - 6 = 0$?
b. Which of the three graphs do you think gave the easiest way to find the solution to this equation?

25. Find the solutions to these equations by graphing a parabola and a line on the same pair of axes. As you saw in problem 24, there may be more than one possible pair of graphs that can be used. You may use any pair that will work.
a. $x^2 = 3x + 4$
b. $x^2 - 5 = -4x$
c. $2x^2 = 18$

DISCOVERY *LAST DIGITS*

26. What is the last digit for each of these numbers: $0^{100}, 1^{100}, 2^{100}, \ldots, 9^{100}$? Most of these numbers have too many digits for the last one to appear in your calculator, so you will have to figure out some other approach. (Hint: Try finding the last digits of smaller powers of these numbers.)

DISCOVERY *LAST DIGITS*

This section could be assigned as a *problem of the week* or as a writing assignment. Or it could be assigned as group problem-solving, followed by the group's presentation of patterns and conclusions to the whole class.

7.6 SOLUTIONS

14.

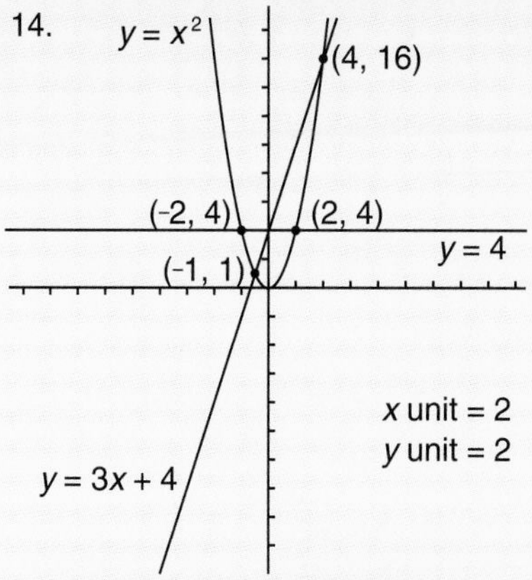

15. Answers will vary. Samples are given.
a. $x^2 = -2x - 1$
b. $x^2 = 4$
c. $x^2 = -x - 1$

16. a. no solution. (The graphs do not intersect.)

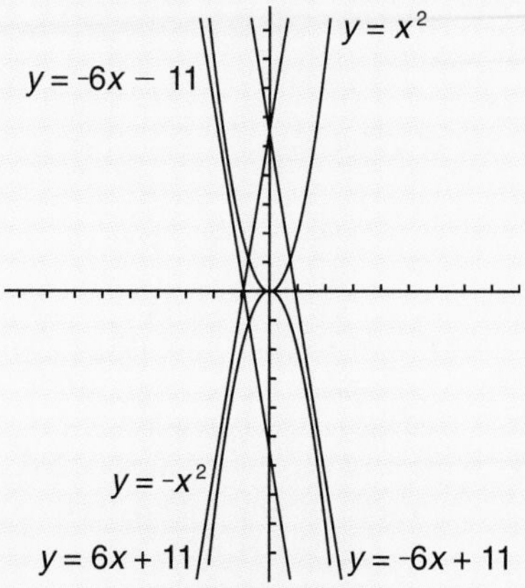

b. Estimates will vary slightly. $x = -7.5$ or $x = 1.5$
c. no solution

17. By trial and error, the answer can be found to be $y = -8x - 16$. A graphing calculator is helpful. Students should confirm that it is a point of tangency, by showing that $x^2 = -8x - 16$ has only one solution.

18. The x-axis.

19. 2 and -2
On one graph, they appear where the graph of $y = x^2$ intersects the graph of $y = 4$. On the other, they appear where the graph of $y = x^2 - 4$ intersects the line $y = 0$, which is the x-axis.

20. The second equation can be converted to the first by adding x to both sides. The third equation can be converted to the first by adding $x + 6$ to both sides.

(Solutions continued on page 523)

▼ 7.7
Equations with Squares

Core Sequence: 1-31

Suitable for Homework: 14-18, 21-31

Useful for Assessment: 4, 18-19

What this Lesson is About:

- Preview of solving quadratic equations
- Factoring wrap-up
- Multiplying polynomials wrap-up

GRAPHICAL SOLUTIONS

This is an application of the strategies, introduced in the previous lesson, to quadratics presented in the form $(x - p)^2 = K$, where K is an expression.

A graphing calculator may be helpful for problems 4b and 5, but if they are unavailable, students should be able to do the work by hand.

LESSON 7.7

Equations With Squares

You will need:

graph paper

the Lab Gear

This lesson is about solving equations. You will use two different methods to approach equations that involve the square of a binomial.

GRAPHICAL SOLUTIONS

The graphs of $y = (x + 3)^2$ and $y = (x - 2)^2$ are shown below.

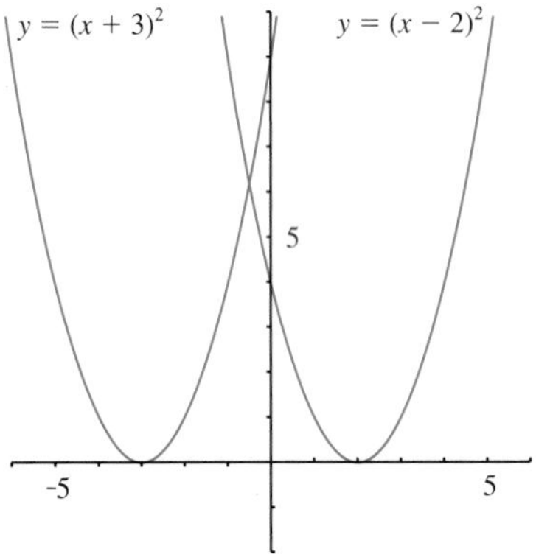

1. Explain why these two graphs never go below the x-axis. (Why is the value of y never negative?)

2. On a piece of graph paper, copy the two graphs. For more accuracy, calculate the coordinates of several points on each curve. Use the graphs to solve these equations.
   a. $(x + 3)^2 = 4$
   b. $(x - 2)^2 = 9$
   c. $(x - 2)^2 = 1$
   d. $(x + 3)^2 = -1$
   e. $(x - 2)^2 = 0$

3. Use your graphs to estimate the solutions to these equations.
   a. $(x + 3)^2 = 12$
   b. $(x - 2)^2 = 6$
   c. $(x - 2)^2 = -2$
   d. $(x + 3)^2 = 5$
   e. $(x + 3)^2 = (x - 2)^2$

4.
   a. Describe what you think the graphs of the functions $y = (x + 2)^2$ and $y = (x - 1)^2$ would look like. (Where would each one intersect the x-axis?)
   b. Check your guess by making tables of values and graphing the functions.

5. Use your graphs to find or estimate the solutions to these equations.
   a. $(x + 2)^2 = 9$
   b. $(x + 2)^2 = 2x + 3$
   c. $(x - 1)^2 = 5$
   d. $(x - 1)^2 = -x$

7.7 SOLUTIONS

1. The square of a number is always nonnegative.
2. a. $x = -5$ or $x = -1$
   b. $x = -1$ or $x = 5$
   c. $x = 1$ or $x = 3$
   d. no solution
   e. $x = 2$

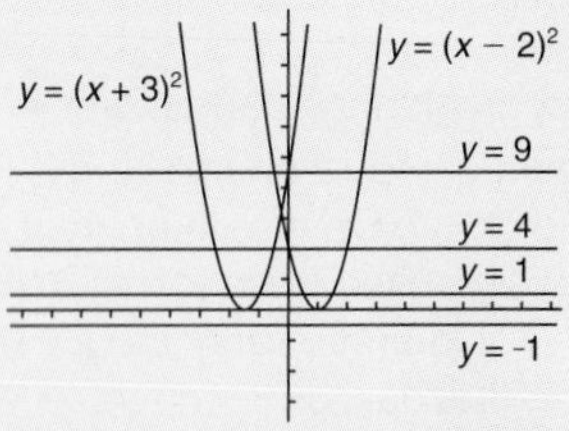

3. Estimates will vary slightly.
   a. $x \approx -6.46$ or $x \approx 0.46$
   b. $x \approx 4.45$ or $x \approx -0.45$
   c. no solution
   d. $x \approx -0.76$ or $x \approx -5.24$
   e. $x = -0.5$

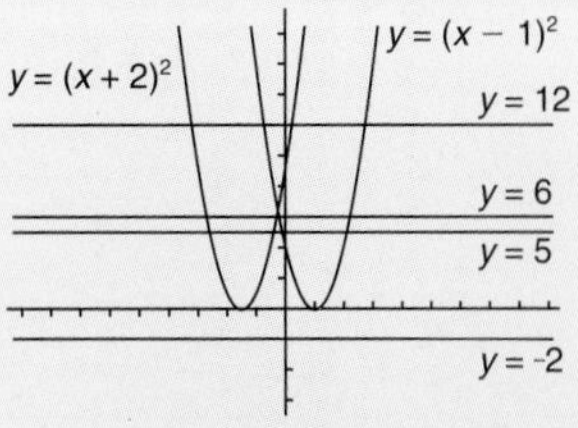

4. a. They would be parabolas that touch the x-axis in one point, the vertex. The first would have a vertex at (-2, 0) and the second would have a vertex at (1, 0).

5. a. $x = -5$ and $x = 1$
   b. $x = -1$
   c. Estimates will vary. $x \approx -1.24$ or $x \approx 3.24$
   d. no solution

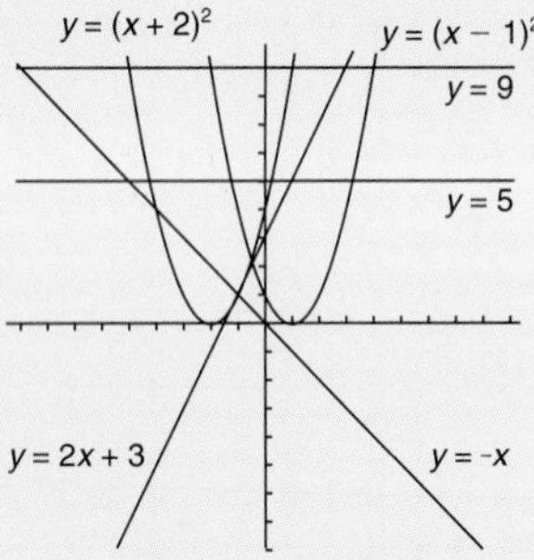

EQUAL SQUARES

The equation $x^2 = 25$ can be illustrated using the Lab Gear. Put out your blocks like this.

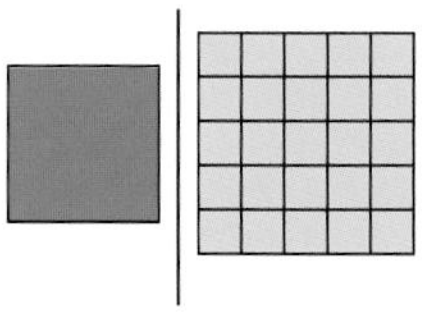

One way to get started with this equation is to remember that if the squares are equal, *their sides must be equal.* (This is true even though they don't look equal. Remember that x can have any value.)

6. Solve the equation. If you found only one solution, think some more, because there are two.

7. Explain why there are two solutions.

8. Write the equation shown by this figure.

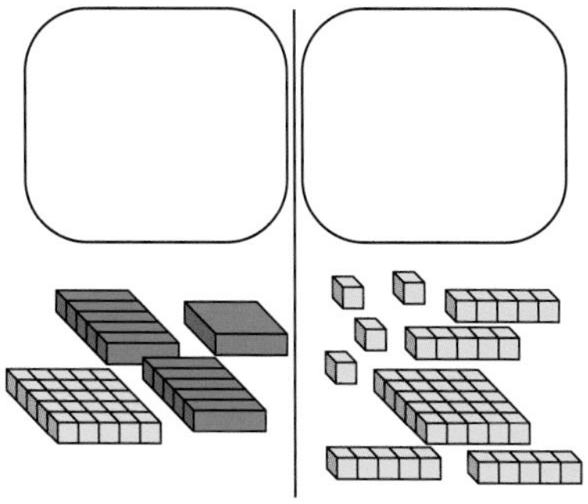

By rearranging the blocks, you can see that this is an *equal squares* problem, so it can be solved the same way. As you can see, $(x + 5)^2 = 7^2$. It follows that $x + 5 = 7$ or $x + 5 = -7$.

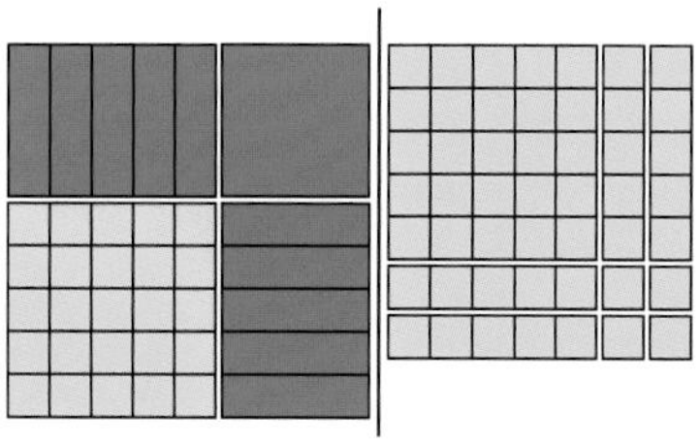

9. Solve the equation. There are two solutions. Check them both in the original equation.

Solve the equations 10-13 using the *equal squares* method. You do not have to use the actual blocks, but you can if you want to. Most equations, but not all, have two solutions.

10. $x^2 = 16$

11. $x^2 + 2x + 1 = 0$

12. $4x^2 = 36$

13. $4x^2 + 4x + 1 = 9$

Solve these equations without the blocks.

14. $4x^2 - 4x + 1 = -9$

15. $x^2 - 10x + 25 = 16$

16. $x^2 + 6x + 9 = 4x^2 - 4x + 1$

17. $-x^2 - 6x - 9 = -25$ (Hint: If quantities are equal, their opposites must be equal.)

18. Explain why some problems had one, or no solution.

EQUAL SQUARES

This section previews completing the square, which we will do in Chapter 13. Note that the Lab Gear method does not show the fact that there are two solutions. Having looked at graphical solutions first should have made clear to the students that they should often expect two solutions for equations of this type. Remind them of that when working on this section.

7.7 SOLUTIONS

6. $x = 5$ or $x = -5$
7. $(5)^2 = 25$ and $(-5)^2 = 25$
8. $x^2 + 10x + 25 = 49$
9. $x = 2$ or $x = -12$
10. $x = 4$ or $x = -4$
11. $x = -1$
12. $x = 3$ or $x = -3$
13. $x = 1$ or $x = -2$
14. no solution
15. $x = 1$ or $x = 9$
16. $x = -2/3$ or $x = 4$
17. $x = 2$ or $x = -8$
18. If the equation can be written as a perfect square on one side and 0 on the other, there will be one solution. If the equation can be written as a perfect square on one side and a negative number on the other, there will be no solutions.
19. a. Answers will vary. Sample answers are given.
    <u>two solutions</u>: $x^2 = 9$
    With the Lab Gear, show x^2 on one side of the workmat and 3^2 on the other. This shows the solution $x = 3$. One must remember to include the negative value of $x = -3$ because $9 = 3^2$ and $9 = (-3)^2$. With the graphical method, graph $y = x^2$ and $y = 9$. This shows two points of intersection, (-3, 9) and (3, 9), so both solutions $x = \pm 3$, are visible.
    <u>one solution</u>: $x^2 + 2x + 1 = 0$
    Using the Lab Gear, show $(x + 1)^2$ on one side of the workmat and 0 on the other. This shows the single solution, $x = -1$. The graphical method shows $y = x^2 + 2x + 1$ and $y = 0$, which intersect where $x = -1$. The methods are comparable because they each show the single solution.
    <u>no solution</u>: $x^2 = -25$
    Using the Lab Gear, show x^2 on one side of the equation and 25 in the minus region on the other side. Since x^2 is nonnegative and -25 is negative, there is no solution. The graphical method shows that $y = x^2$ does not intersect $y = -25$, since the graph of $y = x^2$ does not go below the x-axis.
    <u>no solution</u>: $x^2 + 2x + 1 = x - 1$
    Using the Lab Gear, show $(x + 1)^2$ on one side and $x - 1$ on the other. This is not an equal squares

COMPARING METHODS

Make sure this section is done in class, as it is challenging and requires a solid understanding of the lesson. Group discussion will be necessary, and perhaps also a whole-class discussion.

REVIEW FACTORING PRACTICE

REVIEW MULTIPLICATION PRACTICE

With the next lesson, the chapter changes direction. These sections are intended to wrap up the work on the distributive law and factoring that has been covered in the early part of the chapter and in previous chapters.

COMPARING METHODS

19. Summary

a. Compare the graphical method and the Lab Gear method for the solution of an equal-squares equation. Use examples that can be solved by both methods, and have 0, 1, and 2 solutions.

b. What is the meaning of the *x*-intercept in the graphical method? Where does that number appear in the Lab Gear method?

c. What is the meaning of the *x*- and *y*-coordinates of the intersections of the line and parabola in the graphical method? Where do these numbers appear in the Lab Gear method?

20. Create an equal-squares equation that has two solutions that are not whole numbers. Solve it.

REVIEW FACTORING PRACTICE

Factor these polynomials. One is difficult, one is impossible. The Lab Gear may help for some of the problems.

21. $xy + 6y + y^2$ **22.** $y^2 - 16$

23. $3x^2 + 13x - 10$ **24.** $4x^2 + 8x + 4$

25. $2x^2 + 2x + 1$ **26.** $y^2 - 5y + 6$

27. $y^2 - 4y + 4$ **28.** $x^2 + 8x + 12$

REVIEW MULTIPLICATION PRACTICE

You can multiply polynomials without the Lab Gear and without a table. Picture the table in your mind, and make sure you fill all its spaces. For example, to multiply

$$(2 - x)(7 - 3x + 5y)$$

you would need a 2-by-3 table. To fill the six cells of the table, you would multiply the 2 by 7, by -3*x*, and by 5*y*. Then you would multiply the -*x* by 7, by -3*x*, and by 5*y*. Finally, you would combine like terms. While you think of the six cells of the table, what you actually write on paper looks like this.

$$(2 - x)(7 - 3x + 5y)$$
$$= 14 - 6x + 10y - 7x + 3x^2 - 5xy$$
$$= 14 - 13x + 10y + 3x^2 - 5xy$$

29. Look at the example above, and make sure you understand where each term came from.

Multiply these polynomials without using a table. Combine like terms.

30. a. $(2x - y)(y + 3x)$
b. $(x - 5y)(3x + 2y)$
c. $(ac - b)(2b + 2ac)$
d. $(ab - c)(b - c^2)$

31. a. $(2x - y + 4)(5 - y)$
b. $(2x^2 - y + 4)(5y - x^2)$
c. $(2x - y^2 + 4)(5y - x^2)$
d. $(a + b + c)(2a + 3b + 4c)$

equation, because we cannot write $x - 1$ as a square. Later, we will learn how to turn this into an equal squares problem by using the technique of completing the square.

b. The *x*-intercept is the value of *x* where the expression takes on the smallest possible value. It is the vertex of the parabola. That number is the opposite of the number of *x*-blocks in the Lab Gear model. By setting up the Lab Gear model using the corner piece, it is even easier to see. It is the opposite of the number represented by the yellow blocks forming one side of the square.

c. The *x*-coordinate is the solution to the equation. The *y*-coordinate is the other square. In the Lab Gear method, the *y*-coordinate shows up as the square on the right side. The *x*-coordinate shows up in the last step of the equation, as the number of yellow blocks equal to a single *x*-block.

20. Answers will vary. Sample:
$4x^2 - 4x + 1 = 4$
$(2x - 1)^2 = 4$ so $x = 3/2$ or $x = -1/2$

21. $y(x + 6 + y)$

22. $(y - 4)(y + 4)$

23. $(3x - 2)(x + 5)$

24. $4(x + 1)^2$

25. prime

26. $(y - 3)(y - 2)$

27. $(y - 2)^2$

28. $(x + 6)(x + 2)$

30. a. $6x^2 - xy - y^2$
b. $3x^2 - 13xy - 10y^2$
c. $2a^2c^2 - 2b^2$
d. $ab^2 - abc^2 - bc + c^3$

31. a. $10x - 2xy - 9y + y^2 + 20$
b. $11x^2y - 2x^4 - 5y^2 + 20y - 4x^2$
c. $10xy - 2x^3 - 5y^3 + x^2y^2 + 20y - 4x^2$
d. $2a^2 + 5ab + 6ac + 3b^2 + 7bc + 4c^2$

LESSON 7.8

Power Play

RAFFLE TICKETS

Erin is a senior at Alaberg High School and the director of the senior class play. To help pay for sets and costumes, she plans to raise money through a raffle. She is considering several plans for selling raffle tickets.

Erin's first idea was to have members of each class sell raffle tickets to the class below them. Erin would sell tickets to three 11th graders. Each of them would sell tickets to three 10th graders, who in turn would each sell tickets to three 9th graders, and so on. Erin started to draw a tree-diagram of her plan.

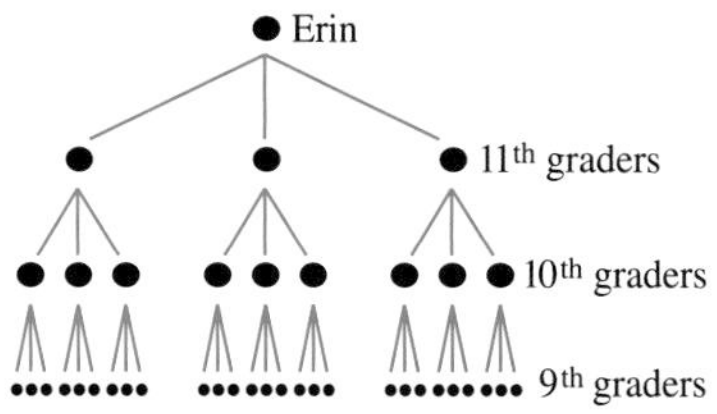

1. If Erin extended her plan all the way down to first grade, how many first graders would be buying tickets? Explain.
2. Make a table like the one following showing how many tickets would be bought by students in each grade. (The first entry in the table is based on the assumption that Erin bought one ticket for herself.) In the last column, express the number of tickets as a power of 3.

Grade	Tickets (number)	Tickets (as a power of 3)
12th	1	
11th	3	3^1
...		
1st		

3. Give several reasons why Erin's plan is not practical.

THE EXPONENT ZERO

The last column in your table above contained increasing powers of 3.

4. a. To follow the pattern, what should the exponent on the first power in the table be?
   b. Based on that pattern, what should 3^0 be equal to?
5. a. Copy and complete this table.

5^5	3125
5^4	
5^3	
5^2	
5^1	

   b. As you move down the columns, how can you get the next row from the previous one?
   c. Add another row to the bottom of the table. Explain how it fits the pattern.

7.8 Power Play

Core Sequence: 1-16, 19-23

Suitable for Homework: 1-7, 13-16, 19-23

Useful for Assessment: 6, 7, 11, 15

What this Lesson is About:

- Preview of exponential growth and laws of exponents
- Preview of geometric sequences and their sums
- The exponent 0
- Review of order of operations
- Review of equal squares and preview of quadratic equations

RAFFLE TICKETS

This section is reminiscent of the work done in Chapter 2, Lesson 5, on **Doing Dishes** and **Chain Letter.** This lesson will go further, and pave the way for Chapter 8's work on the laws of exponents and exponential growth.

Problem 3 should form the basis of a good class discussion. When doing problems like the one that provides the theme for this lesson, do not pretend that the problems are realistic if they're not. Well-chosen contrived problems still offer plenty to learn and think about.

7.8 SOLUTIONS

1. 3^{11} or 177,147 first graders

Erin	11th	10th	9th	8th	7th
1	3^1	3^2	3^3	3^4	3^5
6th	5th	4th	3rd	2nd	1st
3^6	3^7	3^8	3^9	3^{10}	3^{11}

The number of tickets sold by each grade is obtained by multiplying the previous grade's number by 3.

grade	tickets (number)	tickets (as a power of 3)
12th	1	
11th	3	3^1
10th	9	3^2
9th	27	3^3
8th	81	3^4
7th	243	3^5
6th	729	3^6
5th	2187	3^7
4th	6561	3^8
3rd	19,683	3^9
2nd	59,049	3^{10}
1st	177,147	3^{11}

3. Answers will vary. Some possible answers follow. More than one senior will want to go to the play. Few school communities have 177,147 members who would want to see the school play. This puts too much responsibility on the younger students.
4. a. zero
   b. one
5. a. 5^5 3125
   5^4 625
   5^3 125
   5^2 25
   5^1 5
   b. First column: raise 5 to the next lower power. Second column: divide the previous number by 5.
   c. $5^0 = 1$ (It fits the pattern described in part (b).)

THE EXPONENT ZERO

We will return to this in Chapter 8, but the table in the previous section provides a good opportunity to introduce the idea.

A BETTER PLAN

This section gradually leads to a formula. Make sure this work is done in class. In particular, the Exploration in problem 12 would work best as a group project.

6. **Generalization** You have found the values of 3^0 and 5^0. Using patterns in the same way, find the values of 2^0 and 4^0. What generalization can you make?

7. **Summary** Many people think that a number raised to the zero power should be zero. Write a few sentences explaining why this is not true.

A BETTER PLAN

Erin needs a better scheme for selling raffle tickets. She decides to enlist the help of other seniors in the play. Each senior (including Erin) will buy a ticket for himself or herself, and sell a ticket to three juniors; each of the juniors will sell a ticket to three sophomores; and so on, down to the 8th grade.

Four more seniors help out:

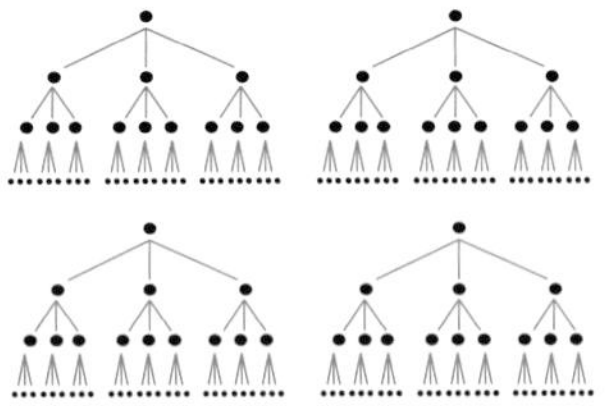

8. Assume Erin gets five seniors to help (including herself).

a. How many 8th graders would buy tickets?

b. How is this number related to the number of 8th graders who would buy tickets if Erin does not get any other seniors to help?

c. Express the answer to (a) as a number times a power of 3. Explain.

9. If Erin gets K seniors to help (including herself), how many 8th graders would buy tickets? Express the answer in terms of K.

10. Assume five seniors are involved, including Erin. As before, each student at every step buys one ticket, but now each student sells two tickets instead of three.

a. How many 8th graders would buy tickets?

b. Express the answer to (a) as a number times a power. Should you use a power of 2, a power of 3, or a power of 5? Explain your answer.

11. Assume K seniors are involved and each student sells M tickets.

a. How many 8th graders would buy tickets? Express your answer in terms of K and M.

b. How many Nth graders would buy tickets? Express your answer in terms of K, M, and N.

12. **Exploration** Erin hopes to sell 1500 tickets altogether. Find several values for K (the number of seniors) and M (the number of tickets sold per person) that make it possible to sell at least 1500 tickets, without going below 7th grade. For each plan, indicate the number of students who would be involved at each grade level. Which of those plans do you think is the most realistic?

7.8 SOLUTIONS

6.

2^4	16	4^4	256
2^3	8	4^3	64
2^2	4	4^2	16
2^1	2	4^1	4
2^0	1	4^0	1

Generalization: A positive number raised to the zero power equals 1.

7. Answers will vary. A convincing argument could be made based on the tables above.

8. a. 405

12th	5
11th	15
10th	45
9th	135
8th	405

b. 405 is 5 times as large as 81, which is the number of eighth graders who would buy tickets under the other scheme.

c. $5(3^4)$

9. $k(3^4)$

10. a. 80 eighth graders

b. $5(2^4)$ Use a power of 2 because each student sells 2 tickets.

12th	5	$5 \cdot 2^0$
11th	10	$5 \cdot 2^1$
10th	20	$5 \cdot 2^2$
9th	40	$5 \cdot 2^3$
8th	80	$5 \cdot 2^4$

11. a. KM^4

b. KM^{12-N}

12. Answers will vary. Sample answers: Five seniors each selling 3 tickets would sell a total of 1820 tickets, if all students down to and including the 7th grade sold 3 tickets each. Fifteen seniors each selling 3 tickets would sell 1815 tickets, if all students down to and including the 8th grade sold 3 tickets each. Fourteen seniors each selling 3 tickets would sell 1694 tickets, if all students down to and including the 8th grade sold 3 tickets each.

REVIEW *WHICH IS GREATER?*

13. Which is greater?
a. $5 \cdot 3^{35}$ or $3 \cdot 5^{35}$
b. $5 \cdot 30^{35}$ or $30 \cdot 5^{35}$
c. $5 \cdot 300^{35}$ or $300 \cdot 5^{35}$

14. Which is greater?
a. $5^{35} \cdot 3^{35}$ or 15^{35}
b. 35^0 or 0^{35}

15. If a and b are each greater than 1, which is greater, $(ab)^{10}$ or ab^{10}? Explain.

REVIEW *A COMMUTATIVE LAW?*

Al announced, "I noticed that $4^2 = 2^4$ and $3^2 = 2^3$, so I generalized this using algebra to say $a^b = b^a$, always."

"That's a great discovery," said Beau. "This means that exponentiation is commutative!"

"Nice try, Al," said Cal. "It's true that 4^2 and 2^4 are both 16, but 3^2 is 9 and 2^3 is 8. They aren't equal."

Al was disappointed. "Round-off error," he muttered. "Close enough."

16. What did Beau mean when she said that exponentiation is commutative? Is she right or wrong? Explain, using examples to support your answer.

17. Is $4^2 = 2^4$ the only case where $a^b = b^a$? If it is, how can you be sure? If it isn't, how can you find others?

18. **Exploration** Which is greater, a^b or b^a? Of course, the answer to this question depends on the values of a and b. Experiment, and try to make some generalizations.

REVIEW/PREVIEW *CHUNKING*

19. Solve for y: $y^2 = 49$. (Remember there are two solutions.)

You can use the strategy of chunking to solve equations involving squares. For example, in problem 20, think of $(x + 3)$ as a chunk, and write two linear equations.

Solve.

20. $(x + 3)^2 = 49$

21. $(2p - 5)^2 = 49$

22. $(5 - 2p)^2 = 49$

23. $(6 + 2r)^2 = 49$

REVIEW *WHICH IS GREATER?*

REVIEW *A COMMUTATIVE LAW?*

This previews the work on exponential growth and the laws of exponents. It also reviews order of operations.

If you decide to assign problems 17 and 18, they should be done in class, allowing time for group discussion.

REVIEW/PREVIEW *CHUNKING*

This reviews the equal squares material from Lesson 7, and previews completing the square, without the support of the Lab Gear.

7.8 SOLUTIONS

13. a. $3 \cdot 5^{35}$
b. $5 \cdot 30^{35}$
c. $5 \cdot 300^{35}$

14. a. They are equal.
b. $35^0 = 1$ and is greater than $0^{35} = 0$

15. $(ab)^{10}$ is greater because both a and b are raised to the 10th power. In the expression ab^{10}, only b is raised to the 10th power.

16. Beau meant that the positions of the base and the exponent could be reversed without affecting the value of the expression. She is wrong. Cal's example that $3^2 = 9$ and $2^3 = 8$ is an example. Another example is $5^2 = 25$ and $2^5 = 32$.

17. It seems to be the only case. Students will probably have no way of being sure. The best way to search for others seems to be trial and error. It looks as if poor Al was really out to lunch.

18. Assume that $a \neq b$ and that a and b are natural numbers. If $b > a$, then $a^b > b^a$, and if $a > b$ the reverse is true. If $a = b$, then $a^b = b^a$. If either a or b equals zero, the expression with the zero exponent is greater than the expression with the base of zero.

19. $y = \pm 7$

20. $x = -10$ or $x = 4$

21. $p = -1$ or $p = 6$

22. $p = -1$ or $p = 6$

23. $R = -6.5$ or $R = 0.5$

THINKING WRITING 7.B
Graphing Inequalities

Core Sequence: 1-10

Suitable for Homework: 1-10

Useful for Assessment: 10

What this Assignment is About:

- Linear and quadratic inequalities
- Compound inequalities
- Preview of quadratic equations
- Preview of square roots

COMPOUND INEQUALITIES

This reviews the material in Chapter 6, Lesson 5. Even though we are dealing with compound inequalities, the examples are straightforward, since the upper and lower bounds are constant, except in the last problem.

This section also offers an opportunity to review graphing lines, including horizontal lines.

THINKING WRITING
7.B Graphing Inequalities

COMPOUND INEQUALITIES

Definition: An inequality that contains more than one inequality symbol is called a *compound inequality.*

Example: $3 < 2x < 8$ is read *2x is between 3 and 8.*

The figure shows the graphs of the line $y = 2x - 4$ and the horizontal lines $y = 2$ and $y = -2$.

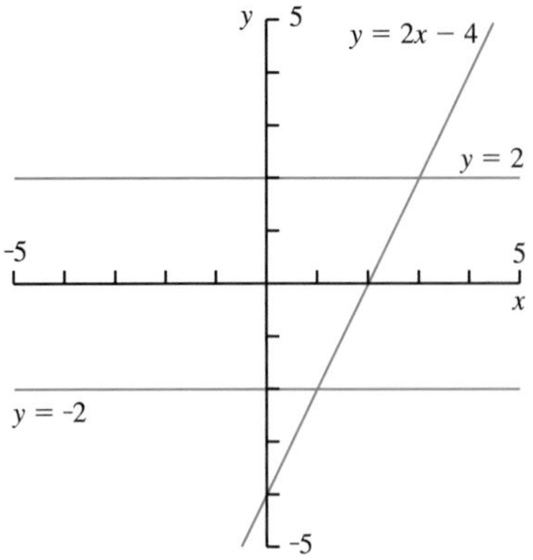

1. What are the coordinates of the points of intersection of $y = 2x - 4$ with each of the horizontal lines?
2. Look only at the part of the line $y = 2x - 4$ that is between the lines $y = 2$ and $y = -2$.
   a. Give the coordinates of some of the points on this part of the line.
   b. On this part of the line, how large can the *y*-coordinate get? How small?
   c. On this part of the line, how large can the *x*-coordinate get? How small?

We say that the *solution* of the compound inequality $-2 < 2x - 4 < 2$ is

$$1 < x < 3.$$

Notice that the solution is also a compound inequality, but it is simpler than the original one. It tells us what values of x make the first inequality true.

3. Explain how the graph above can be used to show that the solution to the inequality is $1 < x < 3$.
4. a. Graph the horizontal lines $y = 3$, $y = 8$, and $y = 3x + 5$.
   b. Use your graph to find the solution of the compound inequality
   $$3 < 3x + 5 < 8.$$

QUADRATIC INEQUALITIES

Sometimes an inequality is not compound, but it has a compound solution. An example is the inequality $x^2 < 4$. The two graphs shown can be used to solve this inequality.

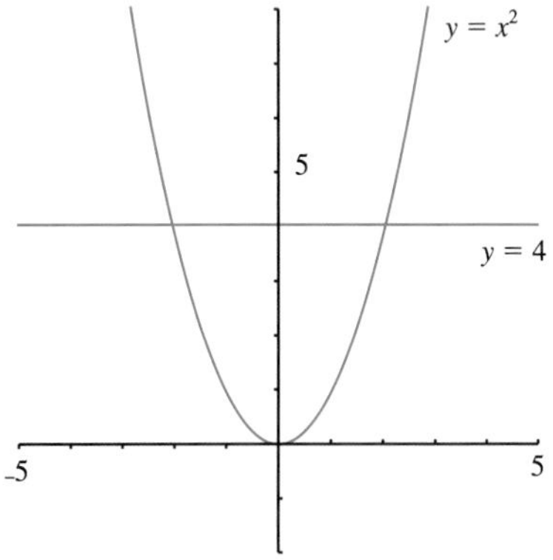

7.B SOLUTIONS

1. (1, -2) and (3, 2)
2. a. Answers will vary. Sample: (2, 0), (2.5, 1), and (1.5, -1)
   b. The largest the *y*-value can get is just less than 2, and the smallest is just larger than -2.
   c. The largest the *x*-value can get is just less than 3, and the smallest is just larger than 1.
3. Looking at the answer to #2c, one can see that the part of the line $y = 2x - 4$ that falls between the horizontal lines $y = 2$ and $y = -2$ has *x*-values larger than 1 and smaller than 3.
4. a.

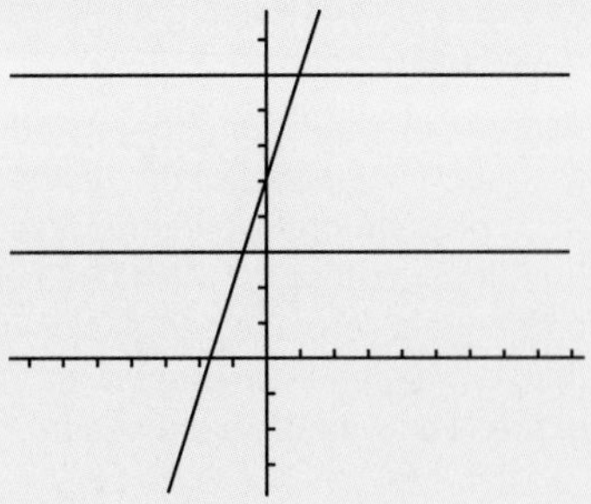

   b. $-2/3 < x < 1$

5. Look at the part of the graph of $y = x^2$ that is below the graph of $y = 4$.
   a. Give the coordinates of four points that lie on this part of the graph.
   b. On this part of the curve, how large can the x-coordinate get? How small?
   c. Write the solution to this inequality.

6. The same graph can also be used to solve the inequality $x^2 > 4$. In this case, the solution cannot be written as a compound inequality. Instead it is written in two parts,

$$x < -2 \text{ or } x > 2.$$

   Explain why the solution has two parts.

7. On the same pair of axes, make an accurate graph of $y = x^2$, $y = 1$, and $y = 9$. Use your graphs to solve these inequalities.
   a. $x^2 < 9$ b. $x^2 > 9$
   c. $x^2 < 1$ d. $x^2 > 1$
   e. $1 < x^2 < 9$

8. Use the graph to estimate the solution to

$$x^2 > 5.$$

9. Solve these without a graph.
   a. $x^2 < 16$ b. $x^2 > 16$
   c. $x^2 > 0$ d. $x^2 < 0$

10. **Report** Write an illustrated report summarizing what you have learned in this assignment. Use examples, including at least one quadratic, and at least one compound, inequality.

QUADRATIC INEQUALITIES

This extends the graphical technique for solving inequalities to quadratic inequalities. Problem 8 previews square roots. Problem 9 is a good way to check whether students are able to visualize these solutions in simple cases.

7.B SOLUTIONS

5. a. Answers vary: Sample: (-1, 1), (0, 0), (1, 1), (0.5, 0.25)
   b. The x-coordinates are between 2 and -2.
   c. $-2 < x < 2$

6. There are two separate parts of the parabola above the line $y = 4$. Each separate inequality represents one of the parts.

7. a. $-3 < x < 3$
   b. $x < -3$ or $x > 3$
   c. $-1 < x < 1$
   d. $x < -1$ or $x > 1$
   e. $-3 < x < -1$ or $1 < x < 3$

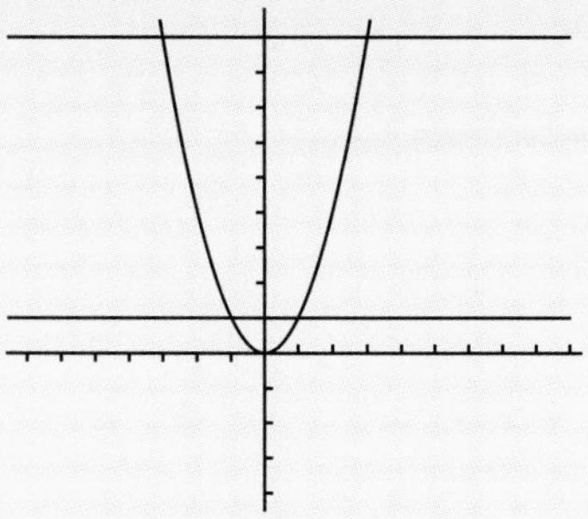

8. Estimates will vary slightly. $x < -2.2$ or $x > 2.2$

9. a. $-4 < x < 4$
   b. $x < -4$ or $x > 4$
   c. $x < 0$ or $x > 0$
   d. no solution

10. Reports will vary.

▼ 7.9
Powers and Large Numbers

Core Sequence: 1-13, 15-18

Suitable for Homework: 7-19

Useful for Assessment: 11-12

What this Lesson is About:

- Exponentiation
- Large numbers
- Introduction to scientific notation
- Review of prime numbers

Lessons 8-11 concentrate on large numbers, scientific notation, and exponentiation. More problems in this area can be found in the book *Innumeracy: Mathematical Illiteracy and its Consequences,* by John Allen Paulos (Hill and Wang, NY, 1988).

The key idea behind Lesson 9 is that instead of just teaching scientific notation by rote, it is possible to give the students some feel for the mathematics behind it. This is achieved by first developing the same system with powers other than ten.

Students need to learn how to use their calculators for exponentiation for this lesson. If students are eager to discuss negative and fractional exponents, reassure them that these are coming in Chapter 8. In this lesson, keep the focus on positive whole-number exponents.

LESSON 7.9

Powers and Large Numbers

Powers provide a shorthand for writing large numbers. Just as multiplication is repeated addition, raising to a power is repeated multiplication. For example,

$$12 \cdot 12 \cdot 12 \cdot 12 \cdot 12 \cdot 12,$$

which equals 2,985,984, can be written 12^6. Not only is this shorter to write than either the repeated multiplication or the decimal number, it is shorter to key into a scientific calculator.

Notation: Calculators use [^], [x^y], or [y^x] for *exponentiation* (raising to a power). We will use [^] to refer to that key.

Calculators can calculate with exponents that are not positive whole numbers. For example, it is possible to get a value for a number like $3^{-2.4}$ using the key for powers on your calculator. (Try it.) In this lesson, you will consider only *positive whole numbers* for exponents. In later chapters, you will use other exponents.

APPROXIMATING LARGE NUMBERS

1. **Exploration** Consider the number 123,456. Use your calculator to approximate the number as closely as you can with a power of 2, a power of 3, a power of 9, and a power of 10. How close can you get with each power? Repeat this experiment with four other numbers. (Use the same numbers as other students, so as to be able to compare your answers. Use only positive whole numbers having six or more digits.) Is it possible to get close to most large numbers by raising small numbers to a power?

For problems 2-4 find the powers of the following numbers (a-d), that are immediately below and above the given numbers.

a. 2 b. 3
c. 9 d. 10

Example: 691,737 (the population of Virginia, the most heavily populated state in 1790) is:
a. between 2^{19} and 2^{20}
b. between 3^{12} and 3^{13}
c. between 9^6 and 9^7
d. between 10^5 and 10^6

2. 3,929,214 (the population of the United States in 1790)
3. 48,881,221 (the number of people who voted for President Bush in 1988)
4. 178,098,000 (approximate number of Americans aged 18 or older in 1988)

CLOSER APPROXIMATIONS

It is possible to combine powers with multiplication to get approximations that are closer than those you were able to get in the previous sections by using only powers. For example, the speed of light is approximately 186,282 miles per second. This number is more than 2^{17} and less than 2^{18}, since

$$2^{17} = 131{,}072 \text{ and } 2^{18} = 262{,}144.$$

By multiplying 131,072 by a number less than 2, it is possible to get quite close to 186, 282.

$1.2 \cdot 131{,}072 = 157{,}286.4$ (too small)
$1.5 \cdot 131{,}072 = 196{,}608$ (too large)
$1.4 \cdot 131{,}072 = 183{,}500.8$ (too small, but pretty close)

7.9 SOLUTIONS

1. Answers will vary. The Exploration is what is important, not the individual answers, but a few sample answers follow: The closest power of 2 is $2^{17} = 131{,}072$, which is 7616 larger than 123,456. The closest power of 3 is $3^{11} = 177{,}147$, which is 53,691 larger than 123,456. The closest power of 9 is $9^5 = 59{,}049$, which is 64,407 less than 123,456. The closest power of 10 is $10^5 = 100{,}000$, which is 23,456 less than 123,456. Yes, it is possible to get close to most large numbers by raising a small number to a power.
2. 3,929,214 is between:
a. 2^{21} and 2^{22}
b. 3^{13} and 3^{14}
c. 9^6 and 9^7
d. 10^6 and 10^7
3. 48,881,221 is between:
a. 2^{25} and 2^{26}
b. 3^{16} and 3^{17}
c. 9^8 and 9^9
d. 10^7 and 10^8
4. 178,098,000 is between:
a. 2^{27} and 2^{28}
b. 3^{17} and 3^{18}
c. 9^8 and 9^9
d. 10^8 and 10^9

5. We showed that the speed of light can be roughly approximated by multiplying 2^{17} by 1.4. Find an even better approximation by changing the number by which you multiply, using more places after the decimal point.

You can approximate the speed of light in many different ways using powers of 2. For example:

$93141 \cdot 2^1 = 186{,}282$
$46570 \cdot 2^2 = 186{,}280$
$23280 \cdot 2^3 = 186{,}240$
$45.5 \cdot 2^{12} = 186{,}368$

We used 2^{17} in the example instead of some other power of 2 because it is the *largest* power of 2 that is less than 186,282. We approximated 186,282 by *multiplying that power of 2, by a number between 1 and 2.*

6. Write an approximation to the speed of light using a power of 3 multiplied by a number between 1 and 3. (Hint: Begin by finding the largest power of 3 that is less than 186,282.)

7. Write an approximation to the speed of light using a power of 9 multiplied by a number between 1 and 9.

8. Write an approximation to the speed of light using a power of 10 multiplied by a number between 1 and 10.

9. Combine a power and multiplication to get a close approximation to the length of the Earth's equator, which is 24,902 miles, to the nearest mile. You can use any base for the power, but multiply the power by a number between 1 and the base.

NAMES FOR LARGE NUMBERS

10. Write 100 and 1000 as powers of 10.

There are common names for some of the powers of ten. *Billion* in the U.S. means 10^9, but in Britain it means 10^{12}. The table gives the common names used in the U.S. for some powers of ten.

Power	Name
10^6	million
10^9	billion
10^{12}	trillion
10^{15}	quadrillion
10^{18}	quintillion
10^{21}	sextillion
10^{100}	googol

11. Someone might think a billion is two millions, and a trillion is three millions. In fact, a billion is how many millions? A trillion is how many millions? Explain.

SCIENTIFIC NOTATION

Definition: To write a number in *scientific notation* means to write it as a power of 10 multiplied by a number between 1 and 10. This is the most common way of writing large numbers in science and engineering.

12. Explain why 10 is used for the base in scientific notation rather than some other number. Use examples.

APPROXIMATING LARGE NUMBERS

In fact, powers of small numbers are not a good way to approximate large numbers, because the gaps between consecutive powers are enormous.

You may ask your students what percent of the U.S. population lived in Virginia in 1790 and what percent of Americans of voting age voted for the President in 1988.

CLOSER APPROXIMATIONS

In problem 5, note that students can get an extremely accurate answer by using division and their calculators.

If students understand problems 5 and 6, they should be able to do the rest of the lesson as homework. Problem 9 gives them the opportunity to try their own base. Of course, 10 is the easiest.

NAMES FOR LARGE NUMBERS

SCIENTIFIC NOTATION

After a brief review of powers of ten, scientific notation is defined, and students are asked to use it to write a few large numbers. Note that they are just applying what they learned earlier in the lesson.

7.9 SOLUTIONS

5. Answers will vary slightly. Sample: $1.42122 \cdot 2^{17} \approx 186282.1$

6. Answers may vary slightly. $1.05157 \cdot 3^{11} \approx 186282.47$

7. Answers may vary slightly. $3.1547 \cdot 9^5 \approx 186{,}281.88$

8. $1.86282 \cdot 10^5 = 186282$

9. Answers may vary. $2.4902 \cdot 10^4 = 24902$

10. $100 = 10^2$
$1000 = 10^3$

11. A billion is 1000 millions because $10^9 = 10^3 \cdot 10^6$

A trillion is a million millions because $10^{12} = 10^6 \cdot 10^6$

12. Ten is used for the base because one can write the exact value of the number. In #6 through #8 above, the best approximation for the speed of light (186,282) was the one using a power of 10. Also, no division or trial and error multiplication on a calculator is needed when using a power of 10. One simply moves a decimal point left to divide or right to multiply.

REVIEW PRIME NUMBERS

Since many of your students should already be familiar with prime numbers, do not spend a lot of class time on this section. We will review prime factorization in Chapter 11, and use that idea in the explanation of the fact that the square root of two is not a rational number.

13. Write in scientific notation.

a. one million
b. 67 million (the average distance from the sun to Venus in miles)
c. 5.3 billion (an estimate of the world's population in 1990)
d. twenty billion
e. 3.1 trillion (the U.S. national debt in dollars as of June 1990)
f. three hundred trillion

14. Project Find four large numbers that measure some real quantity. They should all be larger than 100,000,000. Encyclopedias, almanacs, and science books are good sources of such numbers.

a. Tell what each number measures.
b. Write the number in scientific notation.

REVIEW PRIME NUMBERS

There is only one polyomino rectangle of area 2, and only one of area 3. But there are two polyomino rectangles of area 4, corresponding to the products $2 \cdot 2 = 4$ and $1 \cdot 4 = 4$.

15. What is the smallest number that is the area of a polyomino rectangle in 3 different ways? Sketch the three rectangles and show the products.

16. Repeat the problem for 4 different ways.

17. Can you predict the smallest number that is the area of a polyomino rectangle in 5 different ways? Check your prediction.

Definition: Numbers greater than 1 that can only make a rectangle with whole number dimensions in one way are called *prime numbers.*

18. Here is an ancient method, (invented by the Greek mathematician Eratosthenes,) of finding the prime numbers.

a. On a list of numbers from 1 to 100, cross out the 1.
Circle 2, cross out its multiples.
Circle the first number that is not crossed out, cross out its multiples.
Repeat, until all the numbers are either crossed out or circled.
b. Explain how and why this method works to find the prime numbers.

19. A mathematician once suggested that *every even number greater than 2 may be the sum of two prime numbers.* No one knows why this should be true, but it has worked for every number that's ever been tried. Test this for yourself with at least ten even numbers. (This is known as *Goldbach's conjecture.* A conjecture is a guess that has not yet been proved true or false.)

7.9 SOLUTIONS

13. a. $1.0 \cdot 10^6$ b. $6.7 \cdot 10^7$
c. $5.3 \cdot 10^9$ d. $2.0 \cdot 10^{10}$
e. $3.1 \cdot 10^{12}$ f. $3.0 \cdot 10^{14}$

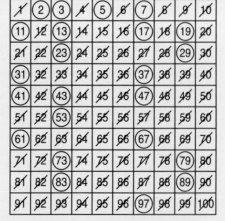

15. 12

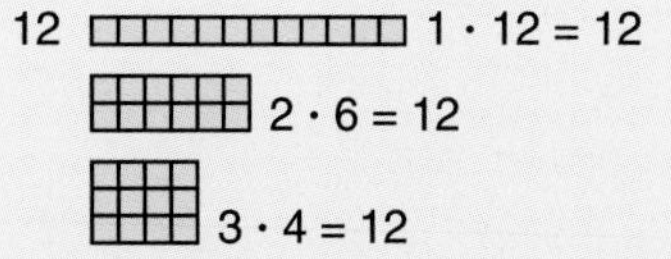

16. 24

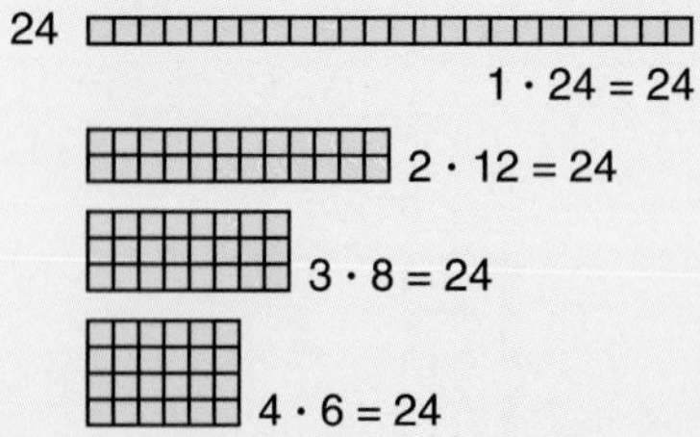

17. 36

18. a.

~~1~~	(2)	(3)	~~4~~	(5)	~~6~~	(7)	~~8~~	~~9~~	~~10~~
(11)	~~12~~	(13)	~~14~~	~~15~~	~~16~~	(17)	~~18~~	(19)	~~20~~
~~21~~	~~22~~	(23)	~~24~~	~~25~~	~~26~~	~~27~~	~~28~~	(29)	~~30~~
(31)	~~32~~	~~33~~	~~34~~	~~35~~	~~36~~	(37)	~~38~~	~~39~~	~~40~~
(41)	~~42~~	(43)	~~44~~	~~45~~	~~46~~	(47)	~~48~~	~~49~~	~~50~~
~~51~~	~~52~~	(53)	~~54~~	~~55~~	~~56~~	~~57~~	~~58~~	~~59~~	~~60~~
(61)	~~62~~	~~63~~	~~64~~	~~65~~	~~66~~	(67)	~~68~~	~~69~~	~~70~~
~~71~~	~~72~~	(73)	~~74~~	~~75~~	~~76~~	~~77~~	~~78~~	(79)	~~80~~
~~81~~	~~82~~	(83)	~~84~~	~~85~~	~~86~~	~~87~~	~~88~~	(89)	~~90~~
~~91~~	~~92~~	~~93~~	~~94~~	~~95~~	~~96~~	(97)	~~98~~	~~99~~	~~100~~

b. Any number that is a multiple of 2 can be written as a product of 2 and another number, so they are crossed out. The number 2 can only be factored into 1 · 2, so it is prime. The next number to circle is 3 which can only be factored into 1 · 3, so it is prime. All of 3's multiples can be written as a product of 3 and another number. So multiples of 3 are crossed out. The next number to be circled is 7. Its multiples are crossed out. The next circled digit is 11, and its multiples are already crossed out. Thirteen is circled next. All multiples of 2, 3, 5, and 7 have already been eliminated. 26, 39, 65, and 91, which are also multiples of 13 have already been crossed out. 13 times 4, 6, or 8 have been eliminated as multiples of 2. The remaining numbers are all prime.

LESSON

7.10 Using Scientific Notation

WITH A CALCULATOR

Calculators can display numbers only up to a certain number of digits. For many calculators, ten digits is the limit.

1. What is the limit for your calculator?
2. What is the smallest power of 2 that forces your calculator into scientific notation?

On many calculators, the answer to problem 2 is 2^{34} which, according to the calculator, is equal to

$\boxed{1.717986918^{10}}$ or $\boxed{1.717986918E10}$.

The expression on the left does *not* mean 1.717986918^{10}, even though that's what it looks like. It is just calculator shorthand for $1.717986918 \cdot 10^{10}$. The actual value is 17179869184, which is too long to fit, so the calculator gives the approximate value of 17179869180, expressed in scientific notation. (For a number this large, this represents a very small error.)

3. Which power of 2 is displayed as $\boxed{2.814749767E14}$?
4. Find a power of 4 and a power of 8 that are also displayed as $\boxed{2.814749767E14}$.
5. Find powers of 3, 9, 27, and 81 that are displayed in scientific notation, in the form ____ $\cdot 10^{17}$. If possible, find more than one solution for each number.

There are three ways to enter numbers in scientific notation into your calculator. For example, to enter $2 \cdot 10^3$, you can key in 2 $\boxed{*}$ 10 $\boxed{\wedge}$ 3, or 2 $\boxed{*}$ $\boxed{10^x}$ 3, or (depending on the calculator) 2 $\boxed{EE}$ 3, or 2 $\boxed{EXP}$ 3. We will refer to this last key as $\boxed{EE}$.

6. Try all the methods listed that are available on your calculator. In each case, the calculator should respond with $\boxed{2000}$ after you press $\boxed{=}$ or $\boxed{ENTER}$.
7. Explain the purpose of the $\boxed{\wedge}$ and $\boxed{EE}$ keys. How are they different?

HOW MUCH FARTHER, HOW MANY TIMES AS FAR?

The table shows the ten brightest objects in the sky, and their *average* distances from Earth, in miles. (The objects are listed in order of average brightness as seen from Earth.)

	Distance
Sun	$9.29(10^7)$
Moon	$2.39(10^5)$
Venus	$9.30(10^7)$
Jupiter	$4.84(10^8)$
Sirius	$5.11(10^{13})$
Canopus	$5.76(10^{14})$
Arcturus	$2.12(10^{14})$
Mars	$1.42(10^8)$
Vega	$1.59(10^{14})$
Saturn	$8.88(10^8)$

8. If you were to divide the objects into two groups, based only on the value of the exponents of 10, what would be in each group? What is the actual significance of the two groups?

7.10 Using Scientific Notation

Core Sequence: 1-23

Suitable for Homework: 8-23

Useful for Assessment: 7, 15

What this Lesson is About:

- Scientific notation on the calculator
- Operations with numbers in scientific notation
- Preview of the laws of exponents

WITH A CALCULATOR

This section is intended to get the students familiar with their calculators. It should be done in class, so that students can help each other. If they are all using different types of calculators, it is interesting to compare the calculator features.

Problems 4 and 5 preview the laws of exponents. There is no need to dwell on them, as they will be a major focus in Chapter 8.

HOW MUCH FARTHER, HOW MANY TIMES AS FAR?

Since the brightness of the planets varies, a mean value was used to order the planets in the table. The brightness of the Moon when it is full was used. (All this is for your information only, and has no bearing whatsoever on the assignment.)

7.10 SOLUTIONS

(7.9 Solutions continued)

19. Answers will vary. For example: $4 = 2 + 2$; $6 = 3 + 3$; $32 = 29 + 3$; $42 = 37 + 5$

1. Answers may vary.
2. Answers may vary. (2^{34} will be a common answer.)
3. The 48th power of 2.
4. 4^{24} and 8^{16} are also displayed as 2.814749767 E14
5. $3^{36} = 1.5 \cdot 10^{17}$ and $3^{37} = 4.5 \cdot 10^{17}$
$9^{18} = 1.5 \cdot 10^{17}$
$27^{12} = 1.5 \cdot 10^{17}$
$81^9 = 1.5 \cdot 10^{17}$
7. The $\boxed{\wedge}$ key raises a number to a power. For example, $A\boxed{\wedge}N$ means A^N.
$\boxed{EE}$ N means 10^N
A$\boxed{EE}$ N means $A(10^N)$.
$\boxed{\wedge}$ can have any number as a base
$\boxed{EE}$ has only 10 as a base.
8. One group would consist of our sun and the planets in our solar system. The other would consist of stars.
9. a. $9.2761(10^7)$ miles farther
b. 389 times as far
10. a. $8.87761(10^8)$ miles farther
b. 3715 times as far
11. a. $5.10999071(10^{13})$ miles farther
b. $5.5(10^5)$ times as far
12. a. $5.759999071(10^{14})$ miles farther
b. $6.2(10^6)$ times as far
13. a. $5.249(10^{14})$ miles farther
b. 11.3 times as far
14. a. 40,000,000 + 5,000,000 = 45,000,000
b. 40,000,000 + 5,000,000 = 45,000,000

Scientists often compare numbers by thinking of their order of magnitude. An order of magnitude ranges from any number to ten times that number. The visible Solar System objects are at distances that range across four orders of magnitude. The four brightest stars are about five orders of magnitude farther than the farthest visible object in the Solar System, and within one order of magnitude of each other.

WITHOUT A CALCULATOR

The purpose of this section is to develop estimation skills and to preview the laws of exponents by using the particularly accessible case of powers of ten.

PREVIEW MULTIPLICATION AND EXPONENTS

Problems 21 and 22 extend the work of the previous section to bases other than ten. This is only a Preview, so you should not expect mastery. We will return to these ideas in Chapter 8.

REVIEW PERFECT SQUARE TRINOMIALS

This reviews and extends Lesson 3.

For each pair of objects given in problems 9-13, answer questions (a) and (b). If an answer is greater than 10,000, give it in scientific notation.

a. The second object is *how many miles* farther from Earth than the first?
b. The second object is *how many times* as far from Earth as the first?

9. The Moon, Venus

10. The Moon, Saturn

11. The Sun, Sirius

12. The Sun, Canopus

13. Sirius, Canopus

WITHOUT A CALCULATOR

14. Convert these numbers to ordinary decimal notation and add them without a calculator.

a. $(4 \cdot 10^7) + (5 \cdot 10^6)$
b. $(40 \cdot 10^6) + (5 \cdot 10^6)$

15. Compare the two computations in problem 14. Which would have been easy to do without converting to ordinary decimal notation? Explain.

Without a calculator it is not easy to add and subtract in scientific notation. One way is to revert to ordinary decimal notation. Another is to write the two quantities with a common exponent for 10, as was done in problem 14b.

16. Add or subtract.

a. $6.2 \cdot 10^3 + 5 \cdot 10^6$
b. $6.2 \cdot 10^6 - 5 \cdot 10^3$
c. $6.2 \cdot 10^5 + 5 \cdot 10^3$
d. $6.2 \cdot 10^3 - 5 \cdot 10^6$

Without a calculator it can be tedious to multiply and divide large numbers. However, if the numbers are written in scientific notation it is easy to estimate the size of the answer.

For the following problems, 17-20:

a. Convert the numbers to ordinary decimal notation.
b. Multiply or divide.
c. Write your answers in scientific notation.

17. $(3 \cdot 10^5) \cdot (6 \cdot 10^3)$

18. $(3 \cdot 10^3) \cdot (6 \cdot 10^5)$

19. $(6 \cdot 10^6) \div (3 \cdot 10^3)$

20. $(3 \cdot 10^6) \div (6 \cdot 10^3)$

PREVIEW MULTIPLICATION AND EXPONENTS

21.

a. In each of problems 17-20, look for a relationship between your answer and the original numbers. How could you have obtained your answer without converting from scientific notation?
b. Explain a shortcut for multiplying and dividing numbers in scientific notation. Include an explanation of what happens to the exponent of 10.

22. Does the shortcut, described in problem 21b, work for multiplying $3(2^4)$ by $5(2^6)$? Explain, giving several examples of this type.

REVIEW PERFECT SQUARE TRINOMIALS

23. All of these are perfect square trinomials. Write each one as the square of a binomial.

a. $c^2x^2 + 2bcxy + b^2y^2$
b. $y^2 + 2xy + x^2$
c. $y^2 + 2by + b^2$
d. $0.25x^2 + 0.2x + 0.04$

7.10 SOLUTIONS

15. Part (b) would have been easy to do without converting to ordinary decimal notation. One would simply add 40 and 5 and multiply the result by 10^6. If $10^6 = x$, the problem would be $40x + 5x$, which is $45x$.

16. a. $0.0062(10^6) + 5(10^6) = 5.0062(10^6)$
b. $6.2(10^6) - 0.005(10^6) = 6.195(10^6)$
c. $6.2(10^5) + 0.05(10^5) = 6.25(10^5)$
d. $0.0062(10^6) - 5(10^6) = -4.9938(10^6)$

17. $(300{,}000)(6000) = 1{,}800{,}000{,}000 = 1.8(10^9)$

18. $(3{,}000)(600{,}000) = 1{,}800{,}000{,}000 = 1.8(10^9)$

19. $6{,}000{,}000/3{,}000 = 2000 = 2.0(10^3)$

20. $3{,}000{,}000/6{,}000 = 500 = 5.0(10^2)$

21. a. The first part of the answer is obtained by multiplying or dividing the first parts (numbers between 1 and 10) of each number. The second part of the answer is obtained by multiplying or dividing the powers of 10.
b. To obtain an answer for multiplication without converting from scientific notation, multiply the two numbers between 1 and 10. Multiply this product by a power of 10. The power of 10 in the answer is obtained by adding the exponents of the powers of 10 in the factors. To divide, divide the two numbers between 1 and 10. Multiply this quotient by a power of 10. The power of 10 in the answer is obtained by subtracting the exponents of the powers of 10 in the factors. If you want your answer to be in scientific notation, adjustments may be needed to make the first part of the answer a number between 1 and 10.

22. Yes. Examples:
$3(2^4) \cdot 5(2^6) = 15(2^{10}) = 15{,}360$
$4(3^5) \cdot 2(3^7) = 8(3^{12}) = 4{,}251{,}528$
$2(4^3) \cdot 5(4^6) = 10(4^9) = 2{,}621{,}440$

23. a. $(cx + by)^2$
b. $(y + x)^2$
c. $(y + b)^2$
d. $(0.5x + 0.2)^2$

LESSON 7.11

Using Large Numbers

TRAVELING IN THE SOLAR SYSTEM

The table below gives the diameter and average distance from the Sun in kilometers (km) of each of the planets in the solar system. The Sun's diameter is also shown.

	Diameter	Distance from Sun	Moons
Sun	$1.39(10^6)$		
Mercury	$4.88(10^3)$	57,700,000	0
Venus	$1.21(10^4)$	108,150,000	0
Earth	$1.23(10^4)$	150,000,000	1
Mars	$6.79(10^3)$	227,700,000	2
Jupiter	$1.43(10^5)$	778,300,000	17
Saturn	$1.20(10^5)$	1,427,000,000	22
Uranus	$5.18(10^4)$	2,870,000,000	15
Neptune	$4.95(10^4)$	4,497,000,000	3
Pluto	$6.00(10^3)$	5,900,000,000	1

1. Convert the diameters to normal decimal notation.
2. Convert the distances to scientific notation.
3. Divide the planets into groups according to:
   a. their diameters. How many groups are there? Explain.
   b. their distance from the Sun. How many groups are there? Explain.
   c. their number of moons. How many groups are there? Explain.
4. Compare the groups you created in problem 3. Find a way to combine your decisions into an overall division of the planets into two or three groups, by *type of planet.* Name each group, and list its characteristics in terms of the data in the table.
5. Light travels approximately 299,793 kilometers per second. Show your calculations, and give your answers in scientific notation. How far does light travel in
   a. one minute? b. one hour?
   c. one day? d. one year?
6. Abe remembers learning in elementary school that it takes about eight minutes for light to travel from the Sun to the Earth. Figure out whether he remembers correctly. Show your calculations.
7. Light from the Sun takes more than one day to reach which planets, if any?
8. When Pluto is at its mean distance from the Sun, how long does it take light from the Sun to reach it?
9. An *Astronomical Unit* is the distance from the Earth to the Sun. What is Pluto's distance from the Sun in Astronomical Units?

SCALE MODELS

10. Make a scale drawing showing the distances of the planets from the Sun. Tell what your scale is, and explain why you chose it.

Project

11. Decide what would be a good scale for a scale model of the solar system, so you could fit the model in your classroom. How large would each planet be? How far would each planet be from the Sun?

7.11 Using Large Numbers

Core Sequence: 1-9

Suitable for Homework: 1-9, 15-19

Useful for Assessment: 4

What this Lesson is About:

- Using scientific notation
- Analyzing numerical data
- Proportional thinking
- Work with exponents

TRAVELING IN THE SOLAR SYSTEM

This is a straightforward application of the work of the past two lessons.

In problem 4 allow any answers, as long as they are backed up with arguments based on the given data. Astronomers usually divide the planets in two groups, the inner planets and the outer planets. The inner planets are smaller and have fewer moons than the outer planets. Pluto is an exception to that pattern, and it is believed to be an escaped moon.

7.11 SOLUTIONS

1. & 2.

	Diameter	Distance from Sun
Sun	1,390,000	
Mercury	4,880	$5.77(10^7)$
Venus	12,100	$1.0815(10^8)$
Earth	12,300	$1.5(10^8)$
Mars	6,790	$2.277(10^8)$
Jupiter	143,000	$7.783(10^8)$
Saturn	120,000	$1.427(10^9)$
Uranus	51,800	$2.87(10^9)$
Neptune	49,500	$4.497(10^9)$
Pluto	6,000	$5.9(10^9)$

3. a. 3 groups:
   diameters between 4,000 and 7,000 km: Mercury (4,880), Mars (6,790), Pluto (6,000)
   diameters between 12,000 and 52,000 km: Venus (12,100), Earth (12,300), Uranus (51,800), Neptune (49,500)
   diameters greater than 100,000 km: Jupiter (143,000), Saturn (120,000)
   b. 2 groups:
   distance from the sun is less than 10^9 km: Mercury, Venus, Earth, Mars, Jupiter
   distance from the sun is greater than 10^9 km: Saturn, Uranus, Neptune, Pluto
   c. 3 groups:
   no moons: Mercury and Venus
   one to three moons: Earth, Mars, Neptune, Pluto
   15 to 22 moons: Jupiter, Saturn, Uranus
4. Answers may vary. (See Notes to the Teacher.)
5. a. 299793 km/sec · 60 sec/min = $1.798758 \cdot (10^7)$ km/min
   b. 299793 km/sec · 3600 sec/hr = $1.0792548(10^9)$ km/hr
   c. $1.0792548(10^9)$ km/hr · 24 hr/day = $2.590(10^{10})$ km/day
   d. $2.590(10^{10})$ km/day · 365 day/year = $9.454(10^{12})$ km/yr
6. $1.798758(10^7)$ km/min · 8 min = 143,900,640 km = $1.439 \cdot 10^8$ km
   He did remember correctly because light will travel $1.439(10^8)$ km in 8 minutes. This is close to the distance from the sun to the earth, which is 1.5×10^8 km.
7. Sunlight travels $2.59 \cdot (10^{10})$ km in one day, which is more than the distance of the farthest planet from the sun. So sunlight leaving the sun can reach all nine planets in one day.

Project **Scale Model**

This is a challenging project that should be seen as a project for a group or for the whole class. It incorporates the use of the data from the table in the previous section, the scientific notation techniques of the past two lessons, and work with proportional thinking. The "astronomical" distances in the solar system mean that for the small planets to be visible in a scale model, the distances between the planets must be substantial. The model would have to be spread out across a midsize town, and the nearest star would be a long drive away.

DOWN TO EARTH

These problems give practice with operations with large numbers and help students get a sense of the relative sizes of large numbers.

12. Decide what would be a good scale for a scale model of the solar system, so you could clearly see even the smallest planet. How far would each planet be from the Sun? How large would each planet be? What objects could you use to represent the planets?
13. Using a map of your town, figure out where you might place the planets and the Sun. Use the scale you calculated in problem 12.
14. The nearest star, Alpha Centauri, is 40 trillion kilometers away from the Sun. Where would it be in your model?

DOWN TO EARTH

15. In 1986 people in the U.S. threw away about 64.7 million tons of paper and cardboard. Write this number in scientific notation.

The number 64.7 million is too large to mean anything to most people. The following problems illustrate some ways of bringing large numbers "down to earth."

For example, to understand how much paper and cardboard was thrown away in the U.S. in 1986, it helps to figure out how much was thrown away *per person.*

Since there are 2000 pounds in a ton, 64.7 million tons is

$(6.47 \cdot 10^7 \text{ tons}) \cdot (2 \cdot 10^3 \text{ lbs/ton})$
$= 12.94 \cdot 10^{10}$ lbs.

16. The U.S. population in 1986 was about 240 million people. Write this number in scientific notation. Then calculate how many pounds of paper and cardboard were thrown away *per person.*
17. The distance around the equator of the Earth is about 24,900 miles. Al bikes to and from school every day, about five miles each way. Biking back and forth to school, about how many school years would it take Al to cover the distance around the equator? (A school year has about 180 days.)
18. Biking back and forth to school, about how many school years would it take Al to cover
    a. the distance from the Earth to the moon?
    b. the distance from the Earth to the Sun?
19. The population of the U.S. was about 250 million in 1990. Approximately $5 \cdot 10^{11}$ cigarettes were smoked in the U.S.
    a. About how many cigarettes were smoked *per person*?
    b. About how many were smoked *per person, per day*?
    c. If 186 million U.S. residents did not smoke any cigarettes, how many cigarettes were smoked *per smoker, per day*?

7.11 SOLUTIONS

8. $[5.9(10^9)$ km$]/[299793$ km/sec$] =$ 19680.25 sec = 19680.25 sec(1 hr/3600 sec) = 5.47 hours
9. Divide $5.9(10^9)$ by $1.5(10^8)$ to get $3.93(10^1)$, or 39.3 Astronomical Units.
10. Answers will vary.
11. This will not work. In order to fit the planets inside the classroom, the distances would have to be so small that the planets could not be seen. For example, suppose a room were 10 meters long. If the distance from the Sun to Mercury were 9 centimeters, then the distance from the Sun to Pluto would be about 9.2 meters. But this would make the smallest planet 0.01 mm in diameter.

12.-14. Answers will vary, depending on how large students decide the smallest planet must be in order to see it clearly. If the smallest planet is given a diameter of 1 mm, Alpha Centauri will be 8197 km away.

15. $6.47(10^7)$
16. $2.40(10^8)$ people threw away 539.2 lbs per person.
17. 13.8 school years
18. a. 132.8 school years
    b. 51,611 school years
19. a. 2000 cigarettes per person
    b. 5.5 cigarettes per day
    c. 64 million smokers
       21.4 cigarettes per smoker per day

LESSON 7.12

As the Crow Flies

You will need:

geoboards

dot paper

SQUARE ROOTS

As you know, the square of a number is the area of a square that has that number for a side. For example, the square of 4 is 16, because a square having side 4 has area 16.

1. a. What is the area of a square having side 9?
b. What is the side of a square having area 9?

2. a. What is the area of a square having side 10?
b. What is the side of a square having area 10?

You can answer question 2b with the help of a calculator, by using trial and error. Or, you may answer it by using the $\boxed{\sqrt{\ }}$ key.

> **Definition:** The *square root* of a number is the side of a square that has that number for area.

For example, the square root of 4 is 2, because a square having area 4 has side 2.

3. a. What is the square of 11?
b. What is the square root of 11?

The square root of 11 is written $\sqrt{11}$. The number given by a calculator is an approximation of the exact value. Many calculators have an $\boxed{x^2}$ key.

4. Use the $\boxed{x^2}$ key to calculate the square of 8.76. Write it down. Clear your calculator. Now use the $\boxed{\sqrt{\ }}$ key to find the square root of the number. What answer did you get? Explain why this is so.

5. Find a number for $\sqrt{5}$. Write it down. Now clear your calculator, enter the number, and use the $\boxed{x^2}$ key. What answer did you get? Compare your answer with other students' answers. Explain.

6. Which number has more digits, $\sqrt{10.3041}$ or $\sqrt{2}$? Make a prediction and check it with your calculator. Explain your answer.

DISTANCE ON THE GEOBOARD

To find the distance between two points on the geoboard, *as the crow flies,* you can use the following strategy.

- Make a square that has the two points as consecutive vertices.
- Find the area of the square.
- Find the side of the square.

In problems 7-9, express your answers two ways: as a square root, and as a decimal approximation (unless the answer is a whole number).

7.12 SOLUTIONS

1. a. 81
   b. 3
2. a. 100
   b. approx. 3.162
3. a. 121
   b. approx. 3.317
4. Taking the square root "undoes" the squaring of a positive number.
5. Squaring "undoes" the taking of a square root.
6. $\sqrt{2}$ gives more digits. $\sqrt{10.3041} = 3.21$. $\sqrt{2}$ is approximately equal to 1.414213562, according to one calculator. We cannot express $\sqrt{2}$ exactly using decimal notation.
7. a. $\sqrt{20} \approx 4.47$
   b. $\sqrt{8} \approx 2.83$
   c. 3
8. $\sqrt{10} \approx 3.16$
9. 5
10. a.

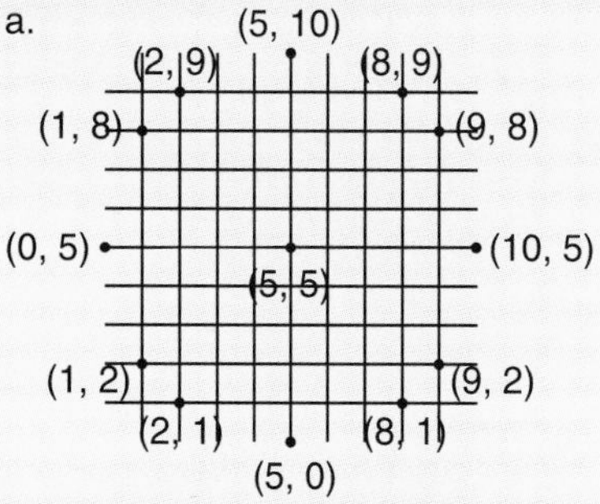

b. The 12 points lie on a circle with center (5, 5) and radius 5.

11. a. 40 b. 68
12. Answers will vary.

7.12 As the Crow Flies

Core Sequence: 1-15

Suitable for Homework: 13-19

Useful for Assessment: 5, 15

What this Lesson is About:

- Square roots
- Distance on the Cartesian plane
- Preview of the Pythagorean theorem
- The square and square root keys on the calculator
- Review of powers of two and scientific notation

This lesson formally introduces square roots, and previews Chapter 9, where the properties of square roots will be investigated in more depth.

SQUARE ROOTS

This section concentrates on a numerical, calculator-based approach. Many students confuse *square* with *square root*. While this problem is much reduced by the geometric work that follows, we try to prevent that confusion by explicit discussion up front.

In problem 5, students may be surprised by the fact that squaring the number the calculator gave for $\sqrt{5}$ does not yield the expected answer of 5. This is because of the fact that the number displayed is just an approximation. It is necessary to clear the calculator and re-enter the number to notice this, because in many calculators, the accuracy is greater than what is shown on the display. As a result, squaring the number given for $\sqrt{5}$ will give 5, because the calculator is squaring a number with more digits than are shown. By re-entering the number shown, you get the calculator to square that number.

DISTANCE ON THE GEOBOARD

Part of the reason for all the geoboard work we have done was to prepare students for this visual interpretation of square roots. The payoff should be a stronger sense of the meaning of square roots, more insight into the rules governing their use, and fewer mistakes when applying the Pythagorean theorem and the distance formula in future courses.

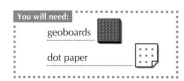

*L*et students find the areas of the squares by any method they please. Some of them may remember the formula developed in Chapter 6, Lesson 12; others may just use generic geoboard techniques involving subtraction of areas. Either approach is acceptable.

*P*roblems 10-13 have a geometrical flavor to them. Students use their new technique for finding distance on the geoboard to investigate geometric ideas such as the set of points at a given distance from a center, or the set of points equidistant from two points.

*T*he Generalization in problem 15 should be reminiscent of the formula derived for the area of a square in Chapter 6, Lesson 12, and again it previews the Pythagorean theorem.

DISCOVERY ***SUMS OF PERFECT SQUARES***

DISCOVERY ***SUMS OF POWERS***

*N*ote that these are substantial problems with a number theoretic flavor. Either of these sections could be assigned as a *problem of the week* or as a writing assignment. Or the sections could be assigned as group problem-solving, followed by the group's presentation of patterns and conclusions to the whole class. Do not assign both sections the same night.

Example: Find the distance between (1, 0) and (0, 1).

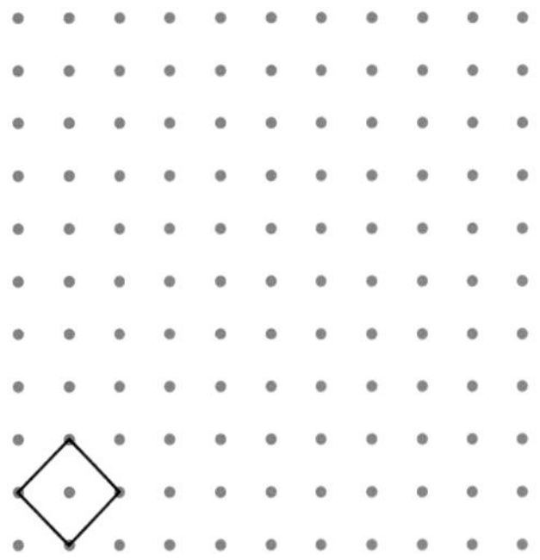

The area of the square is 2, so the distance between the two points is $\sqrt{2}$, or 1.41…

7. Find the distance between:
   a. (4, 3) and (6, 7);
   b. (4, 6) and (6, 4);
   c. (4, 5) and (4, 8).

8. Find the distance between the origin and (3, 1).

9. Find the distance between (5, 5) and (8, 9).

10. a. Find 12 geoboard pegs that are at a distance 5 from (5, 5). Connect them with a rubber band. Sketch the figure.
   b. Explain why someone might call that figure a *geoboard circle.*

11. How many geoboard pegs are there whose distance from (5, 5) is
   a. greater than 5?
   b. less than 5?

12. Choose a peg outside the *circle* and find its distance from (5, 5).

13. Find all the geoboard pegs whose distances from (4, 3) and (6, 7) are equal. Connect them with a rubber band. Sketch.

14. What are the distances between the pegs you found in problem 13 and (4, 3) or (6, 7)?

15. **Generalization** Describe a method for finding the distance between the origin and a point with coordinates (*x*, *y*). Use a sketch and algebraic notation.

DISCOVERY ***SUMS OF PERFECT SQUARES***

16. Any whole number can be written as a sum of perfect squares. Write each whole number from 1 to 25 as a sum of squares, using *as few squares as possible* for each one. (For example, $3^2 + 1^2$ is a better answer for 10 than $2^2 + 2^2 + 1^2 + 1^2$.)

17. You should have been able to write every number in problem 16 as a sum of *four or fewer* perfect squares. Do you think this would remain possible for large numbers? For very large numbers? Experiment with a few large numbers, such as 123, or 4321.

DISCOVERY ***SUMS OF POWERS***

18. Write every whole number from 1 to 30 as a sum of powers of 2. Each power of 2 cannot be used more than once for each number. Do you think this could be done with very large numbers? Try it for 100.

19. Write every whole number from 1 to 30 as a sum of powers of 3 and their opposites. Each power can appear only once for each number. Do you think this could be done with very large numbers? Try it for 100.

7.12 SOLUTIONS

13.

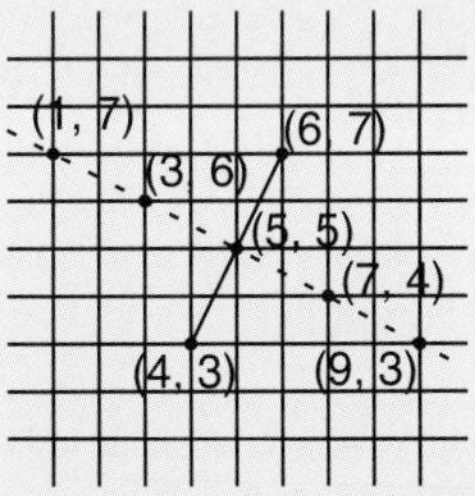

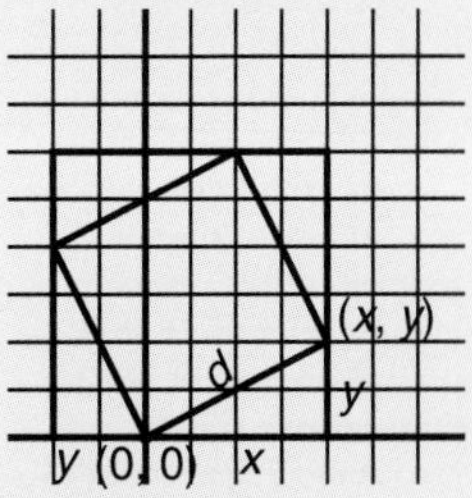

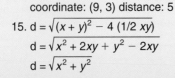

14. coordinate: (1, 7) distance: 5
coordinate: (3, 6) distance: $\sqrt{10} \approx 3.16$
coordinate: (5, 5) distance: $\sqrt{5} \approx 2.24$
coordinate: (7, 4) distance: $\sqrt{10} \approx 3.16$
coordinate: (9, 3) distance: 5

15. $d = \sqrt{(x + y)^2 - 4\,(1/2\ xy)}$
$d = \sqrt{x^2 + 2xy + y^2 - 2xy}$
$d = \sqrt{x^2 + y^2}$

16. $1 = 1^2$
$2 = 1^2 + 1^2$
$3 = 1^2 + 1^2 + 1^2$
$4 = 2^2$
$5 = 2^2 + 1^2$
$6 = 2^2 + 1^2 + 1^2$
$7 = 2^2 + 1^2 + 1^2 + 1^2$
$8 = 2^2 + 2^2$
$9 = 3^2$
$10 = 3^2 + 1^2$
$11 = 3^2 + 1^2 + 1^2$
$12 = 2^2 + 2^2 + 2^2$
$13 = 3^2 + 2^2$
$14 = 3^2 + 2^2 + 1^2$
$15 = 3^2 + 2^2 + 1^2 + 1^2$
$16 = 4^2$
$17 = 4^2 + 1^2$
$18 = 3^2 + 3^2$
$19 = 4^2 + 1^2 + 1^2 + 1^2$
$20 = 4^2 + 2^2$
$21 = 4^2 + 2^2 + 1^2$
$22 = 3^2 + 3^2 + 2^2$
$23 = 3^2 + 3^2 + 2^2 + 1^2$
$24 = 4^2 + 2^2 + 2^2$
$25 = 5^2$

17. $123 = 7^2 + 7^2 + 5^2$
$4321 = 64^2 + 15^2$

18. $1 = 2^0$
$2 = 2^1$
$3 = 2^1 + 2^0$
$4 = 2^2$

(Solutions continued on page 523)

THINKING WRITING

7.C One Googol Zeroes

Scientific notation will help you think about these two very large numbers.

one googol = 10,000,000,000,000,000,000, 000,000,000,000,000,000,000,000,000,000, 000,000,000,000,000,000,000,000,000,000, 000,000,000,000,000,000,000

1. How many zeroes does it take to write one googol? (Count them!)

one googolplex = 1 followed by one googol zeroes

2. Guess how large a sheet of paper one would need to write one googol zeroes.

a. a sheet the size of a table?

b. a sheet the size of a room?

c. a sheet the size of a school?

d. a sheet the size of a city?

3. Let's assume a zero takes up one square centimeter. How many zeroes could you fit on a piece of paper having area

a. one square meter? (There are 100 centimeters in a meter. Use a sketch to figure out how many square centimeters in a square meter. Hint: There are more than 100 square centimeters in a square meter.)

b. one square kilometer? (There are 1000 meters in a kilometer.)

Notation: cm^2 stands for square centimeter; km^2 for square kilometer.

4. a. The area of California is $4(10^5)$ km^2. How many zeroes could fit on a sheet of paper this size?

b. The area of the United States is nearly 10^7 km^2. How many zeroes could fit on a sheet this size?

5. 30,000 sheets of thin paper make a pile one meter high. How many zeroes could be in such a pile, if each sheet is the size of the United States?

6. a. The moon is less than $4(10^5)$ km away. How many zeroes, if our pile of paper extended that far?

b. The sun is $1.5(10^8)$ km away. How many zeroes, if our pile extended that far?

c. The nearest star is $4(10^{13})$ km away. How many zeroes, if our pile extended that far?

7. What fraction of the total number of zeroes does our pile include?

8. **Report** Write a report summarizing your answers to problems 3-6 above. Show your calculations and include any sketches that were useful in figuring out answers. Explain your reasoning. Then show how to figure out the correct answer to problem 2.

9. **Project** Where in the universe would our pile of papers end if it did include one googol zeroes?

The word *googol* was created in 1938 by the eleven-year-old nephew of the American mathematician Edward Kasner. In one sense, a googolplex is the largest number that has a name. But in fact, even without creating any new names, you can name larger numbers. For example, the words *two googolplex* name a larger number.

10. What is the largest nameable number? Explain your reasoning.

7.C SOLUTIONS

1. 100
2. Answers will vary.
3. a. 10,000 zeroes
   b. 10^{10} zeroes
4. a. $4(10^5)(10^{10}) = 4(10^{15})$ zeroes
   b. $(10^7)(10^{10}) = 10^{17}$ zeroes
5. $3(10^4)(10^{17}) = 3(10^{21})$ zeroes
6. a. $4(10^5)(10^3)\ 3(10^{21}) = 12(10^{29}) = 1.2(10^{30})$ zeroes
   b. $1.5(10^8)(10^3)(3)(10^{21}) = 4.5(10^{32})$ zeroes
   c. $4(10^{13})(10^3)(3)(10^{21}) = 12(10^{37}) = 1.2(10^{38})$
7. $1.2(10^{38})/(10^{100}) = 1.2/(10^{62}) = 1.2(10^{-62})$ (A very small fraction!)
8. Reports will vary.
9. $10^{100}/3(10^{21}) = 10^{79}/3 = 3.3(10^{78})$ m away or $3.49(10^{65})$ light years away.
10. Answers will vary. (There isn't one.)

THINKING WRITING

7.C One Googol Zeroes

Core Sequence: 1-8

Suitable for Homework: 8-9

Useful for Assessment: 7

What this Assignment is About:

- Estimation with large numbers
- Multiplication and division in scientific notation
- Infinity

Most people do not have a good feel for very large numbers, and since a googol is much, much larger than most numbers that people have trouble comprehending, it is almost impossible to gain a mental picture of a googol.

This assignment helps students get a handle on the size of a googol. That, in and of itself, is not important, but the work done along the way with scientific notation and large numbers helps students develop a better sense of the meaning of powers of ten and orders of magnitude. (The same sort of techniques can be applied to developing a feel for smaller numbers such as the defense budget.)

The assignment should preferably be started in class. One possible difficulty is that students may need help understanding why there are 10,000 cm^2 in a m^2. A class discussion of the number of square inches in a square foot would help. It is also useful to wrap up the assignment with a class discussion, particularly of problem 7, which most students should find quite surprising.

There are two interesting books around to help students develop a feel for the meaning of powers of ten: *Cosmic view: the universe in 40 jumps* by Kees Boeke (J. Day, NY, © 1957) and *Powers of Ten: a book about the relative size of things in the universe and the effect of adding another zero*, by Philip and Phylis Morrison and the Office of Charles and Ray Eames (Scientific American Library; distributed by W.H. Freeman, San Francisco, © 1982).

There are also two movies on the same topic: *Cosmic Zoom* (Canadian Film Board) and *Powers of Ten* (Charles Eames, 1968). Using these films and/or books will also help preview negative exponents, which are introduced in Chapter 8.

Students should enjoy a class discussion of problem 10, which leads into a discussion of infinity. For more discussion of this question, see *Infinity and the Mind: the science and philosophy of the infinite*, by Rudy Rucker (Birkhauser, Boston, © 1982).

Essential Ideas

RECTANGULAR WINDOWS

The window panes referred to below are those pictured in Lesson 2 of this chapter.

1. Sketch a window having length equal to twice its width that is made up of panes from the A.B. Glare Co. How many panes of each type (corner, edge, and inside) are there?

Use sketches or tables of values to help solve the following problem.

2. How many of each type of pane would you need for windows that are twice as long as they are wide? Your answer will depend on the width of the window. Let the width be W, and find expressions in terms of W for:

a. the length of the window;
b. the number of inside panes;
c. the number of edge panes;
d. the number of corner panes.

3. Draw a pair of axes and label the x-axis *Width* and the y-axis *Number of Panes.* Then make a graph showing each of these as a function of W, the width of the window.

a. the number of inside panes
b. the number of edge panes
c. the number of corner panes

4. As you increase the width of the window, which grows fastest, the number of inside panes, edge panes, or corner panes? Explain, referring to graphs or sketches.

5. The panes described in Lesson 2 cannot be used for windows of width 1.

a. Explain why.
b. Sketch the two types of panes that are needed in this case.
c. Find the number of each type of pane for a window having width 1 and length L.

MULTIPLY

6. Multiply these polynomials.

a. $(3x - 5)(4x - 6)$
b. $(5 - 3x)(6 - 4x)$
c. $(3y + 3x - 1)(-2x + 2y)$
d. $(x + y + z)(-x + y)$

7. Multiply and compare the results. What do you notice? Explain.

a. $(ax - by)(ax - by)$
b. $(by - ax)(by - ax)$
c. $(ax - by)(by - ax)$

REMARKABLE IDENTITIES

8. Find the missing terms.

a. $(ax - \_\_\_\_)^2 = \_\_\_\_ - 2ax + 1$
b. $b^2 - x^2 = (b - x)(\_\_\_\_)$
c. $y^2 - 10y + \_\_\_\_ = (\_\_\_\_)^2$
d. $(ax + \_\_\_)^2 = a^2x^2 + \_\_\_\_ + b^2y^2$

FACTOR

Factor. Look for a common factor and use an identity.

SOLUTIONS

1. Answers will vary.
2. a. $2W$
   b. $2W^2 - 6W + 4$
   c. $6W - 8$
   d. 4
3.

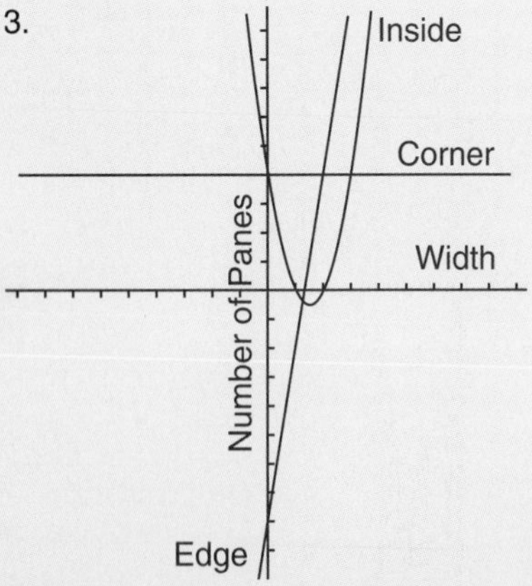

4. The number of inside panes grows faster. The graph is a parabola. The graphs of the other two are straight lines.
5. a. There are no panes with borders on opposite sides or corner panes with borders on three sides.
   b.

inside pane   end pane

   c. $L - 2$ inside panes and 2 end panes
6. a. $12x^2 - 38x + 30$
   b. $30 - 38x + 12x^2$
   c. $6y^2 - 2y + 2x - 6x^2$
   d. $-x^2 - xz + y^2 + yz$
7. a. $a^2x^2 - 2abxy + b^2y^2$
   b. $b^2y^2 - 2abxy + a^2x^2$
   c. $-a^2x^2 + 2abxy - b^2y^2$
   When both factors are replaced by their opposites, the product is not changed. When one factor is replaced by its opposite, the product is the opposite.
8. a. $(ax - 1)^2 = \underline{a^2x^2} - 2ax + 1$
   b. $b^2 - x^2 = (b - x)(\underline{b + x})$
   c. $y^2 - 10y + \underline{25} = (\underline{y - 5})^2$
   d. $(ax + \underline{by})^2 = a^2x^2 + \underline{2abxy} + b^2y^2$
9. a. $5(x + 2)^2$
   b. $6(y + x)^2$
   c. $2(x + 15)^2$
10. a. $100a^2 + 140ab + 49b^2 = (10a + 7b)^2$
    b. $(1/9)x^2 + (1/3)xy + (1/4)y^2 = [(1/3)x + (1/2)y]^2$

9. a. $5x^2 + 20x + 20$
   b. $6y^2 + 12xy + 6x^2$
   c. $2x^2 + 60x + 450$

10. Find the middle term that will make each of these a perfect square trinomial. Then write it as the square of a binomial.
    a. $100a^2 +$ ____ $+ 49b^2$
    b. $(1/9)x^2 +$ ____ $+ (1/4)y^2$

11. Factor these polynomials.
    a. $4x^2 - 20x + 25$
    b. $4x^2 - 25$
    c. $25 - 4x^2$

12. Factor these polynomials. (Hint: First look for common factors.)
    a. $5y^2 + 90xy + 45x^2$
    b. $48x - 27xy^2$
    c. $xy^2 - 6x^2y + 9x^3$

SOLVING EQUATIONS WITH SQUARES

Solve for x. There may be no solution, one solution, or more than one solution.

13. $x^2 = 25$

14. $36x^2 = 49$

15. $x^2 - 6x + 9 = 0$

16. $x^2 - 6x + 9 = 1$

GRAPHING INEQUALITIES

17. Use graphs to help you find the solution to each of these compound inequalities. In each case, you will need to graph two horizontal lines and one other line.
    a. $-3 < 4x - 3 < 5$
    b. $-3 < -4x + 3 < 5$
    c. $-5 < 4x - 3 < 3$
    d. $-5 < -4x + 3 < 3$

18. Use graphs and tables of values to solve these compound inequalities.
    a. $x - 2 < 3x - 4 < x + 5$
    b. $x - 2 < 3x - 4 < -x + 5$

BILLIONS AND BILLIONS

The following was written on an ice cream package: $3 billion is 1% of the U.S. yearly defense budget. If you ate one ice cream cone per hour per day it would take you 342,466 years to consume 3 billion ice cream cones.

19. Check that the calculation is accurate.

20. Assuming that the information is accurate, what is the U.S. *hourly* defense budget?

LIGHT-YEARS

21. A *light-year* is the distance light travels in one year. Figure out how far that is in kilometers, given that light travels approximately 299,793 kilometers per second. Use scientific notation.

WHAT A BARGAIN

22. Say that a particularly expensive necklace costs one googol dollars.
    a. Fortunately, it's on sale at 99% off. How much does it cost now?
    b. What percent-off sale would be needed so that the necklace would cost ten billion dollars?

SOLUTIONS

11. a. $(2x - 5)^2$
    b. $(2x - 5)(2x + 5)$
    c. $(5 - 2x)(5 + 2x)$

12. a. $5(y^2 + 18xy + 9x^2)$
    b. $3x(4 - 3y)(4 + 3y)$
    c. $x(y - 3x)^2$

13. $x = 5$ or $x = -5$

14. $x = \pm 7/6$

15. $x = 3$

16. $x = 2$ or $x = 4$

17. a. $0 < x < 2$
    b. $-1/2 < x < 3/2$
    c. $-1/2 < x < 3/2$
    d. $0 < x < 2$

18. a. $1 < x < 4.5$
    b. $1 < x < 2.25$

19. 24 cones/day · 365 days/yr = 8760 cones/yr
    Then divide 3 billion by this number.
    Yes, the calculation is accurate.

20. $\$3.4 \cdot 10^7$ per hour

21. $9.45 \cdot 10^{12}$ km

22. a. $\$10^{98}$
    b. $[1 - (1/10^{90})] \cdot 100$ percent off

Chapter 8
GROWTH AND CHANGE

Overview of the Chapter

The theme of growth and change ties together two main algebraic concepts.

The first part of the chapter concentrates on the concept of the rate of change of functions, starting with an application and ending with a concentrated effort on linear functions in the form $y = mx + b$.

The next part of the chapter is about exponential growth and decay and the laws of exponents.

By the end of the chapter, students should have a good sense of the difference between exponential and linear growth, as well as a grasp of many traditional algebra skills.

Exponential functions are not part of most first-year algebra courses. We include them for several reasons. First, they have a structure that is parallel to that of linear functions. When the two are studied together, the contrast is interesting and instructive. Second, they arise naturally in many applications that are accessible to students at this level. Through these applications, the operation of exponentiation and the difficult ideas of fractional and negative exponents are made more concrete. Third, by providing experience with the idea of constant multiplication, they help build a good foundation for understanding the laws of exponents.

1. New Ways to Use Tools:

- The focus for linear function diagrams

2. Algebra Concepts Emphasized:

- Rate of change
- Rise and run
- Slope
- Positive, negative, and zero slope
- y-intercept
- Slope-intercept form
- Horizontal and vertical lines
- Linear growth
- Exponential growth and decay
- Product of powers
- Quotient of powers
- Power of a power
- Power of a product
- Power of a ratio
- Negative exponents

CHAPTER 8

The spiral surface pattern of gastropod fossils

Coming in this chapter:

Exploration A population is growing at a rate of about 2% per year. In how many years will the population double? Experiment with different starting values for the population. How does your answer depend on the starting value?

GROWTH AND CHANGE

3. Algebra Concepts Reviewed:

- Proportional thinking
- Scientific notation
- Solving linear equations
- Linear growth
- Percent problems
- Working with decimals
- Reciprocals
- Order of operations

4. Algebra Concepts Previewed:

- Finding the equation of a line from two points and from point-slope
- Fitting a line to data
- Simplifying algebraic fractions
- Rational expressions
- Fractional exponents

5. Problem-Solving Techniques:

- Writing an equation
- Making a table

6. Connections and Context:

- Data analysis
- Discounts
- Taxes and tips
- Simple and compound interest
- Population growth
- Unit conversion

*I*n Lessons 1-4, the concept of slope is introduced in many ways, using many roughly synonymous words: slope, rate of change, magnification, grade. Approaching the concept from a number of perspectives, with a special emphasis on a visual understanding in different contexts, may prove to be more effective than narrowing the focus to one particular interpretation.

*L*essons 5-8 are about exponential growth and decay. The contrast between exponential (*repeated multiplication*) and linear (*repeated addition*) growth is emphasized. The laws of exponents are previewed in this context.

*L*essons 9-12 provide concentrated work with the laws of exponents.

▼ 8.1
Height and Weight

Core Sequence: 1-6, 8-14

Suitable for Homework: 6-7, 10-15

Useful for Assessment: 6, 10-11, 14-15

What this Lesson is About:

- Rate of change
- Data analysis
- Preview of rise and run
- Preview of fitting a line

This lesson introduces the chapter's theme, growth and change, in a context that is close to every teenager's experience: physical growth. More specifically, the lesson introduces the concept of rate of change in preparation for the idea of slope and the slope-intercept form for linear equations.

What is special about linear functions (a constant rate of change) is best appreciated in contrast with a more general situation where the rate of change is not constant, as in the case of the physical growth of children and teenagers.

HEIGHT AS A FUNCTION OF AGE

Make sure students realize that the horizontal spacing between the ages is not uniform. Converting the ages to a common unit (months is the most convenient) would make it easier to locate the points correctly.

LESSON 8.1

Height and Weight

You will need: graph paper

Dr. Terwit, a pediatrician, kept records of her son Joshua's height and weight from birth to age four years. We will use these numbers to learn about *rate of change.*

Age	Height (cm)	Weight (kg)
birth	51	3.4
3 mo	60	5.7
6 mo	66	7.6
9 mo	71	9.1
12 mo	75	10.1
15 mo	79	10.8
18 mo	82	11.4
2 yr	88	12.6
2.5 yr	92	13.6
3 yr	96	14.6
4 yr	103	16.5

HEIGHT AS A FUNCTION OF AGE

1. Make a graph to represent height as a function of age. (Note that the ages given are not evenly spaced.)
2. What is the increase in height between:
   a. birth and three months?
   b. 15 months and 18 months?
   c. birth and one year?
   d. three years and four years?
3. Did Joshua's height grow faster or more slowly as he grew older? Explain your answer by referring to:
   a. the answers to problem 2;
   b. the shape of the graph.
4. If Joshua had grown the same number of centimeters every month, what would his average rate of growth be, in *centimeters per month,* between:
   a. birth and three months?
   b. 15 months and 18 months?
   c. birth and one year?
   d. three years and four years?
5. What was Joshua's *average rate of growth* in centimeters per month during his first four years? Compare this average with the averages you found in problem 4.
6. **Summary** Write a short paragraph summarizing the relationship between Joshua's age, his height, and the rate of his growth. In particular, explain the idea of average rate of growth and how it changed with his age.

8.1 SOLUTIONS

1.

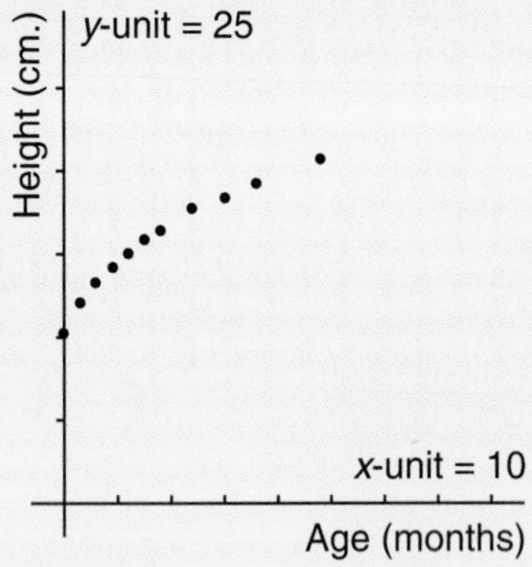

2. a. 9 cm b. 3 cm
   c. 24 cm d. 7 cm
3. a. The previous problem shows the changes in height for two 3-month periods (a and b) and two 12-month periods (c and d). In both cases the change in height decreases for the periods occurring when the child is older.
   b. The right side of the graph shows a more gradual change in height between points than the left side of the graph. The points climb more steeply at the beginning then more gradually as age increases.
4. a. 3 cm per month
   b. 1 cm per month
   c. 2 cm per month
   d. $0.58\overline{3}$ cm per month
5. Joshua's average rate of growth during his first four years was $1.08\overline{3}$ cm per month. This is less than his average rate of growth between birth and three months and birth and one year. It is greater than the rates between 15 months and 18 months and three and four years.
6. As Joshua grew older, his height increased. The increase in height occurred at a slower rate as Josh grew older. For the table below, Joshua's average rate of growth in cm per month is found by dividing the change in height by the number of months in each time period.

One-year period	Average Rate of Growth (cm/mo.)
birth to 12 months	2
1 yr. to 2 yr.	$1.08\overline{3}$
2 yr. to 3 yr.	2/3
3 yr. to 4 yr.	$0.58\overline{3}$

7. **Project** Find out how many sizes there are for babies' and children's clothes in the age range studied here. Is what you find consistent with the information in the table?

WEIGHT AS A FUNCTION OF AGE

This is a graph of weight as a function of age. The straight lines form four *steps* connecting some data points.

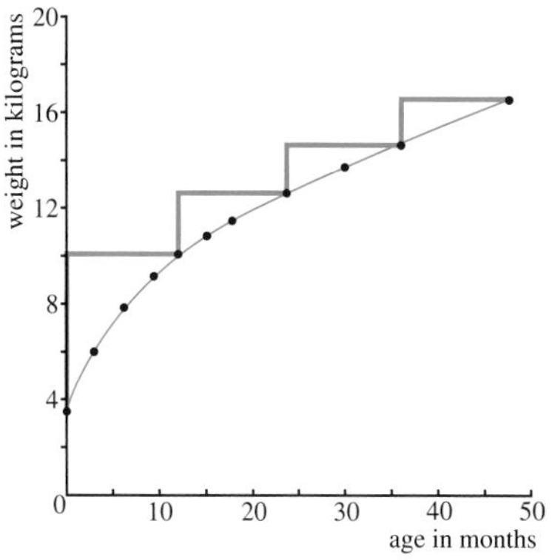

8. Use the data to answer these questions about the graph.
   a. How high is each step? (Give your answer in kilograms.)
   b. How wide is each step? (Give your answer in months.)
   c. Explain the meaning of your answers to (a) and (b) in terms of the *yearly* change in Joshua's weight.

9. Find the average *monthly* weight gain between ages
   a. two and two-and-a-half;
   b. two-and-a-half and three;
   c. two and three.

10. Joshua's weight grew at a fairly constant monthly rate between ages one and four. Explain how this can be seen
    a. on the graph;
    b. numerically.

11. However, his weight grew much more slowly between ages one and four than during his first year. Explain how this can be seen
    a. on the graph;
    b. numerically.

WEIGHT AS A FUNCTION OF HEIGHT

This is a graph of weight as a function of height.

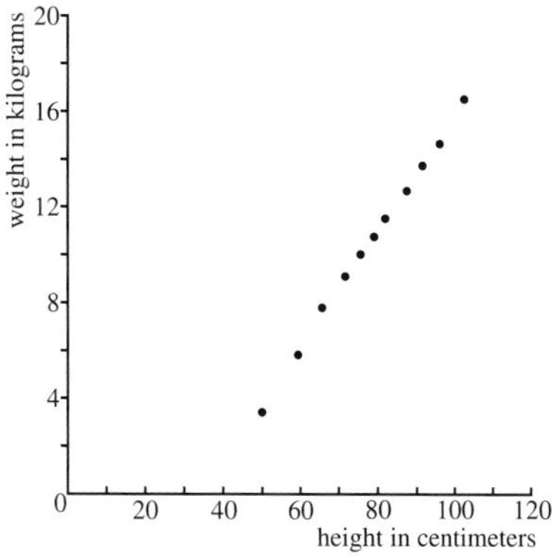

12. How much weight did Joshua gain for each centimeter he gained in height? Answer this question for the following periods:
    a. birth and three months;
    b. ages three and four;
    c. on the average, over the four years.

A key idea behind problems 2-3 is that to discuss how fast growth is occurring you need to compare growth in equal stretches of time.

Problem 4 introduces the idea of average rate of growth, and a unit for it (cm/mo).

Stress that the answer to problem 5 is obtained in the same way as the answers to problem 4, by dividing the increase in height by the number of months, and not by finding the average of different rates of growth.

Problem 7 could be researched by visiting or calling a children's clothing store, or by looking at a catalogue. Or, more simply, have students discuss this with their parents or with the parents of young children. The results of this investigation should confirm what the graph shows: Growth during the first year is much faster than in subsequent years.

WEIGHT AS A FUNCTION OF AGE

The steps preview the idea of rise and run, which will be discussed in greater depth in Lesson 3.

Problem 10 previews the idea of constant rate of change. The graphic representation for such a situation is a straight line, as can be seen in the part of the graph between ages 1 and 4.

8.1 SOLUTIONS

7. For children up to age 4, clothes come in three categories: infant, toddler, and child sizes. Infant has six sizes: newborn, 3 months, 6 months, 12 months, 18 months, and 24 months. Toddler clothes come in three sizes: 2T, 3T, and 4T. There is one child size, 4, for a four year old.

8. The first step has height of 6.7 kg and width of 12 months. This means Joshua gained 6.7 kg during the first year. The second step has height of 2.5 kg and width of 12 months. This means Joshua gained 2.5 kg during his second year. The third step has height of 2 kg and width of 12 months, which means Joshua gained 2 kg during his third year. The fourth step has height of 1.9 kg and width of 12 months, which means Joshua gained 1.9 kg during his fourth year.

   The height of each step shows the change in weight and the width shows the time period in which the weight changed.

9. a. 0.17 kg per month
   b. 0.17 kg per month
   c. 0.17 kg per month

10. a. On the graph, the steps between ages one and four appear to be the same size.
    b.

12-month period	Change in weight (kg)	Average rate of growth in kg per month
From 1 year to 2 yrs.	2.5	$0.208\bar{3}$
From 2 yr. to 3 yrs.	2	0.167
From 3 yr. to 4 yrs.	1.9	$0.158\bar{3}$

The third column shows average rates of growth in kilograms per month which are all approximately equal to 0.2 kg per month.

11. a. The height of the first step is greater than the heights of the following three steps.
    b. The change in weight during the first year was 6.7 kg, so the average rate of growth was 6.7 kg/12 mo. = $0.558\bar{3}$ kg per month. This is much faster than 0.2 kg per month found in #10b.

12. a. 2.3 kg/9 cm. = 0.2556 kg per cm
    b. 1.9 kg/7 cm. = 0.2714 kg per cm
    c. 13.1 kg/52 cm. = 0.2519 kg per cm

WEIGHT AS A FUNCTION OF HEIGHT

Showing time on the x-axis as in the above two sections makes it easier to develop a feel for the idea of rate of change. In this section, however, we will discuss the rate of change of weight as a function of height.

The key difference between this graph and the preceding one, from the point of view of rate of change, is that this one is close to linear; the variation in the rate of change is not very great. This is made clear by the calculations in problems 12 and 13.

BOYS AND GIRLS

This data is for average boys and girls. Obviously there is considerable variation between individuals as to both height and rate of growth at different ages.

Make sure students realize that they should address questions of rate of growth as well as comparisons of absolute heights between boys and girls.

An interesting discussion could be started by these questions: What percent of their adult height have 15-year-old boys and girls reached? Say an average 15-year-old girl dates an average boy of the same height; how old is he? If he is the same age as she is, how tall is he? If he is as mature as she is, how old and how tall is he? (Assume maturity could be measured by percent of adult height, and that adult height is reached by age 18.)

13. Study the preceding graph and table and make calculations to find the time in Joshua's first four years when he gained
    a. the least weight per centimeter;
    b. the most weight per centimeter.

14. Compare the two graphs of weight (as a function of age and as a function of height). How are they alike? How are they different? Discuss the shape of the graphs, the units, and the rate of change.

Because the rate of change of weight as a function of height does not vary much, the data points fall close to a line. You could say that this data is nearly linear. In cases like this, it is a common statistical technique to approximate the data with a line. You will learn more about this in future lessons, but first you need to know more about lines and linear functions.

BOYS AND GIRLS

The following table shows the average height in inches of boys and girls, ages 9 through 18.

	Height (in.)	
Age	Girls	Boys
9	52.3	53.3
10	54.6	55.2
11	57.0	56.8
12	59.8	58.9
13	61.8	61.0
14	62.8	64.0
15	63.4	66.1
16	63.9	67.8
17	64.0	68.4
18	64.0	68.7

15. **Report** Write a report comparing the height and the rate of growth of boys and girls. Include a graph showing the heights of both boys and girls as a function of age, on the same axes. (Since the graphs are close to each other, you may want to distinguish them by using color.) Your report should include, but not be limited to, answers to these questions.
    - How many inches do boys and girls gain per year, on the average?
    - At what ages do they grow fastest?
    - How many inches do they gain per year during those growth spurts?

8.1 SOLUTIONS

13. a. Joshua gained the least weight per centimeter for the period between 15 months and 2 years. For 15 months to 18 months, he had an average gain of 0.2 kg per cm (0.6 kg/3cm = 0.2 kg/cm).
    b. Joshua gained the most weight per centimeter for the period between 3 months and 6 months, when he had an average gain of 0.3167 kg/cm, 1.9 kg/6cm = 0.3167 kg/cm.

14. Answers will vary. The graphs are alike in that the weight increases as both age and height increase. As you look at points from left to right, they increase in height above the horizontal axis. They are different in that the weight vs. age graph is continuous, and the weight vs. height graph is discrete. They both could be discrete, however. The weight vs. age graph increases less than a linear graph, whereas the weight vs. height graph increases in a more linear way.

15. Over the 9-year period, the average rate of growth per year for girls is 1.3 in. per yr., and for boys it is 1.7 in./yr. The data shows that the girls grow steadily from 9 years old to 13 years old, averaging about 2.375 in. per year. This data shows a growth spurt from 12 yrs. to 13 yrs. old. After age 13 the rate of growth increases at a slower and slower rate until girls stop growing after they are 17 yrs. old. Boys grow steadily from ages 9 to 11, averaging about 1.75 in./yr. The growth rate increases each year from 12 yrs. to 15 yrs. with a big spurt between 13 yrs. and 14 yrs. After the age of 15 the growth rate slows down each year. Until the age of 13, girls grow at a faster rate than boys. At ages 11 and 13 girls are taller than boys. Girls reach their tallest height at age 17. Boys are still growing until they are 18 years old, assuming adult height is reached at 18.

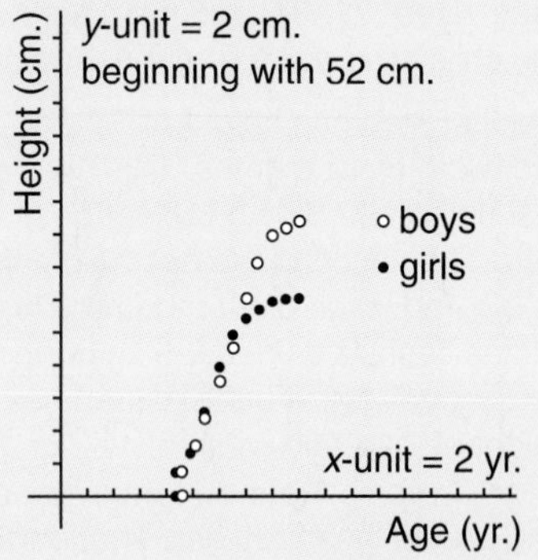

LESSON 8.2

Focus on Function Diagrams

You will need:
graph paper

REVIEW ***PARALLEL-LINE DIAGRAMS***

1. a. Draw a function diagram such that its in-out lines are *parallel* and going uphill (from left to right).
b. Find the function corresponding to the diagram, using an in-out table if you need it.

2. Repeat problem 1 with parallel in-out lines going
a. downhill;
b. horizontally.

3. For the functions you created in problems 1 and 2, when x increases by 1, by how much does y increase? Does it depend on the steepness of the lines?
(To answer this, compare your functions with other students' functions.) Explain your answer.

Problems 4 through 9 refer to the function diagrams shown on the next page.

THE FOCUS

Definition: If an in-out line is horizontal, its input is called a *fixed point.*

For example, both x and y equal 12 in diagram (a), so 12 is a fixed point for that function.

4. What are the fixed points for functions (b-p)?

Definition: In-out lines can be extended to the left or right. If all of them meet in a single point, that point is called the *focus.*

5. **Exploration** Consider the function diagrams shown in figures (a-p). For each one, find the function. You may split the work with other students. Describe any patterns you notice. If you cannot find all the functions or patterns, you will get another chance at the end of the lesson.

MAGNIFICATION

6. Look at function diagram (h). By how much does y change when x increases by:
a. 1? b. 2?
c. some amount A?

In function diagrams that have a focus, changes in y can be found by multiplying the changes in x by a certain number, called the *magnification.*

(change in x) · (magnification) = (change in y)

7. a. What is the magnification for (h)?
b. What other diagrams have the same magnification?

Rule: If y decreases when x increases, the magnification is negative.

8. For which diagrams is the magnification equal to -3? (If x increases by 1, y *decreases* by 3.)

9. Find the magnification for each function diagram. Note that the magnification can be positive or negative, a whole number or a fraction.

8.2
Focus on Function Diagrams

Core Sequence: 1-14, 16-22

Suitable for Homework: 1-3, 12-32

Useful for Assessment: 3, 10, 16, 20, 22

What this Lesson is About:

- Review of function diagrams for the form $y = x + b$
- Rate of change
- Preview of slope-intercept form
- Review of binomial multiplication

This is a substantial lesson, which involves much work and effort. It is worth it, because it lays the groundwork for a full understanding of slope and intercept of linear functions.

REVIEW ***PARALLEL-LINE DIAGRAMS***

This reviews function diagrams for functions of the form $y = x + b$. It is easy, and you can use the opportunity to review the function diagram terminology that will be useful throughout this lesson: in-out lines, x- and y-number lines.

THE FOCUS

The Exploration is important not only to understanding this lesson, but to understanding linear functions. Make sure there is plenty of class time to work on it, preferably in groups. Follow up group work with whole-class discussion.

8.2 SOLUTIONS

1. a.

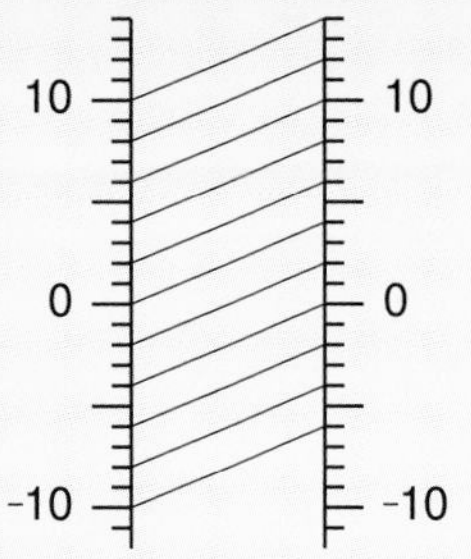

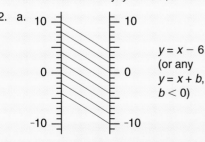

b. Answers will vary. $y = x + b$, $b > 0$.

2. a.

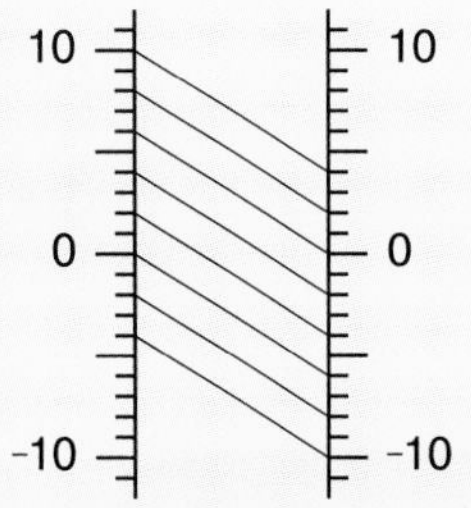

$y = x - 6$ (or any $y = x + b$, $b < 0$)

b.

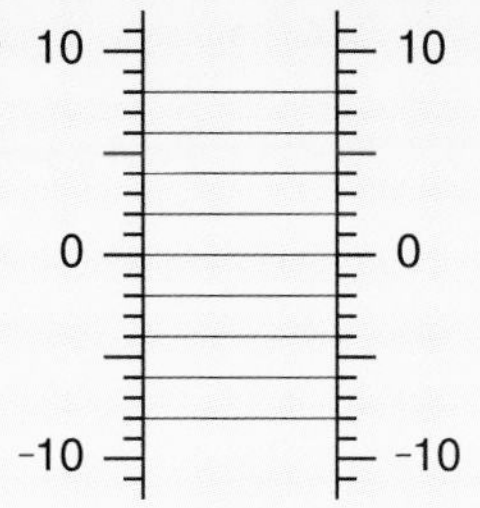

$y = x$

3. When x increases by 1, y increases by 1. It does not depend on steepness. Because in-out lines are parallel, the changes in x and y are the same. If x changes by a certain amount, y changes by the same amount.

4. b through f have a fixed point of 12. g through j have a fixed point of 0. m through p have a fixed point of -6.

5. a. $y = (3/2)x - 6$
b. $y = 3x - 24$
c. $y = -3x + 48$
d. $y = -(1/3)x + 16$
e. $y = (1/3)x + 8$
f. $y = (1/2)x + 6$
g. $y = (3/2)x$
h. $y = 3x$
i. $y = -3x$
j. $y = -(1/3)x$
k. $y = (1/3)x$
l. $y = (1/2)x$
m. $y = (3/2)x + 3$
n. $y = 3x + 12$
o. $y = (1/3)x - 4$
p. $y = (1/2)x - 3$

Patterns to look for: The constant is the y-value when $x = 0$. The focus lies outside the x- and y-number lines when $m > 0$. The focus lies between the x- and y-number lines when

If students have no idea how to begin, you may suggest they make in-out tables based on the diagrams, and try to figure out the patterns from that. You may also encourage them to start with the diagrams (g, h, i, j, k, l) which are substantially easier than the other ones, and can provide a good starting place.

An in-depth discussion of the Exploration will make the rest of the lesson (and the next couple of lessons) much easier. However do not expect full mastery instantly.

MAGNIFICATION

One of the most useful features of the function diagrams of linear functions is the fact that they make the rate of change very clear visually. This section focuses on this visual evidence of "magnification" of the change in x that leads to the change in y.

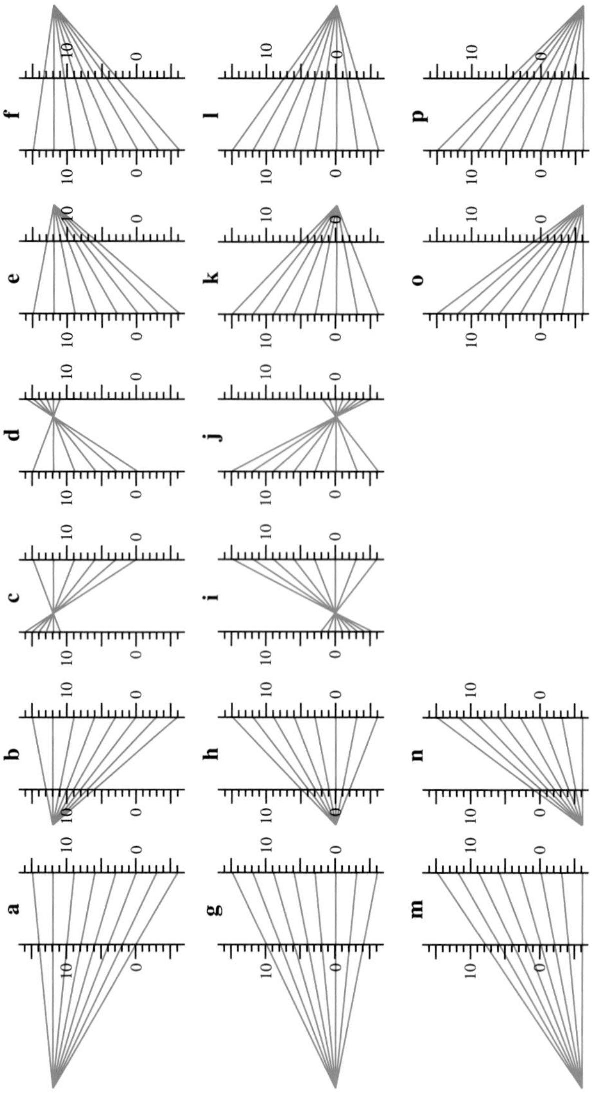

sixteen function diagrams

8.2 SOLUTIONS

$m < 0$. The focus lies to the left of the x-number line when $m > 1$. The focus lies to the right of the y-number line when $0 < m < 1$.

6. a. When x increases by 1, y increases by 3.
   b. When x increases by 2, y increases by 6.
   c. When x increases by A, y increases by $3A$.
7. a. The magnification for h is 3.
   b. b and n have the same magnification of 3.
8. c and i have magnification of -3.
9. a. 3/2
   b. 3
   c. -3
   d. -1/3
   e. 1/3
   f. 1/2
   g. 3/2
   h. 3
   i. -3
   j. -1/3
   k. 1/3
   l. 1/2
   m. 3/2
   n. 3
   o. 1/3
   p. 1/2

THE m PARAMETER

You probably noticed that all the function diagrams represent functions of the form $y = mx + b$. It turns out that this is always true of function diagrams with a focus. As you may remember, the letters m and b in the equation are called *parameters.*

10. Look at the equations you found in the Exploration, problem 5. What is the relationship between the magnification and the m parameter in those equations? Explain.

11. If you move the focus of a function diagram up, how does it affect the value of m? How about if you move it down?

12. Where would the focus be if m was
- a. a negative number?
- b. a number between 0 and 1?
- c. a number greater than 1?

13. What is a possible value of m if the focus is
- a. half-way between the x- and y-number lines?
- b. between the x- and y-number lines, but closer to x?
- c. between the x- and y-number lines, but closer to y?

14. What is a possible value of m if the focus is
- a. far to the left of the x-number line?
- b. close to the left of the x-number line?
- c. close to the right of the y-number line?
- d. far to the right of the y-number line?

15. In some parts of mathematics, parallel lines are said to meet at a point that is *at infinity.* In that sense, parallel-line diagrams could be said to have a focus at infinity. Is this consistent with your answer to problem 14? Explain.

RATE OF CHANGE

Once again, look at the diagrams (a-p).

16. On each diagram, *as x increases,* follow y with your finger. For what values of m does y
- a. go up?
- b. go down?
- c. move fast?
- d. move slowly?

The magnification is often called the *rate of change.*

17. What is the rate of change if y increases by 3 when x increases by:
- a. 1?
- b. 6?
- c. -10?

THE b PARAMETER

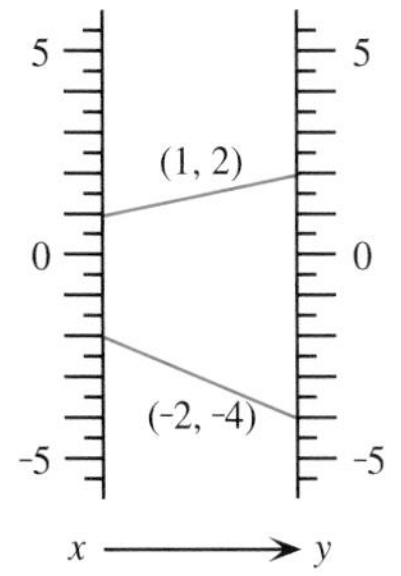

Two in-out lines are shown in the diagram. Each one is labeled with a number pair. The first number in the pair is the input, and the second number is the output.

Notation: Any in-out line can be identified by a number pair. From now on, we will refer to lines on function diagrams this way. For example, the line connecting 0 on the x-number line to 0 on the y-number line will be called the (0, 0) line.

THE m PARAMETER

The main point of this section is that the magnification can be seen explicitly in the equation, if it is written in $y = mx + b$ form. (Could this be the reason the letter m is used, and not a?)

While it is not important for students to memorize the information about the relationship between the position of the focus and the magnification, discussion about it should help reinforce the visual sense of what magnification is about.

Students should be able to do problems 10-13 by discussing them in their groups and looking at the sixteen diagrams in the figure. If they find this difficult, you may lead a class discussion, perhaps based on some function diagrams on the overhead projector.

The answer to problem 14 is based on the fact that if the focus is far to the left, m is a little greater than one. If the focus is far to the right, m is a little less than one. If the focus is *at infinity*, m is exactly equal to one. So the idea of the focus at infinity is consistent with the finite case.

RATE OF CHANGE

This short section serves only to introduce and justify the words *rate of change* as another name for magnification. (The word *slope* that also refers to the same concept will be introduced in the next two lessons.)

8.2 SOLUTIONS

10. The magnification is the same as the parameter m.

11. The value of m is not affected when the focus is moved up or down. See, for example, diagrams n, h, and b which have the same y-values and a focus that moves up. Each equation has magnification of 3.

12. a. When m is negative the focus is between the x- and y-number lines.
    b. When m is between 0 and 1, the focus is outside and to the right of the x- and y-number lines.
    c. When m is greater than 1 the focus is outside and to the left of the x- and y- number lines.

13. a. When $m = -1$, the focus falls half-way between the x- and y-number lines.
    b. Answers will vary. When $m < -1$ the focus falls between the x- and y-number lines, but closer to x.
    c. Answers will vary. When $-1 < m < 0$, the focus falls between the x- and y-number lines, but closer to y.

14. Answers will vary.
    a. Any number slightly greater than 1
    b. The greater the number is above 1, the closer the focus is to the left of the x-axis.
    c. A value of m slightly greater than zero has a focus close to the right of the y-number line.
    d. A positive value of m slightly less than 1 has a focus far to the right of the y-axis.

15. Yes, this is consistent. The closer m is to 1, the farther away the focus is from the x- and y-number lines. If $m = 1$, then as x increases by a number A, y increases by A also. The in-out lines are parallel and there is no focus. One could say the focus is at infinity.

16. a. As x increases, y goes up for positive values of m. This occurs in all diagrams except c, d, i, and j.
    b. As x increases, y goes down for negative values of m, as in c, d, i, and j.
    c. As x increases, y moves fast for large positive values of m, or small negative values of m. Diagrams b, h, n, c, and i have foci close to the x-number line, and as x increases, y moves fast.

THE *b* PARAMETER

The relationship between the *b* parameter and the position of the focus is far from obvious when *b* is not 0. The only way to really see it is to remember the meaning of the in-out lines, and what happens when multiplying by zero.

$y = mx + b$

This wraps up the lesson. If some of your students have not completely mastered the ideas, you can still move on. You will be able to refer back to this lesson while teaching the next two lessons and **Thinking/Writing 8.A**. Out of the comparison of the two approaches (function diagrams and Cartesian graphs), your students should be able to develop a solid grasp of linear functions.

The page of 16 function diagrams is provided on page 573.

18. What can you say about the *b* parameter if the focus is on the (0, 0) line?

19. Look at diagram (n). Its equation is $y = 3x + 12$.

a. Name the in-out lines that are shown.

b. Check that the pairs you listed actually satisfy the equation by substituting the input values for *x*.

c. Among the pairs you checked was (0, 12). Explain why using 0 as input gave the *b* parameter as output.

20. In most of the diagrams (a-p), there is an in-out line of the form (0, ___). How is the number in the blank related to the *b* parameter? Explain.

$y = mx + b$

21. If you did not find all the equations for the function diagrams (a-p), when working on problem 4, do it now. Hint: You may use what you learned about magnification and about the (0, ___) in-out line.

22. **Summary** Write what you learned about function diagrams, the fixed point, the focus, magnification, and the parameters *m* and *b*. Also mention parallel-line diagrams.

REVIEW *BINOMIAL MULTIPLICATION*

Multiply and combine like terms.

23. $(3x + 1)(x - 2)$

24. $(2x - 3)(5 - x)$

25. $(5 + x)(3x - 3)$

26. $(2y - 2)(6 - y)$

27. $(3x - 1)(2 + x)$

28. $(3x + 1)(2 + x)$

29. $(6 + y)(2y + 4)$

30. $(y - 4)(2y + 2)$

31. $(y - 3)(y - 5)$

32. $(6 - x)(2x - 3)$

8.2 SOLUTIONS

d. As *x* increases, *y* moves slowly for $-1 < m < 1$. Diagrams d, e, f, j, k, o, and p all move slowly for *y*, as *x* increases.

17. a. The rate of change is 3.
 b. The rate of change is 1/2
 c. The rate of change is -3/10

18. When the focus is on the (0, 0) line, the *b* parameter is zero.

19. a. (-6, -6), (-5, -3), (-4, 0), (-3, 3), (-2, 6), (-1, 9), (0, 12), (1, 15)
 b. A check for the first one is: $-6 = 3(-6) + 12 = -18 + 12 = -6$
 c. For example for $y = 3x + 12$, we have: $y = 3(0) + 12 = 12$. So we can see the *mx* term equals zero and $y = 12$ at $x = 0$.

20. The number in the blank is equal to the *b* parameter when *x* is 0. The *mx* term is zero in $y = mx + b$: $y = m(0) + b = 0 + b = b$. So when *x* is 0, its *y*-value is the *b* parameter.

22. Refer to the answers to problems 10, 13-16, and 20.

23. $3x^2 - 5x - 2$

24. $-2x^2 + 13x - 15$

25. $3x^2 + 12x - 15$

26. $-2y^2 + 14y - 12$

27. $3x^2 + 5x - 2$

28. $3x^2 + 7x + 2$

29. $2y^2 + 16y + 24$

30. $2y^2 - 6y - 8$

31. $y^2 - 8y + 15$

32. $-2x^2 + 15x - 18$

LESSON 8.3

Slope

You will need:

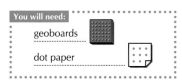

- geoboards
- dot paper

GRADE AND SLOPE

Steep roads sometimes have a sign indicating how steep they are. For example, the sign may say **5% Grade**. This means that you gain 5 units of altitude (the *rise*) for every 100 units you move in the horizontal direction (the *run*).

1. On a 5% grade, how many units of altitude do you gain for every
   a. 200 units you move in the horizontal direction?
   b. 25 units you move in the horizontal direction?
   c. 1 unit you move in the horizontal direction?

5% grade (figure is not to scale)

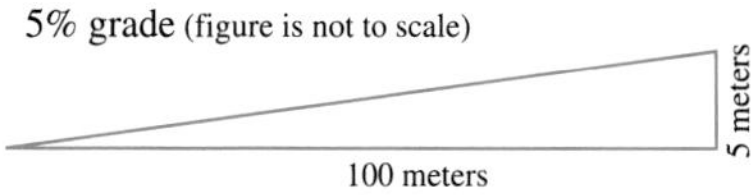

In math a 5% grade is called a *slope* of 0.05.

2. If the slope is 0.05, how many units do you move in the horizontal direction for every
   a. 30 units you gain in altitude?
   b. 0.05 units you gain in altitude?
   c. 0.5 units you gain in altitude?

3. The figure above is not to scale.
   a. What is the actual slope illustrated? (Use a ruler to measure the rise and the run.)
   b. Is it more or less steep than a 0.05 slope?

4. A sign in the mountains says **6% Grade. Trucks Use Low Gear.** Explain what a 6% grade is. Use the words *slope, rise,* and *run* in your answer.

5. In a nonmountainous area, the steepest grade allowed on a freeway is 4%. With this grade, how many meters of altitude do you gain per
   a. kilometer traveled in the horizontal direction? (A kilometer is 1000 meters.)
   b. meter traveled in the horizontal direction?

6. If you are climbing a mountain road with grade 5.5%, and you gain 1000 ft in altitude, how many miles have you traveled? (There are 5280 feet in a mile.)

Definition: Slope is defined as the ratio of rise to run. $\text{slope} = \frac{\text{rise}}{\text{run}}$

7. a. How many units of altitude do you gain for every 100 units traveled on a horizontal road?
   b. What is the grade of a horizontal road?
   c. What is the slope of a horizontal line?

A horizontal road has grade 0. This is because no matter how much you move in the horizontal direction, you do not gain any altitude. The rise is 0 for any run. For example, for a run of 1, the slope is 0/1 which equals 0.

GEOBOARD SLOPE

The figure shows three geoboard right triangles. The side opposite the right angle in a right triangle is called the *hypotenuse*.

8.3 Slope

Core Sequence: 1-21

Suitable for Homework: 1-10, 17-32

Useful for Assessment: 4, 20-21

What this Lesson is About:

- Rise and run
- Slope (positive only)
- Number theory

This lesson tries to develop the geometric intuition for slope, so there is no mention of negative slopes, which will be introduced in the next lesson.

GRADE AND SLOPE

In problem 6, the horizontal distance traveled can be calculated from the information given. If you are concerned that this answer does not exactly reflect the distance traveled by the car along the hypotenuse, you are right. A little trigonometry shows that the distance traveled along the hypotenuse is actually greater, but the two answers differ by about one-hundredth of a mile, out of approximately 3.44 miles. This amounts to 0.2%, which in this context is negligible.

8.3 SOLUTIONS

1. a. 10 units
   b. 1.25 units
   c. 0.05 units
2. a. 600 units
   b. 1 unit
   c. 10 units
3. a. Answers will vary slightly due to the error of measuring. Sample: $1/(7.7) \approx 0.13$.
   b. It is more steep than a 0.05 slope.
4. A 6% grade means that you gain 6 units of altitude (the rise) for every 100 units you move in the horizontal direction (the run). A 6% grade has a slope of 0.06.
5. a. 40 meters
   b. 0.04 meters
6. 3.4 miles is the run. Computation is as follows:
   0.055 = (1000 feet)/run. Run = 18181.81 feet ≈ 3.4 miles. This approximates the distance on the diagonal. See Teacher's Notes.
7. a. 0 units
   b. 0%
   c. 0

GEOBOARD SLOPE

The purpose of this section is to give the students a concentrated experience with slope as ratio, and help develop their feel for it. Calculators are essential if you want answers as decimals.

SLOPES FROM COORDINATES

At the beginning of this section, students can count to find the rise and the run, but by the end they have to use subtraction. This is an important step and students may need help with it. Group work or class discussion may be necessary.

ROLLER COASTERS

This section is a final application of the ideas introduced in this lesson. Assume that the photo described is taken head-on, so that there is no foreshortening of any dimensions.

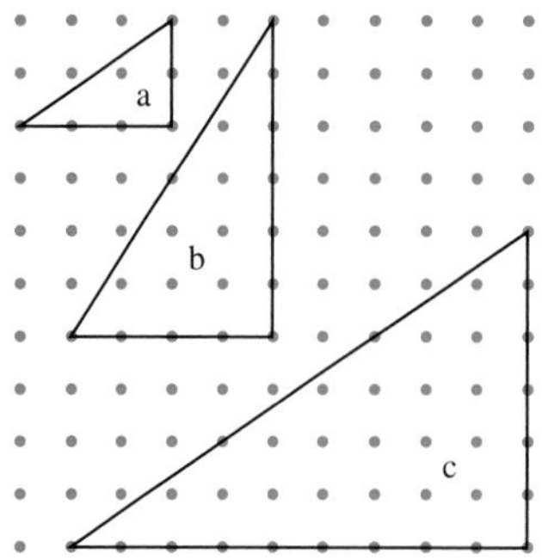

8. Find the slope of each hypotenuse in this figure.

9. How would you use the slope to find which hypotenuse is steeper? Which hypotenuses have the same steepness?

10. Two of the hypotenuses in the figure have the same slope. Explain why someone might make a mistake and believe all three have the same slope.

Do not use horizontal or vertical lines in problems 11-16. Start your lines at the origin.

11. a. What is the smallest slope you can find on a geoboard? Express it as a decimal.
b. Sketch a right triangle, like the ones above, to illustrate it.

12. Repeat problem 11 for the greatest possible geoboard slope.

13. Find a line having slope 1, and sketch several right triangles for it.

14. Find every possible geoboard slope that is a whole number.

15. Find every possible geoboard slope that is greater than 1 and less than 2. Express your answers as decimals.

16. Find every possible geoboard slope that is greater than 0.5 and less than 1. Express your answers as decimals.

SLOPES FROM COORDINATES

You may make a right triangle on your geoboard to help you answer the following questions.

17. What is the slope of the line joining
a. (0, 0) and (4, 5)?
b. (1, 1) and (5, 6)?
c. (0, 1) and (4, 5)?
d. (1, 0) and (5, 6)?

18. What is the slope of the line joining
a. (0, 0) and (8, 10)?
b. (0, 2) and (8, 10)?
c. (2, 3) and (3, 5)?
d. (4, 6) and (6, 10)?

For problem 19, you cannot use the geoboard.

19. What is the slope of the line joining
a. (23, 34) and (65, 54)?
b. (1.2, 3.4) and (5.6, 7.89)?

20. Generalization Explain how to find the slope of the line joining (a, b) and (c, d).

ROLLER COASTERS

Abe and Bea disagree about which roller coaster is steeper, the Plunge of Peril or the Drop of Death.

"The Plunge of Peril," according to the ad for the Great American Super-Park, "drops you 111 feet in seconds, with a mere 20 feet of horizontal displacement."

Abe and Bea have a photograph of themselves standing in front of the Drop of Death. They measured the roller coaster on the photograph, and got a drop of 10.1 cm for a run of 1.8 cm.

8.3 SOLUTIONS

8. a. 2/3
b. 3/2
c. 2/3

9. The larger the number, the steeper the line. Hypotenuses having the same slope have the same steepness.

10. a and c have the same slope of 2/3. If one were not careful to put rise over run, the slope could be mistaken as run over rise for b, which would result in a slope of 2/3.

11. a. The answer depends on the size of the geoboard used. On a 10-by-10 geoboard the smallest slope is 0.1.
b.

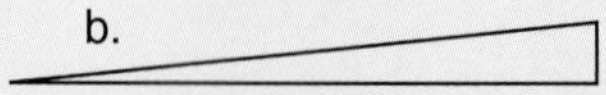

12. a. The largest slope is 10.
b.

13.

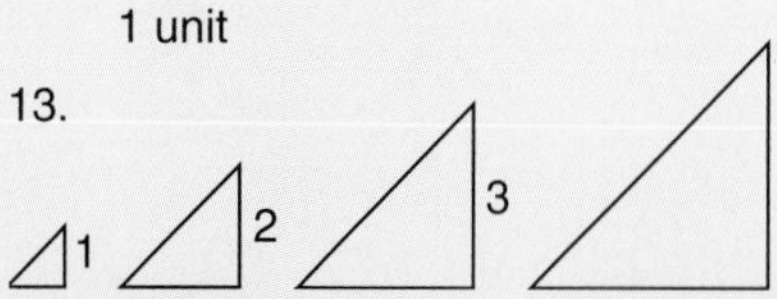

14. The whole-number geoboard slopes are 1 through 10 inclusive.

15. The geoboard slopes between 1 and 2 are: $1.\overline{1}$, 1.125, $1.\overline{142857}$, $1.1\overline{6}$, 1.2, 1.25, $1.\overline{285714}$, $1.\overline{3}$, 1.4, $1.\overline{428571}$, 1.5, 1.6, $1.\overline{6}$, 1.75, 1.8.

16. The geoboard slopes between 0.5 and 1 are: $0.\overline{5}$, $0.\overline{571428}$, 0.6, 0.625, $0.\overline{6}$, 0.7, $0.\overline{714285}$, 0.75, $0.\overline{7}$, 0.8, $0.8\overline{3}$, $0.\overline{857142}$, 0.875, $0.\overline{8}$, 0.9

17. a. 5/4 b. 5/4
c. 1 d. 3/2

18. a. 5/4 b. 1
c. 2 d. 2

19. a. 20/42 = 10/21
b. (4.49)/(4.4) = $1.020\overline{45}$

20. To find the slope of the line joining (*a*, *b*) and (*c*, *d*), where c ≠ a, divide (*d* − *b*) by (*c* − *a*).

21. Use what you know about slope to help them decide which roller coaster is steeper. Explain your method.

22. **Project** The Plunge of Peril and the Drop of Death were invented for this lesson. Find the slopes of some real roller coasters.

DISCOVERY SLUMBER THEORY

Number theory is the branch of mathematics that studies whole numbers and their properties. It has been the source of many challenging problems over the centuries. Slumber theory is a silly offshoot of number theory.

The key concept of slumber theory is that any whole number can be *sliced* into a sequence of whole numbers.

Example: 365 can be sliced in four different ways:

3 | 6 | 5; 36 | 5; 3 | 65; or 365.

(Note that the slices are indicated by a vertical slash. Note also that in slumber theory, not slicing is considered a form of slicing.)

23. How many ways are there to slice a four-digit number?

A number is *slime* if it can be sliced into a sequence of primes.

Examples: 5 is slime, since it is already prime. 2027 is slime (2 | 02 | 7)
4,155,243,311 is slime
(41 | 5 | 5 | 2 | 43 | 3 | 11)

24. Which one of the following numbers is slime?
a. 12 b. 345 c. 6789

25. 2 is the only even prime. Find the first three even slimes.

26. There are no prime squares. Find the first two slime squares.

27. There are no prime cubes. Find the first two slime cubes.

28. 2 and 3 are the only consecutive numbers that are both prime. Find the first three pairs of consecutive numbers that are both slime.

29. There is no triple of consecutive numbers that are all prime. Find the first two triples of consecutive numbers that are all slime.

30. Find the smallest number that is slime in more than one way. (In other words, it can be sliced into two different sequences of primes.)

31. Find the smallest number that is slime in more than two ways.

A number is a super-slime if you get a sequence of primes no matter how you slice it.

Example: 53 is a super-slime since 53 and 5 | 3 are both sequences of primes.

32. Find all the super-slimes.

DISCOVERY SLUMBER THEORY

This is a recreational, problem-solving detour, with no applications to real life whatever. Problem 32 is a satisfying ending, which requires students to use logic and an understanding of divisibility rules to prove they have found all the answers.

8.3 SOLUTIONS

21. The slope of the Plunge of Peril is 111/20 = 5.55. The slope of the Drop of Death is (10.1)/(1.8) = $5.6\overline{1}$. Because $5.6\overline{1}$ is greater than 5.55, the Drop of Death is steeper.
22. Student research will discover many different slopes of roller coasters.
23. 8
24. c
25. 2, 22, 32
26. 25, 225
27. 27, 343
28. 2 and 3
22 and 23
31 and 32
29. 31, 32, 33
71, 72, 73
30. 23 and 2 | 3
31. 223, 2 | 23, 2 | 2 | 3
32. 2, 3, 5, 7, 23, 37, 53, 73, 373

▼ 8.4
Linear Functions

Core Sequence: 1-30

Suitable for Homework: 6-14, 23-30

Useful for Assessment: 3, 7, 26-28

What this Lesson is About:

- Slope-intercept form
- Finding the equation of a line from two points or point-slope in special cases
- Preview of finding the equation from two points or point-slope in the general case

*I*f you have access to graphing calculators, you can carry out a more ambitious version of problem 1, using more designs of greater complexity.

THE SLOPE OF A LINE

*I*n previous lessons, students have been exposed to the geometric idea of slope and have thought about the *m* parameter. This section puts these two concepts together.

*T*his may be a good time to have a class discussion to make the connection between slope and magnification, comparing function diagrams and Cartesian graphs of various linear functions.

LESSON 8.4

Linear Functions

You will need:

graph paper

1. **Exploration** For problems (a-b), find the equations of lines that will create the given design.

a

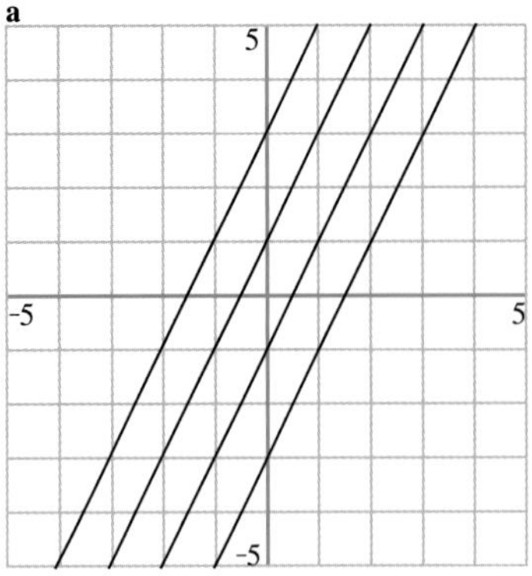

b

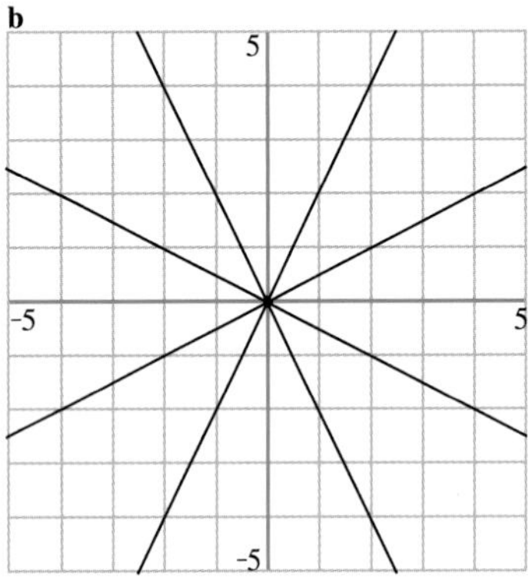

THE SLOPE OF A LINE

Definitions: The *rate of change* of a function is defined as a ratio between the change in *y* and the change in *x*.

$$\text{rate of change} = \frac{\text{change in } y}{\text{change in } x}$$

In the Cartesian plane, a change in *y*-coordinates is called a *rise*. A change in *x*-coordinates is called a *run*.

The *slope of a line* is the ratio obtained when you divide the rise by the run. If you move from left to right, the run is positive. From right to left, it is negative. If you move up, the rise is positive. Moving down, it is negative.

The figure shows right triangles for slopes 0.5, -0.5, 2, and -2.

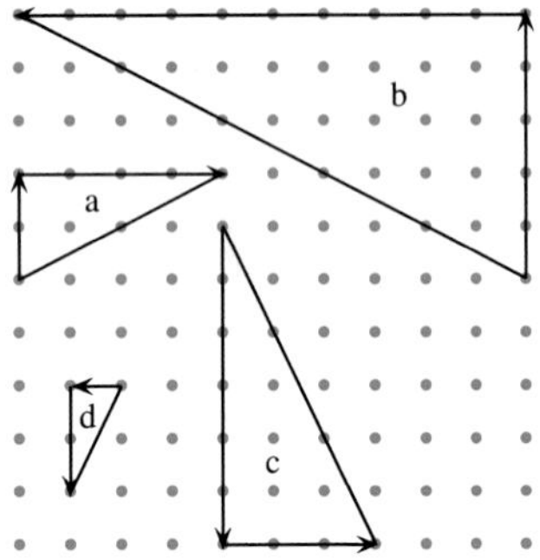

2. Match the slope to the triangle by finding the rise and the run as you move from one end of the hypotenuse to the other
   a. in the direction of the arrows;
   b. in the opposite direction.
   c. Do you get the same answers both ways?

8.4 SOLUTIONS

1. a. $y = 2x + 3$
   $y = 2x + 1$
   $y = 2x - 1$
   $y = 2x - 3$

   b. $y = 2x$
   $y = 0.5x$
   $y = -0.5x$
   $y = -2x$

2. In finding the slope, it doesn't matter if you move in the direction of the arrows or in the opposite direction. In both ways, you get the same number.
   a. 0.5 b. -0.5
   c. -2 d. 2

3. a. The slope is a positive number.
   b. The slope is a negative number.
   c. The slope is zero.

4. a.

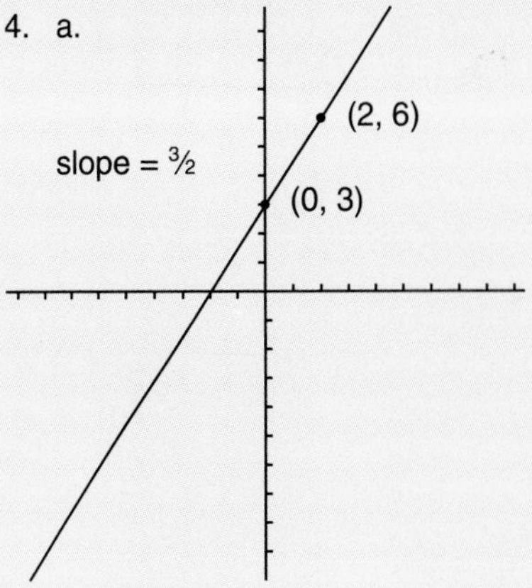

b.

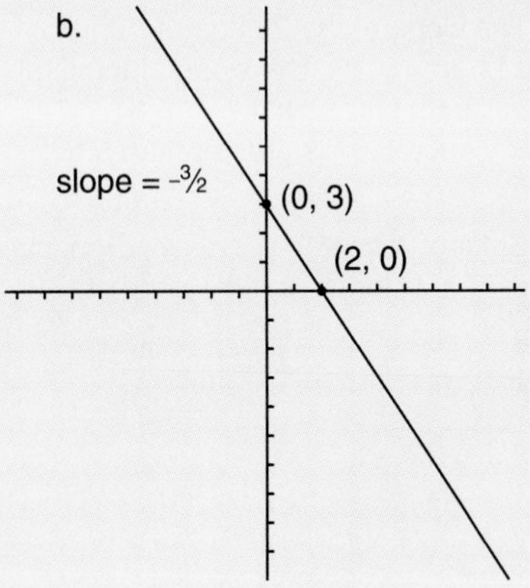

3. What can you say about the slope of a line if, when you follow the line *from left to right,*
   a. it goes up?
   b. it goes down?
   c. it goes neither up nor down?

4. Find two (x, y) pairs that satisfy each equation. Use them to graph the line. Label the two points, and use them to find the slope.
   a. $y = 1.5x + 3$ b. $y = -1.5x + 3$
   c. $y = 2x + 3$ d. $y = -3x + 3$

5. Think of the line with equation $y = 3x + 3$.
   a. Predict its slope.
   b. Check your prediction by graphing.
   c. For this function, when x increases by 1, by what does y increase?

6. Repeat problem 5 for $y = -2x + 3$.

7. How is the coefficient of x related to the slope?

THE y-INTERCEPT OF A LINE

8. For each of these equations, find the y-intercept.
   a. $y = 0.5x + 3$
   b. $y = 0.5x - 3$
   c. $y = 0.5x$
   d. $y = 0.5x + 1.5$

One way to find the y-intercept of a function is to graph it, and see where the graph meets the y-axis. Another way is to remember that *on the y-axis, the x-coordinate is 0.* In other words, all points on the y-axis are of the form (0, ___). So to find the y-intercept of a function, it is enough to substitute 0 for x, and find the value of y.

For each of these linear functions, answer the following questions. Graph the functions if you need to check your answers.
   a. When $x = 0$, what is y?
   b. When x increases by 1, by how much does y increase? (If y decreases, think of it as a negative increase.)
   c. What are the slope and y-intercept?

9. $y = x + 2$ 10. $y = -4 - 3x$
11. $y = -x$ 12. $y = 9$
13. $y = \frac{6x - 7}{8}$ 14. $y = -2(x - 3)$

SLOPE AND y-INTERCEPT

Definition: $y = mx + b$ is called the *slope-intercept form* for the equation of a line.

For each equation below, tell whether it is in slope-intercept form.
   a. If it is, name m and b.
   b. If not, put it in slope-intercept form, then name m and b.

15. $y = 5x - 6$ 16. $y = -4(x - 7)$
17. $y = \frac{5x - 6}{3}$ 18. $y = \frac{x - 7}{-4}$
19. $y = 3(5x - 6)$ 20. $y = -4x - 7$
21. $y + 4 = x$ 22. $y + x = 4$

23. Without graphing each pair of lines, tell whether or not their graphs would intersect. Explain.
   a. $y = 2x + 8$ $y = 2x + 10$
   b. $y = -2x + 8$ $y = 2x + 10$
   c. $y = -2$ $y = 10$
   d. $y = x/4$ $y = 0.25x + 10$
   e. $y = 2(5x - 3)$ $y = 10x$

THE y-INTERCEPT OF A LINE

In addition to a method to find the y-intercept, this section serves as a general introduction to slope-intercept form. It is important for students to look at linear functions that are not in that form, as in problems 13-14, otherwise they overgeneralize, and are unable to recognize *m* and *b*.

SLOPE AND y-INTERCEPT

This section wraps up much of the work in this chapter so far. Pay close attention to how well students understand this material, as they will need to have a reasonably solid grasp of it to be able to do the work in **Thinking/Writing 8.A**.

Because of the importance of problems 15-22, you may want to make sure they are done in class.

8.4 SOLUTIONS

c.

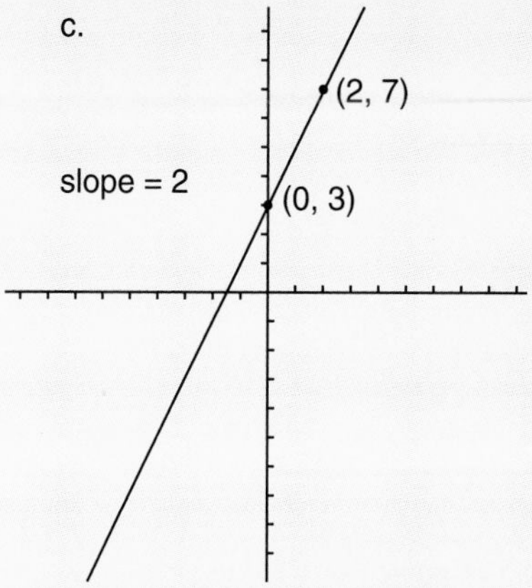

d.

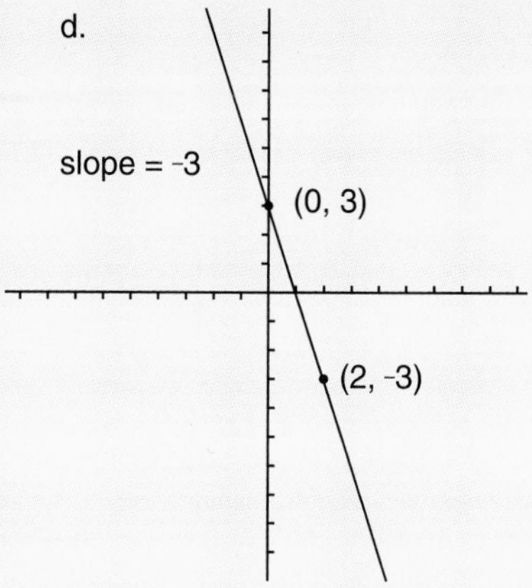

5. a. slope = 3
   b.

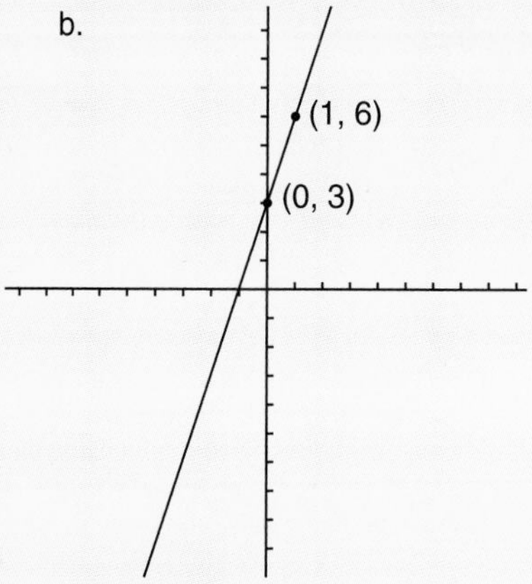

   c. When x increases by 1, y increases by 3.

PREVIEW ***WHAT'S THE FUNCTION?***

Do not teach an equation-solving approach to finding the function yet, as this will be done fully in Chapter 10. The purpose of these problems is to help cement the student's understanding of slope, intercept, and the slope-intercept form. A graphical solution is all you should expect at this point.

24. For (a-c), give the equation of a line that satisfies the following conditions.

a. It passes through the point (0, -2), and goes uphill from left to right.

b. It passes through the origin and (4, -6).

c. It does not contain any point in the third quadrant, and has slope -1.5.

Compare your answers with your classmates' answers.

25. Write three equations of the form $y = mx + b$. For each one, tell how much x changes when y changes by:

a. 1; b. 5; c. K.

26. Did your answers to problem 25 depend on the parameter m, the parameter b, or both?

27. What can you say about the signs of the slope and y-intercept of a line that does not contain any points in:

a. the first quadrant?

b. the second quadrant?

c. the third quadrant?

d. the fourth quadrant?

28. **Report** Explain how to use the slope-intercept form to predict the slope and y-intercept of a line. Make sure you give examples as you answer the following questions.

- What is the value of y when $x = 0$?
- When x increases by 1, by how much does y increase?
- How about when x increases by d?
- If two lines are parallel, what do their equations have in common?
- If two lines meet on the y-axis, what do their equations have in common?
- How is the slope-intercept form useful for graphing lines quickly?

PREVIEW ***WHAT'S THE FUNCTION?***

29. Think of the line that has slope -2 and passes through (1, 4).

a. By graphing, find any other point on the line.

b. Look at the graph to find the y-intercept.

c. What is the equation of the line?

30. Graph the line $y = 2x - 5$. Then graph each line, (a-c), and find its slope, y-intercept, and equation.

a. any line parallel to $y = 2x - 5$

b. the line parallel to it that passes through the origin

c. the line parallel to it that passes through the point (1, 4)

8.4 SOLUTIONS

6. a. slope = -2

b.

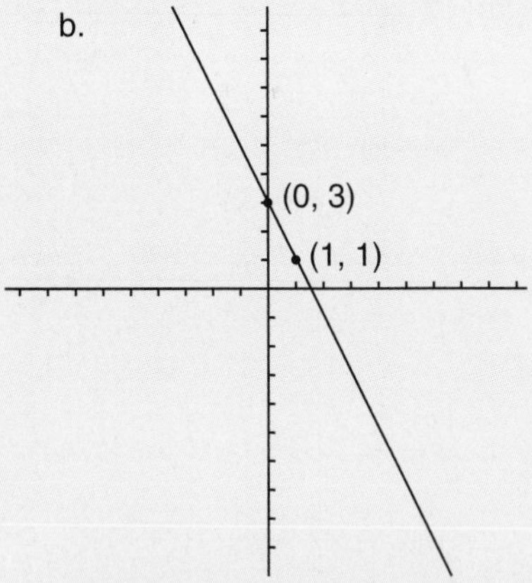

c. When x increases by 1, y increases by -2 (or y decreases by 2).

7. The m parameter is the same as the slope.

8. a. 3 b. -3
c. 0 d. 1.5

9. $y = x + 2$
a. When $x = 0$, y is 2.
b. When x increases by 1, y increases by 1.
c. The slope is 1 and the y-intercept is 2.

10. $y = -4 - 3x$
a. When $x = 0$, $y = -4$.
b. When x increases by 1, y increases by -3.
c. The slope is -3 and the y-intercept is -4.

11. $y = -x$
a. When $x = 0$, $y = 0$.
b. When x increases by 1, y increases by -1.
c. The slope is -1 and the y-intercept is 0.

12. $y = 9$
a. When $x = 0$, $y = 9$.
b. When x increases by 1, y increases by 0.
c. The slope equals zero and the y-intercept is 9.

13. $y = (6x - 7)/8$
a. When $x = 0$, $y = -7/8$
b. When x increases by 1, y increases by 6/8.
c. The slope is 6/8, the y-intercept is -7/8.

14. $y = -2(x - 3)$
a. When $x = 0$, $y = 6$.
b. When x increases by 1, y increases by -2
c. The slope is -2, the y-intercept is 6.

(Solutions continued on page 523)

8.A Slope-Intercept Form

THINKING WRITING

HORIZONTAL AND VERTICAL LINES

1. *REVIEW* What is the equation of:

a. a horizontal line through (2, 3)?
b. a vertical line through (2, 3)?
c. the x-axis?
d. the y-axis?

2. What is the slope of a horizontal line?

To find the slope of a vertical line, notice that the run is 0 for any rise. For example, for a run of 1, the slope should be 1/0, which is not defined. For this reason, vertical lines do not have a slope.

3. a. Explain why vertical lines do not have a y-intercept.
b. Explain why the equations of vertical lines cannot be written in slope-intercept form.
c. How does one write the equation of a vertical line?

FINDING m AND b

4. What are the equations of these lines, (a-d)?

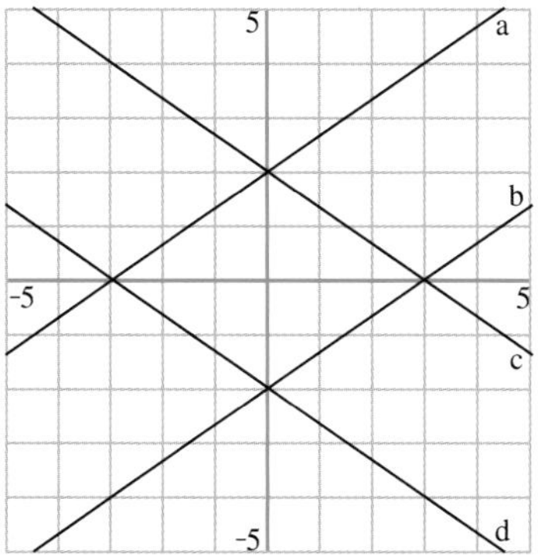

5. a. What are the equations of the two lines in the graph below?
b. What can you say about the equations of lines that pass through the origin and each of the regions A-H? (Your answers should be in the form: For lines in regions A and E, b = ___ and m is between ___ and ___.)

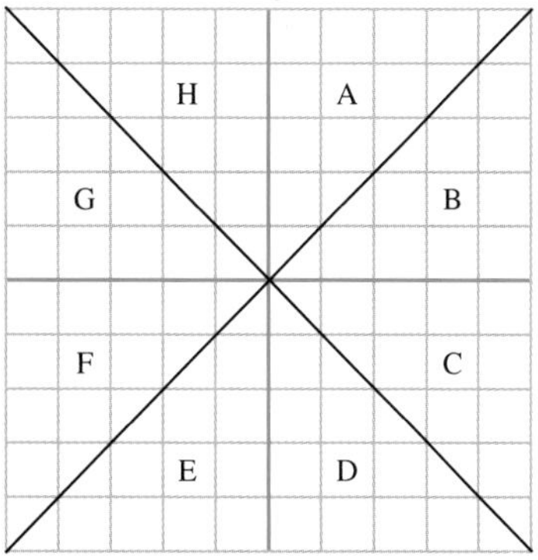

6. What can you say about m if the graph is a very steep line, nearly vertical?

7. This table lists three points that all lie on one line. Find m and b without graphing.

x	y
-3	7
0	6
3	5

THINKING WRITING

8.A Slope-Intercept Form

Core Sequence: 1-10

Suitable for Homework: 1-10

Useful for Assessment: 10

What this Assignment is About:

- Horizontal and vertical lines
- Slope and intercept

Use problems 1-9 as a source of review and in-class discussion about the previous four lessons before assigning the Report.

The only problems that may be somewhat unfamiliar are 7 and 8. If you are concerned about the ability of your students to handle these, you may want to preview them in class with problems of the same type. Note that while m has to be calculated, b is essentially given in problem 7, and easy to guess in problem 8, since points at $x = -1$ and $x = 1$ are given.

8.A SOLUTIONS

1. a. $y = 3$
b. $x = 2$
c. $y = 0$
d. $x = 0$

2. The slope of a horizontal line is zero.

3. a. The y-intercept is one point shared by a line and the y-axis. If the vertical line in question is the y-axis itself then all of its points are on the y-axis, so there is not one point designated as its y-intercept. All other vertical lines do not share a point with the y-axis, so they have no y-intercept.
b. Slope-intercept form is $y = mx + b$ where m is the slope and b is the y-intercept. Vertical lines have no slope so there is no value for the m parameter. They also have no y-intercept so there is no value for the b parameter.
c. The equation of a vertical line is $x = k$, where k is a constant.

4. a. $y = (2/3)x + 2$
b. $y = (2/3)x - 2$
c. $y = (-2/3)x + 2$
d. $y = (-2/3)x - 2$

5. a. $y = x$ & $y = -x$
b. For lines in regions A and E, $b = 0$ and m is between 1 and ∞. For lines in regions B and F, $b = 0$ and m is between 0 and 1. For lines in regions C and G, $b = 0$ and m is between -1 and 0. For lines in regions D and H, $b = 0$ and m is between -1 and $-\infty$.

6. If the graph is very steep, then m is either very large (such as 1,000,000) or very small (such as -1,000,000). Or, the slope approaches $\pm\infty$.

7. $m = -1/3$ and $b = 6$.

The long word list in problem 10 is to encourage students to write a very comprehensive report, including function diagrams. A class discussion of the relationship between function diagrams, Cartesian graphs, and the equation in slope-intercept form is another good way to help prepare students for this assignment.

8.A

8. a. One of these tables lists three points which do not all lie on the same line. Which table is it? Explain how you can tell without graphing, by thinking about slope.
   b. Find m and b for the other two tables.

x	y
-1	-7
1	1
3	9

x	y
-1	2
1	4
3	5

x	y
-1	8
1	0
3	-8

9. For equations (a-e), find m and b without graphing. (You may use graphing to check your answers.)
   a. $y = -2$
   b. $y = 9x$
   c. $y = 2 - 3x$
   d. $y = 4(5x - 6)$
   e. $y = \frac{7x + 8}{9}$

10. **Report** Summarize what you know about slope-intercept form for linear functions. Illustrate your report with graphs and function diagrams. Use the words: equation, fixed point, focus, function, grade, graph, horizontal, linear, magnification, negative, parallel, parameters, positive, rate of change, ratio, slope, table, vertical, y-intercept.

8.A SOLUTIONS

8. a. The second table lists three points which do not all lie on the same line because there are different slopes between pairs of points in the table.
   b. $m = 4$ and $b = -3$ for the first table. $m = -4$ and $b = 4$ for the second table.

9. a. $m = 0$ and $b = -2$
   b. $m = 9$ and $b = 0$
   c. $m = -3$ and $b = 2$
   d. $m = 20$ and $b = -24$
   e. $m = 7/9$ and $b = 8/9$

10. Answers will vary. See solutions to numbers 1 through 3, 6, and 9.

LESSON 8.5

Ideal Population Growth

MATHEMATICAL MODELS

Exponents are useful for making mathematical descriptions of many kinds of growth, including population growth and spread of infectious disease. A mathematical description, or *mathematical model,* usually involves simplifying the real-world situation. Even though some of the idealized situations you study in this course may seem unrealistic, they will help you learn techniques that can be applied to more complicated real-world data.

Bacterial growth is one such situation. In research laboratories, bacteria used for biological studies are grown under controlled conditions. Although no real populations would grow as predictably as the ones described in this chapter, bacterial populations over short periods of time do approximate this kind of growth.

A DOUBLING POPULATION

1. A colony of bacteria is being grown in a laboratory. It contains a single bacterium at 12:00 noon (*time 0*), and the population is doubling every hour. How long do you think it would take for the population to exceed 1 million? 2 million? Write down your *guesses* and compare them with other students' guesses.
2. Make a table of values showing how the population in problem 1 changes as a function of time. Find the population one hour from now, two hours from now, etc. Extend your table until you can answer the questions asked in problem 1. How close were your guesses?
3. Add a third column to your table, writing the population each time as a power of 2.
4. What would the population be after x hours? (Write this as a power of 2.)

HOW MUCH MORE THAN? HOW MANY TIMES AS MUCH?

To determine the rate at which the population is increasing, we compare the populations at different times.

5. Compare the population after 8 hours with the population after 5 hours.
   a. *How much more* is the population after 8 hours? (Compare by subtracting.)
   b. *How many times* as much is it? (Compare by dividing.)
   c. Which of your answers in (a) and (b) can be written as a power of 2? What power of 2 is it?
6. Repeat problem 5, comparing the population after 7 hours with the population after 3 hours.
7. One of the questions, *How much more than?* or, *How many times as much?* can be answered easily with the help of powers of 2. Which question? Explain.
8. Make the comparisons below, answering the question: How many times as much? Write your answers as powers of 2.
   a. Compare the population after 12 hours with the population after 10 hours.
   b. Compare the population after 9 hours with the population after 4 hours.
   c. Compare the population after 4 hours with the population after 12 hours.
9. Compare each pair of numbers. The larger number is how many times as much as the smaller number? Write your answer as a power. In (d), assume x is positive.
   a. 2^6 and 2^9 b. 2^9 and 2^{14}
   c. 2^{14} and 2^6 d. 2^x and 2^{x+3}

8.5 Ideal Population Growth

Core Sequence: 1-19

Suitable for Homework: 10-19

Useful for Assessment: 7, 18-19

What this Lesson is About:

- Exponential growth
- Preview of the product of powers law
- Preview of the quotient of powers law

This lesson previews the basic laws of exponents. The laws are motivated by an application and by the definition of exponentiation as repeated multiplication. Even though the laws have been previewed in the context of scientific notation, do not expect mastery by all students until later in the chapter. (We will continue working with these laws for the rest of the chapter.)

A DOUBLING POPULATION

Exponential growth was previewed in previous chapters, most recently in Chapter 7, Lesson 11.

Note that while it is possible to think of the sequence in the table as a geometric sequence, what concerns us in this chapter is the exponential function and the laws of exponents. For these purposes, it would not be useful to approach these as geometric sequences. Geometric sequences will be studied in Chapter 11.

8.5 SOLUTIONS

1. Guesses will vary. It takes about 20 hours for the population to reach 1 million and 21 hours to reach 2 million.

2 & 3.

Time (hrs. from 12 noon)	Population	Powers of 2
0	1	2^0
1	2	2^1
2	4	2^2
3	8	2^3
4	16	2^4
5	32	2^5
6	64	2^6
7	128	2^7
8	256	2^8
9	512	2^9
10	1024	2^{10}
11	2048	2^{11}
12	4096	2^{12}
13	8192	2^{13}
14	16384	2^{14}
15	32768	2^{15}
16	65536	2^{16}
17	131072	2^{17}
18	262144	2^{18}
19	524288	2^{19}
20	1048576	2^{20}
21	2097152	2^{21}

4. After x hours, the population would be 2^x.
5. a. The population after 8 hours is 224 more than the population after 5 hours.
   b. The population after 8 hours is 8 times greater than the population after 5 hours.
   c. The answer to (b) can be written as 2^3.
6. a. The population after 7 hours is 120 more than the population after 3 hours.
   b. The population after 7 hours is 16 times greater than the population after 3 hours.
   c. The answer to (b) can be written as 2^4.
7. The question "How many times as much?" can be written as a power of 2. In both #5 and #6, part (b) could be written as a power of 2.
8. a. The population after 12 hours is 2^2 times more than the population after 10 hours.
   b. The population after 9 hours is 2^5 times more than the population after 4 hours.

*Nevertheless, emphasize the *constant ratio* of growth, from one hour to the next.

HOW MUCH MORE THAN?
HOW MANY TIMES AS MUCH?

A class discussion based on the tables of values constructed in the previous section may help students understand the pattern.

A TRIPLING POPULATION

This section gives the students an opportunity to test their understanding in a slightly different problem.

Use problem 12d as a reminder of the meaning of the exponent zero. If necessary, use the table from problem 3 to explain why $2^0 = 1$.

MULTIPLYING AND DIVIDING POWERS

This section explains the same pattern from a different perspective, repeated multiplication. Of course, the same results hold. However, the exponent zero is harder to interpret from this perspective. Nevertheless, you should use problems 13d and 14d to highlight the fact that $3^0 = 1$ is perfectly consistent with the pattern discovered in this lesson.

If your students are comfortable with the material in this lesson, you may want to generalize problems 15-16 to the case where the denominator is greater than the numerator. This could start a good discussion of negative exponents, as a preview of the work in Lesson 11.

A TRIPLING POPULATION

A colony of bacteria being grown in a laboratory contains a single bacterium at 12:00 noon (time 0). This population is *tripling* every hour.

10. Make the comparisons below, answering the question: How many times as much? Write your answers as powers of 3. (Hint: It may help to start by making a table showing how the population changes as a function of time.)
   a. Compare the population after 12 hours with the population after 10 hours.
   b. Compare the population after 9 hours with the population after 4 hours.
   c. Compare the population after 4 hours with the population after 12 hours.

11. Compare each pair of numbers. How many times as much as the smaller number is the larger? Write your answer as a power. In (d), assume x is positive.
   a. 3^6 and 3^9 b. 3^9 and 3^{14}
   c. 3^{14} and 3^6 d. 3^x and 3^{x+5}

12. By what number would you have to multiply the first power to get the second power? Write your answer as a power.
   a. $3^5 \cdot \_ = 3^{15}$ b. $3^8 \cdot \_ = 3^{15}$
   c. $3^{11} \cdot \_ = 3^{15}$ d. $3^0 \cdot \_ = 3^{15}$

MULTIPLYING AND DIVIDING POWERS

In a power, the exponent tells how many times the base has been used as a factor. For example, 4^2 means $4 \cdot 4$, and 4^3 means $4 \cdot 4 \cdot 4$, therefore:

$$4^2 \cdot 4^3 = (4 \cdot 4) \cdot (4 \cdot 4 \cdot 4) = 4^5.$$

Use this idea to multiply powers.

13. Write the product as a power of 3.
   a. $3^7 \cdot 3^3 =$ b. $3^5 \cdot 3^5 =$
   c. $3^8 \cdot 3^2 =$ d. $3^8 \cdot 3^0 =$

14. Write the product as a power of 5.
   a. $5^4 \cdot 5^3 =$ b. $5^4 \cdot 5^6 =$
   c. $5^4 \cdot 5^9 =$ d. $5^0 \cdot 5^0 =$

When you divide, the quotient tells you how many times as much the numerator is than the denominator. For example, $4^5/4^2$ means *what times 4^2 equals 4^5*? Since $4^2 \cdot 4^3 = 4^5$, you have $4^5/4^2 = 4^3$. Use this idea to divide powers.

15. Write the quotient as a power of 2.
   a. $\frac{2^{11}}{2^6}$ b. $\frac{2^6}{2^3}$
   c. $\frac{2^{11}}{2^3}$ d. $\frac{2^{11}}{2^0}$

16. Write the quotient as a power of 3.
   a. $\frac{3^7}{3^5}$ b. $\frac{3^6}{3^4}$
   c. $\frac{3^{x+2}}{3^x}$ d. $\frac{3^{11}}{3^0}$

17. Use what you have learned in this lesson to find x.
   a. $5^x \cdot 5^3 = 5^9$
   b. $2^3 \cdot x^4 = 2^7$
   c. $\frac{8^{66}}{8^x} = 8^{54}$
   d. $\frac{10^{x+3}}{10^4} = 10^{a+1}$

18. Summary
   a. Describe the patterns you found in multiplying and dividing powers.
   b. Give examples to show how patterns can make it easier to multiply and divide powers.
   c. In each multiplication and division problem, 15-17, *the bases of the powers are the same.* Does the pattern you described in (a) work if the bases are not the same? Explain, using examples.

19. Generalization Use the patterns you found in this lesson to rewrite each expression as a single power.
   a. $5^x \cdot 5^y$ b. $a^x \cdot a^y$
   c. $\frac{3^y}{3^x}$ d. $\frac{6^{x+5}}{6^x}$
   e. $6^x \cdot 6^x$ f. $6^0 \cdot 6^x$

8.5 SOLUTIONS

c. The population after 12 hours is 2^8 times more than the population after 4 hours.

9. a. 2^3 b. 2^5
   c. 2^8 d. 2^3

10.

Time (hours after 12 noon)	Population	Powers of 3
0	1	3^0
1	3	3^1
2	9	3^2
3	27	3^3
4	81	3^4
5	243	3^5
6	729	3^6
7	2187	3^7
8	6561	3^8
9	19683	3^9
10	59049	3^{10}
11	177147	3^{11}
12	531441	3^{12}
13	1594323	3^{13}
14	4782969	3^{14}

a. The population after 12 hours is 3^2 times greater than the population after 10 hours.
b. The population after 9 hours is 3^5 times greater than the population after 4 hours.
c. The population after 4 hours is $1/(3^8)$ of the population after 12 hours, or the population after 12 hours is 3^8 times greater than the population after 4 hours.

11. a. 3^3 b. 3^5
    c. 3^8 d. 3^5

12. a. 3^{10} b. 3^7
    c. 3^4 d. 3^{15}

13. a. 3^{10} b. 3^{10}
    c. 3^{10} d. 3^8

14. a. 5^7 b. 5^{10}
    c. 5^{13} d. 5^0

15. a. 2^5 b. 2^3
    c. 2^8 d. 2^{11}

16. a. 3^2 b. 3^2
    c. 3^2 d. 3^{11}

17. a. $x = 6$
    b. $x = 2$
    c. $x = 12$
    d. $x = a + 2$
       $(x + 3 - 4 = a + 1$
       $x - 1 = a + 1$
       $x = a + 2)$

(Solutions continued on page 524)

LESSON

8.6 Comparing Populations

EXPONENTIAL GROWTH

Three populations of bacteria are being grown in a laboratory. At time 0: Population A had 10 bacteria; Population B had 100 bacteria; and Population C had 300 bacteria. All three double every hour.

1. Complete the table below to show how the three populations increase as a function of time for the first six hours of growth after time 0.

Population

Time	A	B	C
0	10	100	300
1			

The populations are doubling, which means they are being repeatedly multiplied by 2. Powers of 2 provide a good shorthand for writing the populations.

2. Make another table of the populations of A, B, and C for the first six hours of growth after time 0. This time, use multiplication and a power of 2 to write each population. (Example: For A, the population after four hours is $10 \cdot 2^4$.)

3. Write the expressions for the populations of A, B, and C after:

a. x hours;

b. $x + 3$ hours.

Definitions: This kind of growth is called *exponential growth.* Exponential growth involves *repeated multiplication* by a number. To describe exponential growth, we specify the *starting population* and the *rate of growth.*

For example, if the starting population is 4 and the population triples every hour, this table shows how the population changes as a function of time.

Time	Population	Exponential Expression
0	4	$4 \cdot 3^0$
1	$4 \cdot 3 = 12$	$4 \cdot 3^1$
2	$4 \cdot 3 \cdot 3 = 36$	$4 \cdot 3^2$
3	$4 \cdot 3 \cdot 3 \cdot 3 = 108$	$4 \cdot 3^3$
x	$4 \cdot 3 \cdot ... = ?$	$4 \cdot 3^x$

Generalizations

4. Write an expression for the population after six hours of growth

a. if the starting population is 100 and the population is tripling every hour;

b. if the starting population is 100 and the population is being multiplied by r every hour;

c. if the starting population is p and the population is being multiplied by r every hour.

8.6 Comparing Populations

Core Sequence: 1-23

Useful for Assessment: 5

Suitable for Homework: 8-17, 24-26

What this Lesson is About:

- Exponential growth
- Preview of geometric sequences
- Review of scientific notation
- Simplifying fractions
- Review of factoring

In this lesson, students continue to practice the skills introduced in the previous one. Again, bacterial growth serves as the motivation. Expressions of the form ab^x are divided by each other.

EXPONENTIAL GROWTH

This section goes beyond the material in the previous lesson in that students work with different starting populations. This is very much like the work that was done in Chapter 7, Lesson 11.

8.6 SOLUTIONS

1.

Population

Time	A	B	C
0	10	100	300
1	20	200	600
2	40	400	1200
3	80	800	2400
4	160	1600	4800
5	320	3200	9600
6	640	6400	19200

2.

Population

Time	A	B	C
0	$10 \cdot 2^0$	$100 \cdot 2^0$	$300 \cdot 2^0$
1	$10 \cdot 2^1$	$100 \cdot 2^1$	$300 \cdot 2^1$
2	$10 \cdot 2^2$	$100 \cdot 2^2$	$300 \cdot 2^2$
3	$10 \cdot 2^3$	$100 \cdot 2^3$	$300 \cdot 2^3$
4	$10 \cdot 2^4$	$100 \cdot 2^4$	$300 \cdot 2^4$
5	$10 \cdot 2^5$	$100 \cdot 2^5$	$300 \cdot 2^5$
6	$10 \cdot 2^6$	$100 \cdot 2^6$	$300 \cdot 2^6$

3. a., b.

Population

Time	A	B	C
x	$10 \cdot 2^x$	$100 \cdot 2^x$	$300 \cdot 2^x$
$x + 3$	$10 \cdot 2^{x+3}$	$100 \cdot 2^{x+3}$	$300 \cdot 2^{x+3}$

4. a. $100 \cdot 3^6$
b. $100 \cdot R^6$
c. $P \cdot R^6$

5. a. $100 \cdot 3^x$
b. $100 \cdot R^x$
c. $P \cdot R^x$

6. a. The population of B at 8 hours is $100 \cdot 2^8$, at 11 hours is $100 \cdot 2^{11}$, and at 14 hours is $100 \cdot 2^{14}$. Over each 3-hour period the population is being multiplied by 2^3.

b. $\frac{100 \cdot 2^{x+3}}{100 \cdot 2^x} = 2^3$ because

$100 \cdot 2^x \cdot 2^3 = 100 \cdot 2^{x+3}$

7. a. $\frac{10 \cdot 2^{x+5}}{10 \cdot 2^x} = 2^5$ because

$10 \cdot 2^x \cdot 24^5 = 10 \cdot 2^{x+5}$

b. The population of A at 6 hours is $10 \cdot 2^6$, at 11 hours is $10 \cdot 2^{11}$, and at 16 hours is $10 \cdot 2^{16}$. Over each 5-hour period the population is being multiplied by 2^5.

SAME POPULATION, DIFFERENT TIME

Students have to apply what they learned about dividing powers of the same base. You may also need to remind them of how to simplify fractions when a common factor appears in numerator and denominator.

Problems 6-7 may be made clearer by writing 2^{x+3} like this: $(2 \cdot 2 \cdot \ldots \cdot 2)$ $(2 \cdot 2 \cdot 2)$.

DIFFERENT POPULATIONS, SAME TIME

DIFFERENT POPULATIONS, DIFFERENT TIMES

These problems may be difficult for your students. Give them plenty of time to work on the problems and do not expect mastery.

5. Write an expression for the population after x hours of growth for each situation in problem 4.

SAME POPULATION, DIFFERENT TIME

6. The population of B after five hours is $100 \cdot 2^5$.
   a. Find the population of B at 8 hours, 11 hours, and 14 hours. By how much is the population being multiplied over each three-hour period?
   b. Compare the population of B after x hours with its population after $x + 3$ hours by simplifying this ratio.
   $$\frac{10 \cdot 2^{x+3}}{10 \cdot 2^x}$$
7. The population of A at six hours is $10 \cdot 2^6$.
   a. Compare the population of A after x hours with its population after $x + 5$ hours by simplifying this ratio.
   $$\frac{10 \cdot 2^{x+5}}{10 \cdot 2^x}$$
   b. Check your answer to part (a) by comparing the population of A at 6 hours, 11 hours, and 16 hours.
8. Simplify these ratios.
   a. $\frac{400 \cdot 2^7}{400 \cdot 2^3}$ b. $\frac{100 \cdot 2^{15}}{100 \cdot 2^8}$
9. Simplify these ratios. It may help to substitute values for x and look for a pattern.
   a. $\frac{400 \cdot 2^{x+7}}{400 \cdot 2^x}$ b. $\frac{100 \cdot 2^{3x}}{100 \cdot 2^x}$
10. Solve for x. $\frac{35 \cdot 2^{x+6}}{35 \cdot 2^x} = 2^x$

DIFFERENT POPULATIONS, SAME TIME

11. a. Use the tables you made in problems 1 and 2 to compare the size of A with the size of B at several times. In each case, B is how many times as large? Does this ratio increase, decrease, or remain the same as time goes on?
   b. Repeat part (a), comparing C with B.
12. Simplify these ratios.
   a. $\frac{400 \cdot 2^x}{200 \cdot 2^x}$ b. $\frac{10^0 \cdot 2^{x+4}}{500 \cdot 2^{x+4}}$
13. Solve for x. $\frac{300 \cdot 2^a}{x \cdot 2^a} = 30$

DIFFERENT POPULATIONS, DIFFERENT TIMES

14. Compare these populations using ratios.
   a. B at 10 hours and A at 3 hours
   b. C at 3 hours and A at 6 hours
   c. A at 12 hours and B at 7 hours
   d. C at 1/2 hour and A at 1 hour
15. Compare these populations using ratios.
   a. B at x hours and A at $x + 2$ hours
   b. C at h hours and A at $2h$ hours
   c. A at h hours and B at $h - 5$ hours
16. Simplify these ratios.
   a. $\frac{400 \cdot 2^{x+4}}{25 \cdot 2^x}$ b. $\frac{10 \cdot 2^{4x}}{150 \cdot 2^x}$
17. Solve for x.
   a. $\frac{30 \cdot 2^{a+4}}{x \cdot 2^a} = 60$
   b. $\frac{300 \cdot 2^{a+3}}{x \cdot 2^a} = 24$

8.6 SOLUTIONS

8. a. 2^4
   b. 2^7
9. a. 2^7
   b. 2^{2x}
10. $x = 6$. $(x + 6 - x = x$ so $6 = x)$
11. a. B is 10 times larger than A. The ratio stays the same as time goes on.
   b. C is 3 times larger than B. The ratio stays the same as time goes on.
12. a. 2
   b. 1/500
13. $x = 10$
14. a. Population B at 10 hours is 1280 times greater than population A at 3 hours: $(100 \cdot 2^{10})/(10 \cdot 2^3) = 10 \cdot 2^7 = 1280$
   b. Population C at 3 hours is 3.75 times greater than population A at 6 hours:
   $(300 \cdot 2^3)/(10 \cdot 2^6) = 30/(2^3) = 3.75$
   c. Population A at 12 hours is 3.2 times greater than population B at 7 hours:
   $(10 \cdot 2^{12})/(100 \cdot 2^7) = 2^5/10 = 3.2$
   d. Population C at 0.5 hours is approximately 21.2 times greater than population A at 1 hour:
   $(300 \cdot 2^{.5})/(10 \cdot 2^1) = 30/(2^{.5}) \sim 21.21$
15. a. Population B at x hours is 2.5 times greater than population A at $x + 2$ hours.
   $(100 \cdot 2^x)/(10 \cdot 2^{x+2}) = 10/(2^2) = 2.5$
   b. Population C at h hours is $30/(2^h)$ times greater than population A at 2 hours.
   $(300 \cdot 2^h)/(10 \cdot 2^{2h}) = 30/2^h$
   c. Population A at h hours is 3.2 times greater than population B at $h - 5$ hours.
   $(10 \cdot 2^h)/(100 \cdot 2^{h-5}) = 2^5/10 = 3.2$
16. a. 256
   b. $2^{3x}/15$
17. a. $x = 8$
   b. $x = 100$

POPULATION PROJECTIONS

In 1975 the population of the world was about 4.01 billion and was growing at a rate of about 2% per year. People used these facts to project what the population would be in the future.

18. Copy and complete the table, giving projections of the world's population from 1976 to 1980, assuming that the growth rate remained at 2% per year.

Year	Calculation	Projection (billions)
1976	4.01 + (0.02)4.01	4.09

19. Find the ratio of the projected population from year to year. Does the ratio increase, decrease, or stay the same?

20. There is a number that can be used to multiply one year's projection to calculate the next. What is that number?

21. Use repeated multiplication to project the world's population in 1990 from the 1975 number, assuming the same growth rate.

22. Compare your answer to problem 21 with the actual estimate of the population made in 1990, which was about 5.33 billion.

a. Did your projection over-estimate or under-estimate the 1990 population?

b. Was the population growth rate between 1975 and 1990 more or less than 2%? Explain.

23. At a growth rate of 2% a year, how long does it take for the world's population to double?

REVIEW *FACTORING COMPLETELY*

Example: $16 - 4x^2$ is a difference of two squares, so it can be factored:

$$(4 - 2x)(4 + 2x).$$

However, each of the binomials can be factored further, like this:

$$2(2 - x) \cdot 2(2 + x) = 4(2 - x)(2 + x)$$

Here is another way to factor the same expression:

$$4(4 - x^2) = 4(2 - x)(2 + x).$$

The final expression is the same one we got using the first method. It cannot be factored any further, so we say we have *factored completely*.

Factor each expression completely.

24. $3t^2 - 27s^2$

25. $5x^2 - 180$

26. $x^3y - xy^3$

POPULATION PROJECTIONS

This section previews the next lesson. It features a decimal ratio and will probably require some class discussion. Note that the calculation indicated in the table is somewhat cumbersome. The point is to have the students discover for themselves the fact that a constant percent increase leads to a constant ratio between consecutive terms in the sequence.

Once they see that fact in problem 20 they can use it to solve problem 21.

Problem 22b can be answered qualitatively (the growth rate has decreased). But you may encourage some students to use their calculators and trial and error to find the actual population growth rate in that period. They may be surprised to find that it is only a very little bit lower than 2%.

REVIEW *FACTORING COMPLETELY*

This section reminds students to look for the common factor. This is the most useful and most important factoring technique.

(Hint: Experiment and look for patterns, starting with rectangles whose length and width have no common factors except 1.)

8.6 SOLUTIONS

18.

Year	Calculation	Projection (billions)
1976	4.01 + (0.02)4.01	4.09
1977	4.09 + (0.02)4.09	4.17
1978	4.17 + (0.02)4.17	4.25
1979	4.25 + (0.02)4.25	4.34
1980	4.34 + (0.02)4.34	4.43

19. The ratio of the projected population from year to year stays the same: (4.17)/(4.09) = 1.02, (4.25)/(4.17) = 1.02, etc.

20. 1.02 is the number that can be used to multiply one year's projection to calculate the next.

21.

Year	Projection (billions)
1975	4.01
1976	4.09
1977	4.17
1978	4.25
1979	4.34
1980	4.43
1981	4.52
1982	4.61
1983	4.7
1984	4.79
1985	4.89
1986	4.99
1987	5.09
1988	5.19
1989	5.29
1990	5.4

22. a. The projection on the table in #21 overestimated the 1990 population.

b. The population growth rate between 1975 and 1990 was less than 2%. The projected 1990 population would have been 5.4 billion at 2% growth rate. 5.33 billion is less than 5.4 billion, so the growth rate must have been smaller.

23. About 35 years

24. $3(t + 3s)(t - 3s)$

25. $5(x + 6)(x - 6)$

26. $xy(x + y)(x - y)$

▼ 8.7
Percent Increase

Core Sequence: 1-9, 11-20

Suitable for Homework: 10-31

Useful for Assessment: 8-9, 11

What this Lesson is About:

- Exponential vs. linear growth
- Review of percent problems
- Review of solving linear equations
- Consumer applications

In Lessons 7 and 8, we cover both the idea of percent increase/decrease and the idea of exponential growth/decay. This is deliberate, since without discussion of percent, increase/decrease expressions like $100(1.05)^x$ make no sense. (In previous lessons, we usually limited ourselves to whole number bases.)

AN ALGEBRA TUTOR'S SALARY

This section allows students to compare linear and exponential growth both numerically and graphically.

Problem 8b is key, but may be hard for some students. Even though the idea was previewed at the end of the previous lesson, don't try to force the algebraic derivation right away. (This concept is difficult even for many Algebra 2 students.)

LESSON 8.7

Percent Increase

You will need: graph paper

AN ALGEBRA TUTOR'S SALARY

Bea did so well in algebra that she got a job as an algebra tutor. Her starting salary, as she had no experience, was $10 per week.

1. As Bea got more experience, her salary increased. She got a raise of $1 per week. Copy and complete the table for the first ten weeks that Bea worked.

Weeks	Salary	Amount increase	Percent increase
0	$10		
1	$11	$1	10
2	$12	$1	9
3	$13	$1	8.33

2. a. Explain how to calculate the number in the last column.
b. Explain why the number in the last column decreases each week.

3. Compare Bea's original salary with her salary for the tenth week.
a. What was the total amount of increase in her salary?
b. What percent of her original salary is this total increase? (This is the total *percent increase*.)
c. What percent of her original salary is her salary in the tenth week? (Your answer should be a number greater than 100. Why?)

Abe also got a job as an algebra tutor. He heard that Bea was getting a weekly raise of $1. Since $1 is 10% of $10, Abe asked for a weekly raise of 10%. The first week Bea and Abe both got the same raise.

4. Copy and complete the table for the first ten weeks that Abe worked.

Weeks	Salary	Amount increase	Percent increase
0	$10		
1	$11	$1	10
2	$12.10	$1.10	10
3	$13.31	$1.21	10

5. a. Explain how to calculate the numbers in the third column of the table above.
b. Explain why the numbers in the third column increase each week.

6. Repeat problem 3 for Abe's salary.

7. On the same pair of axes, make graphs of Abe's and Bea's weekly salaries as a function of weeks of experience.

8.
a. Each week's salary for Bea can be obtained from the previous week's salary by *adding* a number. Find this number and use it to write an equation that gives Bea's salary (*S*) as a function of weeks of experience (*W*).
b. Each week's salary for Abe can be obtained from the previous week's salary by *multiplying* by a number. Find this number, experimenting with your calculator if necessary, and use it to write an equation that gives Abe's salary as a function of weeks of experience.

8.7 SOLUTIONS

1.

Weeks	Salary	Amount increase	Percent increase
0	$10		
1	$11	$1	10
2	$12	$1	9.09
3	$13	$1	8.33
4	$14	$1	7.7
5	$15	$1	7.1
6	$16	$1	6.67
7	$17	$1	6.25
8	$18	$1	5.88
9	$19	$1	5.56
10	$20	$1	5.26

2. a. Divide 1 by the previous week's salary to calculate the number in the last column. For example, 1/12 = 8.33.
b. The number in the last column decreases each week because the $1 increase remains the same while the salary grows. Each subsequent percent increase is found by dividing 1 by a larger number than before, so the percent increase grows smaller each week.

3. a. Bea's salary increased by $10.
b. Bea's salary of $20 is a 100% increase in her original salary of $10.00.
c. $20 is 200% of $10. An answer of 100% would mean Bea's salary is 100% of the original amount. This means Bea would have a salary of $10 in the tenth week.

4. Answers may vary a little due to rounding.

Weeks	Salary	Amount increase	Percent increase
0	$10		
1	$11	$1	10
2	$12.10	$1.10	10
3	$13.31	$1.21	10
4	$14.64	$1.33	10
5	$16.10	$1.46	10
6	$17.71	$1.61	10
7	$19.48	$1.77	10
8	$21.42	$1.94	10
9	$23.56	$2.14	10
10	$25.91	$2.35	10

5. a. The amount of increase is found by multiplying the previous week's salary by 0.10.
b. The amount of increase grows each week because the salary increases each week. One is

9. 🔑
   a. Write each equation you wrote on the graphs it belongs to.
   b. Compare the graphs. Which is straight? Which is curved?
   c. Which function describes linear growth? Which describes exponential growth?

10. Repeat the analysis you did for Abe's and Bea's salaries if Bea's raise were \$2 and Abe's raise were 20%.

EQUATIONS WITH PERCENTS

A state has 5% sales tax. If you paid \$12.60 for something, including tax, what was the price without tax? If the price without tax is x, and the increase due to tax is 0.05 of x, then

$$x + 0.05x = \$12.60.$$

11. 🔑 Remember that x can be written $1x$.
   a. Combine like terms on the left side of the equation. (Or factor out the x.)
   b. Then solve for x.

12. Solve for x.
   a. $1.2x = 240$
   b. $x + 0.4x = 18.2$
   c. $x + 0.06x = 23.85$
   d. $1.7x = 78.2$

13. Solve for x.
   a. $(1.10)(1.10)x = 67.76$
   b. $(1.10)(1.10)(1.10)x = 13.31$

The Skolar family eat out once a month. Usually they take turns figuring out the tip, also called the *gratuity.*

14. At one restaurant, they ordered food totaling \$35.95 and received a bill for the total amount they owed. The total was \$43.86, and the bill said "tax and gratuity included." Sue wrote this equation.

$$35.95 + p(35.95) = 43.86$$

   a. Explain the equation. What does p represent?
   b. Solve for p. Is your answer reasonable? Discuss.

15. Another night the Skolar family had \$23.00 to buy dinner. Assuming they'd need 25% of the cost of the dinner to cover the tax and tip, Michael wrote this equation.

$$d + 0.25d = 23.00$$

   a. Explain the equation. What does d represent?
   b. Solve for d.

16. Now assume the Skolars had \$23.00 for their meal and needed only 20% of the cost of the dinner to cover the tax and tip. How much can their actual food order be? Write and solve the equation.

EQUATIONS AND THE PRICE OF WIDGETS

17. A certain retail store sells widgets at the wholesale price, plus a 35% markup. If the wholesale price is W, what is the retail price of the widget? Express your answer as a function of W in two ways: as an addition and as a multiplication.

Instead, encourage students to use trial and error to find the number, then discuss why the number makes sense. We return to this idea in problem 11 and in the next lesson.

EQUATIONS WITH PERCENTS
EQUATIONS AND THE PRICE OF WIDGETS

The main point of these sections is to reinforce the idea that percent growth can be expressed multiplicatively. For a few students, this may be familiar from previous experience with percent problems, but for most this deserves special attention. It is necessary in order to understand exponential growth in all its generality.

8.7 SOLUTIONS

taking 10% of a larger and larger salary each week.

6. a. \$15.91 is the total amount of increase in salary
   b. \$15.91 is 159% of his original salary.
   c. \$25.91 is 259% of his original salary. This answer is greater than 100% because 100% of her original salary is \$10.

7.

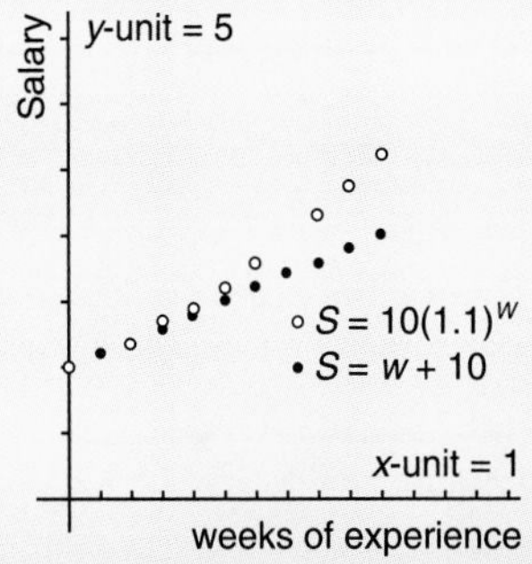

8. a. $S = W + 10$ b. $S = 10(1.1)W$

9. a. See equations written on the graph in problem #7.
   b. Bea's graph, $S = W + 10$ is straight.
   Abe's graph, $S = 10(1.1)W$ is curved.
   c. Bea's function describes linear growth. Abe's function describes exponential growth.

10. Salaries may vary due to rounding.

Weeks	Bea's Salary	Amount increase	Percent increase
0	\$10		
1	\$12	\$2	20
2	\$14	\$2	16.7
3	\$16	\$2	14.3
4	\$18	\$2	12.5
5	\$20	\$2	11.1
6	\$22	\$2	10
7	\$24	\$2	9
8	\$26	\$2	8.3
9	\$28	\$2	7.7
10	\$30	\$2	7.1
W	$2W + 10$	\$2	

Weeks	Abe's Salary	Amount increase	Percent increase
0	\$10		
1	\$12	\$2	20
2	\$14.40	\$2.40	20
3	\$17.28	\$2.88	20
4	\$20.73	\$3.45	20
5	\$24.87	\$4.14	20
6	\$29.84	\$4.97	20
7	\$35.80	\$5.96	20
8	\$42.96	\$7.16	20
9	\$51.55	\$8.59	20
10	\$61.86	\$10.31	20
W	$10(1.2)^W$		

REVIEW SOLVING EQUATIONS

This section reviews the previous lesson. Laws of exponents are formally introduced later in the chapter, in Lessons 9 and 10.

REVIEW EQUATIONS AND INEQUALITIES

These are suitable for homework, unless your students want to use the Lab Gear. Problem 31 is not easily solved using any of the methods discussed, but it can be done by trial and error.

18. The wholesale cost of widgets went up by 8.5%. If the old wholesale price was W, express as a function of W,

a. the new wholesale price;

b. the new retail price;

c. the retail price including a 5% sales tax.

19. After the price increase in the wholesale cost a certain customer purchased a widget at the retail store for \$15.71, including tax.

a. What was the wholesale price on that widget?

b. How much would the customer have saved by buying a widget before the wholesale price increase?

REVIEW SOLVING EQUATIONS

20. Solve for x.

a. $\frac{3^x}{3^2} = 3^5$

b. $\frac{10^{2x-5}}{10^2} = 10^5$

c. $\frac{p^{x-3}}{p^2} = p^6$

REVIEW EQUATIONS AND INEQUALITIES

Use the techniques you have learned to solve these equations and inequalities. You can use trial and error, the cover-up method, tables, graphs, or the Lab Gear. Show your work.

21. $5y > 2y + 57$

22. $3s + 7 = 4 + 3s$

23. $3(m + 4) + 3(m - 4) = 54$

24. $7 + y = 7y$

25. $\frac{10x + 4}{6} + 7 = -4$

26. $\frac{4x}{5} = 2 - x$

27. $\frac{3}{3x} = \frac{7}{4x - 2}$

28. $(2p + 3)^2 = (4p - 2)(p - 8)$

29. $(2p - 1)(3p + 2) = (6p - 1)(p + 1)$

30. $\frac{x}{x + 1} = 2$

31. $\frac{5}{x} + \frac{x}{5} = 2$

8.7 SOLUTIONS

Bea's total increase in salary is \$20, and Abe's is \$51.86. Bea's total increase is 200% of her original salary, and Abe's is 518.6% of his original salary. Bea's final salary is 300% of her original salary, and Abe's is 618.6% of his original salary. Bea's equation is $S = 2W + 10$ which is a linear function, and Abe's is $S = 10(1.2)^W$ which is an exponential function.

11. a. $x + 0.05x = \$12.60$
    $1.05x = 12.60$
    b. $x = \$12.00$

12. a. 200 b. 13
    c. 22.5 d. 46

13. a. 56 b. 10

14. a. p represents the percentage of the cost of the food which is being charged for tax and gratuity. The equation adds the total price of the food, \$35.90, to a percentage of the total price of the food, $p(35.95)$, to get the total of the bill, \$43.86.
    b. $35.95 + p(35.95) = 43.86$
    $p(35.95) = 7.91$
    $p = 0.22$
    This means the tax and gratuity are 22% of the cost of the food. In states where tax is about 7%, this would represent a reasonable tip of 15%.

15. a. d represents the cost of the food ordered before tax and tip. The equation adds the total bill for food, plus 25% of the total bill for food, to get a final bill of \$23.00, including food, tax, and tip.
    b. $d + 0.25d = 23$
    $1.25d = 23$
    $d = 18.4$
    This means the Skolar family can order \$18.40 worth of food to have a total bill of \$23.00. This seems reasonable.

16. $d + 0.20d = 23$
    $1.20d = 23$
    $d = 19.16$
    The Skolars can order \$19.16 worth of food to have a final bill of \$23.00.

17. Retail = $W + 0.35W$ (W = wholesale price)
    Retail = $1.35W$

18. Let N = new wholesale price, W = old wholesale price, & R = new retail price.

LESSON 8.8

Percent Decrease

A CASHIER'S QUANDARY

Sherman's Department Store ran the following ad in the newspaper.

> **3-HOUR EARLY-BIRD SPECIAL!**
>
> ★ ★ ★ ★ ★
>
> This week, all merchandise has been discounted 30% for our year-end clearance sale.
>
> For three hours only, from 9AM to 12 noon on Saturday, get amazing additional savings! We will take an ***additional*** 20% off the sale price at the cash register.

G.D. and Cal were working during the three-hour sale. At the end of the sale, they compared receipts and discovered that they had sold some of the same items, but they had charged customers different prices for them. They made the following table.

Original price	Cal charged	G.D. charged
\$139.99	\$78.39	\$70.00
\$49.95	\$27.97	\$24.98
\$18.89	\$10.57	\$9.44
\$5.29	\$2.96	\$2.65
\$179.00	\$100.24	\$89.50

1. **Exploration** How was Cal calculating the sale price? How was G.D. calculating the sale price? Explain, showing sample calculations. Who do you think was right, and why?

LATE PAPER POLICIES

Mr. Peters, an algebra teacher, has a *10% off* late paper policy. This means that for each day that a paper is late, the student receives 90% of the credit that he or she would have received the day before. For example, if you turned in a perfect paper (assume a score out of 100) one day late, you would receive (0.90)(100) = 90 as your score. If you turned the paper in two days late, you would receive (0.90)(90) = 81 as your score.

2. Copy and extend Mr. Peters's table to show the score you would receive on a perfect paper that is up to ten days late.

Mr. Peters's Late Policy

Days late	Score
0	100
1	90
2	81

3. a. Explain how you figured out the scores in the table. Show some sample calculations.
   b. After how many days would your score for a late paper drop below 50?
   c. Would your score ever reach 0? Explain.

▼ 8.8 Percent Decrease

Core Sequence: 1-16

Suitable for Homework: 4-17

Useful for Assessment: 7-8, 10, 14

What this Lesson is About:

- Exponential vs. linear decay
- Review of percent problems
- Review of solving linear equations
- Consumer applications

A CASHIER'S QUANDARY

This Exploration focuses on the frequent misunderstanding of percent change as being an additive and not multiplicative phenomenon. The question is wrapped up at the end of the lesson.

LATE PAPER POLICIES

A comparison of linear versus exponential decay, using tables and graphs. It is interesting that while linear growth is slow compared to exponential growth, that is reversed in the case of decay.

Problem 9 should provoke a lively discussion. You may ask students to create their own late paper policies.

8.8 SOLUTIONS

(8.7 Solutions continued)

a. $N = 1.085W$

b. $R = 1.35N$ or $1.35(1.085W) = 1.46475W$

c. Total = $1.35N + 0.05(1.35N)$
$= 1.05(1.35N)$
$= 1.4175N$
or Total = $1.4175(1.085W)$
$= 1.5379W$
$= 1.538W$

19. Answers may vary slightly depending on when and/or how one rounds off or truncates.
   a. Total = $1.4175N$
   $15.71 = 1.4175N$
   $N = 11.08$
   Hence, the new wholesale price on the widget was \$11.08.
   b. $\text{Total}_{New} = (\text{Total}_{Old})(1.085)$
   $15.71 = (\text{Total}_{Old})(1.085)$
   $\text{Total}_{Old} = 14.48$
   Hence, the old price was \$14.48.
   The savings is 15.71 − 14.48 = \$1.23.

20. a. $x = 7$ b. $x = 6$ c. $x = 11$

21. $y > 19$

22. No solution

23. $m = 9$

24. $y = 7/6$

25. $x = -7$

26. $x = 10/9$

27. $x = -2/3$

28. $p = 7/46$

29. $p = -1/4$

30. $x = -2$

31. $x = 5$

1. Cal calculated the sale price by finding 70% of \$139.99 or \$97.99 minus 20% of \$97.99 or \$19.60. So \$97.99 minus \$19.60 is \$78.39. G.D. did not calculate 20% of \$97.99, but found 20% of the original price of \$139.99
0.70(139.99) − 0.20(139.99) = 97.99 − 27.99 = 70.00.
Cal was correct because he took 20% off the sale price, and G.D. took 20% off the original price. G.D. reduced the cost too much.

2. **Mr. Peters's Late Policy**

Days late	Score
0	100
1	90
2	81
3	73
4	66
5	59

DISCOUNTER INTRODUCES REDUCTIONS!

This section includes practice on setting up and solving equations for these kinds of percent problems.

The Report may be hard for some students. If so, you may want to spend some class time looking for the algebraic expression.

(Nonmathematical note: The title for this section is an unusual sentence in that each of the three words consists of the same ten letters.)

8.8

Mr. Riley, another algebra teacher, has a *10 points off* policy. This means that you lose ten points for each day that your paper is late.

4. Copy and extend Mr. Riley's table to show the score you would receive on a perfect paper that is up to ten days late.

Mr. Riley's Late Policy

Days late	Score
0	100
1	90
2	80

5. a After how many days would your score for a late paper drop below 50?
b. Would your score ever reach 0? Explain.

6. Graph the data in the two tables showing how the score decreases as a function of the number of days late. Use the same axes for both graphs so that you can compare them.

7. Write an equation that gives your score (S) on a perfect paper as a function of the number of days late (D)
a. in Mr. Peters's class;
b. in Mr. Riley's class.

8.
a. One of the equations you wrote in problem 7 should have an exponent. (If it doesn't, check your work.) Which equation has an exponent, the *percent off* policy, or the *points off* policy?
b. Write each equation you wrote in problem 7 on the corresponding graph. Does the equation containing an exponent correspond to the straight graph or to the curved graph?

9. Compare Mr. Riley's policy with Mr. Peters's policy. Which one do you prefer, and why? Give reasons why some students might prefer one policy and some students another.

DISCOUNTER INTRODUCES REDUCTIONS!

A store offers a 5% discount to students. If something costs \$15.00 after the discount is taken, how much does it cost without the discount? You can use percent decrease and algebra to solve this problem. If the price before the discount is x, and the decrease due to the discount is $0.05x$, then

$$x - 0.05x = \$15.00.$$

10. Remember that x can be written $1x$.
a. Combine like terms on the left side of the equation. (Or factor the x.)
b. Then solve for x.

11. Solve for x.
a. $0.2x = 240$
b. $x - 0.8x = 18.2$
c. $x - 0.06x = 23.50$
d. $x - 0.75x = 22.5$

12. Solve for x.
a. $(0.75)(0.75)x = 11.25$
b. $(0.65)^3x = 4.12$

8.8 SOLUTIONS

6	53
7	48
8	43
9	39
10	35

3. a. To find the score, take 0.90 of the previous score. For example 0.90(66) = 59.4 or 59.
b. A paper's score drops below 50 when it is 7 days late.
c. No, your score would never reach zero, although it would be close to zero. Each score is found by taking 0.90 of the previous day's score which is greater than zero. 90% of any nonzero number is not equal to zero.

4. **Mr. Riley's Late Policy**

Days late	Score
0	100
1	90
2	80
3	70
4	60
5	50
6	40
7	30
8	20
9	10
10	0

5. a. A paper's score drops below 50 when it is 6 days late.
b. Yes, the score reaches zero when it is 10 days late.

6.
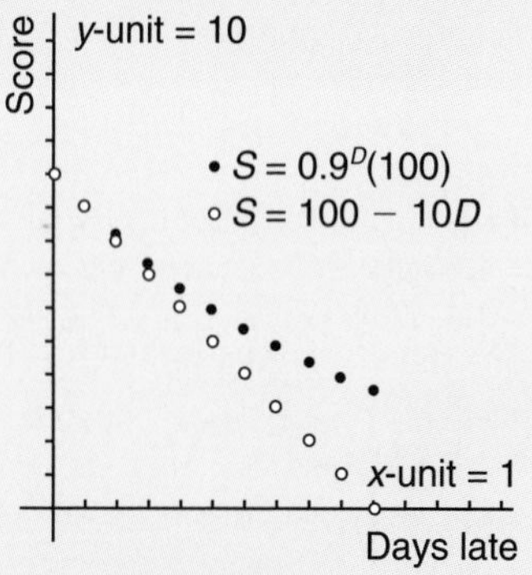

7. a. $S = 0.9^D(100)$
b. $S = 100 - 10D$

8. a. The percent off policy has an exponent.
b. The equation containing an exponent corresponds to the curved graph.

Look back at the ad for Sherman's Store.

13. a. If the clearance sale price is $13.50, what was the original price, before the 30% discount?

b. If the original price was $20.95, what is the 30% discount price?

14. Report Let x be the original price of an item. Write two algebraic expressions for the early-bird price, one that will give the amount Cal would charge, and one for the amount G.D. would charge. Explain how you figured out these two expressions. Show that they work, by substituting the prices from the table into the expression.

REVIEW *RATE OF CHANGE*

15. Find a function $y = mx + b$ for which

a. y increases when x increases;

b. y increases when x decreases;

c. y never increases.

16. Find a function $y = mx + b$, with m positive, for which y changes

a. faster than x;

b. more slowly than x;

c. at the same rate as x.

17. $y = x^7$ and $y = 2^x$ are having a race. When $x = 1$, $x^7 = 1$ and $2^x = 2$, so $y = 2^x$ is ahead. When $x = 3$, $x^7 = 2187$ and $2^x = 8$, so $y = x^7$ is ahead. As x gets larger and larger, who will win the race? Use your calculators and make a table to find out.

REVIEW RATE OF CHANGE

Problems 15-16 again review the concept of slope/rate of change/magnification. If students have questions about it, a class discussion of these two problems, with the help of function diagrams and/or Cartesian graphs may be in order.

Problem 17 forces students to use scientific notation, as $y = 2^x$ "catches up" eventually, but only for very large values of y.

8.8 SOLUTIONS

9. The two policies are the same for papers that are on time or one day late. Mr. Peters's late policy has higher scores than Mr. Riley's policy for papers two or more days late. Some students may prefer Mr. Peters's policy because they get higher scores. Some may prefer Mr. Riley's because it might motivate them more to get papers in on time.

10. $x - 0.05x = \$15.00$
 a. $0.95x = 15$
 b. $x = 15.79$

11. a. $x = 1200$
 b. $x - 0.8x = 18.2$
 $0.2x = 18.2$
 $x = 91$
 c. $x - 0.06x = 23.50$
 $0.94x = 23.50$
 $x = 25$
 d. $x - 0.75x = 22.5$
 $0.25x = 22.5$
 $x = 90$

12. a. $x = 20$ b. $x = 15$

13. a. x = original price
 $0.7x - 0.2(0.7x) = 13.5$
 $x = \$24.11$
 b. x = 30% discount price
 $x = 0.70(20.95)$
 $x = \$14.67$

14. Cal's price $= 0.70x - 0.20(0.70x)$
 $= 0.56x$
 G.D.'s price $= 0.70x - 0.20x = 0.50x$

15. a. Any $y = mx + b$ with $m > 0$
 b. Any $y = mx + b$ with $m < 0$
 c. Any $y = k$ where k is a constant

16. a. Any $y = mx + b$ in which $m > 1$
 b. Any $y = mx + b$ in which $m < 1$
 c. Any $y = mx + b$ with $m = 1$

17. For $x \geq 37$, 2^x is larger than x^7, so 2^x will win the race.

THINKING WRITING 8.B Simple and Compound Interest

Core Sequence: 1-3

Suitable for Homework: 1-5

Useful for Assessment: 3

What this Assignment is About:

- Exponential vs. linear growth
- Preview of fractional exponents

This writing assignment wraps up the last four lessons.

Problems 4-5 are difficult, and should be assigned only to students who have a solid grasp of the basic concepts covered in problems 1-3.

THINKING WRITING 8.B Simple and Compound Interest

Money in a savings account usually earns either *simple* or *compound* interest. For example, suppose you invest \$100 and earn 5% interest per year. If you earn *simple* interest, you will earn \$5 for every year that the money is invested, since 5 is 5% of 100. If you earn *compound* interest, you will earn \$5 for the first year the money is invested. In the next year, if you keep the entire \$105 in the bank, you will earn 5% interest on \$105. In other words, compound interest pays you interest on the interest as well as on the original investment.

The table shows what would happen to your investment in both cases for the first few years.

Total account balance, with:

Year	Simple interest	Compound interest
0	100	100
1	105	105
2	110	110.25
3	115	115.76

1. a. With simple interest, your account balance for each year can be obtained by *adding* a certain amount to the amount from the previous year. Find this amount.

b. With compound interest, your account balance for each year can be obtained by *multiplying* by a certain amount each year. Find this amount.

2. Write two equations (one for simple interest and one for compound interest) giving the account balance as the function of the year for:

a. 5% interest on the amount \$100;

b. 12% interest on the amount \$100;

c. 12% interest on the amount \$500.

3. Report Write a report comparing simple and compound interest. Your report should include, but not be limited to, the following:

- Equations for simple and compound interest that give the account balance as a function of time invested. Show how to change the equations if you change the amount of money invested or the interest rate. Explain how you figured out the equations.
- A comparison of how the amount in the account grows in each case. Which grows linearly and which grows exponentially? Explain how you know.
- An analysis of an example: Choose an amount to invest and an interest rate, and make a table or graph comparing the amount you would have in the account with simple and with compound interest. Assume you leave the money and the interest in the account for 25 years. Use a graph to illustrate.

4. Find a formula for the difference in the account balance after n years for two accounts that start with an original investment of s dollars at p percent interest, if one account earns simple interest and the other earns compound interest.

5. Say you have some money invested at 7% compound interest. How many *months* does it take for your investment to double? (Find a formula, then use decimal exponents on your calculator to find out what fraction of a year past a whole number of years it will take.)

8.B SOLUTIONS

1. a. Each year the balance is obtained by adding \$5.
   b. Each year the balance is obtained by multiplying by 1.05.
2. a. Simple interest: $y = 100 + 5x$
   Compound interest: $y = 100(1.05)^x$
   b. Simple interest: $y = 100 + 12x$
   Compound interest: $y = 100(1.12)^x$
   c. Simple interest: $y = 500 + 60x$
   Compound interest: $y = 500(1.12)^x$
3. Reports will vary. Simple interest equations have the form $y = mx + b$, where b is the amount of money initially invested, m is the product of the interest rate and the initial amount invested, x is the number of years the money is invested, and y is the account balance. Compound interest equations have the form $y = AB^x$, where A is the amount of money initially invested, B is the sum of 1 and the interest rate in decimal form, x is the number of years, and y is the account balance. Simple interest grows linearly, while compound interest grows exponentially.
4. Simple interest: $y = \frac{p}{100} sn + s$

   Compound interest: $y = s(1 + \frac{p}{100})^n$

   Difference: $s(1 + \frac{p}{100})^n - \frac{p}{100} sn + s$
5. $2s = s(1.07)^n$. $n \approx 10.24$ years

LESSON 8.9

Equal Powers

In this lesson, use only whole number exponents.

1. **Exploration** The number 64 can be written as a power in at least three different ways, as 2^6, 8^2, or 4^3.
   a. Find some numbers that can be written as powers in two different ways.
   b. Find another number that can be written as a power in three different ways.

POWERS OF 3 AND 9

2. Using your calculator if necessary, try to find a power of 3 that is equal to each power of 9 below. If any are impossible, say so. Fill in the exponent.
   a. $9^2 = 81 = 3^?$
   b. $9^5 = 59049 = 3^?$
   c. $9^{10} = 3^?$
   d. $9^0 = 3^?$
3. Using your calculator if necessary, try to find a power of 9 that is equal to each power of 3 below. If any are impossible, say so. Fill in the exponent.
   a. $3^8 = 6561 = 9^?$
   b. $3^5 = 243 = 9^?$
   c. $3^{14} = 9^?$
   d. $3^0 = 9^?$
4. a. Can every power of 9 be written as a power of 3? If so, explain why. If not, show some that can and some that can't, and explain the difference.
   b. Can every power of 3 be written as a power of 9? If so, explain why. If not, show some that can and some that can't, and explain the difference.

POWERS OF 2, 4, 6, AND 8

5. Find two powers of 2 (other than 64) that can be written as powers of 8.
6. If the same number is written as both a power of 2 and a power of 8, how do the exponents compare? Explain and give examples.
7. Find at least three powers of 2 that can be written as powers of 4. Compare the exponents and describe what you notice.
8. Find at least two powers of 2 that can be written as powers of 16. Compare the exponents and describe what you notice.
9. a. Which powers of 2 can be written as powers of 8? Explain, giving examples.
   b. Which powers of 8 can be written as powers of 2? Explain, giving examples.
   c. Find the smallest number (besides 1) that can be written as a power of 2, a power of 4, and a power of 8. Write it in all three ways. How do you know that it is the smallest?
10. Can you find a number that can be written as a power of 2, a power of 4, and a power of 6? If so, find it. If not, explain why it is impossible.

WRITING POWERS USING DIFFERENT BASES

11. Write each number as a power using a smaller base.

a. 8^2	b. 27^3	c. 25^3
d. 16^4	e. 49^2	f. 2^0

8.9 Equal Powers

Core Sequence: 1-22

Suitable for Homework: 5-22

Useful for Assessment: 4, 9-10, 15-16, 19-22

What this Lesson is About:

- Power of a power
- Percent-problem equations

Problem 1 gets the students thinking about the essential idea behind this lesson: writing the same number as a power in more than one way.

POWERS OF 3 AND 9

POWERS OF 2, 4, 6, AND 8

WRITING POWERS USING DIFFERENT BASES

You may discuss with your students whether it is more illuminating to use the power key or repeated multiplication on the calculator when working on problems 2-3. Students may come up with the idea of using exponents that are not whole numbers. This lesson requires that they limit themselves to whole numbers, but assure them that they will study other kinds of exponents soon.

After working out specific examples in problems 2-3, the students are asked to look for the underlying pattern in problem 4.

8.9 SOLUTIONS

1. Answers will vary. Samples:
   a. $16 = 2^4$ and 4^2
   $81 = 3^4$ and 9^2
   b. 256 is 2^8, 4^4, and 16^2
2. a. 4 b. 10
   c. 20 d. 0
3. a. 4 b. impossible
   c. 7 d. 0
4. a. Every power of 9 can be written as a power of 3 because if the power of 9 were written as a product of nines, each 9 could be replaced by the product of two threes. So 9 to any exponent is the same as 3 to twice that exponent.
   b. Only even powers of 3 can be written as a power of 9 because if an even power of 3 were written as a product of threes, each pair of threes could be replaced by one 9. So 3 to an even exponent equals 9 to half that exponent. However, an odd power of 3 cannot be expressed as a power of 9.
5. Answers vary. Samples:
   $512 = 2^9 = 8^3$
   $4096 = 2^{12} = 8^4$
6. The exponent of 2 is three times the exponent of 8 since $8^1 = 2^3$. If the power of 8 were written as a product, such as $8^3 = 8 \cdot 8 \cdot 8$, each 8 could be replaced by 2^3 or $2 \cdot 2 \cdot 2$, such as $8^3 = (2 \cdot 2 \cdot 2)(2 \cdot 2 \cdot 2)(2 \cdot 2 \cdot 2) = 2^9$.
7. Answers vary. Samples: $16 = 2^4 = 4^2$, $64 = 2^6 = 4^3$, $256 = 2^8 = 4^4$. The exponent of 2 is twice the exponent of 4.
8. Answers vary. Sample: $256 = 2^8 = 16^2$, $4096 = 2^{12} = 16^3$. The exponent of 2 is four times the exponent of 16.
9. a. The powers of 2 whose exponents are multiples of three can be written as powers of 8. For example, $2^3 = 8^1$, $2^6 = 8^2$, $2^9 = 8^3$
   b. Any power of 8 can be written as a power of 2. The exponent of 2 is three times the exponent of 8. For example, $8^1 = 2^3$, $8^4 = 2^{12}$.
   c. 64 can be written as 8^2, 4^3, and 2^6. It is the smallest power of 8 that is also a power of 4.
10. This is impossible. 6 can be factored into $2 \cdot 3$. All powers of 6 are products of a certain number of twos and threes, for example $6^2 = 6 \cdot 6 = 2 \cdot 3 \cdot 2 \cdot 3$. So, no power of 6 can be expressed as a power of 2 having a whole number exponent because of the presence of the threes in the product.

The next two sections are very much a replay of the same material with different numbers, and so they lend themselves to being done as homework.

A POWER OF A POWER

All of problems 1-15 preview, in a problem-solving context, the idea in this section. As a result, your students should be ripe for understanding the power of a power law. Nevertheless, you may want to discuss with the whole class the step-by-step derivation of the law, as described between problems 17 and 18.

12. Write each number as a power using a larger base.
a. 3^2 b. 9^4 c. 4^8
d. 5^8 e. 6^6 f. 95^0

13. If possible, write each number as a power using a different base. (Do not use the exponent 1.) If it is not possible, explain why not.
a. 3^4 b. 3^3
c. 4^5 d. 3^5

14. Repeat problem 13 for these numbers.
a. 5^4 b. 5^3
c. 25^2 d. 26^4

15. Summary If you exclude the exponent 1, when it is possible to write a number in two or more ways as a power? Does it depend on the base, the exponent, or both? Explain. (Give examples of some equivalent powers and of numbers that can be written as powers in only one way.)

16. Generalization Fill in the exponents.
a. $9^x = 3^?$ b. $4^x = 2^?$
c. $8^x = 2^?$ d. $16^x =$
e. $25^x =$

A POWER OF A POWER

Since $9 = 3^2$, the power 9^3 can be written as $(3^2)^3$. The expression $(3^2)^3$ is a *power of a power* of 3.

17. a. Write 25^3 as a power of a power of 5.
b. Write 8^5 as a power of a power of 2.
c. Write 9^4 as a power of a power of 3.

There is often a simpler way to write a power of a power. For example:

$$(3^5)^2 = (3^5)(3^5)$$
$$= (3 \cdot 3 \cdot 3 \cdot 3 \cdot 3)(3 \cdot 3 \cdot 3 \cdot 3 \cdot 3)$$
$$= 3^{10}$$

18. a. Show how $(2^5)^3$ can be written with one exponent as a power of 2.
b. Write $(3^4)^2$ as a power of 3.

19. Is $(4^5)^3$ equal to 4^8, to 4^{15}, or to neither? Explain.

Generalizations

20. Fill in the exponents.
a. $(x^2)^3 = x^?$ b. $y^4 = (y^2)^?$
c. $y^{10} = (y^5)^?$ d. $y^6 = (y^3)^?$
e. $(x^4)^3 = x^?$

21. Fill in the exponents.
a. $(y^2)^x = y^?$ b. $(y^3)^x = y^?$
c. $(x^4)^y = x^?$ d. $y^{ax} = (y^x)^?$

The generalization you made in problem 21 is one of the *laws of exponents.* It is sometimes called the *power of a power law:*

$(x^a)^b = x^{ab}$, as long as x is not 0.

22. Explain how the ideas you discussed in problem 15 are related to the power of a power law.

8.9 SOLUTIONS

11. a. $8^2 = 2^6$ b. $27^3 = 3^9$
c. $25^3 = 5^6$ d. $16^4 = 4^8$
e. $49^2 = 7^4$ f. $2^0 = 1^0$

12. a. $3^2 = 9^1$ b. $9^4 = 81^2$
c. $4^8 = 16^4$ d. $5^8 = 25^4 = 625^2$
e. $6^6 = 36^3$
f. Answers may vary. Sample: $95^0 = 96^0$. Any base larger than 95 is correct.

13. a. $3^4 = 9^2$
b. $3^3 = 27^1$ (It is impossible to write 3^3 as a power of 9 because the exponent of three must be even.)
c. $4^5 = 2^{10}$
d. $3^5 = 243^1$ (It is impossible to express 3^5 as a power of 9 because the exponent of three is not an even number.)

14. a. $5^4 = 25^2$
b. $5^3 = 125^1$ (It is impossible to express 5^3 as a power of 25 because the exponent of 5 is not an even number.)
c. $25^2 = 5^4$
d. $26^4 = 676^2$

15. Answers will vary. If the base is a power of a smaller number, such as 4, 8, 9, 16, 25, or 27, then the power can be written with a smaller base and higher exponent. For example, $4^3 = 2^6$, $8^5 = 2^{15}$, $27^4 = 3^{12}$.

If the exponent is even, the power can be written with a larger base, which is the square of the original base, and a smaller exponent, which is half the original exponent. For example $2^2 = 4^1$, $3^4 = 9^2$, $3^6 = 9^3$.

If a base, other than 2, cannot be expressed as a power of a smaller number, such as 3, 5, 6, 7, 10, 11, 12, 13, 14, or 15, and if this base is raised to the 3rd, 5th, or 7th power, then it cannot be written differently as a power. For example, 3^3 or 7^3 cannot be written differently as a power.

If the exponent is a multiple of n, then the power can be written with a new exponent ($1/n$) times as large. For example: $5^{15} = (5^3)^5 = 125^5$.

16. a. $2x$ b. $2x$
c. $3x$ d. 4^{2x} or 2^{4x}
e. 5^{2x}

17. a. $25^3 = (5^2)^3$ b. $8^5 = (2^3)^5$
c. $9^4 = (3^2)^4$

18. a. $(2^5)^3 = 2^{15}$ b. $(3^4)^2 = 3^8$

(Solutions continued on page 524)

LESSON 8.10

Working With Monomials

The product of the monomials $3x^2$ and $9x^4$ is also a monomial. This can be shown by using the definition of exponentiation as repeated multiplication.

$$3x^2 = 3 \cdot x \cdot x \text{ and } 9x^4 = 9 \cdot x \cdot x \cdot x \cdot x$$

so

$$3x^2 \cdot 9x^4 = 3 \cdot x \cdot x \cdot 9 \cdot x \cdot x \cdot x \cdot x = 27x^6$$

1. Find another pair of monomials whose product is $27x^6$.

2. **Exploration** If possible, find at least two answers to each of these problems. Write $27x^6$ as:
   a. the product of three monomials
   b. the sum of three monomials
   c. a monomial raised to a power
   d. the quotient of two monomials
   e. the difference of two monomials

PRODUCT OF POWERS

The monomial $48x^9$ can be written as a product in many different ways. For example, $16x^6 \cdot 3x^3$ and $12x^5 \cdot 4x^3 \cdot x$ are both equal to $48x^9$.

3. Write $48x^9$ in three more ways as a product of two or more monomials.

4. Write $35x^4$ as a product in which one of the factors is
   a. a third-degree monomial;
   b. a monomial with a coefficient of 7;
   c. $5x^0$;
   d. $35x^3$.

5. Write $7.2 \cdot 10^8$ in three ways as the product of two numbers in scientific notation.

6. Write x^5 in three ways as a product of two or more monomials.

7. **Generalization** Study your answers to problem 6. Then fill in the exponent.
   $$x^a \cdot x^b = x^?$$
   Explain.

8. If possible, write each expression more simply. If it is not possible, explain why not.
   a. $3x^5 \cdot 6x^4$ b. $x^5 \cdot y^7$
   c. $y^7 \cdot y^3$ d. $4a^4 \cdot 9a^3$

The generalization you made is one of the laws of exponents. It is sometimes called the *product of powers* law. It says that

$$x^a \cdot x^b = x^{a+b}, \text{ as long as } x \text{ is not 0.}$$

However, notice that it works only when the bases are the same.

POWER OF A PRODUCT

The expression $x^4 \cdot y^4 \cdot z^4$ is the product of three powers. Since the bases are not the same, we cannot use the product of powers law. However, notice that since the exponents are the same, it is possible to write a product of powers as a single power

$$x^4y^4z^4 = x \cdot x \cdot x \cdot x \cdot y \cdot y \cdot y \cdot y \cdot z \cdot z \cdot z \cdot z$$
$$= xyz \cdot xyz \cdot xyz \cdot xyz$$
$$= (xyz)^4$$

9. Write $16a^2b^2$ as the square of a monomial. (Hint: First rewrite 16 as a power.)

10. Write p^3q^3 as the cube of a monomial.

11. If possible, write each expression as a single power. If it is not possible, explain why not.
    a. $32n^5m^5$ b. x^2y^3
    c. $(2n)^7 \cdot (3m)^7$ d. $(ab)^4 \cdot (bc)^4$

8.10 SOLUTIONS

1. Answers will vary: Sample: $27x \cdot x^5 = 27x^6$
2. Answers will vary. Samples:
   a. $3x^2 \cdot 3x^2 \cdot 3x^2 = 3x \cdot 9x^2 \cdot x^3 = 27x^6$
   b. $20x^6 + 3x^6 + 4x^6 = 27x^6$
   $5x^6 + 16x^6 + 6x^6 = 27x^6$
   c. $(3x^2)^3 = 27x^6$
   d. $(54x^8)/(2x^2) = (81x^{12})/(3x^6) = 27x^6$
   e. $50x^6 - 23x^6 = 30x^6 - 3x^6 = 27x^6$
3. Answers may vary. Samples: $2x^2 \cdot 24x^7 = 6x^4 \cdot 2x^3 \cdot 4x^2 = 4x \cdot 12x^8 = 48x^9$
4. a. Answers may vary. Sample: $35x^4 = 7x \cdot 5x^3$
   b. Answers may vary. Sample: $35x^4 = 7x^2 \cdot 5x^2$
   c. $35x^4 = 5x^0 \cdot 7x^4$
   d. $35x^4 = 35x^3 \cdot x$
5. Answers may vary. Sample: $(3.6 \cdot 10^2)(2.0 \cdot 10^6) = (2.4 \cdot 10^3)(3.0 \cdot 10^5) = (1.8 \cdot 10^4)(4.0 \cdot 10^4) = 7.2 \cdot 10^8$
6. $(x \cdot x^2 \cdot x^2) = (x^3 \cdot x^2) = (x^4 \cdot x) = x^5$
7. $x^a \cdot x^b = x^{a+b}$. If *a* *x*-monomials are multiplied by *b* *x*-monomials, there are *a* + *b* *x*-monomials being multiplied. This is written x^{a+b}.
8. a. $18x^9$
   b. $x^5 \cdot y^7$ cannot be simplified because the powers have different bases.
   c. y^{10}
   d. $36a^7$
9. $(4ab)^2$
10. $(pq)^3$

8.10 Working With Monomials

Core Sequence: 1-29

Suitable for Homework: 3-29

Useful for Assessment: 7, 23, 27-28

What this Lesson is About:
- Product of powers
- Power of a product
- Power of a ratio
- Preview of ratio of powers
- Simplifying algebraic fractions

In this lesson three laws of exponents are stated. Because they have had a number of opportunities to preview these, some students should already have an understanding of these laws.

Use problems 1-2 to help those students who are still shaky on their understanding of this material. One way to organize work on open questions like these is to have students verify the correctness of each other's solutions within their groups and discuss disagreements or questions. Whole-class discussion of controversial answers can help too.

PRODUCT OF POWERS

This law, also called the Basic Law of Exponents, is the one upon which all the other ones rest. It is a direct consequence of the definition of exponentiation as repeated multiplication, but as students will learn later in their mathematical careers, it also applies to negative and fractional exponents.

When students make mistakes multiplying powers of the same base, it is best to remind them to write out the problem as in the example that opened this lesson. This format makes it easy to remember the product of powers law.

POWER OF A PRODUCT

Again, the best way to address mistakes is to go back to the process demonstrated in the example just before problem 9, and the one after problem 14.

POWER OF A RATIO

This law is often called *power of a quotient*. However, students have often seen the word *quotient* defined as part of the answer to a division, with the other part being the remainder. As a result they may find this terminology confusing. We believe *power of a ratio* is mathematically correct and carries less risk of confusion.

RATIOS OF MONOMIALS

Here, the main obstacle to student understanding is an insufficiently clear grasp of equivalent fractions. Remind students that equivalent fractions are obtained by multiplying or dividing "top and bottom" by the same quantity. Or, equivalently, by "multiplying by 1" in a form such as x/x.

If this section is done as homework, be sure to plan enough time for class discussion of it the next day. This work previews the final law of exponents, the ratio of powers, which will be stated in the next lesson.

You may use problems 22-24 as a springboard for the discussion of negative exponents. In problem 24, if $p < q$, then the expression x^{p-q} could still be used, if negative exponents are defined correctly. (This is the subject of the next lesson.)

SOLVING EQUATIONS

These equations give students a chance to use the laws of exponents for equation solving.

The generalization you used above is another of the laws of exponents. It is sometimes called the *power of a product* law. It says that

$x^a y^a = (xy)^a$, as long as x and y are not 0.

However, notice that it works only when the exponents are the same.

12. Write without parentheses.
a. $(6y)^2$ b. $(3xy)^4$
c. $(5xyz)^3$ d. $(2x)^3$
e. $(2xy)^3$ f. $(2xyz)^3$

13. Write $64x^3y^6z^9$ as the cube of a monomial.

POWER OF A RATIO

14. Write 49/25 as the square of a ratio.

Study this example.

$$\left(\frac{x}{y}\right)^3 = \frac{x}{y}\cdot\frac{x}{y}\cdot\frac{x}{y} = \frac{x\cdot x\cdot x}{y\cdot y\cdot y} = \frac{x^3}{y^3}$$

This law of exponents is called the *power of a ratio* law. It says that

$\frac{x^a}{y^a} = \left(\frac{x}{y}\right)^a$, as long as x and y are not 0.

However, notice that it works only when the exponents are the same.

15. Write as a power of a ratio.
a. $8x^3/y^6$ b. $16x^4/x^{10}$

16. Write as a ratio of monomials.
a. $(5x/7z)^9$ b. $(2xy/yz)^2$

RATIOS OF MONOMIALS

Consider the ratio $6x^5/4x^7$. By multiplying numerator and denominator by x, you can get the equivalent ratio $6x^6/4x^7$. Or you can get an equivalent ratio in lowest terms by noticing that

$$\frac{6x^5}{4x^7} = \frac{3}{2x^2}\cdot\frac{2x^5}{2x^5} = \frac{3}{2x^2}.$$

17. Explain the example above.

18. Write in lowest terms.
a. $8x^8/6x^9$ b. $7x^7/5x^4$

In some cases, a ratio can be simplified to a monomial. For example,

$$\frac{150x^6}{50x^4} = 3x^2.$$

19. a. Explain this example.
b. Write $3x^2$ as a ratio of monomials in three other ways.

20. Write $12y^3$ as a quotient of two monomials in which
a. one is a fourth-degree monomial;
b. one has a coefficient of 5;
c. one is a monomial of degree 0.

21. Write $1.2 \cdot 10^4$ in three ways as the quotient of two numbers in scientific notation.

22. a. Write x^5 as a ratio in three ways.
b. Find three ratios equivalent to $1/x^5$.

23. **Generalization** Study your answers to problem 22. Compare the situations in (a) and (b). Explain how to simplify a ratio whose numerator and denominator are powers of x.

24. Fill in the exponent, assuming $p > q$.

$$\frac{x^p}{x^q} = x^?$$

25. Write these ratios in lowest terms.
a. $3x^5/6x^4$ b. x^5/y^7
c. y^3/y^7 d. $45a^4/9a^3$

26. Write as a power of 6. $\frac{6^{x-5}}{6^{5-x}}$

SOLVING EQUATIONS

Solve for x.

27. a. $\frac{5^{2x}}{5^x} = 5^7$ b. $\frac{(7^2)^x}{7^4} = 7^6$

28. a. $\frac{(3\cdot 5)^3}{108\cdot 5^x} = \frac{1}{20}$ b. $\frac{3^3\cdot 4^7}{3\cdot 4^x} = \left(\frac{3}{4}\right)^2$

29.
a. $\frac{3\cdot 4^{6p}}{9\cdot 4^x} = \frac{1}{3\cdot 4^{4p}}$ b. $\frac{15h^x}{12h^a} = \frac{5}{4h^6}$

8.10 SOLUTIONS

11. a. $(2nm)^5$
b. x^2 and y^3 have different bases.
c. $(6nm)^7$
d. $(ab^2c)^4$

12. a. $36y^2$ b. $81x^4y^4$
c. $125x^3y^3z^3$ d. $8x^3$
e. $8x^3y^3$ f. $8x^3y^3z^3$

13. $(4xy^2z^3)^3$

14. $(7/5)^2$

15. a. $(2x/y^2)^3$ b. $(4/x^3)^2$

16. a. $(1{,}953{,}125x^9)/(40{,}353{,}607z^9)$
b. $(4x^2)/(z^2)$

17. In the numerator $6x^5$ is written as $3 \cdot 2x^5$. In the denominator $4x^7$ is written as $2x^2 \cdot 2x^5$. $(6x^5)/(4x^7)$ is written as the product of two ratios $3/(2x^2)$ and $2x^5/(2x^5)$. Any fraction with the same nonzero numerator and denominator equals 1, so $(2x^5)/(2x^5) = 1$. Hence $3/(2x^2) \cdot (2x^5)/(2x^5) = 3/(2x^2) \cdot 1 = 3/(2x^2)$.

18. a. $4/(3x)$ b. $7x^3/5$

19. 50 goes into 150 three times and $x^6/x^4 = x^{6-4} = x^2$, so $150x^6/(50x^4) = 3x^2$.

20. a. $(12y^4)/y$ b. $(60y^4)/(5y)$
c. $12y^3/y^0$

21. Answers may vary. Sample: $(2.4 \cdot 10^6)/(2.0 \cdot 10^2) = (3.6 \cdot 10^{12})/(3.0 \cdot 10^8) = (5.64 \cdot 10^9)/(4.7 \cdot 10^5) = 1.2 \cdot 10^4$

22. Answers may vary. Samples:
a. $x^{10}/x^5 = x^{12}/x^7 = x^6/x$
b. $x/x^6 = 3/(3x^5) = (10x^8)/(10x^{13}) = 1/x^5$

23. To simplify a ratio whose numerator and denominator are powers of x, write the answer as x to the numerator's exponent minus the denominator's exponent.

24. x^{p-q}

25. a. $x/2$ b. x^5/y^7
c. $1/y^4$ d. $5a$

26. 6^{2x-10}

27. a. $x = 7$ b. $x = 5$

28. a. $x = 4$ b. $x = 9$

29. a. $x = 10p$ b. $x = a - 6$

LESSON 8.11

Negative Bases, Negative Exponents

RECIPROCALS

In previous lessons, we have considered only whole number exponents. Does a negative exponent have any meaning? To answer this, consider these patterns.

$3^4 = 81$	$(1/3)^4 = 1/81$
$3^3 = 27$	$(1/3)^3 = 1/27$
$3^2 = 9$	$(1/3)^2 = 1/9$
$3^1 = 3$	$(1/3)^1 = 1/3$
$3^0 = 1$	$(1/3)^0 = 1$
$3^{-1} = ?$	$(1/3)^{-1} = ?$

1. a. Look at the powers of 3. How is each number related to the number above it? Following this pattern, what should the value of 3^{-1} be?

b. Now look for a pattern in the powers of 1/3. As the exponent increases, does the value of the power increase or decrease? Following this pattern, what should the value of $(1/3)^{-1}$ be?

c. Compare the values of 3^{-1}, 3^1, $(1/3)^1$ and $(1/3)^{-1}$. How are they related?

d. Use the pattern you found to extend the table down to 3^{-4} and $(1/3)^{-4}$.

Another way to figure out the meaning of negative exponents is to use the product of powers law. For example, to figure out the meaning of 3^{-1}, note that:

$$3^{-1} \cdot 3^2 = 3^1$$
$$3^{-1} \cdot 9 = 3$$

But the only number that can be multiplied by 9 to get 3 is 1/3, so 3^{-1} must equal 1/3.

2. Find the value of 3^{-1} by applying the product of powers law to $3^1 \cdot 3^{-1}$.

3. Use the same logic to find the value of:
a. 3^{-2}; b. 3^{-x}.

4. Are the answers you found in problem 3 consistent with the pattern you found in problem 1? Explain.

5. **Summary** People who have not studied algebra (and, unfortunately, many who have) think that 5^{-2} equals a negative number, such as -25.

a. Write a convincing argument using the product of powers law to explain why this is not true.

b. Show how to find the value of 5^{-2} using a pattern like the one in problem 1.

6. a. Show that $5x^2$ and $5x^{-2}$ are not reciprocals, by showing that their product is not 1.

b. Find the reciprocal of $5x^2$.

MORE ON EXPONENTIAL GROWTH

A bacterial culture doubles every hour. At this moment it weighs 10 grams.

7. What did it weigh

a. 1 hour ago?

b. 2 hours ago?

c. x hours ago?

8.

a. Explain why the weight of the bacteria culture x hours from now is given by
$$W = 10 \cdot 2^x.$$

b. Explain the meaning of substituting a negative value for x.

8.11 Negative Bases, Negative Exponents

Core Sequence: 1-20, 23-30

Suitable for Homework: 5-18, 21-31

Useful for Assessment: 5, 8, 10, 19-20

What this Lesson is About:

- Negative exponents
- Review of reciprocals
- Review of order of operations
- Review of the product of powers law
- Review of exponential growth
- Ratio of powers
- Review of scientific notation
- Preview of rational expressions
- Slope-intercept review

This lesson reviews many concepts while introducing negative exponents.

RECIPROCALS

This section introduces negative exponents in two ways: from a pattern in a table in problem 1, and as a consequence of the product of powers law in problem 2. The summary requires students to present both explanations.

The section also serves to review the concept of reciprocal and the product of powers law.

8.11 SOLUTIONS

1. a. Each number is 1/3 the number above it. Following this pattern, 3^{-1} should be 1/3.

b. As the exponent of 1/3 increases, the value of the power decreases. Following this pattern the value of $(1/3)^{-1}$ should be 3.

c. $3^{-1} = 1/3$, $3^1 = 3$, $(1/3)^1 = 1/3$, $(1/3)^{-1} = 3$. 3^{-1} and 3^1 are reciprocals because $(1/3)(3) = 1$ or because $3^{-1} \cdot 3^1 = 3^{-1+1} = 3^0 = 1$.

d.

$3^4 = 81$	$(1/3)^4 = 1/81$
$3^3 = 27$	$(1/3)^3 = 1/27$
$3^2 = 9$	$(1/3)^2 = 1/9$
$3^1 = 3$	$(1/3)^1 = 1/3$
$3^0 = 1$	$(1/3)^0 = 1$
$3^{-1} = 1/3$	$(1/3)^{-1} = 3$
$3^{-2} = 1/9$	$(1/3)^{-2} = 9$
$3^{-3} = 1/27$	$(1/3)^{-3} = 27$
$3^{-4} = 1/81$	$(1/3)^{-4} = 81$

2. $3^1 \cdot 3^{-1} = 1$
$3 \cdot 3^{-1} = 1$
$3^{-1} = 1/3$

3. a. $3^{-2} = 1/9$
b. $3^{-x} = 1/(3^x)$

4. Yes. 3^{-2} is 1/3 of 3^{-1} which would be the number above in the table. In general we can see from the table that $3^{-x} = 1/3^x$.

5. a. $5^2 = 25$
$5^1 = 5$
$5^0 = 1$
$5^{-1} = 1/5$
$5^{-2} = 1/25$
Each number in the table is 1/5 of the number above it. Following this pattern, one gets $5^{-2} = 1/25$ which is a positive number.

b. $5^2 \cdot 5^{-2} = 5^0$
$5^2 \cdot 5^{-2} = 1$
$5^{-2} = 1/(5^2)$

6. a. $5x^2 \cdot 5x^{-2} = 25x^0 = 25$ so $5x^2$ and $5x^{-2}$ are not reciprocals.

b. The reciprocal of $5x^2$ is $1/(5x^2)$ because $5x^2 \cdot$ reciprocal = 1, so reciprocal = $1/(5x^2)$.

7. a. One hour ago the bacterial culture weighed 5 grams.

b. Two hours ago the bacterial culture weighed 2.5 grams.

c. x hours ago the bacterial culture weighed $10(1/2)^x$.

MORE ON EXPONENTIAL GROWTH

This section applies negative exponents to exponential growth, for a "doubling" and a "percent increase" problem, both of which were seen in Lessons 5 and 6.

RATIO OF POWERS

This law has essentially been introduced in Lesson 10, but it could not be stated in all its generality then because negative exponents had not been introduced.

OPPOSITES

This reviews order of operations and provides practice with exponents.

EARLY PAPERS

A class discussion of student plans would be interesting. Students may propose linear and exponential schemes or other schemes. If no one proposes an exponential scheme, encourage students to discuss in their groups how the ideas of **More on Exponential Growth** can be incorporated into an early paper policy.

9. Show your calculations, using the equation in problem 8, to find out:
 a. how much it will weigh in three hours;
 b. how much it weighed three hours ago.

In 1975 the world population was about 4.01 billion and growing at the rate of 2% per year.

10. If it continued to grow at that rate, write a formula for the world population after x years.

If it had been growing at the same rate before 1975, we could estimate the population in previous years by using negative values of x in the formula.

11. Use your calculator to find the value of $(1.02)^4$ and its reciprocal, $(1.02)^{-4}$.

12. Show your calculations using the equation in problem 10 to estimate the population in:
 a. 1971; b. 1979.

13. Assume the world population had been growing at this rate since 1925.
 a. Estimate the world population in 1925.
 b. Compare this number with the actual world population in 1925, which was about 2 billion. Was the population growth rate between 1925 and 1975 more or less than 2%? Explain.

RATIO OF POWERS

Negative exponents often arise when simplifying ratios of monomials.

This law of exponents is sometimes called the *ratio of powers* law:

$$\frac{x^a}{x^b} = x^{a-b}\text{, as long as } x \text{ is not } 0.$$

However, notice that it works only when the bases are the same.

Examples:

$\frac{x^6}{x^7} = x^{6-7} = x^{-1}$ or $\frac{1}{x^1}$

$\frac{x^{3a}}{x^{5a}} = x^{3a-5a} = x^{-2a}$ or $\frac{1}{x^{2a}}$

14. Simplify.
 a. $4x^6/5x^7$ b. $2x^8y^3/2xy$
 c. y^3/y^7 d. $45a/9a^5$

15. Simplify these ratios.
 a. $\frac{400a^5}{25a^2}$ b. $\frac{400x^3}{200x^8}$
 c. $\frac{3m^6}{9m^3}$ d. $\frac{9R^a}{3R^a}$

16.
 a. Write as a power of 4, $4^{3+x}/4^{3-x}$.
 b. Write as a power of 7, $7^{5x-5}/7^{5x-6}$.

17. Solve for x.
 a. $\frac{7^4}{7^{x+2}} = 7^3$
 b. $\frac{3 \cdot 5^{x+2}}{12 \cdot 5^2} = \frac{1}{20}$

18. Divide without using your calculator. Then, if your answer is not already in scientific notation, convert it to scientific notation.
 a. $\frac{4.2 \cdot 10^5}{3.0 \cdot 10^2}$ b. $\frac{3.0 \cdot 10^4}{1.5 \cdot 10^6}$
 c. $\frac{1.5 \cdot 10^3}{3.0 \cdot 10^6}$ d. $\frac{9 \cdot 10^a}{3 \cdot 10^b}$

OPPOSITES

The expression $(-5)^3$ has a negative base. This expression means *raise -5 to the third power.* The expression -5^3 has a positive base. This expression means *raise 5 to the third power and take the opposite of the result.*

8. a.

x hours	$10 \cdot 2^x$
3	80
2	40
1	20
0	10
-1	5
-2	2.5

The table shows that $w = 10 \cdot 2^x$ results in a population that doubles every hour. Changing the value of x in the expression $10 \cdot 2^x$ changes the number of times the population doubles.

 b. A negative value for x represents the number of hours before the moment called the zero hour. For example, x might be considered zero at 12:00 noon so at 11:00 A.M. $x = -1$ and at 8:00 A.M., $x = -4$. If $x = 0$ represents now, a negative x represents a number of hours in the past.

9. a. $W = 10 \cdot 2^x = 10 \cdot 2^3 = 80$. The population weighs 80 grams in three hours.
 b. $W = 10 \cdot 2^{-3} = 10 \cdot 1/8 = 5/4$. So the population weighed 5/4 grams three hours ago.

10. $P = 4.01(1.02)^x$ where P = the world population and x the number of years after 1975.

11. $(1.02)^4 = 1.082432160$
 $(1.02)^{-4} = 0.92384526$

12. a. In 1971, $x = -4$.
 $W = 4.01(1.02)^{-4} = 3.704620158$.
 In 1971 the estimated population was 3.7 billion.
 b. In 1979, $x = 4$. $W = 4.01(1.02)^4 =$ 4.340,552,962. In 1979 the estimated population was 4.34 billion.

13. a. In 1925, $x = -50$ because 1925-1975 = -50.
 So $W = 4.01(1.02)^{-50}$
 $= 4.01(0.3715) = 1.4982$.
 In 1925 the estimated population was 1.49 billion.
 b. In 1925 the actual world population was about 2 billion. At a rate of 2% for 50 years beginning with a population of 2 billion the 1975 population would have been $P = 2(1.02)^{50} = 5.38$. Because 4.01 billion is less than 5.38 billion the rate of growth was less than 2%.

14. a. $4/(5x)$ b. x^7y^2
 c. $1/y^4$ d. $5/a^4$

15. a. $16a^3$ b. $2/x^5$
 c. $m^3/3$ d. 3

16. a. 4^{2x} b. 7

17. a. $x = -1$ b. $x = -1$

19. Which of these expressions represent negative numbers? Show the calculations or explain the reasoning leading to your conclusions.

-5^3 $(-5)^3$ -5^2 $(-7)^{15}$ $(-7)^{14}$

-5^{-3} $(-5)^{-3}$ -5^{-2} $(-7)^{-15}$ $(-7)^{-14}$

20.

a. Is $(-5)^n$ always, sometimes, or never the opposite of 5^n? Explain, using examples.

b. Is -5^n always, sometimes, or never the opposite of 5^n? Explain, using examples.

EARLY PAPERS

Ms. Kem has a policy that penalizes students for turning in papers late. Her students are trying to convince her to give them extra points for turning in their papers early. Some students propose a policy based on adding points. Others propose one based on increasing by a percentage.

21. If you were her student, what kind of early paper policy would you propose?

22. Using your policy, what would your score be, if your paper were x days early?

REVIEW WHICH IS GREATER?

Or are they equal?

23. a. $x - 0.30x$ b. $0.70x$

24. a. $(0.70)(0.70)x$ b. $x - 0.50x$

25. a. $(0.90)(0.90)(0.90)x$

b. $x - 0.10x - 0.10x - 0.10x$

REVIEW EQUATION SOLVING

Solve for x.

26. a. $(0.85)(0.85)(0.85)(0.85)x = 18.79$

b. $x - 0.2x = 160$

c. $0.80x = 500$

27. $\frac{50b^3}{xb} = 2b^2$

28. $\frac{20a^{m+1}}{10a^m} = 2a^x$

REVIEW WHAT'S THE FUNCTION?

29. Find the slope of the line that goes through each pair of points. Then find the equation for the line. (Hint: A sketch may help.)

a. (0, 1) and (2, 3)

b. (0, 4) and (0.5, -6)

c. (0, 7) and (-0.8, 0.9)

30. In problem 29

a. how did you find the y-intercept?

b. how did you find the slope?

31. Find the equation for the line

a. having slope 0.9, passing through (2, -1);

b. having slope 3.4, passing through (6.7, 9);

c. passing through (8, 2) and (1.3, -5.4).

8.11 SOLUTIONS

18. a. $1.4 \cdot 10^3$ b. $2.0 \cdot 10^{-2}$

c. $0.5 \cdot 10^{-3}$ d. $3 \cdot 10^{a-b}$

19. $-5^3 = -125$.

$(-5)^3 = (-5)(-5)(-5) = -125$.

$-5^2 = -25$

$(-7)^{15}$ is negative. The product of 15 negative numbers is negative.

$(-7)^{14}$ is positive. The product of 14 negative numbers is positive.

$-5^{-3} = -1/5^3 = -1/125$

$(-5)^{-3} = 1/(-5)^3 = 1/-125 = -1/125$

$-5^{-2} = -1/5^2 = -1/25$

$(-7)^{-15} = 1/(-7)^{15}$ and $(-7)^{15}$ is negative. So $1/(-7)^{15}$ is negative also.

$(-7)^{-14} = 1/(-7)^{14}$ and $(-17)^{14}$ is positive.

Conclusion: The following expressions represent negative numbers: -5^3, $(-5)^3$, -5^2, $(-7)^{15}$, -5^{-3}, $(-5)^{-3}$, -5^{-2}, and $(-7)^{-15}$.

20. a.

n	$(-5)^n$	5^n	opposite?
4	625	625	no
3	-125	125	yes
0	1	1	no
-1	1/-5	1/5	yes
-2	1/25	1/25	no

Conclusion: When n is odd, $(-5)^n$ and 5^n are opposites. When n is even, $(-5)^n$ and 5^n are equal. So $(-5)^n$ is sometimes the opposite of 5^n.

b.

n	-5^n	5^n	opposite?
4	-625	625	yes
3	-125	125	yes
0	-1	1	yes
-1	-1/5	1/5	yes
-2	-1/25	1/25	yes

Conclusion: -5^n is always negative and 5^n is always positive, so -5^n and 5^n are always opposites.

(Solutions continued on page 524)

REVIEW WHICH IS GREATER?

REVIEW EQUATION SOLVING

These sections review material that is useful when solving percent increase and decrease problems.

Problems 23-25 may generate some interesting discussion. If you assign them as homework, make sure students have a chance to go over them in class.

REVIEW WHAT'S THE FUNCTION?

For problem 29, do not teach an equation-based technique for finding the equation. That will be done in Chapter 10. Since the y-intercepts are given, all the students have to do to find the equation is find the slope. The fact that (b) and (c) involve decimals will force the students to use subtraction to find the rise and run.

Problem 31 is computationally and conceptually challenging, and can be used as a bonus or extra-credit problem. In an average algebra class, you cannot expect mastery of it by every student at this stage in the course. (You will in Chapter 10.) The following comments should help you guide students to a solution, should you want to assign it.

To find a linear equation you need two pieces of information: the slope and the y-intercept. If given the coordinates of two points on the line, your students should already know how to find the slope. For a method that leads to an exact answer for the y-intercept without the use of equation-solving, study the following example. Even if your students are able to solve problem 31 with equation solving, the approach outlined here can give them a better understanding of slope.

Example: Find the equation for the line that has slope 0.6 and passes through (35, 67).

We know that when x increases by 1, y increases by 0.6. Between 0 and 35, x increases by 35. Therefore y increases by $35 \cdot 0.6$, or 21. That means that the y-intercept must be $67 - 21$, or 46. Therefore the equation is

$$y = 0.6x + 46.$$

Check: Substitute the x-coordinate of the original point into the equation: $0.6(35) + 46$. If that is equal to 67, the equation must be correct.

▼ 8.12
Small and Large Numbers

Core Sequence: 1-16

Suitable for Homework: 8-16

Useful for Assessment: 5, 7

What this Lesson is About:

- Review of reciprocals
- Review of scientific notation
- Review of negative exponents
- Review of the power of a product rule

*T*his lesson does not introduce any really new ideas. It serves to review negative exponents by applying them to scientific notation.

SMALL NUMBERS IN SCIENTIFIC NOTATION

*I*n this section, the concept of scientific notation is expanded to include numbers smaller than 1, for which negative exponents of 10 are necessary. Remind students of the definition of scientific notation, which requires multiplying *a number greater than or equal to 1 and less than 10* by a power of 10.

RECIPROCALS

*O*ne approach to this is to apply the power of a product rule with the exponent -1.

LESSON 8.12

Small and Large Numbers

1. Using a power of ten, write the reciprocal of each number.

a. 10^2 b. 10^4 c. 0.001

SMALL NUMBERS IN SCIENTIFIC NOTATION

Any decimal number can be written in many ways as a product of a decimal number and a power of 10. For example, 43,000 can be written:

$$0.43 \cdot 10^5$$
$$4.3 \cdot 10^4$$
$$43 \cdot 10^3$$
$$430 \cdot 10^2$$
$$4300 \cdot 10^1$$

2. Write 43,000 as a product of a decimal number and

a. 10^0; b. 10^{-1}; c. 10^{-2}.

3. a. Write 0.065 in three ways as a product of a decimal number and a power of 10. At least one way should use a negative exponent.

b. Write 0.065 in scientific notation. (Remember that scientific notation requires multiplying a number greater than or equal to 1 and less than 10 by a power of 10.)

4. Which of these numbers would require a negative exponent when written in scientific notation? Explain why.

0.0123 0.123 12.3 1230

5. How can you tell by looking at a decimal number whether or not it will require a negative exponent when it is written in scientific notation?

RECIPROCALS

Al and Abe, having nothing else to do, were arguing about reciprocals. Abe said, "If 10^{-4} is the reciprocal of 10^4, then $2.5 \cdot 10^{-4}$ is the reciprocal of $2.5 \cdot 10^4$." Al said, "I can prove that you're wrong by finding their product."

6. If $2.5 \cdot 10^{-4}$ is the reciprocal of $2.5 \cdot 10^4$, what should their product be?

7. Settle the argument between Al and Abe. If Abe has not found the correct reciprocal of $2.5 \cdot 10^4$, find it for him. Explain.

8. Find an approximation for the reciprocal of $4.6 \cdot 10^{-6}$. Give your answer in scientific notation.

UNITS AND RECIPROCALS

9. Dick walks at the rate of about five miles in one hour. What fraction of an hour does it take him to walk one mile?

10. Stanley can run about ten miles in one hour. What fraction of an hour does it take him to run one mile?

11. A snail travels at the rate of 0.005 miles per hour. How many hours does it take the snail to slither one mile?

Notice that your answers to problems 9-11 are the reciprocals of the rates given. This is not a coincidence. In each case, the rate is given in *miles/hour* and you are asked to find *hours/mile.* Since the units are reciprocals, the rates will also be reciprocals.

12. Sound travels through air at the rate of $1.088 \cdot 10^3$ feet per second at sea level. How long does it take sound to travel one foot?

8.12 SOLUTIONS

1. a. 10^{-2}
   b. 10^{-4}
   c. $0.001 = 10^{-3}$, so its reciprocal is 10^3
2. a. $43{,}000 \cdot 10^0$
   b. $430{,}000 \cdot 10^{-1}$
   c. $4{,}300{,}000 \cdot 10^{-2}$
3. a. Answers will vary. Sample:
   $0.065 = 0.065 \cdot 10^0$
   $0.065 = 0.0065 \cdot 10^1$
   $0.065 = 0.65 \cdot 10^{-1}$
   b. $0.065 = 6.5 \cdot 10^{-2}$
4. 0.0123 and 0.123 are between -1 and 1, so they would require a negative exponent when written in scientific notation.
5. If the number to the left of the decimal point is zero, then it will require a negative exponent when written in scientific notation.
6. Their product should be 1.
7. Al finds that $(2.5 \cdot 10^{-4})(2.5 \cdot 10^4) = 6.25 \cdot 10^0 = 6.25$. Since the product does not equal 1, $2.5 \cdot 10^{-4}$ and $2.5 \cdot 10^4$ are not reciprocals. The reciprocal of $2.5 \cdot 10^{-4}$ is $1/(2.5 \cdot 10^{-4}) = 0.4 \cdot 10^4 = 4.0 \cdot 10^3$.
8. Reciprocal (R) $= 1/(4.6 \cdot 10^6) = 2.17 \cdot 10^{-7}$
9. It takes Dick about 1/5 of an hour to walk one mile.
10. It takes Stanley about 1/10 of an hour to run one mile.
11. It takes the slow snail about 200 hours to slither one mile since 1/0.005 = 200.
12. $1/(1.088 \cdot 10^3) = 0.919 \cdot 10^{-3} = 9.19 \cdot 10^{-4}$ seconds per foot. Hence it takes sound $9.19 \cdot 10^{-4}$ seconds to travel one foot through air.

13. Sound travels much faster through granite than through air. Its speed is about $1.2906 \cdot 10^4$ feet per second. How long does it take sound to travel one foot through granite?

UNITS IN THE METRIC SYSTEM

The metric system of measurement is based on powers of ten. Prefixes indicating powers of ten are used for all measurements within the metric system. Conversion between units is easy, since it involves multiplying by powers of ten.

Example: The prefix *kilo* means to multiply the basic unit of measure by 10^3, or 1000. A kilogram is 1000 grams, a kilometer is 1000 meters, and so on. This table lists some of these prefixes.

To Multiply by	Prefix
10^{12}	tera-
10^9	giga-
10^6	mega-
10^3	kilo-
10^2	hecto-
10^1	deka-
10^0	—
10^{-1}	deci-
10^{-2}	centi-
10^{-3}	milli-
10^{-6}	micro-
10^{-9}	nano
10^{-12}	pico-

14. Express the size of each object in terms of a more appropriate unit of measurement.

a. A redwood tree is 80,023 millimeters high.

b. A protozoan is 0.0000002 kilometers in diameter.

c. A football player weighs 95,130 grams.

15. At the San Andreas fault in Northern California, the ground is moving about $5 \cdot 10^{-5}$ kilometers per year. How long will it take to move one kilometer?

16. If hair grows at the rate of about 10^{-8} miles per hour, how long would it take your hair to reach ankle length? (Why is this problem harder than the previous ones?)

UNITS AND RECIPROCALS

UNITS IN THE METRIC SYSTEM

These are word problems which require students to think of the meaning of reciprocals and powers of ten.

Problem 16 is more difficult, because the units are not in the metric system.

8.12 SOLUTIONS

13. $1/(1.2906 \cdot 10^4) = 0.0000775 = 7.75 \cdot 10^{-5}$. Hence it takes sound $7.75 \cdot 10^{-5}$ seconds to travel through one foot of granite.

14. a. 80,023mm = $80{,}023 \cdot 10^{-3}$ meters = 80.023 meters. A redwood tree is 80.023 meters tall.

b. 0.0000002 km = $0.00000002 \cdot 10^3$ meters = 0.0002 meters = $0.0002 \cdot 10^3$ millimeters = 0.2 millimeters. Therefore a protozoan is 0.2 millimeters in diameter.

c. 95,130g = $95{,}130 \cdot 10^{-3}$ kg = 95.130 kg. Hence a football player weighs 95.12 kg.

15. $1/(5 \cdot 10^{-5}) = 0.2 \cdot 10^5 = 2.0 \cdot 10^4$. Therefore it will take about 20,000 years to move 1 kilometer.

16. This is harder because one is not simply converting a rate in miles per hour to hours per mile. One needs to convert to days per inch. Answers will vary due to different heights. Sample: Suppose your height is 5′8″. Let's say the hair grows from the middle of the back of your head to your ankle. This is about 5′2″ or 62″. It takes hair 10^8 hours to grow one mile.
(10^8 hr/mi) · (1mi/5280ft) · (1ft/12 in.) = = 1578.28 hrs/in.
(1578.28 hr/in.) · (1 day/24 hr) = 65.76 days/in.
(65.76 days/in.) · height = 65.76 days/in. · 62 in. = 4077.12 days.
4077.12 days · (1 yr/365 days) = 11.17 yrs.

Approximately 11.17 years are needed for hair to grow ankle length.

THINKING WRITING 8.C Applying the Laws of Exponents

Core Sequence: 1-3

Suitable for Homework: 1-3

Useful for Assessment: 1-2

What this Assignment is About:

- The laws of exponents

This skills-oriented assignment wraps up the work on the laws of exponents.

THINKING WRITING 8.C Applying the Laws of Exponents

Tina overslept and had to skip breakfast, so she didn't do very well on her math test. Besides, she had forgotten to study the laws of exponents. In fact, she missed *all* the problems.

> Test Name: *Tina A.*
>
> **Exponents**
>
> Instructions: Simplify. Your answer should have only one exponent. Not all are possible.
>
> a. $2^4 \cdot 3^4 = 5^4$
>
> b. $3^{15} + 6^{15} = 9^{15}$
>
> c. $3x^2 \cdot 2x^3 = 5x^5$
>
> d. $\frac{x^7}{y^3} = \left(\frac{x}{y}\right)^4$
>
> e. $10x^5 \cdot 8x^9 = 80x^{45}$
>
> f. $(2x)^7 = 2x^7$
>
> g. $12x^3 \cdot 4y^7 = 48(xy)^{10}$
>
> h. $\left(\frac{3^7}{3^5}\right)^3 = 1^6$
>
> i. $(3x^2)^3 = 3x^5$
>
> j. $x^3 + x^2 = x^5$

1. Summarize the five laws of exponents given in Lessons 9, 10, and 11.
2. Correct Tina's test. For each problem, write the correct answer. If one or more of the laws of exponents was used, tell which law (or laws) was used. If the expression cannot be simplified, say so.
3. Take Tina's make-up test for her. Be careful! (Remember, make-up tests are always harder.)

> Make-up Test Name: *Tina A.*
>
> **Laws of Exponents**
>
> Instructions: Show all work leading to your answer.
>
> a. Write without parentheses: $(4x^2y^3z)^3$
>
> Perform each operation, and *if possible* write the result as a power of 5.
>
> b. $5^{11} - 5^9$
>
> c. $5^{x+3}/5^x$
>
> d. $5^5 \cdot \_\_ = 5^{15}$
>
> e. $5^7 + 5^3$
>
> If possible, write as a power of 12.
>
> f. $3 \cdot 4^3$
>
> g. $(3 \cdot 4)^5$
>
> h. $2 \cdot 6^8$
>
> i. $2^8 \cdot 6^8$
>
> j. $2^8 \cdot 6^5$
>
> Which expression is not equal to the other two?
>
> k. 3^{100} 6^{75} 9^{50}
>
> l. $(y^2)^4$ $(y^4)^2$ y^4y^2
>
> m. a^7 $a^3 + a^4$ $a^3 \cdot a^4$
>
> Write the opposite of the reciprocal of $(1/2)^5$
>
> n. using a negative exponent;
>
> o. using a positive exponent.

8.C SOLUTIONS

1. Power of a power: $(x^a)^b = x^{ab}$
   Product of powers: $x^a \cdot x^b = x^{ab}$
   Power of a product: $x^a \cdot y^a = (xy)^a$
   Power of a ratio: $(x/y)^a = (x^a)/(y^a)$
   Quotient of powers: $(x^p)/(x^q) = x^{p-q}$
2. a. $2^4 \cdot 3^4 = 6^4$. Power of a product
   b. $3^{15} + 6^{15}$ cannot be simplified.
   c. $3x^2 \cdot 2x^3 = 6x^5$. Product of powers
   d. $(x^7)/(x^3) = x^4$. Quotient of powers
   e. $10x^5 \cdot 8x^9 = 80x^{14}$. Product of powers
   f. $(2x)^7 = 128x^7$. Power of product
   g. $12x^3 \cdot 4y^7 = 48x^3y^7$
   h. $(3^7/3^5)^3 = (3^2)^3 = 3^6$. Quotient of powers and Power of a power
   i. $(3x^2)^3 = 27x^6$. Power of a product and Power of a power
   j. $x^3 + x^2$ cannot be simplified.
3. a. $(4x^2y^3z)^3 = 4^3x^6y^9z^3 = 64x^6y^9z^3$
   b. $5^{11} - 5^9 = 46{,}875{,}000$ which is not a power of 5.
   c. $(5^{x+3})/(5^x) = 5^3$
   d. $5^5 \cdot 5^{10} = 5^{15}$
   e. $5^7 + 5^3 = 78250$ which is not a power of 5.
   f. $3 \cdot 4^3 = 192$ which cannot be written as a power of 12.
   g. $(3 \cdot 4)^5 = 12^5$
   h. $2 \cdot 6^8 = 3{,}359{,}232$ which is not a power of 12.
   i. $2^8 \cdot 6^8 = (12)^8$
   j. $2^8 \cdot 6^5 = 2^3 \cdot 2^5 \cdot 6^5 = 2^3(12^5)$ which cannot be written as a power of 12.
   k. 6^{75} is not equal to 3^{100} or 9^{50}.
   l. $y^4 \cdot y^2 = y^6$ which is not equal to the other two terms whose expressions equal y^8.
   m. $a^3 + a^4 \neq a^7$ while the other two expressions equal a^7.
   n. $-(1/2)^{-5}$
   o. The opposite of the reciprocal of $1/(2^5)$ is -2^5.

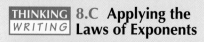

Essential Ideas

POPULATION OF NORTH AMERICA

The table shows the estimated population of North America from 1650 to 1950.

Year	Population (thousands)
1650	5000
1750	5000
1850	39,000
1900	106,000
1950	219,000

1. What is the population increase in each 100-year period?

2. Graph the data.

a. What is the meaning of slope for this data?

b. Is the slope constant or does it increase or decrease? Explain.

3. Estimate the population of North America in the year

a. 1800; b. 2000.

Explain how you arrive at your estimates.

SAME DIAGRAM, DIFFERENT SCALE

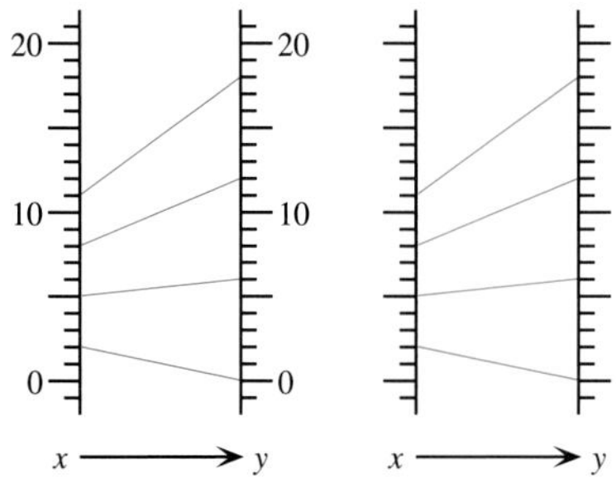

4. Make an in-out table for the function diagram on the left. What is the function illustrated?

5. The function diagram on the right is the same, except that the number lines are not labeled. Copy the diagram, and put labels on it, using the same scale on both the x- and y-number lines. Make an in-out table, and find the function .

6. Repeat problem 5 two times. For each diagram, make an in-out table and find the function.

7. Summary

a. For the functions you found in problems 4-6, when x increases by 1, what does y increase by? Does it depend on the scale you used?

b. Compare the functions you found in problems 4-6. How are they the same? How are they different? Explain.

SLOPE AND INTERCEPT

The following questions are about the graph of $y = mx + b$.

8. Describe the line if $b = 0$ and

a. $m > 1$ b. $0 < m < 1$

c. $m = 0$ d. $-1 < m < 0$

e. $m < -1$

9. In which quadrants does the line lie if

a. $b > 0, m > 0$? b. $b < 0, m > 0$?

c. $b > 0, m < 0$? d. $b < 0, m < 0$?

10. How would lines be the same or different if

a. they have the same value for b and different values for m?

b. they have the same value for m and different values for b?

◆ SOLUTIONS

1.

100-yr. period	Population growth
1650-1750	0
1750-1850	34,000
1850-1950	180,000

2.

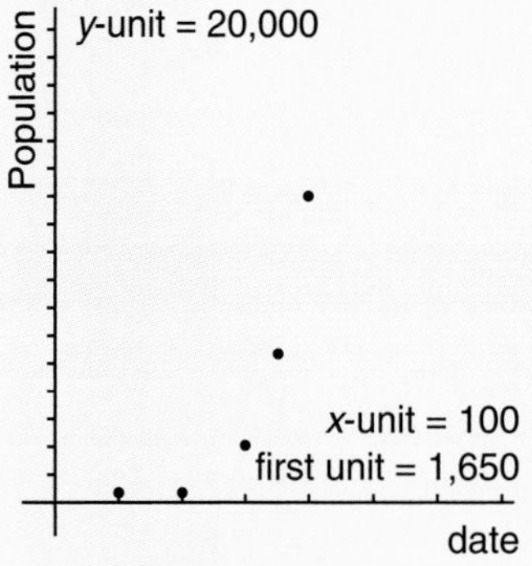

a. Slope for this data shows change in population over a certain number of years.

b. The slope increases. Change in population grows for each successive 100-year period. (See table in #1.)

3. a. Answers will vary. The population in 1800 would be between 10,000 and 20,000. A straight line between point (1750, 5000) and (1850, 39,000) shows that the population would be 20,000 in 1800 if the population growth were linear. But this is more like a curved exponential graph. Sketching in a curve shows an estimated population of about 10,000 in 1800. The population is most likely closer to 10,000.

b. Answers will vary. For the 50-year period of 1900 to 1950, 219000/106000 = 2.066. So the rate of increase was 206.6%. One way to estimate the population in 200 would be to calculate a population increase of 206.6% from the year 1950 when the population was 219,000. 219,000 · 2.066 = 452,454. So one estimate for population in the year 2000 would be 452,454.

4.

x	y
11	18
8	12
5	6
2	0

The function is $y = 2x - 4$

LINEAR AND EXPONENTIAL GROWTH

11. Two populations are growing exponentially. At time 0, both have populations of 100. If one is growing twice as fast as the other, how do their populations compare after:

a. 2 hours? b. 3 hours?
c. x hours?

12. Report A recent college graduate was offered a job with a salary of \$20,000 per year and a guarantee of a 5% raise every year. She was about to accept the job when she received another offer for an identical job with a salary of \$22,000 per year and a guarantee of a \$1200 raise each year. Explain how you would help her decide which job to accept.

LAWS OF EXPONENTS

13. If possible, write as a power of 4.
a. $2 \cdot 2^6$ b. $(2 \cdot 2)^6$
c. $2 \cdot 2^5$ d. $2^7 \cdot 2^5$
e. $2^5 \cdot 2^5$

14. If possible, write as a power of 6.
a. $2 \cdot 3^5$ b. $(2 \cdot 3)^5$
c. 36^7 d. 36^0

15. If possible, write as a power of 3.
a. $9 \cdot 3^5 \cdot 3^2 \cdot 3^0$
b. $9 \cdot 3^5 \cdot 3^2 \cdot 2^0$
c. $9 \cdot 3^5 \cdot 2^2 \cdot 2^0$
d. $81 \cdot (3^5)^4 \cdot 6^0$

16. If possible, write as a single monomial.
a. $8a^{12} - 2(3a^3)^4$
b. $\left(\frac{6t^3}{4}\right)^2 - t^5$

17. Find values of a, b, and c so that
a. $(a \cdot b)^c > a \cdot b^c$;
b. $(a \cdot b)^c = a \cdot b^c$;
c. $(a \cdot b)^c < a \cdot b^c$.

18. Find the number or expression that makes each equation true. Write your answer as a power.
a. $(3x)^4 =$ ____ $\cdot\, x^4$
b. $(5t)^3 =$ ____ $\cdot\, t^3$
c. $(12xy)^3 =$ ____ $\cdot\, (3xy)^3$

19. Simplify each ratio.
a. $(2x^5)/x^5$ b. $(2x)^5/x^5$
c. Explain why your answers to (a) and (b) are different.

20. Find the number that makes each equation true. Write your answer as a power.
a. $100 \cdot (2R)^5 =$ ______ $\cdot\, 100 \cdot R^5$
b. $20 \cdot (2x)^7 =$ ________ $\cdot\, 20 \cdot x^7$
c. $(2xyz)^{10} =$ ________ $\cdot\, (xyz)^{10}$

21. Find the number that makes each equation true. Write your answer as a power.
a. $100 \cdot (3R)^5 =$ ______ $\cdot\, 100 \cdot R^5$
b. $20 \cdot (3x)^7 =$ ________ $\cdot\, 20 \cdot x^7$
c. $(3xyz)^{10} =$ ________ $\cdot\, (xyz)^{10}$

22. Find the reciprocal. Check by showing that the product is 1.
a. $14x^3y^3$ b. $-3a^5$
c. $\frac{1}{3b^2}$

Because of variables in the exponents, these problems are more challenging.

23. Simplify.
a. $\frac{9 \cdot 10^{a+5}}{3 \cdot 10^a}$ b. $\frac{3 \cdot 10^{b+2}}{9 \cdot 10^b}$
c. $\frac{9 \cdot R^{a+5}}{3 \cdot R^a}$ d. $\frac{12 \cdot y^{b+2}}{10 \cdot y^b}$

24. Write as a power of 5.
a. $\frac{5^{2x-2}}{5^{x-5}}$ b. $\frac{5^{x-5}}{5^{2x-2}}$

25. Write as a power of 4. $\left(\frac{4^{3+x}}{4^{3-x}}\right)^3$

S O L U T I O N S

5. The numbers will vary on students' function diagrams. Sample:

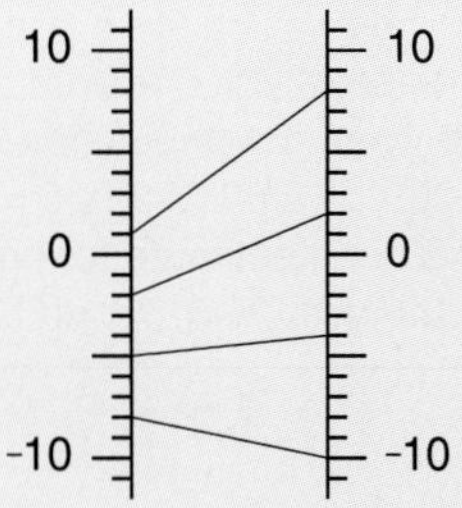

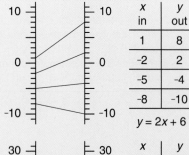

x in	y out
1	8
-2	2
-5	-4
-8	-10

$y = 2x + 6$

6.

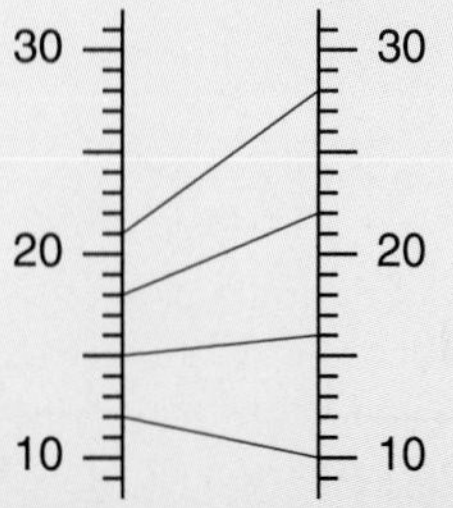

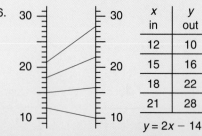

x in	y out
12	10
15	16
18	22
21	28

$y = 2x - 14$

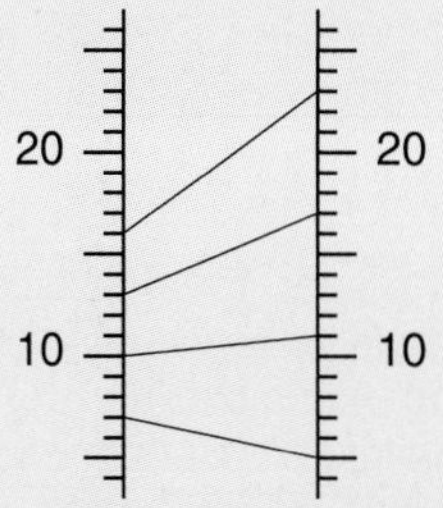

x in	y out
7	5
10	11
13	17
16	23

$y = 2x - 9$

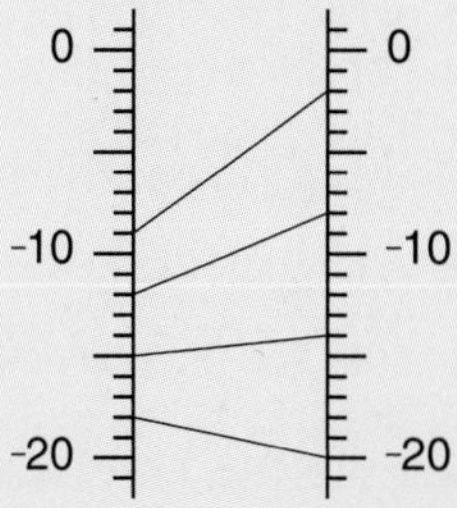

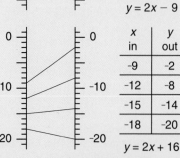

x in	y out
-9	-2
-12	-8
-15	-14
-18	-20

$y = 2x + 16$

7. a. When x increases by 1, y increases by 2. This does not depend on the scale used.
b. Each function has the same value of 2 for m but different values for b in $y = mx + b$.

8. a. The line goes through quadrants III and I. It makes an angle with the x-axis whose measure is between 45 degrees and 90 degrees.
b. The line goes through quadrants III and I. It makes an angle with the x-axis whose measure is between 0 and 45 degrees.
c. The line is the x-axis.
d. The line goes through quadrants II and IV. It makes an angle with the x-axis whose measure is between 45 and 90 degrees.

VERY SMALL NUMBERS

A proton weighs $1.674 \cdot 10^{-24}$ grams, an electron weighs $9.110 \cdot 10^{-28}$ grams, and Ann weighs 48 kilograms.

26. Which is heavier, a proton or an electron? How many times as heavy?

27. Ann weighs the same as how many
   a. electrons?
   b. protons?

28. The mean distance between the Earth and the sun is $1.50 \cdot 10^{11}$ meters. This length is called one *astronomical unit* (AU) and is a convenient unit for measuring distances in the solar system. The distance 10^{-10} meters is called one *angstrom* (after the Swedish physicist Anders Angstrom). It is a convenient unit for measuring atoms. How many angstroms are in one AU?

◆ S O L U T I O N S

e. The line goes through quadrants II and IV making an angle with the x-axis whose measure is between 45 and 90 degrees.

9. a. Quadrants I, II, and III
   b. Quadrants I, III, and IV
   c. Quadrants I, II, and IV
   d. Quadrants II, III, and IV

10. a. The lines would intersect at the same y-intercept but would have different slopes (steepness).
   b. The lines would be parallel. They would have different y-intercepts.

11. a. The larger population is 4 times larger than the smaller.
   b. The larger population is 8 times larger than the smaller
   c. The larger population is 2^x times larger than the smaller.

12.

Year	% raise salary	5% raise	1200 raise salary	raise	% raise
0	20000	1000	22000	1200	0
1	21000	1050	23200	1200	5.5
2	22050	1053	24400	1200	5.2
3	23153	1103	25600	1200	4.9
4	24310	1158	26800	1200	4.7
5	25526	1216	28000	1200	4.5
6	26802	1276	29200	1200	4.3
7	28142	1340	30400	1200	4.1
8	29549	1407	31600	1200	3.9
9	31027	1478	32800	1200	3.8
10	32578	1551	34000	1200	3.7
11	34206	1711	35200	1200	3.5
12	35917	1796	36400	1200	3.4
n	$20000 \cdot (1.05)^n$	$(0.05) \cdot (20000)(1.05)^{n-1}$	$22000 + 1200n$	1200	$1200/22000 + 1200(n - 1)$

Answers will vary in form but should show some calculations of salaries as shown in the table above. If one is looking for long-term employment, the percentage raise leads to higher salaries after the 12th year. For short

(Solutions continued on page 525)

Chapter 9
Measurement and Square Roots

Overview of the Chapter

*T*he theme of measurement ties together the concept of square roots with the work on similar figures that ends the chapter.

*M*uch of the geoboard work that preceded this chapter was intended to lay the geometric foundation on which to build an understanding of square roots. This is developed in the first four lessons. Graphing and function diagrams add a functions perspective, and the calculator adds a numerical perspective. Finally, seeing square roots in the context of exponential growth allows for a review of that essential idea, as well as a preview of fractional exponents and yet another perspective on square roots.

*T*his multi-dimensional approach should yield a more profound and well-rounded understanding of square roots than the repeated manipulation of radicals that constitutes the lion's share of the traditional approach.

*T*he Pythagorean theorem is introduced in the geoboard context. This is a far more meaningful introduction than merely asking students to memorize $a^2 + b^2 = c^2$, but of course it does not fully exhaust the beauty and power of the theorem, which is perhaps the most significant mathematical idea students encounter in secondary mathematics. A full geometric treatment of the theorem, its proofs and applications, can be attended to in the following years. Having viewed the theorem with understanding in this course, and having a better conceptual grasp of square roots, should only enhance that experience for students later.

*L*essons 10-12 and the first part of **Thinking/Writing 9.C** concern similar figures and the ratios of perimeters, areas, and volumes. If you are pressed for time, you may skip this. If you skip it, you may still make use of the second half of **Thinking/Writing 9.C**, **Midpoints**, which concentrates on the material from the beginning of the chapter.

CHAPTER 9

The scroll-like spirals in the capital of a Greek column

Coming in this chapter:

Exploration There are four geoboard segments that start at the origin and have length 5. Find their endpoints. Use this to help you solve the following problem: If you know that two sides of a geoboard triangle are of length 5, what are the possible lengths for the third side?

MEASUREMENT AND SQUARE ROOTS

1. Introduction of New Tools:

- *Radical Gear*
- Scientific calculators to explore square roots

2. Algebra Concepts Emphasized:

- Using the Pythagorean theorem to find distance
- Operations with radicals
- Equivalent radical expressions
- Simple radical form
- Square roots of numbers less than 1
- Domain and range
- The square root function
- Relationship between the square and square root functions
- Midpoint of a segment
- The exponent 1/2

3. Algebra Concepts Reviewed:

- Distance
- Slope
- Average
- Linear and exponential growth
- Equation solving
- Proportions

4. Algebra Concepts Previewed:

- Absolute value
- Fractional exponents
- Rationalizing the denominator

5. Problem-Solving Techniques:

- Trial and error
- Organized searches
- Looking for patterns
- Using diagrams and geometric models
- Solving equations
- Symbol manipulation

6. Connections and Context:

- Taxicab distance
- Surface area
- Right, acute, and obtuse triangles
- The Pythagorean theorem
- Perimeter, area, and volume of similar figures
- Ratio of similarity
- Application of the square root function to police work
- Area of a circle
- Pentomino and SuperTangram puzzles
- Application of similarity to scale models
- Midpoint theorems

▼ 9.1
Distance

Core Sequence: 1-7, 11-19, 21-26

Suitable for Homework: 8-20, 27-28

Useful for Assessment: 6-7, 17-19

What this Lesson is About:

- Review of distance
- Preview of absolute value
- Surface area

Even though taxicab distance is not a traditional algebra topic, it provides an excellent opening to the chapter. Thinking about the difference between taxicab distance and ordinary Euclidean distance, students can avoid some misconceptions. This also lays some important groundwork for understanding distance in the Cartesian plane.

TAXICAB DISTANCE

The reason taxicab distance is included here is that the idea is already in many students' minds. Naming it and contrasting it with Euclidean distance aids in the clearer presentation of the latter, which is the more important concept.

In problem 1, stress that your x- and y-coordinates must keep increasing. Otherwise there is an infinite number of ways to get from the origin to (3, 4), and an infinite number of travel distances. With the given rule, on the other hand, the travel distance is the same no matter what path you follow.

You may show interesting paths on the overhead projector, particularly ones that do not go in whole-number increments.

The problem of counting how many legal paths there are for problem 1 is interesting, but would take us too far from the main purpose of this lesson. We will return to it in a future lesson.

Problem 2e is challenging. If students have trouble understanding how to do it, you may lead a class discussion about it. Essentially, students must resort to subtraction to solve a problem like this. (Sticking to whole numbers allows students just to count, which does not have the generality of subtraction, and does not easily translate into algebraic notation with variables.)

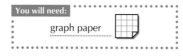

LESSON 9.1

Distance

You will need:

graph paper

TAXICAB DISTANCE

1. Assume you can travel only horizontally and vertically on the Cartesian plane, never letting your x- or y-coordinates decrease.
   a. Find at least three ways to get from the origin to (3, 4).
   b. Does the travel distance depend on the path you found in part (a) or is it the same for all of them? Explain.

Definition: The *taxicab distance* between two points in the Cartesian plane is the length of the *shortest path* between them that consists of *only* horizontal and vertical segments. Taxicab distance gets its name because it models distance in a city with a network of perpendicular streets.

Example: The taxicab distance from (10, 8) to (5, 4) is 9.

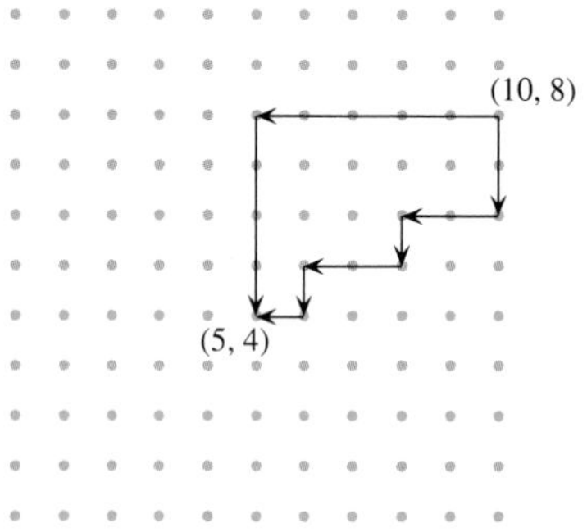

2. What is the taxicab distance between:
   a. (1, 2) and (6, 7)?
   b. (1, 2) and (1, 7)?
   c. (1, 7) and (6, 2)?
   d. (-1, -7) and (6, -2)?
   e. (1.2, 3.4) and (5.67, 8.9)?
3. a. Find all the points that are at taxicab distance 5 from (5, 5). Sketch them.
   b. Describe the shape you found in part (a). Some math teachers call this shape a *taxicab circle*. Explain why.
   c. What else might this shape be called?
4. Describe the set of points whose taxicab distance from (5, 5) is
   a. greater than 5;
   b. less than 5.

TAXICAB vs. EUCLIDEAN DISTANCE

Euclidean distance (named after the ancient Greek mathematician Euclid) is the straight-line distance ("as the crow flies") we studied in a previous lesson.

5. A crow and a taxicab go from the origin to (5, 5). How far does each have to travel?
6. 🔑 Give examples, if possible, and explain.
   a. When are Euclidean and taxicab distances between two points equal?
   b. When is Euclidean distance greater than taxicab distance?
   c. When is taxicab distance greater?
7. 🔑 *A straight line is the shortest path between two points.* Explain how this statement is relevant to problem 6.

9.1 SOLUTIONS

1. a. Answers will vary.
   b. All are the same (7 units).
2. a. 10 b. 5
   c. 10 d. 12
   e. 9.97
3. a.

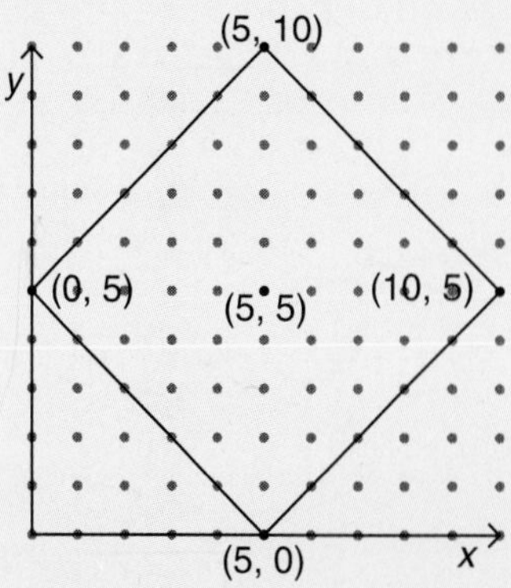

   b. The shape is a square. It is the set of all points equidistant from a given point, when we measure by taxicab distance. The set of all points equidistant from a given point measuring distance "as the crow flies" is a circle. (Perhaps the math teachers saw a black taxicab and mistook it for a crow.)
   c. a diamond
4. a. outside the square
   b. inside the square
5. crow: $5\sqrt{2}$ units taxicab: 10 units
6. a. when traveling only horizontally or vertically
   b. never
   c. always, except when they are equal
7. The taxicab distance is never less than the Euclidean distance.

8. Sketch all the points that are at the same taxicab distance from both (4, 3) and (6, 7).

9. Sketch all the points that are at the same Euclidean distance from both (4, 3) and (6, 7).

10. Find all points P such that:
- the taxicab distance from P to (4, 3) is greater than the taxicab distance from P to (6, 7), **but**
- the Euclidean distance from P to (6, 7) is greater than the Euclidean distance from P to (4, 3).

Explain, using sketches and calculations.

ABSOLUTE VALUE

11. Find the Euclidean distance between:
a. (1, 2) and (6, 2);
b. (6, 2) and (1, 2);
c. (6.7, 3.45) and (8.9, 3.45).

12. Explain in words how to find the distance between (x_1, y) and (x_2, y) if:
a. $x_1 > x_2$; b. $x_1 < x_2$.

If the y-coordinates of two points are the same, the distance between the two can be found by subtracting the x-coordinates. If the result of the subtraction is negative, use its opposite, since distance is always positive. This is called the *absolute value* of the difference.

13. Find the absolute value of the difference between:
a. 2 and 5; b. 3 and -9;
c. -2 and -5; d. -3 and 9.

14. Explain how you find the distance between two points whose x-coordinates are the same. Give an example.

Definition: The *absolute value* of a number x is the distance from x to 0 on the number line.

Example: The absolute value of 3 is 3. The absolute value of -3 is also 3.

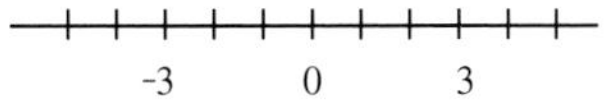

15. Find the absolute value of:
a. 12; b. -1/4.

Notation: The absolute value of a number z is written $|z|$. For example:
$|2| = 2$ $|-2| = 2$

The absolute value of a difference can be written using the same symbol. For example, the absolute value of the difference between a and b is written $|a - b|$.

16. Find the absolute value of:
a. $3 - -5$; b. $-5 - 3$.

17. What is the distance between x and 3 on the number line?
a. Explain in words how to find it.
b. Write a formula, using absolute value notation.

18. Using absolute value notation, the distance between (x_1, y) and (x_2, y) can be written $|x_1 - x_2|$ or $|x_2 - x_1|$. Explain.

19. Use absolute value notation to write the distance between (x, y_1) and (x, y_2).

20. Use absolute value notation to write the taxicab distance between (x_1, y_1) and (x_2, y_2).

TAXICAB VS. EUCLIDEAN DISTANCE

For problem 5 some students may need to be reminded of the "draw a square, find its side" approach to finding Euclidean distance. (See Chapter 7, Lesson 12.)

Problem 7 includes a statement of the triangle inequality in everyday language. It is not necessary at this level to use fancier terminology.

Problems 8-10 present an interesting challenge. (Problem 9 has been previewed on the geoboard in Chapter 7, Lesson 12.) If you want to extend this discussion, you may generalize: Given any two points, how does one find the points equidistant from them in Euclidean terms? In taxicab terms? What are the possible cases? (The points can be on a horizontal line, on a vertical line, on a 45° diagonal, on a line that is closer to vertical, on a line that is closer to horizontal.)

ABSOLUTE VALUE

This is a preview of absolute value, and you should avoid using the formal definition, which is incomprehensible to students at this level. What is important at this point is that the students understand how to use subtraction to find the horizontal or vertical distance between two points.

In problem 17b, students may come up with two different solutions: $|x - 3|$ or $|3 - x|$.

9.1 SOLUTIONS

8. The dotted lines show taxicab circles of different sizes for each point. Points that are the same taxicab distance from (4, 3) and (6, 7) will be those that lie on taxicab circles of the same size relative to both points.

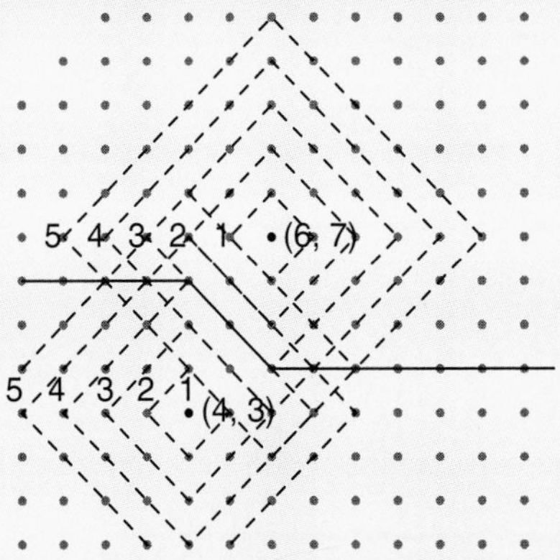

9.

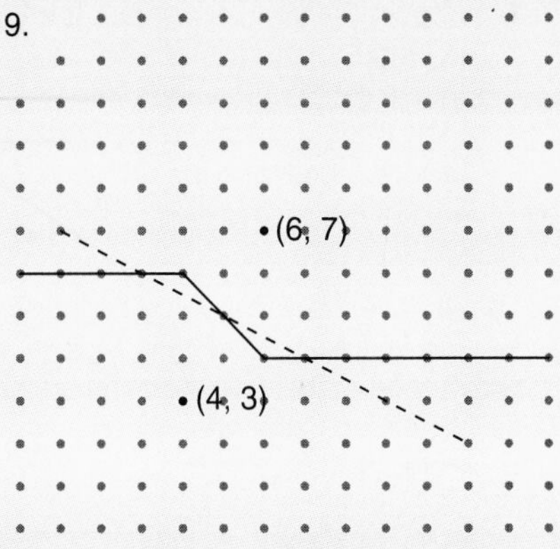

10.

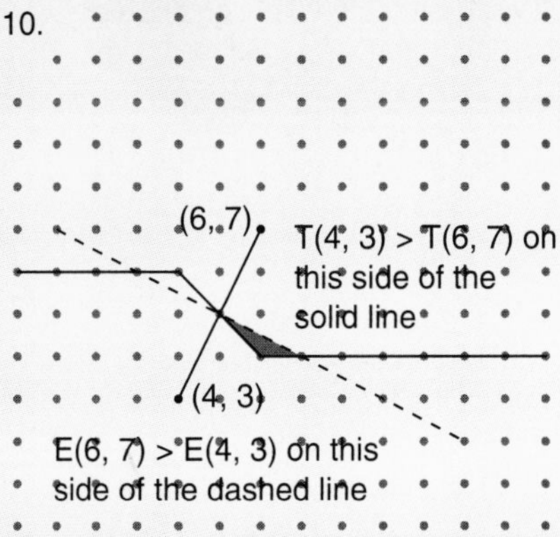

11. a. 5
b. 5
c. 2.2

REVIEW SURFACE AREA OF BUILDINGS

This is the first of three sections of Lab Gear problems about surface area. The remaining two sections are at the end of Lesson 2 and at the end of Lesson 6.

The purpose of the lessons is to preview Lessons 10-12, which concentrate on questions about perimeter, volume, area, and surface area. Of these four concepts, surface area is the most difficult to develop, and a start with the Lab Gear may help students grasp it better.

If access to the blocks is not convenient, you may want to group the three sections into one class session, which can take place at any time before Lesson 10.

If you plan to skip Lessons 10-12, you do not need to cover these surface area problems.

REVIEW SURFACE AREA OF BUILDINGS

Find the volume and surface area of each of these buildings (including the underside).

21. 

22. 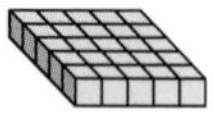

23. 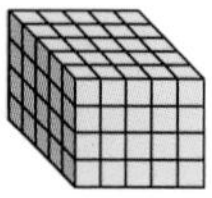

24. 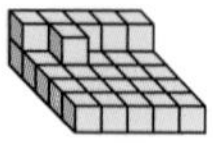

25. 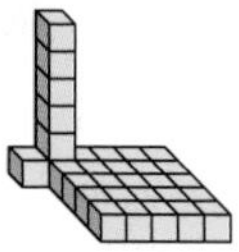

26. 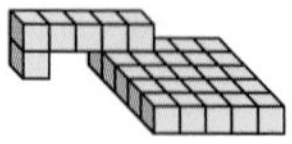

PREVIEW MIXTURES

Tina was thirsty, so Tina and Lana decided to make lemonade. They planned to make a lot, so they could sell some of it at a roadside stand.

Tina started making lemonade using the "taste" method. She added 21 cups of water to 16 cups of lemonade concentrate, but it tasted too lemony. Then she noticed directions on the lemonade package:

> Add water to taste. Most people like a mixture that is 1/5 to 1/4 concentrate.

27. How much water should she add to get a mixture that is 1/5 concentrate?

28. Lana tasted the lemonade after Tina had added water to get a mixture that was 1/5 concentrate. It didn't taste lemony enough. How much lemonade concentrate should they add now to get a mixture that is 1/4 concentrate?

9.1 SOLUTIONS

12. a. Subtract the smaller *x*-coordinate from the larger *x*-coordinate: $x_1 - x_2$
    b. Subtract the smaller *x*-coordinate from the larger *x*-coordinate: $x_2 - x_1$
13. a. 3 b. 12
    c. 3 d. 12
14. Subtract the smaller *y*-coordinate from the larger one. For example, the distance between (-9, 5) and (-9, 12) is 7.
15. a. 12 b. 1/4
16. a. 8 b. 8
17. a. Subtract the smaller number from the larger number. Another method is to subtract one from the other, without regard to their relative sizes, and take the absolute value of the result.
    b. $|x - 3|$ or $|3 - x|$
18. These have the same value because $x_2 - x_1$ is the opposite of $x_1 - x_2$. If two numbers are opposites, they have the same absolute value.
19. $|y_1 - y_2|$ or $|y_2 - y_1|$
20. $|x_1 - x_2| + |y_1 - y_2|$
21. 1 cu. unit; 6 sq. units
22. 25 cu. units; 70 sq. units
23. 100 cu. units; 130 sq. units
24. 31 cu. units; 84 sq. units
25. 31 cu. units; 94 sq. units
26. 31 cu. units; 92 sq. units
27. 43 cups
28. 5 1/3 cups

LESSON 9.2

The Pythagorean Theorem

You will need:

geoboards

dot paper

RIGHT TRIANGLES

The corner of a piece of paper can be used to measure a *right angle.*

1. The figure shows three triangles, having a total of nine angles. To do the following problems, you may copy the figure onto your geoboard.

a. Give the coordinates of the vertex of the right angle.

b. Give the coordinates of the vertex of the angle that is greater than a right angle.

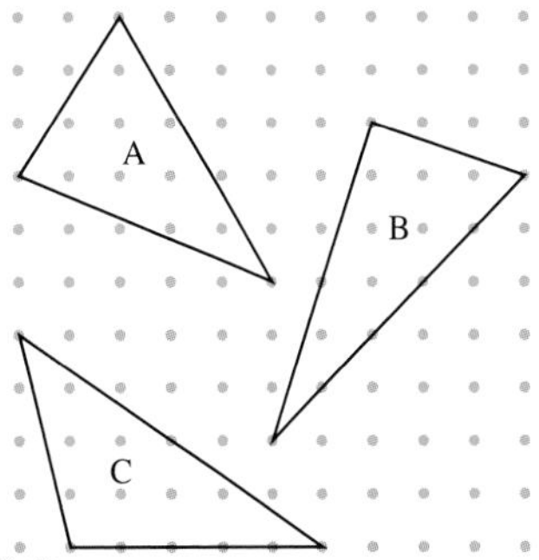

Definitions: An angle that is greater than a right angle is called *obtuse.* An angle that is less than a right angle is called *acute.* A triangle that contains an obtuse angle is called an *obtuse triangle.* A triangle that contains three acute angles is called an *acute triangle.* A triangle that contains a right angle is called a *right triangle.*

2. Which triangle in the preceding figure is acute? Right? Obtuse?

Definition: The two sides forming the right angle in a right triangle are called the *legs.*

The figure shows a right triangle. Three squares have been drawn, one on each of the sides of the triangle.

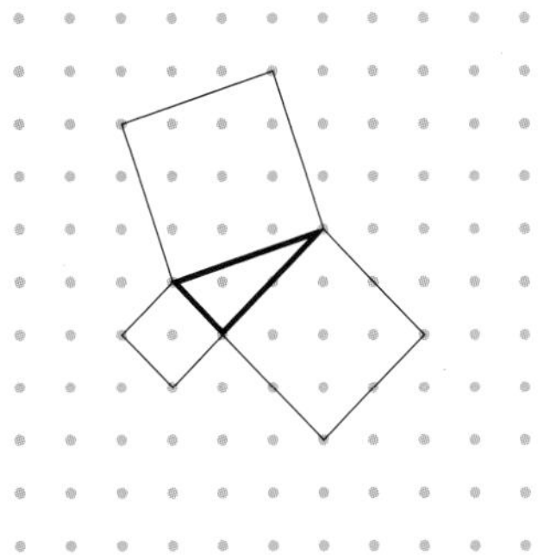

3. What is the area of each of the three squares?

4. **Exploration** Working with other students, make eight figures like the one above (on geoboards or dot paper). Each figure must be based on a different right triangle. For each one, find the areas of the three squares. Fill out a table like the one below. Study the table for any pattern.

Areas of:

Square on short leg	Square on long leg	Square on hypotenuse
...	...	...

9.2 The Pythagorean Theorem

Core Sequence: 1-12, 14-18

Suitable for Homework: 5-13

Useful for Assessment: 7, 11

What this Lesson is About:

- Right, acute, and obtuse triangles
- The Pythagorean theorem
- Using the Pythagorean theorem to find distance
- Review of slope
- Surface area

RIGHT TRIANGLES

You do not need to spend time discussing angle measurement in degrees. It is sufficient for the purposes of this course that students are able to recognize right, acute, and obtuse angles. This can be done by measuring the angles with the corner of a piece of paper. (You can model this on the overhead.)

Problem 4 is extremely important. Students often memorize the Pythagorean theorem without any real understanding of the geometric meaning of the squares in $a^2 + b^2 = c^2$. This leads to mistakes and misunderstandings. Doing this Exploration allows students to discover the relationship for themselves, and to see a concrete meaning to it.

9.2 SOLUTIONS

1. a. (7, 8)
   b. (1, 0)
2. A acute, B right, C obtuse
3. shortest leg: 2 sq. units; other leg: 8 sq. units; hypotenuse: 10 sq. units
4. Drawings will vary. Examples are shown in the figure.

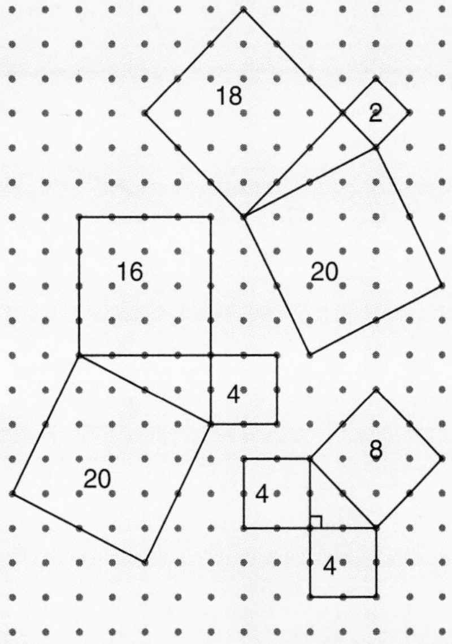

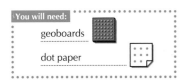

*P*roblems 5-6 should help students appreciate that the Pythagorean theorem applies only to right triangles.

*I*n problem 7, note the formulation

$$leg^2 + leg^2 = hyp^2,$$

which is more meaningful than the traditional $a^2 + b^2 = c^2$.

FINDING DISTANCES FROM COORDINATES

*D*o not teach the distance formula. Memorizing such a formula usually obscures the mathematics behind it, in this case the application of the Pythagorean theorem.

*P*roblem 8 is intended to remind students about using subtraction to find horizontal and vertical distances.

*P*roblem 9 reviews slope.

The pattern you probably discovered is called the Pythagorean theorem, after the ancient Greek mathematician Pythagoras. The pattern is about the relationship of the squares on the legs to the square on the hypotenuse for a right triangle.

5. Make an acute triangle on a geoboard or dot paper. Draw a square on each of its sides. Is the sum of the areas of the two smaller squares equal to, greater than, or less than the area of the large square?

6. Repeat problem 5 with an obtuse triangle.

7. **Summary** Explain the following equation.

$$\text{leg}^2 + \text{leg}^2 = \text{hyp}^2$$

(Is it true of any triangle? For those triangles for which it is true, what does it mean?)

FINDING DISTANCES FROM COORDINATES

The Pythagorean theorem provides us with a way to find distances in the Cartesian plane. (*Distance* usually refers to Euclidean distance.)

Example: What is the distance between (3, 8) and (7, 2)? First sketch the points.

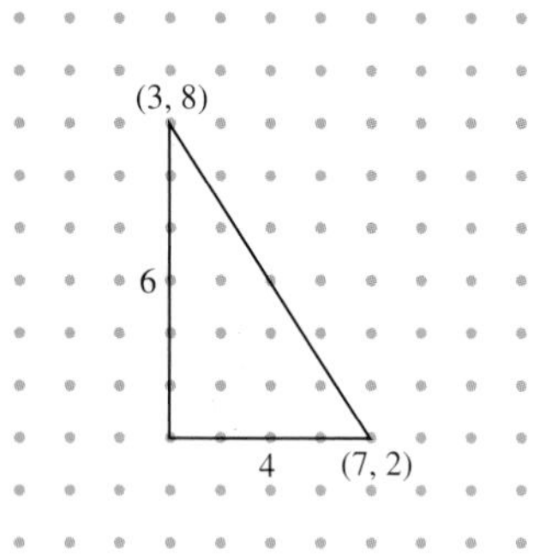

You can see on the sketch that the length of the legs is 4 for the horizontal leg, and 6 for the vertical leg. Since the triangle shown is a right triangle, we can use the Pythagorean theorem, ($\text{hyp}^2 = \text{leg}^2 + \text{leg}^2$). In this case,

$\text{distance}^2 = 4^2 + 6^2 = 16 + 36 = 52$

so, $\text{distance} = \sqrt{52} = 7.21\ldots$

8. For the example, if you did not sketch the figure, how could you find the lengths of the legs directly from the coordinates?

Note that the lengths of the legs have been called the *rise* and the *run* when discussing slope. However keep in mind that rise, run, and slope can be positive, negative, or zero, while distances cannot be negative.

9. Consider the two points (3, -4) and (4, -9). Use a sketch if you need to.
   a. Find the rise between them.
   b. Find the run between them.
   c. Find the slope of the line that joins them.
   d. Find the taxicab distance between them.
   e. Find the Euclidean distance between them.

10. Use any method to find the (Euclidean) distance between:
   a. (-1, 2) and (-1, -7);
   b. (-1, 2) and (5, 2);
   c. (-1, 2) and (5, -7);
   d. (-1, 2) and (-1, 2).

11. For which part of problem 10 is the Pythagorean theorem helpful? Explain.

12. Find the distances between:
   a. (8, 0) and (0, -8);
   b. (-8, 0) and (3, -8);
   c. (1.2, 3.4) and (-5.6, 7.89).

9.2 SOLUTIONS

5. Drawings will vary. The sum of the areas of the smaller squares will be greater than the area of the largest square. One example is shown.
6. Drawings will vary. The sum of the areas of the smaller squares will be less than the area of the largest square. One example is shown.

5., 6.

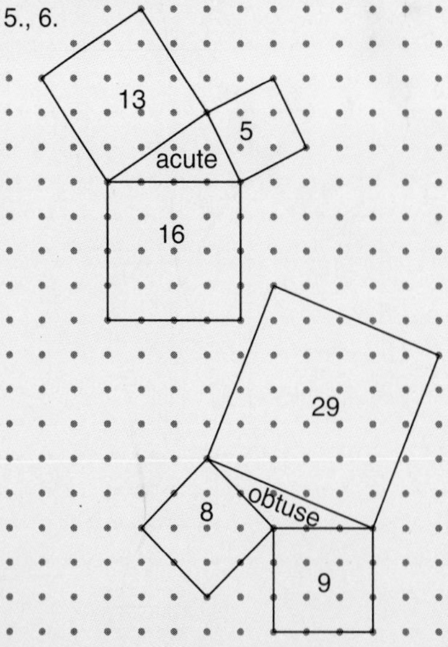

7. This refers to right triangles only. The "hyp" refers to the hypotenuse of a right triangle. It means that if you square the lengths of the legs and then add these two numbers, the result is the same as the square of the hypotenuse. This was illustrated geometrically in the last few problems, when we showed the squares of the lengths by drawing squares.
8. Find the difference of the *x*-coordinates. Square it. Find the difference of the *y*-coordinates. Square it. Add the two squares. The result will be the square of the distance between the two points.
9. a. rise: -5 b. run: 1
   c. slope: -5 d. taxicab distance: 6
   e. Euclidean distance: $\sqrt{26}$

AN OLD PROBLEM

The mathematician Leonardo of Pisa, also known as Fibonacci, posed this problem in 1202.

13. Two towers of height 30 paces and 40 paces are 50 paces apart. Between them, at ground level, is a fountain towards which two birds fly from the tops of the towers. They fly at the same rate, and they leave and arrive at the same time. What are the horizontal distances from the fountain to each tower?

REVIEW *MORE SURFACE AREA*

Imagine these buildings are made by gluing Lab Gear blocks together. The surface area is the total area of all the exposed faces, even the bottom of the building. Find the surface areas.

14. 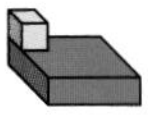

15. 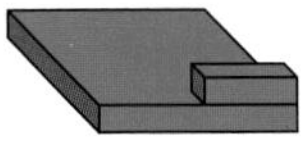

16. 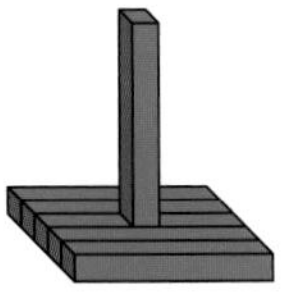

17. 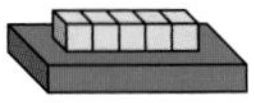

18. 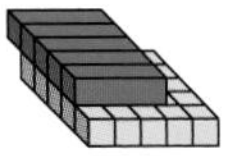

Problem 13 applies the Pythagorean theorem. The x^2 quantities cancel, and the equation is linear.

REVIEW *MORE SURFACE AREA*

See the comments at the end of Lesson 1.

9.2 SOLUTIONS

10. a. 9 b. 6
    c. $\sqrt{117}$ d. 0

11. c

12. a. $\sqrt{128}$
    b. $\sqrt{185}$
    c. $\sqrt{66.4001}$

13. The fountain is 32 paces from the shorter tower and 18 paces from the taller tower.

14. $2x^2 + 4x + 4$

15. $2y^2 + 4y + 2x + 2$

16. $16y + 10$

17. $2xy + 2x + 2y + 12$

18. $80 + 4x$

▼ 9.3
Radicals

Core Sequence: 1-24

Suitable for Homework: 4-22

Useful for Assessment: 7-8, 15, 17

What this Lesson is About:

- Preview of multiplying square roots
- Equivalent radical expressions
- Simple radical form
- Review of the Pythagorean theorem

*R*ules for working with radicals are introduced gradually over Lessons 3-8, so you should not expect instant mastery. This lesson explores the most important rule: the product of radicals.

SQUARES AND ROOTS

*T*his section gives a geometric justification for expressions like $\sqrt{8} = 2\sqrt{2}$.

LESSON 9.3

Radicals

You will need:

geoboards

dot paper

SQUARES AND ROOTS

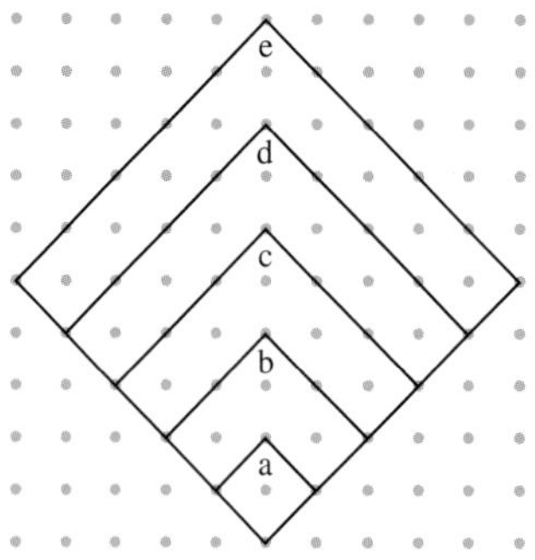

The figure shows five squares. For each one, find

1. its area;
2. its side, written twice: as the square root of the area, and as a decimal number.

The sides of the larger squares are multiples of the side of the smallest square. For example, square (b) has a side that is equal to two times the side of square (a). You can write,

$$\sqrt{8} = \sqrt{2} + \sqrt{2} = 2\sqrt{2}.$$

Note that $2\sqrt{2}$ means 2 times $\sqrt{2}$, just as $2x$ means 2 times x. You can check the equation with a calculator.

$$\sqrt{8} = 2.828427125\ldots$$
$$2\sqrt{2} = 2.828427125\ldots$$

3. Write equations about the sides of squares (c), (d), and (e). Check their correctness with a calculator.

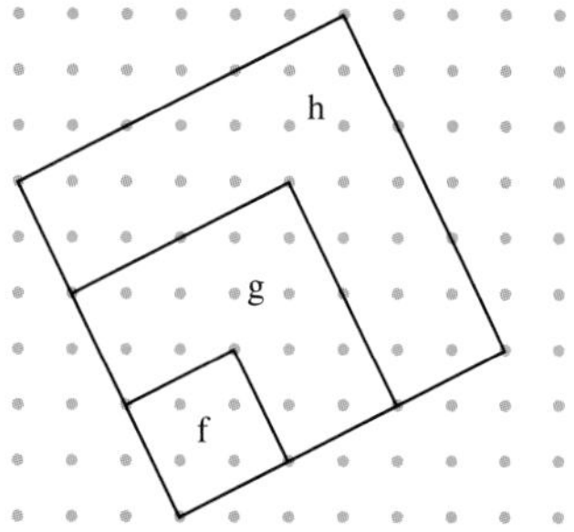

The figure shows three squares. For each one, find

4. its area;
5. its side, written twice: as the square root of the area, and as a decimal number.
6. Write equations involving square roots based on the figure. Check your equations on a calculator.
7. 🔑 True or False? Use a sketch on dot paper to explain your answers.
   a. $\sqrt{2} + \sqrt{2} = \sqrt{4}$
   b. $4\sqrt{2} = \sqrt{8}$
8. 🔑 Is $\sqrt{2 + 2} = \sqrt{4}$? Explain.

RECTANGLES AND ROOTS

In this section do not use decimal approximations.

9. The figure shows three rectangles. For each one, write *length* · *width* = *area.*

9.3 SOLUTIONS

1-6. The answers are summarized in the following table. You may want to suggest that students make a similar table.

square	area	side (square root of area)	side (decimal approx.)	equation relating sides
a	2	$\sqrt{2}$	1.414	
b	8	$\sqrt{8}$	2.828	$\sqrt{8} = 2\sqrt{2}$
c	18	$\sqrt{18}$	4.243	$\sqrt{18} = 3\sqrt{2}$
d	32	$\sqrt{32}$	5.657	$\sqrt{32} = 4\sqrt{2}$
e	50	$\sqrt{50}$	7.071	$\sqrt{50} = 5\sqrt{2}$
f	5	$\sqrt{5}$	2.236	
g	20	$\sqrt{20}$	4.472	$\sqrt{20} = 2\sqrt{5}$
h	45	$\sqrt{45}$	6.708	$\sqrt{45} = 3\sqrt{5}$

7. a. False
   b. False

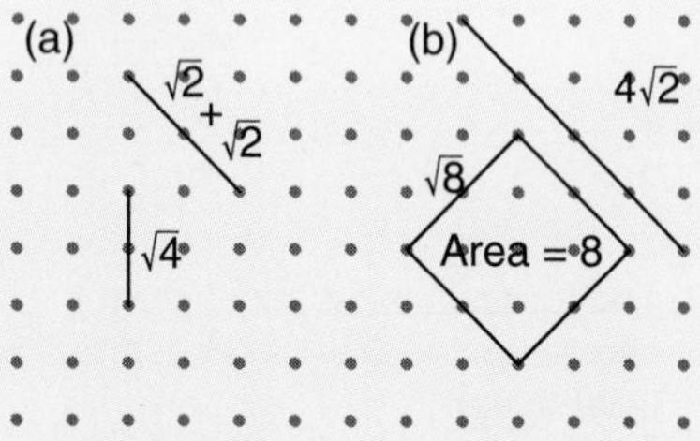

8. Of course! Just simplify inside the radical.
9. top: $\sqrt{10} \cdot 3\sqrt{10} = 30$ middle: $\sqrt{5} \cdot 4\sqrt{5} = 20$ bottom: $\sqrt{2} \cdot 2\sqrt{2} = 4$
10. a. The sides would be $\sqrt{30}$, $\sqrt{20}$, and $\sqrt{4}$ respectively.
    b. It is impossible to show a square of side $\sqrt{30}$, on the geoboard. The others are shown in the figure.

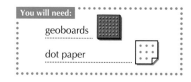

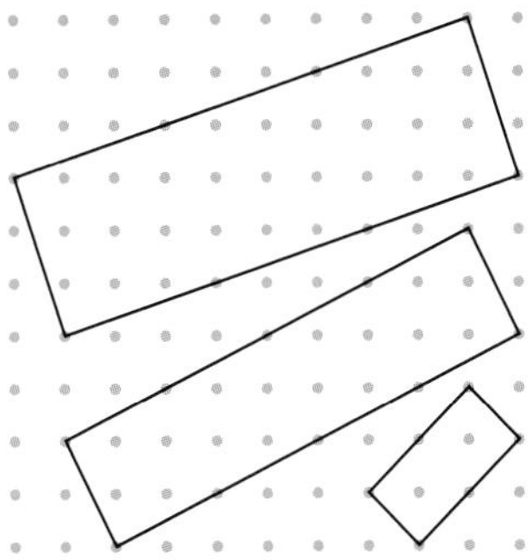

10. For each rectangle above:

a. What is the side of a square having the same area?

b. Sketch this square on dot paper.

Some multiplications involving square roots can be modeled by geoboard rectangles. For example, $2\sqrt{5} \cdot 3\sqrt{5}$ is shown in this figure.

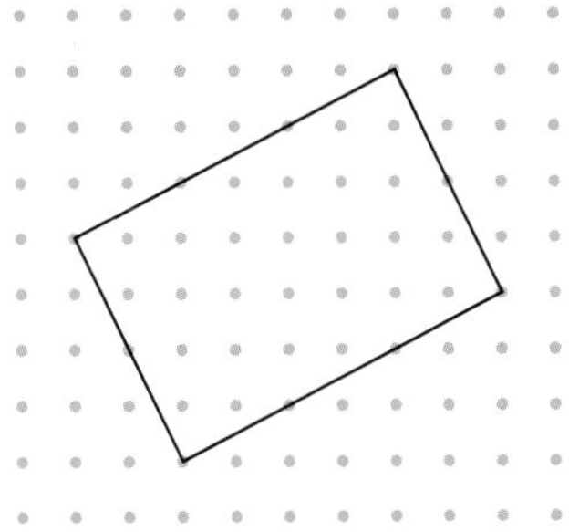

11. Find the product of $2\sqrt{5} \cdot 3\sqrt{5}$ by finding the area of the rectangle.

12. Multiply.

a. $2\sqrt{2} \cdot 3\sqrt{2}$ b. $3\sqrt{2} \cdot 4\sqrt{2}$

c. $4\sqrt{2} \cdot 5\sqrt{2}$ d. $\sqrt{2} \cdot 2\sqrt{2}$

13. Multiply.

a. $\sqrt{2} \cdot \sqrt{18}$ b. $\sqrt{18} \cdot \sqrt{50}$

c. $\sqrt{50} \cdot \sqrt{8}$ d. $\sqrt{8} \cdot \sqrt{32}$

Using the fact that $\sqrt{a} \cdot \sqrt{a} = a$ makes it easy to multiply some quantities involving radicals. For example:

$$6\sqrt{5} \cdot 2\sqrt{5} = 6 \cdot 2 \cdot \sqrt{5} \cdot \sqrt{5} = 12 \cdot 5 = 60$$

14. Multiply.

a. $5\sqrt{2} \cdot \sqrt{2}$ b. $5\sqrt{2} \cdot 4\sqrt{2}$

c. $3\sqrt{5} \cdot \sqrt{5}$

15. Explain your answers by using a sketch of a geoboard rectangle.

a. Is $\sqrt{4} \cdot \sqrt{2} = \sqrt{8}$?

b. Is $\sqrt{5} \cdot \sqrt{20} = \sqrt{100}$?

MULTIPLYING SQUARE ROOTS

Is it always true that $\sqrt{a} \cdot \sqrt{b} = \sqrt{ab}$? We cannot answer this question in general by making geoboard rectangles. A multiplication like $\sqrt{2} \cdot \sqrt{5}$ cannot be shown that way because it is not possible to find those lengths on the geoboard at a right angle to each other.

16. Guess how to write $\sqrt{2} \cdot \sqrt{5}$ as a square root. Check your guess with a calculator.

17. Generalization If a and b are positive,

a. give a rule for multiplying $\sqrt{a} \cdot \sqrt{b}$;

b. explain how to multiply $c\sqrt{a} \cdot d\sqrt{b}$.

18. Multiply.

a. $3\sqrt{5} \cdot 2\sqrt{6}$

b. $(2\sqrt{11})(-11\sqrt{2})$

SIMPLE RADICAL FORM

Definitions: The square root symbol ($\sqrt{\ }$) is called a *radical sign,* or simply *radical.* A *radical expression* is an expression that includes a radical.

Examples:

$$\sqrt{3}, 4\sqrt{7}, 1 + \sqrt{6}, \text{ or } \frac{\sqrt{2}}{x}$$

19. Write each of these in at least two ways as the product of two radical expressions.

a. $\sqrt{70}$ b. $\sqrt{63}$

c. $6\sqrt{80}$ d. $24\sqrt{105}$

RECTANGLES AND ROOTS

MULTIPLYING SQUARE ROOTS

Some products involving square roots can be figured out on a geoboard or on dot paper. A more general rule can be figured out with the help of a calculator.

Lesson 4 will provide more work with multiplying square roots.

SIMPLE RADICAL FORM

Because of calculators, simple radical form is less important than it used to be. This section is mostly interesting in that it helps students develop a better understanding of how to multiply square roots.

It is useful to have a class discussion of problems like 19, so that students can see as many solutions as possible.

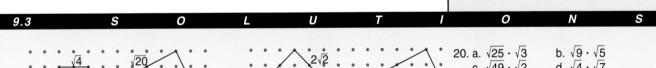

9.3 SOLUTIONS

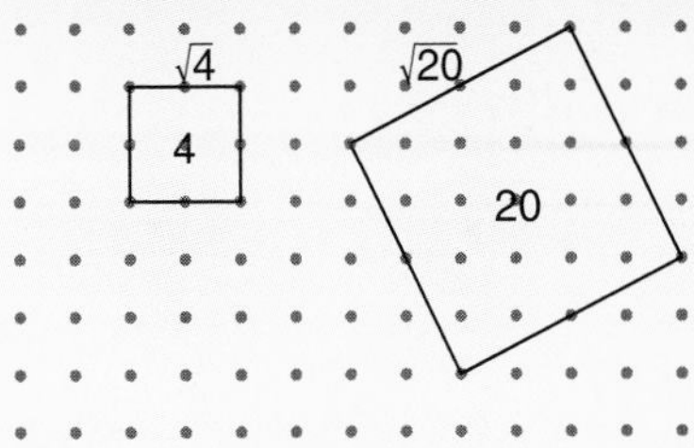

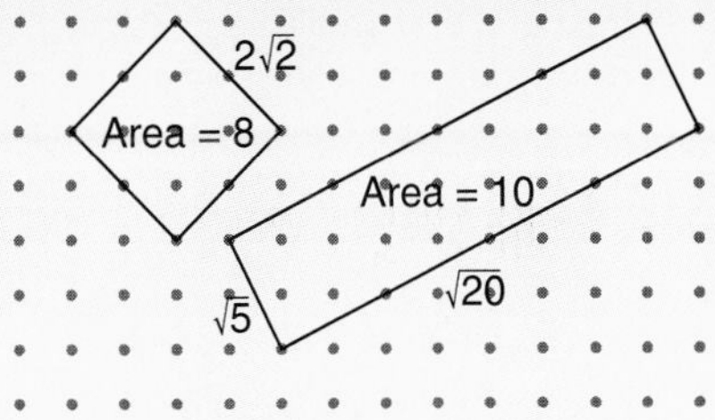

11. 30

12. a. 12 b. 24
c. 40 d. 4

13. a. 6 b. 30
c. 20 d. 16

14. a. 10 b. 40 c. 15

15. a. yes b. yes

16. Guess: $\sqrt{10}$. Check: $1.414 \cdot 2.236 = 3.161$, which is about equal to $\sqrt{10}$.

17. a. $\sqrt{ab}$ b. $cd\sqrt{ab}$

18. a. $6\sqrt{30}$ b. $-22\sqrt{22}$

19. Answers will vary. Sample answers are given.
a. $\sqrt{2} \cdot \sqrt{35} = \sqrt{7} \cdot \sqrt{10}$
b. $\sqrt{9} \cdot \sqrt{7} = \sqrt{21} \cdot \sqrt{3}$
c. $6\sqrt{2} \cdot \sqrt{40} = 6\sqrt{8} \cdot \sqrt{10}$
d. $24\sqrt{5} \cdot \sqrt{21} = 6\sqrt{3} \cdot 4\sqrt{35}$

20. a. $\sqrt{25} \cdot \sqrt{3}$ b. $\sqrt{9} \cdot \sqrt{5}$
c. $\sqrt{49} \cdot \sqrt{2}$ d. $\sqrt{4} \cdot \sqrt{7}$

21. a. $5\sqrt{3}$ b. $3\sqrt{5}$
c. $7\sqrt{2}$ d. $2\sqrt{7}$

22. a. about 8.06
b. about 9.22

23. segments of length 5 have endpoints at: (0, 5), (5, 0), (3, 4), and (4, 3)
segments of length 10 have endpoints at (10, 0), (0, 10), (6, 8), and (8, 6)
segments of length $\sqrt{50}$ have endpoints at (1, 7), (7, 1), (5, 5)

GEOBOARD LENGTHS

*T*his section allows students to practice using the Pythagorean theorem.

*T*he lengths chosen for problem 23 can each be obtained in two essentially different ways, which adds an interesting twist to the problem and makes problems 24-25 possible.

20. Write each of these as the product of two radicals, one of which is the square root of a perfect square.

a. $\sqrt{75}$ b. $\sqrt{45}$
c. $\sqrt{98}$ d. $\sqrt{28}$

Definition: Writing the square root of a whole number as a product of a whole number and the square root of a smallest possible whole number is called putting it in *simple radical form.*

For example, in simple radical form,
$\sqrt{50}$ is $5\sqrt{2}$ $\sqrt{20}$ is $2\sqrt{5}$.

(Note that when using a calculator to find an approximate value, simple radical form is not simpler!)

21. Write in simple radical form.

a. $\sqrt{75}$ b. $\sqrt{45}$
c. $\sqrt{98}$ d. $\sqrt{28}$

GEOBOARD LENGTHS

Since 50 is a little more than 49, $\sqrt{50}$ is a little more than 7. A calculator confirms this: $\sqrt{50} = 7.07\ldots$

22. Estimate the following numbers, and check your answer on a calculator.

a. $\sqrt{65}$ b. $\sqrt{85}$

These numbers may help you with the next problem.

23. **Exploration** There are 19 geoboard line segments that start at the origin and have length 5, 10, $\sqrt{50}$, $\sqrt{65}$, or $\sqrt{85}$. Find them, and mark their endpoints on dot paper.

24. If you know two sides of a geoboard triangle are of length 5, what are the possibilities for length for the third side?

25. Repeat problem 24 for the following side lengths.

a. 10 b. $\sqrt{50}$
c. $\sqrt{65}$ d. $\sqrt{85}$

9.3 SOLUTIONS

segments of length $\sqrt{65}$ have endpoints at (1, 8), (8, 1), (7, 4), and (4, 7) segments of length $\sqrt{85}$ have endpoints at (9, 2), (2, 9), (6, 7), and (7, 6)

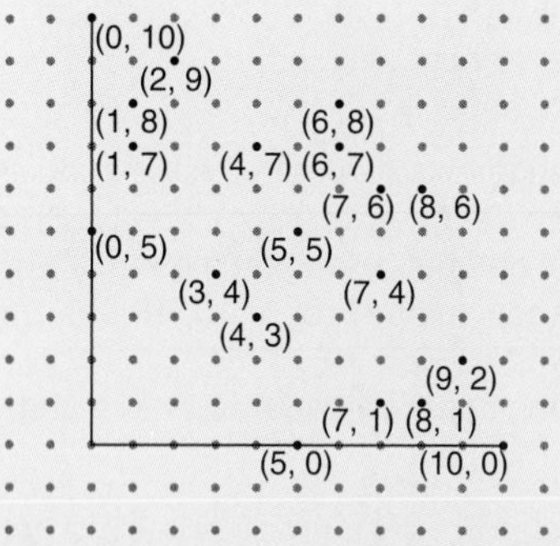

24. The figure shows a strategy for figuring out how many solutions exist. Draw all possible segments of length 5 from the origin. Then form triangles by connecting pairs of endpoints. A total of four triangles is possible. (Some are duplicates, being reflections of each other over the 45° line.) Answers: $\sqrt{10}$, $2\sqrt{5}$, $5\sqrt{2}$, $\sqrt{2}$

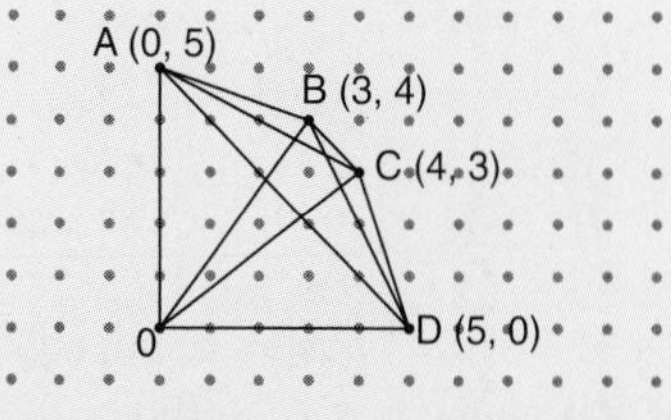

25. The figure shows the geometric strategy for parts (a) and (b). Parts (c) and (d) are similar.

a. $2\sqrt{10}$, $4\sqrt{5}$, $10\sqrt{2}$, $2\sqrt{2}$
b. $6\sqrt{2}$, $2\sqrt{5}$
c. $\sqrt{10}$, $\sqrt{52}$, $7\sqrt{2}$, $3\sqrt{2}$
d. $\sqrt{2}$, $2\sqrt{5}$, $7\sqrt{2}$, $\sqrt{34}$

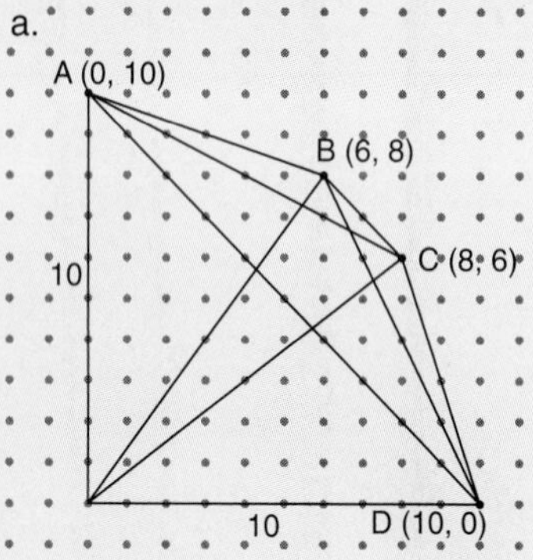

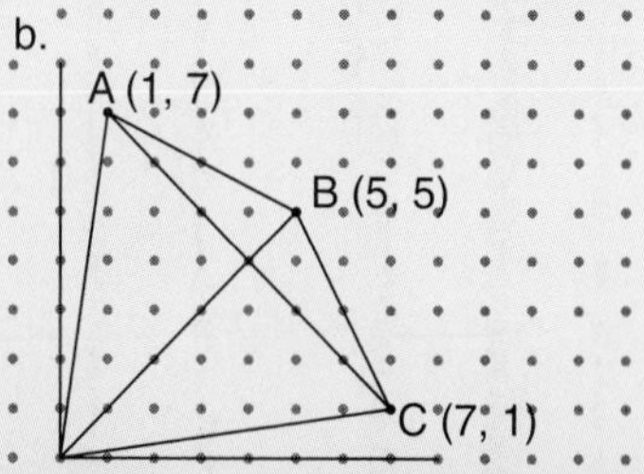

LESSON 9.4

Radical Operations

You will need:

geoboards

dot paper

MULTIPLICATION

1. **Exploration** Using only multiplication, write at least three radical expressions that equal each of the following.
   a. $2\sqrt{3}$ b. 6

Even though you are often asked to simplify expressions, it is sometimes just as important to know how to "complicate" them. For example, $3\sqrt{7}$ is equivalent to all these radical expressions.

$\sqrt{9}\sqrt{7}$ $\sqrt{9 \cdot 7}$ $\sqrt{63}$
$\sqrt{3}\sqrt{3}\sqrt{7}$ $\sqrt{3}\sqrt{21}$

2. Write at least two other radical expressions equivalent to:
   a. $5\sqrt{2}$; b. $2\sqrt{5}$;
   c. $6\sqrt{10}$; d. $10\sqrt{6}$.
3. Write each as the square root of a number. (For example, $3\sqrt{7} = \sqrt{63}$.)
   a. $2\sqrt{2}$ b. $2\sqrt{7}$
   c. $5\sqrt{6}$ d. $4\sqrt{3}$
4. Write each as the product of as many square roots as possible. (For example, $3\sqrt{6} = \sqrt{3} \cdot \sqrt{3} \cdot \sqrt{2} \cdot \sqrt{3}$.)
   a. $5\sqrt{10}$ b. $7\sqrt{5}$
   c. $\sqrt{30}$ d. $10\sqrt{22}$
5. What number times $\sqrt{6}$ equals $3\sqrt{10}$?

To answer problem 5, Tina wrote:

$\_\_\_\_ \cdot \sqrt{6} = 3\sqrt{10}$
$\_\_\_\_ \cdot \sqrt{3}\sqrt{2} = \sqrt{3}\sqrt{3}\sqrt{2}\sqrt{5}$

"First I wrote everything as a product of square roots," she explained. "Then it was easy to see that the missing factors were $\sqrt{5}$ and $\sqrt{3}$, so the answer must be $\sqrt{15}$."

Erin politely told Tina that her method seemed unnecessarily complicated. Erin wrote:

$\_\_\_\_ \cdot \sqrt{6} = 3\sqrt{10}$
$\_\_\_\_ \cdot \sqrt{6} = \sqrt{9}\sqrt{10}$
$\_\_\_\_ \cdot \sqrt{6} = \sqrt{90}$

"My goal was to write $3\sqrt{10}$ as the square root of something. Once I found that $3\sqrt{10} = \sqrt{90}$, it was easy from there. I could use the rule that $\sqrt{a} \cdot \sqrt{b} = \sqrt{ab}$ to see that the answer was $\sqrt{15}$," she explained.

6. What number times $2\sqrt{10}$ equals $10\sqrt{2}$? Find the answer by using
   a. Tina's method;
   b. Erin's method.
7. What number times $\sqrt{8}$ equals 4?
8. What number times $2\sqrt{2}$ equals $4\sqrt{3}$?

DIVISION

9. Divide 5 by $2\sqrt{5}$.

"That's not fair," said Tina. "Ms. Kem never taught us to divide with radicals." "That's true," said Erin, "but we know that multiplication and division are inverse operations." She wrote:

$\_\_\_\_ \cdot 2\sqrt{5} = 5$
$\_\_\_\_ \cdot \sqrt{4}\sqrt{5} = \sqrt{25}$

10. Finish solving the problem using Erin's method.

Another way to solve this problem is to use the following trick: *Write an equivalent fraction without a square root in the denominator.* In this case, we multiply both the numerator and denominator by $\sqrt{5}$.

9.4 Radical Operations

Core Sequence: 1-22

Suitable for Homework: 7-22

Useful for Assessment: 17-18, 20

What this Lesson is About:

- Multiplying square roots
- Dividing square roots
- Simple radical form
- Adding and subtracting square roots

This lesson should not be seen as a lesson in how to perform calculations. In most cases, a calculator should be used to calculate quantities involving square roots. The point of this lesson, instead, is to use operations with radicals to develop insights into the operation of taking a square root and the meaning of the radical sign.

Throughout the lesson you should allow students to use their calculators to check the correctness of their answers. For example, for problem 1a, if a student believes that $2\sqrt{3} = \sqrt{6}$, he or she would discover that this is wrong by calculating each side and finding that $2\sqrt{3} = 3.464\ldots$ while $\sqrt{6} = 2.449\ldots$.

MULTIPLICATION

This section continues the work on multiplying square roots that was started in Lesson 3. It also lays the groundwork for the rest of this lesson.

9.4 SOLUTIONS

1. Answers will vary.
2. a. $\sqrt{25} \cdot \sqrt{2}$ or $\sqrt{50}$
   b. $\sqrt{4} \cdot \sqrt{5}$ or $\sqrt{20}$
   c. $\sqrt{36} \cdot \sqrt{10}$ or $\sqrt{360}$
   d. $\sqrt{100} \cdot \sqrt{6}$ or $\sqrt{600}$
3. a. $\sqrt{4} \cdot \sqrt{2} = \sqrt{8}$
   b. $\sqrt{4} \cdot \sqrt{7} = \sqrt{28}$
   c. $\sqrt{25} \cdot \sqrt{6} = \sqrt{150}$
   d. $\sqrt{16} \cdot \sqrt{3} = \sqrt{48}$
4. a. $\sqrt{5} \cdot \sqrt{5} \cdot \sqrt{5} \cdot \sqrt{2}$
   b. $\sqrt{7} \cdot \sqrt{7} \cdot \sqrt{5}$
   c. $\sqrt{5} \cdot \sqrt{2} \cdot \sqrt{3}$
   d. $\sqrt{2} \cdot \sqrt{5} \cdot \sqrt{2} \cdot \sqrt{5} \cdot \sqrt{2} \cdot \sqrt{11}$
5. $3\sqrt{10} = \sqrt{3} \cdot \sqrt{3} \cdot \sqrt{2} \cdot \sqrt{5} = \sqrt{6} \cdot \sqrt{3} \cdot \sqrt{5} = \sqrt{6} \cdot \sqrt{15}$ so the number is $\sqrt{15}$.
6. a. $\_\_\_ \cdot \sqrt{2} \cdot \sqrt{2} \cdot \sqrt{10} = \sqrt{10} \cdot \sqrt{10} \cdot \sqrt{2}$
   Since $\sqrt{2} \cdot \sqrt{10}$ appears on both sides of the equation, we know that $\_\_\_ \cdot \sqrt{2} = \sqrt{10}$. Hence the missing factor is $\sqrt{5}$.
   b. $2 \cdot \sqrt{10} = \sqrt{4} \cdot \sqrt{10} = \sqrt{40}$
   $10 \cdot \sqrt{2} = \sqrt{100} \cdot \sqrt{2} = \sqrt{200}$
7. One way to solve this is to write 4 as $\sqrt{16}$. Then the missing factor can be seen to be $\sqrt{2}$.
8. Write $2 \cdot \sqrt{2} = \sqrt{8}$ and $4 \cdot \sqrt{3} = \sqrt{48}$. So the missing factor is $\sqrt{6}$.
9. Answers will vary. Some students may find an estimate using a calculator. Others may look for the missing factor. The answer, in simplest radical form, is $\sqrt{5/2}$.
10. $\_\_\_\_ \cdot \sqrt{20} = \sqrt{25}$. The missing factor is $\sqrt{5/4}$.

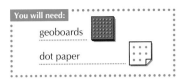

*B*e sure to have a class discussion of students' answers to problem 1, and again of 2, if needed.

DIVISION

MORE ON SIMPLE RADICAL FORM

*T*hese sections apply what was learned at the beginning of the lesson.

ADDITION AND SUBTRACTION

*S*tudents often make the mistake $\sqrt{a+b} = \sqrt{a} + \sqrt{b}$. Problems 14-20 attempt to discourage this by the use of geometric arguments.

*P*roblems 21-22 apply simple radical form to simplifying radical expressions.

$$\frac{5}{2\sqrt{5}} \cdot \frac{\sqrt{5}}{\sqrt{5}} = \frac{5 \cdot \sqrt{5}}{2 \cdot 5} = \frac{\sqrt{5}}{2}$$

11. Explain why $\sqrt{5}$ was chosen as the number by which to multiply.

12. Divide.
a. $\frac{3}{2\sqrt{6}}$ b. $\frac{24}{\sqrt{6}}$ c. $\frac{3\sqrt{10}}{5\sqrt{3}}$ d. $\frac{5\sqrt{3}}{3\sqrt{10}}$

MORE ON SIMPLE RADICAL FORM

Using the fact that $\sqrt{a} \cdot \sqrt{b} = \sqrt{ab}$, we can write $\sqrt{63}$ as $\sqrt{21} \cdot \sqrt{3}$. We can also write it as $\sqrt{9} \cdot \sqrt{7}$, which is especially convenient because 9 is a perfect square. Therefore:

$$\sqrt{63} = \sqrt{9} \cdot \sqrt{7} = 3\sqrt{7}.$$

This last expression is in simplest radical form.

13. Write in simple radical form.
a. $\sqrt{200}$ b. $\sqrt{147}$
c. $\sqrt{700}$ d. $\sqrt{275}$

ADDITION AND SUBTRACTION

14. Use dot paper to illustrate the addition $\sqrt{5} + 2\sqrt{5}$.

15. Using the figure you made in problem 14, explain how to decide which of the two equations $\sqrt{5} + \sqrt{20} = \sqrt{25}$ and $\sqrt{5} + \sqrt{20} = \sqrt{45}$ is correct.

16. Check your answer to problem 15 with a calculator.

17. True or False? Explain.
a. $16 + 9 = 25$
b. $\sqrt{16 + 9} = \sqrt{25}$
c. $\sqrt{16} + \sqrt{9} = \sqrt{25}$
d. $\sqrt{16} + \sqrt{9} = \sqrt{16 + 9}$

18. If a and b are positive numbers, is it always, sometimes, or never true that $\sqrt{a} + \sqrt{b} = \sqrt{a + b}$? Explain, with examples.

The figure shows a right triangle, a square having area a, a square having area b, and a third square.

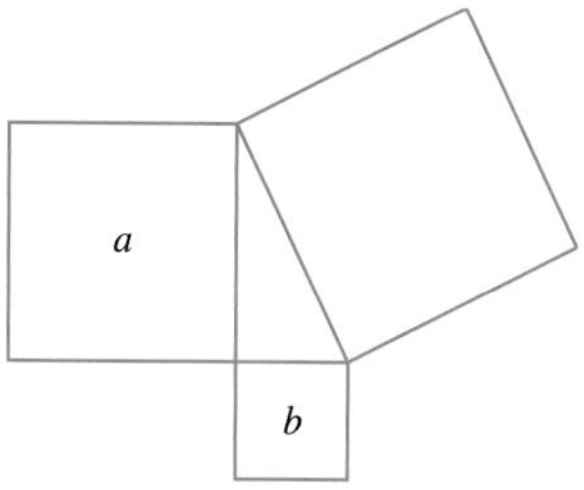

19. In terms of a and b,
a. what is the area of the third square? Explain.
b. What are the sides of the triangle?

20. If a and b are positive numbers, is it always, sometimes, or never true that $\sqrt{a} + \sqrt{b} > \sqrt{a + b}$? Explain, using the figure.

As you see, sums of radical expressions cannot usually be simplified. However, in some cases, simple radical form can help.

21. Simplify, then add or subtract.
a. $\sqrt{18} + \sqrt{32}$
b. $\sqrt{18} - 4\sqrt{20}$
c. $\sqrt{60} - \sqrt{135}$
d. $\sqrt{45} + \sqrt{125}$

You can add or subtract square roots only if they are the roots of the same number. This is similar to combining like terms when adding polynomials.

22. Simplify, then add or subtract, if possible.
a. $5 + 5\sqrt{68} + \sqrt{17}$
b. $6 - 6\sqrt{15} + \sqrt{90}$
c. $\sqrt{8} + \sqrt{16} + \sqrt{32} - \sqrt{64}$
d. $\sqrt{10} + \sqrt{20} - \sqrt{30} + \sqrt{40} - \sqrt{50}$

9.4 SOLUTIONS

11. Since there is already a $\sqrt{5}$ in the denominator, multiplying by $\sqrt{5}$ will eliminate the square root in the denominator.

12. a. multiply by $\sqrt{6/6}$ to get $\sqrt{6}/4$
b. multiply by $\sqrt{6/6}$ to get $4\sqrt{6}$
c. multiply by $\sqrt{3/3}$ to get $\sqrt{30}/5$
d. multiply by $\sqrt{10/10}$ to get $\sqrt{30}/6$

13. a. $10\sqrt{2}$ b. $7\sqrt{3}$
c. $10\sqrt{7}$ d. $5\sqrt{11}$

14. On dot paper you can draw a segment of length $\sqrt{5}$ and connect to it a segment of double that length. The total length will be $\sqrt{5} + \sqrt{5} + \sqrt{5}$, or $3\sqrt{5}$.

15. From the figure, it is clear that $\sqrt{5} + 2\sqrt{5} = 3\sqrt{5}$. Since $2\sqrt{5} = \sqrt{20}$ and $3\sqrt{5} = \sqrt{45}$, the second equation must be correct.

16. $\sqrt{5} \approx 2.236$; $\sqrt{20} \approx 4.472$; $\sqrt{25} = 5$; $\sqrt{45} \approx 6.708$

17. a. true b. true
c. false d. false

18. Answers will vary. A general argument follows: Compare the squares of the two expressions.
$(\sqrt{a} + \sqrt{b})^2 = a + 2\sqrt{ab} + b$
$(\sqrt{a + b})^2 = a + b$
Hence the first expression will always be larger, unless a or b equals 0.

19. a. By the Pythagorean theorem, the area of third square is $a + b$.
b. The legs of the triangle are $\sqrt{a}$ and $\sqrt{b}$ and the hypotenuse is $\sqrt{a + b}$.

20. From the figure, the sum of the lengths of the legs must be larger than the length of the hypotenuse unless one of the legs has length 0.

21. a. $7\sqrt{2}$
b. $3\sqrt{2} - 8\sqrt{5}$
c. $-\sqrt{15}$
d. $8\sqrt{5}$

22. a. $5 + 11\sqrt{17}$
b. $6 - 6\sqrt{15} + 3\sqrt{10}$
c. $-4 + 6\sqrt{2}$
d. $3\sqrt{10} + 2\sqrt{5} - 5\sqrt{2} - \sqrt{30}$

THINKING WRITING 9.A Geoboard Distances

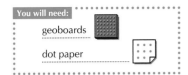

You will need:
- geoboards
- dot paper

1. Find the distance between the origin and each geoboard peg. Use radical expressions for your answers, not decimal approximations. Arrange your results in a table like the one below, with the peg coordinates along the sides. In each space write the peg's distance from the origin. Some examples have been entered to get you started. To speed this up, work with a partner and look for patterns.

10											
9											
8											
7											
6											
5	5										
4				5							
3					5						
2		$\sqrt{5}$									
1			$\sqrt{5}$								
0						5					
	0	1	2	3	4	5	6	7	8	9	10

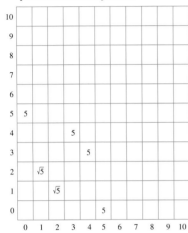

2. Describe the patterns you see in the table.

3. Find the numbers in the table that are not in simple radical form. Put them in that form and describe the patterns you notice.

4. What is the distance from the origin to the furthest peg on a geoboard having dimensions
a. 20 by 20? b. n by n?
c. 20 by 30? d. m by n?

5. On a 20-by-20 geoboard, what would be the largest multiple of:
a. $\sqrt{2}$? b. $\sqrt{5}$?
c. $\sqrt{10}$?

6. Notice that all the multiples of $\sqrt{2}$ lie on a line. What is the slope of this line?

7. a. Why are there two lines containing multiples of $\sqrt{5}$?
b. What are the slopes of these lines?

8. Repeat problem 7(b) for multiples of:
a. $\sqrt{10}$; b. $\sqrt{17}$.

9. List the geoboard distances that are on the line through the origin having slope
a. 5; b. 3/4.

10. Report Summarize your results from this lesson. Describe and explain the patterns you noticed and the generalizations you made.

THINKING WRITING 9.A Geoboard Distances

Core Sequence: 1-10

Suitable for Homework: 4-10

Useful for Assessment: 10

What this Assignment is About:
- The Pythagorean theorem
- Simple radical form
- Review of slope

*T*his assignment involves a lot of initial work, and it is best to do problems 1-3 in class so that students can work in pairs.

*I*n problems 4-5, the geoboard dimensions given refer to the number of units, not the number of pins. For example, the geoboard you have been working with is an 11-pin-by-11-pin geoboard, but in these exercises it would be described as a 10-by-10 geoboard.

9.A SOLUTIONS

1.

10	10	$\sqrt{101}$	$\sqrt{104}$	$\sqrt{109}$	$\sqrt{116}$	$\sqrt{125}$	$\sqrt{136}$	$\sqrt{149}$	$\sqrt{164}$	$\sqrt{181}$	$\sqrt{200}$
9	9	$\sqrt{82}$	$\sqrt{85}$	$\sqrt{90}$	$\sqrt{97}$	$\sqrt{106}$	$\sqrt{117}$	$\sqrt{130}$	$\sqrt{145}$	$\sqrt{162}$	$\sqrt{181}$
8	8	$\sqrt{65}$	$\sqrt{68}$	$\sqrt{73}$	$\sqrt{80}$	$\sqrt{89}$	$\sqrt{100}$	$\sqrt{113}$	$\sqrt{128}$	$\sqrt{145}$	$\sqrt{164}$
7	7	$\sqrt{50}$	$\sqrt{53}$	$\sqrt{58}$	$\sqrt{65}$	$\sqrt{74}$	$\sqrt{85}$	$\sqrt{98}$	$\sqrt{113}$	$\sqrt{130}$	$\sqrt{149}$
6	6	$\sqrt{37}$	$\sqrt{40}$	$\sqrt{45}$	$\sqrt{52}$	$\sqrt{61}$	$\sqrt{72}$	$\sqrt{85}$	$\sqrt{100}$	$\sqrt{117}$	$\sqrt{136}$
5	5	$\sqrt{26}$	$\sqrt{29}$	$\sqrt{34}$	$\sqrt{41}$	$\sqrt{50}$	$\sqrt{61}$	$\sqrt{74}$	$\sqrt{89}$	$\sqrt{106}$	$\sqrt{125}$
4	4	$\sqrt{17}$	$\sqrt{20}$	5	$\sqrt{32}$	$\sqrt{41}$	$\sqrt{52}$	$\sqrt{65}$	$\sqrt{80}$	$\sqrt{97}$	$\sqrt{116}$
3	3	$\sqrt{10}$	$\sqrt{13}$	$\sqrt{18}$	5	$\sqrt{34}$	$\sqrt{45}$	$\sqrt{58}$	$\sqrt{73}$	$\sqrt{90}$	$\sqrt{109}$
2	2	$\sqrt{5}$	$\sqrt{8}$	$\sqrt{13}$	$\sqrt{20}$	$\sqrt{29}$	$\sqrt{40}$	$\sqrt{53}$	$\sqrt{68}$	$\sqrt{85}$	$\sqrt{104}$
1	1	$\sqrt{2}$	$\sqrt{5}$	$\sqrt{10}$	$\sqrt{17}$	$\sqrt{26}$	$\sqrt{37}$	$\sqrt{50}$	$\sqrt{65}$	$\sqrt{82}$	$\sqrt{101}$
0	0	1	2	3	4	5	6	7	8	9	10
	0	1	2	3	4	5	6	7	8	9	10

2. & 3. Answers will vary. The following table shows the numbers in simple radical form, which makes it easier to find patterns.

10	10	$\sqrt{101}$	$2\sqrt{26}$	$\sqrt{109}$	$2\sqrt{29}$	$5\sqrt{5}$	$2\sqrt{34}$	$\sqrt{149}$	$2\sqrt{41}$	$\sqrt{181}$	$10\sqrt{2}$
9	9	$\sqrt{82}$	$\sqrt{85}$	$3\sqrt{10}$	$\sqrt{97}$	$\sqrt{106}$	$3\sqrt{13}$	$\sqrt{130}$	$\sqrt{145}$	$9\sqrt{2}$	$\sqrt{181}$
8	8	$\sqrt{65}$	$2\sqrt{17}$	$\sqrt{73}$	$4\sqrt{5}$	$\sqrt{89}$	10	$\sqrt{113}$	$8\sqrt{2}$	$\sqrt{145}$	$2\sqrt{41}$
7	7	$5\sqrt{2}$	$\sqrt{53}$	$\sqrt{58}$	$\sqrt{65}$	$\sqrt{74}$	$\sqrt{85}$	$7\sqrt{2}$	$\sqrt{113}$	$\sqrt{130}$	$\sqrt{149}$
6	6	$\sqrt{37}$	$2\sqrt{10}$	$3\sqrt{5}$	$2\sqrt{13}$	$\sqrt{61}$	$6\sqrt{2}$	$\sqrt{85}$	10	$3\sqrt{13}$	$2\sqrt{34}$
5	5	$\sqrt{26}$	$\sqrt{29}$	$\sqrt{34}$	$\sqrt{41}$	$5\sqrt{2}$	$\sqrt{61}$	$\sqrt{74}$	$\sqrt{89}$	$\sqrt{106}$	$5\sqrt{5}$
4	4	$\sqrt{17}$	$2\sqrt{5}$	5	$4\sqrt{2}$	$\sqrt{41}$	$2\sqrt{13}$	$\sqrt{65}$	$4\sqrt{5}$	$\sqrt{97}$	$2\sqrt{29}$
3	3	$\sqrt{10}$	$\sqrt{13}$	$3\sqrt{2}$	5	$\sqrt{34}$	$3\sqrt{5}$	$\sqrt{58}$	$\sqrt{73}$	$3\sqrt{10}$	$\sqrt{109}$
2	2	$\sqrt{5}$	$2\sqrt{2}$	$\sqrt{13}$	$2\sqrt{5}$	$\sqrt{29}$	$2\sqrt{10}$	$\sqrt{53}$	$2\sqrt{17}$	$\sqrt{85}$	$2\sqrt{26}$
1	1	$\sqrt{2}$	$\sqrt{5}$	$\sqrt{10}$	$\sqrt{17}$	$\sqrt{26}$	$\sqrt{37}$	$5\sqrt{2}$	$\sqrt{65}$	$\sqrt{82}$	$\sqrt{101}$
0	0	1	2	3	4	5	6	7	8	9	10
	0	1	2	3	4	5	6	7	8	9	10

4. a. $20 \cdot \sqrt{2}$
b. $n\sqrt{2}$
c. $\sqrt{20^2+30^2} = 10\sqrt{13}$
d. $\sqrt{m^2+n^2}$

(Solutions continued on page 525)

▼ 9.5
The Square Root Function

Core Sequence: 1-22

Suitable for Homework: 9-22, 28-29

Useful for Assessment: 8, 10-12, 18, 22

What this Lesson is About:

- Square roots of numbers less than 1
- Domain and range
- The square root function
- Relationship between the square and square root functions

Students often do not have a good understanding of what happens when you take the square root of a number less than one. They also often get confused about the difference and the relationship between squaring a number and taking the square root of a number. Finally, another area of confusion relates to the domain and range of the square root function.

This lesson attempts to help students think about these difficult questions with the help of calculators and three visual supports: geometry, function diagrams, and Cartesian graphs.

LESSON 9.5

The Square Root Function

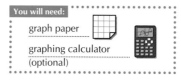

You will need:
graph paper
graphing calculator (optional)

ROOTS OF NUMBERS < 1

The large square in the figure has dimensions 1-by-1 unit. It is divided into 11 smaller squares. For the square on the top left, you could write the following equations, relating the length of its side to its area.

a. $1/4 = (1/2)^2$ b. $1/2 = \sqrt{1/4}$
c. $0.25 = 0.5^2$ d. $0.5^2 = \sqrt{0.25}$

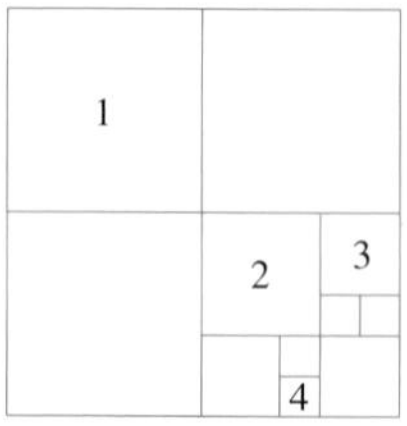

1. Explain the above equations.

2-4. For each numbered smaller square, write equations of the form:
 a. area = side^2, using fractions
 b. side = $\sqrt{\text{area}}$, using fractions
 c. area = side^2, using decimals
 d. side = $\sqrt{\text{area}}$, using decimals

DIAGRAMS FOR SQUARES AND ROOTS

The function diagrams for the same function could look quite different with different scales.

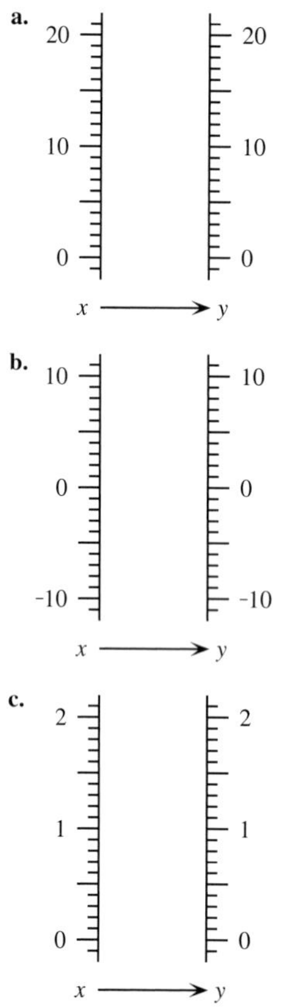

5. Make three function diagrams for the function $y = x^2$, using the scales given in the figure. Use nine in-out pairs for each.

Problems 6 and 7 are about $y = x^2$.

9.5 SOLUTIONS

1. The area of a square is the square of its side length. The side length is the square root of the area. This is expressed in both fractions and decimals. (The equations may look a little surprising to students who are not used to thinking about numbers being smaller than their square roots.)
2. a. $9/100 = (3/10)^2$
 b. $3/10 = \sqrt{9/100}$
 c. $0.09 = (0.3)^2$
 d. $0.3 = \sqrt{0.09}$
3. a. $4/100 = (2/10)^2$
 b. $2/10 = \sqrt{4/100}$
 c. $0.04 = (0.2)^2$
 d. $0.2 = \sqrt{0.04}$
4. a. $1/100 = (1/10)^2$
 b. $1/10 = \sqrt{1/100}$
 c. $0.01 = (0.1)^2$
 d. $0.1 = \sqrt{0.01}$
5.

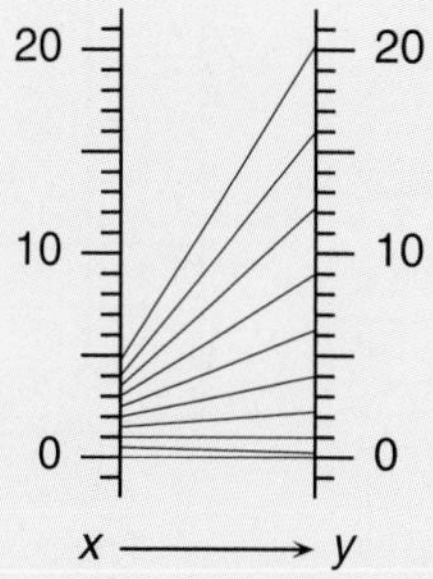

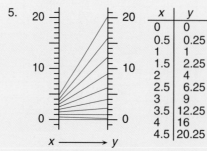

x	y
0	0
0.5	0.25
1	1
1.5	2.25
2	4
2.5	6.25
3	9
3.5	12.25
4	16
4.5	20.25

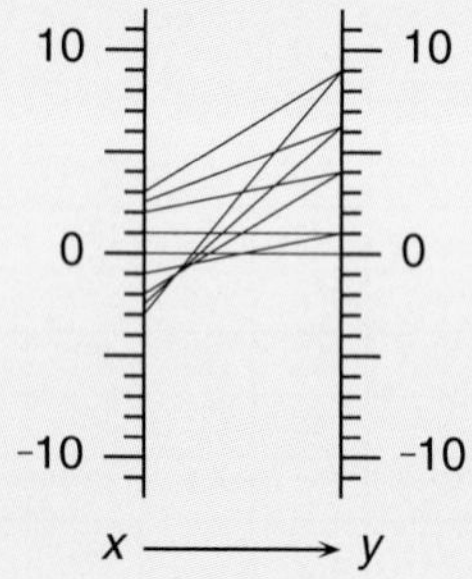

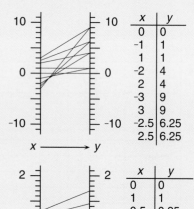

x	y
0	0
-1	1
1	1
-2	4
2	4
-3	9
3	9
-2.5	6.25
2.5	6.25

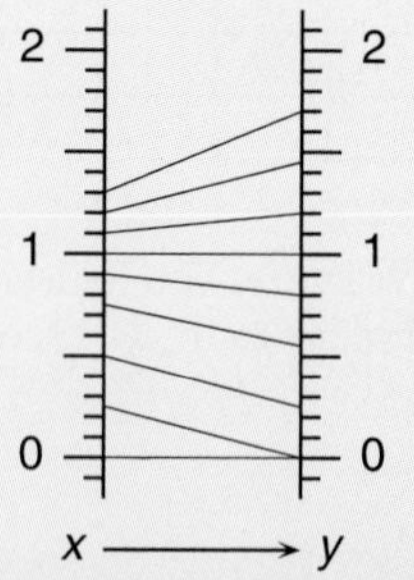

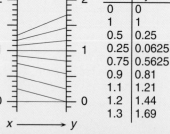

x	y
0	0
1	1
0.5	0.25
0.25	0.0625
0.75	0.5625
0.9	0.81
1.1	1.21
1.2	1.44
1.3	1.69

6. In the function diagrams below, how far would you have to extend the y-number line in the positive direction so that every value you can see on the x-number line has a corresponding y-value on the diagram? How about in the negative direction?

a.

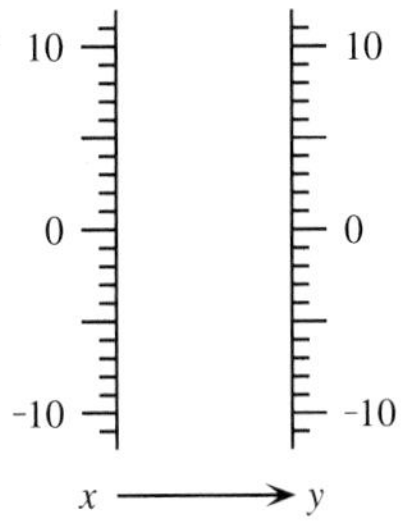

b.

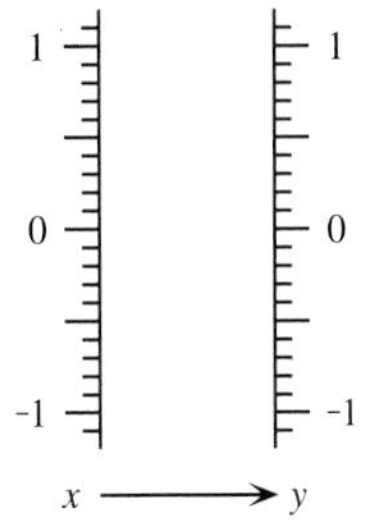

c.

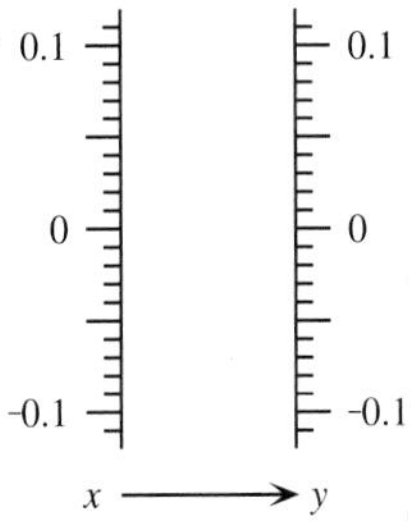

7. In the function diagrams below, how far would you have to extend the x-number line, if at all, so that every value you can see on the y-number line has a corresponding x-value on the diagram?

a.

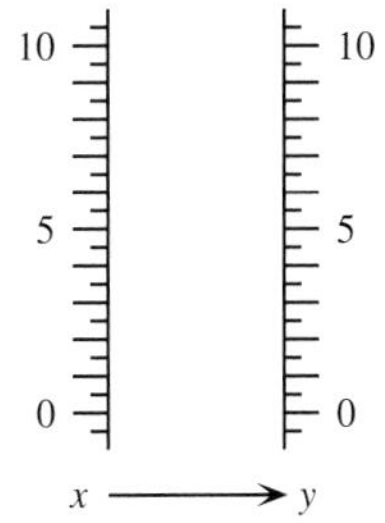

b.

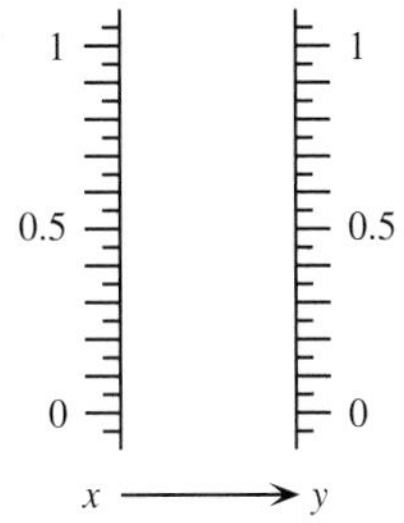

c.

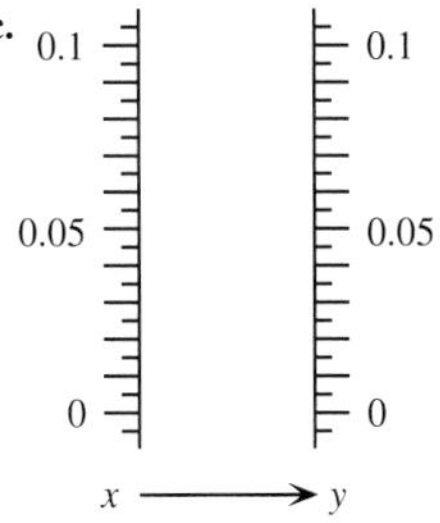

ROOTS OF NUMBERS < 1

Since there are no measurements indicated on the square, students will have to use deduction to figure out the sides of the smaller squares. A good strategy is to call the side of square 4 s, and to use it to measure the other ones. Then the side of square 3 is $2s$, the side of square 2 is $3s$, the side of square 1 is $5s$, and finally the side of the whole square is $10s$. Therefore $s = 1/10$. (Do not give away the whole solution, but if students are frustrated get them started with this strategy.)

An explicit class discussion of the results of this investigation will make it clear that the squares of numbers less than one are less than the original numbers, while the square roots are larger.

9.5 SOLUTIONS

6. a. extend the y-number line to 121 and -121
   b. does not need to be extended
   c. does not need to be extended
7. a. does not need to be extended
   b. does not need to be extended
   c. does not need to be extended
8. If you square 0, the result is zero. A positive number squared is a positive number. A negative number squared is also a positive number. For *any* positive number, it is possible to find two numbers (one negative, one positive) that you can square to get that number.

9.

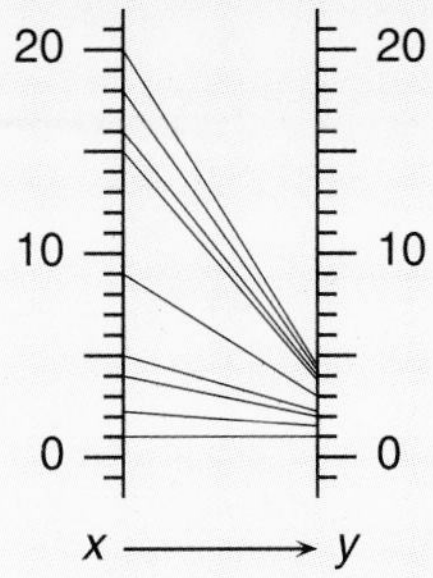

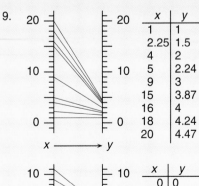

x	y
1	1
2.25	1.5
4	2
5	2.24
9	3
15	3.87
16	4
18	4.24
20	4.47

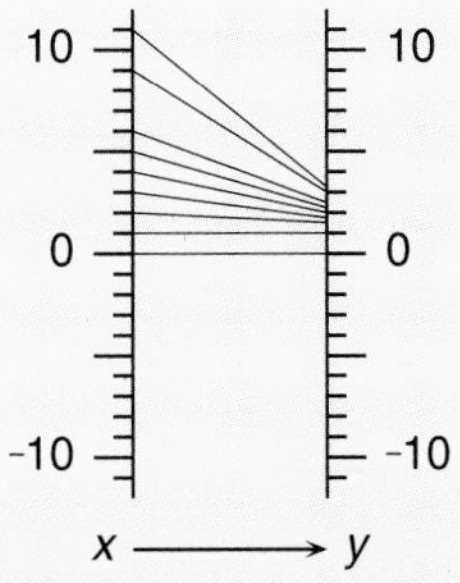

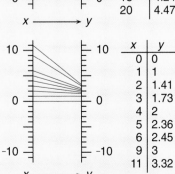

x	y
0	0
1	1
2	1.41
3	1.73
4	2
5	2.36
6	2.45
9	3
11	3.32

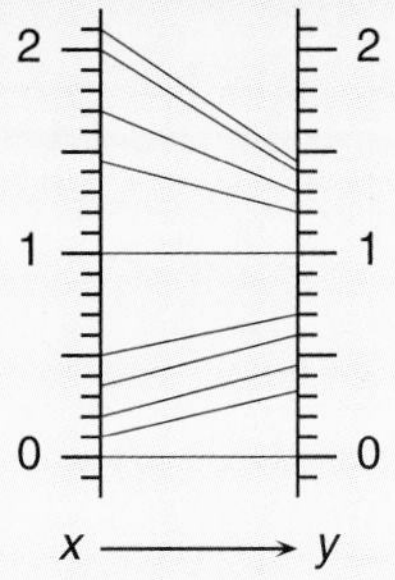

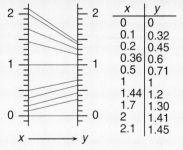

x	y
0	0
0.1	0.32
0.2	0.45
0.36	0.6
0.5	0.71
1	1
1.44	1.2
1.7	1.30
2	1.41
2.1	1.45

10. You cannot take the square root of a negative number.
11. The square root function has domain $x \geq 0$ and range $y \geq 0$.
12. a. nonnegative numbers
    b. all numbers
    c. nonnegative numbers
    d. nonnegative numbers

GRAPHS FOR SQUARES AND ROOTS

Function diagrams and Cartesian graphs make visual what calculators show numerically. The extended discussion made possible by the problems in these sections should help prevent common misunderstandings.

For problems 19-21, students should use calculators and/or graphs. This same idea was covered graphically in Chapter 7, Lesson 7, and **Thinking/Writing 7.B**.

Definitions: The *domain* of a function is the set of the values that the input can take. The *range* of a function is the set of the values the output can take.

Example: The domain of $y = x^2$ is *all numbers*, since any number can be squared.

8. Explain why the range of the function $y = x^2$ is all nonnegative numbers.

Notation: $\sqrt{x}$ represents the nonnegative number whose square is x.

Example: $\sqrt{4}$ represents only 2, even though $(-2)^2$ also equals 4. However we can write

$$-2 = -\sqrt{4}.$$

9. Using the same scales as in problem 5, make three function diagrams for the function $y = \sqrt{x}$.

10. For which scale is the function diagram not a mirror image of the corresponding one for $y = x^2$? Explain.

11. What are the domain and the range of the square root function? Explain.

12. To *be* or to *have*, that is the question.
a. Which numbers have a square root?
b. Which numbers have a square?
c. Which numbers can be a square?
d. Which numbers can be a square root?

GRAPHS FOR SQUARES AND ROOTS

13. Make tables of at least eight (x, y) pairs each for these two functions and graph them on the same axes. Use three values of x between 0 and 1, as well as negative values and whole numbers.
a. $y = x^2$ b. $y = \sqrt{x}$

14. On the same axes, graph the line $y = x$.

15. The curve representing $y = x^2$ is called a *parabola*. What would you call the curve representing $y = \sqrt{x}$?

16. Which of your three graphs grows
a. faster and faster?
b. more and more slowly?
c. always at the same rate?

17. If extended to the right, how high would the curve representing $y = \sqrt{x}$ go? (Can you find an x such that $\sqrt{x}$ is larger than 100? Than 1000?) Explain.

18.
a. What numbers are greater than their squares?
b. What numbers are less than their square roots?
c. What numbers are equal to their square roots?
d. What numbers are equal to their squares?

19. Solve the equations.
a. $x^2 = 5$ b. $x^2 = -5$
c. $\sqrt{x} = 5$ d. $\sqrt{x} = -5$
e. $-\sqrt{x} = -5$

20. Solve the inequalities. (Be careful! Some have compound solutions.)
a. $x^2 < 4$ b. $\sqrt{x} < 2$
c. $x^2 < \sqrt{x}$ d. $x^2 > 6$

21. Solve the equations and inequalities.
a. $P^2 = 456$ b. $P^2 < 456$
c. $\sqrt{K} = 789$ d. $\sqrt{K} < 789$

22. Report Summarize what you know about the functions $y = x$, $y = x^2$, and $y = \sqrt{x}$. Use graphs, diagrams, and examples. Include answers to these questions.
- Which is greatest and which is least among x, x^2, or $\sqrt{x}$? Explain how the answer depends on the value of x.
- What are the domains and ranges of these three functions?

9.5 SOLUTIONS

13., 14.

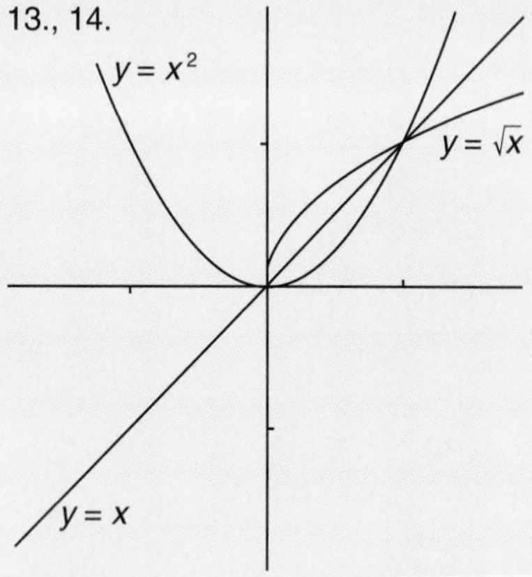

15. Answers will vary. Students should notice that it is half a parabola.

16. a. $y = x^2$
b. $y = \sqrt{x}$
c. $y = x$

17. infinitely high

18. a. numbers between 0 and 1
b. numbers between 0 and 1
c. 0, 1
d. 0, 1

19. a. $x = \sqrt{5}$ or $x = -\sqrt{5}$
b. no solution
c. $x = 25$
d. no solution
e. 25

20. a. x is between -2 and 2 (or $-2 < x < 2$)
b. $0 \le x < 4$
c. $0 < x < 1$
d. $x > \sqrt{6}$ or $x < -\sqrt{6}$

21. a. $P \approx 21.35$ or $P \approx -21.35$
b. $-21.35 < P < 21.35$
c. $K = 622521$
d. $0 \le K < 622521$

22. Reports will vary. Some key ideas follow: x^2 is the greatest and $\sqrt{x}$ the least for $x > 1$. x^2 is greater than x and $\sqrt{x}$ is not defined for $x < 0$. They are all equal for $x = 1$. For $0 < x < 1$, $x^2 < x < \sqrt{x}$.

23. Sketch the graphs of $y = \sqrt{x}$ and $y = \sqrt{-x}$. Think about domain and range!

MORE SQUARE ROOT GRAPHS

Use a graphing calculator if you have one.

24. Graph these equations on the same pair of axes.
   a. $y = 4\sqrt{x}$ b. $y = \sqrt{4x}$
   c. $y = \sqrt{4}\sqrt{x}$

25. In problem 24, which graphs are the same? Explain.

26. Graph these equations on the same pair of axes.
   a. $y = \sqrt{x + 9}$ b. $y = \sqrt{x} + 3$
   c. $y = \sqrt{x} + \sqrt{9}$

27. In problem 26, which graphs are the same? Explain.

PUZZLES PACKING SQUARES

28. A 10-by-10 square can be divided into 11 smaller ones, with no overlaps and no space left over (as in the figure at the very beginning of the lesson). Divide each of the following squares into 11 smaller squares. (The side lengths of the smaller squares must be integers.)
   a. 11-by-11 b. 12-by-12
   c. 13-by-13

DISCOVERY WALKING DISTANCE

Use graph paper as the map of a city. The horizontal and vertical lines represent streets.

29. In your group, agree on the location of various buildings, such as a supermarket, a hospital, a school, a fast food outlet, a bank, etc. Mark them on dot paper. Make a list of their coordinates.

   Make up a problem about finding a good place for a couple to live in your city. Assume that they do not want to drive, and that they work in different places. Each student should choose a different job for each member of the couple.
   a. Where should they live if they want to minimize the total amount of distance walked to work?
   b. Where should they live if, in addition, they want to walk equal amounts?

MORE SQUARE ROOT GRAPHS

These problems make for a good discussion of rules for operations with radicals, but they may be too difficult without a graphing calculator.

PUZZLES PACKING SQUARES

This puzzle is just for fun, though you could ask the same questions about problem 28b, for example, as were asked about the square at the beginning of the lesson.

The puzzles were inspired by Martin Gardner's "Mrs. Perkins' Quilt," a chapter in *Mathematical Carnival* (Vintage Books, © 1975).

DISCOVERY WALKING DISTANCE

This is a side trip. Students can work with taxicab distance to make a mathematical model of the situation. In most cases, problem 29a narrows the apartment search down to a rectangle and 29b to a line segment within that rectangle.

9.5 SOLUTIONS

23.

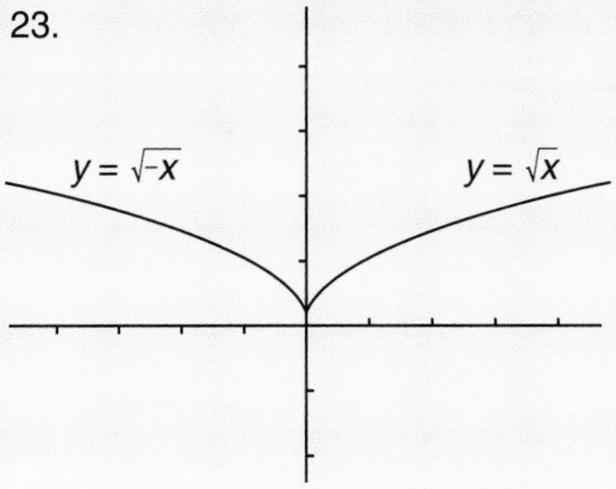

24.

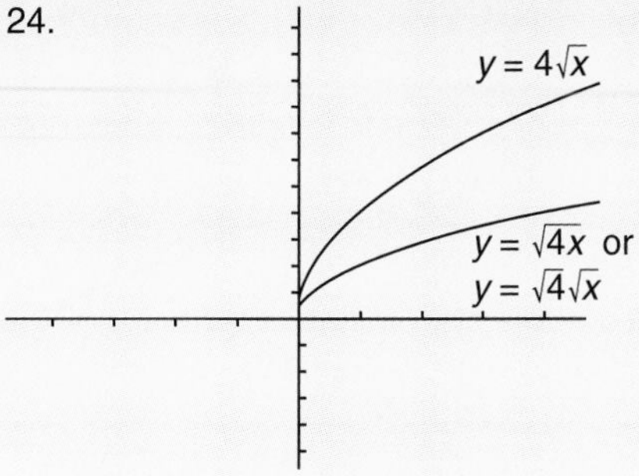

25. The graphs of (b) and (c) are the same, because of the rule about multiplying square roots.

26.

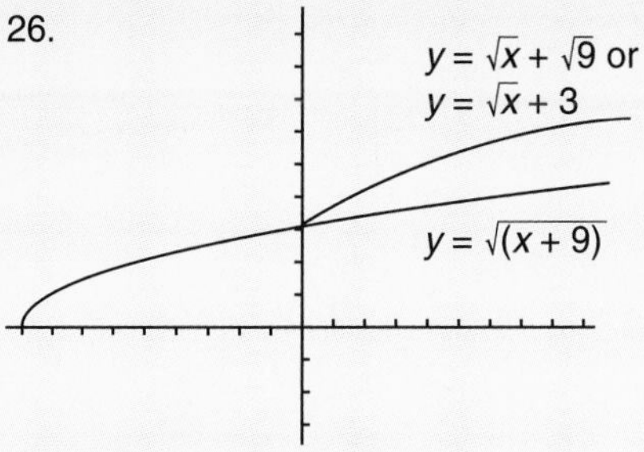

27. The graphs of (b) and (c) are the same, because $\sqrt{9} = 3$.

9.6 Midpoints

Core Sequence: 1-21

Suitable for Homework: 7-18

Useful for Assessment: 5, 13, 18

What this Lesson is About:

- Review of average
- Midpoint of a segment
- Preview of surface area and volume of similar figures
- Review of taxicab distance

While this lesson continues to address the chapter's theme of measurement, it provides a break from the main thrust of the previous lessons (square roots). It also serves as a necessary transition into the next lesson, which puts square roots in the context of exponential growth.

MEETING HALFWAY

FINDING A FORMULA

The first section poses the question of the halfway point and the second guides students to a full answer.

Since it is likely that at least some of your students used "Ruth's method," you may cover the same ground as is in problems 7-12 during a full class discussion of problem 5. In that case, problems 7-13 can be used as homework to consolidate that understanding.

LESSON 9.6

Midpoints

You will need:

graph paper

MEETING HALFWAY

1. Linda works at the corner of Galbrae Avenue and 15th Street. Micaelia works at the corner of Galbrae Avenue and 38th Street. The streets between 15th and 38th are all consecutively numbered streets. Linda and Micaelia agree to meet after work. If they both want to walk the same distance, where should they meet?

2. Change Micaelia's workplace in problem 1. Make her meeting place with Linda at a street corner, not the middle of a block.

3. For what values of n is the halfway point between 15th Street and nth Street in the middle of the block, and for what values is it at a street corner?

4. Find the point on the number line halfway between:

a. 1.5 and 6.8; b. 1/3 and 1/2.

5. Describe how to find the point on the number line halfway between a and b. Use a sketch and explain.

6. Explain how to find the point on the number line

a. 1/3 of the way from 4 to 6;

b. 1/4 of the way from 4 to 7.

FINDING A FORMULA

Sue and Ruth were trying to find the number halfway between 5 and 11.4. Ruth used this method: First she found the distance between 11.4 and 5, which is 6.4. Next she took half of that, which is 3.2. Last she added 3.2 to 5.

7. Use a sketch of the number line to explain Ruth's method.

8. If $B > A$, what is the distance between A and B on the number line? What is half that distance?

9. The formula for Ruth's method is

$$\text{midpoint} = \frac{B-A}{2} + A.$$

Explain.

10. Ruth's formula can be rewritten as two fractions with a common denominator.

$$\text{midpoint} = \frac{B-A}{2} + \frac{2A}{2}$$

Write it as one fraction in lowest terms.

11. Explain the formula you found in problem 10 in words.

12. Sue's method for finding the midpoint between two points on the number line is to take the average of the two points. Does that method work? Test it on some examples, and explain what you find out.

13. **Summary** Compare Ruth's method with Sue's method. Use examples, sketches, and algebra. Does either method work all the time? Which one do you prefer? Do they work when A and/or B are negative?

9.6 SOLUTIONS

1. In the middle of the block between 26th and 27th.
2. Micaelia could move to the corner of 37th Street, or for that matter to the corner of Galbrae and any odd-numbered block.
3. If n is odd, they meet at a corner. If n is even, they meet in the middle of the block.
4. a. 4.15 b. 5/12
5. Answers will vary. One way is to find the distance between the two numbers and add one-half the distance to the smaller number.
6. Answers will vary. One way is to find the distance between the two numbers and add the appropriate fraction of that distance to the smaller number.
   a. 4 + 1/3 (distance between 4 and 6) = 4 + (1/3) (2) = 4 2/3
   b. 4 + 1/4 (distance between 4 and 7) = 4 + (1/4) (3) = 4 3/4
7. Answers will vary.
8. The distance is $B - A$, so half the distance is $(B - A)/2$.
9. Her formula says to take half the distance from A to B and add it to A.
10. $(B - A + 2A)/2 = (B + A)/2$
11. This is the average of A and B.
12. It should work. (See #11.)
13. Answers will vary.

THE MIDPOINT OF LINEAR GROWTH

Between ages 10 and 12, Sue's growth in height was approximately linear as a function of age. This means that the rate of change of height per year was approximately constant.

Sue's Growth (Height)

Age (years)	Height (cm)
10	146
11	—
12	161

14. Estimate Sue's height at age 11.

15. Based on the data, do you think her weight increased linearly as a function of age? If so, estimate her weight at ages 10½ and 11½.

Sue's Growth (Weight)

Age (years)	Weight (lbs)
10	90
11	101
12	112

16. Joel kept a record of his height and weight. When he was 5′5″ tall, he weighed 130 pounds. When he was 5′7″ tall, he weighed 142 pounds. If his weight increased as a linear function of his height, how much did he weigh when he was 5′6″ tall?

MIDPOINT OF A LINE SEGMENT

17. On a graph, plot and label the midpoint of the segment joining each pair of points.

a. (5, 3) and (8, 7)
b. (-5, -3) and (8, -7)
c. (-5.5, 3.5) and (8, 7)
d. (1/4, 3) and (3/4, -7)

18. Using a sketch, explain how to find the coordinates of the midpoint of the segment joining the points (a, b) and (c, d). Check your method for positive and negative numbers. Try to write a formula.

PREVIEW SURFACE AREA SEQUENCES

For each sequence of buildings, find the volume and surface area of the first four buildings. Then, describe and sketch the fifth building, and find its volume and surface area.

19.

20.

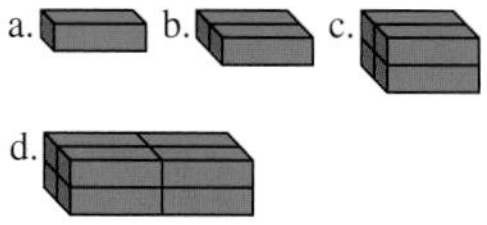

21.

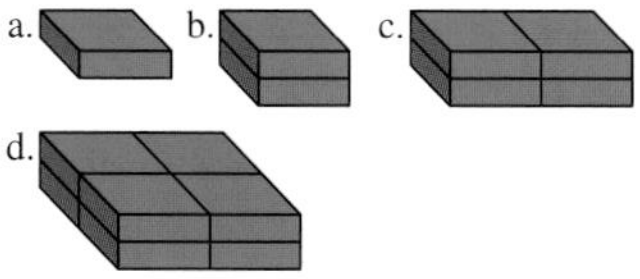

THE MIDPOINT OF LINEAR GROWTH

This problem, while different on the surface, is mathematically identical to the midpoint problem of the previous sections. It should not provide any serious obstacles. In the next lesson, we discuss the midpoint of exponential growth.

MIDPOINT OF A LINE SEGMENT

This is more challenging, because we are working in two dimensions. The sketches should help students discover the pattern. If they are having trouble, you may suggest they draw *rise and run* triangles for each half-segment.

PREVIEW SURFACE AREA SEQUENCES

This completes the work on surface area that started at the ends of Lessons 1 and 2.

9.6 SOLUTIONS

14. 153.5 cm

15. yes; 95.5 pounds at 10 1/2 and 106.5 pounds at 11 1/2

16. 136 pounds

17. a. (6.5, 5)
b. (1.5, -5)
c. (1.25, 5.25)
d. (0.5, -2)

18. Answers will vary. Earlier in the lesson, Ruth and Sue developed midpoint methods for one dimension which can now be applied to two dimensions. Apply one of their methods for finding the midpoint twice—first for the x-coordinates and then for the y-coordinates—to get the x- and y-coordinates of the midpoint. By Sue's method: average the x's to get $(a + c)/2$, then average the y's to get $(b + d)/2$. By Ruth's method, find half the distance and add it to the first number, which gives $(a + 1/2(c - a))$ for the x-coordinate and $b + 1/2(d - b)$ for the y-coordinate. Simplified, these give the same answers as Sue's method. In words, the midpoint can be described as the point (average of the x's, average of the y's). It is better to remember this than to memorize a formula.

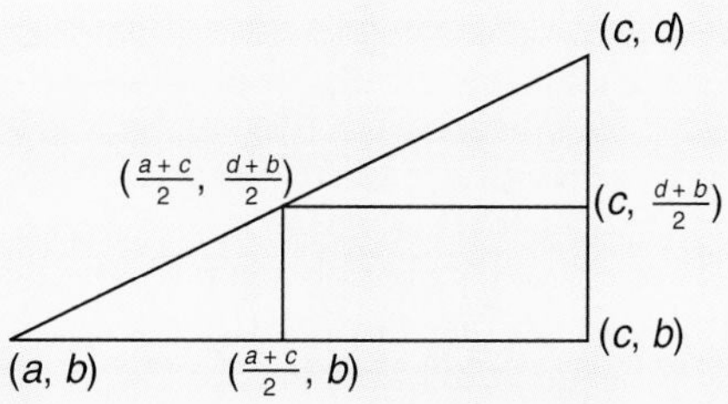

19. a. v = 1; s.a. = 6
b. v = 2; s.a. = 10
c. v = 4; s.a. = 16
d. v = 8; s.a. = 24

20. a. v = x; s.a. = $4x + 2$
b. v = $2x$; s.a. = $6x + 4$
c. v = $4x$; s.a. = $8x + 8$
d. v = $8x$; s.a. = $16x + 8$

21. a. v = x^2; s.a. = $2x^2 + 4x$
b. v = $2x^2$; s.a. = $2x^2 + 8x$
c. v = $4x^2$; s.a. = $4x^2 + 12x$
d. v = $8x^2$; s.a. = $8x^2 + 16x$

▼ 9.7
Halfway Measures

Core Sequence: 1-25

Suitable for Homework: 5-25

Useful for Assessment: 5, 13

What this Lesson is About:

- Review of linear vs. exponential growth
- Review of solving equations
- Review of solving proportions
- Review and preview of radical rules
- Preview of fractional exponents and the exponent 1/2

This lesson reviews many important concepts, however it should not be seen as easy; the concepts are challenging, and they are extended to new levels of difficulty. Moreover, the lesson previews the concept of the exponent 1/2 and of fractional exponents in general.

TWO ACCOUNTS

This section reviews simple and compound interest which were first studied in Chapter 8, **Thinking/Writing 8.B**. What makes it more difficult this time is that the interest rate is not given. Students have to figure it out from the information given.

An algebraic method should work in the case of simple interest, but students will have to resort to trial and error for compound interest. (Do not expect them to take the fourth root of any numbers!)

Problems 1-4 should generate plenty of discussion in groups. It is unlikely that students will succeed with the rest of the lesson if they have trouble with this part, so make sure their questions are answered before forging ahead.

LESSON 9.7

Halfway Measures

TWO ACCOUNTS

1. **Exploration** Janet and Marne had savings accounts. Marne was earning simple interest, and Janet was earning compound interest. Surprisingly, both accounts grew from \$650.00 to \$805.24 in four years. What was the annual interest rate for each account?

2. How much money was in each account after two years?

3. One account increased by the same *amount* every two years. What was the amount?

4. The other account increased by the same *percent* every two years. What was the percent?

5. **Summary** One account was an example of linear growth, the other was an example of exponential growth. In equal time intervals, one account showed constant differences, while the other showed constant ratios. Explain.

THE MIDPOINT OF EXPONENTIAL GROWTH

Dick and Stan had data about the population of their school. There were 325 students in 1980 and 742 students in 1988. They wanted to estimate the population in 1984.

Dick assumed that the population had grown linearly. This means that for equal time intervals the difference in population would be the same. Algebraically,

$$P_{1984} - P_{1980} = P_{1988} - P_{1984}.$$

6. Use algebra to find P_{1984}.

7. If Dick's assumption was correct, what was the population in 1986?

Stan assumed that the population had grown exponentially. This means that for equal time intervals, the population ratios would be the same. Algebraically,

$$\frac{P_{1984}}{P_{1980}} = \frac{P_{1988}}{P_{1984}}$$

$$\frac{P_{1984}}{325} = \frac{742}{P_{1984}}$$

8. Solve for P_{1984}. (Hint: Multiply both sides by 325 and then by P_{1984}.)

9. If Stan's assumption was correct, what was the population in 1986? Explain your reasoning and show your calculations.

10. Assume Stan's assumption was correct and also that the population grew at the same rate from 1980 to 1992. Make a table showing an estimate of the population at two-year intervals during this time period.

LINEAR OR EXPONENTIAL?

Solve these problems in two ways, assuming

a. that the growth is linear;
b. that the growth is exponential.
c. Discuss which assumption is more reasonable, or whether neither one is credible.

11. A tree was 6 feet high in 1930 and 21 feet high in 1980. How high was it in 1955?

12. A tumor was estimated to weigh about 4 grams in January and 7 grams six months later. If it continued to grow in the same way, how much would it weigh after three more months?

9.7 SOLUTIONS

1. simple: 5.97% (found by algebra)
compound: 5.5% (found by trial and error)
2. Marne had \$727.61 and Janet had \$723.47.
3. Marne earned \$77.61 every two years.
4. Janet earned about 11.3% every two years.
5. Janet was earning about 5.5% per year, compounded annually. This means that the ratio of each year's account balance to the previous year's balance is 1.055. Marne was earning about \$38.81 per year. This means that the difference between each year's balance and the previous year's balance is \$38.81. Their financial fate can be summarized in a table.

Year	Marne	Janet
0	650	650
1	688.81	685.75
2	727.61	723.47
3	766.42	763.26
4	805.22	805.24

6. If x is the population in 1984, $x - 325 = 742 - x$. By algebra, find that $x = 533.5$, or approximately 534 students.
7. The growth must have been about 104.25 every two years. Add this to 533.5, to get 637.75, or about 638 students.
8. By Stan's assumption, the population in 1984 was about 491.
9. Let y = the population in 1986. Stan's assumption is one of constant ratios,

13. **Generalization** A growing population is P_1 at a certain time and P_2 at a later time. Use algebra to find its size halfway between these two times, assuming
  a. linear growth;
  b. exponential growth.

USING AN EQUATION

A population grew from 1000 to 2197 in three years.

14. Assume linear growth.
  a. How much did the population grow each year?
  b. Make a table showing the population at the end of one, two, three, and four years.
  c. Write an equation expressing the population as a function of the number of years.
  d. Use the equation to find out the population after 27 months. (Hint: First figure out how many years that is.)

15. Assume exponential growth.
  a. By how much was the population multiplied each year?
  b. Make a table showing the population at the end of one, two, three, and four years.
  c. Write an equation relating the population to the number of years.

Your equation should be in the form $P = 1000b^x$, with x indicating the number of years.

16. Use the equation and your calculator to find the population after:
  a. 27 months; b. 2.5 years;
  c. 1 month.

REVIEW/PREVIEW

CALCULATOR PREDICTIONS

17. a. Predict how your calculator will respond if you try to use it to compute $\sqrt{-9}$.
  b. Explain your prediction.
  c. Check whether you were right.

For each problem, 18-24, two expressions are given.
  a. Predict which is greater or whether they are equal.
  b. Explain your prediction.
  c. Use your calculator to check whether you were right.

18. $\sqrt{2} + \sqrt{8}$ or $\sqrt{18}$
19. $\sqrt{27}$ or $3\sqrt{3}$
20. $2\sqrt{3}$ or $\sqrt{2 \cdot 3}$
21. $\sqrt{3} + \sqrt{3}$ or $\sqrt{6}$
22. $\sqrt{2}/\sqrt{3}$ or $\sqrt{2/3}$
23. $\sqrt{2}\sqrt{3}$ or $\sqrt{2 \cdot 3}$
24. $\sqrt{3} + \sqrt{3} + \sqrt{3}$ or $3\sqrt{3}$
25.
  a. Predict how your calculator will respond if you try to use it to compute $49^{.5}$ (49 to the power one-half).
  b. Explain your prediction.
  c. Use your calculator to check whether you were right.

THE MIDPOINT OF EXPONENTIAL GROWTH
LINEAR OR EXPONENTIAL?
USING AN EQUATION

These sections again contrast linear and exponential growth. A technique for finding the "midpoint of growth" is outlined for both situations.

Problem 16 previews decimal exponents. Except for the exponent 1/2, which will be discussed in Lesson 8, fractional exponents will not be pursued any further in this course. With the help of a calculator and in the context of the exponential functions this is not too difficult for Algebra 1.

With most classes, you should not discuss the relationship of fractional exponents with taking roots. This is beyond the scope of this course. Pursue it only if it comes up as a generalization of the exponent 1/2 in problem 25 at the end of the lesson or in Lesson 8.

REVIEW/PREVIEW CALCULATOR PREDICTIONS

These exercises provide a mixed review/preview of work with radicals. Students have been exposed to the appropriate rules and therefore should theoretically be able to answer the questions accurately without the calculator. However the calculator-check will help reinforce their understanding as well as catch any potential mistakes. In addition, it will strengthen students' feel for radical expressions as numbers.

9.7 SOLUTIONS

so $y/491$ must equal $742/y$. The value of y can be found (by trial and error or by solving a proportion) to be about 604.

10. Answers may vary slightly due to round-off.

year	population
1980	325
1982	400
1984	491
1986	604
1988	742
1990	913
1992	1123

11. a. linear: 13.5 feet
  b. exponential: 11.22 feet
  c. Answers will vary. (Students might consult a biology teacher.)

12. a. linear: 8.5 grams
  b. exponential: 9.3 grams
  c. Answers will vary. If the tumor is growing continuously, the growth is probably better modeled by an exponential function.

13. a. $(P_1 + P_2)/2$
  b. $\sqrt{P_1 \cdot P_2}$

14. a. about 399 people per year
  b. linear growth:

year	population
0	1000
1	1399
2	1798
3	2197
4	2596

  c. $y = 1000 + 399x$
  d. 27 months = 2.25 years
  $y = 1000 + 399(2.25) = 1898$

15. a. By trial and error, the yearly growth can be found to be about 30% per year.
  b. exponential growth:

year	population
0	1000
1	1300
2	1690
3	2197
4	2856

  c. $y = 1000(1.30)^x$

16. a. 27 months = 2.25 years
  $y = 1000(1.30)^{2.25} \approx 1804.57$ or about 1805
  b. $y = 1000(1.30)^{2.5} \approx 1926.90$ or about 1927
  c. $y = 1000(1.30)^{.083} \approx 1022.10$ or about 1022

(Solutions continued on page 525)

▼ 9.8
The Exponent 1/2

Core Sequence: 1-18

Suitable for Homework: 11-18

Useful for Assessment: 5, 9, 11, 17

What this Lesson is About:

- Review of exponential growth
- The exponent 1/2
- Radical rules
- Rationalizing the denominator

THE HALFWAY GROWTH FACTOR

This section continues the work on exponential functions, this time concentrating on the factor corresponding to the "mid-point of growth." This is a real-world application of square root to a very different domain from geometry, which dominated our treatment of square root so far.

A FRACTIONAL EXPONENT

The previous section provided one reason for the square root definition of the exponent 1/2, based on work with the exponential function. This section provides another, this time based on the laws of exponents and makes the connection with the previous section.

LESSON 9.8

The Exponent 1/2

THE HALFWAY GROWTH FACTOR

1. A bacterial population is growing exponentially. It is multiplied by nine every day.

a. Copy and complete the table of the population at half-day intervals.

Time	Population
0	100
0.5	—
1	900
1.5	—
2	—

b. Write an equation giving the population as a function of time (measured in days).

2. Repeat problem 1 for a population that is multiplied by 25 every day.

3. For problems 1 and 2:

a. By how much was the population multiplied in half a day?

b. How are these numbers related to the equation?

4. A tumor that is growing exponentially triples in ten years. By how much is it multiplied in five years?

5. **Generalization** An exponentially growing tumor is multiplied in size by B every ten years and by H every five years. How are B and H related? Explain.

A FRACTIONAL EXPONENT

6. Find x.

a. $2^5 \cdot 2^5 = 2^x$

b. $2^3 \cdot 2^3 = x^6$

c. $(2^4)^2 = 2^x$

7. Find x.

a. $9^x \cdot 9^3 = 9^6$

b. $9^x \cdot 9^x = 9^2$

c. $9^x \cdot 9^x = 9^1$

d. $B^x \cdot B^x = B^1$

8. Find x.

a. $(9^x)^2 = 9^6$ b. $(9^x)^2 = 9^1$

c. $(B^x)^2 = B^6$ d. $(B^x)^2 = B^1$

9. 🔑 Problems 6-8 suggest a meaning for the exponent 1/2. Explain it.

10. Using this meaning of the exponent 1/2, find the following. (Avoid using a calculator if you can.)

a. $16^{\frac{1}{2}}$ b. $400^{\frac{1}{2}}$

c. $25^{-\frac{1}{2}}$ d. $2^{\frac{1}{2}}$

11. 🔑 Does it make sense to use the exponent 1/2 in the equations you found in problems 1 and 2? Explain your answer.

12. A colony of bacteria was growing exponentially. It weighed 6 grams at noon and 15 grams at 8 P.M. How much did it weigh at 4 P.M.? Explain.

9.8 SOLUTIONS

1. a.

Time	Population
0	100
0.5	300
1	900
1.5	2700
2	8100

b. $y = P \cdot 9^x$

2. $y = P \cdot 25^x$

3. a. The first population was multiplied by 3 every half day. The second population was multiplied by 5 every half day.
b. They are both the square roots of the numbers that the population is multiplied by in one full day.

4. $\sqrt{3}$

5. $\sqrt{B} = H$

6. a. $x = 10$
b. $x = 2$
c. $x = 8$

7. a. $x = 3$
b. $x = 1$
c. $x = 1/2$
d. $x = 1/2$

8. a. $x = 3$ b. $x = 1/2$
c. $x = 3$ d. $x = 1/2$

9. Raising a number to the power 1/2 is the same as taking the square root. This is because if $B \cdot B = K$, then B must be the square root of K. By the laws of exponents, it must be $K^{1/2}$. This implies that $\sqrt{K} = K^{1/2}$.

10. a. 4 b. 20
c. 1/5 d. $\sqrt{2}$

11. Yes. The exponent is the time, and if the exponent 1/2 is used, it gives the population after 1/2 day.

12. about 9 grams

13. a. $\sqrt{16} \cdot \sqrt{16} = 4 \cdot 4 = 16$
b. $\sqrt{16} \cdot \sqrt{9} = 4 \cdot 3 = 12 = \sqrt{144} = \sqrt{16 \cdot 9}$
c. $16/\sqrt{16} = 16/4 = 4 = \sqrt{16}$
d. $\sqrt{16}/\sqrt{9} = 4/3 = \sqrt{16/9}$

14. a. $\sqrt{2}$ b. 5
c. 3 d. 2

15. a. $\sqrt{5}/5$ b. $\sqrt{6}/3$
c. 1/5 d. $\sqrt{3}/6$

LAWS OF EXPONENTS AND RADICAL RULES

Rules for operations with radicals can be derived from laws of exponents using the fact that

$$x^{\frac{1}{2}} = \sqrt{x}.$$

The following rules assume a and b are nonnegative.

Exponent Rule	Radical Rule
$a^{\frac{1}{2}} \cdot a^{\frac{1}{2}} = a^1$	$\sqrt{a}\sqrt{a} = a$
$a^{\frac{1}{2}} \cdot b^{\frac{1}{2}} = (ab)^{\frac{1}{2}}$	$\sqrt{a}\sqrt{b} = \sqrt{ab}$
$\frac{a^1}{a^{\frac{1}{2}}} = a^{\frac{1}{2}}$	$\frac{a}{\sqrt{a}} = \sqrt{a}$
$\frac{a^{\frac{1}{2}}}{b^{\frac{1}{2}}} = \left(\frac{a}{b}\right)^{\frac{1}{2}}$	$\frac{\sqrt{a}}{\sqrt{b}} = \sqrt{\frac{a}{b}}$

13. Check all the radical rules by using $a = 16$ and $b = 9$.

The last rule is especially useful for simplifying rational expressions involving radicals. To be in simple radical form, an expression cannot have any radicals in the denominator or fractions under the radical sign.

Examples: $\frac{\sqrt{16}}{\sqrt{8}} = \sqrt{\frac{16}{8}} = \sqrt{2}$

$$\sqrt{\frac{144}{169}} = \frac{\sqrt{144}}{\sqrt{169}} = \frac{12}{13}$$

$$\frac{\sqrt{48}}{\sqrt{32}} = \frac{\sqrt{3}}{\sqrt{2}} = \frac{\sqrt{3}}{\sqrt{2}} \cdot \frac{\sqrt{2}}{\sqrt{2}} = \frac{\sqrt{6}}{2}$$

14. Write problems 14-15 in simple radical form. You can check the answers on your calculator.

a. $\frac{\sqrt{60}}{\sqrt{30}}$ b. $\frac{\sqrt{450}}{\sqrt{18}}$

c. $\frac{\sqrt{18}}{\sqrt{2}}$ d. $\frac{\sqrt{20}}{\sqrt{5}}$

15. a. $\sqrt{\frac{25}{125}}$ b. $\sqrt{\frac{32}{48}}$

c. $\sqrt{\frac{3}{75}}$ d. $\sqrt{\frac{1}{12}}$

SQUARE ROOTS OF POWERS

16. Exploration Use your calculator to make a list of the square roots of the powers of ten, from $\sqrt{10^1}$ to $\sqrt{10^{10}}$. Explain any pattern you discover.

17. Explain the pattern you found in problem 16 by using a law of exponents and the exponent 1/2. (Hint: It is not one of the laws listed before problem 13.)

18. Write in simple radical form.

a. $\sqrt{9(10^8)}$ b. $\sqrt{4(10^7)}$

c. $\sqrt{3(10^6)}$ d. $\sqrt{2(10^5)}$

CHALLENGE *ESTIMATING POPULATION*

19. The population of California was 3,426,861 in 1920 and 15,717,204 in 1960. Assume it grew exponentially and estimate the population in:

a. 1940; b. 1949.

LAWS OF EXPONENTS AND RADICAL RULES

The exponent perspective on radicals allows us to confirm and generalize the rules on the handling of radicals that we had developed in the geometric context. Here, we apply these rules to simplifying radical expressions involving fractions.

While rationalizing the denominator is interesting as an idea, it is not of crucial importance as a skill at this level. Make sure your students understand the rules embodied in problems 14-15, but do not drown them in endless practice.

SQUARE ROOTS OF POWERS

In this section, the idea of the exponent 1/2 is combined with the power of a power law to uncover another rule for radicals.

We deliberately do not do problems of the type *Simplify* $\sqrt{a^5x^6}$, because they build misconceptions that are difficult to overcome in future courses. Even though traditional algebra textbooks stress that in problems of this type a and x are assumed to be positive, students rarely internalize this. As a consequence, in later courses, when asked to graph the function $y = \sqrt{a^5x^6}$ they will tend to believe mistakenly that it is $y = a^2\sqrt{a} \cdot x^3$.

CHALLENGE *ESTIMATING POPULATION*

Problem 19b is quite difficult. One solution requires students to find the yearly growth rate, while only its fortieth power is easy to calculate. Trial and error will work.

9.8 SOLUTIONS

16. & 17.

number	square root	square root (approx.)
10	$\sqrt{10}$	3.16
10^2	10	10
10^3	$10\sqrt{10}$	31.62
10^4	100	10
10^5	$100\sqrt{10}$	316.2
10^6	1000	1000
10^7	$1000\sqrt{10}$	3162.3
10^8	10,000	10000
10^9	$10{,}000\sqrt{10}$	31623
10^{10}	100,000	100,000

18. a. $3 \cdot 10^4$
 b. $2 \cdot 10^{3.5}$ or $2 \cdot 10^3 \sqrt{10}$
 c. $10^3 \cdot \sqrt{3}$
 d. $2 \cdot 10^2 \sqrt{5}$

19. a. If the population grew exponentially, the ratio (pop. in 1940)/(pop. in 1920) should be equal to the ratio (pop. in 1960)/(pop. in 1940). The population in 1940 can be found by trial and error or by solving a proportion. An equivalent approach is to use the generalization from #13b in Lesson 7. The estimate is 7,338,983.
 b. By trial and error, the yearly growth rate can be found to be about 3.9%. (However, it's much easier with logarithms or fractional exponents. What an incentive to study more algebra!) The 1949 population estimate is 10,338,763.

THINKING WRITING 9.B Skidding Distance

Core Sequence: none of the assignment

Suitable for Homework: 2-7

Useful for Assessment: 7

What this Assignment is About:
- Applying the square root function

In Lesson 5, if you skipped the optional section **More Square Root Graphs** your students graphed only the function $y = \sqrt{x}$. However, in real-world applications, functions of the form $y = \sqrt{ax}$ and $y = a\sqrt{x}$ will be a lot more common. This assignment provides students with a chance to work with this form.

THINKING WRITING 9.B Skidding Distance

Police use a formula to estimate the speed a car was traveling before an accident by measuring its skid marks. This is the formula.

$$S = \sqrt{30df}$$

S is the speed the car was traveling (in mph).

d is the distance the car skidded (in feet).

f is a special number (called the *coefficient of friction*) that depends on the road surface and road conditions.

The number f is determined by the police when they investigate an accident. For a dry tar road, f is usually about 1.0, so the formula is

$S = \sqrt{30d(1.0)}$ (dry tar road).

For a wet tar road, f is about 0.5, so the formula is

$S = \sqrt{30d(0.5)}$ (wet tar road).

1. Make tables of values and a graph to show speed as a function of the length of the skid marks. Put both curves on the same axes and use a range for d that will give you values of S up to 125 mph.
2. Why is the coefficient of friction less for a wet road than for a dry road? How does that affect the graph?

Police Report

Weather	Skid marks (ft)
wet	112
dry	321
wet	459
wet	173
dry	100
dry	132

3. This table shows a summary of accidents from a police report. All the accidents took place on tar roads. Use formulas or graphs to estimate how fast the cars were going. Explain how you made your estimates.
4. A police report stated that a car had left 150-foot skid marks on a tar road, but the report did not state the weather. Estimate how fast the car was probably traveling if the road had been wet. Then estimate the speed if the road had been dry.
5. There are two sets of skid marks on the same road. The second set is twice as long as the first. Do you think the second car was going twice as fast as the first? If not, was it going less than twice as fast or more than twice as fast? Explain.
6. The coefficient of friction for a dry concrete road is about 0.8 and for a wet concrete road about 0.4. If a car had been traveling at 50 mph before it skidded, estimate the lengths of skid marks it would have left on each type of road (tar or concrete) and in each type of weather (wet or dry). Compare your answers and comment on the differences you find.
7. **Report** Imagine that you are responsible for giving a lecture on skidding distance to a class of police cadets who are being prepared to join the highway patrol. You are asked to provide an illustrated two-to-three-page report summarizing the information that you think is important for them to know. Use examples. You may also make a poster to help make your talk more interesting and understandable.

9.B SOLUTIONS

1.

d length of skid mark	s dry tar road	d length of skid mark	s wet tar road
10	17.3	10	12.2
20	24.5	20	17.3
30	30	30	21.2
40	34.6	40	24.5
50	38.7	50	27.4
60	42.4	60	30
90	52	90	36.7
100	54.8	100	38.7
150	67.1	150	47.4
200	77.5	200	54.8
300	94.9	300	67.1
400	109.5	400	77.5
500	122.5	500	86.6
600	134.2	600	94.9
800	154.9	800	109.5
1000	173.2	1000	122.5

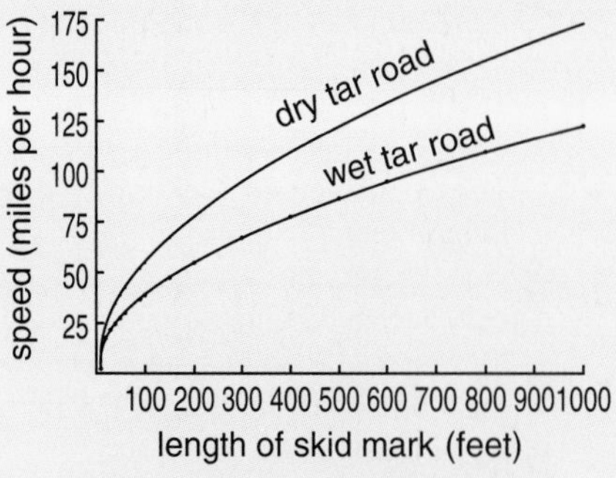

2. You have to be going slower on a wet road than a dry road to have the same length skid marks. There will be less resistance on a wet road.

3.

Police Report

Weather	Skid marks (ft)	Speed (mph)
wet	112	41
dry	321	98
wet	459	83
wet	173	51
dry	100	55
dry	132	63

4. dry: 67 mph; wet 47 mph
5. No. The speed was only $\sqrt{2}$ times as fast. This can be seen by substituting numbers into the formula.
6.

dry tar	wet tar	dry concrete	wet concrete
83	167	104	208

7. Reports will vary.

LESSON 9.9

Radical Expressions

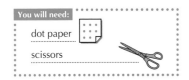

You will need:
- dot paper
- scissors

MAKING RADICAL GEAR

This figure shows how to make *radical gear* from dot paper, to help model multiplications like

$$2\sqrt{5} \cdot (\sqrt{5} + 2).$$

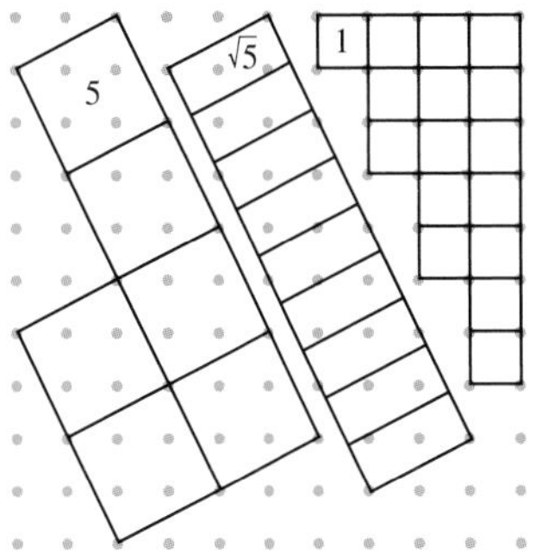

Draw some radical gear on dot paper. Cut it out, then use it in the corner piece to do these multiplications.

1. Multiply.
a. $2\sqrt{5} \cdot (\sqrt{5} + 2)$
b. $\sqrt{5} \cdot (2\sqrt{5} + 2)$
c. $4\sqrt{5} \cdot (\sqrt{5} - 1)$
d. $3\sqrt{5} \cdot (2\sqrt{5} - 1)$

2. Multiply.
a. $(2\sqrt{5} + 1) \cdot (\sqrt{5} + 2)$
b. $(2 + \sqrt{5}) \cdot (\sqrt{5} + 2)$
c. $(2\sqrt{5}) \cdot (2\sqrt{5})$
d. $(2\sqrt{5})(2 + \sqrt{5})$

3. Multiply.
a. $(2\sqrt{5} + 1) \cdot (2\sqrt{5} - 1)$
b. $(\sqrt{5} + 1) \cdot (\sqrt{5} - 1)$
c. $(3\sqrt{5} - 1) \cdot (\sqrt{5} + 1)$
d. $3 + \sqrt{5}(2\sqrt{5} - 1)$

APPLYING THE DISTRIBUTIVE LAW

Rule: As you probably noticed, when multiplying radical expressions, *the radicals are handled as if they were variables* .

Example: You can set up a table to multiply $(\sqrt{3} - 2)(\sqrt{2} - \sqrt{3})$.

	$\sqrt{3}$	-2
$\sqrt{2}$	$\sqrt{6}$	$-2\sqrt{2}$
$-\sqrt{3}$	-3	$2\sqrt{3}$

So the product is $\sqrt{6} - 2\sqrt{2} + 2\sqrt{3} - 3$.

4. Multiply.
a. $7\sqrt{3} \cdot (\sqrt{6} - \sqrt{3})$
b. $(7 + \sqrt{3}) \cdot (\sqrt{6} - \sqrt{3})$
c. $7 + \sqrt{3} \cdot (\sqrt{6} - \sqrt{3})$
d. $(8 - 2\sqrt{3}) \cdot (\sqrt{3} + 4)$

5. Find the missing terms.
a. $(1 + \sqrt{3})$____ $= 3 + \sqrt{3}$
b. $\sqrt{5} \cdot$_____ $= 10 + 4\sqrt{5}$
c. $(6 + \sqrt{7})($___ $+ \sqrt{7}) = 55 + 14\sqrt{7}$
d. $(\sqrt{6} + \sqrt{2}) \cdot$_____ $= 2\sqrt{3} + 2$
e. $(\sqrt{15} - \sqrt{2}) \cdot$_____ $= 5\sqrt{3} - \sqrt{10}$

DISAPPEARING RADICALS

6. Find the product. Simplify your answer.
a. $(x - y)(x + y)$
b. $(x - \sqrt{5})(x + \sqrt{5})$
c. $(\sqrt{3} - x)(\sqrt{3} + x)$
d. $(\sqrt{3} - \sqrt{5})(\sqrt{3} + \sqrt{5})$

9.9 SOLUTIONS

1. a. $10 + 4\sqrt{5}$ b. $10 + 2\sqrt{5}$
c. $20 - 4\sqrt{5}$ d. $30 - 3\sqrt{5}$
2. a. $12 + 5\sqrt{5}$ b. $9 + 4\sqrt{5}$
c. 20 d. $10 + 4\sqrt{5}$
3. a. 19 b. 4
c. $14 + 2\sqrt{5}$ d. $13 - \sqrt{5}$
4. a. $21\sqrt{2} - 21$
b. $7\sqrt{6} + 3\sqrt{2} - 7\sqrt{3} - 3$
c. $4 + 3\sqrt{2}$ d. 26
5. a. $\sqrt{3}$ b. $4 + 2\sqrt{5}$
c. 8 d. $\sqrt{2}$
e. $\sqrt{5}$
6. a. $x^2 - y^2$ b. $x^2 - 5$
c. $3 - x^2$ d. $3 - 5 = -2$
7. Because they are of the form $(a + b)(a - b)$, the result is $a^2 - b^2$. Squaring square roots eliminates the radical.
8. a. $\sqrt{7} + \sqrt{8}$ b. $\sqrt{x} - \sqrt{y}$
c. $2 + \sqrt{y}$
9. To rationalize the denominator, multiply both numerator and denominator by $2 - \sqrt{3}$. The denominator becomes $4 - 3$, or 1. So the fraction is equivalent to $2 - \sqrt{3}$.
10. When he multiplied $2 + \sqrt{3}$ by $2 + \sqrt{3}$, he got $4 + 2\sqrt{3} + 2\sqrt{3} + 3 = 7 + 4\sqrt{3}$. The radical was not eliminated because the middle terms he got from multiplying were not opposites of each other.

9.9 Radical Expressions

Core Sequence: 1-17

Suitable for Homework: 10-18

Useful for Assessment: 7, 10-11, 15, 17

What this Lesson is About:
- Working with binomial radical expressions
- Radicals and the distributive law
- Review of the difference of squares identity
- The conjugate of a radical binomial expression
- Review of many ideas in the chapter

This lesson wraps up the work on square roots and radicals.

MAKING RADICAL GEAR
APPLYING THE DISTRIBUTIVE RULE

Radical gear should be made from the heaviest paper onto which you can duplicate dot paper. However, since it will be used only during this one lesson, ordinary paper will suffice if that is all you have. For this to work best, use centimeter dot paper. Note that the $\sqrt{5}$ "blocks" are rectangles having dimensions 1 by $\sqrt{5}$.

Masters for radical gear and dot paper appear in the reproducible pages in the back of this book.

If you want to do more work along these lines, you may just use the Lab Gear and arbitrarily decide that, for this activity, x is $\sqrt{10}$ and y is $\sqrt{51}$. Then you can say that x^2 is 10, xy is $\sqrt{510}$, and so on, and you can set up products of the type: $(\sqrt{10} + 2)(\sqrt{51} + \sqrt{10})$.

If on the other hand, your students find that they do not need the radical gear, let them do this work by any method they can use successfully. The multiplication-table method certainly can be applied to multiplying radical expressions, as shown in the example.

DISAPPEARING RADICALS

FRACTIONS AND RADICALS

Again, this should be seen more as an opportunity to think and learn about identities, radicals, and fractions than as a time to master a specific symbol manipulation skill.

REVIEW *CALCULATOR EXPERIMENTS*

Some light can be shed on problem 16 by using a function diagram for the square root function, with a scale ranging from 0 to perhaps 4. Then iterating the function can be shown by linking the diagrams as was done in Chapter 3, **Thinking/Writing 3.C**.

REVIEW *GEOBOARD PUZZLES*

Geoboards are not needed for problems 18-19 which could be done on dot paper. These puzzles review the Pythagorean theorem.

7. Explain why there are no radicals in the simplified form of any of the answers to problem 6.

8. For each binomial, find a binomial to multiply it by so that the result has no radicals.

a. $(\sqrt{7} - \sqrt{8})$ b. $(\sqrt{x} + \sqrt{y})$

c. $(2 - \sqrt{y})$

FRACTIONS AND RADICALS

Definition: To *rationalize* the denominator (or numerator) of a fraction is to write an equivalent fraction with *no radicals* in the denominator (or numerator).

9. Rationalize the denominator. $\frac{1}{2 + \sqrt{3}}$

10. In problem 9, Gerald tried to multiply the numerator and denominator by $(2 + \sqrt{3})$. Explain why this did not work.

11. Daniel used the idea in the section **Disappearing Radicals** to rationalize the denominator. Explain what he did, and why it did work.

12. Rationalize the denominator.

a. $\frac{1}{\sqrt{2} + 3}$

b. $\frac{1}{3 - \sqrt{3}}$

c. $\frac{4}{\sqrt{5} - \sqrt{6}}$

d. $\frac{5}{\sqrt{5}}$

13. Rationalize the numerator.

a. $\frac{7 - \sqrt{5}}{4}$ b. $\frac{\sqrt{7} - \sqrt{5}}{4}$

REVIEW *CALCULATOR EXPERIMENTS*

14. Use your calculator to compute
$(\sqrt{9876} - \sqrt{9866})(\sqrt{9876} + \sqrt{9866})$.
Comment on the answer.

15. Bernard believes that the square root of the square of a number is the number itself.

a. Is he right or wrong? Explain.

b. What's the square root of the square of -543? Make a prediction, then use your calculator to check.

16. Choose any number. Find its square root on your calculator. Then find the square root of the result. Continue this until you notice something happening. What is happening? Can you explain it? What starting numbers does it work for?

17. Always, sometimes, or never? Explain, using examples.

a. $x^2 > x$ b. $1/x^2 > 1/x$

c. $\sqrt{x} < x$ d. $1/\sqrt{x} > 1/x$

e. $\sqrt{x} < x^2$ f. $1/\sqrt{x} > 1/\sqrt{x^2}$

REVIEW *GEOBOARD PUZZLES*

18. If two sides of geoboard triangle are $\sqrt{2}$ and $\sqrt{5}$, what are the possibilities for:

a. the third side?

b. the area?

19. Find the geoboard figure having the least area, if its perimeter is

a. 20; b. $4\sqrt{65}$;

c. $10 + 2\sqrt{65}$; d. $10\sqrt{2} + 2\sqrt{85}$.

9.9 SOLUTIONS

11. Daniel multiplied both numerator and denominator by $2 - \sqrt{3}$. He noticed that if $a + \sqrt{b}$ is multiplied by $a - \sqrt{b}$, the result contains no radicals. The middle terms obtained in the multiplication are the only ones containing radicals, and since they are opposites of one another, they are eliminated when the expression is simplified.

12. a. $(3 - \sqrt{2})/7$ b. $(3 + \sqrt{3})/6$
c. $-4(\sqrt{5} + \sqrt{6})$ d. $\sqrt{5}$

13. a. $11/(7 + \sqrt{5})$
b. $1/[2(\sqrt{7} + \sqrt{5})]$

14. 10 (The answer is a difference of squares.)

15. a. He is right only some of the time. The square root of the square of a negative number is a positive number, so if the original number is negative, Bernard is wrong.
b. 543

16. It gets closer to 1.

17. a. sometimes (not true when $0 \le x \le 1$)
b. sometimes (not true when $x \ge 1$)
c. sometimes (true only when $x > 1$)
d. sometimes (true only when $x > 1$)
e. sometimes (true only when $x > 1$)
f. sometimes (true only when $x > 1$)

18. Strategy: On dot paper, draw a segment of length $\sqrt{5}$. Then, from the endpoint, draw a segment of length $\sqrt{2}$ in each of the four possible directions. Four triangles can be found.
a. 1, 3, $\sqrt{13}$, $\sqrt{5}$
b. Sides: $\sqrt{2}$, $\sqrt{5}$, 1 Area: 1/2
Sides: $\sqrt{2}$, $\sqrt{5}$, 3 Area: 1.5
Sides: $\sqrt{2}$, $\sqrt{5}$, $\sqrt{13}$ Area: 1/2
Sides: $\sqrt{2}$, $\sqrt{5}$, $\sqrt{5}$ Area: 1.5

19. We think the best answers are quadrilaterals, and we tried to find the skinniest quadrilaterals possible, in order to minimize the area. You or your students may be able to find better solutions.

LESSON 9.10

Blowups

You will need: graph paper

BIGGER BOXES

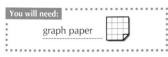

The Real Bag Company makes cardboard boxes. One of the boxes is called the Banker's Box. It has the dimensions: length, 16 in.; width, 12 in.; height, 10 in. Another box, the Square Pak box, has the dimensions: length, 12 in.; width, 12 in.; height, 10 in. Sid, a Real Bag Box Division Manager, decides that new boxes need to be manufactured, the Caterer's Crate and the Great Pak.

1. **Exploration**

a. The Caterer's Crate will have two dimensions the same as the Banker's Box, and the third dimension multiplied by two. Sid asks his colleague Li Ann whether the volume of the box would be increased the most by multiplying the length, the width, or the height by two. What should she answer? Explain.

b. The Great Pak will have a square base and a volume that is double that of the volume of the Square Pak. Sid asks his colleague Annette (who owns a calculator) to find three choices for the dimensions of the new box. What should she answer? Explain.

STRETCHING POLYOMINOES

Sid, Annette, and Li Ann like to spend their lunch breaks working geometric puzzles. (They should have become math teachers.) Here is a puzzle they have been working on, using the tetrominoes.

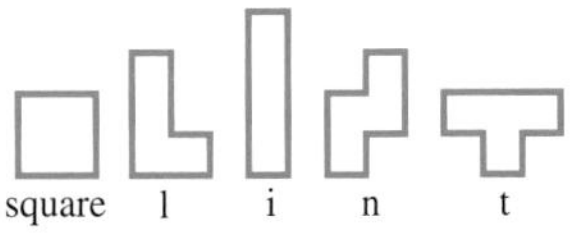

For each of the tetrominoes, they created three new polyominoes. The first one by doubling all horizontal dimensions, the second one by doubling all vertical dimensions, and the third one by doubling both horizontal and vertical dimensions. For example, the t tetromino led to the creation of three new polyominoes.

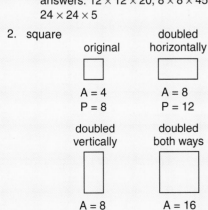

a. original
b. doubled horizontally
c. doubled vertically
d. doubled both ways

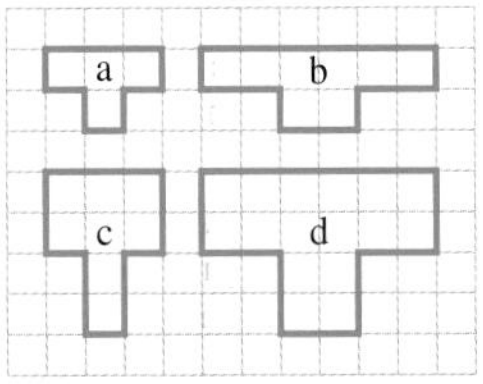

2. **Exploration** Draw all 15 *stretched* tetrominoes. For each one, find its area and perimeter. Keep your work clearly organized, so you can find a pattern to the areas and perimeters. (The area pattern is the easier of the two.) You will need to refer to this data to do the problems in the next two sections.

▼ 9.10 Blowups

Core Sequence: 1-17

Suitable for Homework: 3-32

Useful for Assessment: 5-8, 14, 17

What this Lesson is About:

- Preview of perimeter, area, and volume of similar figures

With this lesson, we change the focus of our work on the theme of measurement. The remainder of this chapter concentrates on perimeter, area, and volume of similar figures. This is a difficult domain to master, but your students should be fairly well prepared because we have been working with ratios and proportions over a long stretch of time. In addition, earlier in the course, we paid attention to the concept of dimensions, which is directly relevant.

BIGGER BOXES

STRETCHING POLYOMINOES

These Explorations should pose the basic questions that will be addressed in the next three lessons. All students should be able to understand some basic aspects of the Explorations, such as problems 1a and 2 on area. However problem 1b and the perimeter patterns in 2 are much tougher. Encourage full discussion before moving on.

9.10 SOLUTIONS

1. a. It doesn't matter. In all cases, the volume would be 3840.
   b. Answers will vary. Sample answers: $12 \times 12 \times 20$; $8 \times 8 \times 45$; $24 \times 24 \times 5$
2. square

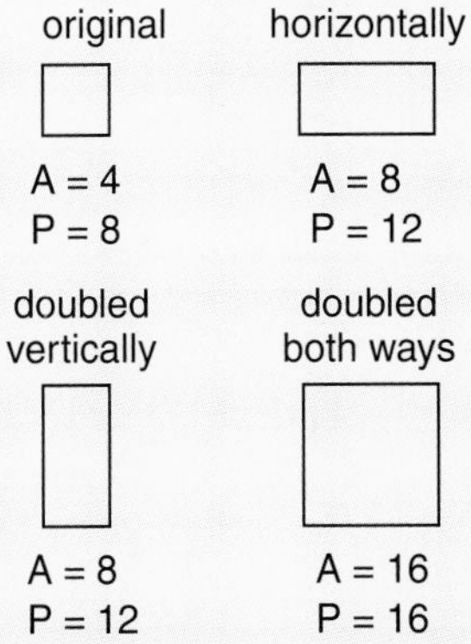

l

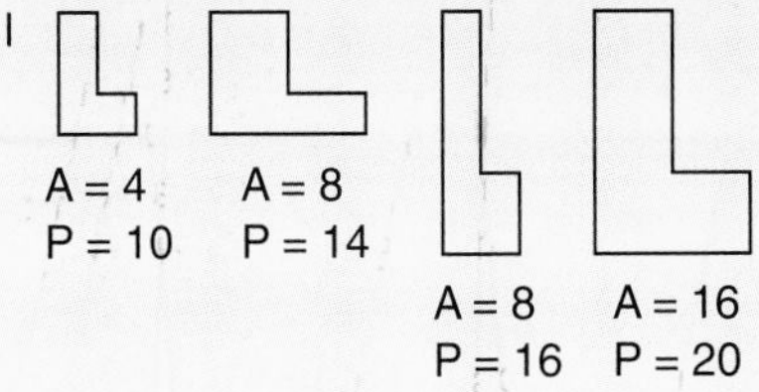

i

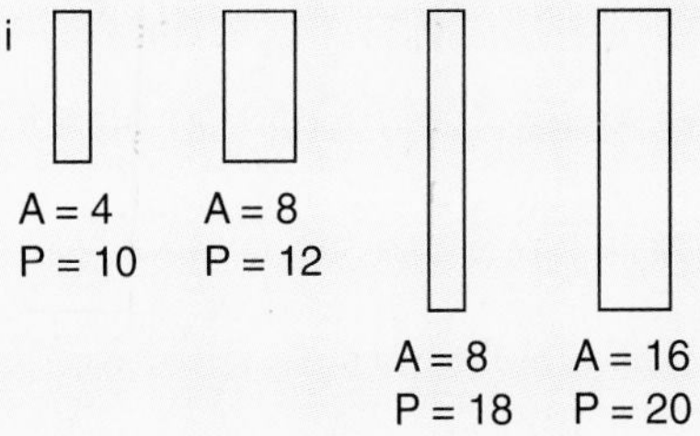

n

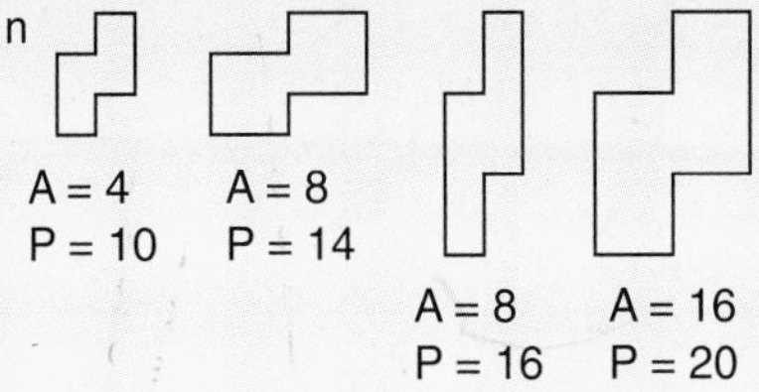

t

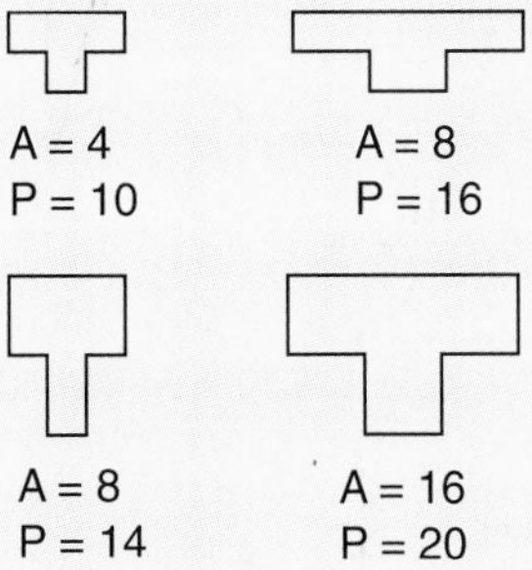

PERIMETER

The content of this section is not important for its own sake. However the section is important in two ways. First, dwelling on horizontal versus vertical stretching lays the basis for better understanding of similarity, where the stretching occurs in both directions. Second, the interplay of geometric insight and algebraic notation provides a good example of how to use algebra to generalize and help generate deeper understanding of a problem.

AREA

Students who enjoy problem 10 will find more problems of this type at the end of Lesson 11.

PERIMETER

Call the perimeter of a tetromino p. It is made up of some horizontal segments and some vertical segments.

Let h = total length of the horizontal segments.
Let v = total length of the vertical segments.

3. Express p in terms of h and v.

4. a. Find h and v for the t tetromino.
b. Show that the perimeter of the vertically stretched t tetromino is $h + 2v$.
c. What is the perimeter of the horizontally stretched t tetromino in terms of h and v?
d. What is the perimeter of the horizontally and vertically stretched t tetromino in terms of h and v?

5. In problem 4 you found formulas that related the perimeters of the three stretched t tetrominoes to the perimeter of the original t tetromino. Explain why these formulas work for all the tetrominoes.

6. What is the sum of the perimeters of the two polyominoes that were stretched in only one dimension? Use factoring to see how this sum is related to the original perimeter.

7. **Generalization**
a. Repeat the perimeter investigation, but stretch the tetrominoes by tripling dimensions. You do not need to draw the tripled tetrominoes, just use algebra. Find a formula relating the perimeters of the tripled tetrominoes to h, v, and p for the original tetromino.
b. Repeat this investigation, but this time stretch by a factor of n.

AREA

8. Refer to your data on the area of the 15 stretched (doubled) tetrominoes, and experiment with other polyominoes. If the original area of a polyomino is A, what is the area of the polyomino stretched by doubling
a. horizontally?
b. vertically?
c. both horizontally and vertically ?

9. a. Draw the l and t tetrominoes, with both their horizontal and vertical dimensions doubled.
b. Repeat part (a), tripling the dimensions instead of doubling.

10. *PUZZLE* Tile the blown-up tetrominoes you drew with copies of the original l and/or t tetrominoes. Example:

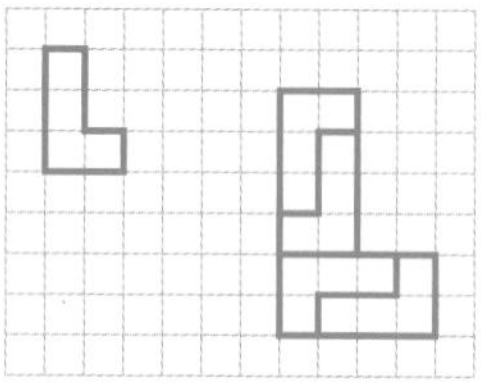

11. How many tetromino tiles did you need to cover the blown-up tetrominoes? How is this related to the area of the blown-up tetrominoes?

12. a. Draw a pentomino.
b. Draw a copy of it, with horizontal and vertical dimensions multiplied by two.
c. Repeat with the original dimensions multiplied by three.
d. Repeat with the original dimensions multiplied by four.

13. Predict the area of each figure you drew in problem 12. Check your predictions.

9.10 SOLUTIONS

3. $p = h + v$

4. a. $h = 6$, $v = 4$
b. For the vertically stretched t tetromino, perimeter is 14, which is $6 + 2(4)$, or $h + 2v$
c. For the horizontally stretched t tetromino, perimeter $2h + v$
d. $2h + 2v$

5. For the horizontally stretched tetromino, all the horizontal segments are doubled and all the vertical segments remain the same, so the perimeter is $2h + v$. For the vertically stretched tetromino, all the vertical segments are doubled and all the horizontal segments remain the same, so the perimeter is $2v + h$. For the tetromino stretched in all directions, both horizontal and vertical segments are doubled, so the perimeter is $2h + 2v$.

6. $(2h + v) + (2v + h) = 3v + 3h = 3(v + h)$

7. Tripled tetrominoes:
vertical stretch: $3v + h$; horizontal stretch: $3h + v$; stretch in both directions: $3h + 3v$
Stretched by a factor of n:
vertical stretch: $nv + h$; horizontal stretch: $nh + v$; stretch in both directions: $nh + nv$

8. a. $2A$ b. $2A$ c. $4A$

9.

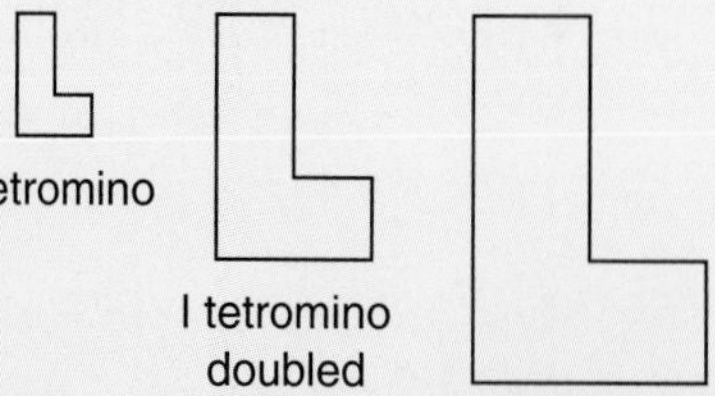

l tetromino

l tetromino doubled

l tetromino tripled

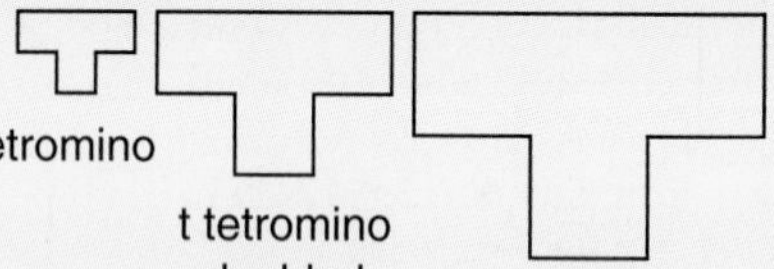

t tetromino

t tetromino doubled

t tetromino tripled

10. No solution needed.

11. The original requires 4 tiles. The blow-ups require $4(2)^2 = 16$ tiles for the doubled ones and $4(3)^2 = 36$ for the tripled ones.

12.

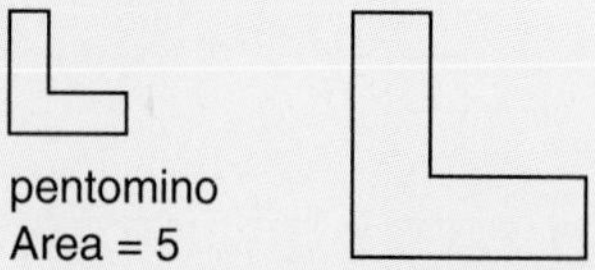

pentomino
Area = 5

doubled pentomino
Area = $20 = 2^2 \cdot 5$

14. **Generalization** When both horizontal and vertical dimensions are multiplied by k, by what is the area multiplied? Explain.

BACK TO WORK

After their lunch break, Sid, Li Ann, and Annette had to attend to more box problems.

15. They created a new box by multiplying all the dimensions of the Banker's Box by two. Make a sketch of the original box and the new box. What would the volume of the new box be? How many times greater is this than the volume of the Banker's Box?

16. If they created a new box by multiplying all the dimensions of the Square Pak by three, what would its volume be? How many times greater is this than the volume of the Square Pak?

17. **Generalization** When all the dimensions are multiplied by k, by what is the volume multiplied?

18. What are the dimensions of a box that is a perfect cube and has the same volume as the Square Pak? Explain.

19. What are the dimensions of a box that is a perfect cube and has double the volume of the Square Pak? Explain.

REVIEW ***SCIENTIFIC NOTATION***

20. In June of 1990 the national debt of the United States was \$3.1 trillion. The population of the U.S. at the same time was about 250 million. Therefore, the debt per person was

$$\frac{3.1 \text{ trillion}}{250 \text{ million}}.$$

a. Express both of these numbers in scientific notation.

b. What was the debt per person? Express your answer in ordinary decimal notation and in scientific notation.

REVIEW ***WHAT'S YOUR SIGN?***

Do not use a calculator for these problems.

21. Is x positive or negative, or is it impossible to know? Explain.

a. $(-2)^x = -524,288$

b. $2^x = 1/131,072$

c. $(-2)^x = 262,144$

d. $x^{11} = -177,147$

e. $x^{12} = 531,441$

f. $x^{13} = 1/1,594,323$

BACK TO WORK

While a generalization is asked for in problem 17, keep in mind that we will return to the volume of similar figures in Lesson 12. If you want to assign problems 18-19, and students are not ready for them now, you can wait until after Lesson 12.

REVIEW ***WHAT'S YOUR SIGN?***

This reviews Lesson 11 in Chapter 8.

9.10 SOLUTIONS

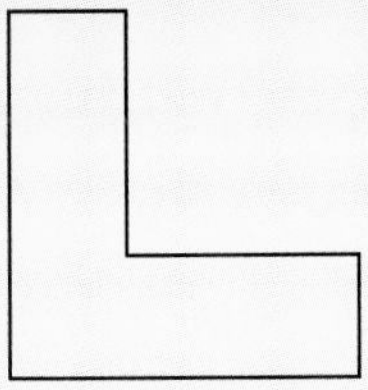

tripled pentomino
Area = 45 = $3^2 \cdot 5$

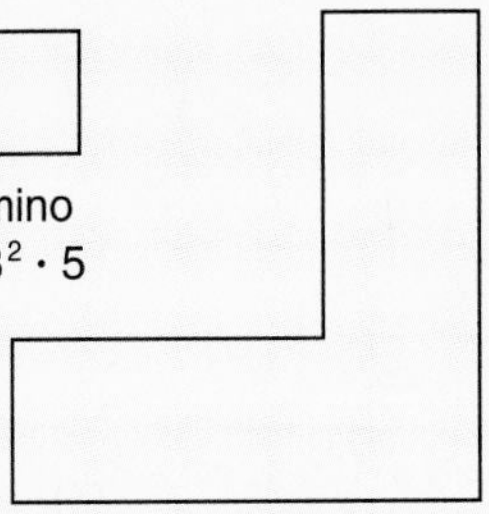

quadrupled pentomino
Area = 80 = $4^2 \cdot 5$

13. See figure.

14. k^2

15. It would have 8 times the volume, since each dimension is multiplied by 2. The total volume is 15,360 cu. in. or about 8.89 cu. ft.

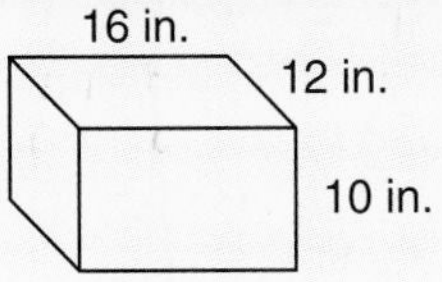

Banker's Box

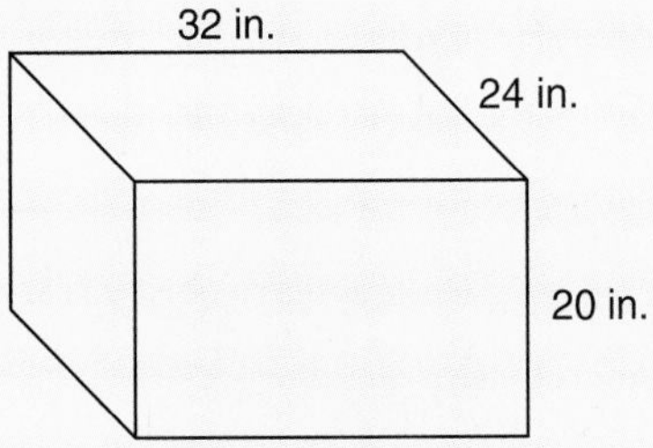

Bigger Banker's Box

16. 1440 (original volume) $\cdot 3^3 = 38,880$ cu. in. or about 22.5 cu. ft.

17. k^3

18. By trial and error, the cube root of 1440 can be found to be about 11.3 in. This would be the length of the side of the cube.

19. By trial and error, the cube root of 2880 can be found to be about 14.23 in. (Notice that the ratio of this side to the side of the cube found in problem 18 is 1.27, which is about the cube root of 2.)

20. a. $3.1 \cdot 10^{12}$ and $2.50 \cdot 10^8$
b. about \$12,400

21. a. x is a positive number. If x were negative, the power would equal a number between -1 and 0 or 0 and 1. (Using a calculator, $x = 19$.)

REVIEW ***THE CHESSBOARD***

This is similar to the **Doing Dishes** problem from Chapter 2, Lesson 5. The larger numbers here require the use of scientific notation.

DISCOVERY ***DECIMAL EXPONENTS***

It is not necessary for first-year algebra students to have a full understanding of fractional exponents. However, the idea of exponential growth which has been explored in this chapter does lead to it in a natural way.

REVIEW ***THE CHESSBOARD***

According to an old legend, a King decided to reward the inventor of the game of chess. "I am immensely rich. Whatever you ask for will be yours." The inventor replied, "All I ask is for one cent on the first square of the chessboard; two cents on the next square; four cents on the next square; and so on, doubling the amount each time, until the last square on the chessboard." (The legend actually specifies grains of rice, not cents.)

22. Find out how many cents the King owed the inventor. Express the final answer two ways: in terms of a power of two, in cents; and as a number of dollars, in scientific notation.

23. **Project** Is the money paid the inventor as much as the budget of:
a. a toy store?
b. a multi-national corporation?
c. the State of New York?
d. the United States?

DISCOVERY ***DECIMAL EXPONENTS***

24. Use decimal exponents (to the nearest hundredth) to approximate 100 as a power of:

a. 2	b. 3	c. 4
d. 8	e. 9	f. 10

REVIEW ***EQUAL RATIOS***

Solve for N.

25. $\frac{3N-2}{5} = \frac{N+2}{2}$

26. $\frac{3N-2}{15} = \frac{N+2}{6}$

Solve for x. If you cannot find an exact value, approximate to nearest thousandth.

27. $\frac{x}{8} = \frac{3}{4}$

28. $\frac{4}{10} = \frac{400}{x}$

29. $\frac{1}{x} = \frac{x}{2}$

REVIEW ***DISTRIBUTIVE LAW PRACTICE***

Find these products.

30. $2y(2x - y + 6)$

31. $3x(2x - 3)$

32. $(y - 4)(y + 3)$

9.10 SOLUTIONS

b. x is negative. A negative exponent equals the reciprocal of the base raised to the opposite of the negative exponent. 1/131,072 is the reciprocal of a power of 2. (Using a calculator, $x = -17$.)

c. x is a positive number because the power equals a large positive number. (Using a calculator, $x = 18$.)

d. x is negative. A negative base raised to an odd exponent is negative. (Using a calculator, $x = -3$.)

e. It is impossible to know if x is positive or negative because the exponent is even. A negative or positive base raised to the 12th power equals a positive number. (Using a calculator, $x = \pm 3$.)

f. x is positive, because a positive base raised to an odd exponent is positive. (Using a calculator, $x = 1/3$.)

22. The chessboard has 64 squares.

# of the square	# of cents on the square	Sum
1	2^0	1
2	2^1	$3 = 2^2 - 1$
3	2^2	$7 = 2^3 - 1$
4	2^3	$15 = 2^4 - 1$
n	2^{n-1}	$2^n - 1$
64	2^{63}	$2^{64} - 1$

The king gives the inventor $2^{64} - 1$ cents = $1.845 \cdot 10^{19}$ cents or $1.845 \cdot 10^{17}$ dollars, which is approximately $184 quadrillion

23. Answers will vary according to students' research.

24. a. 6.64
b. 4.19
c. 3.32
d. 2.21
e. 2.1
f. 2

25. $N = 14$

26. $N = 14$

27. $x = 6$

28. $x = 1000$

29. $x = \pm 1.414$

30. $4xy - 2y^2 + 12y$

31. $6x^2 - 9x$

32. $y^2 - y - 12$

LESSON 9.11

Let's Eat!

PIZZA PRICES

Lana and Tina were studying for their semester exam one Sunday afternoon. They needed more energy and decided to order a pizza. They called Pinky's and Primo's to compare prices.

Pinky's Prices

Size	Diameter	Price
small	8 in.	\$4.25
medium	12 in.	\$8.50
large	14 in.	\$10.20

Primo's Prices

Size	Diameter	Price
small	10 in.	\$6.44
medium	12 in.	\$8.84
large	14 in.	\$9.91

1. **Exploration** Assuming the pizzas are of the same thickness and similar quality, which is the better buy for the large pizza? The medium pizza? The small pizza? Explain, showing your calculations.

The area of a circle is given by the formula πr^2, where r is the radius, and π is approximately equal to the number 3.1415926536.

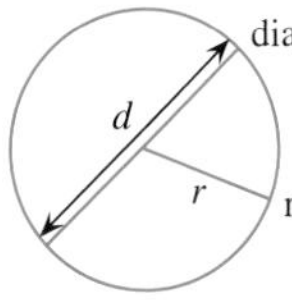

Example: A circle having diameter 14 in. has a radius of 7 in. Its area is $\pi(7)^2$, or 49π square inches.

2. Use your calculator to find the area of a circle having diameter 14 in., to the nearest tenth of a square inch. (Scientific calculators have a π key.)

Tina thought Pinky's medium pizza looked expensive. "It's twice as expensive as an 8-inch pizza," she said. "For twice as much, I ought to be able to get a 16-inch pizza."

3. a. Find the area of a 16-inch pizza. Compare it with the area of an 8-inch pizza. How many times as large is it?
   b. How many times as large is a 12-inch pizza as an 8-inch pizza? Show your calculations.
   c. Comment on Tina's remark.
4. a. Copy and complete the tables below, giving an approximation for the area of each pizza and the price per square inch.
   b. Which pizza is the best buy, based on price per square inch?

Pinky's

Diameter (in.)	Area (sq in.)	Price	Price per sq in.
8	16π	\$4.25	—
12	—	\$8.50	—
14	—	\$10.20	—

9.11 Let's Eat

Core Sequence: 1-13, 20-23

Suitable for Homework: 4-23

Useful for Assessment: 6-9, 11-12

What this Lesson is About:

- Area of a circle
- Area of similar figures
- Puzzles involving similar figures
- Review of simple radical form

This lesson concentrates on the area of similar figures, in a real-world context.

PIZZA PRICES

Students' first guesses as to how to compare the value of the small pizzas may involve finding the price *per inch*. If no one thinks of making a comparison based on area, you may keep a poker face and move on to the rest of the lesson, returning to problem 1 at the end of the section. However, if anyone hits upon the idea of finding the area, you should encourage a full class discussion of the issue.

Make sure students understand the difference between radius and diameter, so they can calculate the areas correctly.

Unlike Lesson 10, the ratios in this lesson are not whole numbers.

9.11 SOLUTIONS

1. Students' conclusions will vary. (The correct answers are that Primo's is the better buy for the large and small sizes, and Pinky's offers a slightly cheaper medium pizza.)
2. 153.9 sq. in.
3. a. A 16-inch pizza has area 64π, or about 201.1 square inches. An 8-inch pizza has area 16π, or about 50.3 square inches. The 16-inch is 4 times as large.
   b. $36\pi/16\pi = 2.25$
   c. A 12-inch pizza is more than twice as large as an 8-inch pizza. Actually, Tina is getting a discount for quantity. The 12-inch is a better buy than the 8-inch.
4. a.

Pinky's

diameter (in)	area (sq in)	price	price per sq in
8	$16\pi \approx 50.3$	\$4.25	8.45¢
12	$36\pi \approx 113.1$	\$8.50	7.52¢
14	$49\pi \approx 153.9$	\$10.20	6.63¢

Primo's

diameter (in)	area (sq in)	price	price per sq in
10	$25\pi \approx 78.5$	\$6.44	8.20¢
12	$36\pi \approx 113.1$	\$8.84	7.82¢
14	$49\pi \approx 153.9$	\$9.91	6.44¢

   b. Primo's large is the cheapest.
5. a. 4 times
   b. 1.36 times
6. $(4\pi r^2)/(\pi r^2) = 4$
7. a. $\pi(3r)^2/\pi r^2 = (9\pi r^2)/(\pi r^2) = 9$
   b. $\pi(kr)^2/\pi r^2 = (k^2\pi r^2)/(\pi r^2) = k^2$

You may generalize problem 9 algebraically, by discussing: If $a > b$, which is greater, ab^2 or a^2b?

BAKING BROWNIES

This section should be more straightforward, since students should be more comfortable with the area of squares than with the area of circles.

Problem 13 involves some tricky algebra with fractions. Remind students that to divide by a fraction, you multiply by its reciprocal. Alternately, work the problem using a circle having radius r and a square having side $2r$.

Primo's

Diameter (in.)	Area (sq in.)	Price	Price per sq in.
10	—	—	—
12	—	—	—
14	—	—	—

5. Compare the areas of these pizzas. How many times as big is the larger than the smaller?
   a. a 12-inch pizza and a 6-inch pizza
   b. a 14-inch pizza and a 12-inch pizza

6. To compare a pizza having radius r with a pizza having radius $2r$, you can use the ratios of the areas. Simplify this ratio.

$$\frac{\pi(2r)^2}{\pi(r)^2}$$

7. **Generalization** Write and simplify the ratios to compare the area of:
   a. a pizza having radius r with a pizza having three times this radius;
   b. a pizza having radius r with a pizza having radius kr.

8. If you double the diameter of a pizza, why does the price more than double?

9. For a party Tina was going to buy ten 8-inch pizzas from Pinky's, but she got mixed up and bought eight 10-inch pizzas from Primo's instead. Did she have the right amount of pizza, too much, or too little? Explain, showing your calculations.

BAKING BROWNIES

An hour after they had polished off their pizza, Lana and Tina were having trouble concentrating on studying exponents. "Maybe we're just hungry," said Lana. "I'm feeling a little faint," Tina agreed. "We should probably bake some brownies."

The recipe said to use an 8-inch-square pan.

Lana wanted to double the recipe. "OK," said Tina, "but we'll need a 16-inch-square pan."

10. a. Using the same scale, make a sketch of an 8-by-8-inch pan and a 16-by-16-inch pan.
    b. How many 8-by-8 pans would fit inside a 16-by-16 pan?
    c. Comment on Tina's remark.

11. How many times as big is the larger than the smaller square? (The measurement refers to the side length.)
    a. a 12-inch square and a 6-inch square
    b. a 14-inch square and a 12-inch square

12. **Generalization** What is the ratio of the areas of two squares, if the ratio of the sides is
    a. 5? b. k?

13.
    a. Write the ratio of the area of a circle having diameter s to that of a square having side s.
    b. Simplify the ratio. Which is larger, the circle or the square? How many times as large is it?

9.11 SOLUTIONS

8. Because the area quadruples — (The price doesn't quadruple, because you usually get a break for buying in quantity.)
9. Ten 8-inch pizzas: $10 \cdot \pi(4)^2 = 160\pi$
   Eight 10-inch pizzas: $8 \cdot \pi(5)^2 = 200\pi$
   She had more pizza than she needed.
10. a.

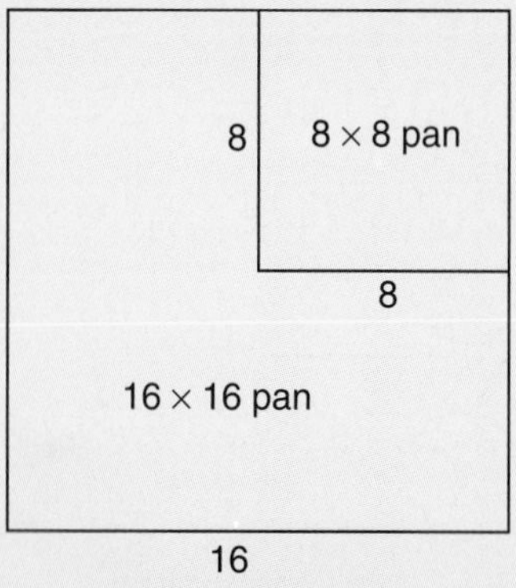

    b. 4
    c. She would get crisp brownies if she doubled the recipe and quadrupled the pan size because the layer of batter in the pan would be half as thick as required by the recipe. Most people prefer chewy brownies, so I wouldn't recommend Tina's course of action.
11. a. 4
    b. 1.36
12. a. 25
    b. k^2
13. a. $[\pi s^2/4]/s^2 = \pi/4$
    b. The square is $4/\pi$ times as large.
14.

15.

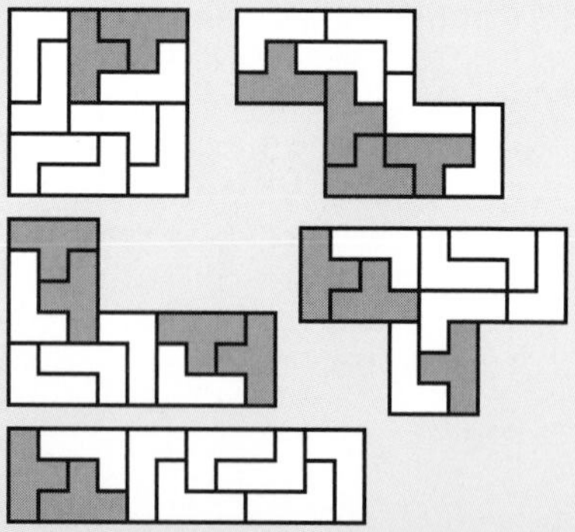

PUZZLES *MORE POLYOMINO TILINGS*

14. Draw all the tetrominoes with their dimensions doubled. Tile the blowups with the l and/or t tetrominoes.

15. Repeat with the tripled tetrominoes.

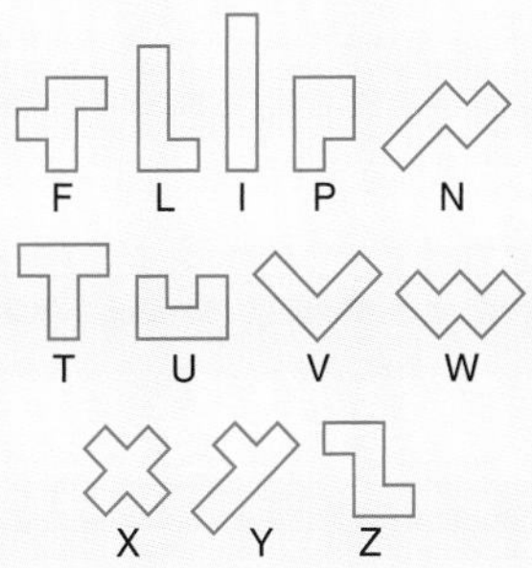

16. Draw all the pentominoes with their dimensions doubled. Tile the blowups with the P and/or N pentominoes.

17. Repeat with the tripled pentominoes.

Projects

18. Can you use the same tiles to cover bigger and bigger blown-up tetrominoes and pentominoes? Experiment and report on your discoveries.

19. What is the smallest rectangle you can tile with a given pentomino? Experiment and report on your discoveries.

REVIEW *A SQUARE NUMBER OF SQUARES*

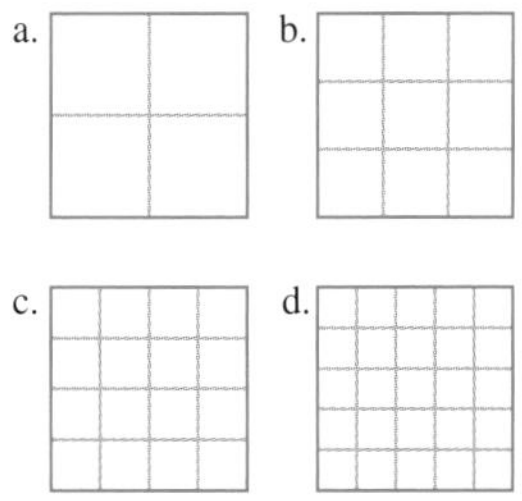

Each of the four large squares has area 75. Each has been divided into a square number of smaller squares.

20. Find the area of each small square.

21. Express the side of each small square as a square root.

22. Explain why $\sqrt{75} = 5\sqrt{3}$, using

a. the figure;

b. radical rules;

c. decimal approximations.

23. Divide a square having area 72 into a square number of smaller squares, in such a way that you can use the figure to help write $\sqrt{72}$ in simple radical form.

PUZZLES *MORE POLYOMINO TILINGS*

*E*ach of the problems is a major assignment. Assign these only if you have time for them or as extra credit for students who enjoy geometric puzzles.

*T*he focus of problem 18 could be narrowed by trying to tile quadrupled tetrominoes with just the l and/or t tetrominoes. Another option would be to take a single pentomino, say the N, and try to tile it using the P and the N at greater and greater degrees of magnification.

*P*roblem 19 is easy for some pentominoes, impossible for some, and challenging for the Y.

REVIEW *A SQUARE NUMBER OF SQUARES*

*P*roblems 20-23 review simple radical form visually.

9.11 SOLUTIONS

16.

19. 2 L pentominoes

20. a. 75/4
b. 75/9
c. 75/16
d. 75/25 = 3

21. a. $\sqrt{75/4}$
b. $\sqrt{75/9}$
c. $\sqrt{75/16}$
d. $\sqrt{75/25} = \sqrt{3}$

22. a. Figure (d) has 25 small squares, each of side $\sqrt{3}$. Hence the length of the side of the large square is $5\sqrt{3}$. But if the area of the entire large square is 75, its side must be $\sqrt{75}$. Hence $5\sqrt{3} = \sqrt{75}$.
b. $\sqrt{75} = \sqrt{25} \cdot \sqrt{3} = 5\sqrt{3}$
c. $5\sqrt{3} \approx 5 \cdot 1.732 \approx 8.66$ and $\sqrt{75} \approx 8.66$

23. Divide the squares into 36 small squares. Each will have area 2 and side $\sqrt{2}$. Since there are six of these on each side of the large square, the large square has side length $6\sqrt{2}$. Since the large square has area 72, its side has length $\sqrt{72}$, so $\sqrt{72} = 6\sqrt{2}$.

▼ 9.12
Similar Figures

Core Sequence: 1-24

Suitable for Homework: 8-12, 16-24

Useful for Assessment: 2, 6, 11-12, 14, 17

What this Lesson is About:

- Ratio of similarity, ratio of areas, ratio of volumes
- Application to scale models

RATIO OF SIMILARITY

This section reviews the concept of ratio of similarity, which has been in the background of Lessons 10 and 11. Here it is defined precisely, and perhaps taken a little further, as a discussion of the fact that the same pair of similar figures can be thought of in two different ways, yielding ratios of similarity which are reciprocals of each other.

AREA, PERIMETER

Problems 7 and 13 should help students test their understanding of the definition of similarity. They would be good problems for group discussion.

LESSON 9.12

Similar Figures

You will need:

the Lab Gear 

RATIO OF SIMILARITY

The polycubes in this figure were obtained by doubling the dimensions of the original tetracube in succession: first the height, then the length, and finally the width.

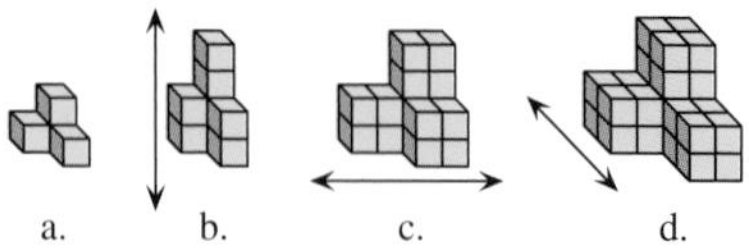

a. b. c. d.

1. Find the volume and surface area of each of these polycubes.

Definitions: Two figures are *similar* if *all* the dimensions of one can be obtained by multiplying the dimensions of the other by the same number, called the *ratio of similarity.*

(In Chapter 3, similar figures were defined as being enlarged or shrunk *without distortion.* That definition is equivalent to this one.)

2. Which two of the four polycubes are similar to each other? Explain.

3. Sketch buildings similar to this tetracube, but larger, with ratio of similarity
   a. 2 b. 3

The two buildings you sketched in problem 3 are similar to each other.

4. You could get the dimensions of the larger building by multiplying the dimensions of the smaller one by what number?

5. You could get the dimensions of the smaller building by multiplying the dimensions of the larger one by what number?

6. Either of the numbers you found in problems 4 and 5 could be considered the ratio of similarity. How are the two numbers related? Explain this.

AREA, PERIMETER

7. Make a list of pairs of similar polyominoes in this figure. (Hint: There are six pairs.)

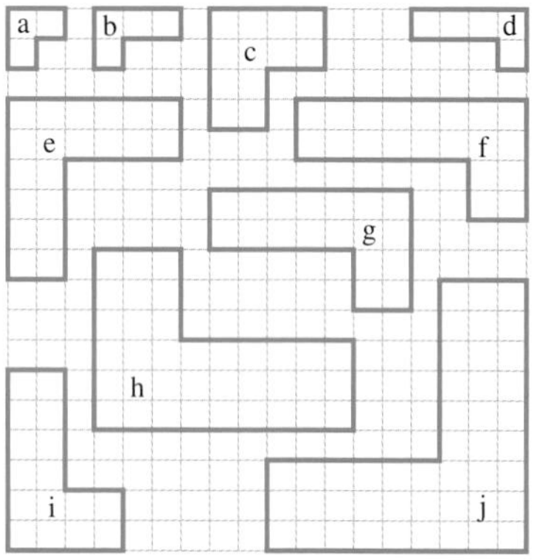

For each pair of similar polyominoes you found, find

8. the ratio of similarity;

9. the ratio of the areas.

10. Give the dimensions of a rectangle similar to the domino shown above, but larger, such that the ratio of areas is
    a. 25; b. 9;
    c. 2; d. 5.

9.12 SOLUTIONS

1. a. volume: 4; surface area: 18
   b. volume: 8; surface area: 30
   c. volume: 16; surface area: 48
   d. volume: 32; surface area: 72
2. Figures (a) and (d) because to create (d) we could double all the dimensions of (a)
3. 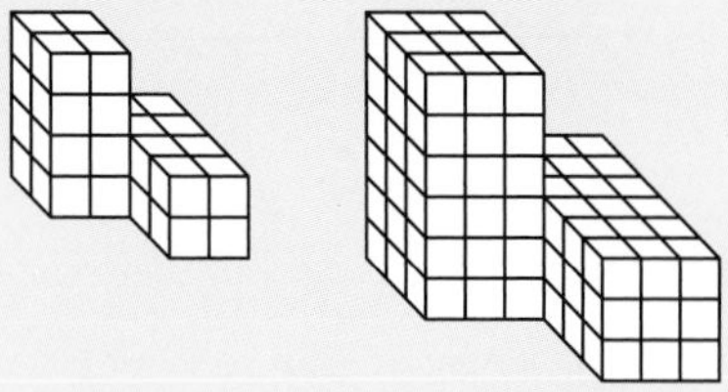
4. 3/2
5. 2/3
6. They are reciprocals. You can compare the figures in either order. Whether you get 2/3 or 3/2 depends on whether your reference figure is the smaller or the larger.

7., 8., 9.

Figures	Ratio of Similarity		Ratio of Areas
a & c	c : a	2 : 1	12/3 = 4
b & h	h : b	3 : 1	36/4 = 9
e & j	j : e	3 : 2	45/20 = 9/4
d & f	f : d	2 : 1	20/5 = 4
h & i	h : i	3 : 2	36/16 = 9/4
b & i	i : b	2 : 1	16/4 = 4

10. a. 10 by 5
    b. 6 by 3
    c. $2\sqrt{2}$ by $\sqrt{2}$
    d. $2\sqrt{5}$ by $\sqrt{5}$
11. a. $(R_s)^2$
    b. $\sqrt{R_A}$
12. The ratio of similarity between two figures will be the same as the ratios of their perimeters. It is not necessary to find the perimeters to figure this out. We find from the work with tetrominoes that to create similar figures, we stretch in all directions; therefore, the new perimeter will be a multiple of the old perimeter.
13. Answers will vary.
14. a. No, two rectangles can be different shapes.
    b. Yes, since all sides of a square have equal length, all squares are similar.
    c. Yes, since all sides of a cube have equal length, all cubes are similar.
15.

cube	volume	surface area
1^3	1	6
5^3	125	150
$(x+1)^3$	x^3+3x^2+3x+1	$6x^2+12x+6$
y^3	y^3	$6y^2$

11. **Generalization**
   a. If the ratio of similarity of two figures is R_S, what is the ratio of areas? Explain.
   b. If the ratio of areas is R_A, what is the ratio of similarity? Explain.

12. Using the data from problems 7-8, find the relationship between the ratio of similarity and the ratio of perimeters.

13. Make a figure using three 2-D Lab Gear blocks (including some blue blocks).
   a. Sketch the figure.
   b. Find its perimeter and area.
   c. Use blocks to make a figure similar to the original figure.
   d. Predict its perimeter and area.
   e. Check your prediction.

VOLUME, SURFACE AREA

14. True or False? Explain each one.
   a. Any two rectangles are similar.
   b. Any two squares are similar.
   c. Any two cubes are similar.

15. Build the following cubes using the Lab Gear: 1^3, 5^3, $(x + 1)^3$, and y^3. Find the volume and surface area of each cube.

16. There are six pairs of similar buildings among the four cubes you built. For each pair, find
   a. the ratio of similarity;
   b. the ratio of surface areas;
   c. the ratio of volumes.

17. **Generalization** If you know the ratio of similarity between two figures, R_S, explain how you can find
   a. the ratio of surface areas, R_A;
   b. the ratio of volumes, R_V.

18. What should be the dimensions of a cubical box that would hold 27 times as much as a box having dimensions 2 in.-by-2 in.-by-2 in.?

19. Repeat problem 18 for a cubical box that would hold 10 times as much as a box having dimensions 2 in.-by-2 in.-by-2 in.

TRAIN SETS

Model train sets come in different scales. The scale is the ratio of similarity between the model and the actual train that is being modeled. This table shows some of the available scales.

Name	Scale
Z	1/220
N	1/160
O	a quarter inch to one foot
HO	an eighth of an inch to one foot
LGB	half an inch to one foot

20. Order the scales from smallest to largest.

21. The LGB scale is also known as 1/25. Comment on this.

George wanted to buy an HO set that would cover an area of 15 square feet.

22. How much area would be covered by the actual train being modeled by this set?

23. How much area would be covered by a similar set in each of the other scales?

24. How many times heavier or lighter do you estimate a similar set would be in each of the other scales? (Assume that you can estimate the ratio of weights by using the ratio of volumes.)

VOLUME, SURFACE AREA

TRAIN SETS

*P*roblem 14a is false, which can best be explained with a counter-example.

*U*nderstanding similarity in three dimensions makes it possible to think of many real-world problems much more clearly, especially issues of scaling.

*I*n problem 22, it may be useful to discuss the length and width of a rectangle with the area found, in order to develop more of a feel for the size of it.

9.12 SOLUTIONS

16.

pair	ratio of similarity	ratio of volumes	ratio of surface areas
$5^3 : 1^3$	$5 : 1$	$125 : 1$	$25 : 1$
$(x+1)^3 : 1^3$	$(x+1) : 1$	$(x+1)^3 : 1$	$(x+1)^2 : 1$
$y^3 : 1^3$	$y : 1$	$y^3 : 1$	$y^2 : 1$
$(x+1)^3 : 5^3$	$(x+1) : 5$	$(x+1)^3 : 5^3$	$(x+1)^2 : 5^2$
$(x+1)^3 : y^3$	$(x+1) : y$	$(x+1)^3 : y^3$	$(x+1)^2 : y^2$
$5^3 : y^3$	$5 : y$	$5^3 : y^3$	$5^2 : y^2$

17. a. $R_A = (R_S)^2$
   b. $R_V = (R_S)^3$

18. 6 by 6 by 6

19. $\sqrt[3]{10} \cdot 2$

20. Z, N, HO, O, LGB

21. The LGB scale is 1/2 in. : 1 ft. or 1/2 in. : 12 in. which is 1/24 or approximately 1/25.

22. $R_S = 1/96$ so $R_A = (1/96)^2 = 1/9216$

   To get the area of the actual train, multiply the area of George's train by 9216 to get 138,240 square feet.

23. Z scale: 2.86 square feet
   N scale: 5.40 square feet
   O scale: 60 square feet
   LGB scale: 240 square feet

24. These are comparisons with the HO scale.
   Z : multiply by 0.083
   N: multiply by 0.216
   O: multiply by 8
   LGB: multiply by 64

THINKING WRITING 9.C SuperTangrams, Midpoints

Core Sequence: 1-7

Suitable for Homework: 6-7, 12-14

Useful for Assessment: 7, 13

What this Assignment is About:

- Review of the Pythagorean theorem
- Review of operations with radical expressions
- Review of similar figures
- Review of slope
- Review of distance
- Preview of midpoint theorems

These assignments are substantial. Do not assign both at once! Even though they provide review, you will need to allow plenty of class time to get students started.

SUPERTANGRAMS

This assignment reviews most concepts that were developed in this chapter.

Problems 1-2 are an excellent activity for group work and for developing students' visual sense.

For problem 3 students may use calculators to rank the radical expressions.

If you have access to plastic Super-Tangrams, your students can reproduce, on inch graph paper, the similar figures shown before problem 4 and try to cover each shape with SuperTangrams.

THINKING WRITING 9.C SuperTangrams, Midpoints

SUPERTANGRAMS

You will need:

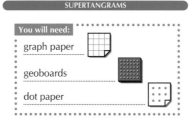

- graph paper
- geoboards
- dot paper

In the world of geometric puzzles, half a unit square (cut along the diagonal), is called a *tan*.

Figures created by combining tans are called *polytans*. Here are the ditans.

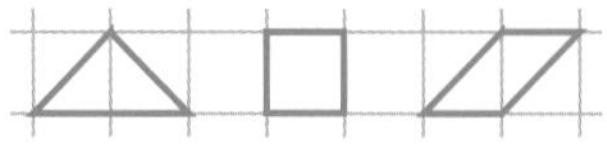

The tans must be combined side-to-side. The following arrangements are not acceptable.

1. Find all four tritans.

2. Find all fourteen tetratans.

3. Tetratans are usually called *SuperTangrams*. Find the perimeter and area of each SuperTangram, using radical expressions when appropriate. Rank the perimeters from shortest to longest.

This figure shows one of the SuperTangrams and four blown-up versions of it.

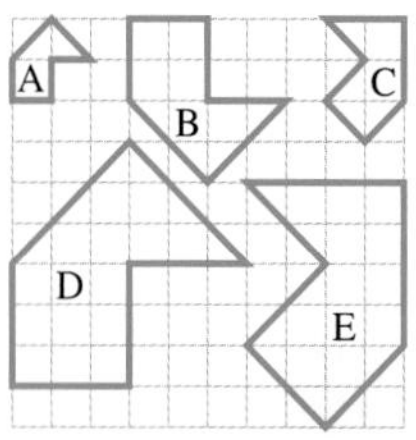

4. Find the perimeter and the area for the SuperTangram and each blowup.

5. Compare shape A with shape C.

a. What is the ratio of similarity?

b. Verify your answer to part (a) by showing that multiplying the perimeter of A by the ratio of similarity yields the perimeter of C.

6. Repeat problem 5 for each other pair of shapes in the figure. (You should find nine more ratios of similarity.)

7. Report Write a report summarizing your work in problems 3-6. Include a discussion of:

- using the Pythagorean theorem;
- perimeter and area of similar figures;
- operations with radical expressions.

9.C SOLUTIONS

1.

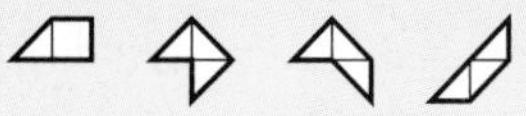

2., 3.

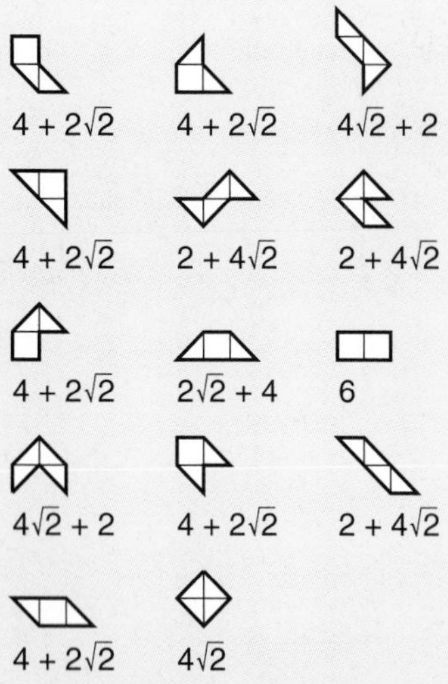

4.

Figure	Perimeter	Area
A	$4 + 2\sqrt{2}$	2
B	$8 + 4\sqrt{2}$	8
C	$4 + 4\sqrt{2}$	4
D	$12 + 6\sqrt{2}$	18
E	$8 + 8\sqrt{2}$	16

5., 6.

	Ratio of Similarity(R)	R · Second Perimeter	First Perimeter
B : A	2 : 1	$2(4 + 2\sqrt{2})$	$8 + 4\sqrt{2}$
C : A	$\sqrt{2}$: 1	$\sqrt{2}\,(4 + 2\sqrt{2})$	$4 + 4\sqrt{2}$
D : A	3 : 1	$3(4 + 2\sqrt{2})$	$12 + 6\sqrt{2}$
E : A	$2\sqrt{2}$: 1	$2\sqrt{2}\,(4 + 2\sqrt{2})$	$8 + 8\sqrt{2}$
C : B	$1 + \sqrt{2} : 2 + \sqrt{2}$	$\frac{1 + \sqrt{2}}{2 + \sqrt{2}}(8 + 4\sqrt{2})$	$4 + 4\sqrt{2}$
D : B	$6 + 3\sqrt{2} : 2(2 + \sqrt{2})$	$\frac{6 + 3\sqrt{2}}{2(2 + \sqrt{2})}(8 + 4\sqrt{2})$	$12 + 6\sqrt{2}$
E : B	$2(1 + \sqrt{2}) : 2 + \sqrt{2}$	$\frac{2(1 + \sqrt{2})}{2 + \sqrt{2}}(8 + 4\sqrt{2})$	$8 + 8\sqrt{2}$
D : C	$3(2 + \sqrt{2}) : 2(1 + \sqrt{2})$	$\frac{3(2 + \sqrt{2})}{2(1 + \sqrt{2})}(4 + 4\sqrt{2})$	$12 + 6\sqrt{2}$
E : C	2 : 1	$2\,(4 + 4\sqrt{2})$	$8 + 8\sqrt{2}$
E : D	$4(1 + \sqrt{2}) : 3(2 + \sqrt{2})$	$\frac{4(1 + \sqrt{2})}{3(2 + \sqrt{2})}(12 + 6\sqrt{2})$	$8 + 8\sqrt{2}$

7. Reports will vary. To show that the third and fourth columns of the table are equivalent, students will have to use rules about operations with radical expressions. This might be included in the report. The report might also include a discussion of how the Pythagorean theorem was used to help find the perimeters. A table like the preceding one can be made to compare areas, showing how one can obtain the area of a similar figure by multiplying by the square of the ratio of similarity.

MIDPOINTS

8. Draw five geoboard segments whose midpoints are on a peg.
9. Make a triangle such that all of its sides have their midpoints on a peg. Connect the midpoints, making a smaller triangle. Study the figure, looking for parallel lines, equal segments, and similar figures.
10. Find the slopes of lines you believe are parallel. Find the lengths of the segments you believe are equal. Find the ratio of similarity for figures you believe are similar.
11. Make a quadrilateral such that all of its sides have their midpoints on a peg. Make the quadrilateral as irregular as you can, avoiding equal or parallel sides. Connect the midpoints, making a smaller quadrilateral. Study the figure, looking for parallel sides and equal segments.
12. Find the slopes of lines you believe are parallel. Find the lengths of the segments you believe are equal.
13. **Report** Write a report on midpoints of triangles and quadrilaterals. Do you think what you found in the case you investigated will always be true? Explain.
14. Try to make a triangle such that exactly two of its sides have their midpoints on pegs. If you find such a triangle, draw it on dot paper. If you believe such a triangle does not exist, explain why.

You will probably want to discuss problem 5 in class before assigning problems 6 and 7 for homework. You may need to have some discussion about how to verify the ratio of similarity by comparing the perimeters. For example, shape A has perimeter $4 + 2\sqrt{2}$ and shape C has perimeter $4 + 4\sqrt{2}$. Showing that the second perimeter can be obtained from the first by multiplying by $\sqrt{2}$ is a good application of operations with radicals.

Other SuperTangram puzzles can be found in *SuperTangrams for Beginners* and *SuperTangram Activities*, by Henri Picciotto. (Creative Publications, © 1987 and 1986.)

MIDPOINTS

The activity is fairly straightforward. You should encourage students to make sure they start with different triangles and quadrilaterals from each other's, so that they can check the generality of their observations.

A challenging extension is to generalize what was discovered by using variables for the coordinates of the vertices.

9.C SOLUTIONS

8. Answers will vary. Sample answers are given in the figure.

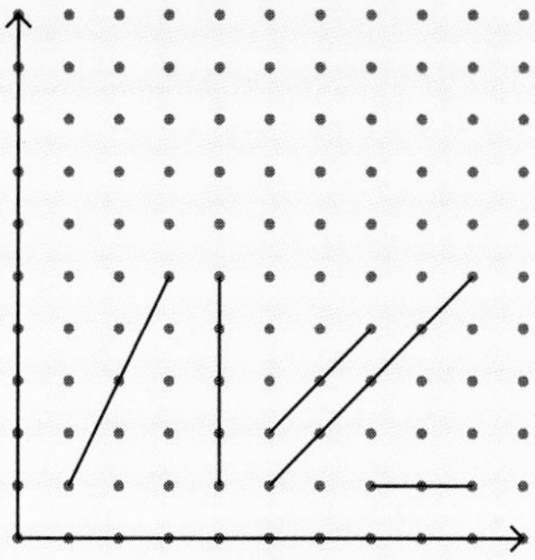

9. Answers will vary. Sample answers are given in the figure.

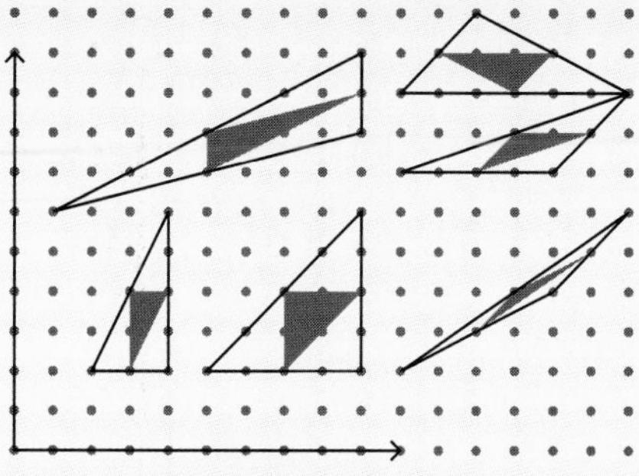

10. Answers may vary. As can be seen in the figure for #9, four smaller triangles are formed. Each one is similar to the original triangle. The ratio of similarity of the larger to the smaller triangles is 2 : 1. The segment joining the midpoints of two sides is parallel to the third side. Students may notice other relationships as well.

11. Answers will vary. A sample is given.

11., 12.

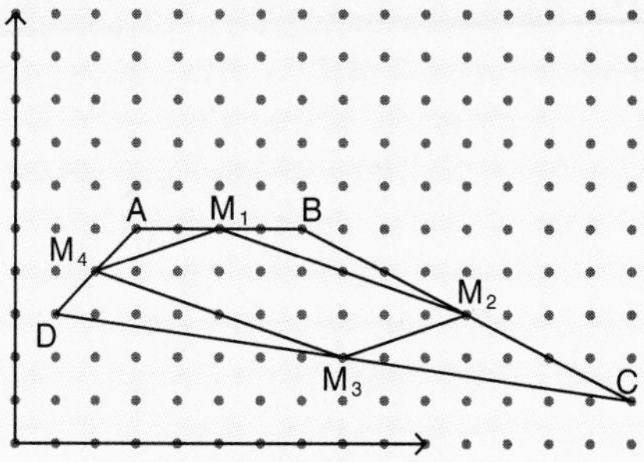

12. A parallelogram will be formed. Students may make other observations.
13. Reports will vary.
14. Such a triangle does not exist. Students' explanations will vary.

◆ Essential Ideas

Do not assign problems 28-32 if you skipped Lessons 10-12.

Essential Ideas

DISTANCE

1. On the number line, what is the distance between:
a. 12 and -34? b. 12 and 34?
c. 12 and x?

2. On the number line, what points are at distance 7.5 from 6.89?

3. On the number line, what point is halfway between:
a. 12 and -34? b. 12 and 34?
c. 12 and x?

4. (5, 6) is the midpoint of a segment from what point to:
a. (7, -8)? b. (-9.1, 2.34)?

5. What is the biggest possible difference between taxicab and Euclidean distance between two geoboard pegs on a 10-by-10 geoboard? (Give a decimal approximation.)

6. On graph paper, show as many points as possible that are at distance 10 from the origin, using
a. taxicab distance;
b. Euclidean distance.

7. What is the distance from (5, 6) to:
a. (7, -8)? b. (-9.1, 2.34)?

THE PYTHAGOREAN THEOREM

8. How long is the diagonal of a square if the side of the square is
a. 10? b. x?

9. How long is the side of a square if the diagonal is
a. 10? b. x?

10. How long is the other leg of a right triangle, if the first leg is half the hypotenuse, and the hypotenuse is
a. 10? b. x?

FROM ONE POINT TO ANOTHER

11. Given the two points (1, 2.3) and (-4.5, 6), find
a. the taxicab distance between them;
b. the slope of the line that joins them;
c. the Euclidean distance between them.

SQUARE ROOTS

12. 🔑 Explain why $\sqrt{-4}$ is not a real number.

13. 🔑 Is $\sqrt{-x}$ a real number? Explain.

14. a. Give three values of x for which $-x$ represents a positive number.
b. Make a table of values and graph $y = \sqrt{-x}$.
c. What is the domain of $y = \sqrt{-x}$?

15. Hal noticed something interesting. He saw that if he squared a number and took its square root, he would get back the same number. Jacob said he could find many numbers for which that wouldn't work. Can you? List some.

16. Ruth thought you could write:
$-\sqrt{25} = \sqrt{-25}$ and $-\sqrt{-25} = \sqrt{25}$.
Explain why she is wrong.

17. Which is greater? Explain.
a. $\sqrt{80}$ or $8\sqrt{10}$
b. $\sqrt{40} + \sqrt{40}$ or $\sqrt{80}$
c. $\sqrt{63} - \sqrt{28}$ or $\sqrt{63 - 28}$
d. $\frac{\sqrt{4}}{\sqrt{9}}$ or $\sqrt{\frac{4}{9}}$

◆ S O L U T I O N S

1. a. 46
b. 22
c. $|12 - x|$
2. -0.61 and 14.39
3. a. -11
b. 23
c. $(12 + x)/2$
4. a. (3, 20)
b. (19.1, 9.66)
5. $20 - 10\sqrt{2} \approx 5.86$
6.

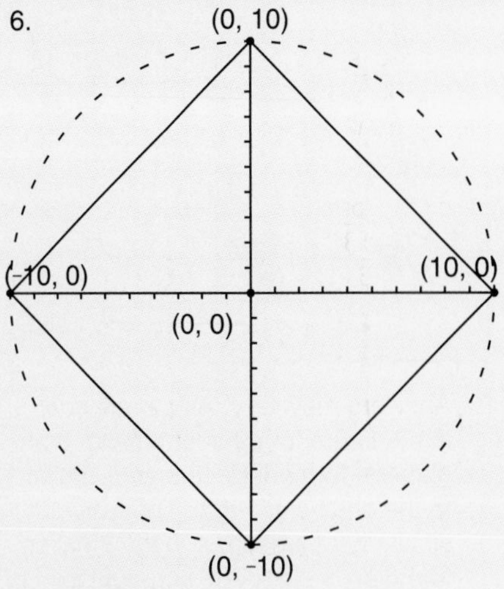

7. a. $10\sqrt{2}$
b. about 14.57
8. a. $10\sqrt{2}$
b. $x\sqrt{2}$
9. a. $5\sqrt{2}$
b. $(x\sqrt{2})/2$
10. a. $5\sqrt{3}$
b. $(x\sqrt{3})/2$
11. a. 9.2
b. -0.673
c. 6.6
12. There is no number that you can multiply by itself to get -4.
13. If $x \le 0$, it is a real number, since the opposite of a negative number is positive, and positive numbers have real square roots.
14. a. Answers will vary. Any negative number will work.

MULTIPLYING AND DIVIDING

18. What is the area of a rectangle having sides
a. 3 and $\sqrt{6}$?
b. $\sqrt{3}$ and $\sqrt{6}$?
c. $4\sqrt{3}$ and $5\sqrt{6}$?
d. $(4 + \sqrt{3})$ and $5\sqrt{6}$?

19. A rectangle has area $8\sqrt{7}$. Give three possibilities for the sides.

20. 💡 A rectangle has area $15 + 6\sqrt{7}$. Give three possibilities for the sides.

21. Write without radicals in the denominator.
a. $\frac{2}{\sqrt{3}}$ b. 💡 $\frac{4}{\sqrt{5} + 6}$

ADDING AND SUBTRACTING

22. True or False? Explain.
a. $36 + 64 = 100$
b. $\sqrt{36 + 64} = \sqrt{100}$
c. $\sqrt{36} + \sqrt{64} = \sqrt{100}$
d. $\sqrt{36 + 64} = \sqrt{36} + \sqrt{64}$

23. Simplify, then add or subtract.
a. $\sqrt{8} + \sqrt{72}$
b. $\sqrt{20} - \sqrt{5}$
c. $\sqrt{30} - \sqrt{36} + \sqrt{120} + \sqrt{121}$
d. $15 - \sqrt{15} + 60 - \sqrt{60}$

THE MIDPOINT OF GROWTH

24. Joel invested \$200 in 1970 and forgot about it. In the year 2010 he discovered that he had \$5227 in the account. How much did he have in the account in 1990 if he was getting
a. simple interest?
b. compound interest?

RADICAL RULES

25. If a and b are nonnegative, write an expression equivalent to each of the following. Explain each rule with an example.
a. $\sqrt{a}\sqrt{a}$ b. $\sqrt{a}\sqrt{b}$
c. $a/\sqrt{a}$ d. $\sqrt{a}/\sqrt{b}$

26. Simplify.
a. $\sqrt{2^9}$ b. $\sqrt{2^{10}}$

27. 💡 Simplify $\sqrt{2^n}$ assuming n is
a. even; b. odd.

SIMILAR FIGURES

28. Assume you want to use a copy machine to blow up a picture from a 3-inch-by-5-inch index card to 4-inch-by-6-inch card.
a. What percent setting should you use so that you get as large an image as possible, but one which does not extend beyond the edge?
b. How much is the area increased at that setting?

29. Answer the questions in problem 28 about blowing up a picture from a 3-inch-by-5-inch size to an 8.5-inch-by-11-inch size.

30. Assume you want to use a copy machine to reduce an image so its area gets divided by two. What percent setting should you use?

Assume that the amount of material needed to make clothes is proportional to the surface area, while the amount of food needed is proportional to the volume.

31. How many times as much material would be needed to dress a five-foot Alice as a ten-inch Alice?

32. How many times as much food would be needed to feed a five-foot Alice as a ten-inch Alice?

◆ S O L U T I O N S

b.

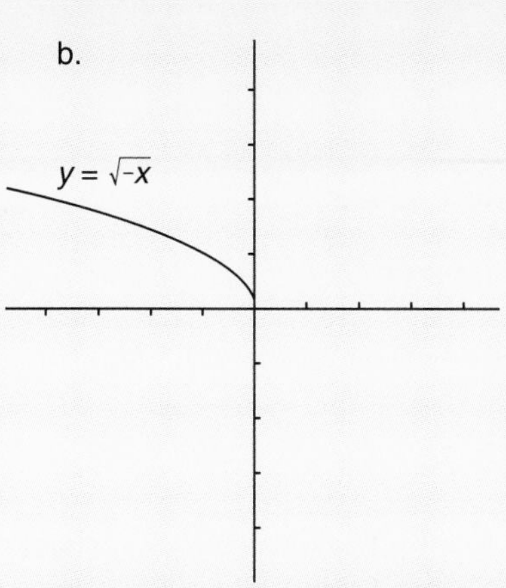

c. $x \le 0$

15. Any negative number will work.

16. Ruth was trying to "distribute" a negative sign across the square root symbol, as if it were parentheses.

17. a. $8\sqrt{10}$ is larger
b. $\sqrt{40} + \sqrt{40}$ is larger
c. $\sqrt{63 - 28}$ is greater.
d. equal

18. a. $3\sqrt{6}$
b. $\sqrt{18}$ or $3\sqrt{2}$
c. $20\sqrt{18}$ or $60\sqrt{2}$
d. $20\sqrt{6} + 5\sqrt{18}$ or $20\sqrt{6} + 15\sqrt{2}$

19. 4 and $2\sqrt{7}$ OR 2 and $4\sqrt{7}$ OR 1 and $8\sqrt{7}$ OR 8 and $1\sqrt{7}$

20. Answers will vary. Samples: 3 and $(5 + 2\sqrt{7})$ OR 5 and $(3 + (6/5)\sqrt{7})$ OR 15 and $(1 + (6/15)\sqrt{7})$

21. a. $(2/3)\sqrt{3}$
b. $(4\sqrt{5} - 24)/(-31)$

22. a. True b. True
c. False d. False

23. a. $8\sqrt{2}$ b. $\sqrt{5}$
c. $5 + 3\sqrt{30}$ d. $75 - 3\sqrt{15}$

24. Joel earned a total of \$5027 in interest in 40 years.
a. If he had been earning simple interest, his interest would have been \$125.675 per year, so in 1990 he would have had \$2713.50.
b. For compound interest, his rate would have been about 8.5% per year. In 1990 he would have had about \$1022.

25. a. a b. $\sqrt{ab}$
c. $\sqrt{a}$ d. $\sqrt{a/b}$

26. a. $2^4\sqrt{2}$ b. 2^5

27. a. $2^{n/2}$ b. $2^{(n-1)/2}\sqrt{2}$

28. a. 120% b. 144%

29. a. 220% b. 484%

(Solutions continued on page 525)

Chapter 10
SATISFYING CONSTRAINTS

The Last Five Chapters

*I*f you are using this book in a one-year course, before proceeding with Chapter 10 you should look over Chapters 10-14 and decide what you want to cover in the limited time you have left. For detailed suggestions, see the section entitled **End-of-Year Options** in the Course Planning Guide in the back of this Teacher's Edition.

Overview of the Chapter

*T*his chapter is primarily about simultaneous linear equations in two variables, a traditional algebra topic that retains much relevance. However our treatment of it departs significantly from the traditional approach.

*W*e start from real-world applications, where linear constraints on two variables introduce students to the essential question. The first techniques we use in addressing this topic are trial and error and table-building, then we work with the Lab Gear, then with symbols, and finally with graphs. The multiplicity of approaches is intended to give students a multi-dimensional grasp of the question. Since we do this in an applied context, students learn many strategies to solve word problems, including the standard one. The last part of the chapter concerns the related question of finding the equation of a line given two points on it. This is useful in understanding how a mathematical formula can be derived to model the relationship between two real-world variables. We end the chapter with examples of this application.

*W*hen teaching this chapter, do not rush to teach everything about simultaneous equations right away. Give students a chance to discover for themselves, and encourage discussion and comparison of the different methods. This will prepare students for learning standard techniques later on.

*I*n particular, do not expect students to know how to write equations about word problems spontaneously; they need to work their way up to that.

CHAPTER 10

The spiral groove of a record, from the outer rim to the inner

Coming in this chapter:

Exploration I have pennies, dimes, and quarters, and two bags to put them in. I put all the coins of one kind into one bag, and coins of the other two kinds into the other. There is the same number of coins in each bag, and the total value of each bag's contents is the same. How much money might I have?

SATISFYING CONSTRAINTS

1. New Uses for Tools:

- Tables, graphs, Lab Gear, and symbol manipulation for simultaneous equations

2. Algebra Concepts Emphasized:

- Graphing linear equations
- Simultaneous equations
- Solving simultaneous equations graphically
- Solving simultaneous equations by substitution
- Solving simultaneous equations by linear combinations
- Solving for one variable in terms of another
- Systems having one solution, no solutions, or an infinite number of solutions
- Algebraic relationship between standard form and slope-intercept form
- Effect of the parameters on the graph of $Ax + By = C$
- Quick graphing of linear equations in standard and line-intercept form
- Word problems
- Finding the equation of a line, given its slope and one point on it
- Finding the equation of a line, given two points on it

3. Algebra Concepts Reviewed:

- Proportions
- x- and y-intercepts
- Exponents and exponential functions
- Slope-intercept form
- Percent
- Direct variation

4. Algebra Concepts Previewed:

- Using linear functions as mathematical models

5. Problem-Solving Techniques:

- Using equations
- Making a table
- Organized searches

6. Connections and Context:

- Mixture problems
- Number patterns
- Fitting a line to data
- Fahrenheit-Celsius conversion

▼ 10.1
The Van Pool

Core Sequence: 1-23

Suitable for Homework: 8-23

Useful for Assessment: 13, 17

What this Lesson is About:

- Using graphs and equations to model a real-world problem
- Preview of graphical solution of simultaneous equations
- Review of proportions
- Review of exponents and exponential functions
- Preview of mixture problems

*P*roblem 1 poses the problem that this lesson investigates. Trial and error is the most likely approach. Do not suggest or encourage any strategies, as the main purpose of this Exploration is to get students to understand for themselves what issues are involved.

*I*n fact you will need to hold back throughout the lesson: Do not explain how to get an equation out of the problem's given, let alone how to solve the equation. Students will have a chance to discover such ideas for themselves in the course of the next few lessons.

SHARING COSTS

*T*he wording of problem 2c is debatable, since values in only whole numbers of cents are actually possible. Nevertheless, it is useful to draw the graph as a line, and close enough to a correct graph, given the resolution of the graph.

*N*ote that the graphs are meaningful only in the first quadrant, since no one will be charged a negative fare. (You may want to discuss this with your class.) The graph for problem 2 is the familiar "constant sum" graph, but the ones for problems 3-4 are not. Finding the equation (in problem 5) may be difficult for some students. Encourage discussion in the groups or by the whole class, but do not reveal how to do it.

*T*he equations are likely to be in the form $ax + by = c$, but of course any mathematically correct equation should be accepted. If more than one form surfaces, you can discuss the merits of each form. Specifically, the parameters a, b, and c in the $ax + by = c$ form are easy to interpret in this context.

LESSON 10.1

The Van Pool

You will need: graph paper

In the town of Braun a group of people decided to organize a van pool to get to and from work and school. They estimated mileage costs to be about \$11 per day, so the total cost including the bridge toll would be \$12 per day round trip. Then they had to discuss how to share costs. They agreed that children and adults might have different fares.

1. **Exploration** Say there are three children and four adults in the van pool. Find several possible fares you could charge children and adults.

SHARING COSTS

In the following problems, let x stand for a child's daily fare, and let y stand for an adult's daily fare.

2. If only one adult and one child joined the van pool, there is more than one possible pair of values for x and y.
   a. List three possible (x, y) pairs.
   b. Plot these (x, y) pairs on coordinate axes.
   c. Make a graph showing all possible (x, y) pairs. Label the x-intercept and the y-intercept.
3. Repeat problem 2, assuming that one child and two adults join the van pool. Use the same axes for your graph.
4. Repeat problem 2, assuming that two adults and three children join the van pool. Use the same axes for your graph.
5. a. Write equations for the graphs you drew in problems 2-4.
   b. For each equation, interpret the coefficients of x and y and the constant term in terms of the situation.
   c. Find the x-intercept and the y-intercept on each of your graphs. Interpret them in terms of the situation.

NEGOTIATIONS

In this section, assume that the van pool has four children and three adults.

6. a. Make a table showing several possible (x, y) pairs representing the daily fare for children and adults. Draw a graph that shows all possible (x, y) pairs.
   b. Label and interpret the x-intercept and the y-intercept on your graph.
   c. Write an equation for the graph.

The members of the van pool discussed how to divide the cost among themselves. Some thought the adults' and children's fares should be different, and others thought they should be the same. They discussed several possible plans.

10.1 SOLUTIONS

1. Answers vary. Sample answers: If children are free, then each adult pays \$3.00. If children pay \$1 each, adults each pay \$2.25. If each child pays half the adult cost, then each child pays \$1.09 and each adult pays \$2.18, with someone chipping in the extra penny.
2. a. Answers will vary. Sample answers: (1, 11), (2, 10), (3, 9)

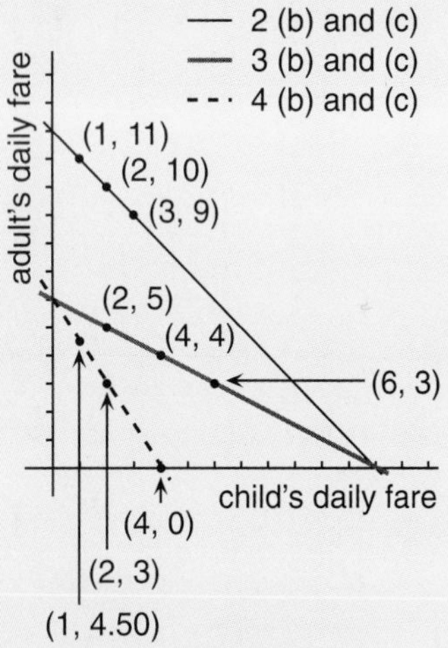

3. a. Answers will vary. Sample answers: (2, 5), (4, 4), (6, 3)
   b. See the figure for #2 b and c.
   c. See the figure for #2 b and c.

In each case described in problems 7-12:

a. Figure out what the daily fare for adults and for children would be. Show your work.

b. Plot a point on the graph from problem 6 to represent your solution.

7. Frances suggested that adults pay twice as much as children because they have more money.

8. John thought that adults should pay $1 more than children.

9. Kathleen said that adults should pay $2 more than children.

10. Joanna argued that there was no reason to have different fares, since an adult and a child each occupy one seat.

11. Allan thought it was unfair to have adults pay more than children, since adults take turns driving the van. He argued that children should pay twice as much as adults.

12. Louise remembered that van pools are exempt from the bridge toll, so she subtracted $1 from the total cost. She agreed with Allan that children should pay twice as much as adults.

INFLATION

The cost of commuting kept increasing. Since the van could legally carry nine people, including the driver, the members decided to let two more children join the pool. They had six children and three adults. Over the years, the cost went up, first to $14, then to $15, and finally to $18 per day.

13. On the same pair of axes, draw three graphs, one for each of the three values for the total cost.

14. Label each graph with its equation.

15. Assume that the adults' fare is twice the children's fare. Mark the points on your graph representing those fares for adults and children, if the total cost is the following amounts:

a. $14 b. $15 c. $18

16. Look at the three points you marked in problem 15. You should be able to connect all of them with a straight line.

a. Find an equation that fits your line.

b. Interpret your equation. (What do the coefficients mean in terms of the problem?)

17. Repeat problems 15-16, assuming that the children's fare is twice the adults' fare.

In several places in this and subsequent lessons students are asked to "interpret" points and parameters. Each point on the graph represents a certain cost for children and a certain cost for adults. For example, (0, 12) represents a cost of $0 for children and $12 for adults.

NEGOTIATIONS

Students can use calculators and trial and error to solve these problems. You may want to agree that rounding to the nearest penny (or nickel) is close enough so that no one feels cheated.

The main observation of this section is that each solution is a number pair that is represented by a point that lies on the graph of $4x + 3y = 12$, (except for problem 12, where the total cost is no longer $12. This is likely to come up in discussion, since students are asked to plot the points on their graph from problem 6, and in this case it is impossible).

INFLATION

There are two things to notice here: With the same number of children and adults, but different total costs, the graphs are parallel lines; and, solutions based on the same relationship between child and adult fares form a line.

By now the groundwork has been laid for the graphic solution of a system of equations, which will be formally introduced in Lessons 5 and 6.

10.1 SOLUTIONS

4. a. Answers will vary. Sample answers: (1, 4.50), (2, 3), (4, 0)
   b. See the figure for #2 b and c.
   c. See the figure for #2 b and c.
5. a. $x + y = 12$, $x + 2y = 12$, and $3x + 2y = 12$
   b. For all three equations, 12 is the total round trip cost each day. For $x + y = 12$, the coefficients of x and y are both 1 because there is one child and one adult riding in the van.
   For $x + 2y = 12$, the coefficient of x is 1 because there is one child. The coefficient of y is 2 because there are two adults.
   For $3x + 2y = 12$, the coefficient of x is 3 because there are three children. The coefficient of y is 2 because there are two adults.
   c. For $x + y = 12$, (12, 0) and (0, 12) are the x-intercept and y-intercept when the child pays $12, the adult pays $0. When the adult pays $12, the child pays $0.
   For $x + 2y = 12$, (12, 0) and (0, 6) are the x-intercept and y-intercept when the child pays $12, the adults pay $0. When the child pays $0, each adult pays $6.
   For $3x + 2y = 12$, (4, 0) and (0, 6) are the x- and y-intercepts. When each child pays $4, each adult pays $0. When each child pays $0, each adult pays $6.
6. a. Tables will vary. Sample table:

x	y
0	4
3	0
1	2.67
2	1.33

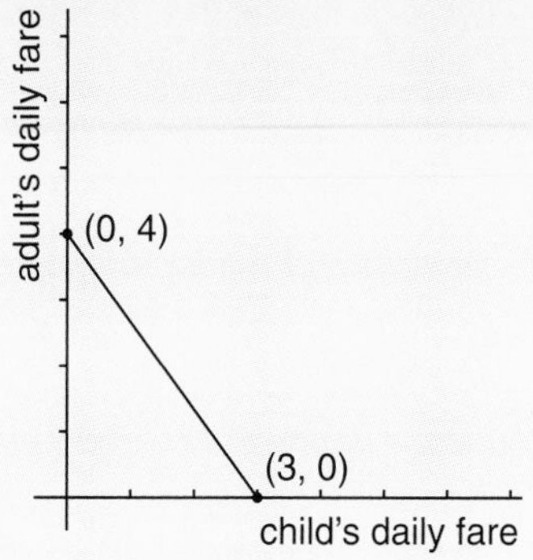

   b. (0, 4) and (3, 0)
   c. $4x + 3y = 12$
7. a. Each child pays $1.20 and each adult pays $2.40.
   b. See the figure for #6. Point is (1.20, 2.40)
8. a. Each child pays $1.29 and each adult pays $2.29. (Note: This

REVIEW/PREVIEW ***RECIPES***

This section reviews proportions, and previews Lesson 2. It consists of mixture problems in the special case where all of the proportions are multiples of one of them. This makes it easy to think about them as problems having one variable.

REVIEW ***EXPONENTS***

If students have trouble with this review, encourage them to look back at their work in Chapter 8.

For problem 23, replacing x by a number, then by another, may help students see the pattern.

Problem 23 could make for a good class discussion if you have time for it. Do not let students limit their investigation to values of x that are greater than 1. This is also fun to do on the graphing calculator.

REVIEW/PREVIEW ***RECIPES***

These are the instructions on a can of orange juice concentrate.

> Mix one part juice concentrate with three parts water.

18. How much concentrate should you use to make
a. 6 cups of orange juice?
b. 10 cups of orange juice?

19. Using this recipe, how much of each ingredient would you need to make 160 cups of punch for the 80 people who are expected at the piano recital?

> **Piano Recital Punch**
>
> *Mix:*
> 4 parts iced tea, sweetened
> 4 parts apple juice
> 4 parts cranberry juice
> 2 parts orange juice
> 1 part lemon juice
>
> *Garnish with lemon and orange slices.*

20. How much Piano Recital Punch could you make if you had an unlimited amount of the other ingredients but only
a. 3/4 cup of lemon juice?
b. 3 cups of orange juice?

REVIEW ***EXPONENTS***

21. Write without parentheses.
a. $(4x^2)^3$ b. $(4x^2y)^3$

22. Simplify each ratio.
a. $\frac{80 \cdot 2^{x+2}}{4 \cdot 2^x}$
b. $\frac{4 \cdot 2^{x+2}}{80 \cdot 2^{x+1}}$
c. $\frac{4 \cdot 2^{x+1}}{80 \cdot 2^{x+2}}$

23. Use your calculator to compare $3 \cdot 2^x$ and $2 \cdot 3^x$. Which is greater for different values of x? For what value of x are they equal?

10.1 SOLUTIONS

yields a total of $12.03. Students might settle for $1.29 and $2.28 to get a total of exactly $12.00.)
b. See the figure for #6. Point is (1.29, 2.29)

9. a. Each child pays $0.86 and each adult pays $2.86, which yields a total of $12.02.
b. See the figure for #6. Point is (0.86, 2.86)

10. a. Everyone pays $1.72, which yields a total of $12.04.
b. See the figure for #6. Point is (1.72, 1.72)

11. a. Each child pays $2.20 and each adult pays $1.10, which yields a total of $12.10. If someone wanted to chip in the extra penny, they could get a total of $11.99 by having adults pay $1.09 and children pay $2.18, but it is probably not worth all the fiddling around with pennies. They could put the extra 10 cents per day into an ice cream fund, or donate it to charity.
b. See the figure for #6. Point is (2.20, 1.10)

12. a. They can get exactly $11 by having each adult pay $1 and each child pay $2.
b. See the figure for #6. Point is (2.00, 1.00). Note that this point is not on the graph of $4x + 3y = 12$.

13., 14., 15.
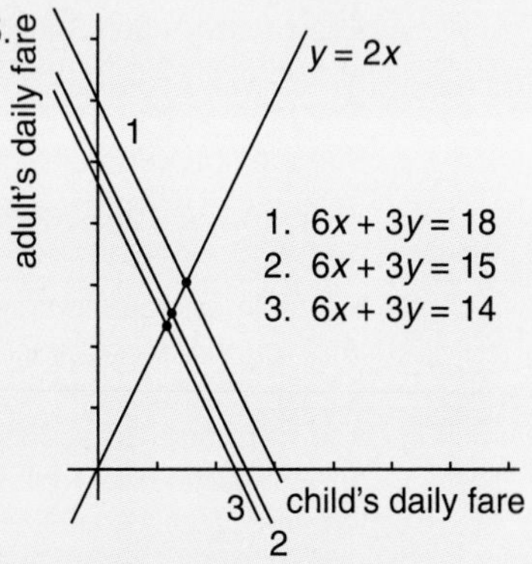

15. a. plot (1.17, 2.34) (This yields $14.04, so will be slightly off the line.)
b. plot (1.25, 2.50)
c. plot (1.50, 3)

(Solutions continued on page 525)

LESSON 10.2

How Much of Each Kind?

AT THE LAUNDROMAT®

1. **Exploration** Some dimes and quarters have a total value of \$3.95. How many of each coin might there be? (Find all the possibilities.) What is the fewest coins there could possibly be? The most? Explain, showing your method of thinking about this problem and commenting on any patterns you notice.

Dan needs nickels and quarters to do his laundry at Science and Math Quick Wash. He has a five-dollar bill. The table shows one possible combination of coins he might get if he asks for change in nickels and quarters only. (The value is given in cents.)

Nickels		Quarters		Total Coins	
no.	value	no.	value	no.	value
45	225	11	275	56	500

2. Add at least six more possibilities to the table and comment on any patterns you notice. (If you don't see any patterns, add more possibilities until you do.)
3. What is the fewest coins Dan might get? The most?
4. Would it be possible for Dan to have an even number of coins? An odd number? Explain.
5. Would it be possible for Dan to have the same number of quarters as nickels? If so, how many of each would he have?

If Dan gets x nickels and y quarters, the entry in the table would look like this.

Nickels		Quarters		Total Coins	
no.	value	no.	value	no.	value
x	$5x$	y	$25y$	—	—

6. a. Explain the meaning of the expressions $5x$ and $25y$ in the table.
   b. Complete the entry, giving the total number of coins and their value *in terms of x and y*.

Any possible whole number pair of values (x, y) giving a possibility for the number of nickels and quarters that Dan might get in change will satisfy this *equation*,

$$5x + 25y = 500.$$

For example, it is easy to show by substitution that the pair (45, 11) satisfies this equation: $5(45) + 25(11) = 500$. This pair also satisfies this condition, or *constraint:*

The total number of coins is 56.

7. Is there another (x, y) pair that satisfies the same equation and the same constraint? If so, what is it?
8. Find (x, y) pairs that satisfy both the equation $5x + 25y = 500$ and the constraints given. (You may want to extend the table you made. You can save work by looking for patterns in your table.) Some may not be possible.
   Constraints:
   a. The total number of coins is 80.
   b. There are 20 times as many nickels as quarters.
   c. There are 12 more nickels than quarters.
   d. There are 8 more quarters than nickels.

10.2
How Much of Each Kind?

Core Sequence: 1-26

Suitable for Homework: 10-26

Useful for Assessment: 12, 15-19, 26

What this Lesson is About:

- Using tables and equations to model real-world problems
- Preview of solving simultaneous equations with numerical tables
- Introduction to mixture problems

In this lesson we show how to use tables of values to solve simultaneous equations. You may extend this lesson by teaching your students how to use a spreadsheet computer program, which automates table-building. To use a spreadsheet students need to be able to figure out what formulas to use. This lesson should help them with that. Even if you don't teach your students how to use a spreadsheet, this lesson helps prepare them for that tool.

Using tables helps students develop a feel for the numerical structure underlying simultaneous linear equations.

AT THE LAUNDROMAT®

We have already seen coin problems in Chapter 5 (after Lesson 5 and in Lesson 8). If you skipped them then, consider assigning them now. Here we use coin problems as a way to get more insight into simultaneous equations.

10.2 SOLUTIONS

1. Methods of solution will vary. One method is to use a table to look for patterns.

number of dimes	number of quarters	number of coins
37	1	38
32	3	35
27	5	32
22	7	29
17	9	26
12	11	23
7	13	20
2	15	17

From the table, you can see the pattern: As the number of dimes decreases by 5, the number of quarters increases by 2. The smallest possible number of coins is 17, with 2 dimes and 15 quarters. $2(10) + 15(25) = 20 + 375 = 395$. The largest possible number of coins is 38, with 37 dimes and 1 quarter. $37(10) + 1(25) = 370 + 25 = 395$.

2. Additional entries in the table will vary. A sample is given below.

Nickels		Quarters		Total Coins	
no.	value	no.	value	no.	value
45	225	11	275	56	500
100	500	0	0	100	500
95	475	1	25	96	500
90	450	2	50	92	500
85	425	3	75	88	500
80	400	4	100	84	500
75	375	5	125	80	500
70	350	6	150	76	500
0	0	20	500	20	500

Some patterns: As the number of nickels decreases by 5, the number of quarters increases by 1 and the total number of coins decreases by 4. The value is always 500. Students will find other patterns.

3. The fewest number of coins Dan might get is 20, consisting of 20 quarters and no nickels. The most would be 100 nickels and no quarters.
4. Dan will always have an even number of coins. The total number of coins is always a multiple of 4, from 20 to 100.
5. It is not possible for Dan to have the same number of quarters as nickels. The closest he could get would be 17 quarters and 15 nickels.
6. a. The variable x represents the number of nickels, each of which is worth 5 cents. To find the total value of x nickels, one multiplies x by 5 to get $5x$. Similarly, y represents the number of quarters, each

Problems 1-5 help students get a feel for the problem. Problems 6-9 concentrate on writing equations. The problem is presented as consisting of an equation in two variables (the one indicating the total value of the coins is \$5.00) which has many possible solutions. However, when adding an additional constraint on the numbers of coins, the number of solutions is narrowed down. In problems 7-9, the constraint is an additional linear equation. In problem 10, the constraint is an inequality: There must be enough nickels and quarters to do the maximum number of washes, but greater numbers are also acceptable.

CRANBERRY-APPLE JUICE

This section is slightly more complex since we are mixing a mixture with straight apple juice, but students are guided through it step by step. It should work well as a homework assignment.

Again, the main point is to use tables as a lead-in to equations. A further twist: The mixture cannot possibly contain less than 50% apple juice, since the original liquids don't.

The most important problems are 16-19, in which students have to interpret equations in terms of the problem. This is necessary preparation for being able to write equations describing a problem.

There will be more mixture problems in **Thinking/Writing 10.A**.

9. Each of the constraints in problem 8 can be expressed as an equation in x and y. Write each equation.

10. At Science and Math Quick Wash, the machines take three quarters and one nickel to wash and one quarter to dry. If Dan wants to do as many loads as possible,

a. how many loads of wash will he be able to do?

b. what change should he request for his five-dollar bill? (Find all possible answers.)

CRANBERRY-APPLE JUICE

Nelson works for the G. Ale Bar Company, a chain of soda fountains. He is trying to create a special recipe to make a best-selling juice. For a taste test, he wants to prepare several 20-cup batches of different mixtures of pure apple juice with a cranberry-apple juice that is 50% apple and 50% cranberry.

Apple juice		Cranberry-apple		Mixture	
apple	cran	apple	cran	apple	cran
15	0	2.5	2.5	17.5	2.5
8	0	6	6	14	6
6	0	—	—	—	—
—	—	8	—	—	—
—	—	—	9.5	—	—
x	—	$0.50y$	—	$x+0.50y$	—

11. Copy and complete the table. Add several more numerical possibilities. (The last row is based on x cups of apple juice and y cups of cranberry-apple.)

12. What are the largest and smallest amounts of cranberry juice possible in one of Nelson's mixtures? What about apple juice? Explain.

13. For the mixture in the first row, what percent *of the total* is cranberry? (Be careful! You can't get the answer by dividing 2.5 by 17.5)

14. Add a **% cran** column to your table, and repeat problem 13 for all the rows.

15. What are the largest and smallest *percentages* of cranberry juice possible in one of Nelson's mixtures? What about apple juice? Explain.

16. Explain why the expression $x + 0.50y$ represents the total amount of apple juice in the mixture.

17. What is the expression for the total amount of cranberry juice in the mixture? Explain.

18. Explain why $x + y$ equals 20 for every possibility listed in the table.

19. What does the $x + 0.50y = 10$ mean in this situation? Is there an (x, y) pair that satisfies this equation? Explain.

For each equation, 20-25:

a. Interpret the equation in terms of this situation.

b. If possible, find a value of x and of y that satisfies the equation, given the constraint that x and y add up to 20.

20. $0.50y = 4$

21. $x + 0.50y = 15$

22. $x + 0.50y = 4$

23. $x + 0.5y = 11.5$

24. $x + 0.50y = 0.75(x + y)$

25. $x + 0.50y = 0.25(x + y)$

26. Which of the equations 20-25 were impossible to solve? Would they have been possible if the total amount had been 30 cups? Explain.

10.2 SOLUTIONS

of which is worth 25 cents. To find the total value of y quarters, one multiplies y by 25 to get $25y$.

b. number: $x + y$ value: $5x + 25y$

7. no

8. a. (75, 5) b. (80, 4)
c. not possible d. (10, 18)

9. a. $x + y = 80$ b. $x = 20y$
c. $x = y + 12$ d. $x + 8 = y$

10. a. $3(25) + 5 + 25 = 105$
$500/105 = 4.76$ He will be able to do 4 loads for \$4.20 of his \$5.00.

b. Each load is 4 quarters and 1 nickel. So four loads would require 16 quarters and 4 nickels, with 80 cents left over. The 80 cents could come in various combinations of coins. The combinations shown below assume that he wants his extra 80 cents in nickels and quarters, too. He could also request dimes or pennies, unless he wants to save the 80 cents in change for his next trip to the laundromat. (If there is a candy machine at the laundromat that takes a specific combination of coins, he may take that into account when deciding how he wants the 80 cents. However, candy machines are usually more flexible than washers and dryers.)

Nickels		Quarters		Total Coins	
no.	value	no.	value	no.	value
16	80	0	0	16	80
11	55	1	25	12	80
6	30	2	50	8	80
1	5	3	75	4	80

Assuming he wants only nickels and quarters, there are four possibilities:

nickels	quarters
20	16
15	17
10	18
5	19

(Solutions continued on page 526)

LESSON 10.3

Two Variables, Two Equations

You will need:

the Lab Gear 

MYSTERY CONTAINERS

The Lab Gear may help you solve this problem.

1. A crate contains two small containers and three large containers. The total weight of the crate is 16 pounds.

a. What are some possible weights of the small and the large containers? How many possible weights are there?

b. Find the weight of four small containers and six large containers.

c. Two containers are removed from the crate, and it is weighed again. Now it weighs ten pounds. Using this additional information, find possible weights for the small container and the large container. Comment on your answers.

ONE EQUATION, ONE CONSTRAINT

The workmat shows the equation

$$y + 4x = 12.$$

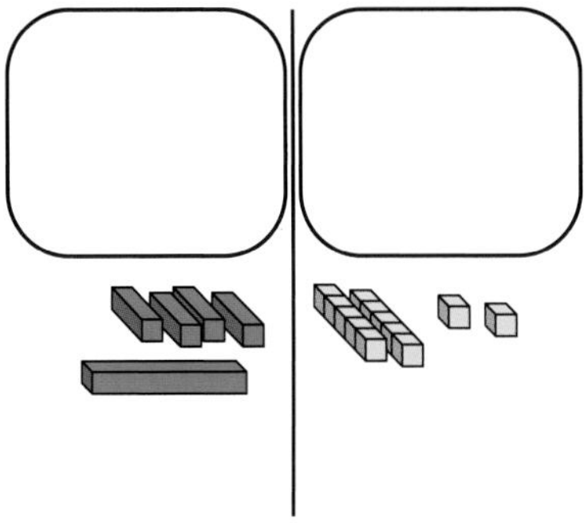

2. Using trial and error, find some values of x and y that make the equation true. (How many possible values are there?)

One of the (x, y) pairs satisfying this equation also satisfies the constraint, or condition, that y is twice x. If y is twice x, then each y-block can be replaced with two x-blocks.

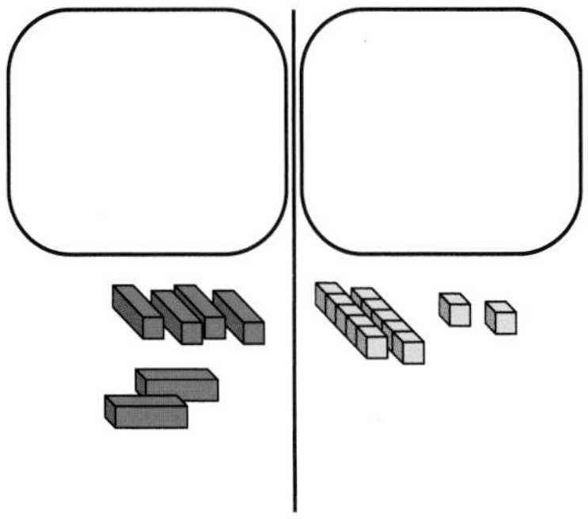

The resulting equation is $6x = 12$.

3. Solve for x in the equation above. Then find the (x, y) pair that satisfies both the equation $y + 4x = 12$ and the constraint that $y = 2x$.

For each problem, 4-7, model the equation on the workmat with the blocks. Then use the blocks to find an (x, y) pair that satisfies both the equation and the constraint. Check your final answers in the original equations.

4. $4x - 7 = y + 3$
Constraint: y is two more than x.

5. $2y + x = 5$
Constraint: x is six less than y.

6. $2x + y = 9$
Constraint: x is three more than y.

▼ 10.3
Two Variables, Two Equations

Core Sequence: 1-27

Suitable for Homework: 12-17, 26-27, 30-33

Useful for Assessment: 15, 17, 26-27

What this Lesson is About:

- Preview of simultaneous equations
- Use of the Lab Gear for simultaneous equations
- Solving for one of the variables
- Converting equations from standard form to slope-intercept form
- Using algebraic symbols to solve number problems
- Number of factors of a whole number

Again, do not teach any methods for solving simultaneous equations. At most, provide hints. Solving techniques will be taught formally in the next lesson, and that lesson will have its maximum impact if students have already been thinking creatively about the problem of solving simultaneous equations.

MYSTERY CONTAINERS

Let students solve problem 1 by any method. Using the Lab Gear may help, with x for the small container and y for the large one (or vice versa). The size of the blocks is, of course, irrelevant.

Problem 1c really is three problems in one, since either two large containers, two small containers, or one of each were removed. One solution (with a negative weight for the large container) is not plausible.

ONE EQUATION, ONE CONSTRAINT

This section is harder than the next one, since students have to translate the "constraint" into an equation. Let them struggle with this, and don't teach equation solving methods to save time. The time spent pays off in the next section, since students have a better understanding of the two equations as conditions to be satisfied.

Insist on students checking their solutions by substituting the values in the original equation.

10.3 SOLUTIONS

1. a. Answers vary. Sample answers:

weight of each small container (lbs)	weight of each large container (lbs)
0.5	5
2	4
3.5	3

There is an infinite number of possibilities.

b. Let x = the weight of each small container
y = the weight of each large container
$4x + 6y$ = the total weight of the containers
Since it is given that $2x + 3y = 16$, it must be true that $4x + 6y = 32$. So the weight of 4 small and 6 large is 32.

c. The small container weighs 2 pounds and the large container 4 pounds. Because of the additional information, there is no longer an infinite number of answers. There is only one answer.

2.

x	y
0	12
1	8
2	4
3	0

3. $x = 2$, $y = 4$

4. $x = 4$, $y = 6$

5. $x = -2\frac{1}{3}$, $y = 3\frac{2}{3}$

6. $x = 4$, $y = 1$

SIMULTANEOUS EQUATIONS

Do not teach any particular method. You can give hints along the way, for example by reminding students that they can add two equal things to both sides of the equation, regardless of how strange those equal things look. Students will invent some very interesting ways of solving these equations. Don't interfere too much!

Let students work with or without the Lab Gear, but if both approaches are used in one group, encourage discussion between group members. At the very least, students should make sure they get the same answers as each other.

MIND READING

Again, do not teach any strategy for problems 12-14. Instead, ask students to share strategies with their groups and with the class.

REVIEW/PREVIEW *EVALUATING*

Problems 16-17 preview equivalent equations, and so are essential to the development of the ideas in this chapter. Some class discussion of problem 17 in particular could be helpful as preparation for the next lesson.

REVIEW/PREVIEW *SOLVING FOR y*

If your students are very comfortable with algebraic manipulation, you may assign this for homework and do it without the Lab Gear. However most classes would benefit from using the blocks, at least initially.

This section serves as preview in two ways. On the one hand, solving for y is a necessary part of the "substitution" approach to equation solving, which will be formally introduced in Lesson 4. On the other hand, and what is more important, the problems provide a bridge between standard form and slope-intercept form for linear equations. This is particularly useful to help preview Lesson 5.

7. $2y + x = 4$
Constraint: x and y add up to six.

For each problem you just solved, the constraint could have been written as an equation. For example, the constraint that the sum of x and y is six can be written $x + y = 6$. This means that in each of problems 4-7, you found an (x, y) pair that *satisfied both of two given equations*. We say that you *solved* a system of simultaneous equations.

SIMULTANEOUS EQUATIONS

Solve each system of simultaneous equations. If you want to use the Lab Gear, begin by modeling the first equation with the blocks. Then use the second equation to substitute blocks for the y-blocks or for the x-blocks. Check your answers.

8. $\begin{cases} 2x - y = 2 \\ y = 3x \end{cases}$ **9.** $\begin{cases} 4x + y = 10 \\ y = 6x - 20 \end{cases}$

10. $\begin{cases} x - 4y = 23 \\ x = -5y - 4 \end{cases}$ **11.** $\begin{cases} 3y + 2x = 7 \\ 3y = 4x - 5 \end{cases}$

MIND READING

What numbers am I thinking of?

12. Their sum is 7. Their difference is 3.

13. Their sum is 18. The second is twice as large as the first.

14. The first minus the second is 3. Twice the first, minus twice the second is 6.

15. One of problems 12-14 has more than one answer. How many answers does it have? Why?

REVIEW/PREVIEW *EVALUATING*

16. Two (x, y) pairs that satisfy the equation $2x + 3y = 16$ are given in the table below. Copy and complete the table.

x	y	$2x + 3y$	$x + y$	$x - y$	$4x + 6y$	$x + 1.5y$
-1	6	16	5	—	—	8
2	4	16	—	-2	32	—
—	5	16	—	—	—	—
—	-6	16	—	—	—	—
—	—	16	—	—	—	—
-4	—	16	—	—	—	—

17. Study the table you made. In which columns are all the values the same? Why?

REVIEW/PREVIEW *SOLVING FOR y*

Set up these problems with the Lab Gear, and rearrange the blocks so that y is by itself on one side of the equation. Write equations to show your steps. In some cases, you will need to finish the problem without the blocks.

18. $-4x + y = 6$ **19.** $4x + 2y = 10$

20. $-6x + y = 4$ **21.** $-6x + 3y = 9$

22. $6x - 3y = 12$ **23.** $x + 2y = 8$

24. $x - y = 1$ **25.** $6x - 5y = 0$

26. Explain how to solve for y (without the Lab Gear), with the help of an example.

27. **Generalization** Solve for y.
$Ax + By = C$

10.3 SOLUTIONS

7. $x = 8, y = -2$
8. $x = -2, y = -6$
9. $x = 3, y = -2$
10. $x = 11, y = -3$
11. $x = 2, y = 1$
12. 5 and 2
13. 6 and 12
14. There is an infinite number of answers. Any pair of numbers that has a difference of 3 will work.
15. #14 has an infinite number of answers. The first and second conditions are equivalent and can be represented by equivalent equations; hence, we have only one constraint. Any (x, y) pair satisfying $x - y = 3$ will also satisfy $2x - 2y = 6$.
16. For some table entries, answers will vary. These are shown in italics.

x	y	$2x + 3y$	$x + y$	$x - y$	$4x + 6y$	$x + 1.5y$
-1	6	16	5	-7	32	8
2	4	16	6	-2	32	8
0.5	5	16	5.5	-4.5	32	8
17	-6	16	11	23	32	8
8	*0*	16	*8*	*8*	32	8
-4	8	16	4	-12	32	8

17. The value of $2x + 3y$ was given to be 16. Hence $4x + 6y$ must be 32 since $2(2x + 3y) = 4x + 6y$ and $2(16) = 32$. Also, $x + 1.5y$ must be 8 since $0.5(2x + 3y) = x + 1.5y$ and $0.5(16) = 8$.
18. $y = 4x + 6$ 19. $y = -2x + 5$
20. $y = 6x + 4$ 21. $y = 2x + 3$
22. $y = 2x - 4$ 23. $y = -0.5x + 4$

DISCOVERY *CONSECUTIVE NUMBERS*

28. Compute, and look for a pattern.
a. $1 \cdot 2 \cdot 3 + 2$
b. $2 \cdot 3 \cdot 4 + 3$
c. $4 \cdot 5 \cdot 6 + 5$
d. $(5 - 1) \cdot 5 \cdot (5 + 1) + 5$
e. $9 \cdot 10 \cdot 11 + 10$
f. $(10 - 1) \cdot 10 \cdot (10 + 1) + 10$

29. Use algebra to explain the pattern.

30. The product of three consecutive numbers divided by their sum is 1. What are the numbers?

31. Repeat problem 30, if the product divided by the sum is the following:
a. 5 b. 16

32. What can you say about the middle number if the product of three consecutive numbers divided by their sum is a whole number?

DISCOVERY *NINE FACTORS*

33. **Project** The number 1 has one whole number factor, itself; 2 has two factors, 1 and 2; 3 has two factors; and 4 has three factors. (What are they?) Find some numbers having *nine factors*. Explain.

DISCOVERY *CONSECUTIVE NUMBERS*

These problems can be solved by looking for numerical patterns. However, greater insight is attained by using algebraic symbol manipulation. If you do problems 28-29 in class, it will help prepare students for problems 30-32. (Or you can assign 28-29 and 30-32 on different days.)

DISCOVERY *NINE FACTORS*

This is a substantial, *problem-of-the-week*-sized problem. Do not expect immediate solution, and do not assign it if you cannot give students sufficient time for a full investigation.

Homework on this problem would be most effective if there were some group and class discussion of the issues that arise during the work.

10.3 SOLUTIONS

24. $y = x - 1$
25. $y = \frac{6}{5}x$
26. Answers will vary. (This should be discussed in class.)
27. $Ax + By = C$
$By = -Ax + C$
$y = -\frac{A}{B}x + \frac{C}{B}$
28. a. 8
b. 27
c. 125
d. 125
e. 1000
f. 1000
29. $(x - 1)(x)(x + 1) + x = x^3$
30. 1, 2, and 3 or -1, -2, and -3
31. a. 3, 4, 5 or -3, -4, -5
b. 6, 7, 8 or -6, -7, -8
32. The middle number cannot be 0, because the denominator would be -1 + 0 + 1, or 0. Division by 0 is undefined.
33. Sample answer: The number 36 has nine factors: 1, 2, 3, 4, 6, 9, 12, 18, 36.

▼ 10.4 Solving Systems

Core Sequence: 1-23

Suitable for Homework: 9, 10, 16-23

Useful for Assessment: 13, 17

What this Lesson is About:

- Solving simultaneous equations by substitution
- Solving simultaneous equations by linear combinations

In this lesson you will finally teach students techniques for solving equations. Since many of these ideas will have already emerged in the previous lessons, this should not be too difficult.

As usual, the important thing is for students to understand the underlying concepts. Programmable calculators and mathematical computer software make solving systems of equations of any size easy, with the help of matrices. Systems having two variables can easily be solved graphically. (We will use that approach in Lesson 6.) What must be achieved at this level is a sense of what it means to solve systems of equations.

Equivalent equations were introduced in Chapter 6, Lesson 4, in the context of graphing. (Equivalent equations have the same graph.) They were previewed informally at the end of Lesson 3.

LESSON 10.4

Solving Systems

You will need:

the Lab Gear

Definitions: In real-world applications we often need to find a solution that satisfies two or more equations simultaneously. We call the group of equations a *system of simultaneous equations*. To *solve a system* means to find the (x, y) pairs that satisfy every equation in the group.

In this course, you will learn techniques for solving systems of two equations. In later courses you will learn how to solve systems of more than two equations.

In an earlier chapter, you studied equivalent equations. *Equivalent equations have all the same solutions.*

1. Find some (x, y) solutions to these equations.
   a. $y = 2x + 6$
   b. $3y = 6x + 18$
2. Use algebra to show that the two equations in problem 1 are equivalent.

SOLVING TECHNIQUES: SUBSTITUTION

Example: Solve the system.

$$\begin{cases} 5x + 3y = -15 & (A) \\ y = 2x + 6 & (B) \end{cases}$$

The figure shows how to model the system on two workmats.

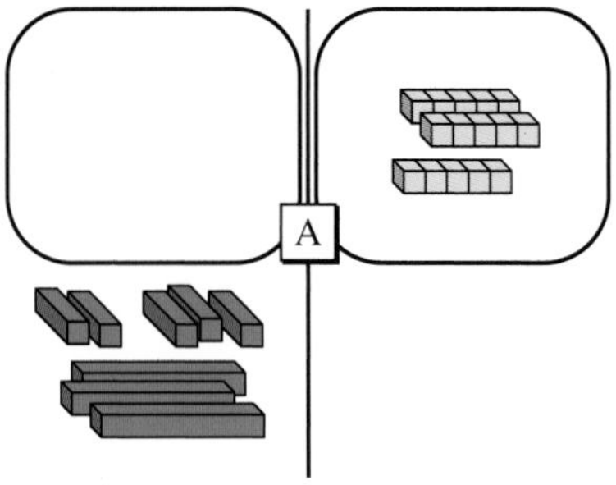

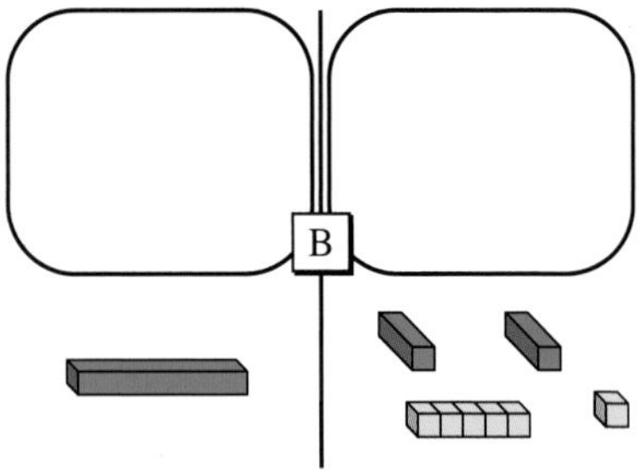

By multiplying both sides of Equation (B) by 3, you get Equation (C), which is equivalent to Equation B.

$$3y = 6x + 18 \quad (C)$$

The figure shows how to model Equation (C) on the second workmat.

10.4 SOLUTIONS

1. Answers vary. Samples:
   a. (0, 6) (-1, 4) (2, 10)
   b. (0, 6) (-1, 4) (2, 10)
2. Multiply both sides of $y = 2x + 6$ by 3 to get $3y = 6x + 18$.

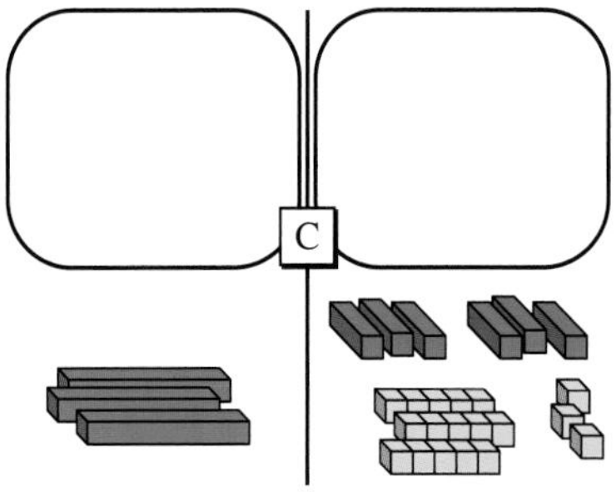

Since $3y = 6x + 18$, we can replace the $3y$ in the first equation with $6x + 18$ to get a new equation that has only x-blocks and yellow blocks.

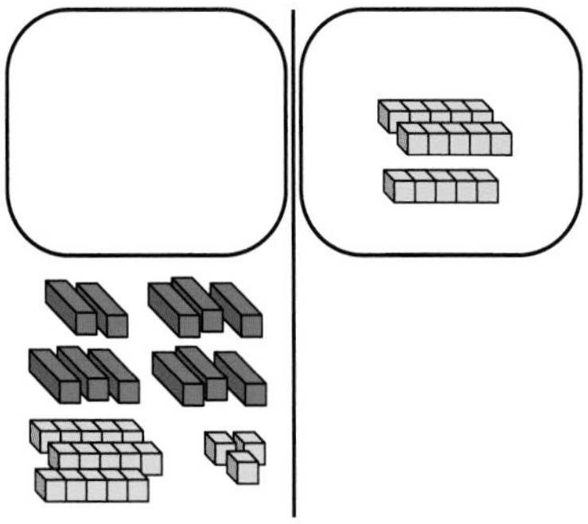

3. Write the new equation. Then solve for x.

4. a. Substitute the value of x into Equation (B) and solve for y.
b. Substitute this (x, y) pair into Equation (A). If it doesn't satisfy the equation, check your work to find your mistake.
c. Write the (x, y) pair that is the solution to the system.

Solve each system, 5-10. If you use the Lab Gear, you may set up the first equation with the blocks. Then use the second equation to eliminate the x- or y-blocks by substitution. In some cases, you may first need to write an equation equivalent to the second equation.

5. $\begin{cases} 5y - 4x = -9 \\ 5y = 3x - 7 \end{cases}$ **6.** $\begin{cases} 5x + 3y = -15 \\ y = 2x + 6 \end{cases}$

7. $\begin{cases} 5x - 3y = -29 \\ x = 2 - 2y \end{cases}$ **8.** $\begin{cases} 2x + 3y = 9 \\ 4x = 6 - 2y \end{cases}$

9. $\begin{cases} 4x - y = 5 \\ 3y = 6x + 3 \end{cases}$ **10.** $\begin{cases} 6x - 2y = -16 \\ 4x + y = 1 \end{cases}$

SOLVING TECHNIQUES: SUBSTITUTION

Using the Lab Gear to introduce this idea helps students see what substitution is about. However, do not insist that they use the blocks when solving for themselves.

The approach to substitution presented here is slightly different from tradition. Instead of solving for y in the example, we solve for $3y$. This approach helps prepare students for the more powerful linear combinations technique.

SOLVING TECHNIQUES: LINEAR COMBINATIONS

SYSTEMATIC PRACTICE

Students are guided through increasingly difficult systems. Do not use the Lab Gear after problem 12.

10.4 SOLUTIONS

3. $11x + 18 = -15$
$11x = -33$
$x = -3$

4. a. $y = 0$
c. $(-3, 0)$

5. $(2, -\frac{1}{5})$

6. $(-2, 2)$

7. $(-4, 3)$

8. $(0, 3)$

9. $(3, 7)$

10. $(-1, 5)$

SOLVING TECHNIQUES: LINEAR COMBINATIONS

Here is another technique for solving systems.

Example: Solve the system.

$$\begin{cases} x + 2y = 11 & \text{(A)} \\ x - 2y = 3 & \text{(B)} \end{cases}$$

The figure shows two workmats, with one equation modeled on each.

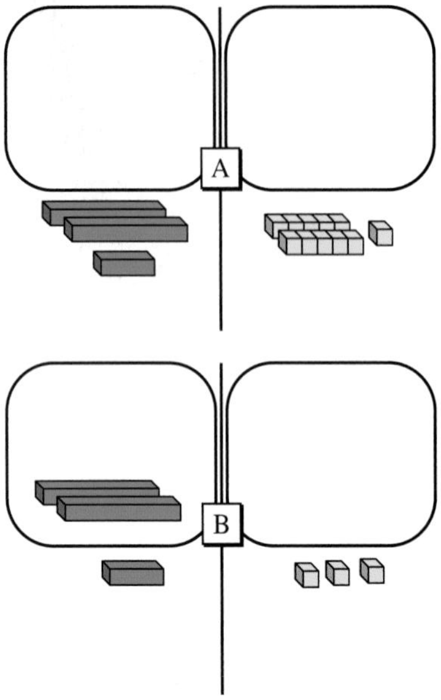

You can add equal quantities to both sides of Equation (A) to get an equivalent equation. For example, you could add 3 to both sides, or even $x - 2y$ to both sides. Also, since Equation (B) says that $x - 2y = 3$, you could add 3 to one side and $x - 2y$ to the other side, as shown on the figure.

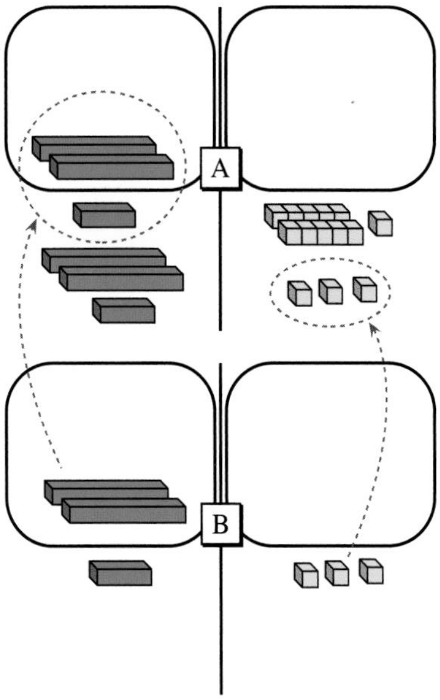

11. Write the equation shown in equation (A) in the figure. Simplify and solve for x. (What happened to y?)

12. Find the (x, y) pair that is the solution to the system. Check by substituting into both of the original equations.

Solving the system in the example was easier than solving most systems, since when you added one equation to the other there were no y's left. The next example is more difficult.

Example: Solve the system.

$$\begin{cases} 2y - 6x = 16 & \text{(A)} \\ 4x + y = 1 & \text{(B)} \end{cases}$$

10.4 SOLUTIONS

11. $2x + 2y - 2y = 14$
$2x = 14$
$x = 7$
The y's dropped out because $2y - 2y = 0$.

12. (7, 2)
Check by substituting:
$7 + 2(2) = 11$
$7 + 4 = 11$
$11 = 11$ ✓
$7 - 2(2) = 3$
$7 - 4 = 3$
$3 = 3$ ✓

By multiplying both sides of Equation (B) by -2, you get Equation (C), which is equivalent to Equation (B). Here is the new system, which is equivalent to the original.

$$\begin{cases} 2y - 6x = 16 & \text{(A)} \\ -8x - 2y = -2 & \text{(C)} \end{cases}$$

13. Why was Equation (B) multiplied by -2?

14. Solve the system. Show your work. Check your answers by substituting into both equations of the original system.

Mr. Richards gave the class this hard system to solve.

$$\begin{cases} 3x + 5y = 17 & \text{(A)} \\ 2x + 3y = 11 & \text{(B)} \end{cases}$$

Charlotte suggested multiplying the first equation by 3 and the second equation by -5 to get a new system.

15. Use Charlotte's method to write a new system. Solve the system and check your answer.

Definition: The equation you get by adding multiples of the two equations together is called a *linear combination* of the two equations.

Leroy thought it would be easier if they got a linear combination by multiplying by smaller numbers. He suggested multiplying the first equation by -2 and the second equation by 3.

16. Use Leroy's method to write a new system. Solve the system.

17. Compare the two ways you solved this problem. Which do you prefer? Can you think of a third way? Explain.

SYSTEMATIC PRACTICE

Solve these systems. Some have one (x, y) solution. Others have an infinite number of solutions, or no solution.

18. $\begin{cases} 5x + 7y = 1 \\ x + 7 = 1 \end{cases}$

19. $\begin{cases} 3 - x = 4y \\ x = -2y - 9 \end{cases}$

20. $\begin{cases} 8x - 4y = 0 \\ 2x = y \end{cases}$

21. $\begin{cases} y = 4 + x \\ y = 7x + 10 \end{cases}$

22. $\begin{cases} 4x - y = 2 \\ y = 4x + 1 \end{cases}$

23. $\begin{cases} 6x - 2y = -16 \\ 4x + y = 1 \end{cases}$

10.4 SOLUTIONS

13. Equation B was multiplied by -2 so that the y terms in the two equations will be opposites of one another. The sum of opposites is 0, so there will be no y terms in the equation obtained from adding Equation A to Equation C.
14. (-1, 5)
15. The two new equations are $9x + 15y = 51$ and $-10x - 15y = -55$. The solution is (4, 1).
16. The two new equations are $-6x - 10y = -34$ and $6x + 9y = 33$. The solution is (4, 1).
17. Answers will vary. Other ways might include: (1) making tables of values for each equation and finding the (x, y) pair common to both tables (tedious!) (2) solving for x or y in one equation and substituting into the other (messy!), or (3) graphing both equations on a graphing calculator and finding the point of intersection (easy, as long as you've got a graphing calculator).
18. $(-6, 4\frac{3}{7})$
19. (-21, 6)
20. True for all ordered pairs satisfying $2x = y$.
21. (-1, 3)
22. No solution. Solving for y in the first equation, we see that $y = 4x - 2$. It is impossible for a number to equal $4x - 2$ and $4x + 1$ at the same time.
23. (-1, 5)

THINKING WRITING

10.A Juice Experiments

Core Sequence: 1-16

Suitable for Homework: 1-16

Useful for Assessment: 16

What this Assignment is About:

- Using tables and equations to solve mixture problems

This is a challenging lesson, but it has been thoroughly previewed. If your class had trouble with Lessons 1-4, you may want to start this assignment in class. Otherwise, students should be able to tackle it as homework.

THINKING WRITING

10.A Juice Experiments

Nelson is continuing his quest for the perfect juice. You have been hired as a consultant to the G. Ale Bar Company to assist him. He ran out of apple juice and is making the 20-cup batches for the taste test using two kinds of juice.

Fruity Flavor: 50% cranberry and 50% apple

Berry Blend: 20% cranberry and 80% apple

Fruity Flavor		Berry Blend		Mixture	
apple	**cran**	**apple**	**cran**	**apple**	**cran**
5	5	8	2	13	7
7.5	7.5	4	1	11.5	8.5
$0.50x$	—	$0.80y$	—	—	—

1. Make a table like the one above. List at least six possible mixtures. Add two columns to the table, showing the percents of cranberry and apple in the mixture.
2. Find the minimum and the maximum amount of cranberry juice possible in one of Nelson's mixtures. Then find the minimum and the maximum *percent*.
3. Repeat problem 2 for apple juice.

How many cups of Fruity Flavor and Berry Blend would you need to use to make 20 cups each of the cranberry-apple mixtures in 4-7? (Some are impossible.)

4. 30% cranberry, 70% apple
5. 25% cranberry, 75% apple
6. 10% cranberry, 90% apple
7. Choose your own percentages.
8. In the last line of the table, what is the meaning of x and y?
9. For Nelson's mixtures, what is the sum of x and y?

For each equation, 10-15:

a. Write, in words, an interpretation of it in terms of the situation.

b. If possible, find a value of x and of y that satisfies the equation, keeping in mind the answer to problem 9.

10. $0.50x + 0.20y = 7$
11. $0.50x + 0.80y = 8$
12. $0.50x + 0.80y = 0.25(x + y)$
13. $0.50x + 0.20y = 0.25(x + y)$
14. $x + y = 25$
15. $x - y = 10$
16. Report Write an illustrated report summarizing the results of this investigation. Your report should include, but not be limited to, answers to the following questions:
    - What determines the maximum and the minimum amount of each kind of juice possible in the mixture?
    - What determines the maximum and the minimum percent of each kind of juice in the mixture?
    - How could you use systems of equations to solve problems like 4 through 6? Give examples.

10.A SOLUTIONS

1.

Fruity Flavor (x)		Berry Blend (y)		Mixture			
apple	cran	apple	cran	apple	cran	%apple	%cran
6	6	6.4	1.6	12.4	7.6	62	38
7	7	4.8	1.2	11.8	8.2	59	41
1	1	14.4	3.6	15.4	4.6	77	23
2	2	12.8	3.2	14.8	5.2	74	26
10	10	0	0	10	10	50	50
0	0	16	4	16	4	80	20

2. 4 cups of cranberry juice is the minimum amount possible.
   10 cups of cranberry juice is the maximum amount possible.
   20% is the minimum percentage of cranberry juice in the mixture.
   50% is the maximum percentage of cranberry juice in the mixture.
3. 10 cups of apple juice is the minimum amount.
   16 cups of apple juice is the maximum amount.
   50% is the minimum percentage of apple juice possible.
   80% is the maximum percentage of apple juice possible.
4. 6 and 2/3 cups of Fruity Flavor
   13 and 1/3 cups of Berry Blend
5. 3 and 1/3 cups of Fruity Flavor
   16 and 2/3 cups of Berry Blend
6. Not possible. See the answers for problems 2 and 3.
7. Answers will vary.
8. x is the number of cups of Fruity Flavor and y is the number of cups of Berry Blend in the total mixture.
9. $x + y = 20$. The sum is 20.
10. a. There are 7 cups of cranberry juice in the mixture of x cups of Fruity Flavor and y cups of Berry Blend.
    b. (10, 10)
11. a. There are 8 cups of apple juice in the 20-cup batch of x cups of Fruity Flavor and y cups of Berry Blend.
    b. This is impossible. The minimum number of cups of apple juice is 10 cups. (See #3.)
12. a. Apple juice is 25% of the total 20-cup batch of juice, or there are 5 cups of apple juice in the 20-cup batch.
    b. Impossible. Apple juice cannot be less than 50% of the juice.
13. a. Cranberry juice is 25% (5 cups) of the 20-cup batch.
    b. (3 and 1/3, 16 and 2/3)

(Solutions continued on page 527)

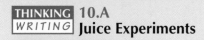

LESSON 10.5

Standard Form

You will need:

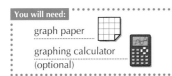

- graph paper
- graphing calculator (optional)

Definitions: An equation of the form $Ax + By = C$ is called the *standard form* of a linear equation. A, B, and C are the *parameters* for the equation.

In this lesson you will investigate how the values of the parameters affect the graphs of linear equations in standard form.

INTERCEPTS

Do not use graphing calculators for this section. These equations of lines are in standard form. For each equation:

a. Find the parameters A, B, and C.
b. Find the x-intercept and the y-intercept.
c. Graph the line by plotting the intercepts.

1. $3x + 2y = 12$ **2.** $3x - 2y = 18$

3. $x + y = 6$ **4.** $x - y = 6$

5. $-3x + 4y = 10$

6. **Generalization**

a. Explain how to find the x-intercept and the y-intercept of the line whose equation is $Ax + By = C$.
b. A fast way to graph a line is by finding and plotting the intercepts. Show how to use this technique to graph a line of the form $Ax + By = C$. (Choose specific values for A, B, and C.)

7. a. Write the equation of a line that has x-intercept (6, 0). Graph it and find its y-intercept.
b. Write the equation of a line that has y-intercept (0, -4). Graph it and find its x-intercept.
c. Write the equation of a line that has y-intercept (0, 4) *and* x-intercept (-6, 0).

8. **Generalization** Show how to find the equation of a line having intercepts $(p, 0)$ and $(0, q)$.

THE CASE WHEN $A = B$

9. a. Graph $x + y = 10$.
b. On the same axes, graph $2x + 2y = 10$.
c. In the equations you graphed in parts (a) and (b), what are A, B, and C?
d. When you doubled A and B in the equation but left C the same, how did the graph change?

10. Draw the graphs of at least two other equations of the form $Ax + By = C$ for which A is equal to B and $C = 10$. Label the graphs with their equations.

11. Compare all the graphs you drew in problems 9-10. (What stayed the same, and what changed? How do the graphs compare in steepness?)

12. a. Graph $x + y = 4$.
b. On the same axes, graph $2x + 2y = 8$.
c. In the equations you graphed in parts (a) and (b), what are A, B, and C?

13.
a. When you doubled A, B, and C, how did the graph change?
b. If you triple A, B, and C, what will the equation be? How do you think the graph will change? Explain.

10.5 SOLUTIONS

	Parameters A	B	C	x-intercept	y-intercept
1.	3	2	12	(4, 0)	(0, 6)
2.	3	-2	18	(6, 0)	(0, -9)
3.	1	1	6	(6, 0)	(0, 6)
4.	1	-1	6	(6, 0)	(0, -6)
5.	-3	4	10	$(-3\frac{1}{3}, 0)$	$(0, 2\frac{1}{2})$

1. c.

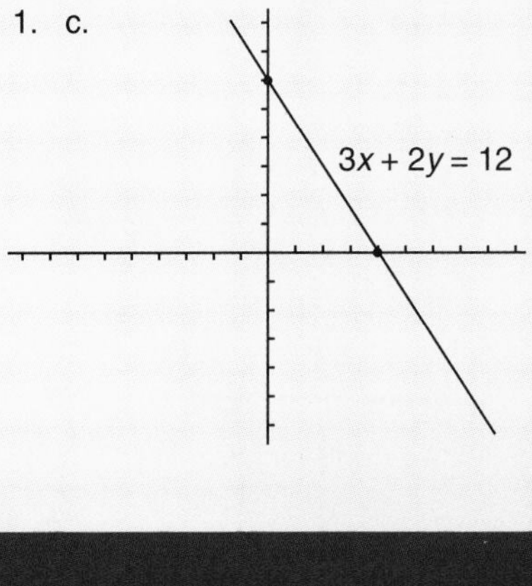

2. c.

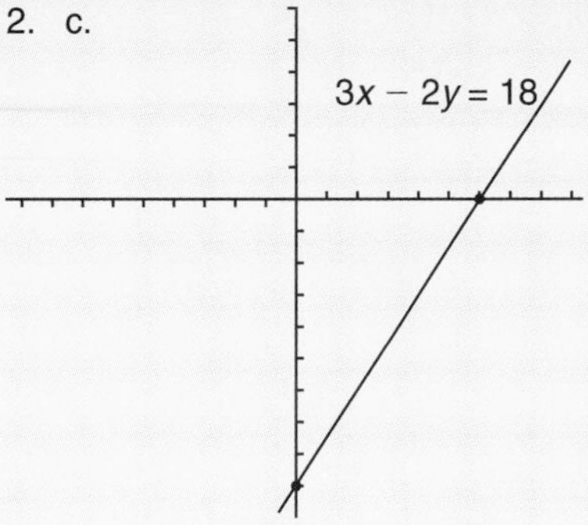

3. c.

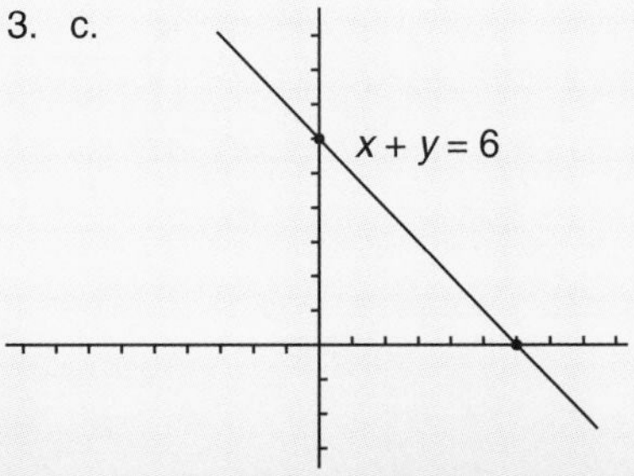

▼ 10.5 Standard Form

Core Sequence: 1-15, 23

Suitable for Homework: 1-13, 23-27

Useful for Assessment: 6, 8, 11, 13, 15, 18, 21-23

What this Lesson is About:

- Review of x- and y-intercepts
- Quick graphing of linear equations given in standard form
- Effect of the parameters on the graph of $Ax + By = C$
- A number pattern
- Review of sides of squares

INTERCEPTS

This section reviews the important idea that to find the x-intercept, you set y equal to 0, and to find the y-intercept, you set x equal to 0. Secondarily, this serves as a graphing shortcut for lines whose equations are given in standard form.

Students also learn to find the equation of a line, if given its intercepts. If this section is done at home, make sure to have some class time to discuss problems 6 and 8. The latter especially may be difficult for some students. Do not require students to memorize any formulas that result from it. Instead, have students who solved it share their approach with their group and with the class.

THE CASE WHEN $A = B$

This section serves as a transition from the case where $A = B = 1$, which students have worked on under the name of "constant sums" graphs, and the general case where A and B are independent of each other. In a way, this section previews **Varying C** below.

VARYING A
VARYING B
VARYING C

*These sections will work best if students have access to a graphing calculator that will accept equations in the form $Ax + By = C$. If not, you should skip the optional part of the lesson, because it is much too long and tedious to be done by hand by every student. Alternatively, use one of the following strategies:

- **Without an electronic calculator:** All groups should do the first two sections. Then have each group do just one section (**Varying** ***A***, **Varying** ***B***, or **Varying** ***C***) and present their findings to the class.
- **With an electronic calculator that requires you to enter equations of functions:** You have two options, both based on the Preview **Solving for** ***y*** located after Lesson 3.
  - ◊ Have students work in teams, as suggested above, and solve each equation for *y*, in order to enter it into the graphing calculator.
  - ◊ Have students enter a program to query the user on the value of the parameters *A*, *B*, and *C*, and graph the corresponding linear equation. Such a program would be based on the formula discovered at the end of Lesson 3.
- **With a teacher's "demonstration" electronic calculator:** You can enhance and support any of the above approaches, or run the lesson as a whole-class guided discovery.

To specify a line uniquely, we need to know only two parameters, for example the *M* and the *B* in $y = Mx + B$. If we change the parameters, the line changes. However, in the equation $Ax + By = C$, there are three parameters. What's going on? As the students will discover in this lesson, and as was seen in previous lessons, you can get the same line with different values of *A*, *B*, and *C*. That's because what really matters are the two ratios *A*/*C* and *B*/*C*. (Discuss this with your class only if it comes up naturally.)

Your goals should be to help students explore what happens as they change the parameters, and write clearly about what they have discovered. This level of thinking about linear equations helps provide the conceptual framework to understand the graphical solution of systems of equations better, as well as to broaden and deepen students' grasp of linear relationships.

VARYING A

14. a. Graph $x + 2y = 5$.
b. Graph $2x + 2y = 5$ on the same axes.
c. Draw several more graphs, changing the value of *A*, leaving *B* equal to 2, and *C* equal to 5. Use both positive and negative values for *A*.

15. Compare all the graphs you drew in problem 14.
a. When you changed the value of *A* in the equation, what features of the graph changed and what stayed the same? Did the steepness change? Did the intercepts change?
b. How are the graphs having a positive value of *A* different from the graphs having a negative value of *A*?
c. Is it possible to pick a value of *A* so that the graph will be a horizontal line? A vertical line? Explain.

16. Show what you think the following graphs would look like. You don't have to graph them accurately, but you should make a rough sketch and explain your work.
a. $500x + 2y = 5$
b. $-500x + 2y = 5$
c. $0.01x + 2y = 5$
d. $-0.01x + 2y = 5$

VARYING B

17. a. Graph $2x + y = 8$.
b. Graph $2x + 2y = 8$ on the same axes.
c. Draw several more graphs, changing the value of *B*, leaving *A* equal to 2, and *C* equal to 8. Use both positive and negative values for *B*.

18. Compare all the graphs you drew in problem 17.
a. When you changed the value of *B* in the equation, what features of the graph changed and what stayed the same? Did the steepness change? Did the intercepts change?
b. How are the graphs having a positive value of *B* different from the graphs having a negative value of *B*?
c. Is it possible to pick a value of *B* so that the graph will be a horizontal line? A vertical line? Explain.

19. Show what you think the following graphs would look like. You don't have to graph them accurately, but you should make a rough sketch and explain your work.
a. $2x + 100y = 8$
b. $2x - 100y = 8$
c. $2x + 0.02y = 8$
d. $2x - 0.02y = 8$

VARYING C

20. Where do you think the graph of $3x + 2y = 5$ will intersect the graph of $3x + 2y = 6$? You may want to check your prediction by graphing.

21. Describe what will happen to the graph of $3x + 2y = 6$ when you change the value of *C* but keep *A* and *B* constant. What will change and what will stay the same? Make several graphs to convince yourself that your answers are correct.

22. Report Write a report summarizing what you learned in this lesson. Explain how the values of the parameters *A*, *B*, and *C* affect the graph of $Ax + By = C$, specifically its slope and intercept. Use examples.

10.5 SOLUTIONS

4. c.

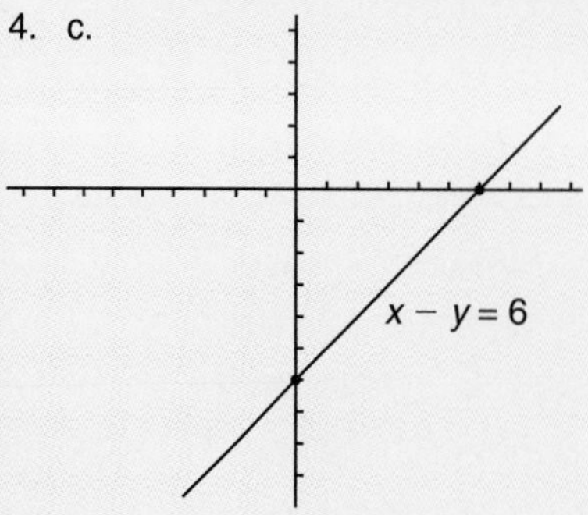

5. c.

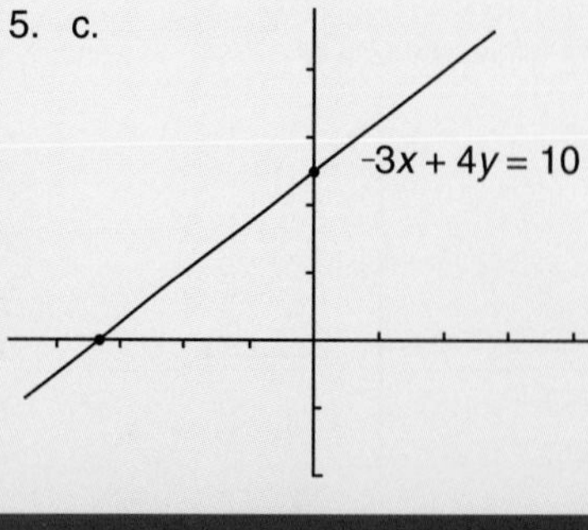

6. a. The *x*-intercept is the value of *x* when $y = 0$. Substitute 0 for *y* in $Ax + By = C$ and solve for *x*.
$Ax + B(0) = C$
$Ax + 0 = C$
$Ax = C$
$x = -\frac{C}{A}$
The *y*-intercept is the value of *y* when $x = 0$. Substitute 0 for *x* in $Ax + By = C$ and solve for *y*.
$A(0) + By = C$
$0 + By = C$
$By = C$
$y = -\frac{C}{B}$
b. Answers will vary. Sample: To graph $3x + 4y = 12$, find the *x*-intercepts and *y*-intercepts. $x = \frac{12}{3} = 4$ and $y = \frac{12}{4} = 3$. Plot (4, 0) and (0, 3) and draw the line.

7. a. Answers will vary. Sample:
$x + 2y = 6$ *y*-intercept is (0, 3)

DISCOVERY *DIFFERENCES OF PERFECT SQUARES*

23. Project The number 17 can be written as the difference of the squares of whole numbers, $9^2 - 8^2$. Which other whole numbers can be written as the difference of two squares of whole numbers? Which cannot? Look for patterns, and try to explain what you discover.

REVIEW *SIDES OF SQUARES*

24. The length of a side of a square is given. Find the area of the square.

a. $\sqrt{2}$ b. $2 + \sqrt{2}$
c. $2 - \sqrt{2}$ d. $2\sqrt{2}$
e. $\sqrt{2}/2$ f. $2/\sqrt{2}$

25. The side lengths of two squares are given. Which of the two squares has the larger area? Explain how you know.

a. $\sqrt{10} - \sqrt{5}$ and $\sqrt{5}$
b. $2\sqrt{8}$ and $\sqrt{16}$

26. Which has the larger area, or are they the same?

a. a rectangle with sides $\sqrt{2}$ and $\sqrt{5}$ or a square with side $\sqrt{10}$
b. a rectangle with sides $\sqrt{4}$ and $\sqrt{8}$ or a square with side $2\sqrt{2}$

27. Which has the larger perimeter, or are they the same?

a. a rectangle with sides $\sqrt{10}$ and $\sqrt{5}$ or a square with side $2\sqrt{5}$
b. a rectangle with sides $2 + 2\sqrt{2}$ and $\sqrt{2}$ or a square with sides $2 + \sqrt{2}$

DISCOVERY ***DIFFERENCES OF PERFECT SQUARES***

Only odd numbers and multiples of four can be written as a difference of squares. (In some cases, this can be done in more than one way.) This can be explained algebraically as follows:

If $n = a^2 - b^2$, then $n = (a + b)(a - b)$. We have two possible cases.

- If a and b are both even or both odd, then $(a + b)$ and $(a - b)$ are both even, and therefore n is a multiple of four.
- If one of a or b is even, and the other odd, then $(a + b)$ and $(a - b)$ are both odd, and n must be odd.

(This is too difficult for students to discover, though some may be able to understand the argument if led to it through specific examples.)

Students may discover that odd numbers are equal to the difference of the squares of consecutive numbers on either side of half of the original number, as in the example given in the statement of the problem.

Though it is more difficult, they may also notice the fact that multiples of four are equal to the difference of the squares of the number preceding or following the number that is one fourth of the original number. For example, $12 = 4^2 - 2^2$. (4 and 2 are on either side of 3 which is 12/4.)

REVIEW ***SIDES OF SQUARES***

This section reviews radicals and their use, in the context of the geometric meaning of square root.

10.5 SOLUTIONS

b. Answers will vary. Sample: $2x - 4y = 16$ x-intercept is (8, 0)
c. $-2x + 3y = 12$

8. The equation of a line with intercepts $(p, 0)$ and $(0, q)$ is $qx + py = pq$. Explanations of how to find the equation will vary.

9. a. & b.

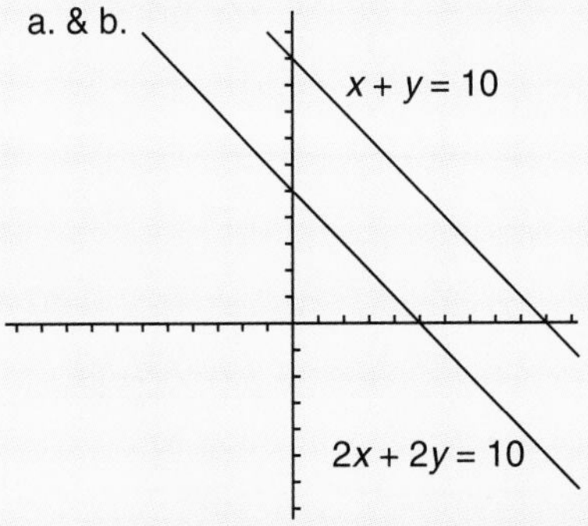

c. For $x + y = 10$, $A = 1$, $B = 1$, $C = 10$
For $2x + 2y = 10$, $A = 2$, $B = 2$, and $C = 10$
d. The intercepts were halved.

10. Graphs will vary. The two lines should be parallel, both with slopes -1.

11. The slopes of all the lines remained the same but their intercepts changed.

12. a. & b.

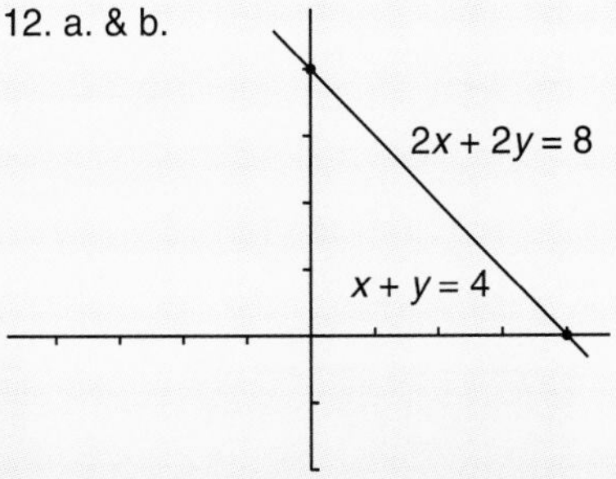

c. For $x + y = 4$, $A = 1$, $B = 1$, $C = 4$
For $2x + 2y = 8$, $A = 2$, $B = 2$, $C = 8$

13. a. The graph did not change.
b. The equation will be $3x + 3y = 12$, and the graph will not change. All three are equivalent equations.

14. a., b.

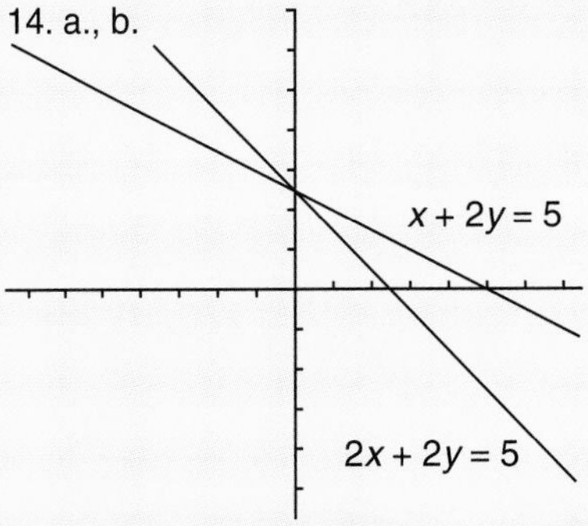

(Solutions continued on page 527)

▼ 10.6
Line Intersections

Core Sequence: 1-20, 27-30

Suitable for Homework: 13, 20, 26-30

Useful for Assessment: 6, 13, 20, 26-29

What this Lesson is About:

- Solving systems of equations graphically
- Systems with one solution, no solutions, or an infinite number of solutions
- Review of slope-intercept form
- Quick graphing of lines in slope-intercept form

This lesson is pivotal, and much of it should be done in class to ensure full discussion of the important ideas it contains.

POINTS ON LINES

This section prepares students for a full discussion of the graphical solution of systems of equations. Understanding the ideas presented here is an important prerequisite to the rest of the lesson. So make sure to have a class discussion of problem 6. Have most students found the answers by graphing lines? Have some made tables? Have some solved equations? This is a good place to compare methods and make connections between this lesson and previous lessons.

LESSON 10.6

Line Intersections

You will need:

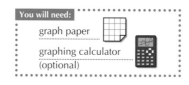

- graph paper
- graphing calculator (optional)

POINTS ON LINES

1. On the same pair of axes, make accurate graphs of these three equations.
a. $3x + 5y = 9$ b. $6x + y = 18$
c. $4x + 2y = 30$

2. There is a point on each of the lines in problem 1 where the y-value is three times the x-value.
a. Find these points. Show your work.
b. The three points you found in part (a) should all lie on one straight line. What is the equation of this line?

3. Graph the line $4x + 2y = 6$. Then mark and label a point on the line for which
a. the y-coordinate is four times the x-coordinate;
b. y is twice x;
c. x is three less than y;
d. y is three less than x.

4. Add the graphs of the following lines to the axes you used in problem 3. Notice where each one intersects the line $4x + 2y = 6$.
a. $y = 4x$ b. $y = 2x$
c. $x = y - 3$ d. $y = x - 3$

5. Find the point on the line $2x - y = 6$ for which
a. the y-coordinate is one more than the x-coordinate;
b. the x-coordinate is 2/3 of the y-coordinate.

6. Explain the method you used to solve problem 5.

HOW MANY INTERSECTIONS?

7. Graph these three lines on the same pair of axes. Describe what you observe.
a. $x + 3y = 9$
b. $2x + 6y = 18$
c. $x + 3y = 10$

8. Graph the line $2x - 3y = 4$. Then write an equation that has
a. the same graph;
b. a parallel graph.

For each pair of equations 9-12 tell whether the two graphs will be
a. the same graph;
b. parallel graphs;
c. intersecting graphs.

9. $2x + 9 = y$
$-4x - 18 = -2y$

10. $x - y = 7$
$x + y = 7$

11. $x + 6 = y$
$x + y = 6$

12. $x + y = 9$
$x + y = 7$

13. Summary Explain how to tell without graphing whether the equations of two lines have the same graph, parallel graphs, or intersecting graphs. Give examples.

HOW MANY SOLUTIONS?

Some pairs of equations 14-19 represent parallel lines. Some represent intersecting lines. Others represent the same line. *Without graphing*, find the point of intersection of each pair of lines, if it exists.

14. $2x - 3y = 7$
$3x - 4y = 15$

15. $x = 6 + 3y$
$3y = 3 + x$

10.6 SOLUTIONS

1.

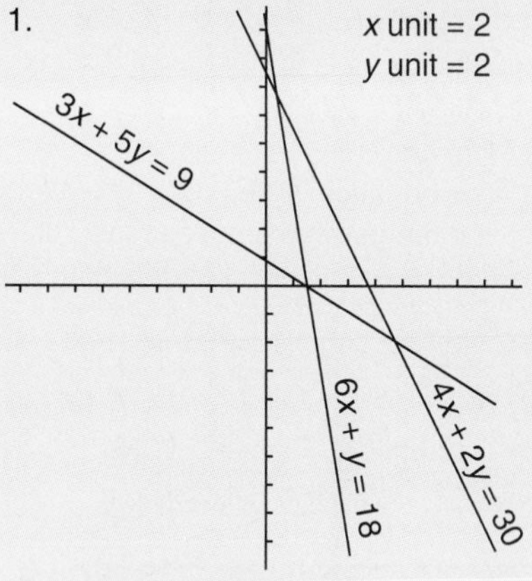

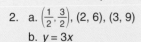

2. a. $\left(\frac{1}{2}, \frac{3}{2}\right)$, (2, 6), (3, 9)
b. $y = 3x$

3. a. (0.5, 2) b. (0.75, 1.5)
c. (0, 3) d. (2, -1)

3., 4.

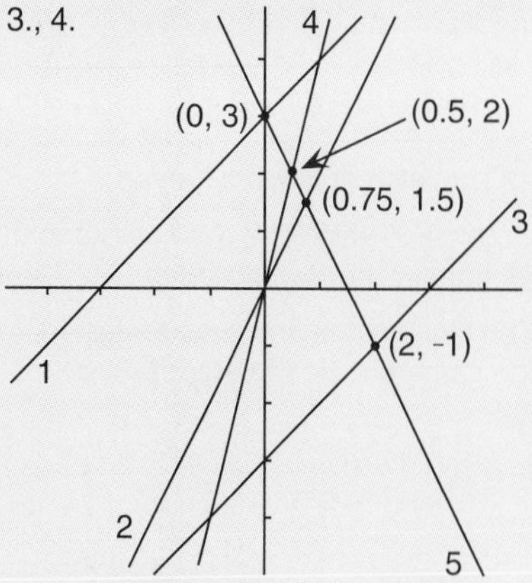

1. $x = y - 3$ 4. $y = 4x$
2. $y = 2x$ 5. $4x + 2y = 6$
3. $y = x - 3$

5. a. (7, 8) b. (12, 18)

6. Answers will vary. Sample: For #5a, graph $2x - y = 6$ and $y = x + 1$ on the same pair of axes. The two lines intersect at (7, 8). For #5b, graph $2x - y = 6$ and $x = (2/3)\,y$ on the same pair of axes. The two lines intersect at (12, 18).

7. The graphs of $x + 3y = 9$ and $2x + 6y = 18$ are the same line, which is parallel to the graph of $x + 3y = 10$.

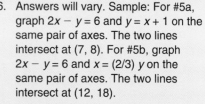

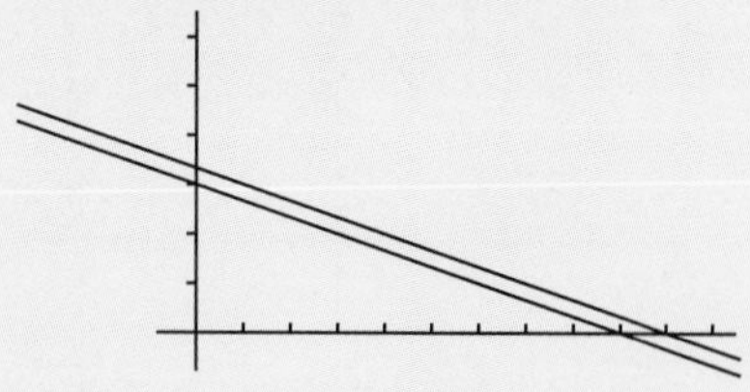

16. $y - 12 = 4x$
$2y - 8x = 24$

17. $y = 42 - 4x$
$6x = 50 + 5y$

18. $y - 12 = 4x$
$2y = 8x + 24$

19. $2y - 2x = 7$
$y - x = 3.5$

20. Summary Explain, giving examples, and compare what happens when you try to solve the system if
a. the lines are parallel;
b. the equations represent the same line;
c. the lines meet in one point.

ADDING LINES

21. a. Graph the two lines on the same pair of axes.
$3x + y = 7$
$-2x + y = -8$
b. Label the point of intersection.
c. Add these two equations to get a third equation. Graph it on the same pair of axes. What do you notice?

22. a. Graph these two lines on the same pair of axes.
(A) $5x - 2y = 3$
(B) $2x + y = 3$
b. Label the point of intersection.
c. Get a third equation by adding.
(A) + (B) + (B)
Graph this equation on the same pair of axes. What do you notice?

23. Solve the system. $\begin{cases} 5x - 2y = 3 \\ 2x + y = 3 \end{cases}$

24. Here are two equations of lines.
$2x + 3y = 5$
$x + 2y = 4$
Use addition of these equations to get the equation of a *horizontal* line that passes through their intersection.

25. Solve the system. $\begin{cases} 2x + 3y = 5 \\ x + 2y = 4 \end{cases}$

26. Summary Explain how "adding lines" to get horizontal and vertical lines is related to solving systems of equations.

MORE MIND READING

27. Which of these problems has one solution? Which has an infinite number of solutions? Which has no solution? Explain.
a. I'm thinking of two numbers. Their sum is 10. Twice the first plus twice the second is 20.
b. I'm thinking of two numbers. Their sum is 6. Their difference is 10.
c. I'm thinking of two numbers. The second is 5 more than the first. The second minus the first is 6.

HOW MANY INTERSECTIONS?
HOW MANY SOLUTIONS?

These sections go over standard territory. Note that all the preparatory work that has preceded them should make it possible for students to find the relationships between symbolic and graphical solutions, rather than be told what they are.

ADDING LINES

This section will work best with an electronic calculator that can graph $Ax + By = C$. (See the Teacher's Notes for Lesson 5.) For more examples, you can go back to the equations in Lesson 4 and follow their solutions graphically.

10.6 SOLUTIONS

8.

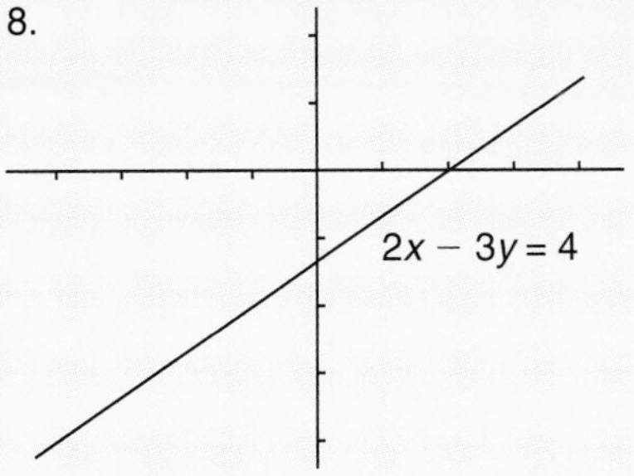

a. Answers will vary for different values of k, where $2kx - 3ky = 4k$, for $k \neq 0$.
b. Answers will vary for different values of k, for $2x - 3y = k$, for $k \neq 4$.

9. a
10. c
11. c
12. b

13. Students' level of understanding will vary. The basic ideas are:
(1) Two equations have the same graph if they are equivalent equations.
(2) $Ax + By = C$ and $kAx + kBy = kC$ are the same graph. Two lines are parallel if they differ only in the constant term.
(3) If two equations of the form $Ax + By = C$ have the same value for A and different values of B and C, then they intersect.
(4) If two equations' parameters are different and the equations are not equivalent (such as $3x + 5y = 10$ and $4x + 3y = 7$) then they intersect.

14. (17, 9)

15. No solution. The lines are parallel.

16. All ordered pairs satisfying $y - 12 = 4x$ also satisfy $2y - 8x = 24$. They are equivalent equations.

17. (10, 2)

18. The equations are equivalent, so any ordered pair satisfying $y - 12 = 4x$ also satisfies $2y = 8x + 24$.

19. The equations are equivalent, so any ordered pair satisfying $2y - 2x = 7$ also satisfies $y - x = 3.5$.

20. a. Parallel lines: If you try to add or subtract the equations or use substitution, the result is a contradiction; that is, an equation that is *never* true such as 0 = 8. This means there is no solution to the system. (Graphically, the lines do not intersect.)

MORE MIND READING

REVIEW ***SLOPE-INTERCEPT FORM***

These sections should work well as homework. Problems 28-29 should be discussed in class on the following day.

REVIEW ***SLOPE-INTERCEPT FORM***

28. The following questions are about the graph of $y = \frac{2}{3}x - 1$.

a. Where does it meet the y-axis?

b. If you move 2 units up and 3 units to the right from the y-intercept, where are you? Is that point on the graph? Explain.

c. If you move 2 units up and 3 units to the right from the point you found in part (b), where are you? Is that point on the graph? Explain.

d. Start anywhere on the line. Move 6 units up and m units to the right, to end up on the graph. What is m? Explain.

29. Describe a fast way to graph a line whose equation is given in slope-intercept form. Use an example.

30. Write these equations in slope-intercept form.

a. $3y = 4(2 - x)$

b. $4 - 3x = y - 2$

c. $y - 4 = 3(x - 2)$

d. $\frac{y}{2} = \frac{2 - 4x}{6}$

10.6 SOLUTIONS

b. Equations representing the same line: If you multiply one equation by a constant and then add or subtract, both variables will be eliminated, leaving an equation such as 0 = 0, that is *always* true. This means that every ordered pair satisfying one equation also satisfies the other.

c. The lines meet in one point: One variable can be eliminated and the resulting equation can be solved for the other variable.

21. a.

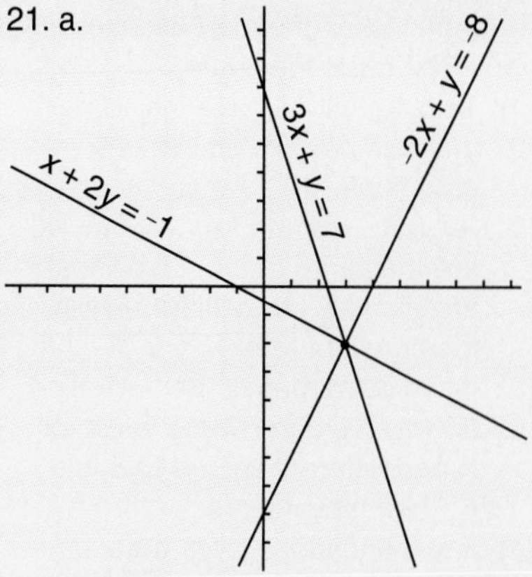

b. The point of intersection is (3, -2).

c. When you add the two lines together, you get the graph $x + 2y = -1$. It intersects the two original lines at their common point, (3, -2).

22. a.

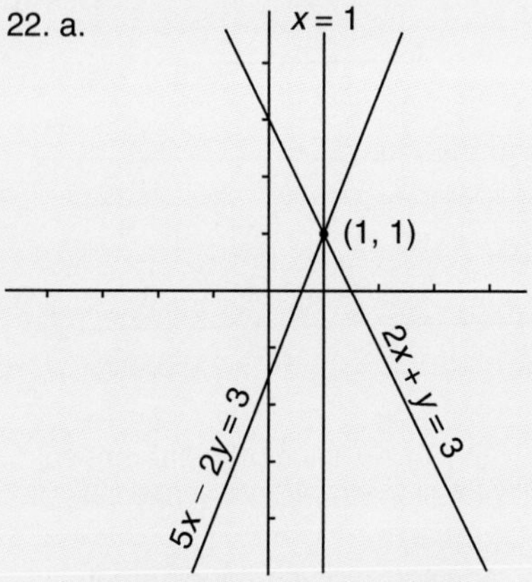

b. The point of intersection is (1, 1).

c. The third equation obtained by adding the first two is $x = 1$. Miraculously, it is the vertical line through the point of intersection of the original two equations!

(Solutions continued on page 528)

LESSON 10.7

Using Simultaneous Equations

WRITING EQUATIONS

Some problems can be solved by solving systems of equations.

Example: The members of the advanced music class of Alaberg High School gave a spring concert. Afterwards they wanted to know how many adults had attended the concert. They knew they had sold 351 tickets, and receipts totaled $1078.50. If adult tickets were $4.00 and student tickets were $2.50, how many of each kind had they sold?

Identify the variables:

Let x = the number of adult tickets.

Let y = the number of student tickets.

Write the equations:

$x + y = 351$

$4.00x + 2.50y = 1078.50$

1. Interpret the two equations in terms of this problem.
2. Solve the system. Interpret your answer.
3. The following year 536 tickets were sold, with total receipts of $1656.50. If the ticket prices were the same, how many of each type were sold? Write and solve a system of equations.
4. Compare the system you wrote in problem 3 with the one in the example. What is the same, and what is different? Explain.

Writing and solving a system of equations is an efficient way to solve the problems in this lesson. However, there are other ways to solve them, such as using tables, graphs, or by trial and error. Regardless of what method you use, show your work clearly and express your solutions in terms of the original problem.

GADGETS AND WIDGETS

5. Ken walked into Kate's Store. "How much for five of those gidgets and eight of those gadgets?" he asked. "That would be $11.27 without tax," Kate replied. "Oops," said Ken. "I really need eight of the gidgets and five of the gadgets." The total was $11.87 before tax. What was the cost of a gidget? What was the cost of a gadget?
6. It takes 2.5 kg of copper and 4 kg of nickel to manufacture a widget. A smidget requires 7 kg of copper and 3 kg of nickel. How many widgets and how many smidgets could you manufacture if you had
   a. 74 kg of copper and 61 kg of nickel?
   b. 80 kg of copper and 43 kg of nickel?

MOZART

7. Liza planned to tape a 12-hour Mozart Marathon. She wanted to use a combination of 90-minute and 60-minute tapes and to fill each one completely.
   a. What possible combinations of tapes could she use?
   b. If she used a total of ten tapes, and filled all of them completely, how many of each did she use?
8. Shelly earned some money assisting with preparations for Mozart's 200th birthday party. She made $6 per hour for addressing invitations and $8 per hour for helping to set up the stage and auditorium for the concert. She received a total of $352. How many hours did she work at each job?

10.7 Using Simultaneous Equations

Core Sequence: 1-17

Suitable for Homework: 5-18

Useful for Assessment: 4

What this Lesson is About:

- Solving word problems with simultaneous equations
- Review of percent

This lesson is about traditional material. After the previous six lessons, students should be ready to apply simultaneous equations to word problems. However, allow students to solve the problems any way they want.

WRITING EQUATIONS

This is the heart of the lesson and should be done in class. It is now that you must establish the importance of working neatly and carefully, with a record of what the variables stand for and a final solution expressed as the answer to the question posed by the problem.

GADGETS AND WIDGETS
MOZART

These are standard word problems.

10.7 SOLUTIONS

1. $x + y = 351$ means the total number of tickets sold was 351.
   $4.00x$ is the money obtained from selling adult tickets.
   $2.50y$ is the money obtained from selling student tickets.
   $4.00x + 2.50y = 1078.50$ means the amount of money from both kinds of tickets is $1078.50.
2. $x = 134$ and $y = 217$
   There were 134 adult tickets and 217 student tickets sold.
3. The equations are $x + y = 536$ and $4.00x + 2.50y = 1656.50$. There were 211 adult tickets and 325 student tickets sold.
4. The total number of tickets and the total amount of the receipts were different, so the right-hand sides of the equations were different. The price of the tickets remained the same, so the coefficients in the second equation were the same.
5. Each gidget costs $0.99 and each gadget costs $0.79.
6. a. 10 widgets and 7 smidgets
   b. 3 widgets and 10 smidgets
7. a. Answers may vary. Samples:

# of 90-minute tapes	# of 60-minute tapes
2	9
4	6
6	3

   b. four 90-minute tapes and six 60-minute tapes
8. Let x be the number of hours addressing invitations and y be the number of hours helping to set up the stage. Then $6x + 8y = 352$. There are many possible (x, y) pairs that will satisfy this equation. Examples:

x	y
0	44
2	42.5
4	41
6	39.5
8	38

There is not enough information to determine a unique answer to this problem.

COLLEGE APPLICATIONS

*T*his section reviews percent in the context of simultaneous equations problems.

MEXICAN FOOD

CHEMISTRY

GEOMETRY

*M*ore standard word problems.

PROBLEMATIC PROBLEMS

*I*f they cared about those numbers, one may legitimately ask why the members of the advanced music class, or their teacher, did not keep a record of how many of each type of ticket was sold, for example, by using different-colored tickets or some kind of bookkeeping.

*G*idgets, widgets, gadgets, and smidgets do not exist, (though some can be found in the dictionary).

*G*iven the relatively low cost of cassette tapes, Liza is more likely to organize the taping in terms of musical, rather than mathematical criteria.

*T*he only way Shelly's pay could have been computed was from knowing the number of hours she worked at each job. (Did she then lose that information?)

*T*he only way the Garabel College newspaper could have known the total number of applications and the percent increase was to know the numbers that are being asked for. If this was a true story, one could call the reporter, or Ms. Pavlov, and just ask for the answers!

*T*he assumption of the restaurant problem is that there is no break for buying a Family Feast instead of a Couple's Combo. This is, of course, unlikely.

*Y*ou can extend this kind of discussion to the whole book or to other math books.

COLLEGE APPLICATIONS

9. Garabel College newspaper reported that 1089 students had applied to the college in the two-year period 1992-1994. There were 20% more applicants in the 93-94 school year than in the 92-93 school year. How many students applied to Garabel in each of the two years?

10. The number of students applying to Garabel in 92-93 was a 12% increase over the number in 91-92. How many students applied in 91-92?

11. Ms. Pavlov, the Director of Admissions, congratulated the admissions staff. "We had 32% more applicants in 93-94 than in 91-92." What is wrong with her statement?

12. The admissions department is expanding. Their budget has been increased by $1800 per week to hire new staff. They will hire some part-time student interviewers and tour guides at $5.25 per hour and student secretaries at $6.50 per hour. Interviewers and tour guides work approximately 10 hours per week, and secretaries work 15 hours per week. If they need one secretary for every five interviewers and tour guides, how many of each should they hire?

MEXICAN FOOD

At La Brea's Mexican Restaurant, you can buy a Family Feast of eight enchiladas and twelve tamales for $19.60. The Couple's Combo has four tamales and four enchiladas, and sells for $8.00.

13. Based on these prices, what price would you recommend for the Single's Special, which has two tamales and one enchilada?

14. Mr. G. La Brea wants to add a new item to the restaurant's menu. How should he price the Double Dozen, which has a dozen enchiladas and a dozen tamales?

CHEMISTRY

15. One solution is 80% acid. Another is 20% acid. Rosemary wants 500 liters of a solution that is 70% acid. How much of each solution should she use?

GEOMETRY

16. A 30-cm string loop goes around two thumbtacks that are ten cm apart. A third thumbtack is added, so that the loop makes a right triangle. How far is the new tack from the old ones?

17. A rectangle has perimeter 30. If you add 3 to the width, and subtract 4 from the length, the area does not change. What are the length and width of the original rectangle?

PROBLEMATIC PROBLEMS

Systems of simultaneous linear equations are an important and widely-used application of mathematics. Usually they involve many variables and are solved with the help of more advanced math, plus computers or programmable calculators. The lessons in this chapter were intended to give you an introduction to this sort of mathematics. However, some of the problems in this lesson are not very realistic.

18. Report Discuss:
- How could some of the problems be solved (or avoided) without using algebra?
- Which problems are backwards? (You are given information that could have been figured out only by someone who already knew the answer to the problem.)
- Which problems seem to start from unrealistic numbers?
- Which problems could arise in the real world?
- Which problems are really puzzles created to help you learn algebra?

10.7 SOLUTIONS

9. 594 students applied in 1993-1994 and 495 applied the previous year.
10. 495 = (1.12)x so x = 441.96. There were 442 applicants in 1991-1992.
11. In '93-'94 there were 594 applicants. In '91-'92 there were 442 applicants.
$594 = (1 + p)442$
$594 = 442 + 442p$
$152 = 442p$
$p = 0.34$
The correct percentage is 34%.
12. The admissions department can hire a group of 25 tour guides and interviewers and 5 secretaries.
13. The Single's Special should cost $2.90.
14. The Double Dozen should cost $24.
15. x = 416 and 2/3
y = 83 and 1/3
16. $x + y = 20$
$y^2 = x^2 + 10^2$
$(20 - x)^2 = x^2 + 100$
$400 - 40x + x^2 = x^2 + 100$
$300 = 40x$
$x = 7.5$
$y = 12.5$
The new thumbtack is 7.5 cm from one tack and 12.5 cm from the other old tack.
17. Solve the equations $l + w = 15$ and $(w + 3)(l - 4) = lw$
The length is 10 and 2/7 and the width is 4 and 5/7 units.
18. See Notes to Teacher.

LESSON 10.8

Lines Through Points

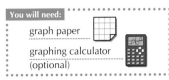

You will need:
- graph paper
- graphing calculator (optional)

1. **Exploration** The linear equation $y = x - 1$ has (2, 1) as a solution. Make up several more linear equations in x and y that have (2, 1) as a solution. Compare your solutions with those of other students. How many different linear equations have this solution?

FINDING COORDINATES

Hint: The problems in this section and the following one can be solved by graphing carefully.

2. A line having slope -2 passes through the point (-4, 3). Give the coordinates of three more points on the line.
3. A line having slope -3 passes through the point (5, 12). The points (a, 5) and (0, b) are on the same line. Find a and b.
4. A line passes through (2, 1) and (-2, -1). Give the coordinates of three more points on the line.
5. The points (7, -2) and (6, 2) are on a line. The points (a, 5) and (0, b) are on the same line. Find a and b.

LINES THROUGH A POINT

6. Which of the following lines pass through the point (1, -1)?
   a. $5x - 5y = 10$ b. $5x + 5y = 10$
   c. $2x - 3y = 6$ d. $-3x + 2y = 6$
7. The line $y = mx - 1$ passes through the point (3, 2). What is m?
8. The line $y = (-1/3)x + b$ passes through the point (3, 2). What is b?

FINDING THE EQUATION OF A LINE

9. Graph the line that passes through the points (1, 3) and (3, 8). Find its equation.

Ellen and Sandor wanted to find the equation of a line passing through (4, 5) and (8, -3) *without using graphing*.

10. Ellen could tell by imagining the graph that the slope of the line must be negative and the y-intercept must be greater than 5. Explain.

Ellen knew that the equation could be written in slope-intercept form as $y = mx + b$. "All I have to do is find m and b," she thought. Using the point (4, 5), she substituted values for x and y and wrote this equation in m and b,

$$5 = m(4) + b$$

which she rewrote as $5 = 4m + b$.

11. What equation in m and b did she write, using the point (8, -3)?

10.8 SOLUTIONS

1. Equations will vary. There is an infinite number of equations with (2, 1) as a solution. Samples: $y = (1/2)x$
   $x + y = 3$
   $y = 2x - 3$
2. Answers vary. Sample: (-3, 1), (-2, -1), (-1, -3), (0, -5). Any pair that satisfies the equation $y = -2x - 5$ will work.
3. $a = 7$ and $1/3$ $b = 27$
4. Answers will vary. Sample (10, 0), (4, 2), (6, 3). Any pair that satisfies $x = 2y$
5. $a = 5$ and $1/4$, and $b = 26$
6. $5x - 5y = 10$ is the only one that passes through (1, -1). This can be determined by substituting the coordinates into the equations.
7. $m = 1$
8. $b = 3$
9.

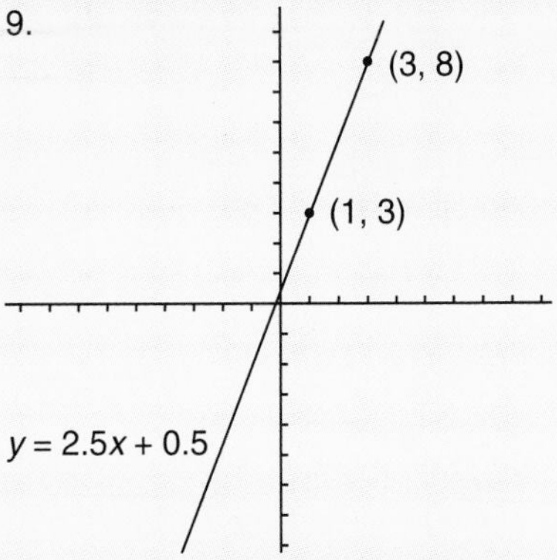

10. The line would fall from (4, 5) in quadrant I to (8, -3) in quadrant IV, so the slope must be negative. The line would fall from the y-intercept (0, b) to (4, 5) so the intercept must be greater than 5.

10.8 Lines Through Points

Core Sequence: 1-21

Suitable for Homework: 2-10, 28

Useful for Assessment: 17, 26

What this Lesson is About:
- Finding the equation of a line given its slope and one point on it
- Finding the equation of a line given two points on it
- Application to discovering the formula relating Fahrenheit to Celsius degrees
- Review of direct variation

This is a substantial lesson, which you may consider doing entirely in the classroom.

Answers to problem 1 should be discussed, as well as the methods students used to get them.

FINDING COORDINATES
LINES THROUGH A POINT

These sections help prepare students for the main point of the lesson, by providing problems that can be solved by graphing, with no need for algebraic manipulation. This will make it possible for the students to get a better understanding of the problem before tackling it symbolically in the next section.

FINDING THE EQUATION OF A LINE

In this section students use what they learned about simultaneous equations to find the equation of a line. This is better than learning a formula, since a formula is easy to forget, and to a beginner it can mask the underlying mathematics.

Expect some difficulty with problem 13, since there are three unknowns. If students are frustrated, you may hint that any convenient value can be chosen for A, B, or C, and the other two unknowns can be found by solving the system. As usual when there are many possible solutions, it is important to have a class-wide discussion of the answers.

In problems 15-17 students may prefer to use slope-intercept form, since it has only two parameters, and since m is either given or can be found as *rise over run*.

CELSIUS-FAHRENHEIT CONVERSION

This formula was introduced in Chapter 3, Lesson 8, and again in Chapter 4, Lesson 7. Here students derive the formula from two data points as an application of the techniques they learned in this lesson. This technique will be used again in **Thinking/Writing 10.B**.

12. a. Find the values of m and b that satisfy both of Ellen's equations.
b. Write the slope-intercept equation of the line passing through the points.

Sandor knew that the equation could be written in standard form as $Ax + By = C$. He substituted values for x and y and wrote two equations. One was $A(4) + B(5) = C$, which he rewrote as $4A + 5B = C$.

13. a. What was the other equation?
b. Find some values of A, B, and C that satisfy both equations. (Many solutions are possible.)
c. Write in standard form an equation of the line passing through the points.
d. Compare your answer to (c) with other students' answers.

14. Show that Ellen and Sandor got equivalent answers, one in slope-intercept form and the other in standard form.

15. Find the equation of a line having slope 1.5 that passes through the point (0.5, 4).

16. Find the equation of the line through the points (2.3, 4.5) and (-6, -7). (You may round off the parameters.)

17. Summary Explain, with examples, your strategies for finding the equation of a line,
a. when you know its slope and the coordinates of a point on it;
b. when you know the coordinates of two points on it.

CELSIUS-FAHRENHEIT CONVERSION

Water freezes at 0° Celsius, which is 32° Fahrenheit. Water boils at 100° Celsius, which is 212° Fahrenheit.

18. A temperature reading can be converted from Fahrenheit to Celsius by using the formula $C = mF + b$. Find m and b by using the fact that $C = 0$ when $F = 32$, and $C = 100$ when $F = 212$.

19. Find a formula for converting Celsius to Fahrenheit.

20. What is the relationship between the formulas that you found in problems 18-19?

21. When the temperature increases by n degrees on the Celsius scale, by how much does it increase on the Fahrenheit scale? Explain.

10.8 S O L U T I O N S

11. $-3 = 8m + b$

12. a. $m = -2$, $b = 13$
b. $y = -2x + 13$

13. a. $8A - 3B = C$
b. Answers will vary. Sample answers:

A	B	C
2	1	13
6	3	39
-4	-2	-26
2k	k	13k

c. Answers will vary. Sample answers: $2x + y = 13$, $6x + 3y = 39$, $-4x - 2y = -26$
d. All answers should be equivalent equations of the form $2kx + ky = 13k$ for $k \neq 0$.

14. Sandor's equation should be $2x + y = 13$, or some multiple of it. Ellen's equation should be $y = -2x + 13$. Adding $2x$ to both sides of the second equation yields the first equation.

15. $y = 1.5x + 3.25$ or $6x - 4y = -13$

16. Answers will vary slightly, due to round-off. All should be equivalent (approximately) to $115x - 83y = -109$.

17. Answers will vary. Samples:
a. You can substitute the slope and coordinates into $y = mx + b$ and solve for b. Replacing the values of the slope and intercept for the parameters of m and b results in the slope-intercept form of the line.
b. Use the two points to calculate the slope (find the ratio of rise to run) and then use the method in 17(a) with the slope and one of the pairs. (Use the other pair to check your answer.)

18. Use the equations $0 = 32m + b$ and $100 = 212m + b$. Solve them simultaneously to get $C = (5/9)F - (17 \text{ and } 7/9)$ or $C = (5/9)(F - 32)$.

19. $F = (9/5)C + 32$

20. If the first equation is solved for F in terms of C, the result is the second equation.

21. It increases $(9/5)n$ degrees on the Fahrenheit scale for every one degree increase on the Celsius scale.

ADDING POINTS

A line passes through the points (2, 4) and (6, 8). If you add the x-coordinates and the y-coordinates of these points you get the point (8, 12). Call this point the *sum* of the points.

22. What point is the *difference* of the points?

23. a. Find the equation of the line through (2, 4) and (6, 8).

b. Does this line also pass through the sum and the difference of (2, 4) and (6, 8)?

24. Write the equation of any line and find the coordinates of two points on the line. Find their sum and difference. Does the line pass through the sum and difference points?

25. Find the equation of a line such that the sum and the difference of any two points on the line is also on the line. To find this line, it may help to experiment with graphs. Compare your answers to problems 23-24 with other students' answers.

26. **Summary** What kinds of lines contain the sum and the difference of any two points on the line? Explain, giving examples and counter-examples.

27. What's wrong with this reasoning? (Hint: Think about problems 18-26.)

0°C = 32°F

100°C = 212°F

Adding equals to equals:

100°C = 244°F

DISCOVERY *REAL WORD PROBLEM*

28. Rearrange the letters in the sentence

I'm a pencil dot.

to create an appropriate mathematical two-word phrase. (Hint: The second word has five letters.)

ADDING POINTS

This section offers an interesting opportunity to work with direct variation. You can motivate it by introducing the section with a discussion of the apparent paradox in problem 27. An algebraic explanation, which would be too hard for most students to understand at this level, goes as follows:

If $y_0 = mx_0$ and $y_1 = mx_1$, then:

$$y_0 + y_1 = mx_0 + mx_1 = m(x_0 + x_1)$$

so the sum is on the line.

However, if $y_0 = mx_0 + b$ and $y_1 = mx_1 + b$, then:

$$\begin{aligned} y_0 + y_1 &= (mx_0 + b) + (mx_1 + b) \\ &= mx_0 + mx_1 + b + b \\ &= m(x_0 + x_1) + 2b \end{aligned}$$

so the "sum" is on the line only if $2b = b$, or $b = 0$.

Perhaps a geometric argument would reach more students.

10.8 SOLUTIONS

22. Either (-4, -4) or (4, 4)

23. a. $y = x + 2$
    b. no

24. Answers vary.

25. Answers vary. $y = mx$ for $m \neq 0$. Sample: $y = 3x$ goes through the points (1, 3) and (3, 9). The sum (4, 12) is also on the line. The difference (-2, -6) is also on the line.

26. Any line through the origin that is neither horizontal nor vertical contains the sum and difference of any two points on the line.

27. $F = (9/5)C + 32$ is not a line through the origin, so the sum of any two points on its graph does not lie on its graph.

28. Decimal point

THINKING WRITING **10.B Fitting a Line**

Core Sequence: 1-7

Suitable for Homework: 1-5, 7-10

Useful for Assessment: 7

What this Assignment is About:

- Finding the equation of a line from the coordinates of points
- Fitting a line to data

This idea was previewed in Chapter 4, Lesson 7. In that case, the line passed through the origin, but the same suggestions still apply.

- Make sure the students do not connect the dots in the graph. The idea of fitting a line is to use it, rather than line segments connecting the dots, to approximate the relationship between the variables.
- Have students use uncooked spaghetti to place on the graph as a help in finding the line of best fit. At this level, eyeballing the best fit is satisfactory.
- If you use a graphing calculator, do not use the automatic line-fitting feature. Instead, plot the points, and try graphing various lines until you find one that provides a satisfactory fit.

THINKING WRITING 10.B Fitting a Line

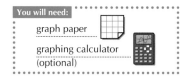

You will need:
graph paper
graphing calculator (optional)

These data are about *average* 45-year-olds.

	Weight (lbs)	
Height	**Men**	**Women**
4′10″		118
5′		123
5′2″	140	129
5′4″	149	136
5′6″	158	143
5′8″	167	150
5′10″	176	158
6′	186	168
6′2″	197	
6′4″	208	

1. On the same axes, graph weight as a function of height for men and women.

The points appear to lie on two straight lines. However by looking at the differences between consecutive entries, you can see that for women, a two-inch difference in height means five more pounds between 4′10″ and 5′, while it means six more pounds between 5′ and 5′2″. This shows that the slope changes, and therefore the points are not lined up exactly.

2. Between what heights is the relationship between height and weight linear? In other words, between what heights do the points lie exactly on a line?
   a. Answer this for men and for women.
   b. Find the slope of those lines.
   c. Find the equations of the lines, in the form $W = mH + b$. (Express heights in inches.)

The equations you found can be used to predict the average weight for 45-year-old men and women *in that range*.

3. Use the equation you found to calculate the weights of a man and a woman who are each 5′5″ tall. Check that your answers are consistent with the data in the table.
4. The unit of height is the inch, the unit of weight is the pound. What is the unit and meaning of the slope in these graphs?
5. In what ranges is the slope less? Greater? Explain why, in terms of the real-world meaning of the data.

It is more difficult to find a linear function relating weight to height if you try to do it over the whole range. Finding such a function is called *fitting a line to the data*. The equation of such a line is useful as an approximate formula.

6. **Exploration** Draw a line that is close to all the data points for the men. Find its equation. (Start out by finding two points on the line you drew and use their coordinates. They do not need to be points from the table.) Do this again for the women. Compare your answers with those of other students.

10.B SOLUTIONS

1.

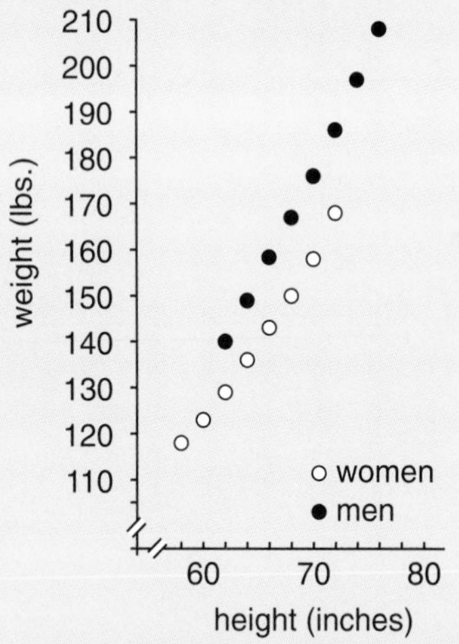

2. a. For men, there is a linear relationship between 5′2″ and 5′10″ and between 6′ and 6′4″. For women, there is a linear relationship between 5′2″ and 5′8″.
   b. The slope is 9/2 for men between 5′2″ and 5′10″ and 11/2 for men between 6′ and 6′4″. The slope is 7/2 for women between 5′2″ and 5′8″.
   c. $W = \frac{9}{2}H - 139$ for $62 \le H \le 70$ for men
   $W = \frac{11}{2}H - 210$ for $72 \le H \le 76$ for men
   $W = \frac{7}{2}H - 88$ for $62 \le H \le 68$ for women
3. For men,
   $W = \frac{9}{2}(65) - 139 = 153.5$ lbs.
   For women,
   $W = \frac{7}{2}(65) - 88 = 139.5$ lbs.
4. The unit of slope is pounds per inch. Slope shows the change in weight for each one-inch change in height.
5. The slope is less in lower heights and more for greater heights. This means that a 1-inch increase in height means, on the average, a greater increase in weight for a taller person than for a shorter person.
6. Answers will vary.

7. **Report** Explain how you found a linear equation for these data. Your report should answer the following questions, but not be limited to them.
   - In a paragraph, summarize the information contained in the table.
   - Why is it impossible to find an exact formula relating weight and height?
   - What is the meaning of slope in this context?
   - What does your formula predict for the weight of a 5′ man? Of a 6′2″ woman? Are those predictions probably too high or too low?

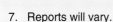

DISCOVERY *BEYOND SQUARE ROOTS*

8. With which of the following numbers of blocks could you build a single cube with no blocks left over? If you could build a cube, give its dimensions. (You may want to use the Lab Gear or make a sketch.)
   a. 8 b. 81
   c. 216 d. 729

Say that we have:

$$64^x \cdot 64^x \cdot 64^x = 64.$$

Using the product of powers law of exponents it is easy to see what x must be:

$$64^{1/3} \cdot 64^{1/3} \cdot 64^{1/3} = 64^1.$$

9. a. What must be the value of $64^{1/3}$? (Hint: What number could you substitute for it in this equation?)
   b. Use the same reasoning to find the value of $27^{1/3}$.

   The 1/3 power of a number is called the cube root of a number. Explain why.

10. Use a law of exponents to simplify.
   a. $64^{2/3}$
   b. $8^{4/3}$
   c. $64^{1/4}$

It would be best for students do problem 6 as part of the homework, but it would be too difficult for them if you don't do a similar problem in class as an introduction. You may, for instance, use the data about Joshua's growth in Chapter 8, Lesson 1, and find a formula that gives an approximate weight for him as a function of his height.

We will return to fitting a line in Chapter 12. At that point, we will teach an algorithm for doing it.

DISCOVERY *BEYOND SQUARE ROOTS*

This section extends the idea of fractional exponents a little further. It is not intended as a full lesson on this subject, which should be covered in depth in a future course. Do not expect mastery.

10.B SOLUTIONS

7. Reports will vary.
8. a. 2^3
   b. impossible
   c. 6^3
   d. 9^3
9. a. 4
   b. 3
10. a. 16
   b. 16
   c. 2 times the square root of 2

Essential Ideas

BIKES AND TRIKES

Kathryn counted 41 wheels in the preschool yard. All of them were on bikes and trikes. (She did not count training wheels.)

1. Make a table showing some possible numbers of bikes and trikes.
2. Jana counted a total of 16 bikes and trikes in the same yard. How many of each kind were there?

LETTERS AND CARDS

Bill is on vacation and wants to write to his friends. He is going to write letters and postcards, and wants to spend no more than $4.75 on postage. Postcard stamps are 19 cents, and letter stamps are 29 cents.

3. a. If Bill writes only cards, how many can he write?
   b. If he writes only letters, how many can he write?
   c. If he has 20 friends and wants to write as many letters and as few postcards as possible, how many of each kind should he send?

LINEAR EQUATIONS

4. Which of these equations have the same set of (x, y) solutions as each other? Make two groups. Show your work.
   a. $2x + 3y = 0.4$ b. $10x = 2 - 15y$
   c. $15x + 10y = 5$ d. $x + 1.5y = 0.2$
   e. $y = -1.5x + 0.5$ f. $3x + 2y = 1$
5. Write in standard form, $y = 6x + 7$.
6. What is the equation of a line having slope 8 that passes through (9, 11)?

SYSTEM SOLVING

Solve each system. Check first to see if you can tell that the system has no solution or an infinite number of solutions.

7. $\begin{cases} 6m - 4b = 0 \\ 5m + 8b = 0 \end{cases}$ 8. $\begin{cases} 4m - 3b = 2 \\ 3m + 4b = 5 \end{cases}$

9. $\begin{cases} 3a + 8b = 20 \\ 3a + b = 13 \end{cases}$ 10. $\begin{cases} 6m - 2n = 12 \\ n = 3m - 4 \end{cases}$

LEGS

11. Jeanne saw some cows and chickens. She had nothing to do, so she counted their legs and heads, over and over. Here are her results.

    The first time: 93 legs, 31 heads
    The second time: 66 legs, 16 heads
    The third time: 82 legs, 29 heads

    She counted accurately only one time. Which time was it? How many cows and how many chickens were there? Comment.

12. Jonathan saw some three-legged stools and four-legged chairs. He was bored, so he counted their legs. There were 59 legs. Then he put six pennies on each stool, and eight nickels on each chair. (He thought it would make a good math problem.)
    a. He used 118 coins. Can you tell how many chairs and stools there were? Explain.
    b. The total value of the coins was $3.74. Can you tell how many chairs and stools there were? Explain.
    c. How many of each kind of coin did he use?

SOLUTIONS

1. Answers will vary. All pairs of values should satisfy the equation $2b + 3t = 41$.
   Sample table:

bikes	trikes
1	13
4	11
7	9
10	7
13	5

2. 7 bikes and 9 trikes
3. a. 25 cards b. 16 letters
   c. Find the maximum value of L that satisfies the equation $C + L = 20$ and the inequality $0.19C + 0.29L \le 4.75$.
   He should send 9 letters and 11 postcards, spending a total of $4.70.
4. a, b, and d have the same set of (x, y) solutions, and so do c, e, and f. This problem can be solved graphically, by showing that the equations in each group all have the same graph, or algebraically, by showing that the equations are equivalent.
5. $6x - y = -7$
6. $y - 11 = 8(x - 9)$
7. $m = 0$, $b = 0$
8. $m = 23/25$, $b = 14/25$
9. $a = 4$, $b = 1$
10. no solution
11. The third count was the only one that could possibly have been correct, with 12 cows and 17 chickens. The first count means there were 15 and 1/2 cows and 15 and 1/2 chickens. The second count means there were 17 cows and -1 chickens. However, if I were Jeanie, I would count again, just to make sure. Her third count was not impossible, but that doesn't mean it was correct, and Jeanie doesn't seem to have a very good track record.
12. a. No. The information leads to two equivalent equations: $3s + 4c = 59$ and $6s + 8c = 118$.
    b. Yes. The information leads to two different equations: $3s + 4c = 59$ and $6s + 40c = 374$. Solving these equations simultaneously, we conclude that there were 9 stools and 8 chairs.
    c. There were 54 pennies and 64 nickels.

GOING NUTS

The G. Ale Bar Company also sells nuts. Cashews are \$4.95 a pound, and peanuts are \$1.95 a pound.

13. Ginger was asked to create a mix of cashews and peanuts that would cost \$2.95 a pound. What percent of the mix should be peanuts and what percent should be cashews?

CREATING SYSTEMS OF EQUATIONS

14. Create a system of equations that has the solution $x = 2$, $y = 7$. Compare your answer with other students' answers.

15. Create two different systems of equations that have the solution $x = 4$, $y = -1$. Compare answers.

16. Explain your strategy for making up a system of equations having a given (x, y) solution.

17. Make up a word problem having two variables. The problem should have a unique solution. You might use one of the following themes: different-sized bottles or cans, alien creatures having different numbers of eyes or arms. Or choose anything else you want. Be creative, but make sure the math works out.

EQUATIONS AND GRAPHS

18. The graphs of $y = 2x + 3$ and $y = -4x - 5$ meet at a point having x-coordinate $-4/3$. Solve the system.

$$\begin{cases} y = 2x + 3 \\ y = -4x - 5 \end{cases}$$

19. One of (2.5, 0.5) and (0.5, 2.5) is the solution to the system $\begin{cases} 6x + 2y = 8 \\ 9x - y = 2 \end{cases}$

Where do the graphs of $6x + 2y = 8$ and $9x - y = 2$ intersect?

POINTS ON A LINE

Susan connected (6, 0) to (2, 10) with a rubber band on her geoboard. (5, 3) and (4, 5) appeared to be on the line she formed. She wondered whether they really were.

20. Find the equation of the line through (6, 0) and (2, 10). Use algebra to check whether (5, 3) and (4, 5) are on it.

21. Mark thought the question could be answered without finding the equation of a line, by using the slope of the line connecting one point to another. Use his method and explain it.

A HEIGHT-WEIGHT FORMULA?

Many people do not like to reveal their weight, but most people don't mind telling their height. Lewis thought it would be useful to have a formula giving weight as a function of height. Lewis is 5 feet 6 inches tall and weighs 141 pounds. He made up a formula that relates his weight (in pounds) to his height (in inches).

$$W = 2(H) + 9$$

22. Verify that this formula works for Lewis's height and weight.

23. Lewis's friend Doug weighs 162 pounds and is 6 feet 1 inch tall. Does Lewis's formula work for Doug? Explain.

24. Find a formula that works for both Lewis and Doug.

25. Find two people who will tell you their height and weight. Find a formula that relates their weights to their heights.

26. Check whether the formula you found in problem 25 works to predict your weight from your height. Comment.

SOLUTIONS

13. 67% of the mix would be peanuts and 33% would be cashews.
14. Answers will vary. Sample: $5x + 2y = 24$ and $x + y = 9$
15. Answers will vary. Sample: $5x + 2y = 18$ and $x + y = 3$ Sample: $3x - 4y = 16$ and $2x + y = 7$.
16. Answers will vary.
17. Answers will vary.
18. When $x = -4/3$, $y = 1/3$
19. By substitution, we can see that (2.5, 0.5) does not satisfy both equations, but (0.5, 2.5) does.
20. The equation connecting (6, 0) and (2, 10) is $5x + 2y = 30$. By substitution, you can find that (5, 3) is not on the line, but (4, 5) is.
21. Mark uses the idea that you can use any two points to calculate the slope of a line. The slope from (6, 0) to (2, 10) is -2.5. The slope from (6, 0) to (5, 3) is -3, so (5, 3) is not on the same line. The slope from (6, 0) to (4, 5) is also -2.5, so it is on the line.
22. 141 = 2(66) + 9
23. No. 2(73) + 9 = 155, which is less than Doug's weight.
24. The equation satisfying both (66, 141) and (73, 162) is $W = 3H - 57$.
25. Answers vary, depending on the data collected.
26. Answers will vary.

Chapter 11
Interpreting Ratios

Overview of the Chapter

*R*atio and proportion are ideas that have permeated the whole course. In this chapter they are the starting point for work on rational and irrational numbers, probability, and unit conversion. The lessons address profound, fundamental, and difficult concepts in mathematics, probability, and science. Do not be misled by the apparent shortness of the lessons; many of them will require a considerable amount of time.

Note: The first half of the chapter depends heavily on your class's having done Chapter 5, Lessons 9-11, and **Thinking/ Writing 5.C.** If you did not do that work then, do it now.

1. Introduction of New Tools:

- An algorithm for adding geometric sequences
- Graphing applied to probability

2. Algebra Concepts Emphasized:

- Sums of geometric sequences
- Converting decimals to fractions
- Definition of rational numbers
- Existence of irrational numbers
- Irrationality of $\sqrt{2}$

CHAPTER 11

A spiral staircase

Coming in this chapter:

Exploration On graph paper, you want to go from (0, 0) to (p, q), where p and q are positive whole numbers. If you travel only up and to the right, following graph paper lines, how many ways are there to do it? If you travel in a straight line, how many graph paper squares do you cross?

INTERPRETING RATIOS

3. Algebra Concepts Reviewed:

- Comparing by ratio and comparing by difference
- Geometric sequences
- Converting fractions to decimals
- Slope
- Equivalent fractions
- Direct variation
- Prime factorization
- Square roots
- Constant sum graphs
- Proportional thinking
- Reciprocals

4. Algebra Concepts Previewed:

- Convergence and limits
- Pascal's triangle

5. Problem-Solving Techniques:

- Using variables
- Using a diagram
- Starting with a simpler problem

6. Connections and Context:

- Distance traveled by a bouncing ball
- Review of geoboard area
- Review of taxicab distance
- Introduction to probability
- Fair games
- Experiment, outcome, and event
- Preview of the multiplication counting principle
- Definitions of probability
- Two-dice experiment
- Coin experiments
- Random walks
- Unit conversion
- Calibration of speedometers

▼ 11.1 Sums of Geometric Sequences

Core Sequence: 3-17, 19-22

Suitable for Homework: 16-28

Useful for Assessment: 8, 10-11, 15, 21-22

What this Lesson is About:

- Review of comparing by ratio and comparing by difference
- Review of geometric sequences
- Sums of geometric sequences
- Application of geometric sequences to the distance traveled by a bouncing ball

Geometric sequences were previewed in: Chapter 2, Lesson 5; Chapter 5, **Thinking/Writing 5.C;** Chapter 7, Lesson 8; and Chapter 8, Lessons 5 and 6.

THE BOUNCING BALL

The experiment in problems 1-2 (and in 18) is optional, but it greatly increases students' interest in the lesson. It also serves to review comparing by ratio versus comparing by difference. The result of the experiment should be to observe that (even taking measurement error into account) the ratio is much more constant than the difference.

Problems 3-5 should give students a chance to get some experience with the basic problem of the lesson. They will use calculators to answer the questions.

In problem 4 make sure students include the travel in both directions. It is easy to make a calculating mistake in problem 4b, but students should get answers that are close to each others', since the terms get smaller and smaller.

They should be able to make fairly good guesses for problem 5, either by using their calculators or by making an estimate based on the observation that the terms get smaller and smaller. It is not important for the guess to be accurate. Students will get a chance to revise their answer when they get to problem 16.

USING SYMBOLIC NOTATION

FINDING THE SUM

The terms *geometric sequence* and *common ratio* were introduced in Chapter 5, **Thinking/Writing 5.C.**

LESSON 11.1

Sums of Geometric Sequences

You will need:

- a ball
- yardstick (or meterstick)

THE BOUNCING BALL

When you drop a ball, it bounces back, but not quite to the height from which you dropped it.

1. Do an experiment in which you drop a ball from various heights and see to what height it bounces back. Use a yardstick or meterstick to make your measurements. Make a table like this.

Dropped from	Bounced to	Ratio	Difference
—	—	—	—

2. As you vary the height, what remains closer to constant, the ratio or the difference?

For a certain "ideal" ball, the bounce-height to drop-height ratio (or *bounce ratio*) is consistently 0.8. The ball is dropped from a height of two meters.

3. a. How high does it bounce on the first, second, and third bounces?
b. How many bounces until it bounces to fewer than 80 centimeters?
c. How many bounces until it bounces to fewer than 10 cm?

4. What is the total distance traveled by the ball (both down and up) if someone catches it at the top of its bounce after:
a. 2 bounces? b. 20 bounces?

5. Make a guess about the total distance traveled by the ball after 200 bounces. Justify your guess.

USING SYMBOLIC NOTATION

Say the bounce ratio is r. Then we have:

$$\frac{\textit{bounce height}}{\textit{drop height}} = r$$

Or: $\textit{bounce height} = r \cdot \textit{drop height}$

Assume that the initial drop height is H.

6. How high does the ball bounce on the first, second, third, and fourth bounces? Express your answers in terms of H and r.

To analyze the problem of the total distance traveled, it is easier to separate the upwards and downwards motions. First find the downwards distance traveled in the first four bounces.

$$D_4 = H + Hr + Hr^2 + Hr^3$$

As you see, the terms of the sum form a *geometric sequence* having first term H and *common ratio* r.

7. Write an expression for D_6 the downwards distance traveled in the first six bounces.

8. 🔑 What is the last exponent in the expression for the downwards distance traveled in the first n bounces? Explain why the exponent is not the same as the number of bounces.

9. Write an expression for the upwards distance traveled in:
a. the first four bounces, U_4;
b. the first six bounces, U_6.

10. 🔑 What is the last exponent in the expression for the upwards distance traveled in the first n bounces? Why does this differ from the expression for the downwards distance?

11.1 SOLUTIONS

1. Answers will vary.
2. ratio
3. a. first bounce: $2(0.8) = 1.6$ meters; second bounce: $2(0.8)^2 = 1.28$ meters; third bounce: $2(0.8)^3 = 1.024$
   b. fourth bounce: $2(0.8)^4 = 0.8192$; fifth bounce: $2(0.8)^5 = 0.655$
   It bounces to fewer than 80 centimeters on the fifth bounce.
   c. 13th bounce: $2(0.8)^{13} = 0.11$; 14th bounce: $2(0.8)^{14} = 0.088$
   It bounces to fewer than 10 centimeters on the fourteenth bounce.
4. These problems can be solved by making a table.
   a. about 6.48 meters
   b. about 17.8 meters
5. Answers will vary. (See #16.)
6. first bounce: Hr; second bounce: Hr^2; third bounce: Hr^3; fourth bounce: Hr^4
7. $H + Hr + Hr^2 + Hr^3 + Hr^4 + Hr^5$
8. The last exponent is $n - 1$. The first downward distance traveled depends on the drop height (H) only, not on the bounce ratio (r).
9. a. $U_4 = Hr + Hr^2 + Hr^3 + Hr^4$
   b. $U_6 = Hr + Hr^2 + Hr^3 + Hr^4 + Hr^5 + Hr^6$
10. The last exponent is n. This is because beginning with the first bounce the distance traveled upward depends on the bounce ratio.

FINDING THE SUM

Here is a shortcut for calculating the sum of a geometric sequence. We will use the example of the ideal ball having bounce ratio 0.8, dropped from a height of two meters, and caught at the top of its fourth bounce. First write the downwards motion.

Eq. 1: $D_4 = 2 + 2(0.8) + 2(0.8)^2 + 2(0.8)^3$

Do not calculate the sum! You will soon see why.

Multiplying both sides by 0.8, we get:

Eq. 2: $D_4(0.8) = 2(0.8) + 2(0.8)^2 + 2(0.8)^3 + 2(0.8)^4$

Subtracting one equation from the other:

Eq. 1-Eq. 2: $D_4 - D_4 \cdot (0.8) = 2 - 2(0.8)^4$

11. Explain why there are so few terms after subtracting.

12. *Solve* for D_4. (Hint: Factor, then divide.)

13. Use this *multiply-subtract-solve* technique to find U_4. You found an expression for U_4 in problem 9.

14. What is the total distance traveled by the ball in four bounces?

When adding only four terms, the multiply-subtract-solve technique is not much of a shortcut. However, when adding large numbers of terms, it is extremely convenient. For example, for 20 bounces, you would start by writing:

$D_{20} = 2 + 2(0.8) + ... + 2(0.8)^{18} + 2(0.8)^{19}$

15. Explain why in this case the last terms do not contribute very much to the sum.

16. Use the multiply-subtract-solve technique to check the correctness of your answers for problems 4b and 5.

OTHER BOUNCE RATIOS

17. What is the total distance traveled in 200 bounces by a ball having the following bounce ratios, after being dropped from a height of two meters?

a. a super-ball, having bounce ratio 0.9

b. a flat basketball, having bounce ratio 0.3

18. Repeat problems 3-5 for a real ball. (First, you must find the bounce ratio, perhaps by averaging the ratios you found in problem 1.) Verify your predictions for problem 3 with experiments.

An absent-minded professor invents a hyper-ball having a bounce ratio of 1.1.

19. Repeat problems 3-5 for the hyper-ball.

20. Repeat problems 3-5 for a defective hyper-ball having a bounce ratio of only 1.

21. **Summary** Summarize what you learned about the sum of geometric sequences.

a. Explain the multiply-subtract-solve method. (What does one multiply by? What does one subtract? What does one solve for, and how?)

b. What is the effect of the common ratio on the sum? (What if r is less than 1? What if it is equal to 1? What if it is greater than 1?)

22. **Generalization** Use the multiply-subtract-solve technique for each sum S.

a. $S = a + ar + ar^2 + ... + ar^{n-1}$

b. $S = a + ar + ar^2 + ... + ar^n$

11.1 SOLUTIONS

11. Everything cancels out except the first and last terms.

12. $D_4 - D_4 \cdot 0.8 = 2 - 2(0.8)^4$

$D_4[1 - 0.8] = 2[1 - (0.8)^4]$

$D_4 = \frac{2[1 - (0.8)^4]}{1 - 0.8}$

$D_4 = 10[1 - (0.8)^4] = 10[0.5904] = 5.904$

13. $U_4 - U_4 \cdot 0.8 = 2(0.8)^1 - 2(0.8)^5$

$U_4[1 - 0.8] = 2(0.8)[1 - (0.8)^4]$

$U_4 = \frac{2(0.8)[1 - (0.8)^4]}{1 - 0.8}$

$U_4 = 8[1 - (0.8)^4] = 8[0.5904] = 4.723$

14. $10[0.5904] + 8[0.5904] = 5.904 + 4.723 = 10.627$

15. The terms involve 0.8, a number less than one, raised to higher and higher powers. Powers of numbers less than one decrease as the exponent increases.

16. The last step for D_{20} is:

$D_{20} = 10[1 - (0.8)^{20}] \approx 9.88$

The last step for U_{20} is:

$U_{20} = 8[1 - (0.8)^{20}] \approx 7.91$

$D_{20} + U_{20} \approx 17.79$

The last step for D_{200} is:

$D_{200} = 10[1 - (0.8)^{200}] \approx 10$

The last step for U_{200} is:

$U_{200} = 8[1 - (0.8)^{200}] \approx 8$

$D_{20} + U_{20} \approx 18$

17. a. Use the pattern developed in the multiply-subtract-solve technique:

$D_{200} = \frac{2[1 - (0.9)^{200}]}{1 - 0.9} \approx 20$

$U_{200} = \frac{2(0.9)[1 - (0.9)^{200}]}{1 - 0.9} \approx 18$

$D_{200} + U_{200} = 38$

The point of this lesson is not to introduce the formula for the sum. There is more gained at this level by students using algebraic manipulation when calculating the sum, than "efficiently" calculating the sum with a formula. Students at this level do not have the maturity to keep in mind both the formula and its derivation. Moreover, it is easy to apply the formula incorrectly because of not remembering whether to use $n - 1$, or n, or $n + 1$ in a given problem. Finally, formula-wielding students often confuse the formula for the nth term with the formula for the sum.

(Any student who is conceptually ready to use the formula will be able to do it after problem 22.)

Note that each ball bouncing problem includes the calculation of two sums of geometric sequences, with the second term of one being the first term of the other. This forces students to keep alert and to remember what they are doing.

You may want to introduce the multiply-subtract-solve technique at the chalkboard, before letting students work on problems 11-15.

OTHER BOUNCE RATIOS

This section will allow students to practice what they have learned, but also to think about the difference between a common ratio r such that $r < 1$, and one such that $r \geq 1$.

You do not need to define convergence formally. At this level, all students need to realize is that the higher the exponent of r (if $r < 1$), the smaller the corresponding term.

There will be more applications of sums of geometric sequences in the following lessons. In addition, you can go back to the problems in Chapter 2, Lesson 5, and Chapter 7, Lesson 8.

DISCOVERY ***FOUR NUMBERS***

This section allows students to review the meaning of the four operations and the numerical value of fractions. Even though it is not essential to solving these problems, allow calculator use.

DISCOVERY ***FOUR NUMBERS***

23. a. Replace each box with one of the numbers: 1, 2, 3, 4. (Use each number exactly once.)

$$\frac{\square}{\square}+\frac{\square}{\square}$$

How many possible arrangements are there?

b. Which arrangement gives the smallest sum? What is the smallest sum?

c. Which arrangement gives the largest sum? What is the largest sum?

d. Are the arrangements that give the smallest and the largest answer *unique*? That is, is there only one arrangement that gives the same sum?

24. Repeat problem 23 for $\frac{\square}{\square}-\frac{\square}{\square}$, this time finding the arrangements that give the smallest and the largest difference. How are the smallest and the largest difference related? Explain.

25. Repeat problem 23 for $\frac{\square}{\square}\cdot\frac{\square}{\square}$, this time finding the arrangements that give the smallest and the largest product. How are the smallest and the largest product related? Explain.

26. Repeat problem 23 for $\frac{\square}{\square}\div\frac{\square}{\square}$, this time finding the arrangements that give the smallest and the largest quotient. How are the smallest and the largest quotient related? Explain.

27. Choose four numbers a, b, c, d such that $a < b < c < d$. Repeat problems 23-26 for these numbers. Compare your answers with other students' answers. Were you able to use the answers from problems 23-26 to help you?

28. **Report** Write a report summarizing your findings in problems 23 through 27. Describe the strategies you used for finding the smallest and the largest values. Explain why you were sure that they were the smallest and the largest.

11.1 SOLUTIONS

b. Use the pattern developed in the multiply-subtract-solve technique:

$$D_{200}=\frac{2[1-(0.3)^{200}]}{1-0.3}\approx 2.86$$

$$U_{200}=\frac{2(0.3)[1-(0.3)^{200}]}{1-0.3}\approx 0.86$$

$$D_{200}+U_{200}=3.72$$

18. Answers will vary.

19. Hyperball: bounce ratio 1.1
first bounce $2(1.1) = 2.2$
second bounce $2(1.1)^2 = 2.42$
third bounce $2(1.1)^3 = 2.66$
It never bounces fewer than 80 centimeters or 10 centimeters. The bounce height is always increasing. The total distance after n bounces is $D_n + U_n$ where

$$D_n=\frac{2[1-(1.1)^n]}{1-1.1}$$

$$U_n=\frac{2(1.1)[1-(1.1)^n]}{1-1.1}$$

If $n = 2$, $D_2 + U_2 = 4.2 + 4.62 = 8.82$
If $n = 20$, $D_{20} + U_{20} = 114.55 + 126.00 = 240.55$
If $n = 200$, $D_{200} + U_{200} = 3{,}798{,}105{,}509 + 4{,}177{,}916{,}060 = 7{,}976{,}021{,}569$

20. Defective hyperball: bounce ratio 1.0
first bounce $2(1.0) = 2.0$
second bounce $2(1.0)^2 = 2.0$
third bounce $2(1.0)^3 = 2.0$
The multiply-subtract-solve technique doesn't work. The denominator would be zero, which would make the expressions for D_n and U_n undefined. For n bounces, the total amount traveled is $4n$.

21. Answers will vary. Some main ideas follow:
   a. Write an equation for the sum of the sequences. Multiply both sides of this equation by the bounce ratio r. Subtract the second equation from the first equation. Solve for the sum by dividing, factoring out $1 - r$ from the left side and dividing by $1 - r$.
   b. If $r < 1$, the sum converges to $\frac{a}{1-r}$ because the term $1 - r^n$ in the numerator approaches 1 as n gets larger. If r is equal to 1, the sum is just an. If r is greater than 1, the sum gets larger and larger, and diverges.

22. a. $S = a + ar + ar^2 + ... + ar^{n-1}$
Multiply by r: $rS =$
$ar + ar^2 + ar^3 + ... + ar^n$

LESSON 11.2

Decimals and Fractions

WRITING FRACTIONS AS DECIMALS

1. How do you convert a fraction to a decimal number? Give examples.

When converting fractions to decimals, sometimes you get a *terminating* decimal like 3.4125, and sometimes you get a *repeating* decimal, like 7.8191919.... This last number is often written $7.8\overline{19}$.

Problems 2 and 3 are easier if you work with lowest-term fractions.

2. **Exploration** For what fractions do you get a repeating decimal? Does it depend on the numerator or the denominator? (Hint: Pay attention to the prime factorization of the numerator and the denominator.)

3. **Exploration** For repeating decimals, is there a pattern to the number of digits in the repeating part? What is the longest possible repeating string for a given denominator? (Hint: Use long division rather than a calculator to explore this.)

4. Explain why the decimals obtained as a result of a division *must* repeat or terminate.

5. Explain why some calculators give a decimal that does not seem to repeat for 2/3: 0.6666666667.

WRITING DECIMALS AS FRACTIONS

Example: 3.4125 can be converted to a fraction by multiplying it by 10^4, which gets rid of the decimal, and then dividing by 10^4, which gets us back to the original number.

$$\frac{34{,}125}{10{,}000}$$

6. Convert these decimals to fractions.

a. 6.0 b. 3.2

c. 0.015 d. 3.41

The case of repeating decimals is more difficult. Take $7.8\overline{19}$. Clearly, it is greater than 7.81 and less than 7.82. So it is between 781/100 and 782/100.

To find a single fraction it is equal to, we can rewrite it as:

$7.80\overline{19}$

$= 7.8 + 0.0\overline{19}$

$= 7.8 + 0.019 + 0.00019 + 0.0000019 + \ldots$

Observe that:

$$0.00019 = 0.019(0.01)$$
$$0.0000019 = 0.019(0.01)^2$$

7. Write the next term in the sum as a decimal, and as a product of 0.019 and a power of 0.01.

As you see, $7.8\overline{19}$ is the sum of 7.8 and a geometric sequence with first term 0.019 and common ratio 0.01. The sum of the first three terms of the geometric sequence can be written:

$$S = 0.019 + 0.019(0.01) + 0.019(0.01)^2$$

Multiply both sides by 0.01:

$$S(0.01) = 0.019(0.01) + 0.019(0.01)^2 + 0.019(0.01)^3$$

Subtract:

$$S(1 - 0.01) = 0.019 - 0.019(0.01)^3$$

Solve:

$$S = \frac{0.019 - 0.019(0.01)^3}{0.99}$$

Multiplying numerator and denominator by 1000:

$$S = \frac{19 - 19(0.01)^3}{990}$$

11.2. Decimals and Fractions

Core Sequence: 1-2, 5-16

Suitable for Homework: 8-16

Useful for Assessment: 5, 9, 16

What this Lesson is About:

- Review of converting fractions to decimals
- Converting decimals to fractions
- Definition of rational numbers

This lesson is mostly an application to decimals-fractions conversion of the previous lesson on sums of geometric sequences.

WRITING FRACTIONS AS DECIMALS

Problems 1-2 can be solved with the help of a calculator. However, remind students that the limited display of the calculator is not the most appropriate place to study the questions we address in this section, since the decimal expansion may terminate or repeat beyond the level of accuracy allowed by the calculator. The key idea is that denominators whose prime factors (in lowest terms) are exclusively 2 and 5 will terminate. All others will repeat.

11.2 SOLUTIONS

(11.1 Solutions continued)

Subtract: $S - rS = a - ar^n$

Factor and divide: $S(1 - r) = a(1 - r^n)$

$S = \frac{a(1 - r^n)}{1 - r}$

b. $S = a + ar + ar^2 + \ldots + ar^n$

Multiply by r: $rS = ar + ar^2 + ar^3 + \ldots + ar^{n+1}$

Subtract: $S - rS = a - ar^{n+1}$

Factor and divide: $S(1 - r) = a(1 - r^{n+1})$

$S = \frac{a(1 - r^{n+1})}{1 - r}$

1. Divide numerator by denominator. Examples will vary.
2. It depends on the denominator. If the prime factorization consists of twos and fives only, the decimal will terminate. Otherwise, it will repeat.
3. Answers will vary. One thing to note is that the number of repeating digits will never be more than the divisor.
4. There is only a certain number of remainders possible. Once a remainder appears again, the cycle will be repeated.
5. The calculator rounds off.
6. a. 60/10 or 6/1
   b. 32/10
   c. 15/1000
   d. 341/100
7. $0.019(0.01)^3$

*P*roblems 3-4 require the use of long division. The basic idea is that only so many remainders are possible. When they have all been used, the expansion must terminate or repeat. A full answer to problem 3 is difficult, but some partial answers are:

- If the denominator is d, the length of the repeating string must be $< d$.
- In fact, the length of the repeating string is often a factor of $(d - 1)$.

*P*roblem 5 is an opportunity to distinguish between a decimal approximation and a decimal representation for a given fraction.

WRITING DECIMALS AS FRACTIONS

RATIONAL NUMBERS

*Y*ou should probably demonstrate on the chalkboard how to apply the multiply-subtract-solve technique to the conversion of repeating decimals to fractions.

*P*roblem 16 can be answered by using the multiply-subtract-solve technique. However, do not be concerned if some students do not find the argument convincing. A real understanding of limits requires more mathematical maturity.

$$7.8\overline{19} = 7.8 + S$$

$$= 7.8 + \frac{19 - 19(0.01)^3}{990}$$

$$= \frac{7.8(990) + 19 - 19(0.01)^3}{990}$$

So

$$= \frac{7741 - 19(0.01)^3}{990}$$

$$= \frac{7741 - 0.000019}{990}$$

The sum is very close to 7741/990.

8. Use the multiply-subtract-solve technique to add:

a. the first 4 terms;

b. the first 5 terms.

9. The numerator differs from 7741 by $19(0.01)^n$ if we add up the first n terms. Explain.

If we use large values for n, we find that the sum can get as close to 7741/990 as we want. (Even with fairly small values of n, the sum of the first n terms differs from 7741/990 by a *very* small number.) Mathematicians say that the whole infinite sum *converges* to 7741/990, and they agree that we can write an equality:

$$7.8\overline{19} = 7741/990.$$

10. Check that this equality is correct, by converting the fraction back to a decimal.

A quick way to find the fraction is to use the multiply-subtract-solve technique on the decimal itself:

$$R = 7.8191919...$$
$$0.01\,R = 0.0781919...$$

Subtract:

$$R - 0.01R = 7.8191919... - 0.0781919...$$
$$(1 - 0.01)R = 7.819 - 0.078$$

(Notice that the infinite sequence of 19s disappeared.)

$$0.99R = 7.741$$
$$R = \frac{7.741}{0.99} = \frac{7741}{990}$$

11. Convert to a fraction.

a. $0.\overline{65}$ b. $4.\overline{321}$

RATIONAL NUMBERS

Definition: A *rational number* is a number that can be written as a fraction having an integer numerator and denominator.

Examples: 7, 0.5, and -0.66666... are rational numbers, because they can be written as 7/1, 1/2, and -2/3.

Show that the following numbers are rational.

12. a. 0.3

b. 0.3333...

13. a. 0.142857

b. $0.\overline{142857}$

14. a. 0.0909090...

b. 0.9090909...

15. a. 0.1111111...

b. 0.2222222...

16. Mathematicians believe that 0.99999... = 1. Explain why.

11.2 SOLUTIONS

8. a. $\frac{7741 - 19(0.01)^4}{990} \approx \frac{7741}{990}$

b. $\frac{7741 - 19(0.01)^5}{990} \approx \frac{7741}{990}$

9. When n terms are added, the quantity subtracted from 7741 in the numerator is $19(0.01)^n$.

10. It works.

11. a. 65/99
b. 4317/999

12. a. 3/10
b. 3/9

13. a. 142857/1000000
b. 1/7

14. a. 9/99 = 1/11
b. 90/99

15. a. 1/9
b. 2/9

16. This can be written as the sum of a geometric series. Using the multiply-subtract-solve technique, one can show that we can get as close to 1 as we like by adding more terms.

LESSON 11.3

Stairs and Squares

You will need:

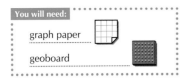

- graph paper
- geoboard

STAIR SAFETY

In most houses, stairs have a riser (or rise) of eight inches and a tread (or run) of nine inches. However, safety experts claim that such stairs are the cause of many accidents. They recommend what they call 7/11 stairs: a riser of seven inches, and a tread of eleven inches.

1. What are the slopes of the stairs described in the previous paragraph? (Express the answer as a decimal.)
2. If a staircase makes a vertical rise of about nine feet from one floor to the next, how much horizontal distance does it take
   a. for 8/9 stairs?
   b. for 7/11 stairs?
3. Why do you think 8/9 stairs are more common?
4. **Exploration** Donna wants to build a staircase that is less steep than an 8/9 staircase would be, but that does not take up as much horizontal space as a 7/11 staircase would. What are the possibilities for the riser and tread of Donna's stairs? Make the following assumptions:
   - The riser and tread must each be a whole number of inches.
   - The riser should be between six and nine inches, inclusive.
   - The tread should be between eight and twelve inches, inclusive.

   Express your answer numerically and graphically.

STAIRS ON LINES

To build a staircase on the graph of a line:

a. Sketch the graph.
b. Find the coordinates of a point on the graph. Call this point the starting point.
c. Find two numbers (the rise and the run) such that if you draw a step having those dimensions, you end up on the line.

The figure shows a staircase for the line $y = -x + 2$.

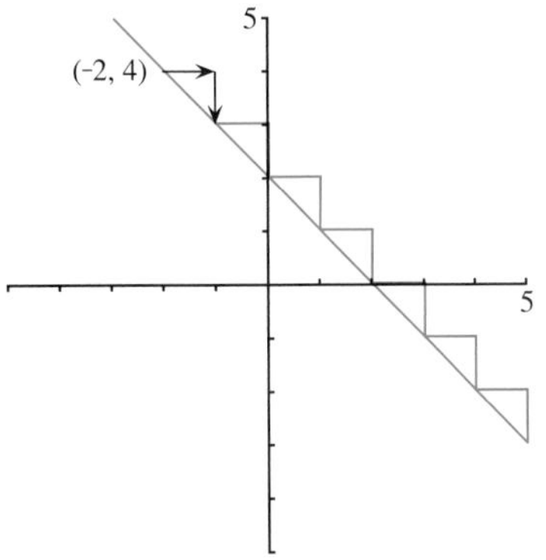

The starting point is (-2, 4), the rise is -1, and the run is 1.

5. Create a staircase for the same line, using a different starting point and a different rise and run.
6. Create *two* staircases for each line. They must have a different starting point and a different rise and run.
   a. $y = -4 + 3x$
   b. $y = -0.5x$
   c. $y = 9$

▼ 11.3 Stairs and Squares

Core Sequence: 1-13

Suitable for Homework: 5-19

Useful for Assessment: 12-13, 18

What this Lesson is About:

- Review of slope
- Review of equivalent fractions
- Review of direct variation
- Slope relationships

STAIR SAFETY

STAIRS ON LINES

These sections review slope.

Students may be interested in measuring the risers and tread of actual stairs, both at school and at home. Interviews with carpenters, contractors, and architects will yield interesting stories relating to the design of stairs in actual buildings.

Problem 4 is presented in such a way as to prepare students for the emphasis on lattice points in the latter part of the lesson. An excellent graphical representation of the solution is to draw a rectangle with $8 \le x \le 12$ and $6 \le y \le 9$. Lattice points in this rectangle are possible candidates for Donna's stairs. However her slope requirements limit the solution to the ones between the lines $y = (8/9)x$ and $y = (7/11)x$. Of course, the solution can also be found by calculation.

11.3 SOLUTIONS

1. $7/11 = 0.6\overline{36}3$
   $8/9 = 0.8\overline{8}$
2. a. $8/9 = 9/x$ so $x = 10.125$ feet
   b. $7/11 = 9/x$ so $x = 14\ 1/7$ feet
3. They use less horizontal space.
4. The possibilities are shown in the table. One way of solving this problem is to convert all the fractions to decimals and compare the results with the decimal equivalents of 7.11 and 8/9.

riser					
9	9/8	9/9	9/10	9/11	9/12
8	8/8	8/9	8/10	8/11	8/12
7	7/8	7/9	7/10	7/11	7/12
6	6/8	6/9	6/10	6/11	6/12
tread →	8	9	10	11	12

Another approach is to graph the lines $y = (7/11)x$ and $y = (8/9)x$. All lines of the form $y = mx$ with slopes between 7/11 and 8/9 will lie between these two lines. To tell whether a staircase will have a steepness between 7/11 and 8/9, plot the point (tread, riser). If it lies between the two graphs, it fits Donna's specifications. See the graph.

4.

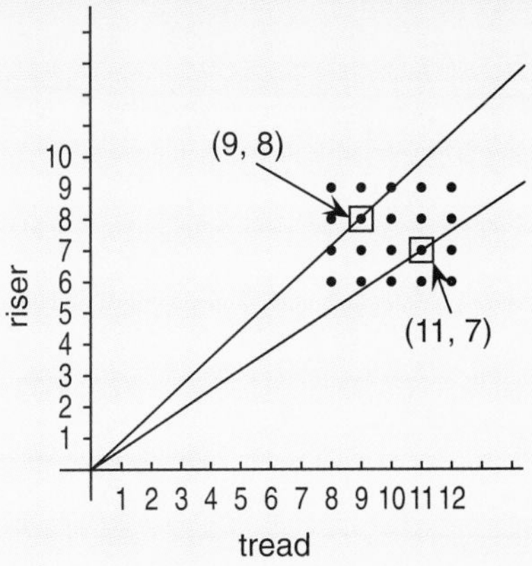

LATTICE POINTS AND FRACTIONS

This section reviews the work on direct variation, which took place in Chapter 4. This provides a different emphasis and connects it with the idea of rational and irrational numbers.

Problem 11 previews the question of the existence of irrational numbers that is addressed in the next lesson.

GEOBOARD DIAGONALS

Problem 14 is difficult and works well as a *problem of the week,* because students can find partial answers by experimenting. If you use it that way, give students enough time to think about it. Otherwise use it in class, as a group exploration.

Students are guided through a solution in problems 15-17. Note that the solution relies on an understanding of the ideas in the previous section.

d. $y = \frac{6x - 7}{8}$

e. $y = -2(x - 3)$

7. Find a rise and a run for a staircase connecting the following pairs of points:
a. (3, -5) and (2, 2.5)
b. (-3, 5) and (2, 2.5)

8. A staircase having the given rise and run starts at the given point. What is the equation of the corresponding line?
a. rise = 4, run = 6, point = (-3, 6)
b. rise = -2, run = -3, point = (0, 8)

LATTICE POINTS AND FRACTIONS

Definition: A *lattice point* is a point on the Cartesian plane having integer coordinates.

Examples: (2, 3) is a lattice point, but (4.5, 6) is not.

9. The graph of each of the following equations is a line through the origin. Find two other lattice points on each line.

a. $y = 7x$ b. $y = \frac{2}{3}x$
c. $y = 4.5x$ d. $y = 6.78x$

If a line passes through the origin and the lattice point (9, 8), it will also pass through the lattice points $(9n, 8n)$ for all integer values of n.

10. If a line passes through the origin and the point (2.4, 3.6),
a. what are the lattice points on the line that are closest to the origin?
b. what is a general description of all the lattice points on the line?
c. what is the equation of the line?

11. Do all lines through the origin pass through another lattice point sooner or later? Discuss.

Generalizations

12. What is the slope of a line that passes through the origin and a lattice point (p, q), where $p \neq 0$?

13. Describe the lattice points on the line $y = (p/q)x$, where $p \neq 0$.

GEOBOARD DIAGONALS

If you connect (0, 0) to (5, 3) with a straight line, you go through seven unit squares.

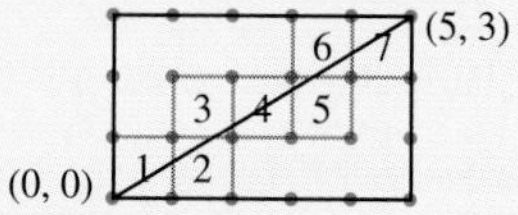

14. Exploration If you connect (0, 0) to (p, q) with a straight line, how many unit squares do you go through? Experiment and look for patterns. (Assume p and q are positive whole numbers.) Keep a record of your work.

Definition: A *lattice line* is a line having equation $x = b$ or $y = b$, where b is an integer.

The following problems are about the diagonal connecting (0, 0) to (p, q). Give answers in terms of p and q.

15. a. How many horizontal lattice lines does it cross? (Look at some specific cases and make a generalization. Do not guess.)
b. How many vertical lattice lines does it cross?

11.3 SOLUTIONS

5.

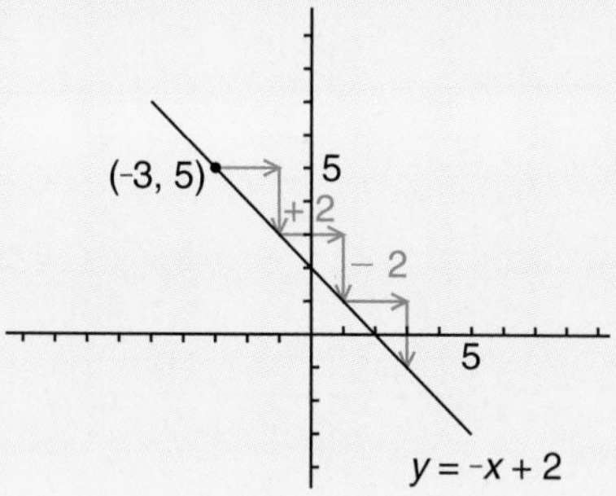

6. a.

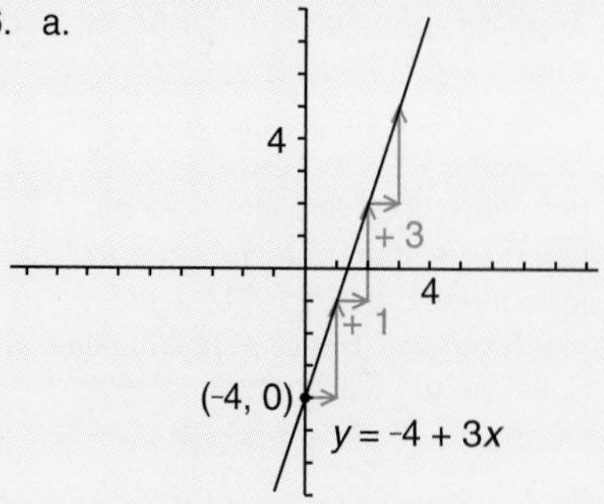

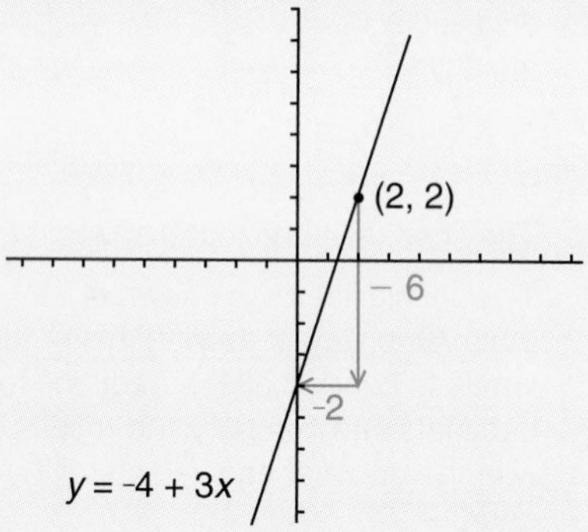

16. How many lattice points does it cross,
a. if the greatest common factor of p and q is 1?
b. if the greatest common factor of p and q is n, where $n > 1$? (Experiment and reason. Do not guess.)

17. The diagonal starts in the first unit square, then every time it crosses a lattice line it enters a new square.
a. If it crosses no lattice points, how many squares does it go through altogether?
b. If it crosses n lattice points, how many squares does it cross?

18. Report How many squares do the diagonals of geoboard rectangles go through? Write an illustrated report, including examples.

DISCOVERY SLOPE RELATIONSHIPS

Lines	Slopes
parallel	opposite
perpendicular	opposite of reciprocal
symmetric across horizontal line	reciprocal
symmetric across the line $y = x$	reciprocal of opposite
symmetric across vertical line	same

The first column shows possible relationships between two lines. The second column shows possible relationships between the slopes of two lines.

19. Project Experiment to find out if it is possible to match relationships in the first column with relationships in the second column. (For example, parallel lines have the same slope.) Support your answers with examples, sketches, and explanations.

DISCOVERY SLOPE RELATIONSHIPS

This is a good way to review slope while investigating an interesting mathematical question. Students may use graphing calculators and/or graph paper. The slope of perpendicular lines was previewed on geoboards in Chapter 6, Lesson 12.

11.3 SOLUTIONS

6. b.

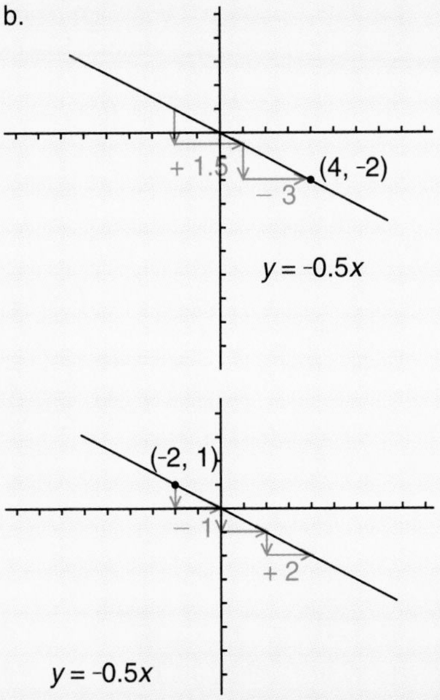

6. c.

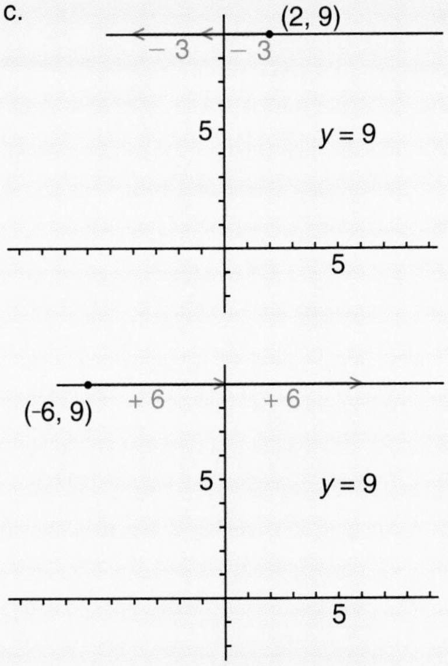

6. d.

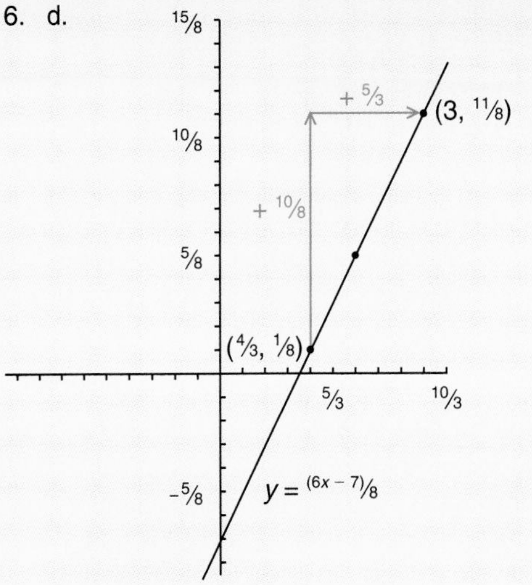

(Solutions continued on page 528)

▼ 11.4
Irrational Numbers

Core Sequence: 1-18

Suitable for Homework: 2-9, 14-21

Useful for Assessment: 8-9, 14-15, 18

What this Lesson is About:

- Existence of irrational numbers
- Review of prime factorization
- Irrationality of $\sqrt{2}$

The example given of an irrational number can be adapted to answering problem 1. Because this number is created in such an artificial way, students may conclude that irrational numbers are the exception. However the opposite is true; there are infinitely more irrational numbers than rational.

PRIME FACTORIZATION

The fact that the prime factorization of any number is unique is the key to this lesson. We will not attempt to prove it formally.

Your students should have learned in middle school how to find the prime factorization of numbers. However they may not be familiar with the results presented in problems 7-9.

If your class is ready for this, you may discuss those problems by using algebraic notation. For problem 8: If a number has prime factorization $p_1 \cdot p_2 \cdot \ldots \cdot p_n$, its square will be $(p_1 \cdot p_2 \cdot \ldots \cdot p_n)^2 = p_1^2 \cdot p_2^2 \cdot \ldots \cdot p_n^2$, an even number of prime factors. Problem 9 can be discussed in a similar way.

THE SQUARE ROOT OF TWO

The basic argument presented in this section should probably be the subject of a class discussion.

An alternate approach, which is less general but is intimately related to the one presented here, does not require a full grasp of prime factorization. It is based on first establishing that the square of an even number is a multiple of four, while the square of an odd number is odd. Moreover, students need to agree that a multiple of four is always equal to twice an even number, never twice an odd number. Then, if we assume p/q is in lowest terms, we know that at least either p or q must be odd. Since $p^2 = 2q^2$, p must be even, and q must be odd. Therefore p^2 must be a multiple of

LESSON 11.4

Irrational Numbers

In Lesson 2 you learned how to show that any terminating or repeating decimal can be converted to a fraction. In other words, you know how to show that terminating or repeating decimals are rational numbers.

If a decimal is neither repeating nor terminating, it represents an *irrational number* (one that is not rational).

For example, the number

0.010110111011110111110...,

created by inserting one, two, three, ... 1's between the 0's, never ends or repeats. Therefore it cannot be written as a fraction, because if it were, it would have to terminate or repeat.

1. Create an irrational number that is
   a. greater than 1 and less than 1.1;
   b. greater than 1.11 and less than 1.12.

While most numbers we deal with every day are rational, and even though there is an infinite number of rational numbers, mathematicians have proved that most real numbers are irrational.

$\sqrt{2}$ and $\sqrt{3}$ are familiar examples of irrational numbers. They cannot be written as a fraction having whole number numerators and denominators. In order to prove this, we will need to review prime factorization.

PRIME FACTORIZATION

Every whole number can be written as a product of prime factors.

Example: $990 = 99 \cdot 10$
$= 9 \cdot 11 \cdot 2 \cdot 5$
$= 2 \cdot 3 \cdot 3 \cdot 5 \cdot 11$

Note that 990 has a total of five prime factors. (Three is counted twice since it appears twice.)

2. Start the factorization of 990 by writing $990 = 3 \cdot 330$. Do you get the same prime factors?
3. Start the factorization of 990 a third way. Do you get the same prime factors?

Each whole number greater than 1 has *only one* prime factorization. Find it for the following numbers:

4. 12
5. 345
6. 6789
7. Find the prime factorization of several perfect squares. Try to find one having an odd number of prime factors.

Take the numbers 6 and 8. We have

$$6 = 2 \cdot 3 \text{ and } 8 = 2^3.$$

Six has two prime factors, an even number. Eight has three prime factors, an odd number. When we square them, we get:

$$6^2 = (2 \cdot 3)^2 = 2^2 \cdot 3^2$$
$$8^2 = (2^3)^2 = 2^6$$

8. Explain why any perfect square *must* have an even number of prime factors.
9. Explain why any number that is equal to twice a perfect square *must* have an odd number of prime factors.

THE SQUARE ROOT OF TWO

This section explains why $\sqrt{2}$ is not a rational number. The way we are going to do this is to show that if it were, it would lead to an impossible situation. This is called proof by contradiction.

11.4 SOLUTIONS

1. Answers will vary. Sample answers are given.
   a. 1.010010001 ...
   b. 1.11010010001 ...
2. Answers will vary. All will lead to the same prime factorization.
3. yes
4. $3 \cdot 2^2$
5. $5 \cdot 3 \cdot 23$
6. $3 \cdot 31 \cdot 73$
7. impossible
8. Suppose that the number is greater than 1 and $(p \cdot q \cdot r \cdot s)$ is a prime factorization. Then the prime factorization of its square is $p^2 \cdot q^2 \cdot r^2 \cdot s^2$. Every prime factor appears twice as many times in the square as it does in the original number. That is, if the original number has n prime factors, the square has $2n$, which is an even number.

   If the original number was equal to 1, then it has 0 prime factors, and its square has 0 prime factors. Since 0 is an even number, the statement is true here too.
9. It has an even number plus 1, since by multiplying by 2 we have added one more prime factor.

If p and q were nonzero whole numbers and we had

$$\frac{p}{q} = \sqrt{2}$$

It would follow that $\left(\frac{p}{q}\right)^2 = (\sqrt{2})^2$

$$\frac{p^2}{q^2} = 2$$

$$p^2 = 2q^2$$

10. Explain each step in the previous calculations.

11. Explain why p^2 must have an even number of prime factors.

12. Explain why $2q^2$ must have an odd number of prime factors.

13. Explain why p^2 cannot equal $2q^2$.

We conclude that there can be no whole numbers p and q such that $\sqrt{2} = p/q$, and therefore $\sqrt{2}$ is irrational.

14. Use the same method to show that $\sqrt{3}$ is irrational.

15. Show why the method does not work to prove that $\sqrt{4}$ is irrational.

16. Does the decimal expansion of $\sqrt{2}$ terminate or repeat?

17. Does the line $y = \sqrt{2}x$ pass through any lattice points?

18. Do all lines through the origin eventually pass through a lattice point? Discuss.

19. Research π is probably the world's most famous irrational number. Find out about its history.

DISCOVERY *SUM FRACTIONS*

20. Find two lowest-term fractions having different denominators whose sum is 8/9.

DISCOVERY *COMPARING COUPONS*

21. Which is a better deal, 15% off the purchase price, or \$1 off every \$5 spent? Make a graph that shows how much you save with each discount, for various purchases from \$1 to \$20. Write about your conclusions.

four, but $2q^2$ cannot be, since it is equal to twice an odd number.

Problems 14-18 will allow you to check students' understanding of the ideas presented in this section.

DISCOVERY *SUM FRACTIONS*

This seemingly simple problem will offer an opportunity to review the addition and subtraction of fractions.

DISCOVERY *COMPARING COUPONS*

At first sight, the \$1 off every \$5 spent appears to be a better deal, since that is 20%. However, on closer inspection, it turns out that the problem is a little more complicated than it appears. The graph will involve a step function. Step functions were previously seen in Chapter 2, Lesson 6; Chapter 4, Lesson 11; and Chapter 6, Lesson 3.

11.4 SOLUTIONS

10. Square both sides. Then multiply both sides by q^2.
11. It is a perfect square. (See #8.)
12. It is twice a perfect square. (See #9.)
13. One must have an even number of prime factors and the other must have an odd number. Since the prime factorization of any whole number is unique, the two numbers could not possibly be equal.
14. Suppose $(p/q) = \sqrt{3}$. Then $(p/q)^2 = 3$. So $p^2/q^2 = 3$ and hence $p^2 = 3q^2$. Since p^2 and q^2 both have an even number of prime factors, $3q^2$ has an odd number of prime factors. Therefore $p^2 \neq 3q^2$, since they cannot have the same number of prime factors. Hence our assumption that $\sqrt{3}$ can be written in the form p/q where p and q are integers is incorrect. It is not a rational number.
15. 4 is $2 \cdot 2$, so in the third step of the argument we would get $p^2 = 2 \cdot 2 \cdot q^2$. Both sides could have an even number of prime factors, so they could be equal.
16. No, it is irrational.
17. None except the origin. It would have to pass through points of the form (qn, pn), where p and q are integers $p/q = \sqrt{2}$. We have shown that $\sqrt{2}$ cannot be written in the form p/q.
18. No. Lines of the form $y = mx$ will pass only through lattice points other than the origin if m is a rational number.

THINKING WRITING

11.A Nested Squares

Core Sequence: 1-10

Suitable for Homework: 10

Useful for Assessment: 10

What this Assignment is About:

- Review of geoboard area
- Review of square roots
- Application of geometric sequences and sums of geometric sequences

This reviews the work on geoboard area and square roots, particularly Chapter 7, Lesson 12, and Chapter 9, **Thinking/Writing 9.C.**

Students may not realize that the sequences for the sides and perimeters are geometric. Those sequences appear to be geometric sequences having ratio 1/2, if one looks only at even or odd terms. The common ratio if looking at all the terms is $1/\sqrt{2}$. You should give students enough time on this assignment so that if there is a need for class discussion of this point, you will be able to have it.

THINKING WRITING

11.A Nested Squares

You will need:
geoboard
and/or dot paper

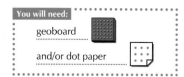

1. Using your geoboard or dot paper, make an 8-by-8 square. Calculate its area and perimeter.
2. Now make a square that is nested in the original square, like in the diagram. Its vertices should be the midpoints of the sides of the original square. Find its area and perimeter.

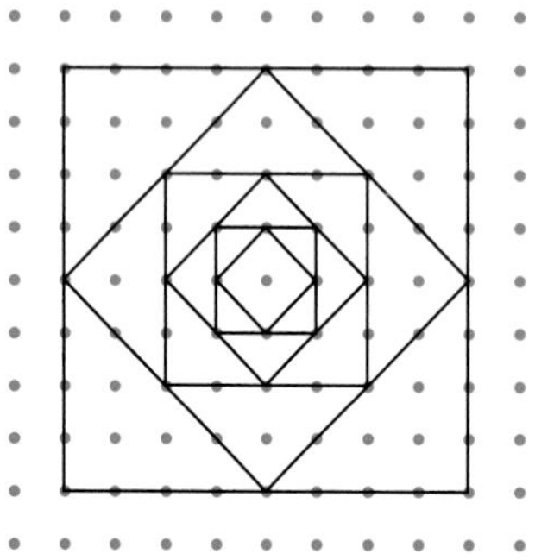

3. Continue the process, making smaller and smaller nested squares. As you work, extend and complete a table like the following one up to Square #5. When the numbers involve square roots, write them in simple radical form.

Square #	Area	Side	Perimeter
1	64	8	32

4. Look for a pattern in each of the columns. Describe the patterns for the
   a. areas;
   b. sides;
   c. perimeters.
5. Use the pattern you found in problem 4. For the 10th nested square, find
   a. the area;
   b. the side;
   c. the perimeter.
6. Repeat problem 5 for the nth nested square.
7. For the first ten squares, what is the sum of:
   a. the areas;
   b. the sides;
   c. the perimeters.
8. Repeat problem 7 for the first n squares.
9. With larger and larger values of n, the sums get closer and closer to a certain number. What is that number for:
   a. the areas?
   b. the sides?
   c. the perimeters?
10. **Report** Write a report on nested squares.

11.A SOLUTIONS

1.-8. See the table.

square #	area	side-length	perimeter	sum of areas	sum of side lengths	sum of side perimeters
1	64	8	32	64	8	32
2	32	$4\sqrt{2}$	$16\sqrt{2}$	96	$8 + 4\sqrt{2}$	$32 + 16\sqrt{2}$
3	16	4	16	112	$12 + 4\sqrt{2}$	$48 + 16\sqrt{2}$
4	8	$2\sqrt{2}$	$8\sqrt{2}$	120	$12 + 6\sqrt{2}$	$48 + 24\sqrt{2}$
5	4	2	8	124	$14 + 6\sqrt{2}$	$56 + 24\sqrt{2}$
6	2	$\sqrt{2}$	$4\sqrt{2}$	126	$14 + 7\sqrt{2}$	$56 + 28\sqrt{2}$
7	1	1	4	127	$15 + 7\sqrt{2}$	$60 + 28\sqrt{2}$
8	0.5	$1/\sqrt{2}$	$4/\sqrt{2}$	127.5	$15 + 7.5\sqrt{2}$	$60 + 30\sqrt{2}$
9	0.25	1/2	2	127.75	$15.5 + 7.5\sqrt{2}$	$62 + 30\sqrt{2}$
10	0.125	$1/(2\sqrt{2})$	$\sqrt{2}$	127.875	$15.5 + 7.75\sqrt{2}$	$62 + 31\sqrt{2}$
n	$(1/2)^{n-1} \cdot 64$	$(1/\sqrt{2})^{n-1} \cdot 8$	$(1/\sqrt{2})^{n-1} \cdot 32$	See (i) below.	See (ii) below.	See (iii) below.

(i) $64\,[1 + 1/2 + \ldots (1/2)^{n-1}]$
(ii) $8\,[1 + 1/\sqrt{2} + \ldots (1/\sqrt{2})^{n-1}]$
(iii) $32\,[1 + 1/\sqrt{2} + \ldots (1/\sqrt{2})^{n-1}]$

9. a. 128
   b. $8\,[2 + 2\sqrt{2}]$
   c. $32\,[2 + 2\sqrt{2}]$

10. Reports will vary. They might include a comparison of the numbers in #9 with the area, side-length, and perimeter of the original square. A table may help students identify patterns to be discussed and analyzed in the report.

LESSON 11.5

Dice Games

You will need:

dice 

TWO GAMES

1. **Exploration** Play these two games with another person. To play a game, roll a pair of dice 20 times. After each roll, add the numbers on the uppermost faces. Keep track of how many rolls each player wins. (See below.) Whoever wins the most rolls, wins that game.

   Game One: If the sum is 3, 5, 7, 9, or 11, Player A wins. If the sum is 2, 4, 6, 8, 10, or 12, Player B wins.

   Game Two: If the sum is 5, 6, 7, 8, or 9, Player A wins. If the sum is 2, 3, 4, 10, 11, or 12, Player B wins.

   For each game, who wins more often? Why?

TWO-DICE SUMS

If you roll a red die and a blue die, there are many possible outcomes. We will use (4, 3) to refer to the outcome in which 4 dots appear uppermost on the red die and 3 dots appear uppermost on the blue die. Likewise (3, 4) refers to 3 on the red die and 4 on the blue die.

(4, 3) 

(3, 4) 

Both of the outcomes in the figure show a sum of seven.

2. Copy and extend this table to show all possible two-dice sums. For each sum, list all the possible ways it can be obtained, and give the total number of ways. The sums of 2 and 7 have been done to get you started.

Sum	2	...	7	...	12
Possible ways	(1, 1)	...	(1, 6) (2, 5) (3, 4) (4, 3) (5, 2) (6, 1)	...	...
# of ways	1	...	6	...	...

3. Which sums have the most ways of occurring? Which sums have the fewest ways of occurring?

4. **Summary** Analyze the games in problem 1 using the table you made. Explain why some sums are more likely to occur than others and how this determines who wins more often.

Definition: A game is *fair* if each of the players is equally likely to win.

5. Is Game One fair? How about Game Two? Explain.

OUTCOMES AND EVENTS

Definition: We call one roll of the dice an *experiment*. Each of the different possibilities you listed in the table is called an *outcome* of the experiment.

11.5 SOLUTIONS

1. See the solution to #4 below.
2.

Sum	2	3	4	5	6	7	8	9	10	11	12
Possible ways	(1,1)	(1,2) (2,1)	(1,3) (2,2) (3,1)	(1,4) (2,3) (3,2) (4,1)	(1,5) (2,4) (3,3) (4,2) (5,1)	(1,6) (2,5) (3,4) (4,3) (5,2) (6,1)	(2,6) (3,5) (4,4) (5,3) (6,2)	(3,6) (4,5) (5,4) (6,3)	(4,6) (5,5) (6,4)	(5,6) (6,5)	(6,6)
# of ways	1	2	3	4	5	6	5	4	3	2	1

3. The "inside" sums have the most ways of occurring. The "outside" sums have the fewest.
4. There are 36 possible outcomes, as can be seen from the table. Eighteen of these yield odd sums and eighteen yield even sums, so in Game 1 the first player and the second player have the same number of winning possibilities. In Game 2 the first player has 24 winning possibilities, while the second player has only 12.
5. Game One is fair. Game Two is not, since one player is twice as likely to win as the other.

▼ 11.5 Dice Games

Core Sequence: 1-18

Suitable for Homework: 2-8, 13-22

Useful for Assessment: 4-5, 17-18

What this Lesson is About:

- Introduction to probability
- Fair games
- Experiment, outcome, and event
- Preview of the multiplication counting principle
- Quantities and constraints

You will need a pair of dice for each pair of students. It is best if the dice in each pair are of different colors.

TWO GAMES

You may have students play these games without opening the book. This will reduce the temptation to read ahead for the analysis of the game.

After students have played each game once, (and some will have time to play twice), combine all the results on the chalkboard in a format like this:

Game One:

Player A rolls: 9, 8, 8, 11, 10, …
Player B rolls: 11, 12, 12, 9, 10, …
Totals for class:
Player A wins 14 games
Player B wins 16 games
Player A wins 289 rolls (48%)
Player B wins 311 rolls (52%)

And similarly for Game Two.

Students are often surprised by the results of Game Two, particularly when they see that what happened in their group was replicated in the other groups.

You may discuss the reasons for these results. If some of your students have played Dungeons and Dragons (or studied probability in previous classes) they may have some insights into the games that they can share with the class. In any case, a full analysis of the game is presented in the next section.

TWO-DICE SUMS

This section serves as a transition. On the one hand, it provides an analysis of the games in problem 1, and on the other hand, it previews the ideas of outcomes and events that are discussed in the next section.

Note that the layout of the table in problem 2 makes it look like a histogram.

This section is easy enough to be homework.

OUTCOMES AND EVENTS

These definitions help organize students' thinking about probability experiments. A formal definition of probability will appear in Chapter 11, Lesson 6. It depends on an understanding of the definitions presented here.

Problems 6-8 preview the multiplication counting principle.

Because the definitions are subtle, it is best to discuss them in class.

For problems 11-14, students can construct tables like the ones presented in the text. However, if they have some other way to get the answers, allow that. These tables will be useful in answering questions in Lesson 6. Students may want to keep these tables and charts for use then.

6. When you roll a red die and a blue die, how many outcomes are possible?

7. If you flip a penny and a nickel, how many outcomes (heads and tails) are possible? Make a list.

8. If you roll a red, a blue, and a yellow die, how many outcomes are possible?

When an experiment is performed, we are usually interested in whether or not a particular *event* has occurred. An event consists of one or more outcomes.

In the two-dice experiment, an example of an event could be: *The sum of the dots is even.* This event was important in Game One of problem 1. In that game, 36 outcomes were possible. However, we were not interested in the individual outcomes, but only in which of the two events had occurred: an even sum or an odd sum.

9. In what events were we interested in Game Two of problem 1?

10. The outcome of a two-dice experiment is (3, 2). Which of the following events occurred?
a. The difference is even.
b. The product is even.
c. One die shows a multiple of the other.
d. The sum is a prime number.

The table you made in problem 2 was organized to show these *events*: the sum of the dots is 2, the sum of the dots is 3, etc. In that table, each column corresponds to one event. A table like the following one is another way to represent the two-dice experiment. It is organized around the *outcomes*. Each cell corresponds to one outcome.

Blue Die

Red Die	1	2	3	4	5	6
1	(1, 1)	(1, 2)	(1, 3)	(1, 4)	(1, 5)	(1, 6)
2	(2, 1)	(2, 2)	(2, 3)	(2, 4)	(2, 5)	(2, 6)
...	...	...	...	...	...	...

In the two-dice experiment, figure out how many outcomes make up each event in problems 11-14.

You can make the same kind of table to help answer problems 11-14. For example, to think about problem 11a, you would write the products in the cells.

Blue Die

Red Die	1	2	3	4	5	6
1	1	2	3	4	5	6
2	2	4	...	...	...	...

11. a. The product is even.
b. The difference is even.
c. One die shows a multiple of the other.

12. a. The sum is 2, 3, or 4.
b. The sum is 9, 10, or 12.

13. a. a double
b. not a double

14. a. The sum is prime.
b. The product is prime.
c. The difference is prime.

11.5 SOLUTIONS

6. 36
7. Four possibilities: TT, TH, HT, HH
8. For every possibility in #6, there are six possibilities for the yellow die, so the total number is $6 \cdot 6 \cdot 6 = 216$.
9. The "inside" sums and the "outside" sums
10. (b) and (d)
Making the tables below will help students answer #11 - #14.

Outcomes:

Blue Die

Red Die	1	2	3	4	5	6
1	(1, 1)	(1, 2)	(1, 3)	(1, 4)	(1, 5)	(1, 6)
2	(2, 1)	(2, 2)	(2, 3)	(2, 4)	(2, 5)	(2, 6)
3	(3, 1)	(3, 2)	(3, 3)	(3, 4)	(3, 5)	(3, 6)
4	(4, 1)	(4, 2)	(4, 3)	(4, 4)	(4, 5)	(4, 6)
5	(5, 1)	(5, 2)	(5, 3)	(5, 4)	(5, 5)	(5, 6)
6	(6, 1)	(6, 2)	(6, 3)	(6, 4)	(6, 5)	(6, 6)

Products:

Blue Die

Red Die	1	2	3	4	5	6
1	1	2	3	4	5	6
2	2	4	6	8	10	12
3	3	6	9	12	15	18
4	4	8	12	16	20	24
5	5	10	15	20	25	30
6	6	12	18	24	30	36

Sums:

Blue Die

Red Die	1	2	3	4	5	6
1	2	3	4	5	6	7
2	3	4	5	6	7	8
3	4	5	6	7	8	9
4	5	6	7	8	9	10
5	6	7	8	9	10	11
6	7	8	9	10	11	12

11. a. 27 b. 18
c. 22
12. a. 6 b. 8
13. a. 6 b. 30
14. a. 15 (sums 2, 3, 5, 7, and 11)
b. 6 (products 2, 3, and 5, which each appears twice)
c. 16

CREATE DICE GAMES

15. Name two events in the two-dice experiment that each consist of nine outcomes.

16. Name an event in the two-dice experiment that consists of:

a. 17 outcomes;

b. 19 outcomes.

17. Create a dice game that is fair. Write the rules. Then write an explanation of why the game is fair.

18. Create a dice game that appears to favor one player, but that actually favors the other. Or, make up a dice game that appears to be fair, but that actually favors one player. Write the rules and an explanation of the game.

DISCOVERY THREE QUANTITIES, THREE CONSTRAINTS

These problems were invented by algebra students. You may want to use colored slips of paper to solve them. In each one, there are three unknown quantities and three constraints. Try to find the three unknown quantities.

19. The red and yellow marbles add up to 5.
Blue and red add up to 7.
There are 8 yellows and blues altogether.

20. The blue and red add up to 9.
There are two times as many yellows as blues.
There are 15 marbles altogether.

21. Blue + 9 = Black
Blue times 3 = Red
Black + 1 = Red

22. $A + B = 11$
$A + C = 7$
$B + C = 6$
How many of each?

CREATE DICE GAMES

Students' answers to problems 15-18 should be discussed and compared. Problem 18 in particular lends itself to oral presentations.

In problems 17-18, many students will create variations on the games in problem 1. However they do not need to limit the games to that format, nor do they need to limit the games based on the two-dice experiment.

Be sure that students use the terms they learned in this lesson in their explanations.

DISCOVERY THREE QUANTITIES, THREE CONSTRAINTS

This extends the work on simultaneous equations. Allow students to solve the systems algebraically, but do not teach any formal techniques. Encourage students who are stuck to use trial and error.

11.5 SOLUTIONS

15. Answers will vary. Two possibilities:
(1) The product is odd.
(2) The sum is 5 or 6.

16.-18. Answers will vary.

19. R = 2, Y = 3, B = 5

20. R = 6, B = 3, Y = 6

21. Red = 15, Black = 14, Blue = 5

22. $A = 6$, $B = 5$, $C = 1$

▼ 11.6 What is Probability?

Core Sequence: 1-19

Suitable for Homework: 6-10, 16-19

Useful for Assessment: 3-4, 7, 10, 14-15

What this Lesson is About:

- Definitions of probability
- Two-coin experiment
- Review of the two-dice experiment
- Graphing probability

RELATIVE FREQUENCY

Make sure students understand the experiment before they start doing it. A result of one or two heads represents success; that of no heads represents failure.

Note that the same data will be graphed again later in the lesson, so students should not discard the results of the experiment.

You should compile class totals to see what happens in the long run.

You may want to have at least one group of students use a transparency to make their graph for problem 2. You can use it for a class discussion of problems 3 and 15.

LESSON 11.6

What is Probability?

You will need:

two coins

This lesson will introduce you to three interpretations of probability.

RELATIVE FREQUENCY

While waiting for his food at the Slow Food Café, Zoltan asked himself, "What is the probability of getting at least one head when tossing two coins?" He thought it might be 1/2, since there was an equal chance of getting heads or tails, or 1/3, since there were three possibilities (two heads, one head, no heads). He decided to find out by doing an experiment. Here are his notes on the first eight tosses (or *trials*).

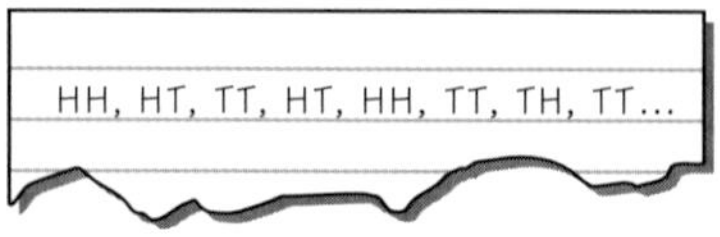

He made a table of the results. A *success* is a toss where one or two heads appeared.

Definition: The *relative frequency* of the successes is the ratio of successes to trials.

Trials so far	Successes so far	Relative frequency
1	1	1/1 = 1.00
2	2	2/2 = 1.00
3	2	2/3 = 0.67
4	3	3/4 = 0.75
5	4	4/5 = 0.80
6	4	4/6 = 0.67
7	5	5/7 = 0.72
8	5	5/8 = 0.63

He graphed the results, with relative frequency on the *y*-axis, and trials on the *x*-axis.

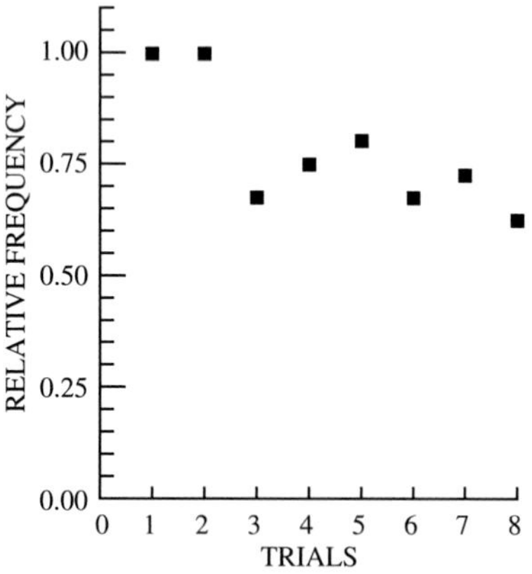

11.6 SOLUTIONS

1. Answers will vary. A sample table is shown.

Trials so far	Successes so far	Relative Frequency
1	1	1/1 = 1.00
2	2	2/2 = 1.00
3	2	2/3 = 0.67
4	3	3/4 = 0.75
5	4	4/5 = 0.80
6	5	5/6 = 0.83
7	6	6/7 = 0.86
8	7	7/8 = 0.88
9	8	8/9 = 0.89
10	9	9/10 = 0.90
11	10	10/11 = 0.91
12	11	11/12 = 0.92
13	12	12/13 = 0.92
14	13	13/14 = 0.93
15	13	13/15 = 0.87
16	13	13/16 = 0.81
17	13	13/17 = 0.76
18	13	13/18 = 0.72
19	14	14/19 = 0.74
20	15	15/20 = 0.75
21	16	16/21 = 0.76
22	16	16/22 = 0.73
23	17	17/23 = 0.74
24	18	18/24 = 0.75
25	18	18/25 = 0.72
26	19	19/26 = 0.73
27	19	19/27 = 0.70
28	20	20/28 = 0.71
29	21	21/29 = 0.72
30	22	22/30 = 0.73

2.

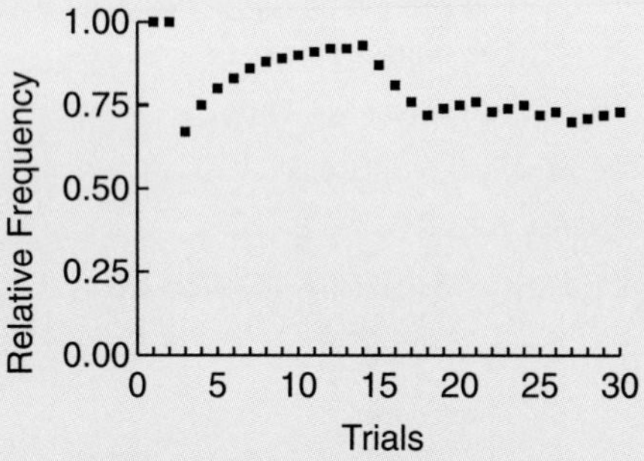

3. Answers will vary. (The relative frequency should approach 3/4.)

1. Toss a pair of coins 30 times. Make a table like Zoltan's.
2. Make a graph like Zoltan's for the data in your table.
3. If you tossed the coins 100 times, what do you think your graph would look like? What if you tossed them 500 times? Explain.

First Definition: The *probability* of an event is often interpreted to mean the relative frequency with which that event occurs if the experiment is repeated many, many times.

Example: If you roll a die many times, you expect the relative frequency of threes to be approximately 1/6.

4. Explain why the relative frequency of an event is a number from 0 to 1.

EQUALLY LIKELY OUTCOMES

This definition is the most common interpretation of probability.

Second Definition: The *probability* of an event A is

$$P(A) = \frac{e}{t}$$

where:

e = the number of equally likely outcomes in the event.

t = the total number of equally likely outcomes possible.

Example: In the two-dice experiment, say that event D is the event that the sum is 8. Then

$D = \{(2, 6), (3, 5), (4, 4), (5, 3), (6, 2)\}$

Since D consists of five equally likely outcomes, and the total number of equally likely outcomes is 36,

$$P(D) = \frac{5}{36}.$$

5. For the two-dice experiment, find an event having the following probabilities:
   a. $\frac{2}{36}$ b. $\frac{1}{12}$
6. For the two-dice experiment, find the probability of these events.
   a. The product is more than 25.
   b. The product is less than 50.
   c. The sum is 7 or 11.
7. Explain why any probability p will always satisfy the inequality $0 \le p \le 1$.
8. For the two-dice experiment, find an event having the following probabilities:
   a. 0 b. 1
9. List all the equally likely outcomes in Zoltan's two-coin experiment. (Hint: Think of the coins as a penny and a nickel. Make a table.)
10. What is the probability that there will be at least one head when tossing two coins? Explain.

THEORETICAL vs. OBSERVED PROBABILITY

Zoltan graphed his results another way. This time he put the number of successes on the y-axis and the number of trials on the x-axis.

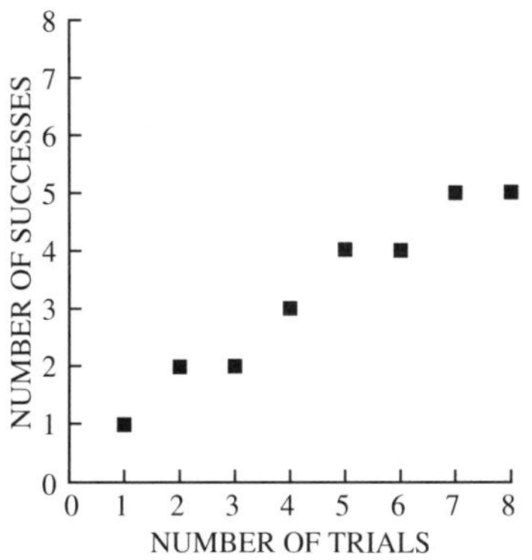

EQUALLY LIKELY OUTCOMES

This section reviews and extends the work on the two-dice experiment and applies the ideas to the two-coins experiment.

THEORETICAL VS OBSERVED PROBABILITY

This section presents another way to graph the data from problem 1. While in the first graph, data points tend to get closer and closer to the horizontal line at $y = 0.75$, in this graph it is the line through the origin and the data point that gets closer and closer to the line having equation $y = 0.75x$. The data points themselves do not necessarily have a tendency to get closer to the line.

This idea is probably too subtle for students to grasp, but it is explained by the fact that it is the ratio of successes to trials that approaches 0.75. As the number of trials gets very large, the difference between the expected number of successes and the actual number can increase, even as the relative frequency gets closer and closer to 0.75.

As with problem 2, in problem 11 you may want to have a group of students make their graph on a transparency to help with discussion of problems 12-14. A wrap-up of this section could include discussion and comparison of the graphs from problems 2 and 11.

11.6 SOLUTIONS

4. The relative frequency is the ratio of successes to trials. The number of successes will be between 0 and the number of trials (inclusive), so the ratio of successes to trials has to be between 0 and 1, inclusive. (It will be 0 if none of the trials results in a success, and 1 if they all result in a success.)
5. a. getting a sum of 3
   b. getting a sum of 4
6. a. 1/12
   b. 1
   c. 8/36 = 2/9
7. $e \le t$ so $(e/t) \le 1$
8. a. the difference is 8
   b. the sum is ≤ 12
9.

Penny	Nickel
H	H
T	T
H	T
T	H

10. The probability of at least one head is 3/4. There are four equally likely outcomes. Of these, three have at least one head.

11.

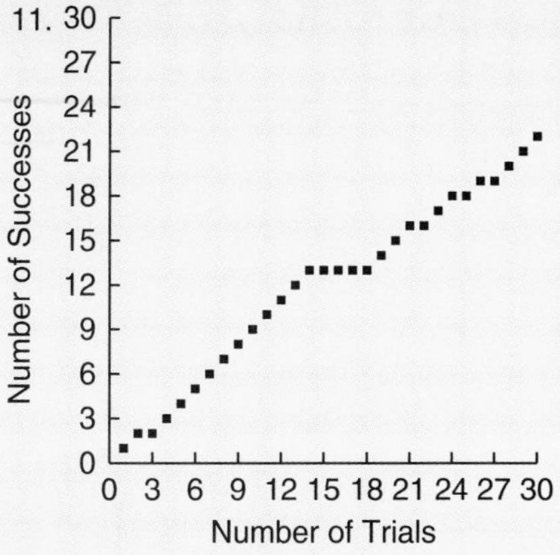

SUBJECTIVE PROBABILITY

*Though it is infrequently defined this way in elementary courses, this is a common interpretation of the word *probability* in daily life and in some approaches to statistics.*

11. Make a graph like Zoltan's for the data in the table you made in problem 1.

12. On your graph, draw lines having equations:

    successes = trials
    successes = 0.75 · trials
    successes = 0.67 · trials
    successes = 0.50 · trials

13. What do rise and run each measure on this graph? What does slope represent?

On a graph like this, the *theoretical probability*, as predicted by the analysis of equally likely outcomes, can be represented as a line through the origin, having slope equal to the probability. The *observed probability* as seen in the experiment is represented by the slope of the line through the origin and the corresponding data point. Note that data points rarely land exactly on the theoretical line.

14. Which line that you drew in problem 12 represents the theoretical probability? Explain.

15. Add a line representing the theoretical probability to the graph you made in problem 2. Explain.

SUBJECTIVE PROBABILITY

A third interpretation of probability is *subjective probability*. This is the probability that a person assigns to an event based on his or her own knowledge, beliefs, or information about the event. Different people may assign different probabilities to the same events.

Example: Before Mark took his driving test, Karen said, "I think you've got about a 60% chance of passing."

What subjective probability would you assign for each of the following events? Explain your reasons.

16. It will be cloudy on a night with a full moon this month.

17. You will be assigned no math homework this Friday.

18. School will be cancelled next week due to bad weather.

19. Exactly half of the students in your math class next year will be boys.

12.

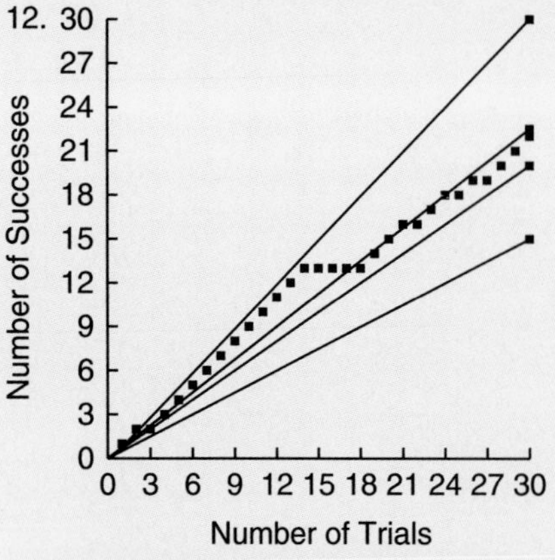

13. Rise represents the number of successes. Run represents the number of trials. Slope represents "successes per trial," or relative frequency.

14. $y = 0.75x$

15. Add the line $y = 0.75$ to the graph. In this case, the y-value represents the relative frequency. In the long run, we would expect the relative frequency, or observed probability, to be close to the theoretical probability.

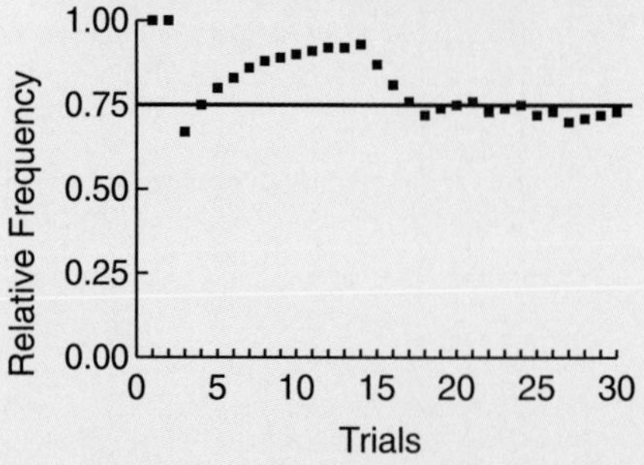

16.-19. Answers will vary.

LESSON 11.7

Random Walks

You will need:

dot paper 

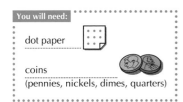

coins 
(pennies, nickels, dimes, quarters)

The Mad Probabilist takes a random walk on dot paper. Starting at the origin, he goes from lattice point to lattice point, flipping a coin each time to determine where to go next.

- *Heads* means to move east, increasing just the *x*-coordinate by 1.
- *Tails* means to move north, increasing just the *y*-coordinate by 1.

The map shows the path H, H, T, T, H, T, H, H.

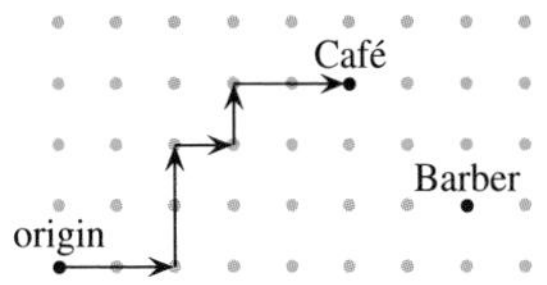

1. **Exploration** Find another sequence of heads and tails that would get the Mad Probabilist from the origin to (5, 3), where the Slow Food Café is located. Compare your sequence with that of a classmate. How many ways are there to reach (5, 3)?

A FOUR-COIN EXPERIMENT

2. If you toss a penny, a nickel, a dime, and a quarter, which do you think is most likely to occur: 0 heads, 1 head, 2 heads, 3 heads, 4 heads? Or are they all equally likely? Explain your reasoning.

3. Use a penny, a nickel, a dime, and a quarter. Toss them and record the number of heads. Repeat this experiment 20 times.

If you toss a penny, a nickel, a dime, and a quarter, the event *three heads* consists of the following equally likely outcomes: HHHT, HHTH, HTHH, and THHH, depending on which coin comes up tails.

4. Find all possible equally likely outcomes when tossing four coins.

5. Count the outcomes for each of these events: 0 heads, 1 head, 2 heads, etc.

6. Are the results of your experiment in problem 3 consistent with your analysis in problems 4 and 5? Comment.

If you toss one coin, there are two equally likely possible outcomes, H and T. In Lesson 6 you studied the tossing of two coins, (HH, HT, TH, TT), and in problems 5-6 the tossing of four coins.

7. Figure out how many equally likely outcomes are possible if you toss
   a. three coins; b. five coins.

8. **Generalization** How many equally likely outcomes are possible if you toss *n* coins? Explain.

Tossing the same coin repeatedly works in a similar way. For example, one possible string of eight tosses is: TTHTHTTH, just as one possible outcome of tossing eight coins is TTHTHTTH.

9. If you toss one coin eight times, how many possible outcomes are there? How about *n* times?

11.7 Random Walks

Core Sequence: 1-15

Suitable for Homework: 7-15, 18-19, 21-25

Useful for Assessment: 6, 8, 11, 13-15, 19, 25

What this Lesson is About:

- Coin probability
- Review of constant sum graphs
- Review of taxicab distance
- Random walks
- Pascal's triangle

Problem 1 poses the question that ties together coin probability and Pascal's triangle. It is a problem that is easy to state, but difficult to solve. You may suggest that students start with an easier problem, i.e. a destination nearer the origin. Analyzing it makes it possible to start seeing a pattern. Students are guided to a solution in the section **Making a Map,** below.

A FOUR-COIN EXPERIMENT

In problem 2, some students may be ready to apply some of what they learned in previous lessons to an analysis of the problem. Most will probably just guess.

The experiment in problem 3 should be enough to convince students that the event *two heads* is more likely than the other

11.7 SOLUTIONS

1. Answers will vary. By the end of the lesson, students should be able to figure out that the correct answer is 56.
2. Answers will vary. See #4 and #5
3. Answers will vary.
4. Use a table.

Penny	Nickel	Dime	Quarter	# Heads	# Tails
H	H	H	H	4	0
H	H	H	T	3	1
H	H	T	H	3	1
H	T	H	H	3	1
T	H	H	H	3	1
H	H	T	T	2	2
H	T	T	H	2	2
T	T	H	H	2	2
T	H	H	T	2	2
T	H	T	H	2	2
H	T	H	T	2	2
H	T	T	T	1	3
T	H	T	T	1	3
T	T	H	T	1	3
T	T	T	H	1	3
T	T	T	T	0	4

5.

Event	# Outcomes
0 heads	1
1 head	4
2 heads	6
3 heads	4
4 heads	1

6. Answers will vary. One would not expect the experimental results to be exactly the same as the theoretical analysis.
7. a. 8
   b. 32
8. 2^n
9. 2^8, 2^n

ones, especially if the class data are combined into one chart on the chalkboard or overhead.

Students are guided through a systematic analysis and generalization. This information will be essential in analyzing the Mad Probabilist's random walk problem.

THE MAD PROBABILIST

This section limits itself to analyzing how far (in taxicab distance) various points are from the origin. This, together with the information about coin experiments from the previous section, is necessary for finding the denominator in the probability fraction for the Mad Probabilist's question.

MAKING A MAP

This section shows how to find the number of paths leading to any point that is potentially on the Mad Probabilist's random walk. This information in turn allows us to find the numerator in the probability fraction.

The key is to see that to get to any point, e.g., (5, 3), you must have come from (5, 2) or (4, 3). So if there were m ways to get to (5, 2) and n ways to get to (4, 3), there must be $m + n$ ways to get to (5, 3). Do not start by telling your students this, but help them discover it by starting with points near the origin.

THE MAD PROBABILIST

10. How many moves does it take the Mad Probabilist to get to (5, 3)?

11. **Generalization** How many moves does it take him to get to (p, q)? Explain.

12. a. Where might he be after six moves?

b. Make a list of the points he could get to in seven moves.

13. How would you describe the set of points you listed in problem 12b? (How many points does it consist of? What equation relates their coordinates?) Explain.

14. **Generalization** Describe the set of points he could reach in n moves. Explain.

15. Which is greater, the number of possible points he could end up on after eight tosses of a coin, or the number of possible strings of eight tosses? Explain.

MAKING A MAP

The Mad Probabilist wants to calculate the *probability* of getting to a lattice point like (5, 3). He decides to make a map on a piece of dot paper. He draws diagonal lines to separate the points he may reach in one, two, three, etc., moves.

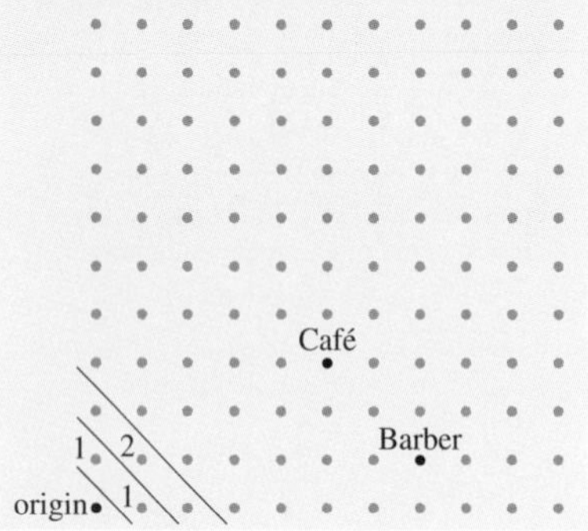

Then he writes how many ways there are to reach each point on the map. For example, there is only one way to get to (1, 0): a toss of H. There is only one way to get to (0, 1): T. There is only one way to get to (2, 0): HH. There are two ways to get to (1, 1): HT or TH.

As he makes his map, he finds it helpful to ask himself for each point, "Where could I have come from to get here?"

16. Continue the Mad Probabilist's map, until you get to (5, 3).

The Mad Probabilist reasons, "At the end of eight moves, I will be at one of these points, one of which is the Slow Food Café." He marks the points on his map. "The outcomes are eight-move paths; the event is those paths that end up at (5, 3). To find out the probability of this event, I need a numerator and a denominator." He writes:

$$P(5, 3) = \frac{\text{\# of paths that get to (5, 3)}}{\text{\# of 8-move paths}}$$

17. What is $P(5, 3)$? In other words, what is the probability the Mad Probabilist's random walk will end up at the Slow Food Café?

18. What is the probability it will end up at (7, 1), where the barbershop is? Explain.

19. **Summary** Explain how you can find the probability of getting to any lattice point in the first quadrant.

11.7 SOLUTIONS

10. 8

11. It takes him $p + q$ moves. He must move p horizontal segments and q vertical segments.

12. a. He will be at any point (a, b), where $a + b = 6$.

b. (0, 7), (6, 1), (5, 2), (3, 4), (7, 0), (1, 6), (2, 5), (4, 3)

13. They lie on the line $x + y = 7$.

14. any point (p, q) with integer coordinates such that $p + q = n$

15. The number of possible strings of eight tosses is greater than the number of possible points he could end up on after eight tosses. This is because there are many paths to each point.

16.

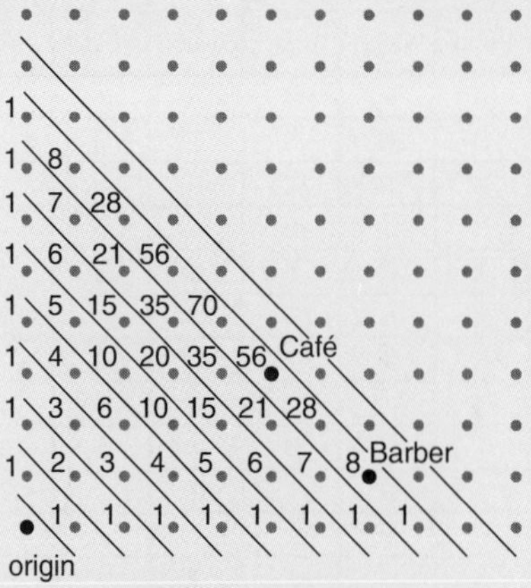

17. From the map, one can see that there are 56 paths to (5, 3). The total number of 8-move paths is 2^8. Hence the probability is $56/2^8$, or 0.21875.

18. There are only 8 paths to (7, 1), so the probability is $8/2^8 = 0.03125$.

19. To find the probability of getting to any lattice point (p, q), continue the Mad Probabilist's map. The number on his map corresponding to (p, q) is the numerator. The denominator is $2^{(p+q)}$.

DISCOVERY ***PASCAL PATTERNS***

This is one of the most important arrays of numbers in mathematics. It is called Pascal's triangle.

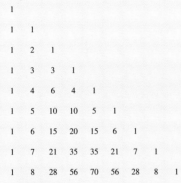

1								
1	1							
1	2	1						
1	3	3	1					
1	4	6	4	1				
1	5	10	10	5	1			
1	6	15	20	15	6	1		
1	7	21	35	35	21	7	1	
1	8	28	56	70	56	28	8	1

20. **Exploration** Study this triangle, looking for patterns. Explain any patterns that you find.

21. Find a pattern that will enable you to write the next row in the triangle.

22. Find the pattern in the third column.

23. Find the pattern in the sums of the rows.

24. Find the pattern in the sums of the upward diagonals.

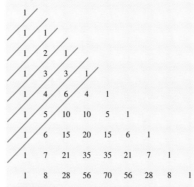

1								
1	1							
1	2	1						
1	3	3	1					
1	4	6	4	1				
1	5	10	10	5	1			
1	6	15	20	15	6	1		
1	7	21	35	35	21	7	1	
1	8	28	56	70	56	28	8	1

25. **Report** Write an illustrated report about the patterns you found in Pascal's triangle. Include a section on the relationship between Pascal's triangle and coin-tossing experiments.

DISCOVERY ***PASCAL PATTERNS***

This section can be done independently of the main body of the lesson. Pascal's triangle is interesting for its own sake, as a mathematical object that is rich with patterns and a good context in which to review many ideas of this course.

However doing it in the context of the Mad Probabilist's walk helps show its connection with coin tossing experiments, thereby giving the triangle more real-world relevance.

Problem 21 reviews the ideas that led to problem 16.

Problem 22 reviews triangular numbers, which were seen in Chapter 1, Lesson 11, and Chapter 5, Lesson 9.

Problem 23 reviews problems 7-9, and, more generally, powers of 2 that appeared in Chapter 2, Lesson 5; Chapter 5, Lesson 9; Chapter 7, Lesson 9; and Chapter 8, Lessons 5 and 9.

Problem 24 reviews the Fibonacci sequence, previously encountered in Chapter 2, Lesson 6.

11.7 SOLUTIONS

20. Answers will vary.
21. To get a number in the current row, add the number directly above in the previous row to the number to the left in the previous row. The next row is: 1, 9, 36, 84, 126, 126, 84, 36, 9, 1.
22. The differences between terms form the arithmetic sequence: 2, 3, 4, 5, ... etc.
23. The sums are powers of 2.
24. Fibonacci sequence
25. Reports will vary.

▼ 11.8
Unit Conversion

Core Sequence: 1-16

Suitable for Homework: 8-16, 19-25

Useful for Assessment: 5, 7, 9, 12, 14

What this Lesson is About:

- Unit conversion
- Review of proportions
- Review of direct variation
- Application of reciprocals
- Review of solving systems

You may start this lesson with a discussion of how quickly students can run, skip, walk backwards, etc., in miles per hour. The discussion will probably lead to some of the issues addressed in this lesson. If you do problem 17 you will know the answer!

Problem 1 is intended to remind students about simplifying fractions by cancelling, a key idea in this lesson.

TWO RULERS

This appears to be an extension of the two-ruler problem from Chapter 5, Lesson 1. However it is quite different mathematically.

In problem 2, students should see a direct variation relationship (though they may not remember these terms). However, Alice's table is a little misleading because of the

LESSON 11.8

Unit Conversion

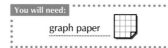

You will need: graph paper

1. Find the missing numerator and denominator in each equation. (You should be able to solve most of these without multiplying or dividing.) Compare your answers with other students' answers.

a. $\frac{2}{3} \cdot \frac{5}{7} \cdot \frac{\triangle}{\square} = \frac{2}{3}$

b. $\frac{2}{3} \cdot \frac{\triangle}{7} \cdot \frac{5}{\square} = \frac{2}{3}$

c. $\frac{7}{12} \cdot \frac{14}{11} \cdot \frac{12}{5} \cdot \frac{\triangle}{\square} = \frac{7}{11}$

d. $\frac{1}{3} \cdot \frac{5}{x} \cdot \frac{2}{5} \cdot \frac{x}{2} \cdot \frac{\triangle}{\square} = \frac{8}{3}$

e. $\frac{8}{7} \cdot \frac{3}{x} \cdot \frac{7}{6} \cdot \frac{y}{\square} \cdot = \frac{y}{x}$

f. $\frac{a}{b} \cdot \frac{\triangle}{a} \cdot \frac{b}{\square} = \frac{x}{y}$

TWO RULERS

Alice had a new ruler. Oliver suggested she measure it with another ruler, as in this figure.

Alice's ruler

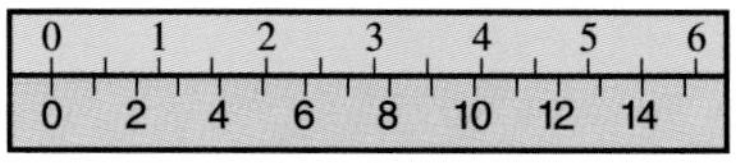

Oliver's ruler

Oliver and Alice had to write about functions for algebra. They decided to use the rulers as a way to get tables of x- and y-values. Here are the tables they got from the ruler setup.

Alice

x	y
1	2.5
2	5.1
3	7.6

Oliver

x	y
1	0.4
2	0.8
3	1.2

2. Describe the pattern for the numbers in each table.

3. What do you think the units of each ruler are?

4. Write a function of the type y = *an expression in terms of* x for each table. (Because of measurement error, this may have to be an approximation.)

5. 🔑 If you were to graph these functions, explain why the graph would

a. be a line;

b. pass through the origin.

6. According to an almanac, 1 inch = 2.54 centimeters, exactly. Using that information, what is the exact length of a centimeter, in inches?

When converting inches to centimeters, we multiply by 2.54. When converting centimeters to inches, we multiply by 1/2.54. As you can see from the equations, this conversion of units involves direct variation.

Definition: In the case of unit conversion, the proportionality constant (the number you multiply by) is called the *conversion factor*.

11.8 SOLUTIONS

1. a. 7/5
   b. 7, 5
   c. 5/14
   d. 8/1
   e. 4
   f. *x, y*
2. Alice: *y* is approximately 2.5 times *x*
   Oliver: *y* is approximately 0.4 *x*.
3. Alice's ruler is in inches. Oliver's is in centimeters.
4. Alice: $y = 2.5x$ Oliver: $y = 0.4x$
5. These functions are of the form $y = mx$, so they will be lines through the origin.
6. 1 centimeter = (1/2.54) inches

Conversion factors have units. For example, the conversion factor from inches to centimeters is 2.54 *cm/in*.

7. What is the conversion factor from centimeters to inches? (Include its unit.) Explain.

MULTIPLYING BY ONE

When converting a quantity from one unit to another, the way the quantity is measured is changed, not the amount of it. We can think of the conversion factor as having the value 1.

Example: Two miles are how many feet?

$$2 \text{ miles} \cdot \frac{5280 \text{ feet}}{1 \text{ mile}} = 10{,}560 \text{ feet}$$

The conversion factor is 5280/1 and its units are feet/mile. Since 5280 feet = 1 mile, the numerator equals the denominator in the fraction, so we can think of this conversion as multiplying by a form of 1. To make the units work out, we multiplied by feet and divided by miles.

In problems 8-10, when writing a conversion factor, include its unit.

8. a. What is the conversion factor used to convert feet to miles?
b. Mount Everest, the world's tallest peak, is 29,028 feet high. How many miles is that?

9.
a. What is the conversion factor used to convert seconds to minutes?
b. What is the conversion factor used to convert minutes to seconds?
c. How are the answers to (a) and (b) related? Explain.

10. Convert 1000 inches to:
a. feet; b. miles;
c. meters; d. kilometers.

TWO-STEP CONVERSIONS

In science, speeds are sometimes given in feet per second. To convert feet per second to miles per hour, there are two steps:

- Convert feet to miles.
- Convert seconds to hours.

The steps can be combined:

$$\frac{\text{feet}}{\text{second}} \cdot \frac{1 \text{ mile}}{5280 \text{ feet}} \cdot \frac{3600 \text{ seconds}}{1 \text{ hour}} = \frac{\text{miles}}{\text{hour}}$$

We chose the conversion factors in order to divide by feet and multiply by seconds so that those units did not appear in the final answer.

11. Convert the speed of sound in cold water (4938 feet per second) to miles per hour. Show your calculations.

12. To convert feet per second to miles per hour, what single number could you multiply by? Explain how you obtained this conversion factor.

13. Find the conversion factor between each of these common measures of speed. Show all your work. Summarize your results in a table like this one. Give approximations to the nearest thousandth. (Note: m/sec means meters per second.)

From: \ To:	mi/hr	km/hr	m/sec	ft/sec
mi/hr	—	—	—	—
km/hr	—	—	—	—
m/sec	—	—	—	—
ft/sec	—	—	—	—

14. In your table, find pairs of numbers that are reciprocals of each other. Explain why they should be reciprocals.

measurement error. You will need to discuss this in detail, because it forces the answer to problem 4 to be merely an approximation.

Problem 6 is the first of several in this lesson that revolve around the fact that to make a unit conversion in the opposite direction, the needed conversion factor is the reciprocal of the original one.

MULTIPLYING BY ONE

TWO-STEP CONVERSIONS

The most common error students make in conversion problems is multiplying instead of dividing — or in the language of this lesson, multiplying by the reciprocal of the correct conversion factor. The key idea of the canceling of units should help reduce this kind of mistake.

This is material that is usually taught at the beginning of science courses. As applications of mathematics take a greater and greater role in our classes, it is necessary to increase the focus on topics such as this one. Science teachers will be grateful.

Problem 13 is a substantial one, as it involves 16 answers, 12 of which are not 1. Be aware of this when assigning homework.

11.8 SOLUTIONS

7. (1/2.54) inches per centimeter

8. a. $\frac{1 \text{ miles}}{5280 \text{ feet}}$
b. about 5 and 1/2 miles

9. a. $\frac{1 \text{ minute}}{60 \text{ seconds}}$
b. $\frac{60 \text{ seconds}}{1 \text{ minute}}$
c. They are reciprocals. Both the units and the numbers are reciprocals.

10. a. 83.33 b. 0.0158
c. 25.40 d. 0.02540

11. $\frac{4938 \text{ feet}}{1 \text{ second}} \cdot \frac{1 \text{ mile}}{5280 \text{ feet}} \cdot \frac{3600 \text{ seconds}}{1 \text{ hour}}$
= 3366.82 mph

12. The single number is $\frac{3600}{5280}$ = 0.682, as can be seen from the above calculations.

13.

From: \ To:	mi/hr	km/hr	m/sec	ft/sec
mi/hr	1	1.609	0.447	1.467
km/hr	0.621	1	0.278	0.911
m/sec	2.237	3.600	1	3.281
ft/sec	0.682	1.097	0.305	1

14. Reciprocals: 0.621 and 1.609, 0.447 and 2.237, 0.682 and 1.467, 0.911 and 1.097, 0.305 and 3.281, 3.600 and 0.278. When the units are reciprocals, so are the numbers.

Doing one of problems 17-18 will help make this lesson more relevant to students. There are a number of challenges, such as:

- How to measure out the distance. We've used a tailor's measuring tape, but there may be better ways.
- How to time both departure and arrival. We've used stopwatches, those found on student wrists and those borrowed from coaches. We've stationed a student with a stopwatch at the finish line, and an assistant at the start, who signals to the timer when to start the stopwatch.

REVIEW SOLVING SYSTEMS

A routine review of systems of linear equations.

15. Use your table to convert
   a. the speed of light (299,792,500 m/sec) into miles per hour;
   b. the speed of sound in cold air (1,088 ft/sec) into miles per hour.

16. A fast runner can run a mile in four minutes. How fast is that in miles per hour?

17. **Project** Find out how fast students in your class walk, skip, run, move backwards, etc., by timing how long it takes them to cover a measured distance. Convert the speeds to miles per hour.

18. **Project** Find out how fast cars drive on a nearby street or road, by timing how long it takes them to cover a measured distance. Convert the speeds to miles per hour.

REVIEW SOLVING SYSTEMS

Solve each system. Check first to see if you can tell that the system has no solution or an infinite number of solutions.

19. $\begin{cases} 2x + 6 = 3y \\ 4y = 12 - 3x \end{cases}$

20. $\begin{cases} -m - b = 25 \\ -m + b = 13 \end{cases}$

21. $\begin{cases} 2r + 2s = 60 \\ r - 2s = 5 \end{cases}$

22. $\begin{cases} 2m + n = -1 \\ m + 3n = -18 \end{cases}$

23. $\begin{cases} r - s = 1 \\ r + 3s = -11 \end{cases}$

24. $\begin{cases} \frac{2}{3}x + \frac{2}{5}y = 4 \\ x - 2y = 5 \end{cases}$

25. $\begin{cases} y = \frac{3}{7}(x - 8) \\ y - 4 = \frac{3}{7}(x + 6) \end{cases}$

11.8 SOLUTIONS

15. a. about 670,635,823 miles per hour
    b. about 742 miles per hour
16. 15 miles per hour
19. $x = 12/17$ $y = 42/17$
20. $m = -19$ $b = -6$
21. $r = 65/3$ $s = 25/3$
22. $m = 3$ $n = -7$
23. $r = -2$ $s = -3$
24. $x = 75/13$ $y = 5/13$
25. No solution

THINKING WRITING 11.B Calibrating a Speedometer

You can check the accuracy of a car's speedometer by using a stopwatch and the mile markers on a highway. The driver should maintain a steady speed while a passenger uses a stopwatch to time the travel time between mile markers. This travel time tells you the number of seconds it takes you to go one mile, which you can convert to miles per hour.

1. Convert 0.123 hours to minutes and seconds.
2. Convert 4.567 hours to hours, minutes, and seconds.
3. A car is traveling at 55 miles per hour.
   a. What fraction of an hour does it take to go one mile?
   b. How many minutes and seconds does it take to go one mile?
   c. How many seconds does it take to go one mile?
4. How would you convert
   a. miles per hour to miles per second?
   b. miles per second to miles per hour?
   c. miles per second to seconds to go one mile?
   d. seconds to go one mile to miles per second?
5. If it takes you 65 seconds to go one mile, how many miles per hour are you going? Explain how you figured this out, showing calculations.
6. Describe a general strategy for converting seconds per mile to miles per hour.
7. Make a table like this one to help people check their speedometers.

Seconds between mile markers	Speed in mi/hr
...	...

8. a. Graph the ordered pairs in the table you made.
   b. Let y stand for the speed in mi/hr, and x stand for the number of seconds between markers. Write an equation relating x and y.

Say that the person in charge of timing can be off by one second in starting the stopwatch, and one second in stopping it.

9. What is the maximum error in using the table, resulting from the inaccuracy in timing?
10. If, instead of measuring the time to go one mile, you measure the time to go four miles and use the average one-mile time, what is the maximum error?
11. **Report** Write an explanation for the general public of how to check the accuracy of a speedometer. Include your table, some illustrations, and an explanation of what to do to get an exact answer between values given in the table.

THINKING WRITING 11.B Calibrating a Speedometer

Core Sequence: 1-11

Suitable for Homework: 6-11

Useful for Assessment: 11

What this Assignment is About:

- Unit conversions
- Application of reciprocals
- Application to automobiles

Some of the key ideas in this lesson were previewed in Chapter 8, Lesson 12.

Problems 1-2 are not very difficult, but students may need some help. Some calculators have a built-in function to do this conversion, but it's probably best to ignore it. If students want to use it, let them figure out how, and teach others. Your emphasis should be on helping students apply the ideas of Lesson 5 to this slightly different case.

Problems 3-5 guide students through the process they will need to apply in this lesson. Doing them in class will allow you to be sure the students are ready to tackle the rest of the assignment at home.

11.B SOLUTIONS

1. 7 minutes, 22.8 seconds
2. 4 hours, 34 minutes, 1.2 seconds
3. a. 1/55 hours per mile
   b. about 1 minute, 5.5 seconds
   c. about 65.45 seconds
4. a. divide by 3600
   b. multiply by 3600
   c. take the reciprocal
   d. take the reciprocal
5. First take the reciprocal to get $\frac{1 \text{ mile}}{65 \text{ seconds}}$. Then multiply by 3600:
   $$\frac{1 \text{ mile}}{65 \text{ seconds}} \cdot \frac{3600 \text{ seconds}}{1 \text{ hour}} = 55.4 \text{ mph}$$
6. Take the reciprocal to convert seconds/mile to miles/second. Then multiply by 3600 to convert miles/second to miles/hour. A shortcut would be just to divide 3600 by the number of seconds to go one mile.
7.

Seconds between mile markers	Speed in mi/hr
45	80
50	72
55	65.5
60	60
65	55.4
70	51.4
75	48
80	45
85	42

8. a.

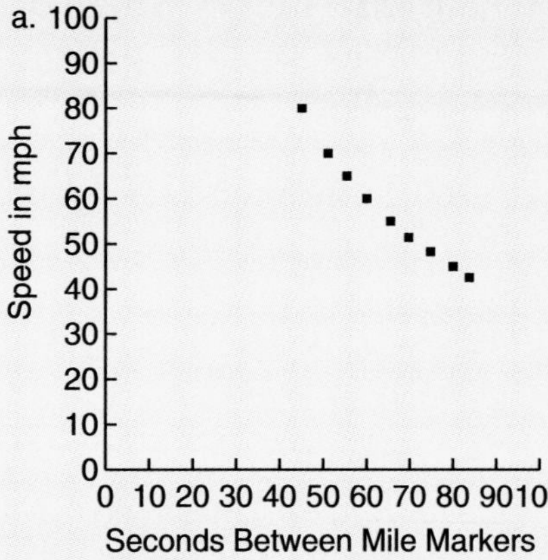

   b. $y = \frac{3600}{x}$
9. Look at the extremes in the table, and figure out what the estimated speed would be if your measurement were 2 seconds off:

(Solutions continued on page 529)

Essential Ideas

SUMS

1. Find each sum.
   a. $\frac{1}{2} + \left(\frac{1}{2}\right)^2 + \left(\frac{1}{2}\right)^3$
   b. $\frac{1}{2} + \left(\frac{1}{2}\right)^2 + \left(\frac{1}{2}\right)^3 + \left(\frac{1}{2}\right)^4$
   c. $\frac{1}{2} + \left(\frac{1}{2}\right)^2 + \left(\frac{1}{2}\right)^3 + \left(\frac{1}{2}\right)^4 + \left(\frac{1}{2}\right)^5$
   d. $\frac{1}{2} + \left(\frac{1}{2}\right)^2 + \left(\frac{1}{2}\right)^3 + \ldots + \left(\frac{1}{2}\right)^n$

2. This sum goes on for ever. (We call it an *infinite series*.) Use the pattern you found in problem 1 to estimate the sum of this infinite series.

$$\frac{1}{2} + \left(\frac{1}{2}\right)^2 + \left(\frac{1}{2}\right)^3 + \ldots$$

3. Estimate the sums of these infinite series.
   a. $\frac{1}{3} + \left(\frac{1}{3}\right)^2 + \left(\frac{1}{3}\right)^3 + \ldots$
   b. $\frac{1}{4} + \left(\frac{1}{4}\right)^2 + \left(\frac{1}{4}\right)^3 + \ldots$
   c. $\frac{1}{k} + \left(\frac{1}{k}\right)^2 + \left(\frac{1}{k}\right)^3 + \ldots$

   (Assume that k is a positive integer.)

GEOMETRIC SEQUENCES

4. Some of the following sequences are geometric; find their common ratio. Some are arithmetic; find their common difference.
   a. $2/3, (2/3)^2, (2/3)^3, (2/3)^4, \ldots$
   b. 1/3, 4/3, 7/3, 10/3, ...
   c. 10, 10/8, 10/64, 10/512, ...
   d. 10, 80, 640, 5120, ...
   e. 1/3, 8/3, 64/3, 512/3, ...

5. Find the sum of the first 50 terms for the sequences in problems 4a and e.

6. Two of the sequences in problem 4 are such that if you add the entire infinite sequence, the sum converges to a finite number.
   a. Explain how you can tell which sequences they are.
   b. Find the sum they each converge to.

INHERITANCE

The brothers Able and Earl inherited from their father an acre of land, which they divided equally. Each brother willed his land to his family. Able's family was large, and Earl's was small. Able's family needed more land, so they bought 40% of the land belonging to Earl's family. In the next generation, Able's family again bought 40% of Earl's family land. This continued for several generations.

7. Copy and and extend this table to show the amount of land owned by each family up to the eighth generation.

Generation	Able's land	Earl's land
1	0.5	0.5
2	0.7	0.3

8. Study the data. At this rate, will Able's family ever own the whole acre? Explain.

DECIMALS AND FRACTIONS

9. Write as a fraction.
   a. $0.\overline{21}$
   b. $0.3\overline{21}$
   c. $0.\overline{321}$

SOLUTIONS

1. a. 0.875
   b. 0.9375
   c. 0.96875
   d. $1 - (1/2)^n$
2. As n gets larger and larger, $(1/2)^n$ approaches 0, so $1 - (1/2)^n$ approaches 1.
3. a. 3/2
   b. 4/3
   c. $1/(1 - 1/k) = k/(k - 1)$
4. a. geometric $r = 2/3$
   b. arithmetic $d = 1$
   c. geometric $r = 1/8$
   d. geometric $r = 8$
   e. geometric $r = 8$
5. a. Use the pattern found in Lesson 1. The sum is $[a(1 - r^n)/(1 - r)]$. In this case, a is 2/3, r is 2/3, and n is 50. The sum is approximately 2.
   b. In this case, the sum does not converge. Using the formula, $a = 1/3$, $r = 8$, and $n = 50$. The sum is approximately $6.79 \cdot 10^{43}$.
6. The sums of (a) and (c) will converge. They are geometric sequences with $r < 1$. The sum of the sequence in (a) converges to 2. The sum of the sequence in (c) converges to 80/7.
7.

Generation	Able's land	Earl's land
1	0.5	0.5
2	0.7	0.3
3	0.82	0.18
4	0.892	0.108
5	0.9352	0.0648
6	0.96112	0.03888
7	0.97667	0.023328
8	0.986003	0.0139968
9	0.99160192	0.00839
10	0.994961	0.00503885

8. In theory, he won't. In practical terms, Earl's share will eventually be so small that Able might as well own the whole acre.
9. a. 21/99
   b. 3/10 + 21/990 = 318/990
   c. 321/999

10. Find whole numbers p and q such that:
    a. $0.45 < p/q < 0.46$
    b. $0.\bar{4} < p/q < 0.45$

PRIME FACTORIZATION

11. Explain why the square of an even number must be a multiple of four.
12. Explain why the square of an odd number must be odd.
13. Explain why the double of an odd number is an even number, but not a multiple of four.

LATTICE POINTS

Imagine that you are standing at the origin, and that you cannot see lattice points that are hidden behind other lattice points. For example, you cannot see (2, 2) because (1, 1) is in the way. Let us call (1, 1) *visible* and (2, 2) *hidden*.

14. List three visible lattice points and three hidden ones. Explain.
15. By looking at its coordinates, how can you tell whether a lattice point is visible?
16. Give the equation of a line that includes no lattice points except the origin.
17. Give the equation of a line that includes no lattice points at all.
18. Which line on an 11-by-11 geoboard contains the greatest number of visible lattice points?

GAMES AND PROBABILITY

19. If you choose a letter at random from the alphabet, what's the probability that it's a vowel?
20. If you choose a month at random, what's the probability that its name
    a. begins with J?
    b. contains an R?
21. Assume that you draw one card from an ordinary deck of 52 playing cards. What's the probability that you draw
    a. a 7?
    b. a heart?
    c. a 7 or a heart?
    d. a 7 of hearts?
22. Which game, if either, is fair? Explain.
    a. Roll a pair of dice and multiply the numbers on the uppermost faces. If the product is 18 or greater, Player A wins. If the product is less than 18, Player B wins.
    b. Toss three coins. If the number of heads is even, Player A wins. If it is odd, Player B wins.
    c. Repeat part (b) for six coins.

UNIT CONVERSION

23. Given that 1 pound is approximately 454 grams, 1 kilogram is approximately how many pounds?
24. Find conversion factors for converting the following measurements. (Note: Even though these problems look different, you can use the technique you learned in Lesson 8. Remember that $in.^2$ means in. · in.)
    a. $in.^2$ to ft^2 b. ft^2 to $in.^2$
    c. $in.^3$ to cm^3 d. cm^3 to $in.^3$
25. The density of water is approximately 1 $gram/cm^3$. What is it in $pounds/ft^3$?

◆ SOLUTIONS

10. Answers will vary. Sample answers are given.
    a. 455/1000 b. 445/1000
11. An even number has at least one prime factor that is 2. Therefore, its square has at least two prime factors of 2, so it has a factor of 4.
12. The prime factorization of the odd number has no factors of 2. Therefore, its square will have no factors of 2.
13. An odd number has no prime factors of 2. If we multiply it by 2, it has only one factor of 2. Hence it must be even, but it is not a multiple of 4.
14. Answers will vary. Sample answers are given.
    Visible: (2, 5), (3, 8), (7, 11)
    Hidden: (6, 8), (4, 6), (100, 200)
    For an explanation, see #15.
15. The point (p, q) is visible if and only if p and q are relatively prime.
16. The line $y = \sqrt{2}x$ contains no lattice points except the origin.
17. The line $y = \sqrt{2}x + \sqrt{2}$ passes through no lattice points. To convince yourself of this, substitute any whole number n for x. You will find that y cannot also be a whole number: $y = \sqrt{2}n + \sqrt{2} = \sqrt{2}(n + 1)$. This could only be a whole number if $\sqrt{2}$ was a fraction with a denominator that was a factor of $n + 1$. Since $\sqrt{2}$ is irrational, that is impossible.
18. Every lattice point on the geoboard line $x = 1$ is visible, since the fraction $k/1$ is in lowest terms for any k. Other lines with many visible points are lines with equation $x + y = p$, where p is a prime number. This is true because $k/(p - k)$ is in lowest terms for any k if $0 < k < p$. On the geoboard, the line of this type with the most visible points is $x + y = 11$. The $x + y = p$ lines stand out if all visible points are marked on a graph of the first quadrant.
19. 5/26
20. a. 1/4 b. 8/12
21. a. 7/52 b. 4/52
    c. 16/52 d. 1/52
22. a. Not fair. This can be seen by looking at the table of two dice products in Lesson 11.5.

(Solutions continued on page 529)

Chapter 12
MATHEMATICAL MODELING

Overview of the Chapter

This chapter concentrates on mathematical modeling in the sense of the use of functions and families of functions as models for real-world phenomena. This is of course an essential application of algebra throughout science and technology. There are almost no radically new ideas in the chapter. Instead, we rely heavily on concepts that have been developed previously. The chapter serves as an opportunity to review many key ideas in the course, by applying them.

1. New Uses for Tools:

- Cartesian graphs to model motion problems

2. Algebra Concepts Emphasized:

- Dependent and independent variables
- Direct and inverse variation
- The effect of parameters in a formula
- Recognizing functions from data points
- Average speed
- Iterating linear functions
- Recurrence equations
- Fixed points

CHAPTER 12

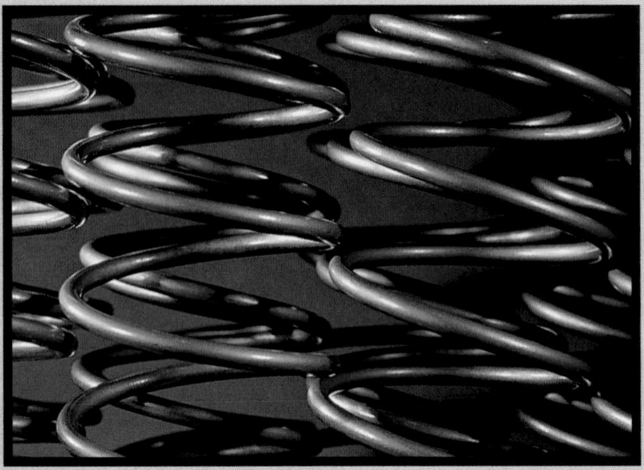

The spiral coils of car springs

Coming in this chapter:

Exploration By measuring people's feet and asking for their shoe size, find a formula relating foot length, in inches, to shoe size,

a. for men;
b. for women.

MATHEMATICAL MODELING

3. Algebra Concepts Reviewed:

- Exponential and linear growth
- The midpoint of growth
- Linear functions
- Constant product
- Constant ratio
- Slope and magnification
- Foci in function diagrams
- Simultaneous equations
- Domain and range

4. Algebra Concepts Previewed:

- Convergence
- Families of functions
- Absolute value graphs
- Radical expressions involving variables

5. Problem-Solving Techniques:

- Using equations
- Using graphs and function diagrams

6. Connections and Context:

- The importance of assumptions when choosing a mathematical model
- Extrapolating and interpolating
- Fitting a line to data
- Uses and limits of mathematical models
- Public safety
- Linear functions and equations in science
- Interpreting graphs
- Data from experiments
- Gears
- Unit conversion
- Circumference of a circle

▼ 12.1
The U.S. Population, 1890-1990

Core Sequence: 1-9, 13-19

Suitable for Homework: 1-4, 13-19

Useful for Assessment: 9-10, 12, 16, 18

What this Lesson is About:

- Review of exponential and linear growth
- Review of the midpoint of growth
- The importance of assumptions when choosing a mathematical model
- Extrapolating and interpolating

This lesson reviews the work on linear and exponential growth, from Chapter 2, Lesson 5; Chapter 7, Lesson 8; and several lessons of Chapters 8 and 9.

This lesson uses some very informal approaches to mathematical modeling. Comparisons between actual data and numbers obtained from a model illustrate the importance of careful examination of assumptions underlying any mathematical model. It provides motivation for the somewhat more sophisticated approach presented in the next lesson.

If you have access to computers with spreadsheet software (including graphing capabilities), you may use this lesson as an opportunity to teach your students how to use this powerful tool. In fact any software that allows for convenient calculations of tables and graphing of data could be used.

Otherwise, be sure to have students work in groups, at least for problems 5-11, because the large amount of work involved in building the tables and graphs would be tedious otherwise.

EXAMINING DATA

It would be a good idea to assign problems 1-4 for homework as preparation for this lesson.

Students can ask parents or history teachers for help with problem 2. Population growth reflects the birth rate, the death rate, immigration, and emigration. All are subject to historical variations.

If possible, problem 5 should be done on poster-size graph paper, or on graph paper transparencies, to facilitate whole-class discussion of the results.

LESSON 12.1

The U.S. Population, 1890–1990

You will need:
- graph paper
- colored pens

The Bureau of the Census conducts a census every ten years, as required by the U.S. Constitution. Census results are now used for many purposes, but their original purpose was primarily to determine how many seats each state would be allocated in the House of Representatives. As population patterns change, these seats are divided up differently among the states. Here are some census results from 1890 through 1990.

Census Table

Year	Population	# increase	% increase
1890	62,979,766	12,790,557	25.5
1900	76,212,168	13,232,402	21.0
1910	92,228,496	16,016,328	21.0
1920	106,021,537	13,793,041	15.0
1930	123,202,624	17,181,087	16.2
1940	132,164,569	8,961,945	7.3
1950	151,325,798	19,161,229	14.5
1960	179,323,175	27,997,377	18.5
1970	203,302,031	23,978,856	13.4
1980	226,545,805	23,243,774	11.4
1990	248,709,873	22,164,068	9.8

EXAMINING DATA

1. Use the information given to estimate the 1880 population.
2. Write a paragraph describing anything interesting you see in the data. What factors affect population growth? Can you think of historical events that might be associated with periods of low or high growth rates?
3. Over what ten-year period was
   a. the number increase the smallest? The largest?
   b. the percent increase the smallest? The largest?
4. From 1890 to 1990, what was the overall
   a. number increase?
   b. percent increase?
5. Using a large piece of graph paper, make a graph of the population as a function of time. You will add to this graph when you do other problems in this lesson. Choose the scale carefully.
6. Approximately when did the population reach its halfway point between 1890 and 1990? Explain how you calculated this, and show the point on your graph. Is the halfway point in population before or after the halfway point in years?

MAKING PREDICTIONS

If you had lived in 1890 and wanted to predict the population of the United States in 1900 and 1990, you might have assumed that the increase for every future ten-year period would be the same as it had been in the ten-year period from 1880 to 1890. (We will call 1880-1890 the *base period.*)

12.1 SOLUTIONS

1. 62,979,766 − 12,790,557 = 50,189,209
2. Answers will vary.
3. a. The smallest increase was in 1930-1940 (8,961,945 people). The largest increase was in 1950-1960 (27,997,337 people).
   b. The smallest percent increase was in 1930-1940 (7.3%). The largest percent increase was in 1880-1890 (25.5%).
4. a. 248,709,873 − 62,979,766 = 185,730,107
   b. 185,730,107/62,979,766 = 2.949 The percent increase was almost 295%.
5. 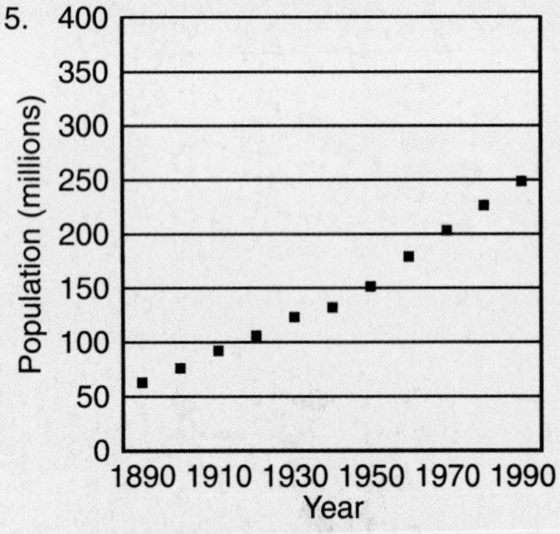

6. Answers will vary. Students have learned how to find the halfway point for linear or exponential growth. However, it is not clear which (if either) assumption is appropriate here, and students will assume that "halfway" in this case refers to the

7. For each assumption below, make a table showing what the population would have been in each decade.
   a. The number increase in each decade was the same as in the base period.
   b. The percent increase in each decade was the same as in the base period.

8. In this problem, add to the graph you made in problem 5. Use a different color for each set of data.
   a. Graph the data in your table from problem 7a. Write a description on your graph telling what assumption was used to obtain the numbers.
   b. Repeat part (a) for the data in your table in problem 7b.

9. Compare the three graphs.
   a. Which of the two assumptions in problem 7 gave a closer prediction of the population in 1900? How close was each estimate?
   b. Which predicted the population in 1990 more accurately? How close was each estimate?

Say you were living in 1940, had access to the data for the period 1890-1940, and wanted to predict the population for 1950 and 1990.

10. a. Why might you *not* want to use the growth from 1930 to 1940 to help you make the predictions?
    b. What numbers might you choose instead to model a constant number increase? What about a constant percent increase?

11. Repeat problem 7, starting with the 1940 population and using the numbers you chose in problem 10. Do you get better predictions?

12. Predict the population of the U.S. in the years 2000 and 2040. Explain how you arrive at your numbers.

ESTIMATING MISSING DATA

It is very expensive to conduct a census of the entire population, and it cannot be done every year. However, census data can be used to estimate the population in other years.

13. Use the 1940 and 1950 data to estimate the population in 1945 assuming
    a. linear growth;
    b. exponential growth.

14. Use the 1930 and 1950 data to estimate the population in 1940 assuming
    a. linear growth;
    b. exponential growth.

15. Use the 1890 and 1990 data to estimate the population in 1940 assuming
    a. linear growth;
    b. exponential growth.

16. Compare your answers to problems 14 and 15. Did you get closer to the actual 1940 population using
    a. the 1930 and 1950 data or the 1890 and 1990 data?
    b. the linear model or the exponential model?

EXAMINING ASSUMPTIONS

Definitions: When we know data points and use them to determine data values between those points, the process is called *interpolation*. When we know data points and try to use them to predict data values at a later or earlier time, the process is called *extrapolation*.

MAKING PREDICTIONS

Problems 7-9 show that both assumptions are reasonably accurate in the short run. However, in the long run, the exponential model overestimates and the linear model underestimates.

(In fact the graph for problem 8b is likely to go off the page. You may have the students extend the page upwards, or just not graph the last points.)

If you want to get further in this discussion, you can assign problems 10-11. Clearly, from the vantage point of 1940, the growth in the last decade seemed abnormally low, so one would look for other numbers to use in making forecasts. Some possibilities are to use the mean or the median of the growth in the previous two or three decades, going all the way back to 1890. If different groups use different possibilities, it would be interesting to compare the accuracy of their results.

For problem 12 a good prediction would take into account the persistent dropping of both the numerical increase and the percent increase since 1960.

12.1 SOLUTIONS

arithmetic mean, or average, computed as follows: (248,709,873 + 62,979,766)/2 = 311,689,639/2 = 155,844,820. The U.S. had this population sometime between 1950 and 1960. This was after the halfway point in years, which was 1940.

7. See the table.

Year	#7(a)	#7(b)	Actual Population
1890	62,979,766	62,979,766	62,979,766
1900	75,770,323	79,039,606	76,212,168
1910	88,560,880	99,194,706	92,228,496
1920	101,351,437	124,489,356	106,021,537
1930	114,141,994	156,234,142	123,202,624
1940	126,932,551	196,073,848	132,164,569
1950	139,723,108	246,072,679	151,325,798
1960	152,513,665	308,821,212	179,323,175
1970	165,304,222	387,570,621	203,302,031
1980	178,094,779	486,401,130	226,545,805
1990	190,885,336	610,433,418	248,709,873

8.

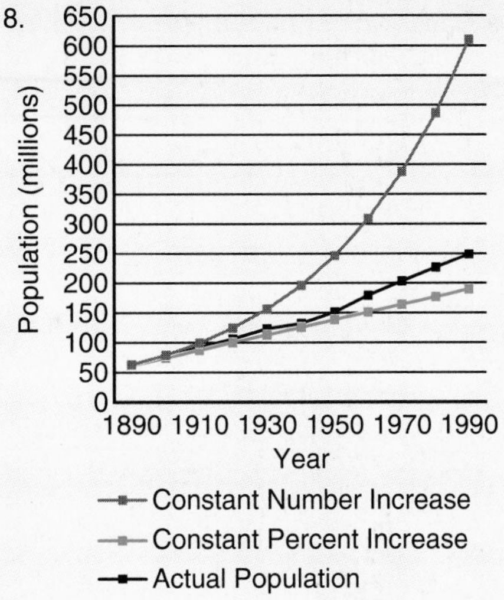

9. a. The assumption of constant number increase slightly underestimated the population in 1900. It was off by 76,212,168 − 75,770,323 = 441,845. The assumption of constant percent increase gave an estimate that was farther off. It overestimated the population by 79,039,606 − 76,212,168 = 2,827,438.

ESTIMATING MISSING DATA

*I*n this section, students will need to realize that the assumption of linear growth corresponds to constant number increase, and the assumption of exponential growth corresponds to constant percent increase. This section also uses the idea of the midpoint of growth, which we saw in Chapter 9, Lesson 7.

EXAMINING ASSUMPTIONS

*T*he main point of this lesson is that mathematical models cannot be applied blindly. Careless or mechanical use of mathematics is no more accurate than random guessing and could be more dangerous, since it claims scientific validity. Mathematical models can be a useful tool, but only in cases where they really make sense. Students will learn that long term predictions are more greatly affected by inappropriate assumptions.

*Y*ou can expect more from problem 18 if students have done problems 10-12.

REVIEW LINE THROUGH TWO POINTS

*T*his problem reviews an idea from Chapter 10, Lesson 8, that will be needed in the next lesson.

17. Which of the problems in this lesson involved extrapolation? Which ones involved interpolation?

It is important to examine assumptions when analyzing from data. People who analyze data often make incorrect projections and draw wrong conclusions because of making inappropriate assumptions.

18. Report Write a report summarizing what you learned in this lesson. Your report should include but not be limited to comments on:

- the suitability of the linear and exponential models as applied to the growth of the U.S. population during this century;
- the validity of results from extrapolating and interpolating using these models;
- a comparison of the accuracy of short-term and long-term predictions;
- how ideas outside of mathematics can help improve the quality of a mathematical model.

REVIEW LINE THROUGH TWO POINTS

19. Find the equation of the line through:

a. (0, 0) and (12, 34);
b. (5, 6) and (7, 11);
c. (8.9, -10) and (12.3, -4.3).

12.1 SOLUTIONS

b. The assumption of constant number increase considerably underestimated the population. The difference between the estimated population and the actual population is 57,824,537. The assumption of constant percent increase drastically underestimated the population. The difference between actual and estimated is 361,723,543. The percent error is 145%.

10. a. This decade was atypical, with the lowest growth rate in the 100-year period.
b. Answers will vary. Students might use a mean or median of previous growth rates.

11. Answers will depend on the choice made in 10(b).

12. Answers will vary depending on the assumptions made.

13. a. linear growth: (132,164,569 + 151,325,798)/2 = 141,745,183
b. exponential growth: $\sqrt{132164569 \cdot 151325798)}$ = 141,421,034

14. a. linear growth: (123,202,624 + 151,325,798)/2 = 137,264,211
b. exponential growth: $\sqrt{123202624 \cdot 151325798)}$ = 136,542,065

15. a. linear growth: (62,979,766 + 248,709,873)/2 = 155,844,820
b. exponential growth: $\sqrt{62979766 \cdot 248709873)}$ = 125,154,663

16. a. The 1930 and 1940 data gave a close estimate. The estimate based on the linear assumption was off by 5,099,642, and the estimate based on the exponential assumption was off by 4,377,496.
b. In both cases, the exponential model was closer.

17. The problems in the section called "Making Predictions" involved extrapolation. Those in the section called "Estimating Missing Data" involved interpolation.

18. Reports will vary.

19. a. $y = (17/6)x$
b. $y = (5x - 13)/2$
c. $y = 1.68x - 24.92$

LESSON 12.2

The Median-Median Line

You will need: graph paper

FITTING A LINE

The table shows fuel efficiency data for 28 automobiles equipped with manual transmission.

Highway vs. City Mileage

EPA Fuel Efficiency Data for 28 Cars with Manual Transmission

Car	miles per gallon City	miles per gallon Highway
Corvette	16	25
Firebird	17	26
Thunderbird	17	24
Nissan 300ZX	18	24
Subaru XT	18	25
Stealth	19	24
Saab 9000	19	25
Sunbird	19	28
Volvo 740	20	26
Shadow	20	28
Probe	21	27
Sonata	21	28
Nissan NX	22	28
Colt Vista	22	29
Celica	22	30
Eclipse	23	32
Accord	24	29
Acclaim	24	34
Capri	25	31
Cabriolet	25	32
Impulse	26	33
Geo Prizm	28	34
Colt 5-speed	29	35
Escort	29	36
Sentra	29	37
Colt 4-speed	31	36
Civic CRX	32	36
Tercel	33	37

1. Explain the meaning of the words *city mileage* and *highway mileage.*

Can average highway mileage be predicted from average city mileage? A graph of highway mileage versus city mileage shows that the data points lie approximately in a straight line. In this lesson you will learn a formal method for fitting a line to data. You can then use this line to make predictions for other cars.

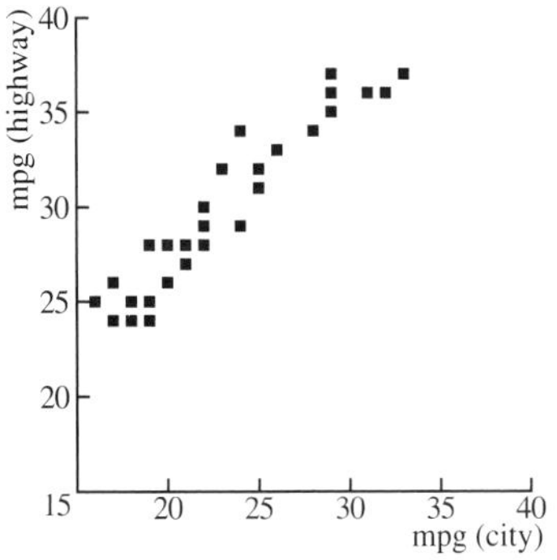

12.2 SOLUTIONS

1. These have precise definitions used by the EPA when performing fuel efficiency tests. Informally, city mileage refers to the number of miles the car gets per gallon when doing primarily city driving, and highway mileage refers to the number of miles the car gets per gallon when doing primarily highway driving.

2.-6.

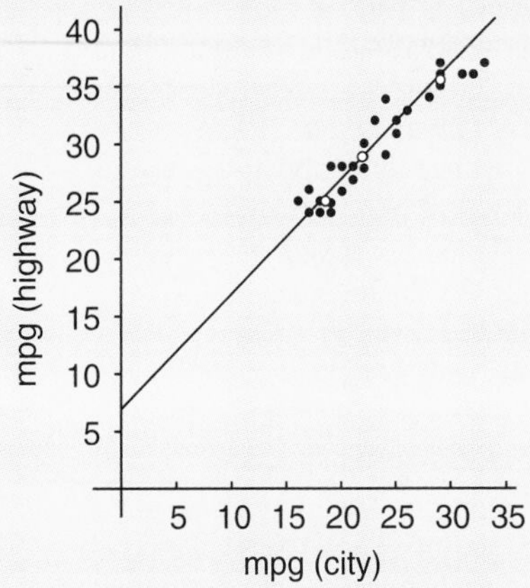

12.2 The Median-Median Line

Core Sequence: 1-18

Suitable for Homework: 11-19

Useful for Assessment: 8-12, 18-19

What this Lesson is About:

- Fitting a line to data
- Interpolation and extrapolation
- Uses and limits of mathematical models

While Lesson 1 warned about the limits of mathematical models, this lesson shows that in some cases it is fairly easy to construct a reasonably accurate model for real-world data. Be sure to precede this lesson with problem 19 in Lesson 1 to review finding the equation of a line.

For many more ideas and activities on this topic, see the excellent book *Exploring Data,* by James M. Landwehr and Ann E. Watkins (Dale Seymour Publications, 1986).

FITTING A LINE

The idea of fitting a line to data has been previewed in Chapter 4, Lesson 7; Chapter 8, Lesson 1; and Chapter 10, **Thinking/Writing 10.B**.

The method presented here is easy to understand and apply. It is not as commonly used by statisticians as least squares regression, but it is satisfactory at this level. Graphing calculators and computer software make it possible to fit a line to data automatically. Because of the "black box" nature of this capability, we prefer to use the median-median line, which gets the students directly involved with the data.

At any rate, what is most important at this level is not the procedure for getting a line, but a discussion of when fitting a line is appropriate, and what the limits of such a model are.

Students do not need to do problem 2 if you provide them with a copy of the graph on page 575.

Problem 7 uses a concept that was reviewed after Lesson 1.

EXAMINING THE MODEL

This section is the heart of the lesson. In it, students must interpret the graph. At least problems 8-10 should be done in class.

Problems 8-9: The slope of 1 indicates that this line is a constant difference graph. On average in this range, the highway mileage can be obtained from the city mileage by adding a constant number, the one corresponding to the y-intercept. Note that in another sense, the y-intercept is meaningless here, since there is no car with mileage zero miles per gallon in the city.

In problem 9, students may have trouble with the fact that the graph in the text has origin (15, 15). However the one in the back of the Teacher's Guide has origin (0, 0). As a result, the graph in the text cannot be used to find the y-intercept graphically.

Problem 10: Points that are above the fitted line represent cars for which the highway mileage is greater than the city mileage by more than seven miles per gallon.

USING THE MODEL

This is straightforward. You may want to discuss the fact that in the vast majority of cases (if C is the city mileage and H the highway mileage), we have

$$C + 5 < H < C + 9.$$

2. On your own graph paper, make a full-page graph of the data. Your graph should have both scales starting at (0, 0). Use vertical lines to divide the data points into three approximately equal sets of points, as shown in the following graph. There are ten points in the first set, eight in the middle set, and ten in the third set.

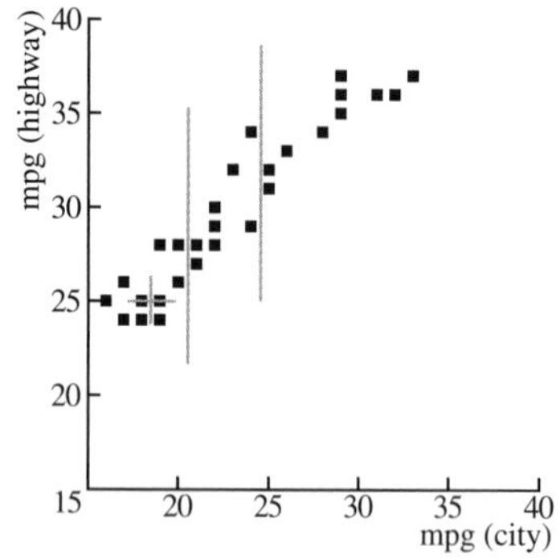

Look at the first set of data points. In your table, this is (16, 25) through (20, 28). It is easy to see on the graph that the median of the x-values in this first set of points is 18.5, and the median of the y-values is 25. The median point is marked with a +. Five points are to the left of it and five to the right. Five points are below it, (or even with it), and five are above, (or even with it).

3. Plot the point (18.5, 25) on your graph to show the medians of the x-values and y-values. Mark it with a +.

4. Find the median of the x-values and the median of the y-values for the second set of points. Mark it with a +.

5. Repeat for the third set of points.

The three +'s do not all lie exactly on the same line, but we can find a line that is close to all of them.

6. Place your ruler next to the first + and the third +, as if you were going to connect them with a line, but do not draw a line. Instead, move your ruler slightly toward the second +, about one-third of the way. Then draw the line.

7. Using two points on the line, find its equation. (Use points on the line, not actual data points — unless they happen to lie on the line.)

The line for which you found the equation is called the *median-median* line. Its equation provides an approximate relationship between city and highway mileage for a given car.

EXAMINING THE MODEL

Summary

8. What is the slope of the fitted line? What is its meaning in terms of this application?

9. What is the y-intercept of your line? What is its meaning in terms of this application?

10. Find two data points that are at least two units above the fitted line. What cars do they represent? What does it mean for points to be above the fitted line?

11. Find two data points that are at least two units below the fitted line. What cars do they represent? What does it mean for points to be below the fitted line?

12. Find two data points that are exactly on the line, or very near it. What cars do they represent? What does it mean for points to be on or near the fitted line?

12.2 SOLUTIONS

3. See the figure.
4. (22, 29)
5. (29, 35.5)
6. See the figure.
7. Answers will vary slightly. All should be quite close to $H = C + 7$.
8. The slope is 1. It means that an increase of 1 mpg in city mileage corresponds to an increase of 1 mpg in highway mileage.
9. The y-intercept is about 7. This means that one can estimate the highway mileage by adding 7 to city mileage for the same car.
10. Points above the line represent cars whose highway mileage is more than 7 mph greater than the city mileage. If the point lies at least two points above the line, it represents a car for which there is at least a 9 mpg spread between city mileage and highway mileage. These points lie at least two units above the line:
    (16, 25) Corvette
    (17, 26) Firebird
    (19, 28) Sunbird
    (23, 32) Eclipse
    (24, 34) Acclaim
11. Points below the line represent cars whose highway mileage is less than 7 mph greater than the city mileage. If the point lies at least two points below the line, it represents a car for which highway mileage is at most 5 mpg greater than city mileage. These points lie at least two units below the line:
    (19, 24) Stealth
    (24, 29) Accord
    (31, 36) Colt 4-Speed
    (32, 36) Civic CRX
    (33, 37) Tercel
12. If a point lies exactly on the line, it represents a car for which the line will predict exactly the highway mileage from the city mileage.
    (17, 24) Thunderbird
    (21, 28) Sonata
    (25, 32) Cabriolet
    (26, 33) Impulse
    (29, 36) Escort
    (22, 29) Colt Vista
    (18, 25) Subaru XT

USING THE MODEL

13. Using your model (the equation of your fitted line), predict the highway mileage for a car that got city mileage of:

a. 30 miles per gallon;

b. 27 miles per gallon.

14. For a city mileage of 26, what is the

a. actual highway mileage based on the data?

b. predicted highway mileage based on the fitted line?

15. For a highway mileage of 28,

a. what range of city mileages might you expect, based on the data?

b. what city mileage would you expect, based on the fitted line?

EXTENDING THE MODEL

16. Use the equation of the fitted line to predict highway mileage, if the city mileage is the following:

a. 53 b. 11

17. Based on your model, what city mileage would you expect for highway mileage of:

a. 58? b. 15?

Car	miles per gallon	
	City	Highway
Lamborghini	9	14
Ferrari	10	15
BMW M5	11	20
Suzuki Swift	45	50
Civic HF	49	52
Geo Metro	53	58

This table shows data for cars with very high and very low mileage.

18.

a. Does your model seem to work for very high and very low values?

b. For what range of values does your model work well? Explain.

YOUR OWN DATA

19. Project Collect your own data (at least twenty *pairs* of numbers), either from an almanac, newspaper, or magazine, or by surveying people you know. Graph the data. *If the points seem to fall more or less in a line*, find the median-median line and find an equation for it. In any case, write a paragraph about what you find out. The following are possible topics, but you may choose any two variables which are related.

a. arm span vs. height

b. weight vs. height

c. height vs. shoe size

d. points scored vs. time on the court

e. hits vs. times at bat

In other words, almost all the data points are enclosed between two parallel lines, one two units above and the other two units below, the fitted line.

EXTENDING THE MODEL

While this model is fairly useful and accurate, it works well only within the limits of the given data. It appears that for extreme values the difference may be less pronounced.

YOUR OWN DATA

This project will give the students a chance to apply their new skill to a different data set.

If more than one data point falls on the same point in the graph, it can be replaced by a number on the graph (e.g., the number 2 instead of a point would indicate two data points are in that spot). Or, the points can be displaced so all can be seen. This is visually preferable, even though it is slightly less accurate.

If the data points do not seem to line up, it is meaningless to fit a line. You may compare student data sets by looking at their graphs, and discussing which ones show an association between the two variables (an increase in x clearly leads to an increase or a decrease in y); and which ones do not (an increase in x leads to no recognizable change in y). In the latter case, students should not fit a line!

Make sure students get a chance to share their projects with the class.

12.2 SOLUTIONS

13. a. 37
 b. 34

14. a. 33
 b. 33

15. a. 19-22
 b. 21

16. a. 60
 b. 18

17. a. 51
 b. 8

18. a. It works fairly well, but it slightly overestimates the highway mileage for all but one of the cars given. (See the table.)
 b. Answers will vary. It doesn't do a bad job of predicting in the entire range given, but it seems best in the range of 17-29 mpg for city driving.

Miles per Gallon

Car	City	Actual Highway	Predicted Highway
Lamborghini	9	14	16
Ferrari	10	15	17
BMW M5	11	20	18
Suzuki Swift	45	50	52
Civic HF	49	52	56
Geo Metro	53	58	60

▼ 12.3
Safe Driving

Core Sequence: 1-16

Suitable for Homework: 4-20

Useful for Assessment: 7, 10, 15-16

What this Lesson is About:

- Direct and inverse variation
- Application of algebra to public safety
- The effect of parameters in a formula

One of the purposes of this lesson is to develop the skill of using and interpreting formulas. It is one of the few places where we give a formula instead of having students derive it.

Mathematically, the formula at the heart of the lesson involves three variables. By fixing one of the three, a function can be found that relates the other two to each other.

You may discuss this lesson with a health or a biology teacher, to get more insights into how to lead a discussion of this life-and-death topic.

A FORMULA

This lesson shows how a single formula can embody both direct and inverse variation, depending on which variable is fixed and which varies.

LESSON 12.3

Safe Driving

You will need: graph paper

There is no safe way to drive after drinking. Alcohol reaches a person's brain very soon after it has been absorbed into the bloodstream, and it impairs vision, hearing, muscular coordination, judgment, and self-control.

A person can begin to show mild effects from drinking alcohol when the blood alcohol concentration (BAC) is as low as 0.02%. Most people do not experience impairment until the BAC is about 0.05%, but each situation is different. A person who is tired or sick, or has taken drugs or medicines, may experience impairment with a lower BAC. In any case, a BAC of 0.10% is very unsafe for driving.

A FORMULA

Blood alcohol concentration depends on many factors, but it can be estimated by using a person's weight and the amount of alcohol consumed, using this formula.

$$B = \frac{7.6 \cdot A}{W}$$

B = blood alcohol level, or BAC (in %).
A = alcohol consumed (in ounces).
W = body weight (in pounds).

The number 7.6 in the formula was derived by taking into account physiological factors (such as the percentage of alcohol that will be absorbed into the blood) and conversion of units.

Definition: We say that y is *inversely proportional* to x if the product of x and y is constant. Expressed algebraically

$xy = k$ or $y = k/x$ for some constant k.

1. In the formula is B
  a. directly or inversely proportional to W?
  b. directly or inversely proportional to A?

2. Use the formula to estimate the blood alcohol concentration of:
  a. a 152-pound person who consumed one ounce of alcohol;
  b. a 190-pound person who consumed two ounces of alcohol.

3. a. Solve the formula for W in terms of the other two variables.
  b. Use your equation to estimate the weight a person would have to be in order to have a blood alcohol concentration of 0.05 after drinking three ounces of alcohol.

4. a. Solve the formula for A in terms of the other two variables.
  b. Estimate the amount of alcohol a person probably consumed if he or she weighed 170 lbs. and had a BAC of 0.10.

GRAPHING BAC vs. ALCOHOL

The formula has three variables, so we cannot graph it on a two-dimensional Cartesian coordinate system. However, we can use two-dimensional graphs to study this problem by fixing the value of one variable and graphing the resulting function.

12.3 SOLUTIONS

1. a. inversely
   b. directly
2. a. 0.05%
   b. 0.08%
3. a. $W = (7.6A)/B$
   b. $W = 7.6(3)/0.05 = 456$ pounds!
4. $(170 \cdot 0.10)/7.6 = 2.24$ or about 2.25 ounces

5. a. Substitute 152 for W in the formula to find the function that expresses how BAC depends on the amount of alcohol consumed for a 152-pound person.
   b. Make a graph of the function you wrote in part (a). Label the y-axis *BAC (%)* and the x-axis *Alcohol (oz)*.
   c. Label your graph so people can see what it refers to.
6. Repeat problem 5 for three other reasonable weights. Use the same axes for all four graphs.
7. Describe the four graphs you drew. For a given body weight, is BAC directly proportional or inversely proportional to the amount of alcohol consumed? Explain.

GRAPHING BAC vs. WEIGHT

8. a. Substitute 1 for A in the formula to find the function that expresses how BAC depends on weight for people who have consumed one ounce of alcohol.
   b. Make and label the graph of the function you wrote in part (a).
9. Repeat problem 8 for three other amounts of alcohol (between two ounces and eight ounces). Use the same axes for all four graphs.
10. Describe the four graphs you drew. For a given amount of alcohol, does the BAC vary directly or inversely as the weight of the person? Explain.

THE EFFECT OF TIME

Alcohol does not stay in a person's blood forever. The amount remaining as time passes depends on many factors. A rule of thumb is that 40 minutes after drinking, blood alcohol starts to decrease at the rate of 0.01% per 40 minutes. In using this rule, you must remember to account for the first 40 minutes.

Example: Using the formula, a woman's blood alcohol level was estimated to be about 0.06%. Eighty minutes later she might expect it to be about 0.05%.

11. A man's blood alcohol concentration was estimated to be about 0.09%. How long would he have to wait for his BAC to drop below 0.02%?
12. A woman's blood alcohol concentration was estimated to be about 0.12%. How long until her BAC was below 0.04%?

SAFE DRIVING GUIDELINES

13. A 115-pound woman had two ounces of alcohol to drink. Her 240-pound companion drank three ounces. Two hours later, do you think either person could drive safely? If so, which one? Explain your answer.
14. People know how much they have had to drink, but they do not know how much alcohol they have consumed. Calculate the amount of alcohol in each of these drinks.
    a. 12 ounces of beer that is 4% alcohol
    b. 4 ounces of wine that is 12% alcohol
    c. 6 ounces of wine that is 12% alcohol
    d. 4 ounces of a drink that is 20% alcohol
15. A woman drank two 12-ounce beers. She weighs about 120 pounds. How long should she wait before driving? Explain.
16. **Report** Write a report that will give information to people to help them use good judgment in driving if they have been drinking. Include the following components in your report:
    - Summarize what you learned about blood alcohol concentration in your investigation. You may wish to include graphs or tables.

In problems 3-4, students have to solve for one variable in terms of another, a skill that is very important in science.

GRAPHING BAC VS. ALCOHOL
GRAPHING BAC VS. WEIGHT

These are straightforward graphing activities, that review constant ratio and constant product graphs.

THE EFFECT OF TIME
SAFE DRIVING GUIDELINES

This is where the information presented in this lesson is put to use in answering real-world questions.

12.3 SOLUTIONS

5. a. $B = 0.05A$

5. - 6.

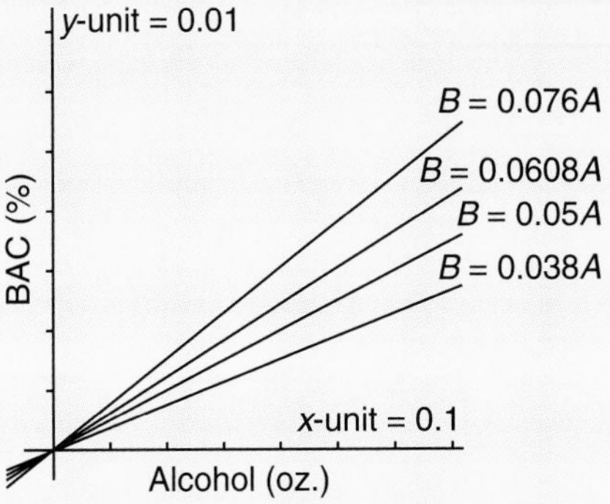

6. Answers will vary. Some possibilities are given below and on the graph.

$W = 100$	$B = 0.076A$
$W = 125$	$B = 0.061A$
$W = 150$	$B = 0.051A$
$W = 152$	$B = 0.050A$
$W = 175$	$B = 0.043A$
$W = 200$	$B = 0.038A$
$W = 250$	$B = 0.030A$

7. It varies directly. (The graphs are all straight lines through the origin.) This makes sense, since the more alcohol you drink, the higher the BAC.

8. a. $B = 7.6/W$

8. - 9.

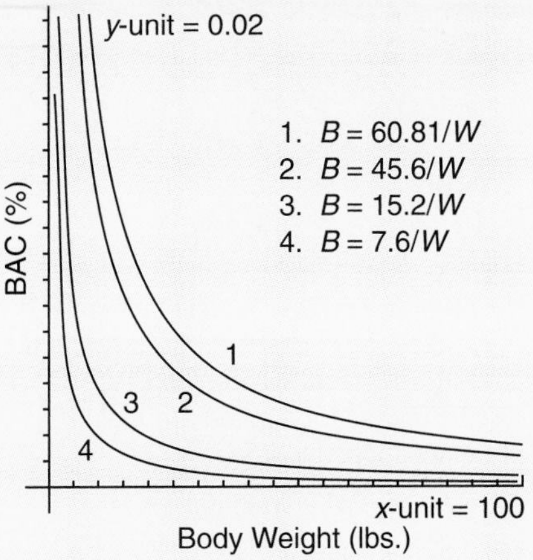

REVIEW COMPARING FRACTIONS

This section reviews the meaning of fractions in a form which will be helpful in Lesson 5.

Problem 18 reviews reciprocals. For the rest, instead of teaching any algorithms, encourage students to pay attention to whether numerators or denominators are the same, and to use reasoning and/or calculations. Class discussion of how students answered these questions would be useful.

- Make a chart or diagram that you think will help give people information about blood alcohol concentration. They should be able to look up their weight and the amount they have had to drink in your table and estimate their BAC. Include information on the amount of alcohol in some typical drinks.

17. Research Find out about the DUI (driving under the influence of alcohol or drugs) laws in your state. In some states the laws are different for people under age 18 or 21. You may want to find statistics about the relationship between BAC and the chance of being involved in an accident.

- Summarize what you find out about DUI laws.
- Give your own opinion about the DUI laws in your state.

REVIEW COMPARING FRACTIONS

Explorations

18. Find several values of x for which:

a. $\frac{x}{40} > \frac{40}{x}$ b. $\frac{x}{40} < \frac{40}{x}$

19. Which is greater?

a. $\frac{x}{40}$ or $\frac{x}{45}$ b. $\frac{40}{x}$ or $\frac{45}{x}$

20. Which is greater?

a. $\frac{d}{40} - \frac{d}{45}$ or $\frac{d}{40} - \frac{d}{50}$

b. $\frac{d}{40} - \frac{d}{45}$ or $\frac{d}{45} - \frac{d}{50}$

12.3 SOLUTIONS

9. Answers will vary. Some possibilities are given below and on the graph.

$A = 2$	$B = 15.2/W$
$A = 3$	$B = 22.8/W$
$A = 4$	$B = 30.4/W$
$A = 5$	$B = 38/W$
$A = 6$	$B = 45.6/W$
$A = 7$	$B = 53.2/W$
$A = 8$	$B = 60.8/W$

10. The graphs are constant product graphs. The BAC varies inversely to the weight of the person. As the weight increases, the BAC decreases for a given amount of alcohol consumed.

11. 5 hours and 20 minutes

12. 6 hours

13. Neither one could drive safely after two hours. The smaller person would need to wait more than 6 hours before her BAC dropped below 0.05, and the larger person would need to wait about 4 hours. After two hours, the smaller person would have a BAC of about 0.11% and the larger one would have a BAC of about 0.075%.

14. a. 0.48 or about 1/2 oz
 b. 0.48 or about 1/2 oz
 c. 0.72 or about 3/4 oz
 d. 0.80 oz

15. Her BAC after 80 minutes will be about 0.051%. She should wait at least an hour and a half.

16. Answers will vary.

17. Answers will vary.

18. Answers will vary. If $x > 0$,
 a. any value greater than 40 will work;
 b. any value less than 40 will work.

19. Answers will depend on the value of x.
 a. If $x > 0$, $x/40$ will be greater.
 b. If $x > 0$, $45/x$ is greater.

20. Answers will depend on the value of d. If $d > 0$,
 a. the second expression is greater;
 b. the first expression is greater.

LESSON 12.4

Mathematical Models in Science

You will need:

- graph paper
- materials for experiments (See below)

HEATING AND COOLING GASES

Doing science often means finding mathematical models that fit experimental data. In 1787 the French scientist Jacques Charles discovered that when a gas is kept at constant pressure, it expands when heated and contracts when cooled. For gases under constant pressure, *volume is a linear function of temperature*.

At a certain pressure a gas has a volume of 500 cubic centimeters at 27°C. Kept at the same pressure, it expands to 605cc at 90°C.

1. Find an equation that gives the volume (V) of this gas as a linear function of the temperature (T).
2. Find the volume of the gas at 0°C.
3. When kept at this pressure, how much does this gas expand for every 1°C increase in temperature?

When they get cold enough, gases condense (turn into liquids). If they did not, the temperature for which the volume would be 0 is called *absolute zero*, the lowest possible temperature.

4. Use the equation you wrote in problem 1 to figure out what temperature absolute zero must be.

This graph shows how the volume of a certain gas varies with temperature, when kept at constant pressure. Each line represents a different pressure. The point where the red line ends and the blue line starts is the condensation point. Only the red lines represent actual data.

Charles's Law

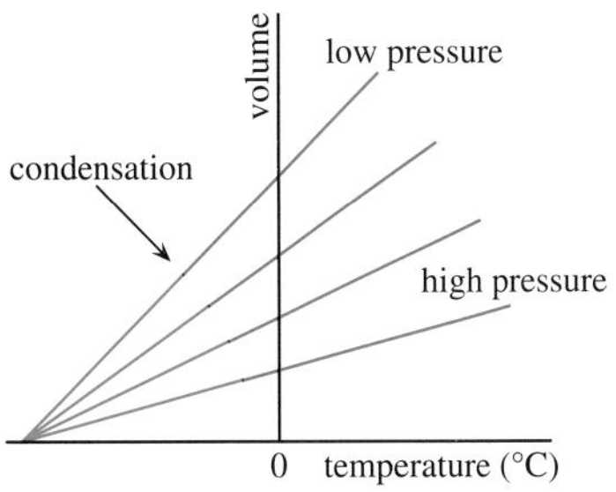

Summary

5. As the pressure increases, what happens to the slopes of the lines? What does this mean in terms of the application?
6. What is the meaning of the y-intercept of the lines? As the pressure increases, how does it change?
7. How does the condensation point vary with pressure?
8. Why do all the blue lines intersect at one point? What is the point's significance?

▼ 12.4 Mathematical Models in Science

Core Sequence: 1-16

Suitable for Homework: 9-16, 20-21

Useful for Assessment: 5-8, 10-11, 15-16, 21

What this Lesson is About:

- Linear functions and equations in science
- Interpreting graphs
- Dependent and independent variables
- Data from experiments

HEATING AND COOLING GASES

The day before this lesson you may hand out a balloon to each student. Ask them what they think would happen if they blow up the balloon when they get home and put it in the freezer. This experiment should increase the interest in this section and make its real-world content more believable. Students should observe what happens when the balloon has been in the freezer for a while, and when it gets back to room temperature.

Problems 1-4 are applications of linear functions and linear equations to a problem from the physical sciences. Problems 5-8 are problems in interpreting graphs. Throughout this section students may have difficulty making the connection between what they are reading and the math they have studied in the past. Group and class discussion may be helpful.

12.4 SOLUTIONS

1. $V = (5/3)T + 455$
2. $V = 455$
3. 5/3 cubic centimeters
4. $T = -273$ degrees Celsius
5. The slopes decrease as the pressure increases. This means that when the gas is at higher pressure, there is less increase in volume for each degree increase in temperature. (The answer in #3 refers to one particular pressure only.)
6. The y-intercept is the volume of the gas at 0 degrees C. As the pressure increases, the volume at 0 degrees decreases.
7. As the pressure increases, the condensation point increases.
8. This is absolute zero.

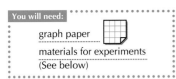

STRETCHING IT

*A*gain, the problems require applying math ideas to a science problem, and interpreting graphs. You may precede this section with problem 17 if you prefer to begin with a hands-on experience for your students.

*F*or problem 10 you may tell students that there is a point beyond which the spring gets permanently distorted. This is called the *elastic limit* of the spring. And beyond that, there is a point where the spring breaks. These things must be kept in mind if you do problem 17.

DEPENDENCE AND INDEPENDENCE

*T*he idea of dependent and independent variable is useful in deciding how to set up the graphs for experiments in the next section.

STRETCHING IT

The length of a spring is related to the weight that hangs from it. The following figure shows a graph from an experiment with a certain spring.

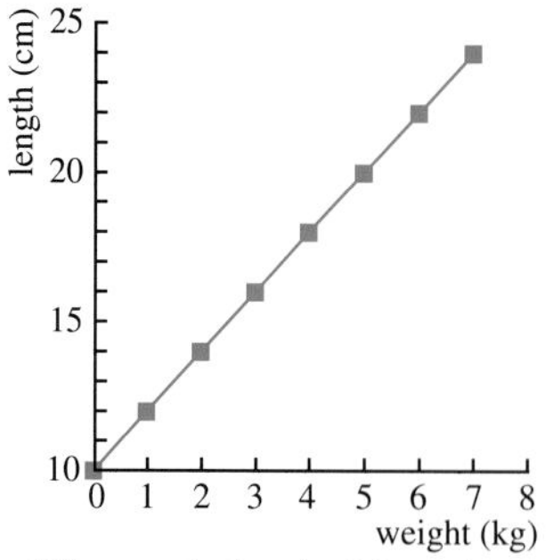

9. a. What was the length of the spring before any weight was added?

b. How many centimeters did the spring stretch for each kilogram of weight?

c. What is the equation that relates length to weight?

10. Can the graph be indefinitely extended to the right? Explain.

11. This graph shows data for two other springs. Which spring is stiffer? Which one is longer? Explain.

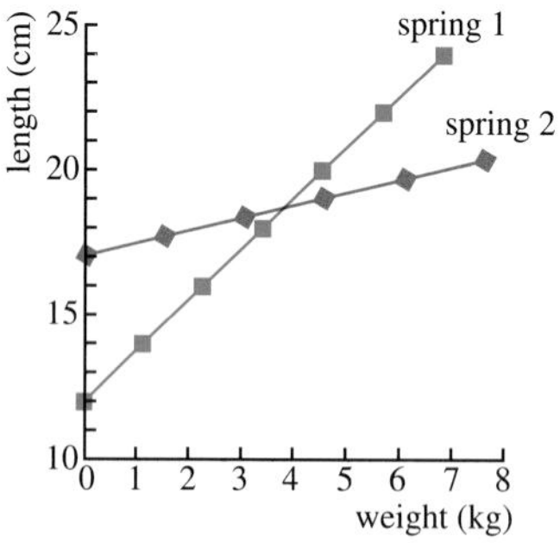

DEPENDENCE AND INDEPENDENCE

Paul, a forest lover, knew how to estimate the temperature from listening to cricket chirps. His grandmother had taught him to count the number of chirps per minute, divide by 4, and add 40 to get the temperature in Fahrenheit.

12. Write an equation for the temperature (T) as a function of the number of chirps (C).

13. What would Paul estimate the temperature to be if he counted 180 chirps per minute?

14. According to the model, at what temperature would the crickets cease to chirp?

Since the number of chirps depends on the temperature, and not vice-versa, we call number of chirps the *dependent* variable and temperature the *independent* variable.

In algebra we usually call the independent variable x and use the horizontal axis for it. We call the dependent variable y and use the vertical axis for it. Likewise, we often express the relationship between the two variables by writing the dependent variable as a function of the independent variable.

15. Write an equation for the dependent variable (number of chirps) as a function of the independent variable (temperature). Hint: Use your equation from problem 12 and solve for C in terms of T.

In an experiment the independent variable is the variable we change or manipulate. Then we observe and record the effect on the dependent variable.

16. Which variable is dependent and which is independent in problem 9? Explain.

12.4 SOLUTIONS

9. a. The spring is 10 cm.
   b. 2
   c. $L = 10 + 2W$
10. No, the spring will reach its elastic limit.
11. Spring 2 is stiffer. Spring 2 is longer to start with. If 4 kg were added to each spring, they would be the same length. When more weight than that is added, Spring 1 becomes longer.
12. $T = C/4 + 40$
13. Substitute 180 for C in the above equation. $T = 85$
14. Substitute 0 for C in the above equation. $T = 40$
15. $4(T - 40) = C$
16. Length is the dependent variable and weight is the independent variable.

YOUR OWN EXPERIMENTS

For each experiment, problems 17-20, do the following:

a. Discuss the relationship you expect between the two variables.
b. Identify the dependent and independent variables.
c. Carry out the experiment and collect the data in a table.
d. Make a graph.
e. Interpret the graph.
f. If possible, write an equation relating the variables.
g. Draw some conclusions.

17. *Spring:* The length of a spring as a function of the weight that hangs from it — **You will need** a spring and several identical weights. Start by letting the spring hang freely. Measure its length. Then add the weights one by one, each time measuring the length of the spring as it stretches.

18. *Fall:* The time it takes for Lab Gear blocks to fall as a function of the number of blocks — **You will need** a stopwatch and 20 or more x^2-blocks. Line up x^2-blocks so that if the first one is pushed, each block will knock down the next block in succession.

19. *Summer:* The time it takes to do "the wave" as a function of the number of people involved. **You will need** a stopwatch. Decide on an order for the wave. Appoint a student (or the teacher) to be the timer. When the timer says "Go," take turns getting up and sitting down. Repeat the experiment for different numbers of people.

20. *Winter:* The height of an ice column as a function of the height of the corresponding water column — **You will need** some drinking straws, chewing gum, ice (or access to a refrigerator). Plug the bottom of a straw with gum. Fill it to a certain height with water. Mark and measure the height of the water column. Do it again with different amounts of water in other straws. Freeze them. Mark and measure the height of the column of ice.

21. **Report** Write an illustrated lab report on an experiment you conducted. This can be one of the ones presented in this section or another one of your own design. Include the data you collected, a graph, and an equation, if you found one. Describe the conditions in which you conducted the experiment, your expectations, and your conclusions.

YOUR OWN EXPERIMENTS

You may choose to do one or more of the experiments, but you probably cannot do all of them in one day. Be sure to try each one yourself before doing them with the class, so you can anticipate what difficulties might arise.

Each experiment should be preceded by a group and/or class discussion of the nature of the two variables and what relationship can be expected between them. The main ideas in the discussion should be incorporated into the introduction to the report.

The variables can be named x and y, which would help specify which variable is dependent and which is independent, and make it easier to set up the graph. Or, if you prefer, the variables can be named in a way that reflects their meaning.

For problem 17, borrow springs from a physics teacher, or use miniature Slinkies®. Depending on the spring, the weights can be washers, paper clips, M&M's®, or coins. You may need a container hanging from the spring. A film container does the job, suspended with the help of a paper clip.

For problem 18, keep the distance between the blocks constant as much as possible. The blocks fall so fast that you should plan on having long trains for more accurate measurement. Instead of Lab Gear blocks, you can use dominoes.

Problem 20 can be assigned as homework. It would be interesting to compare the results different students get.

12.4 SOLUTIONS

17.-21. Results and reports will vary.

12.A Equations from Data

THINKING WRITING

Core Sequence: 1-11

Suitable for Homework: 11

Useful for Assessment: 11

What this Assignment is About:

- Recognizing functions from data points
- Review of direct variation, inverse variation, and linear functions
- Review of constant product and constant ratio
- Review of slope

You may introduce the lesson by playing *What's my Function?* (See Teacher's Notes for Chapter 2, Lesson 7.)

Problems 1-6 are deliberately difficult, so that students will not be able to see the solutions by inspection. They should not be assigned for homework, as they are likely to be frustrating for some students. Instead, assign these as a group problem-solving activity in class. If the groups seem to be getting frustrated, you might suggest graphing the points to help reveal a pattern. After most of the equations have been found by at least one group, have students explain how they found the equations. Use this as a springboard for discussion of general methods.

Computer spreadsheets are a convenient way to explore numerical relationships like these. If you introduced that tool in Lesson 1, you may want to use it again here. However calculators are certainly sufficient.

Constant products were seen in Chapter 5, especially in Lesson 2 and **Thinking/Writing 5.A**. Constant ratios were seen in Chapter 6, **Thinking/Writing 6.B**, and in many lessons on direct variation. The idea of constant rate of change was seen in Chapter 8 and in many lessons on slope.

If students cannot solve problem 7 without help, you can suggest they start with simple examples of each type of function, and see which test applies. In addition, you may lead them to see how the constant product and constant ratio tests can be justified symbolically. For example, if $y = mx$, then dividing both sides by x yields $y/x = m$.

Both direct variation and more general linear functions involve constant slope. The key is that direct variation *also* requires constant ratios.

THINKING WRITING

12.A Equations from Data

Each of the tables below gives four (x, y) pairs for a function. Each function is one of the following types and has an equation of the corresponding form.

Type of Function	Form of Equation
direct variation	$y = mx$
inverse variation	$y = k/x$
linear	$y = mx + b$

For each table in problems 1 through 6,

a. decide whether the function is direct variation, inverse variation, or linear;

b. find the equation of the function.

1.

x	y
0.05	5
0.5	0.5
5	0.05
50	0.005

2.

x	y
0.05	0.002
0.5	0.02
5	0.2
50	2

3.

x	y
0.9	0.6
1.5	1.0
2.7	1.8
5.1	3.4

4.

x	y
200	125
100	62.5
120	75
320	200

5.

x	y
0.01	0.73
0.1	0.55
1.5	-2.25
3	-5.25

6.

x	y
4	-2
8	-1
18	1.5
25	3.25

7. Each of the following three tests can be used to recognize a certain type of function among direct variations, inverse variations, and linear functions. Match the test to the type of function. Make sure your answer works for problems 1-6.

a. constant xy product

b. constant slope

c. constant y/x ratio

Because of measurement error, the numbers obtained in scientific experiments do not usually give perfect number patterns. For tables 8-10, find an equation that is approximately right.

8.

x	y
1.5	0.50
1.6	0.53
1.7	0.55
1.8	0.60
1.9	0.63
2.0	0.65

9.

x	y
12.5	6.8
13	6.5
13.5	6.3
14	6.1
14.5	5.9
15	5.6

10.

x	y
0.6	4.12
0.7	4.26
0.8	4.37
0.9	4.49
1.0	4.61
1.1	4.71

11. **Report** Summarize what you know about how to find the equation corresponding to experimental data, if it is one of the following types:
- direct variation
- linear function
- inverse variation

Include examples. Explain both how to recognize the type of function and how to find the actual equation.

12.A SOLUTIONS

For problems 8 and 10, the median-median line is not usable, because there are too few points. However using the mean or median ratio for problem 8, and the mean or median product for problem 9 should provide a satisfactory equation. Problem 10 is a little more difficult since it involves two parameters. One possible approach is to use a mean or median slope and choose a line that passes through one of the given points. Or students can eyeball a line with a good fit and find its equation. Finally, experimenting with a graphing calculator, in combination with using a mean or median slope, makes it possible to find an equation quickly.

1. a. inverse variation b. $xy = 0.25$
2. a. direct variation b. $y = x/25$
3. a. direct variation b. $y = (2/3)x$
4. a. direct b. $y = 0.625x$
5. a. linear
   b. $y = -2x + 0.75$
6. a. linear
   b. $y = 0.25x - 3$
7. a. constant xy product: inverse variation
   b. constant slope: linear, direct variation
   c. constant y/x ratio: direct variation
8. $y = 0.25x + 0.125$
9. $xy = 85$
10. $y = 1.2x + 3.4$
11. Reports will vary.

LESSON 12.5

Modeling Motion

You will need: graph paper

AVERAGE SPEED

Definition: Average speed is total distance traveled divided by total travel time.

1. Joan goes to work at 6 A.M. She averages 60 mph on the interstate highway. She returns during rush hour, when she averages 15 mph. What is her average speed for the round trip if she travels 30 miles in each direction?

Many problems in this lesson can be understood better by making distance-time graphs, like this one about Joan's commute.

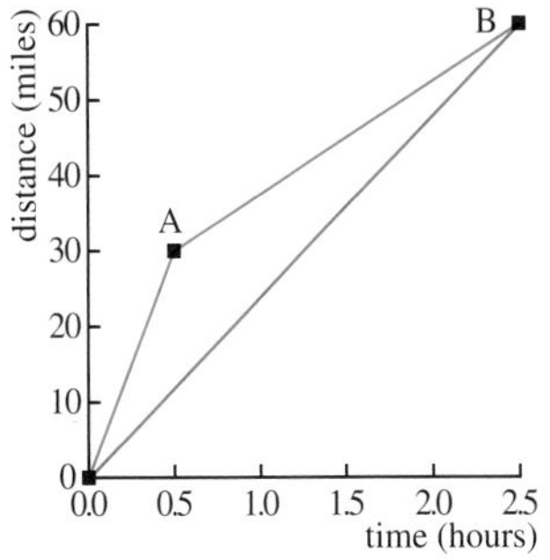

2. Explain how the coordinates of points A and B were obtained from the given information.

3. How does Joan's morning speed of 60 mph show up on the graph? Her return speed? Her average speed?

4. Joan calculated her average speed by adding the two speeds and dividing by 2.

$$(60 + 15)/2 = 37.5$$

Explain why this is wrong.

5. Jill traveled for two hours at 30 mph and two hours at 60 mph. Jack traveled for 90 miles at 30 mph and for 90 miles at 60 mph. Which of them had an average speed of 45 mph? Which one did not? Explain.

6. **Generalization**

a. I travel for t hours at v mph and t more hours at w mph. What is my average speed?

b. I travel to work, which is d miles away, at v mph, and travel back at w mph. What is my average speed?

RELAY RACE

Alaberg High's Track Team has a relay race team. These tables show the times in seconds of the individual runners in the 4 × 100 meter race at the meet with the Lean County School. The runners are listed in running order.

Alaberg		Lean	
Mal	12.2	Neil	12.1
Cal	12.0	Neal	12.3
Hal	12.4	Alan	12.2
Zal	11.4	Allen	10.9

7. Imagine you are the radio announcer for this event. Describe the teams' performances. Who was ahead at various times? How did it end up? What was the key to the winning team's victory?

12.5 Modeling Motion

Core Sequence: 1-12, 25

Suitable for Homework: 7-25

Useful for Assessment: 5-6, 12, 14, 18, 22-23, 25

What this Lesson is About:

- Using Cartesian graphs to model motion problems
- Average speed

You may not want to do the whole lesson consecutively. The first two sections form a coherent whole, but the last two can be assigned a few problems at a time over the next week or two.

The use of Cartesian graphs helps students think about time, distance, and rate more carefully. At the same time, this approach reinforces concepts of slope and interpretation of graphs.

AVERAGE SPEED
RELAY RACE

Problem 1 is a classic trick question, often posed on standardized tests. Do not be surprised if most students get it wrong. They will get a chance to correct it in the course of these two sections. We try to throw light on the difficulty, by using graphical analysis (problems 2-3) and the algebraic generalization in problem 6.

12.5 SOLUTIONS

1. Joan will spend 1/2 hour traveling to work and 2 hours traveling home. Her average speed is (total distance/total time). Since her total distance is 60 miles, her average speed is 60/2.5, or 24 miles per hour.

2. Point A shows that Joan traveled 30 miles in 1/2 hour, which was obtained by dividing 30 by 60. Point B shows that she traveled the next 30 miles (her return trip) in 2 hours, which was obtained by dividing 30 by 15.

3. Her morning speed is this slope of the line from (0, 0) to A. Her return speed is the slope of the line from A to B. Her average speed is the slope of the line from (0, 0) to B.

4. Average speed is calculated by dividing the total distance by the total time.

5. Jill traveled a total distance of 180 miles in 4 hours, so her average speed was 180/4, or 45 mph. Jack traveled a total distance of 180 miles in 4.5 hours, so his average speed was 40 mph. (Note that if Jack's average speed were computed incorrectly by averaging his two speeds of 60 mph and 30 mph, one would come to the wrong conclusion that his average speed was 45 mph.)

6. a. The total distance traveled is $tv + tw$ and the total time is $2t$. Hence the average speed is $(tv + tw)/(2t)$ or $(v + w)/2$. Notice that since the times at each speed are the same, the formula for average speed reduces to the average of the two speeds.

   b. The total time is $(d/w) + (d/v)$. The total distance is $2d$, so the average speed is $2d/[(d/w) + (d/v)]$.

7. Radio announcements will vary. This was a pretty exciting race. First, with Mal and Neil starting, Lean County was ahead. Then, thanks to Cal, Alaberg pulled ahead. Hal and Alan finished neck and neck, so it was up to Zal and Allen to determine who would win the race. Thanks to Allen's stunning performance, Lean County won by 1/2 second.

Do not belabor problem 6 if it is too difficult for your students, but your top students should find it interesting. The answer to problem 6a simplifies nicely.

The key to these problems is to remember the definition of average speed.

Students may find a graph useful for problem 7, but the points are so close that it may be difficult to see what's happening, unless a lot of attention is paid to the scale. (The time axis needs to be made as long as possible, while the distance axis should be somewhat squashed.)

Again, students may make a mistake on problem 10. They may consider that the difference is not very big, and that is true, but there are cases where the difference would be much greater (e.g., problem 1). At any rate, the discussion in problems 11-12 should help throw light on the subject. Any approach that does not yield the same answer as *total distance/total time* must be wrong!

8. a. Compare the median running times for the two teams.
b. Compare the mean running times for the two teams.
c. Which is more relevant to winning the race?

9. Find each runner's speed in m/sec.

10. Find the average speed of each team in m/sec.

11. Show how each student answered problem 10 and find their answers.
a. Andrea divided 100 by the mean running time for each team.
b. Beth divided 400 by the total time for each team.
c. Carolyn took the average of the individual members' speeds.

12. **Summary** Discuss the three methods presented in problem 11. Which ones are equivalent to each other? Which one is incorrect? Explain.

CATCH UP AND MEET

13. Jane is traveling at 60 mph along a road. She has traveled for four hours when Joe catches up with her. How fast must Joe have been traveling if he left the same place one hour after Jane?

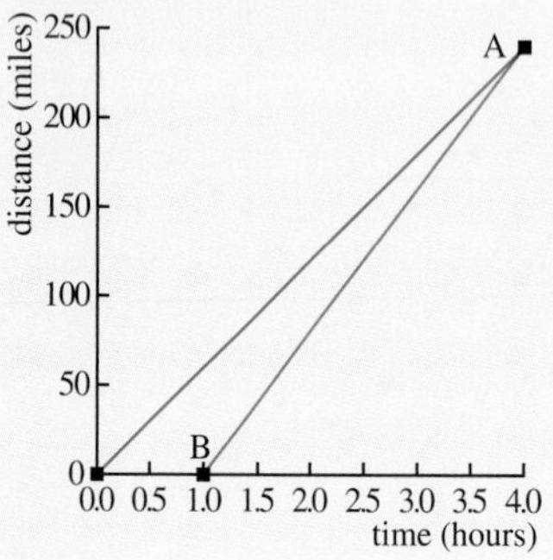

14. Look at the graph in problem 13. Explain how the coordinates of points A and B were chosen, and how the graph can help solve the problem.

15. Jim is traveling at 40 mph. Jorge leaves two hours later and travels at 50 miles per hour. How long until he catches up? How far have they gone?

16. Juan leaves at noon and travels at 45 mph. Jo leaves two hours later. How fast must she travel to catch up by:
a. 8 P.M.? b. 8:30 P.M.?
c. 11 P.M.? d. *H* P.M.?

17. Jacquey and Gigi start out at the same time, traveling towards each other. Jacquey travels at 50 mph. Gigi travels at 40 mph. They start out 250 miles apart. When and where do they meet?

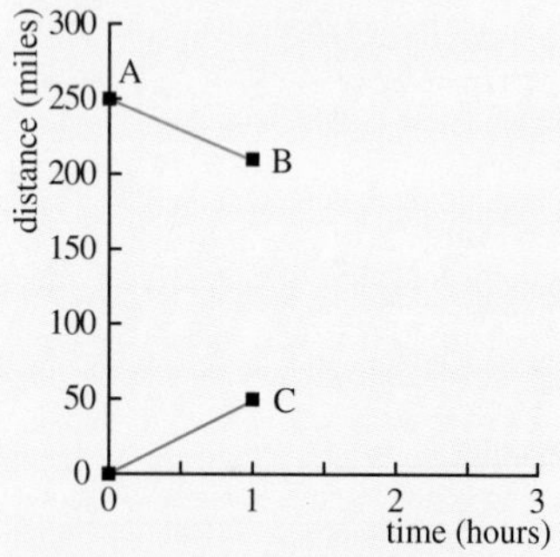

18. The graph shows Jacquey and Gigi's progress during the first hour. (Jacquey's graph starts at the origin.) Explain how the coordinates of points A, B, and C were obtained, and how to use a graph like this to solve problem 17.

19. Greg starts out going towards Cary, traveling 50 mph. Cary starts out two hours later going 40 mph, going towards Greg. If they are 250 miles apart to begin with, when and where do they meet?

12.5 SOLUTIONS

8. a. median for Alaberg: 12.1
   median for Lean: 12.15
   b. mean for Alaberg: 12
   mean for Lean: 11.875
   c. mean

9. See the table for each runner's speed in m/sec.

Alaberg	
Mal	8.197
Cal	8.333
Hal	8.065
Zal	8.772

Lean	
Neil	8.264
Neal	8.130
Alan	8.197
Allen	9.174

10. The average speed of each team is found by dividing the total distance of 400 meters by the team's total time.
   Alaberg High: 400/48 = 8.333
   Lean County School: 400/47.5 = 8.421

11. a. Alaberg: 100/12 = 8.333
   Lean: 100/11.875 = 8.421
   b. Alaberg: 400/48 = 8.333
   Lean: 400/47.5 = 8.421
   c. Add the average speeds of the individuals and divide by 4.
   Alaberg: 8.342 Lean: 8.441

12. Andrea's and Beth's methods are equivalent to each other. Note that the ratios in (b) are the same as those in (a), since both numerator and denominator have been multiplied by 4. Carolyn's method is incorrect. Hers does not take into account the fact that the individuals ran for different lengths of time.

13. 80 mph

14. B represents Joe's starting time and place. A represents the time and place where Jane and Joe meet.

15. Solve for t: $40t = 50(t - 2)$. Jorge catches up when he has been traveling 8 hours and Jim has been traveling 10 hours. They have both gone 400 miles.

16. a. 60 mph
   b. 58.85 mph
   c. 55 mph
   d. $45H/(H - 2)$

17. Solve for t: $250 - 40t = 50t$. They have been traveling about 2 hours and 47 minutes. They meet about 139 miles from Jacquey's starting place.

SAVING TIME

Paige travels to work so early that he meets hardly any traffic. He can drive at the speed limit the whole way. He wishes that the speed limit, which is 40 mph, would be raised so that he could sleep a little later in the morning.

20. How many minutes would Paige save if the speed limit were raised to 45 mph and he lives 30 miles from work?

21. Tara lives on the same road, 45 miles from work. How much time would she save?

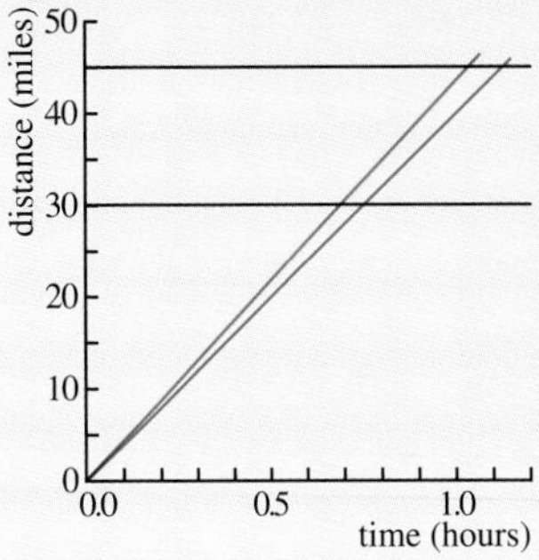

22. Explain how you can use a graph like this one to think about problems 20 and 21.

23. Generalization How much time would be saved for people who live *d* miles from work if the speed limit were raised from 40 to 45 mph?

24. If Leon lives 60 miles from work, to what would the speed limit have to be raised (from 40 mph) in order for him to save

a. 6 minutes? b. 12 minutes?

25. Rina is taking a 60-mile trip. Which is greater: the time saved if she can travel 50 mph instead of 40 mph, OR the time saved if she can travel 60 mph instead of 50 mph? Explain.

CATCH UP AND MEET
SAVING TIME

You may assign problems 13-16 as one group, then 17-19, then 20-23, then 24-25. You may also stop after any of these groups.

Note the difference between the vertical axis for the graph of problem 17, where instead of *distance traveled* what is represented is *distance from Jacquey's starting place*.

12.5 SOLUTIONS

18. A represents Gigi's starting place. The origin is Jacquey's starting place. B and C represent where they end up after one hour of travel. These points are determined by the rates given in the problem. To solve the problem of their meeting place and time graphically, one could extend the lines and find their point of intersection.
19. Solve for *t*: $50t = 250 - 40(t - 2)$. They meet after 3 and 2/3 hours. This is 183 and 1/3 miles from Greg's starting place.
20. It takes him 3/4 of an hour, or 45 minutes with the present speed limit. It would take him 2/3 of an hour, or 40 minutes if the speed limit were raised. He would save 5 minutes.
21. She would save 7.5 minutes.
22. Look at the horizontal distance between the two lines to determine the amount of time saved. Notice that the longer you travel, the more time you save.
23. $(d/40) - (d/45)$
24. a. 42.86 miles per hour
    b. 46.15 miles per hour
25. The 60-mile trip would take her 1.5 hours at 40 mph, 1.2 hours at 50 mph, and 1 hour at 60 mph. The difference between 40 mph and 50 mph is greater than the difference between 50 mph and 60 mph.

▼ 12.6
Gearing Up

Core Sequence: none of the lesson

Suitable for Homework: 1-10

Useful for Assessment: 3, 6, 8, 10-11

What this Lesson is About:

- An application of ratio
- Review of unit conversion
- Review of the circumference of a circle

It is best to introduce this lesson by bringing one or more real bicycles into the classroom and analyzing their gears. If you cannot bring bikes in, you may take students on a mini field-trip to some place where they can look at bikes and study the gears.

LESSON 12.6

Gearing Up

In this lesson you will learn about the mathematics of gears. This will help you understand the decisions people have to make when they buy or design bicycles.

BIG WHEELS

1. How far does a bicycle travel for every revolution of the wheel for each wheel diameter below?

a. 20 in. b. 27 in.
c. 50 in. d. 64 in.

Old-fashioned bicycles had huge front wheels. Most of these high-wheelers, as they were called, had a 50-inch front wheel and a 17-inch rear wheel, but some of the makers got carried away and built front wheels as high 64 inches! The pedals were in the center of the front wheels.

2. Why did bicycle makers make such big wheels?

Highwheelers had two drawbacks. First, the rider had to work very hard to get started, and most of these bicycles had to be pushed or dragged up hills. Second, their height made them a dangerous and impractical means of transportation. The rider had to jump down from the seat when the bicycle stopped, hoping to land feet-first.

The invention of gears on bicycles was a key development. Gears allowed the rider to travel longer distances for each turn of the pedals, without requiring such big wheels.

HOW GEARS WORK

Example: A bicycle has a chainwheel having 45 teeth and a rear sprocket having 15 teeth.

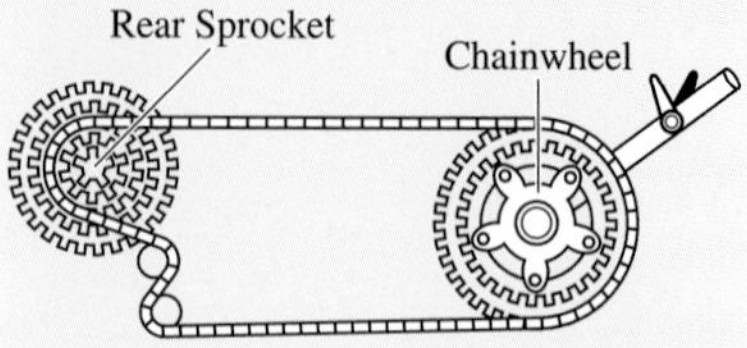

Each time the chain passes over one tooth on the chainwheel, it also passes over one tooth on the rear sprocket. Therefore, the rear sprocket will go through three revolutions for every one revolution of the chainwheel.

3. Explain why riding a 27-inch bicycle having these gears would be like riding an 81-inch bicycle in terms of the distance covered in one turn of the pedals.

Definition: The *gear ratio* is the ratio of the number of teeth on the chainwheel to the number of teeth on the rear sprocket.

4. If the gear ratio is 2.5, how many turns does the rear wheel make for each turn of the pedals?

12.6 SOLUTIONS

1. Multiply each diameter by π to get the circumference. Approximations are given.
   a. 62.83 in.
   b. 84.82 in.
   c. 157.08 in.
   d. 201.06 in.
2. One turn of the pedals would cause the bicycle to travel a great distance.
3. The rear sprocket would turn 3 times for each turn of the pedal, so the wheel would go through 3 revolutions. The distance traveled in three revolutions of a 27″ wheel would be the same as that traveled in one revolution of an 81″ wheel, since the circumference is directly proportional to diameter.
4. 2.5

A ten-speed bicycle has two chainwheels and five rear sprockets. Each combination of chainwheel and sprocket is a different gear.

5. Make a table to show how the gear ratio changes as a function of the number of teeth on the gears of a ten-speed bicycle, with two chainwheels having 40 and 54 teeth, and five rear sprockets having 14, 17, 22, 28, and 34 teeth.

	14	17	22	28	34
40	—	—	—	—	—
54	—	—	—	—	—

6. **Generalization** Write the gear ratio (g) as a function of the number of teeth on the chainwheel (c) and the number of teeth on the rear sprocket (r).

GEAR

Definition: The *gear* is the gear ratio multiplied by the diameter of the rear wheel. It gives the diameter of the wheel that would travel the same distance in one revolution of the pedals. (The unit of gear is inches, but it is usually omitted.)

Example: The gear ratio is 40/20, or 2, when using a chainwheel having 40 teeth and a rear sprocket having 20 teeth. On a bicycle having 26-inch wheels, the gear would be 2 × 26, or 52. This means that each turn of the pedals when the bicycle is in this gear would move the bike a distance equivalent to one turn of a 52-inch wheel.

7. If the gear is 52, how far would the bike travel with each turn of the pedals?

8. **Generalization**

a. Write the gear (G) as a function of the number of teeth on the chainwheel (c), the number of teeth on the rear sprocket (r), and the size of the wheel (w).

b. If the gear is G, how far would the bike travel with every turn of the pedals?

c. Write a formula that gives the distance (d) that the bike would travel with each turn of the pedals as a function of c, r, and w.

CADENCE

Definition: The *cadence* is the pace of pedaling.

A good cadence to maintain is 65 to 85 pedal revolutions per minute. Better cyclists like to maintain a cadence of 90 turns per minute.

9. Julio's ten-speed bike has wheels 27 inches in diameter. Its gears were described in problem 5. At a cadence of 90 pedal revolutions per minute, how fast, in miles per hour, would Julio be going in the highest gear? (Hint: Find a conversion factor to get directly from pedal revolutions per minute to miles per hour.)

10. If Julio knows his cadence, find a way for him to calculate his speed mentally in miles per hour when riding in the highest gear.

Work on as many of the ideas of the lesson as possible by having groups study actual bikes, and then assign the lesson itself as homework. Be sure to draw on the expertise of any students who happen to know a lot about bicycles.

12.6 SOLUTIONS

5.

	14	17	22	28	34
40	2.86	2.35	1.82	1.43	1.18
54	3.86	3.18	2.45	1.93	1.59

6. $g = c/r$

7. 52π inches, or about 163.36 inches

8. a. $G = (c/r)w$
   b. $G\pi$
   c. $d = (c/r)\pi w$

9. The highest gear is 3.86. Multiply this by 27π to get the number of inches per revolution. Then multiply by 90 rev/min to get the number of inches per minute.
$3.86 \cdot 27\pi \cdot 90 = 29467.5$ inches per minute
To convert this to miles per hour, convert inches to miles by dividing by $12 \cdot 5280$. Then convert minutes to hours by multiplying by 60. The result is 27.9 miles per hour.

10. This amounts to finding a single conversion factor from revolutions per minute to miles per hour. This conversion factor is $(3.86 \cdot 27\pi \cdot 60)/(12 \cdot 5280) = 0.31$. A good rule of thumb for Julio to use would be to multiply his cadence by 3 and divide by 10 to get his speed in miles per hour.

*H*owever, it is best to do problem 11 in class, with students working in pairs. This will allow them to use all the ideas they have learned in the course of the lesson and avoid the temptation of just using numbers from an actual bicycle.

DESIGN A BIKE

11. Project Design a bicycle. First describe the future owner of the bicycle and his or her needs. Will the rider be climbing steep hills? Be racing? Choose a size for the wheel, and the number of teeth for the gears of a 10-, 15-, or 18-speed bicycle. The following information may be helpful. Describe how each gear would most likely be used.

Wheel diameters
24, 26, and 27 inches are common.
Teeth on the chainwheel
24 to 58
Teeth on the rear sprocket
12 to 38
Sample Gears
- Very low gear, for climbing steep hills and for easy starts: 33
- Medium gear, for general use: 54
- Very high gear, for going downhill fast, and for racing: 100

Progression
Some cyclists like an approximately geometric progression of gears, because the common ratio makes the change feel the same from one gear to the next.

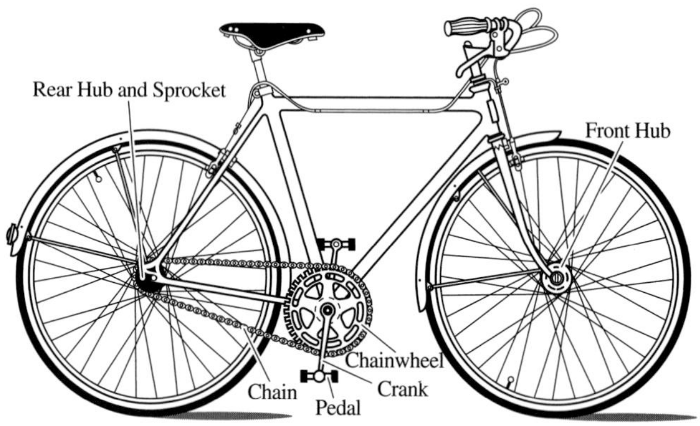

12.6 SOLUTIONS

LESSON 12.7

Iterating Linear Functions

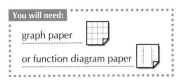

You will need:
- graph paper
- or function diagram paper

TREE HARVESTING

Paul's Forestry Products owns two stands of trees. This year there are about 4500 trees in Lean County and 5500 in Cool County. So as not to run out of trees, the yearly harvesting policy at each location is to cut down 30% of the trees and then plant 1600 trees. For example, in Lean County this year they will cut 1350 trees and plant 1600 trees.

1. Make a table of values showing how many trees they would have at each location every year for nine years.
2. Describe the change in the number of trees at each location. Is it increasing or decreasing? Is it changing at a constant rate from year to year? What do you think will happen in the long run?
3. Write a formula that would give the number of trees next year in terms of the number of trees this year. (Use y for next year's number and x for this year's number. What you get is called a *recurrence equation*.)
4. How many trees would they have at each location after 30 years?

DRUGS

To control a medical condition, Shine takes ten milligrams of a certain drug once a day. Her body gets rid of 40% of the drug in a 24-hour period. To find out how much of the drug she ends up with over the long run, we can use function diagrams.

5. If x is the amount of the drug Shine has in her body on a certain day, and y is the amount on the next day, explain why the recurrence equation is $y = 0.6x + 10$.
6. Make a table of values for the recurrence equation, using these values for x: 0, 5, 10, 15, 20, 25, 30, 35, 40.

Here is a function diagram for the recurrence equation.

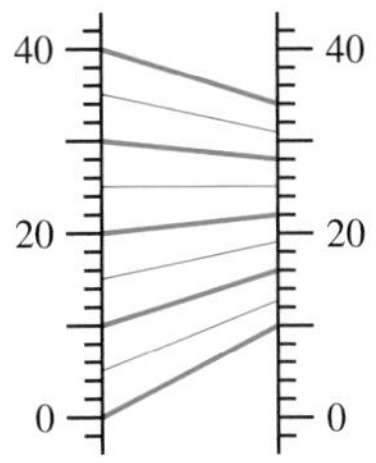

This function diagram can be repeated to show what happens over the long run. The linked diagrams show how the y-values for one become the x-values for the next.

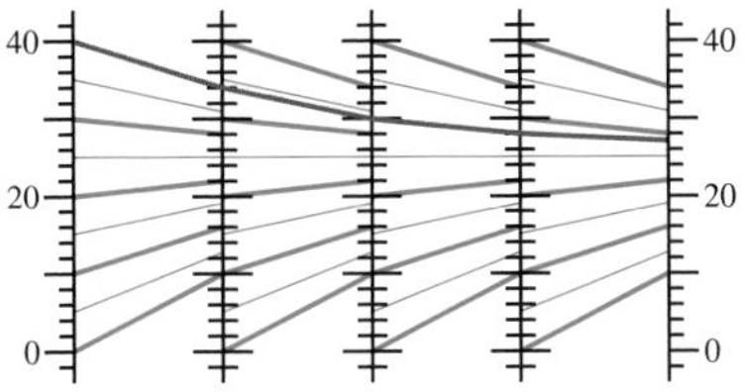

7. Use the diagram to predict what happens in the long run if Shine takes 10 mg a day of the drug after an initial dose of:
   a. 10 mg; b. 25 mg;
   c. 40 mg.
8. Check your predictions by calculation.

12.7 SOLUTIONS

1.

Year	Lean County	Cool County
0	4500	5500
1	4750	5450
2	4925	5415
3	5048	5391
4	5134	5374
5	5194	5362
6	5236	5353
7	5265	5347
8	5286	5343
9	5300	5340
10	5310	5338

2. The number of trees in Lean County is increasing, but the amount of the increase decreases every year. The number of trees in Cool County is decreasing, but the amount of the decrease decreases every year. In the long run, it looks as if they will end up with the same number of trees. (This can be confirmed by extending the table a few more years.)
3. $y = 0.70x + 1600$
4. Lean: 5332; Cool: 5335
5. Her body will still have 60% of the drug left when she adds 10 milligrams.
6.

x	$0.6x + 10$
0	10
5	13
10	16
15	19
20	22
25	25
30	28
35	31
40	34

▼ 12.7 Iterating Linear Functions

Core Sequence: 1-21

Suitable for Homework: 5-13, 21-25

Useful for Assessment: 13-14, 17-18, 20-21

What this Lesson is About:
- Iterating linear functions
- Recurrence equations
- Convergence
- Fixed points

The ideas in this lesson were previewed in Chapter 3, Lesson 1, and **Thinking/Writing 3.C**. In more advanced classes students may study an extension of these ideas to nonlinear functions. This is the essential core of the science of chaos and dynamical systems.

This lesson was inspired by an article in the *Mathematics Teacher*, vol. 83, no. 9, December 1990: "The difference equation $x_n = ax_{n-1} + b$," by Lawrence E. Spence.

A hands-on experiment to bring this topic to life in the classroom with water and food coloring is described in the *Mathematics Teacher*, vol. 85, no. 2, February 1992: "Drugs and Pollution in the Algebra Class," by James T. Sandefur. In the experiment an empty glass container represents the body, a quart of water represents the blood in the body, and 16 ml of food coloring represents 16 mg of medicine. The elimination of 25% of the medicine in a four-hour period is modeled by removing one cup of the mixture, and replacing it with a cup of clear water.

TREE HARVESTING

These three problems introduce the basic idea of the lesson. Calculators are essential, and programmable calculators or computer spreadsheets are particularly convenient.

DRUGS
SAVINGS

Function diagrams help students visualize what happens in the long run. In particular, students should see a major difference between the drugs and the savings problems, in that the in-out lines converge in the first case and diverge in the other.

Note that in the case of the drug problem, if one uses the equation $y = 0.6(x + 10)$, the numbers will converge to a different number. This is because, in this case, the formula describes the amount of the drug in the body just before taking the next dose. The equation in the text reflects the amount in the body just after taking a dose.

Problem 14 should remind students about the analysis of the focus of function diagrams for linear functions (from Chapter 8, Lesson 2). We deliberately ignore the cases where $m \le 0$ for the purposes of this lesson. They can be analyzed in roughly the same way.

There is a reproducible page of linked function diagrams to use with this lesson on page 568.

THE FIXED POINT

In the long run, the sequence of inputs and outputs gradually gets closer and closer to, or farther and farther from, the function's fixed point, depending on whether $m < 1$ or $m \ge 1$.

It is interesting that the initial input does not affect the outcome that much. The only thing that matters is whether the initial input is above or below the fixed point.

Note that a fixed point will have the same x- and y-coordinates. Hence, on a Cartesian graph, any fixed point lies on the line $y = x$. So you can imagine where the fixed point of a linear function is by visualizing where the function intersects the line $y = x$. However, it is much easier to see convergence on a function diagram than on a Cartesian graph.

Remember that instead of linked diagrams like in the figure, you could use a single function diagram of the function. Just follow an in-out line, then move horizontally across back to the x-number line; then repeat the process, using the in-out line that starts at that point.

SAVINGS

Glinda puts $50 a month into a savings account paying yearly compound interest of 6%.

9. What is the interest per month?

10. How much money will she have at the end of one year?

11. Write a recurrence equation for problem 10, expressing the amount in the account at the end of each month as a function of the amount the previous month.

12. Make a function diagram.

13. How does what happens in the long run for problem 10 differ from the problems in the previous sections? Explain.

Definition: To *iterate* a function means to use its output as a new input.

All the problems in this lesson involve iterating linear functions. We will use function diagrams and algebraic symbols to get a more general understanding of this kind of problem.

14. Describe the difference between function diagrams for $y = mx + b$ for the following:

a. $0 < m < 1$ b. $m = 1$

c. $m > 1$

THE FIXED POINT

Definition: A fixed point of a function is one in which the output is the same as the input.

Example: For the function $y = 7x - 12$, when the input is 2, the output is also 2.

15. What is the fixed point for each of the functions in problems 3 and 5? Why was it important in understanding the problems?

16. Find the fixed points.

a. $y = 3x - 6$ b. $y = 3x + 5$

c. $y = 3x$ d. $y = x$

e. $y = x + 3$ f. $y = x^2 - 2$

17. Function diagrams may help you think about these questions.

a. There is a linear function that has more than one fixed point. What is it? Explain.

b. What linear functions have no fixed points? Explain.

18. Generalization

a. Find a formula for the fixed point for the function $y = mx + b$. (Hint: Since the output is the same as the input, substitute x for y and solve for x.)

b. Explain why $m = 1$ is not acceptable in the formula you found. What does that mean in terms of the existence of the fixed point for equations of the form $y = x + b$?

ANALYZING THE SEQUENCES

When iterating a function, you get a sequence of numbers.

19. Exploration Start with the equation $y = 2x + 3$. Change one number in the equation so that when iterating the function, starting with any input, you get

a. an arithmetic sequence;

b. a geometric sequence;

c. a sequence where the values get closer and closer to a fixed point.

Compare your answers with other students' answers.

7. Both the table and the function diagram suggest that she will end up with 25 miligrams in her body over the long run, regardless of the initial dose.
8. The predictions can be checked by iterating the function $y = 0.6x + 10$ with the starting values given in #7.
9. 0.5%, or 0.005
10. $53.08, if the interest is compounded monthly.
11. $y = 1.005x$

12.

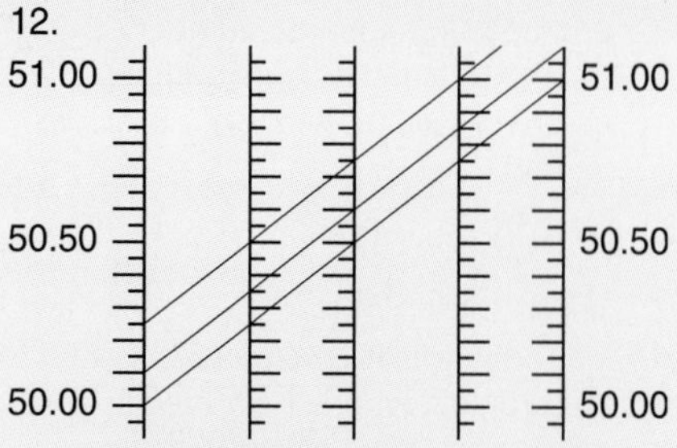

linked function diagrams for the recurrence equation $y = 1.005x$

13. The amount always increases. It does not get closer and closer to a fixed number.
14. a. The focus is to the right of the y-number line.
    b. The in-out lines are parallel.
    c. The focus is to the left of the x-number line.

15. The fixed points were 5333 and 25. The fixed points were important because in each case the situation reached a steady state, regardless of the starting point.
16. Note: The fixed points can be found by iterating the functions or by replacing y with x in the equation and solving for x.
    a. $x = 3$
    b. $x = -5/2$
    c. $x = 0$
    d. Every point is a fixed point.
    e. No point is a fixed point.
    f. $x = 2$ or $x = -1$
17. a. The function $y = x$ has an infinite number of fixed points, since the output is always the same as the input.

20. **Generalization** When iterating $y = mx + b$, different things may happen, depending upon the value of the parameters. Find the values of m and b which lead to the following situations:

a. arithmetic sequences;

b. geometric sequences;

c. sequences where the values get farther and farther from the fixed point;

d. sequences where the values get closer and closer to the fixed point.

21. **Report** Summarize what you know about iterating linear functions. Include, but do not limit yourself to these topics.

- real-world applications
- use of function diagrams
- the fixed point
- these special cases:
  - ◊ $b = 0$
  - ◊ $0 < m < 1$
  - ◊ $m = 1$
  - ◊ $m > 1$

DISCOVERY *TWO RULERS*

Alice's ruler

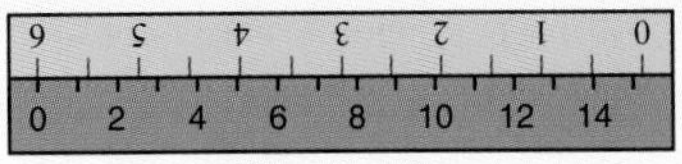

Oliver's ruler

Alice and Oliver lined up her inch ruler against his centimeter ruler, as in the above figure. This yielded the following table of numbers.

x	y
0	6.0
2	5.2
4	4.4
6	3.6

22. a. Graph these data.

b. What is the equation for y in terms of x?

c. Interpret the slope and y-intercept in terms of the rulers.

Place an inch ruler and a centimeter ruler against each other so that they run in opposite directions.

23. Using the ruler arrangement you made as a source of (x, y) pairs, make a table like Alice's and Oliver's. Then make a graph.

24. Write an equation for the function that shows the relationship between the numbers in your table.

25. Interpret the slope and y-intercept in your equation and graph in terms of your rulers and their positions.

ANALYZING THE SEQUENCES

This section pulls together everything that was discovered in this lesson.

DISCOVERY ***TWO RULERS***

This is the third appearance of the two-ruler problem. (The first two were in Chapter 5, Lesson 1, and Chapter 11, Lesson 8.)

Be sure to compare the different equations obtained by students for their own rulers setup. If they followed the instructions correctly, the slope should be close to -2.54, or -1/2.54, depending on which ruler is used for x and which for y. The intercept will reflect the different positions of the zeros.

12.7 SOLUTIONS

b. Linear functions of the form $y = x + b$ (where $b \neq 0$) have no fixed points. It is impossible for the output to equal the input if you add a nonzero number to the input to get the output. In other words $x \neq x + b$ unless $b = 0$.

18\. a. Solve $x = mx + b$ for x to get $x = b/(1 - m)$, where $m \neq 1$

b. Substituting 1 for m in the equation would make the denominator 0. Division by 0 is undefined. There are no fixed points in this case, except in the special case where $m = 1$ and $b = 0$.

19\. a. $y = x + 3$

b. $y = 2x$

c. $y = 0.2x + 3$ (Answers will vary.)

20\. a. $m = 1$ b. $b = 0$

c. $m > 1$ d. $0 < m < 1$

21\. Reports will vary. Of special importance are the conclusions from #19 and #20.

22\. a.

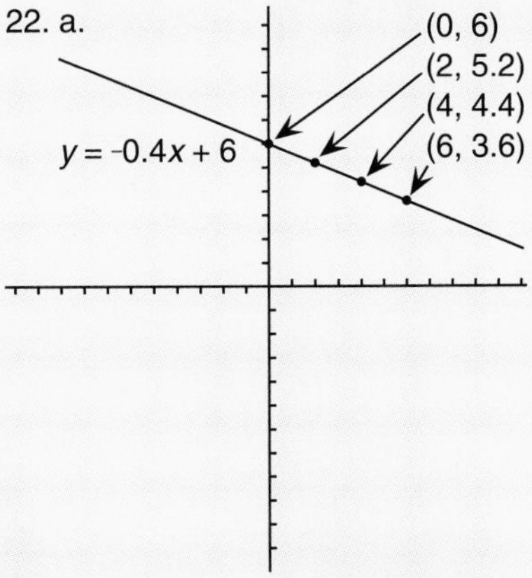

b. $y = -0.4x + 6$

c. The slope is the ratio of the two scales. It is negative because the rulers are arranged so that one increases as the other decreases. The intercept is 6 because 6 on one ruler corresponds to 0 on the other.

Answers will vary for problems 23-25.

▼ 12.8
Representing Functions

Core Sequence: 1-23

Suitable for Homework: 5-23

Useful for Assessment: 3, 5, 9-10, 15, 18-19, 22-23

What this Lesson is About:

- Review of linear functions
- Review of linear function foci in function diagrams
- Review of simultaneous equations
- Families of linear functions

We used function diagrams to introduce functions early in the course, and we use them again, this time to review basic ideas about linear functions, and to point out an interesting duality between points and lines. Some students will appreciate the deeper, more theoretical ideas in the lesson, but everyone will benefit from the opportunity to review basic ideas.

POINTS AND LINES
FOCUS ON SIMULTANEOUS EQUATIONS

We first encountered the focus in Chapter 8, Lesson 2. As it turns out, there is a one-to-one correspondence between foci and linear functions with $m \neq 1$. Each function has a unique focus, and each focus corresponds to a unique function.

LESSON 12.8

Representing Functions

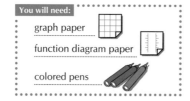

You will need:
- graph paper
- function diagram paper
- colored pens

POINTS AND LINES

As you know, an (x, y) pair is represented as a point on a Cartesian graph and as an in-out line on a function diagram. In this section we will review how an equation of the form $y = mx + b$ is represented in these formats.

1. For the function represented by this Cartesian graph,
   a. write the equation;
   b. draw a function diagram.

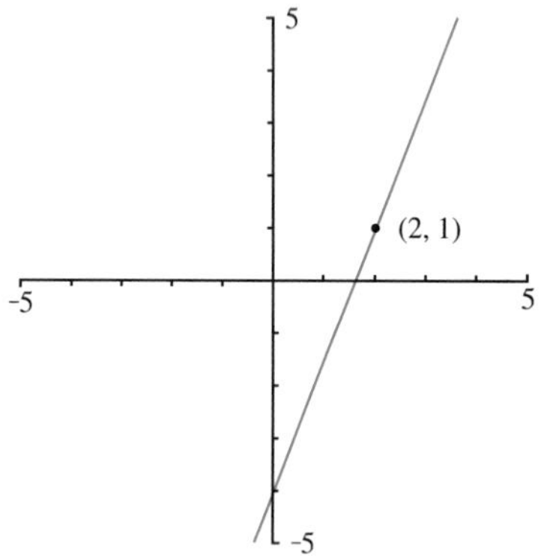

2. Extend the in-out lines in the function diagram you made in problem 1. They should meet in one point, called the focus.

3. What is the minimum number of lines you need to draw to find the focus? Explain.

Actually, a function of the form $y = mx + b$ can be represented by just the focus, as you will see in the next problem.

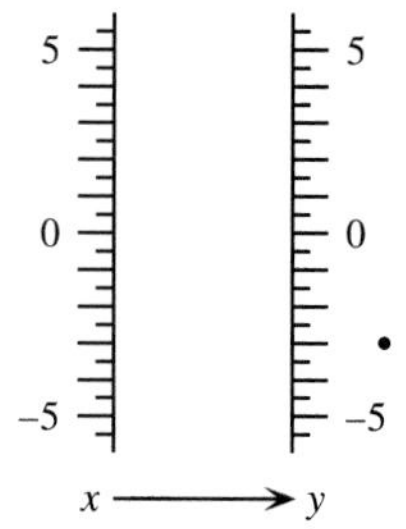

4. The figure shows the focus of a certain function of the form $y = mx + b$.
   a. Place a ruler on the focus, and find three in-out lines. Do not draw the lines, but keep a record of the (x, y) pairs.
   b. Find the equation.

5. If you were to make a Cartesian graph of this function, what is the minimum number of points you would need to plot? Explain.

This table shows how points and lines appear in the two representations. Notice how points and lines are switched when going from one representation to the other.

Object	Representation	
	on Cartesian graph	on function diagram
(x, y) pair	one point	one line (in-out)
linear equation	one line	one point (the focus)

12.8 SOLUTIONS

1. a. $y = (5/2)x - 4$

1.-2.

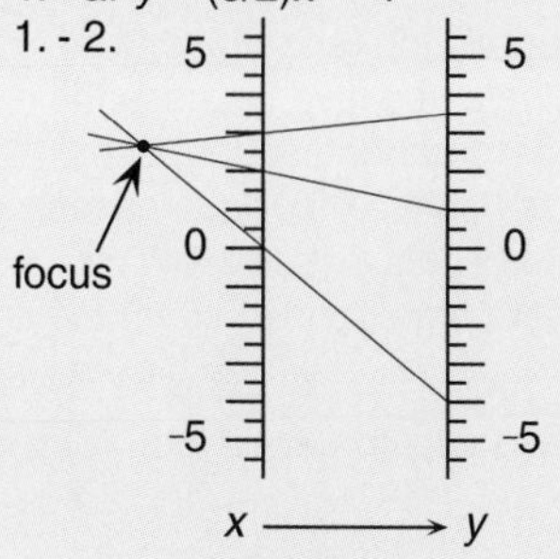

$y = (5/2)x - 4$

2. See the function diagram.

3. Two lines are the minimum. They will intersect in a point, which must be the focus since all lines for that function must pass through the focus.

4. a. Answers will vary. Four possible in-out pairs are (-3, -3), (3, -1), (-5, -3.67), (0, -2).
   b. $y = (1/3)x - 2$

5. Two. Two points determine a line.

FOCUS ON SIMULTANEOUS EQUATIONS

This graph shows $y = -3x$ and $y = -x + 2$.

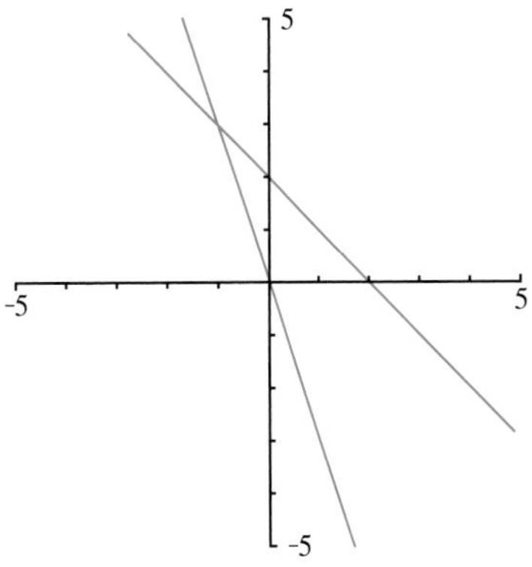

6. What point do the two lines have in common?

The function diagram shows the foci of $y = -3x$ and $y = -x + 2$. (Foci is the plural of focus.)

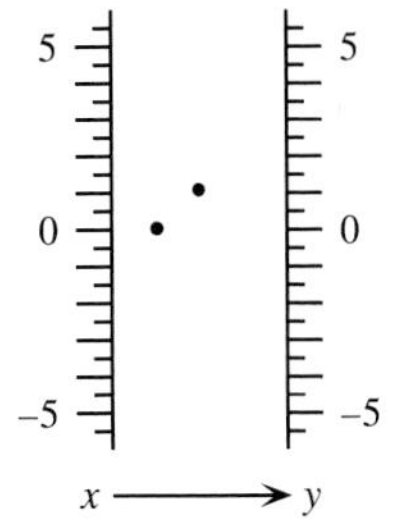

7. Check that the foci are placed correctly.

a. Place a ruler on the focus and find three in-out lines for each function. Do not draw the lines, but keep a record of the (x, y) pairs.

b. Check that the (x, y) pairs you found satisfy the equations.

8. If you were to draw an in-out line containing both foci, what (x, y) pair would it represent?

9. How is the solution of a system of linear equations represented on:

a. a Cartesian graph?

b. a function diagram?

10. Explain how to solve this system by using a function diagram. (Hint: First find each focus, then find the solutions.)

$$\begin{cases} y = 0.5x + 2 \\ y = 2x - 1 \end{cases}$$

Because two lines meet in a point, the solution to a system of simultaneous equations is represented on a Cartesian graph by a point. Because two points determine a line, the solution to a system of linear equations is represented on a function diagram by a line (an in-out line).

FAMILIES OF FUNCTIONS

Definition: A *family* of functions is a group of functions that share a certain attribute.

11. All functions having equations of the form $y = 5x + b$ belong to the $m = 5$ family.

a. Sketch the graphs of two members of the family.

b. What do all graphs for this family have in common?

12. All functions having equations of the form $y = mx + 7$ belong to the $b = 7$ family.

a. Sketch the graphs of two members of the family.

b. What do all graphs for this family have in common?

All functions in the same b-family have foci that lie on the same in-out line.

*F*or problem 1, students should have no trouble finding the slope and intercept from the graph, but for problem 4 they may not think of looking for the m and b parameters directly in the diagram. After they have found the equations, it would be interesting to compare strategies.

*T*he most effective way is to find the in-out line through the focus and the point 0 on the x-number line. That will give the y-intercept (0, -2), so $b = -2$. Then one can look for the magnification m by looking for one other in-out line, preferably one having integral coordinates, and finding the ratio between the change in y-values and the change in x-values. Though other choices are possible, the in-out line (-3, -3) is convenient. It allows us to see that when x changes by 3, y changes by 1. Therefore the magnification must be 1/3. (However, you may hold off on presenting this approach until after having done the next section, where the function diagram representation of m and b is reviewed.)

*P*roblems 6-10 review familiar material in a new setting.

*P*roblems 3, 5, 9, and the closing paragraphs of both sections address the point-line duality that is inherent in these representations. The idea of point-line duality is not important for students to master at this level, but those who appreciate this aesthetically should be encouraged to stick with mathematics. Duality is fundamental to projective geometry, a branch of mathematics they will have a chance to study in college.

12.8 SOLUTIONS

6. (-1, 3)
7. Answers will vary.
8. (-1, 3)
9. a. a point
   b. an in-out line
10. Draw two in-out lines for each function in order to find its focus. Then draw the in-out line that passes through both foci. The (x, y) pair corresponding to this in-out line is the solution to the system.

11. a.

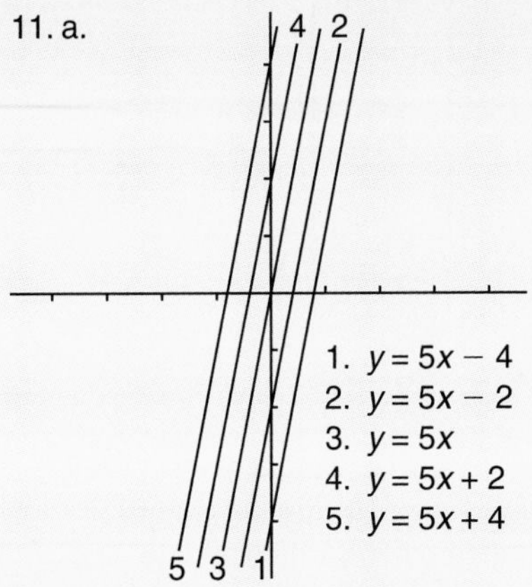

b. They have the same slope.

12. a.

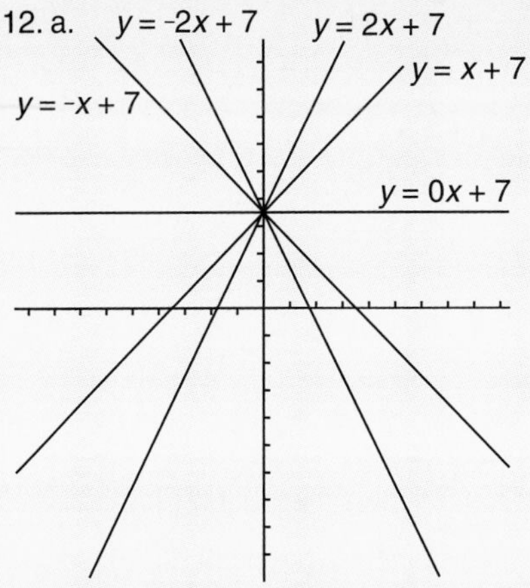

b. They all have the same y-intercept.

FAMILIES OF FUNCTIONS

You may use the idea in problem 23 as a motivation in the real world for the concept of families of functions. However, we concentrate on m and b families, which helps us review once again the significance of those parameters.

To speed up the making of the function diagrams in this section, remind the students that all they need is to find the focus, which can be done by sketching two in-out lines. (A third one can be used as a check.)

Problem 18 reviews the previous section, since all systems where both equations are of the form $y = mx - 2$ will have (0, -2) for a solution.

When discussing m families, you may have a class discussion of how the position of the focus is related to the value of m, and of how m is the magnification from the x- to the y-number line. (See Chapter 8, Lesson 2.)

Note that problem 21 adds an important footnote by reminding students that some linear functions do not have a focus, because their in-out lines are parallel. Alternately, for those functions, we think of the focus being a point *at infinity*, which makes it possible to preserve the duality. (All the points at infinity make up the line at infinity.)

13. These four functions are in the same b-family. For each one, draw in-out lines to find the focus and mark it with a colored pen or pencil. Do all four on the same diagram.

a. $y = 0.5x - 2$ b. $y = 2x - 2$
c. $y = -2x - 2$ d. $y = -0.5x - 2$

14. What is the family name for the functions in problem 13?

15. Why do all the foci of the functions in problem 13 lie on the same in-out line? Which in-out line is it? Explain.

16. The foci for all functions in the family $b = -3$ also lie on one in-out line. Which line? Explain how you know.

Many m-families also have foci that lie on the same in-out line in a function diagram.

17. a. On a function diagram, find and mark the focus for $y = -2x + 3$.
b. On the same function diagram, find and mark the focus for $y = -2x + 1$.
c. Find and mark the focus for several other graphs of the form $y = -2x + k$.

18. What is the family name for all the functions in problem 17? Explain why the foci are all on the same line. Describe the line.

19. If two functions both have a focus on the same vertical line, what would their Cartesian graphs have in common?

20. What is the family name for all functions having focus half-way between the two number lines?

21. There is one m family for which the function diagrams have no focus, because the in-out lines do not meet. Which m family is this?

22. Summary On a function diagram, what is true of the foci of all linear functions in the same
a. m family? b. b family?

23. The functions representing Charles's Law for gases in the graph in Lesson 4 form a family that is neither an m nor a b family. If you were to make function diagrams for them, the foci would all be on a certain in-out line. Which one? Explain.

12.8 SOLUTIONS

13.
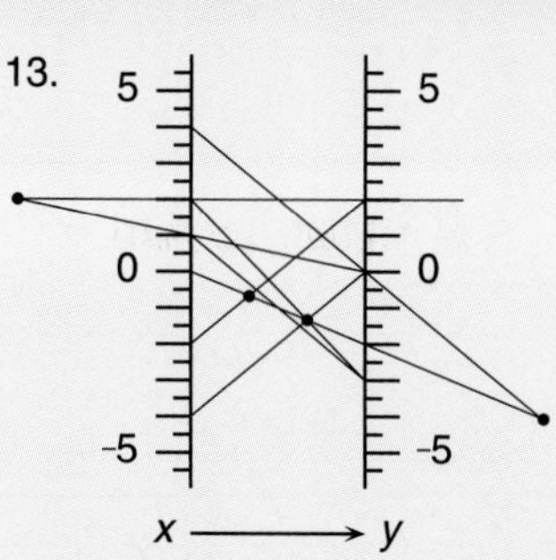

14. $b = -2$

15. They all share the point (0, -2), so their foci must lie on this in-out line.

16. They all share the point (0, -3), so their foci must lie on this in-out line.

17.
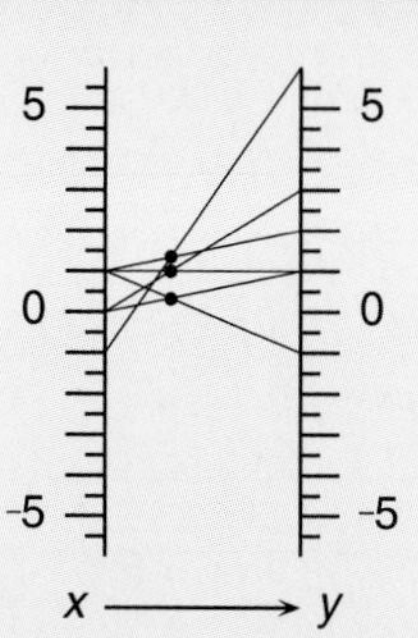

18. They are in the $m = -2$ family. Since they have the same magnification, or slope, their foci are the same distance from the x-number line. The foci all lie on a vertical line between the two axes.

19. slope

20. $m = -1$

21. $m = 1$

22. a. They all lie on a single vertical line.
b. They all lie on the in-out line (0, b).

23. They will all lie on the in-out line (-273, 0), which represents absolute zero. From the graph in Lesson 4, we can see that all the lines on the Cartesian graph go through the point (-273, 0), so on a function diagram this will be an in-out line common to all the functions.

THINKING WRITING

12.B V-Shaped Graphs

You will need:

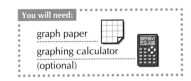

- graph paper
- graphing calculator (optional)

THE SQUARE ROOT OF x^2

As you know, the radical sign means *the non-negative square root of.*

1. Make a table of values, and a graph, for the function $y = \sqrt{x^2}$. Use at least six values for x, including positive numbers, negative numbers, and zero.
2. Find a linear function that has the same graph as $y = \sqrt{x^2}$, when
   a. x is positive; b. x is negative.
3. True or False? $\sqrt{x^2} = x$. Explain.

ABSOLUTE VALUE

As you may remember, the absolute value of a number is the distance between that number and zero.

4. Repeat problems 1-3 for the function $y = |x|$.

Graph the functions in problems 5 through 10. Use separate axes for each one. Write each equation on its graph.

5. $y = |x| + 2$
6. $y = |x| - 2$
7. $y = -|x|$
8. $y = 2|x|$
9. $y = |x + 2|$
10. $y = |x - 2|$

11. **Exploration** Find equations of the form $y = A|x - H| + V$ for these four graphs.

a.

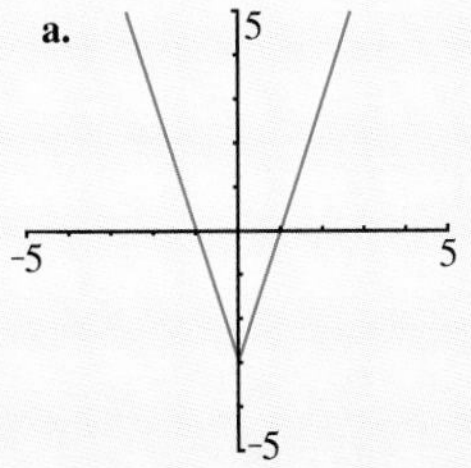

b.

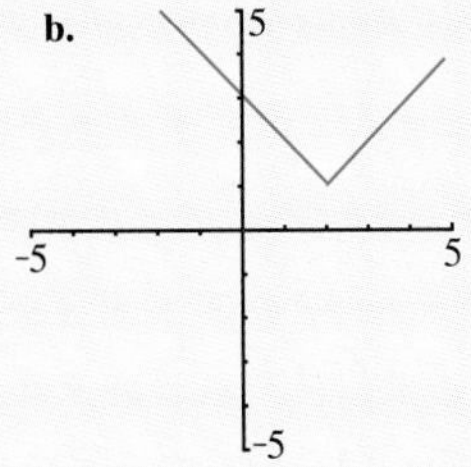

c.

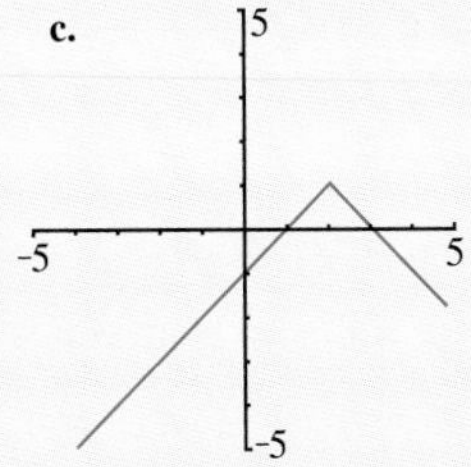

d.

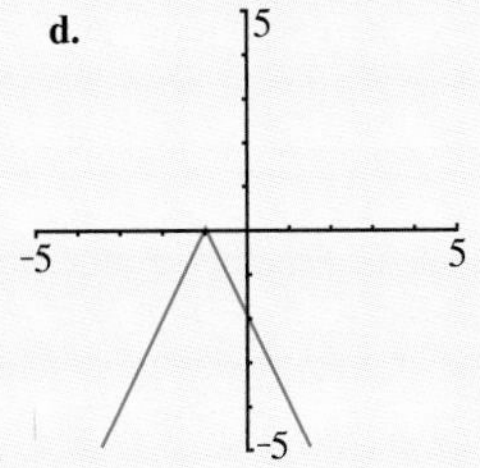

12.B SOLUTIONS

1.

x	y
0	0
-1	1
-2	2
-5	5
6	6
3	3

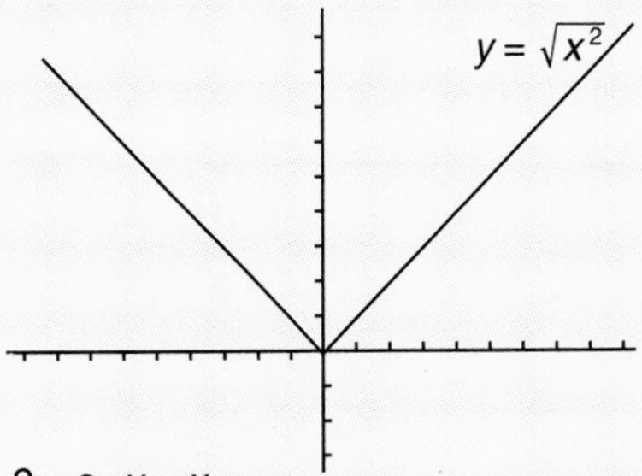

2. a. $y = x$
   b. $y = -x$
3. False. This is true only when $x \geq 0$.
4. The solutions are the same.
5.

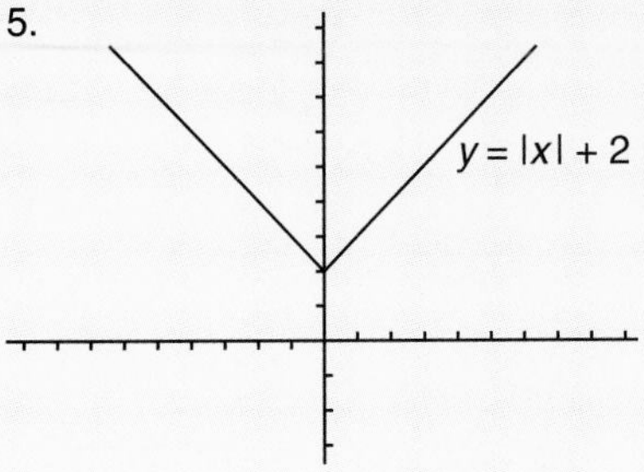

6.

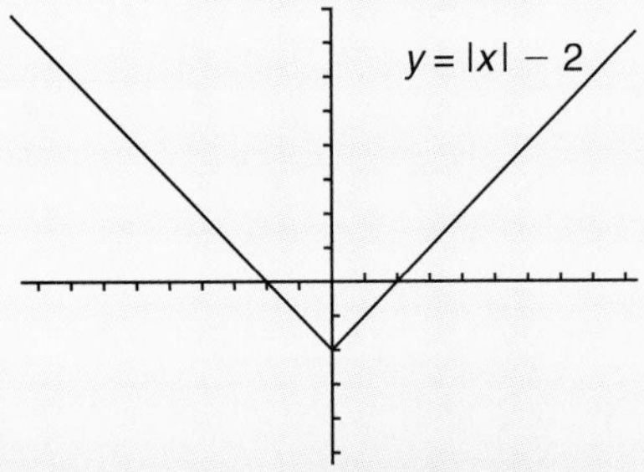

THINKING WRITING

12.B V-Shaped Graphs

Core Sequence: none of the assignment

Suitable for Homework: 12-18

Useful for Assessment: 3, 12-14

What this Assignment is About:

- Review of domain and range
- Absolute value graphs
- Preview of radical expressions involving variables
- Preview of quadratics in the form $y = a(x - h)^2 + k$
- Applications of absolute value graphs

THE SQUARE ROOT OF x^2

In Chapter 9, we deliberately avoided problems requiring simplification of expressions such as $\sqrt{x^6}$. In problems of this type, traditional textbooks emphasize that x must be nonnegative, but students rarely understand (or even notice) the need for this restriction. In more advanced courses, however, students will need to understand the concept of the domain and range of functions of this type, and we preview it here via a graphical exploration of $y = \sqrt{x^2}$.

Students are likely to understand the idea better if you begin by using tables and pencil-and-paper graphing, but you may wish to introduce the graphing calculator during a class discussion of problem 3. A wrap-up of that problem might include having students explain when $\sqrt{x^2}$ is equal to x and when it is equal to the opposite of x. Encourage students to say "the opposite of x" instead of "negative x" to avoid confusion, or at least to bring attention to that issue.

ABSOLUTE VALUE

Students may be surprised to see that the graph of $y = |x|$ is the same as the graph of $y = \sqrt{x^2}$.

Beginning with problem 5, you may wish to have students use a graphing calculator again. It will be especially useful in problem 11.

Note that this section serves to preview work with graphing quadratic expressions in the form $y = a(x - h)^2 + k$.

If you assign problem 12 as a written report, you may lead a class discussion about it beforehand, having groups share their findings from problems 5 through 11. The discussion should include a review of the meaning of domain and range.

A ROUND TRIP

This is an application of absolute value graphs that connects with previous work on motion in this chapter.

REVIEW *LIKE TERMS*

Students often find these manipulations difficult. This reflects a weak grasp of fractions, and/or a weak grasp of the distributive law. These exercises should help.

Discuss problem 18 if necessary. You can suggest either using a common denominator, or start by distributing the division by 5 in the first fraction.

12. Report Write an illustrated report describing graphs of the form $y = A|x - H| + V$. Describe how each of the parameters A, H, and V affects the graph. What are the slopes? Where is the vertex? What are the domain and range? Give examples, including both negative and positive values of all the parameters.

A ROUND TRIP

This graph shows a plane's trip. It was sighted passing over Alaberg at time $t = 0$.

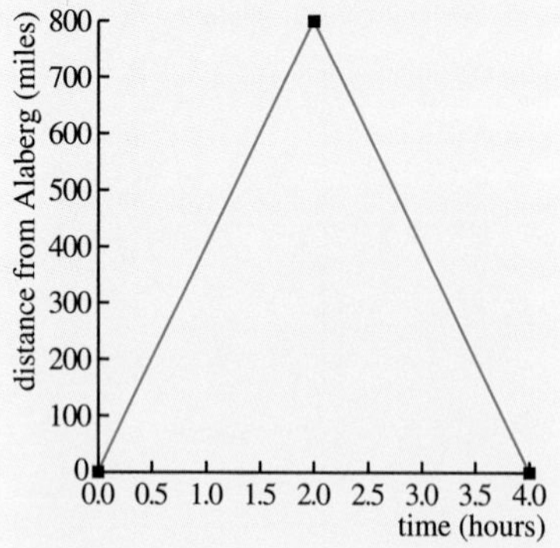

13. Describe the plane's trip.

14. The equation of the graph is of the form $y = A|x - H| + V$. What are A, H, and V?

15. If the plane were going at 300 miles per hour,

a. how would the graph be different?

b. how would the equation be different?

REVIEW LIKE TERMS

When combining terms involving fractions, it is sometimes useful to write the fractions with common denominators. However, it is often more convenient to use the method that is demonstrated in the following example.

Example: $\frac{x}{60} - \frac{11x}{70}$

$= \frac{1}{60}x - \frac{11}{70}x$

$= \left(\frac{1}{60} - \frac{11}{70}\right)x$

$= -0.14x$

(A calculator was used for the last step.)

Combine like terms.

16. $\frac{2x}{3} - 4x$

17. $\frac{5x}{6} + \frac{7}{8} + \frac{9x}{4}$

18. $\frac{3x + 2}{5} - \frac{x}{2}$

12.B SOLUTIONS

7.

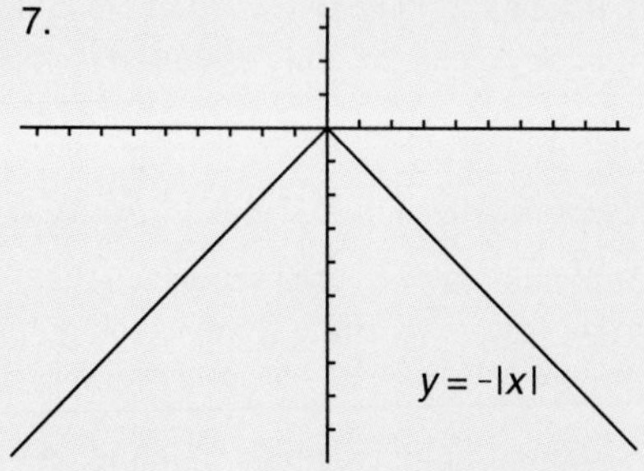

8.

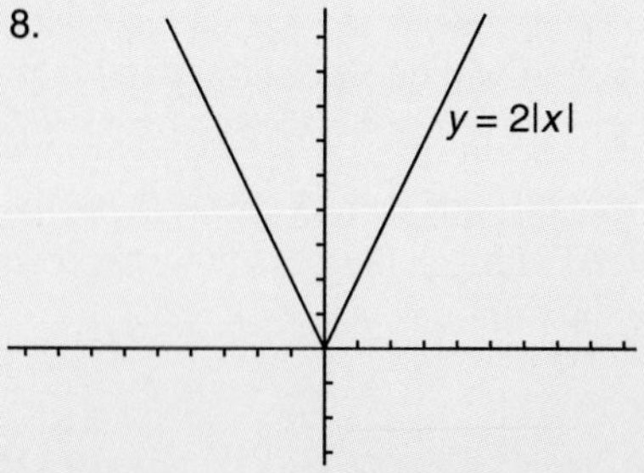

9.

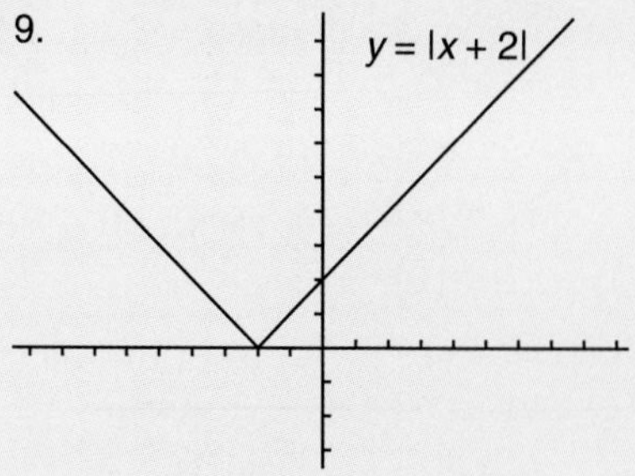

10.

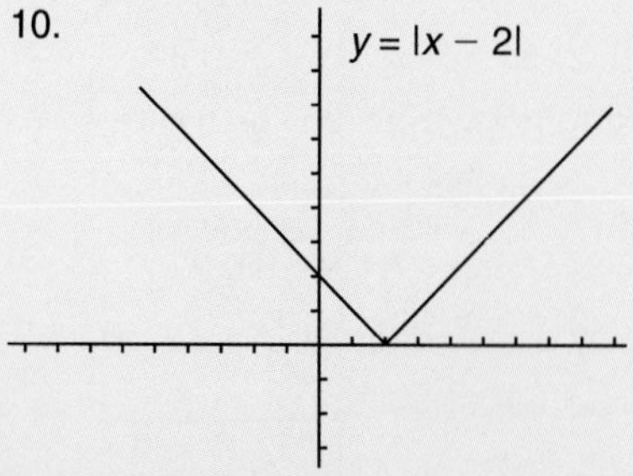

11. a. $y = 3|x| - 3$
b. $y = |x - 2| + 1$
c. $y = -|x - 2| + 1$
d. $y = -2|x + 1|$

12. Reports will vary. Some key ideas follow: The graphs will be V-shaped, composed of two half-lines of slopes $-A$ and A. The vertex of the graph is (H, V). The domain is all real numbers. If $A < 0$, the range is $y \le V$. If $A > 0$, the range is $y \ge V$.

13. The plane traveled at a constant speed of 400 mph for 2 hours. Then it turned around and flew back at the same speed for 2 hours. It was sighted again over Alaberg at $t = 4$.

14. The equation would be $y = -400|x - 2| + 800$, so $A = -400$, $H = 2$, $V = 800$.

(Solutions continued on page 529)

Essential Ideas

FIRST CLASS STAMPS

This table shows the costs in cents of first-class stamps over the past sixty years. The dates indicate the year when there was an increase in the first-class rate.

Year	Cost
1932	3
1958	4
1963	5
1968	6
1971	8
1974	10

Year	Cost
1975	13
1978	18
1981	20
1985	22
1988	25
1991	29

Interpolation is not relevant since all the data are known within the given period. However extrapolation may be possible.

1. Graph the data as a step function. For example, the cost was 3 cents from 1932 to 1957.
2. In 1985 Barbara wanted to use the average cost increase in the period 1932-1985 to predict the cost of stamps in 1991.
   a. What was the average yearly increase?
   b. Based on this, what cost did she predict for 1991?
3. In 1985 Sue used a computer to find the average percent increase over the 53-year period. The computer indicated that on the average, the cost went up by 3.8% a year. Based on this, what cost did she predict for 1991?

In 1991 they used the same methods to find the average increases over the 59-year period. Barbara found an average increase of 0.44 cents a year, and Sue found an average percent increase of 3.9% a year.

4. Make a prediction for the cost of stamps in the year 1999 and 2032. Explain.

THE MILE RUN

Year	Time
1868	4:29.0
1868	4:28.8
1874	4:26.0
1875	4:24.5
1880	4:23.2
1882	4:21.4
1882	4:19.4
1884	4:18.4
1894	4:18.2
1895	4:17.0
1911	4:15.6
1911	4:15.4
1913	4:14.6
1915	4:12.6
1923	4:10.4
1931	4:09.2
1933	4:07.6
1934	4:06.8
1937	4:06.4
1942	4:06.2

Year	Time
1942	4:04.6
1943	4:02.6
1944	4:01.6
1945	4:01.4
1954	3:59.4
1954	3:58.0
1957	3:57.2
1958	3:54.5
1962	3:54.4
1964	3:54.1
1965	3:53.6
1966	3:51.3
1967	3:51.1
1975	3:51.0
1975	3:49.4
1979	3:49.0
1980	3:48.8
1981	3:48.53
1981	3:48.40
1981	3:47.33

▼ Essential Ideas

THE MILE RUN

There is a reproducible graph to use with this section on page 576.

◆ S O L U T I O N S

1.

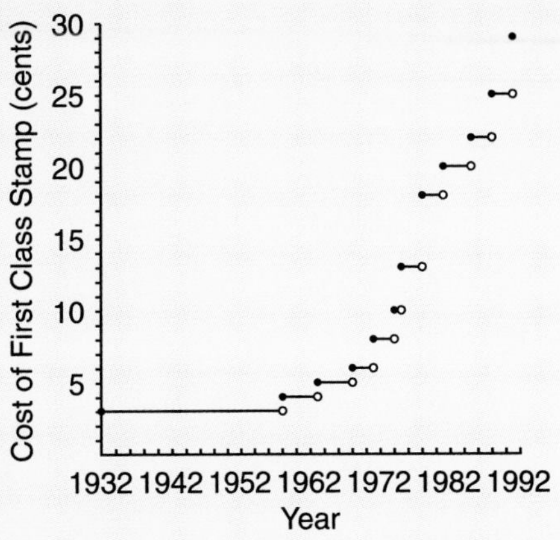

2. a. $19/53 = 0.36$ The average yearly increase was 0.36 cents per year.
   b. $22 + (0.36) \cdot 6 = 22 + 2.16 = 24.16$ or about 24 cents
3. $22(1.038)^6 = 27.5$ or about 27 to 28 cents
4.

Year	Linear Prediction: $29 + 0.44x$	Exponential Prediction: $29(1.039)^x$
1999	about 33 cents	about 39 cents
2032	about 47 cents	about $1.39

The prediction was made by using 1991 as the starting point and the rate of increase from 1932-1991. The variable x represents the number of years after 1991.

5.–6.

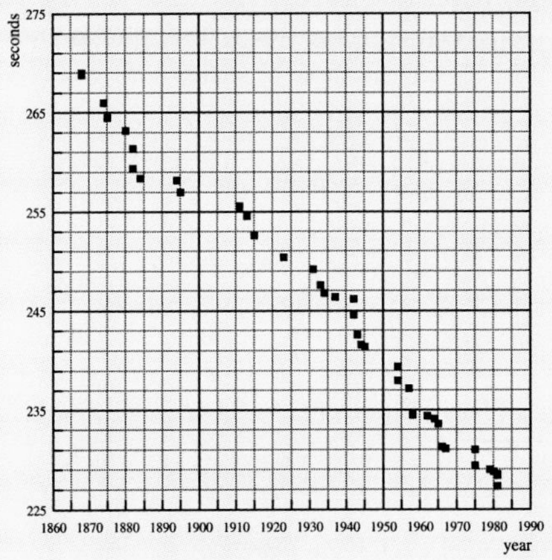

5. The table shows the world record for the mile run from 1868 to 1981. Plot the time *in seconds* as a function of year.

6. Use the median-median line method to fit a line.

7. What is the equation of your fitted line?

8. Richard Webster of Great Britain ran the mile in 4:36.5 in 1865. How does this compare with the time for 1865 predicted by your fitted line?

9. Steve Cram of Great Britain ran one mile in 3:46.31 in 1985. How does this compare with the time predicted by your fitted line?

10. a. According to your model, when would the mile be run in 0 seconds?
    b. For how many more years do you think your fitted line will be a good predictor of the time?

WIRES

When a metal wire changes temperature, it expands or contracts, according to the equation

$$L = L_0(1 + kT),$$

where L is the length of the wire, L_0 is its length at 0°C, T is the temperature, and k depends on the metal. For copper, $k = 1.8(10^{-5})$.

11. A copper wire is 100.05 meters long at 40°C. If it is cooled to -10°C, how much will it shrink? (Hint: First find its length at 0°C.)

12. Two poles are 100 meters apart. They are connected by a 100.05-meter copper wire in the summer, when the temperature is 40°C. In the winter the temperature drops to -10°C.
    a. Explain why the wire breaks.
    b. How long should the wire be so as not to break in the winter?

A nickel-iron alloy is created. Measurements are made in a lab on a wire made of the alloy. It is found that a wire that is 10 meters long at 0°C expands by one half a millimeter at 100°C. The alloy is called *Invar*.

13. Find the value of k for Invar.

14. Would an Invar wire that measures 100.01 meters at 40° C work to connect the poles in problem 12? Explain.

EQUATIONS FROM DATA

a.

x	y
0.4	15
0.6	10
0.8	7.5
1	6

b.

x	y
0.4	0.667
0.6	1.00
0.8	1.33
1	1.67

c.

x	y
0.4	-4.4
0.6	-2.6
0.8	-0.8
1	1

15. Find an equation for each table. Hint: One is a direct variation, one an inverse variation, and one a linear function.

THE CAR TRIP AND THE BICYCLE TRIP

Reread **Thinking/Writing 2.B** (Chapter 2). The function diagram is shown below.

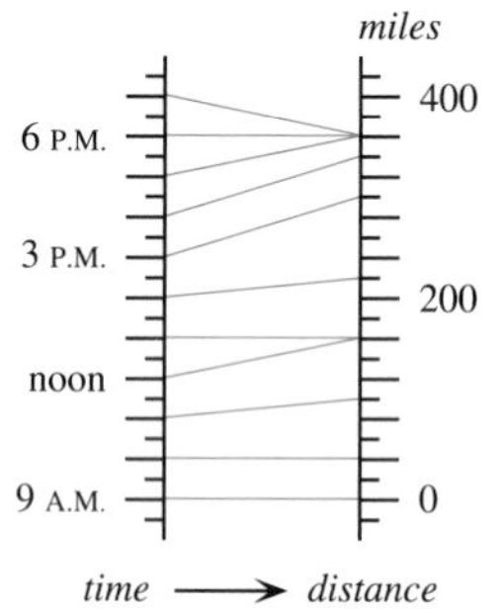

Car Trip

SOLUTIONS

7. Answers will vary. One possible solution is given.
   The line seems to go through the points (1954, 238) and (1895, 257). Use these points to get the line
   $y = -0.322x + 867.18$.

8. $y = -0.322(1865) + 867.18$
   $y = 266.65$
   This underestimates Webster's time of 276.50 seconds by about 10 seconds.

9. $y = -0.322(1985) + 867.18$
   $y = 228.01$
   This is within 2 seconds of Cram's time of 226.31.

10. a. $0 = -0.322x + 867.18$
    $x = -867.18/(-0.322) = 2693$
    The mile would be run in 0 seconds in the year 2693!
    b. Answers will vary. (It certainly won't be a good predictor in 2693!)

11. Its length at 0 degrees is 99.98 m. At -10 degrees, it will be 99.96 m.

12. a. It shrinks to less than 100 m, as shown in #11.
    b. First find the length at 0 degrees, based on the fact that in order not to break it must have been 100 m at -10 degrees. Its length at 0 degrees would have been 100.018, which means that it should have been 100.09 m at 40 degrees.

13. The wire is 10 meters long at 0 degrees C. It expands by 1/2 mm = 0.5 mm or 0.0005 m at 100 degrees C. Using the formula:
    $L = L_0(1 + k \cdot T)$
    Substituting: $10.0005 = 10(1 + k \cdot 100)$
    $10.0005 = 10 + 1000k$
    $0.0005 = 1000k$
    $5 \cdot 10^{-4} = 10^3 \cdot k$
    $k = 5 \cdot 10^{-7}$

14. Use k and the length of the wire at 40 degrees to find L_0.
    $L = L_0(1 + kT)$
    $100.01 = L_0[1 + 5 \cdot 10^{-7} \cdot (40)]$
    $\frac{100.01}{1.00002} = L_0$
    $100.008 = L_0$
    We can use L_0 to find the length of the wire at -10 degrees.
    $L = 100.008[1 + 5 \cdot 10^{-7} \cdot (-10)]$
    $L = 100.0075$
    The length at -10 degrees will be 100.0075 cm, which is greater than 100 cm, so it will not break.

15. a. $xy = 6$
    b. $y = (5/3)x$
    c. $y = 9x - 8$

16. Make a Cartesian graph for the car trip, as best you can from the information given.

17. What is the car's average speed,
   a. if you include the time the car was stopped in the middle of the day?
   b. if you include only the driving time?

Reread **Thinking/Writing 4.A** (Chapter 4). The graph is shown below.

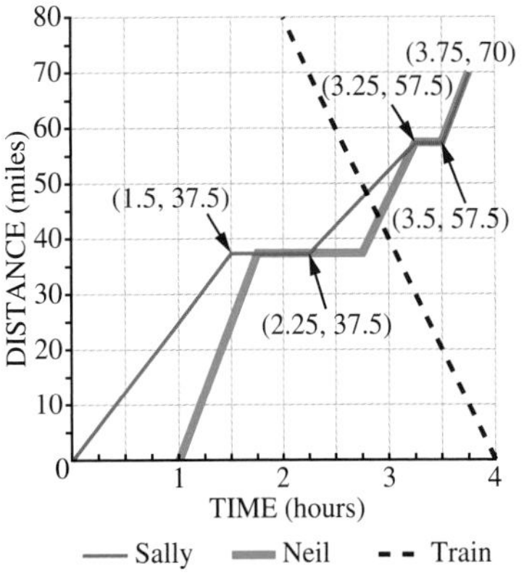

18. Repeat problem 17 for the van Neil drove.

19. If Neil were to make the return trip in the same length of time, but traveling at a constant speed and never stopping, what would be his speed?

20. a. Write an equation for Sally's graph during the leg of the trip when she and the train passed each other.
   b. Solve the system of equations consisting of the equations representing Sally's and the train's motion.
   c. Interpret the point of intersection.

ASTHMA

For her asthma Lynne takes 360 mg of the drug *theophylline* twice a day. After 12 hours, 60% of the drug has been eliminated from her body.

21. Assume Lynne has x_a mg of the drug in her body immediately after taking the dose. Explain why $y_a = 0.4x_a + 360$ is the recurrence equation that says how much will be in her body immediately after taking the next dose.

22. Assume she has x_b mg of the drug in her body immediately before taking the dose. Explain why $y_b = 0.4(x_b + 360)$ is the recurrence equation that says how much will be in her body immediately before taking the next dose.

The amount of theophylline in Lynne's body is constantly changing, but the lowest amount (right before taking the drug) and the highest amount (right after) eventually approach a stable level.

23. Find that level, using tables, function diagrams, or equations. What is the level before taking the dose? What is it after?

◆ SOLUTIONS

16.

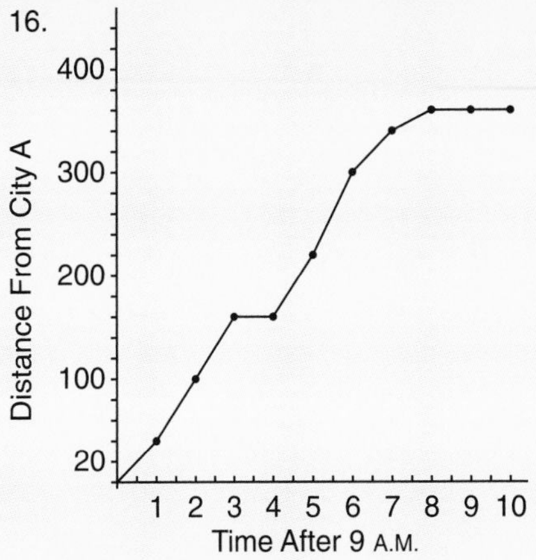

17. a. Total time from 9 A.M. to 5 P.M. is 8 hours. Total distance is 360 miles. Average speed is 360/8 = 45 mph.
   b. Total travel time is 7 hours. Average speed is 360/7 ≈ 51.4 mph.

18. a. Neil's total time was 2.75 hours. The total distance he traveled was 70 miles. His average speed was 70/2.75 or about 25.5 mph.
   b. Neil's total driving time can be found by adding the three legs of his trip: 45 min + 30 min + 15 min = 1.5 hours. His total distance is 70 miles, so his average speed is 70/1.5 = 46 2/3 miles per hour.

19. If the time used is 2.75 hours, his speed would be about 25.5 mph. If the time used is 1.5 hours, the speed would be about 46 2/3 mph. In other words, it is the same as the average speed.

20. a. This segment has endpoints (2.25, 37.5) and (3.25, 57.5). Using these points, the equation of Sally's motion can be found to be $D = 20T - 7.5$.
   b. The equation of the train's motion is $D = -40T + 160$. (This was given in the lesson.) Solving this simultaneously with the equation of Sally's motion gives the point (2.79, 48.4).
   c. This means that Sally and the train passed each other about 2 hours and 48 minutes after Sally left the staging area. She had gone a little less than 48 and 1/2 miles.

(Solutions continued on page 529)

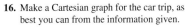

Chapter 13
MAKING DECISIONS

Overview of the Chapter

*T*his chapter starts with a set of real-world problems which we analyze with the help of linear and quadratic functions. In particular, the question of optimization leads us to pay attention to the vertex of parabolas and to its position in relation to the x-intercepts. In this context we also meet the zero product property and the use of factoring to solve some quadratic equations.

*I*n the second part of the chapter (Lessons 6-8) we zero in on quadratic expressions in the form $x^2 + bx + c$ and $(x - H)^2 + V$. This is more technical and will be difficult for some students. However our presentation makes this material much more accessible than the traditional treatment does, first of all because of the use of the Lab Gear and Cartesian graphs to throw light on the symbol manipulations.

*M*uch of the work in this chapter serves to preview Chapter 14, where we work with quadratic expressions in the form $ax^2 + bx + c$ where a is not necessarily 1, and to introduce the quadratic formula.

CHAPTER 13

The spiraling vortex of a whirlpool

Coming in this chapter:

Exploration You want to make pens for Stripe, your pet zebra, and Polka Dot, your pet leopard. You have 100 feet of fencing. If you use all of it to make two pens of equal area, what is the biggest area possible?

MAKING DECISIONS

1. New Uses for Tools:

- Combining the Lab Gear and Cartesian graphs for a better understanding of quadratic functions

2. Algebra Concepts Emphasized:

- Parabolas through the origin
- Quadratic functions in the form $y = a(x - p)(x - q)$
- The zero product property
- Solving quadratic equations by factoring
- Symmetry of parabolas
- Vertex of parabolas
- Intercepts of parabolas
- Completing the square
- Translations of the graph $y = x^2$
- Quadratic functions in the form $y = (x - H)^2 + V$
- Quadratic functions in the form $y = x^2 + bx + c$
- Vertex methods of solving quadratics

3. Algebra Concepts Reviewed:

- Constant sum graphs
- Constant product graphs
- Factoring
- Equal squares
- Simultaneous equations

4. Algebra Concepts Previewed:

- The quadratic formula
- Equations that lead to quadratic equations
- Graphs of rational functions
- Cubic functions

5. Problem-Solving Techniques:

- Using diagrams
- Using graphs and tables
- Using equations

6. Connections and Context:

- Optimization
- Constraints
- Area and perimeter
- Volume and surface area

▼ 13.1 Rectangular Pens: Constant Perimeter

Core Sequence: 1-22

Suitable for Homework: 2-12, 23-26

Useful for Assessment: 4-6, 9-12, 15, 18, 20

What this Lesson is About:

- Using graphs and tables to analyze a real-world problem
- Optimization
- Review of constant sum graphs
- Parabolas through the origin
- Preview of the quadratic formula
- Review of fixed points

Problem 1 poses the question that is explored in problems 2-12. Any method students use to solve it is acceptable. The most likely approach is trial and error. You may deepen the discussion of the problem, with the book closed, by asking these questions:

- What is the width of the pen as a function of its length?
- What is the area of the pen as a function of its length?

Let students (working in groups) take the initiative about how to proceed. You may hint that tables, graphs, and equations may be helpful in providing a full understanding of the problem. Students may even find a use for function diagrams or geoboards.

LESSON 13.1

Rectangular Pens: Constant Perimeter

You will need:

graph paper

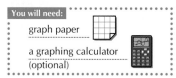

a graphing calculator (optional)

1. **Exploration** You want to make a rectangular pen for Stripe, your pet zebra. Even though Stripe takes many walks around town, you want to make sure she has as much space as possible inside the pen. You have 50 feet of fencing available. If you use all of it to make the pen, what is the biggest area possible? Find out by trying various dimensions for the pen.

WIDTH AS A FUNCTION OF LENGTH

You have 28 feet of fencing to make a rectangular pen. There are many possible dimensions for this pen. One possible pen, 10 feet wide by 4 feet long, is shown below. In this section you will investigate how the length and width change in relation to one another if you keep the perimeter constant.

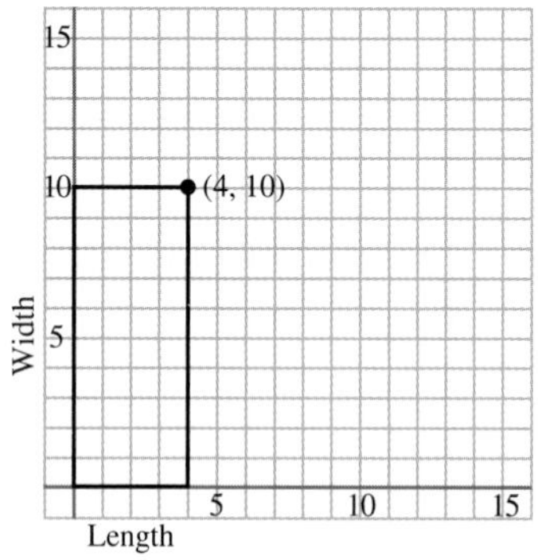

2. a. On graph paper, draw axes and at least six pens having a perimeter of 28.

b. The upper right corner of the pen in the figure has been marked with a • and labeled with its coordinates. Do this for the pens you drew. Then connect all the points marked with a •. Describe the resulting graph.

3. a. Make a table showing all the coordinates on your graph. Look for a pattern and make three more entries in the table.

b. Write an equation for the function described by your graph and table.

Summary

4. The point whose coordinates are (4, 10) is on the graph.

a. What does the sum of these numbers represent in this problem?

b. What does the product represent?

5. a. What is the greatest possible length of a pen? How can you see this on your graph?

b. How many rectangles are possible if the dimensions are whole numbers? How many are possible otherwise?

c. Explain why the graph should not be extended into quadrants II and IV.

6. If you increase the length by one foot, does the width increase or decrease? Does it change by the same amount each time? Explain.

13.1 SOLUTIONS

1. Answers will vary. See solutions to #11 and #12.

2. a.

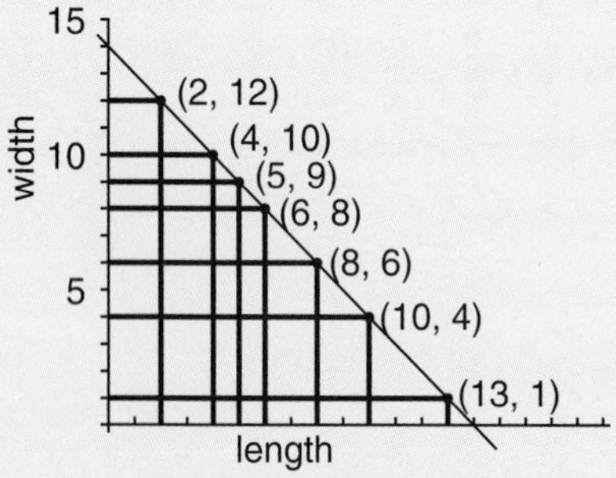

b. The graph is a straight line. It is a constant sum graph.

3. a.

W	L
1	13
2	12
3	11
4	10
5	9
6	8
7	7
8	6
9	5
10	4
11	3
12	2
13	1

b. $L + W = 14$ or $W = 14 - L$

4. a. one-half the perimeter
b. area

5. a. The x-intercept is (14, 0). The length must be less than 14.
b. There are 7 whole number possibilities and an infinite number of other possibilities. An 8-by-6 pen is the same as a 6-by-8 pen, and a 9-by-5 pen is the same as a 5-by-9 pen, etc.
c. Length and width cannot be negative.

6. The width will decrease by one foot each time. (The slope of the line is -1.)

AREA AS A FUNCTION OF LENGTH

In the previous section you may have noticed that the area of the rectangles changed even though the perimeter remained constant. In this section you will investigate how the area changes as a function of length, if you keep the perimeter constant.

7. Write the area of the corresponding rectangle next to each of the points marked with a • on the graph from problem 2.

8. Make a graph of area as a function of length. Show length on the x-axis and area on the y-axis. Connect the points on your graph with a smooth curve. What kind of curve is it?

9.

a. Label the highest point on your graph with its coordinates. Interpret these two numbers in terms of this problem.

b. Where does the graph cross the x-axis? What do these numbers mean?

c. If you increase the length by one foot, does the area increase or decrease? Does it change by the same amount each time? Explain.

10. Summary

a. Describe in words how you would find the area of the rectangular pen having perimeter 28 if you knew its length.

b. If the perimeter of a rectangular pen is 28 and its length is L, write an algebraic expression for its area in terms of L.

c. If you had 28 feet of fencing and wanted to make the largest possible rectangular pen, what would its length, width, and area be? Explain.

Generalizations

11. Say the perimeter of a rectangle is P and its length is L. Write the following expressions in terms of P and L. (A sketch may help.)

a. an expression for the width

b. an expression for the area

12. Explain how to find the length that gives the maximum area. Write an algebraic expression for it in terms of P only.

PARABOLAS THROUGH THE ORIGIN

13. Graph each of the following functions, using graph paper. Since you will want to compare your graphs in the end, use the same pair of axes for all your graphs. Use a scale that will show values from -5 to 20 for x and from -20 to 100 for y. This will allow you to see all four graphs clearly.

a. $y = x(8 - x)$ b. $y = x(15 - x)$

c. $y = x(12 - x)$ d. $y = x(20 - x)$

14. For each of the four parabolas in problem 13,

a. label the graph with its equation;

b. label the x-intercepts;

c. label the vertex.

15. Generalization

a. Describe the graph of a parabola having equation $y = x(b - x)$. Write expressions for the coordinates of its intercepts and vertex in terms of b.

b. Do these expressions work for negative values of b? Explain, using examples.

16. Graph.

a. $y = x(x - 8)$ b. $y = x(x - 15)$

c. $y = x(x - 12)$ d. $y = x(x - 20)$

WIDTH AS A FUNCTION OF LENGTH
AREA AS A FUNCTION OF LENGTH

After having done problem 1 students can be assigned these sections for homework, as plenty of guidance is provided. However, some students may have difficulty making the generalization to variables, so be sure to have a class discussion on problems 9-12 after students have had a chance to try them on their own.

Problem 6 should alert students to the possibility of noninteger values for the sides of the rectangle.

Problem 7 shows an interesting way to represent data when three variables are involved, but problem 8 helps focus on the variables we are concerned with in this section.

PARABOLAS THROUGH THE ORIGIN

This section should be done in class. Graphing calculators would help. If they are not available, the students should work in groups, sharing the work on making the graphs. Otherwise, graphing many parabolas would get tedious.

This section starts work that will lead to equations of the type $y = a(x - p)(x - q)$. This was started in Chapter 5, Lesson 5, and will continue in Lessons 2 and 3. We will look at other forms of the equations of parabolas in Chapter 14.

13.1 SOLUTIONS

7. See the figure for #2.

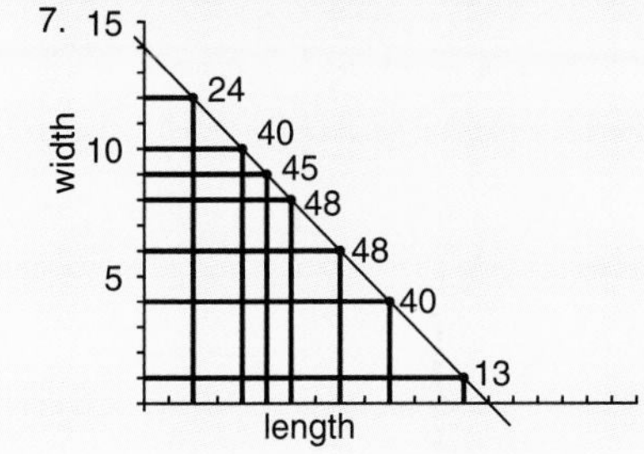

8.-9. $A = L(14 - L)$

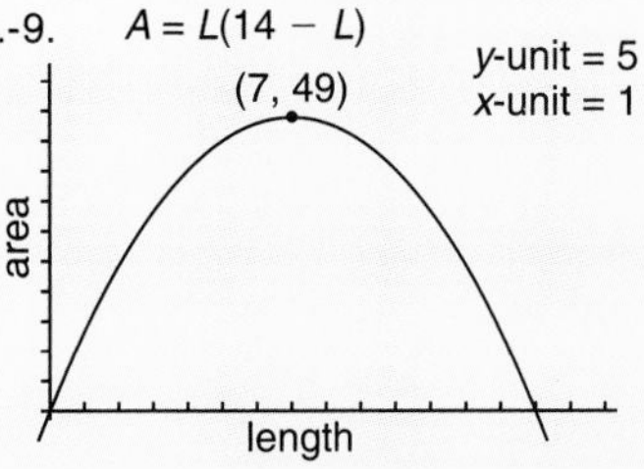

parabola

9. a. This gives the length and the area of the largest rectangle.
 b. (0, 0) and (14, 0). If the length were 0 or 14, the area would be 0.
 c. It does not increase or decrease at the same rate. This would be true only if the graph were a straight line.

10. a. Subtract the length from 14 to get the width. Then multiply length times width to get the area.
 b. $A = L(14 - L)$
 c. $L = 7$, $W = 7$, and $A = 49$. This is a square, which gives the greatest possible area.

11. a. $(P - 2L)/2$
 b. $A = L(P - 2L)/2$

12. The length that gives the maximum area will be the length that makes a square. This can be found by dividing the perimeter by 4. The length will be $P/4$ and the area $P^2/16$.

13.-14.

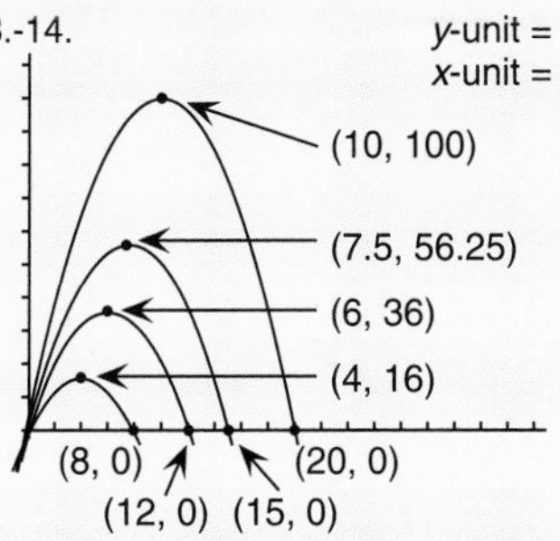

15. a. These are "frown" parabolas with one x-intercept at the origin. The intercepts are (0, 0) and (b, 0). The vertex is (b/2, b^2/4).
 b. Yes, they will work. If b is negative, one x-intercept will be to the left of the origin. For example, $y = x(-15 - x)$ looks just like

We start with an equation of the form $y = x(b - x)$, because that is where the applied problem from the previous sections led us. Careful discussion will be necessary to manage the transition to the form $y = x(x - q)$, but such discussion should be productive.

Notice that in problems 15 and 18, students are asked to write expressions for the vertex in terms of b and q. This begins a preview of a graphical understanding of the quadratic formula, which will be completed in Chapter 14.

REVIEW ***FIXED POINTS***

Do this section only if you have done Chapter 12, Lesson 7. In that lesson we saw fixed points in the function diagram representation. Here we look at them in the Cartesian representation.

17. How do the graphs differ from the ones in problem 3? Discuss the vertex and the intercepts.

18. **Generalization**

a. Describe the graph of a parabola having equation $y = x(x - q)$. Write expressions for the coordinates of its intercepts and vertex in terms of q.

b. Do these expressions work for negative values of q? Explain, using examples.

19. Graph $y = ax(x - 3)$ for:

a. $a = 1$ b. $a = -1$

c. $a = 2$ d. $a = -3$

20. What is the effect of a on the position of:

a. the vertex?

b. the x-intercepts?

Find equations of the form $y = ax(x - q)$ for parabolas *through the origin*, with the given x-intercept and the vertex with the given y-coordinate.

		x-intercept	y-coordinate of vertex
21.	a.	4	4
	b.	4	8
	c.	4	2
	d.	4	-6
22.	a.	8	4
	b.	2	4
	c.	-4	4
	d.	-6	-6

REVIEW ***FIXED POINTS***

23. Find the fixed point for the function $y = 6x + 8$.

24. Solve the system: $\begin{cases} y = 6x + 8 \\ y = x \end{cases}$

25. Explain the statement: *To find the fixed points of a function, find the intersection of its graph with the line $y = x$.*

26. Test whether the statement is true by finding the fixed points of $y = x^2$.

13.1 S O L U T I O N S

$y = x(15 - x)$ except that one intercept is (-15, 0) instead of (15, 0) and the x-coordinate of the vertex is -15/2 instead of 15/2.

16.

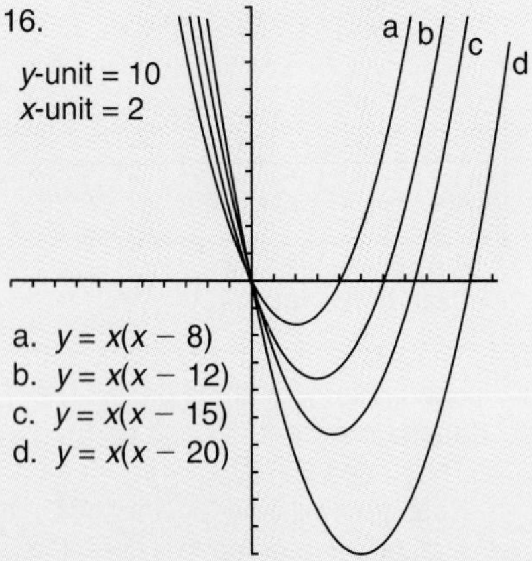

17. The intercepts are the same, but the vertex is the reflection over the x-axis of the vertex of the corresponding parabola in #13. These parabolas are "smiles"; those in #13 are "frowns."

18. a. The parabola with equation $y = x(x - q)$ has intercepts at the origin and the point $(q, 0)$. It is a smile parabola with vertex $(q/2, -q^2/4)$.

b. Yes. If q is negative, the x-intercept is to the left of the origin, but the vertex is still below the x-axis. (Note that the expression $-q^2/4$ is always negative.)

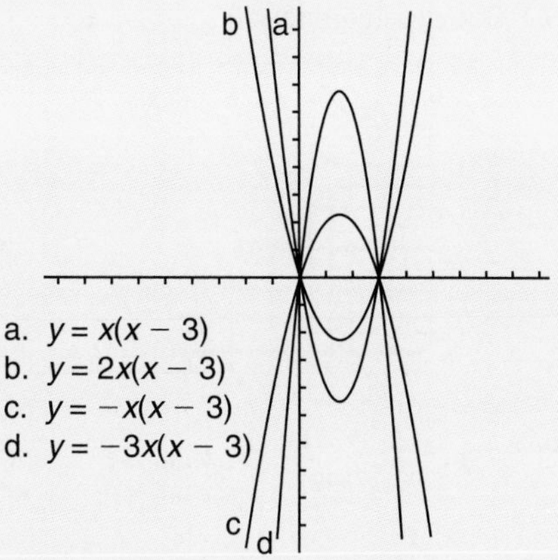

20. a. moves it up or down

b. none

21. a. $y = -1x(x - 4)$ b. $y = -2x(x - 4)$

c. $y = -0.5x(x - 4)$ d. $y = 1.5x(x - 4)$

(Solutions continiued on page 529)

LESSON 13.2

Advanced Penmanship

You will need:

graph paper

PEN PARTITIONS

Assume that you have 50 feet of fencing to build a rectangular pen. You plan to use the garage wall as one side of the pen, which means you need to use your fencing for only three of the four sides. Since you are considering adopting more pets, you want to investigate what happens when you use some of the fencing to divide the pen into two or more parts by building partitions inside the pen, at a right angle to the wall.

1. Make a rough sketch of what this pen might look like,
   a. having no internal partitions;
   b. divided into two sections.
2. With no partitions, is it possible to get a square pen? If so, what are its dimensions?
3. With one partition, is it possible to get two square sections? If so, what are their dimensions?

Call the side of the pen parallel to the wall the *length,* and the distance between the wall and the side opposite the wall x.

4. Imagine you are dividing the pen into two parts. Make a table having three columns: x, the length, and the total area of the pen.

Generalizations

5. Look for patterns in your table. Express algebraically as functions of x,
   a. the length; b. the area.
6. What is the equation that expresses the length as a function of x, if the pen is divided into the given number of parts. (Make sketches. If you need to, make tables like those in problem 4.)
   a. 1 b. 3
   c. 4 d. n
7. Repeat problem 6, but this time find the area as a function of x.

GRAPHS OF AREA FUNCTIONS

This section is about the graphs of functions like the ones you found in problem 7.

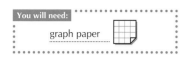

8. Using graph paper, graph each of the following functions. To make comparison easier, use the same graph, or at least the same scale, for all your graphs. To see all four graphs clearly, use a scale that will show values from -5 to 15 for x and from -50 to 50 for y. When making a table of values, use both negative and positive values for x. Keep these graphs, because you will need them in the next section.
   a. $y = x(12 - x)$
   b. $y = x(12 - 2x)$
   c. $y = x(12 - 3x)$
   d. $y = x(12 - 4x)$
9. For each graph,
   a. label the graph with its equation;
   b. label the x-intercepts;
   c. label the vertex.
10. Write a brief description comparing the four graphs. Describe how the graphs are the same and how they are different.

13.2 Advanced Penmanship

Core Sequence: 1-22

Suitable for Homework: 1-7, 18-22

Useful for Assessment: 5-7, 10, 13, 22

What this Lesson is About:

- Using sketches and tables to analyze a real-world problem
- Optimization
- Review of parabolas through the origin
- Role of a and q in $y = ax(x - q)$
- Review of factoring
- Preview of the quadratic formula

PEN PARTITIONS

The issues explored here closely parallel those addressed in Lesson 1. These sections can therefore be assigned as homework if students seemed comfortable with the original pen problem. However, you may want to introduce the homework with a class discussion to make sure students understand what is being asked. Encourage the use of labeled sketches.

For problems 6-7 students may be able to move more directly to an equation, by looking carefully at a sketch of the pen, and reasoning to come up with an expression. If they are unable to do that, they can always use tables of values as a help in finding the algebraic expression.

13.2 SOLUTIONS

1. a.

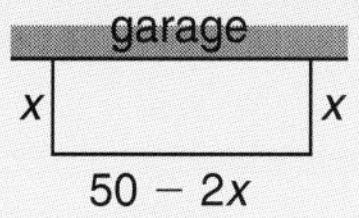

b.

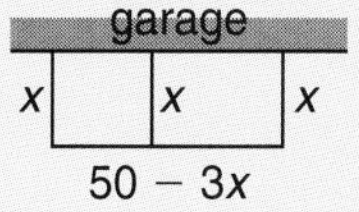

2. Yes. Divide the total amount of fencing by 3. Make a pen whose length and width are both 50/3 feet.
3. Yes. With one partition, there would need to be 5 segments of fencing of equal length. (See the figure.) Each one would have length 50/5 or 10, so the two square pens would be 10 by 10.

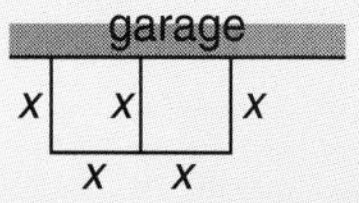

4. Answers will vary. A sample table is given.

x	length	area
2	44	88
4	38	152
8	26	208
10	20	200
15	5	75
16	2	32

5. a. length = $50 - 3x$
   b. area = $x(50 - 3x)$
6. a. length = $50 - 2x$
   b. length = $50 - 4x$
   c. length = $50 - 5x$
   d. length = $50 - (n + 1)x$
7. a. area = $x(50 - 2x)$
   b. area = $x(50 - 4x)$
   c. area = $x(50 - 5x)$
   d. area = $x[50 - (n + 1)x]$

8.-9.

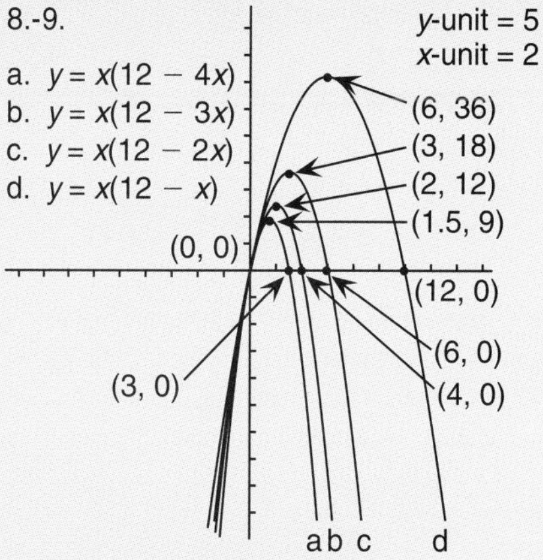

10. Answers will vary. They are all frown parabolas passing through the origin. The other x-intercept varies.

*F*unctions like the ones found in problem 7 will be graphed in the next section.

GRAPHS OF AREA FUNCTIONS

DIFFERENT FORMS

*T*hese sections continue the work on parabolas through the origin that was started in Lesson 1. We start out with functions in the format they are likely to have appeared in the application in the previous section. A graphing calculator would be helpful in solving problem 8.

*T*hen we review the form we learned about in Lesson 1, and review factoring, which provides a way to convert functions into that form.

*I*n problem 13 we continue our preview of a graphical interpretation of the quadratic formula.

MAXIMIZING AREA

*T*his section can be used like a Thinking/Writing assignment. It gives students a chance to apply and extend what they have learned so far.

*A*s an added challenge, you may suggest considering whether making the internal partitions parallel to the garage wall yields a larger maximum area.

11. Without graphing, guess the vertex on the graph of $y = x(12 - 6x)$. Explain how you arrived at your guess.

DIFFERENT FORMS

As you learned in Lesson 1 the equations of parabolas through the origin can be written in the form $y = ax(x - q)$.

12. For each parabola described in (a-d), find a function of the form $y = ax(x - q)$:

a. x-intercepts: 0 and 12, vertex: (6, 36)
b. x-intercepts: 0 and 6, vertex: (3, 18)
c. x-intercepts: 0 and 4, vertex: (2, 12)
d. x-intercepts: 0 and 3, vertex: (1.5, 9)

13. How are the intercepts and the vertex related to the values of a and q in the equation $y = ax(x - q)$?

The equations in problems 8 and 12 have the same graphs. You can verify this by checking that they have the same vertices and intercepts, and in fact that for any x they yield the same y. In other words, the equations are equivalent. We can use the distributive law to confirm this. For example, for problem 8a:

$$y = x(12 - x) = 12x - x^2$$

And for problem 12a:

$$y = -x(x - 12) = -x^2 + 12x$$

14. Show that the other three pairs of equations in problems 8b-d and 12b-d are equivalent.

It is possible to convert equations like the ones in problem 8 to the form $y = ax(x - q)$ by factoring. For example:

$$x(24 - 6x) = 6x(4 - x) = -6x(x - 4)$$

15. Fill in the blanks:

a. $x(24 - 2x) = 2x(\_\_\_\_\_)$
b. $x(24 - 3x) = -3x(\_\_\_\_\_)$
c. $x(24 - 4x) = \_\_\_(x - 6)$

16. Write in the form $y = ax(x - q)$ and find the vertex and the intercepts.

a. $y = x(12 - 6x)$
b. $y = x(50 - 5x)$
c. $y = x(50 - 3x)$
d. $y = x(50 - (n + 1)x)$

MAXIMIZING AREA

17. If you have to use part of the 50 feet of fencing for a partition to divide the pen into two equal parts, what is the largest total area you can get for the enclosure? Explain how you got your answer, including a sketch and graph if necessary.

18. Solve problem 17 if you want to divide the pen into three equal parts.

19. Solve problem 17 if you want to divide the pen into n equal parts.

20. Look at your solutions for problems 17, 18, and 19. In each case look at the shapes of the subdivisions of the pen having the largest area. Are they always squares? Are they ever squares? Does the answer to this depend on the value of n? Explain.

21. Look at your solutions for problems 17, 18, and 19. In each case look at how much of the fencing was used to construct the side parallel to the garage for the pen having maximum area. What fraction of the fencing was used to construct this side? Does the answer depend on the value of n? Explain.

22. Report Imagine you are the representative of a fencing company presenting information to a customer. Write a complete illustrated report, making clear who the customer is and what the pens are needed for. Explain how to maximize the area of the pens for a given amount of fencing. Discuss both divided and undivided pens.

13.2 SOLUTIONS

11. No solution necessary.

12. a. $y = -x(x - 12)$
b. $y = -2x(x - 6)$
c. $y = -3x(x - 4)$
d. $y = -4x(x - 3)$

13. The intercepts are (0, 0) and (q, 0). The vertex is ($-aq^2$)/4.

14. Answers will vary. (Those found in #12 are the factored form of those in #8. Students will see this more clearly after doing the next few problems.)

15. a. $x(24 - 2x) = 2x(12 - x)$
b. $x(24 - 3x) = -3x(x - 8)$
c. $x(24 - 4x) = -4x(x - 6)$

16. a. $y = -6x(x - 2)$
intercepts: (0, 0) and (2, 0)
vertex: (1, 6)
b. $y = -5x(x - 10)$
intercepts: (0, 0) and (10, 0)
vertex: (5, 125)
c. $y = -3x(x - 50/3)$
intercepts: (50/3, 0) and (0, 0)
vertex: (25/3, 625/3)
d. $y = ax(x - q)$
intercepts: (0, 0) and ($50/(n + 1)$, 0)
vertex: ($25/(n + 1)$, $625/(n + 1)$)

17. Find the vertex of $y = x(50 - 3x)$. The y-coordinate of the vertex is $208\frac{1}{3}$, and this is the largest possible area.

18. This involves finding the y-coordinate of the vertex of $y = x(50 - 4x)$, which is 156.25.

19. This involves finding the y-coordinate of the vertex of $y = x[50 - (n + 1)x]$, which is $625/(n + 1)$.

20. They are never squares. They have dimensions $25/n$ by $25/(n + 1)$.

21. The answer is independent of n. It is always 1/2.

22. Reports will vary.

LESSON 13.3

The Zero Product Property

You will need:

graph paper

or a graphing calculator (optional)

1. Given that you have 50 feet of fencing and that you can use the wall of the garage for the fourth side of your pen, what dimensions should you choose to make a rectangular pen having area 200 square feet? Solve by trial and error or by graphing. (There is more than one solution.)

This problem can be solved by writing the equation $x(50 - 2x) = 200$, where x is the distance from the wall to the side opposite it. One way of doing it is to find the intersection of the graphs of $y = x(50 - 2x)$ and $y = 200$.

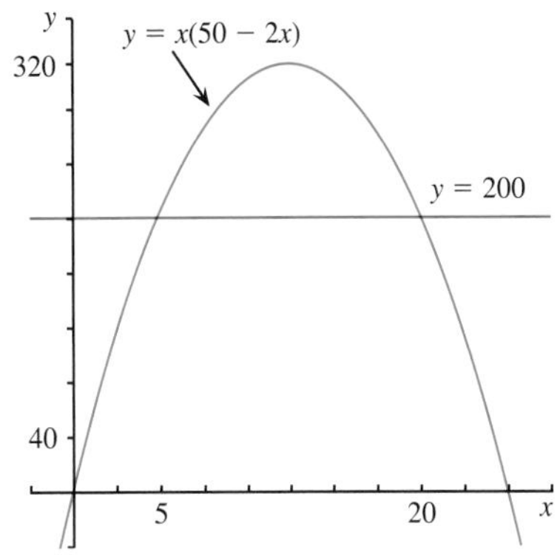

2. Use this method to find the dimensions for the following areas:
   a. 300 b. 250

Another method of solving this kind of problem is to write a quadratic equation and factor it, as explained in the following sections.

ZERO PRODUCTS

3. If $ab = 0$, which of the following is impossible? Explain.
   a. $a \neq 0$ and $b \neq 0$
   b. $a \neq 0$ and $b = 0$
   c. $a = 0$ and $b \neq 0$
   d. $a = 0$ and $b = 0$

Zero Product Property: When the product of two quantities is zero, one or the other quantity must be zero.

An equation like $(x + 6)(2x - 1) = 0$ can be solved using the zero product property. Since the product in the equation is zero, you can write these two equations.

$$x + 6 = 0 \quad \text{or} \quad 2x - 1 = 0$$

4. You know how to solve these equations. Write the solutions.
5. There are two solutions to the equation $(x + 6)(2x - 1) = 0$. What are they?

Solve these equations.

6. $(3x + 1)x = 0$
7. $(2x + 3)(5 - x) = 0$
8. $(2x - 2)(3x - 1) = 0$

▼ 13.3 The Zero Product Property

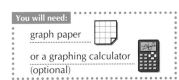

Core Sequence: 1-23

Suitable for Homework: 6-24

Useful for Assessment: 3, 21

What this Lesson is About:

- The zero product property
- Solving quadratics by factoring
- The form $y = a(x - p)(x - q)$
- Symmetry of parabolas
- Vertex and intercepts of parabolas
- Preview of the quadratic formula
- Two definitions of absolute value

The opening problem can be solved in many ways. The most likely solution for most students will be by trial and error. A graphic solution is presented, reviewing the method introduced in Chapter 7, Lesson 6.

ZERO PRODUCTS

SOLVING QUADRATIC EQUATIONS

This is standard material. Solving quadratics by factoring is not important as a skill, and we do not emphasize this aspect of it. However, it does throw light on some important ideas, such as the zero product property, and later, the Fundamental Theorem of Algebra.

13.3 SOLUTIONS

1. Two solutions: Make the side parallel to the garage 10 feet and the other two sides each 20 feet, or make the side parallel to the garage 40 feet and the other two sides each 5 feet.
2. a. Determine graphically where the line $y = 300$ intersects the parabola $y = x(50 - 2x)$. The intersections are at $x = 10$ and $x = 15$. These correspond to pens of dimensions 10 by 30 and 15 by 20 respectively.
   b. Determine graphically where the line $y = 250$ intersects the parabola $y = x(50 - 2x)$. The intersections are approximately at $x = 6.91$ and $x = 18.09$, which correspond to pens of dimensions 6.91 by 36.18 and 18.09 by 13.82.
3. It is impossible for a and b both to be unequal to zero. If the product is zero, at least one of the factors must be zero.
4. $x = -6$ and $x = 1/2$
5. $x = -6$ and $x = 1/2$
6. $x = -1/3$ and $x = 0$
7. $x = -3/2$ and $x = 5$
8. $x = 1$ and $x = 1/3$

In this lesson, we concentrate on using the zero product property along with property of parabolas to solve a variety of problems about quadratic functions and equations. This helps set the stage for a graphical treatment of the quadratic formula, which will be done in Chapter 14.

SYMMETRY

VERTEX AND INTERCEPTS

More standard material. The work of the past two lessons on parabolas is wrapped up here. More work on quadratics will be done in the next chapter, using other forms for the equations.

SOLVING QUADRATIC EQUATIONS

Some quadratic equations can be solved using the zero product property.

Example: Find the values of x for which

$$x^2 + 6x = -5.$$

First rewrite the equation so you can apply the zero product property.

$$x^2 + 6x + 5 = 0$$

In factored form, this is written:

$$(x + 5)(x + 1) = 0.$$

Since the product is 0, at least one of the factors must be 0. So $x + 5 = 0$ or $x + 1 = 0$.

9. What are the two solutions of the equation $(x + 5)(x + 1) = 0$?

Example:

Find the values of x for which $6x^2 = 12x$.

First rewrite the equation so that you can apply the zero product property.

$$6x^2 - 12x = 0$$

In factored form, this is written:

$$6x(x - 2) = 0.$$

10. What are the two solutions to the equation $6x(x - 2) = 0$?

11. Factor and use the zero product property to solve these quadratic equations.

a. $x^2 - x = 2$

b. $2L^2 - L = 3$

c. $W^2 + 10W + 16 = 0$

d. $3M^2 + 30M + 48 = 0$

To solve problem 2a, write the equation:

$$x(50 - 2x) = 300$$
$$-2x^2 + 50x - 300 = 0$$
$$2x^2 - 50x + 300 = 0$$
$$x^2 - 25x + 150 = 0$$

12. Explain the four steps.

13. Factor the final equation and use the zero product property to solve it.

Unfortunately, most quadratic equations cannot easily be solved by factoring. In the next chapter you will learn a way that always works to solve quadratic equations.

SYMMETRY

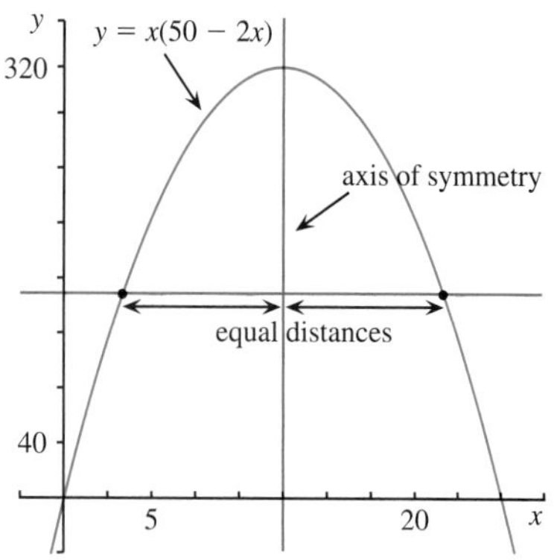

The vertical line through the vertex of a parabola is called its *axis of symmetry*.

14. How far is each x-intercept from the axis of symmetry in the preceding graph?

The x-intercepts are *equidistant* from the axis of symmetry. (They are at an equal distance from it.) As you can see in the figure, this is also true of any pair of points of the parabola that lie on the same horizontal line as each other.

15. Refer to the graph for problem 1.

a. Show that the two solutions to problem 1 are equidistant from the axis of symmetry.

b. Is this also true of the two solutions to problem 2a? What about problem 2b? Show your work.

13.3 SOLUTIONS

9. $x = -5$ and $x = -1$

10. $x = 0$ or $x = 2$

11. a. $(x - 2)(x + 1) = 0$
   $x = 2$ or $x = -1$
   b. $(2L - 3)(L + 1) = 0$
   $L = 3/2$ or $L = -1$
   c. $(W + 8)(W + 2) = 0$
   $W = -8$ or $W = -2$
   d. $3(M + 8)(M + 2) = 0$
   $M = -8$ or $M = -2$

12. First step: Distribute the x. Subtract 300 from both sides.
   Second step: Multiply both sides by -1.
   Third step: Divide both sides by 2.

13. $(x - 15)(x - 10) = 0$. Therefore, by the zero product property, $x = 15$ or $x = 10$.

14. 12.5 units

15. a. The solutions are 5 and 20. They are both 7.5 units from the axis of symmetry, which is at $x = 12.5$.
   b. This is true for 2(a). The solutions are both 2.5 units from the axis of symmetry. It is also true for 2(b). The solutions are both 5.59 units from the axis of symmetry.

16. At the y-intercept, $x = 0$ and $y = -24$.

17. At the x-intercepts, $y = 0$ and $x = -3$ or $x = 4$, by the zero product property.

VERTEX AND INTERCEPTS

In an equation like $y = 2(x + 3)(x - 4)$, you can quickly find the intercepts and the vertex.

16. What is the value of x at the y-intercept? Substitute this value for x in the equation and find the y-intercept.

17. What is the value of y at the x-intercepts? Substitute this value for y in the equation and find the x-intercepts with the help of the zero product property.

18. If you know the x-intercepts, how can you find the x-coordinate of the vertex? Find it.

19. If you know the x-coordinate of the vertex, how can you find its y-coordinate? Find it.

20. Find the intercepts and vertex for:
a. $y = 0.5(x - 0.4)(x - 1)$
b. $y = 2(x + 3)(x + 4)$

21. Explain how you would find the intercepts and vertex for a function of the form

$$y = a(x - p)(x - q).$$

22. Find the equation and the vertex for a parabola having the following intercepts:
a. (3, 0), (6, 0), (0, 36)
b. (3, 0), (6, 0), (0, 9)
c. (-3, 0), (-6, 0), (0, -9)
d. (-3, 0), (6, 0), (0, 6)

23. The vertex and one of the two x-intercepts of parabolas are given. Find the equation and the y-intercept.
a. vertex: (2, -2); x-intercept: (1, 0)
b. vertex: (1, -12); x-intercept: (-1, 0)
c. vertex: (3, 4.5); x-intercept: (6, 0)

DISCOVERY *TWO DEFINITIONS*

Definition: The absolute value of a number is the distance between that number and zero.

Browsing through Ginger's calculus book, Mary and Martin noticed this definition:

Definition: $|x| = \begin{cases} x \text{ for } x > 0 \\ -x \text{ for } x < 0 \end{cases}$

"That $-x$ must be a misprint," Mary commented. "Absolute value can't be negative."

24. Report Write a letter to Mary explaining everything you know about absolute value. Restate the two definitions presented above in your own words. Using examples, explain why they are equivalent, and why Mary was wrong about the misprint.

Problems 16-19 guide students through the process that would lead to finding intercepts and vertex from the equation, by using what they should know about the meaning of those words and by taking advantage of the symmetry. Then, in problem 20, students have to apply this method.

If these sections are done as homework, make sure to spend some class time the next day discussing them. Problems 21-23 in particular are a real test of understanding. Don't expect mastery of problems 22-23. Some students may not be able to do this algebraically, or may not know how to get started. Encourage group work and discussion. For problem 23, you may give the hint that they should start by finding the other x-intercept, which can be done easily on a graph.

DISCOVERY *TWO DEFINITIONS*

While the second definition is more commonly seen, it is less general than the first one, which generalizes to complex numbers, for instance. Furthermore, the second definition is very difficult to understand.

13.3 SOLUTIONS

18. The x-coordinate of the vertex is halfway between the x-intercepts. It is at $x = 1/2$.

19. Substitute $x = 1/2$ into the equation $y = 2(x + 3)(x - 4)$ to get $y = -24.5$.

20. a. x-intercepts: $x = 0.4$ and $x = 1$, y-intercept: (0, 0.2), vertex: (0.7, -0.045)
b. x-intercepts: $x = -3$ and $x = -4$, y-intercept: (0, 24), vertex: (-3.5, -0.5)

21. The x-intercepts are (p, 0) and (q, 0), so the x-coordinate of the vertex is $(p + q)/2$. To find the y-coordinate of the vertex, substitute the x-coordinate into the equation. The y-coordinate is $-a(p - q)^2/4$.

22. a. $y = a(x - 3)(x - 6)$
$36 = a(0 - 3)(0 - 6)$
$a = 2$
The equation is $y = 2(x - 3)(x - 6)$.
b. $9 = a(0 - 3)(0 - 6)$
$9 = a(0 - 3)(0 - 6)$
$a = 1/2$
The equation is $y = (1/2)(x - 3)(x - 6)$.
c. $y = a(x + 3)(x + 6)$
$-9 = a(0 + 3)(0 + 6)$
$a = -1/2$
The equation is $y = (-1/2)(x + 3)(x + 6)$.
d. $y = a(x + 3)(x - 6)$
$6 = a(0 + 3)(0 - 6)$
$a = -1/3$
The equation is $y = (-1/3)(x + 3)(x - 6)$

23. a. The other x-intercept must be (3, 0). The equation must be of the form $y = a(x - 1)(x - 3)$. Then $-2 = a(2 - 1)(2 - 3)$, so $a = 2$. The equation is $y = 2(x - 1)(x - 3)$.
b. The other x-intercept is (3, 0). The equation is $y = 3(x + 1)(x - 3)$.
c. The other x-intercept is (0, 0). The equation is $y = (-1/2)x(x - 6)$.

24. Reports will vary.

▼ 13.4
Rectangular Pens: Constant Area

Core Sequence: 1-16

Suitable for Homework: 2-20

Useful for Assessment: 4-5, 14-16, 20

What this Lesson is About:

- Review of constant product and constant sum graphs
- Preview of graphs of rational functions

We conclude our Exploration of the pen problem by reversing it; this time the area is constant and the perimeter varies. Students should be able to carry out the Exploration on their own.

You can extend the Exploration, with the book closed, by asking these questions:

- What is the width of the pen as a function of its length?
- What is the perimeter of the pen as a function of its length?

WIDTH AS A FUNCTION OF LENGTH

PERIMETER LINES

This reviews constant product and constant sum graphs, which were seen in Chapter 5, Lessons 1, 2, and **Thinking/ Writing 5.A**.

LESSON 13.4

Rectangular Pens: Constant Area

You will need:

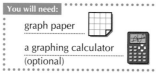

- graph paper
- a graphing calculator (optional)

1. Exploration You bought 45 square feet of artificial turf for the floor of Stripe's backyard. You can cut it up any way you like, but you want to use all of it. Since you're almost broke (artificial turf is expensive) you would like to spend as little money as possible on fencing. What's the least amount of fencing you could buy and still make a rectangular pen that surrounded the artificial turf on all four sides? Find out by trying various dimensions for the pen.

WIDTH AS A FUNCTION OF LENGTH

Suppose you want to make a rectangular pen having area 36.

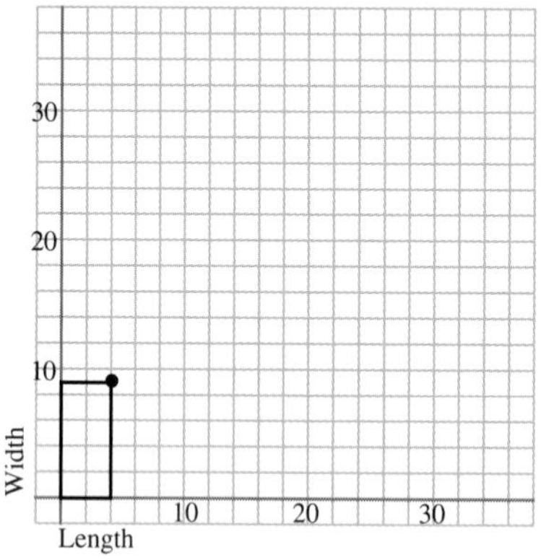

2. a. On graph paper draw a pair of axes and show five rectangular pens that would have an area of 36 square feet. The lower left corner should be at the origin. An example is shown in the figure.

b. Mark with a • the upper right corner of each rectangle you drew. Then write in the coordinates of each of these points.

c. Connect the •s. Do they lie in a straight line or on a curve? Describe any patterns you notice.

3. Make a table showing some of the coordinates on your graph. Look for a pattern in your coordinates and make three more entries in the table.

4. 🔑 Write an algebraic equation that expresses the width as a function of the length.

5. 🔑

a. Would it be possible to have a pen having length greater than 30? 32? 36? Explain your answers, giving examples.

b. Explain why your graph will never touch the x-axis or the y-axis.

c. If you increase the length by one foot, does the width increase or decrease? Does it change by the same amount each time? Explain.

PERIMETER LINES

In the previous section you probably noticed that the perimeter of the rectangles changed even though the area remained constant. In this section you will investigate how the perimeter varies as a function of length if you keep the area constant.

13.4 SOLUTIONS

1. Answers will vary. See the solutions to #14-#16.
2. The graph will be a constant product curve.

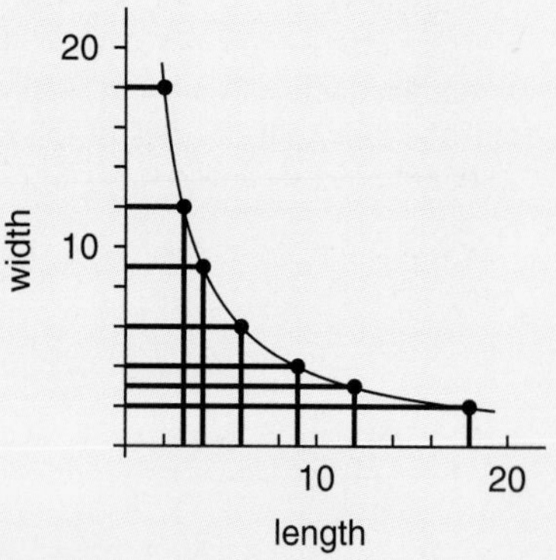

3. Answers will vary.

L	W
1	36
2	18
3	12
4	9
6	6
9	4
12	3
18	2
36	1

4. $W = 36/L$
5. a. Yes, the length can be (theoretically) as long as you want. For example, if the length is 72, the width is 1/2. If the length is 144, the width is 1/4.

   b. The product of the length and the width is 36. If the product is nonzero, both of the factors must be nonzero.

   c. Decrease. No, this would be true only if the graph were a straight line.

6.-8.

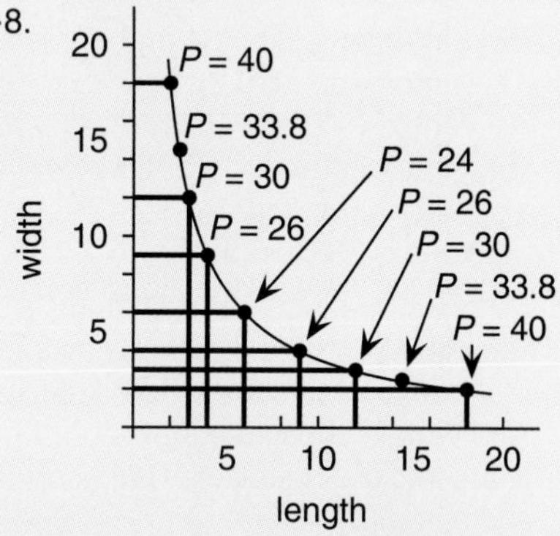

7. The intercepts are (15, 0) and (0, 15). They represent the extremes of length and width.

6. Write the perimeter of the corresponding rectangle next to each • you marked on the graph. Look for patterns.

Your graph should show pairs of points that correspond to the same perimeter. For example, (3, 12) and (12, 3) both correspond to the perimeter 30.

7. Connect (3, 12) and (12, 3) to each other by a straight line. Extend it to its intercepts. Interpret the intercepts in terms of this problem.

8. On your graph find two points that both correspond to a perimeter of 26. Repeat problem 7 for these points. Then find other pairs of points that both correspond to the same perimeter and repeat problem 7 for each of these pairs. What patterns do you see?

9. Use the graph to estimate the dimensions of a rectangle having area 36 and perimeter 36.

PERIMETER AS A FUNCTION OF LENGTH

10. Make a graph of perimeter as a function of length. Show length on the x-axis and perimeter on the y-axis. Connect the points on your graph with a smooth curve. Describe the shape of the curve.

11. Label the lowest point on your graph with its coordinates. Interpret these two numbers in terms of the problem.

Note: The graph is *not* a parabola, and its lowest point is *not* called a *vertex*.

12. Explain why your graph will never touch the x-axis or y-axis.

13. If you increase the length by one foot, what happens to the perimeter? Can you tell whether it will increase or decrease? Does it increase or decrease by the same amount each time? Explain.

14. **Summary**
    a. For a fixed area of 36 square feet, explain in words how you would find the perimeter of the rectangular pen if you were given the length.
    b. If the area of a rectangular pen is 36 and its length is L, write an algebraic expression for its perimeter.
    c. If you had to enclose a rectangular area of 36 square feet and wanted to use the least amount of fencing, what would the length, width, and perimeter be? Explain.

Generalizations

15. If the area of a rectangular pen is A and its length is L,
    a. write an algebraic expression for its width in terms of A and L;
    b. write an algebraic expression for its perimeter in terms of A and L.

16. Explain how to find the length that gives the minimum perimeter. Write an algebraic expression for it in terms of A only.

NUMBER PUZZLES

17. Find two numbers x and y whose product is 75 and whose sum is 20. Explain your method.

18. Graph the equations $xy = 75$ and $x + y = 20$ on the same pair of axes. Find their point of intersection. How is this point related to your answer to problem 17?

19. Find two numbers whose product is 75 and whose sum is 23.75.

20. If two numbers have a product of 75, what is the smallest value their sum could take? What is the largest? Explain.

13.4 SOLUTIONS

8. The lines are parallel constant sum lines.

9. This involves graphically estimating the intersection of $xy = 36$ with $x + y = 36$. The (x, y) pairs are approximately (1.03, 34.97) and (34.97, 1.03).

10.-11.

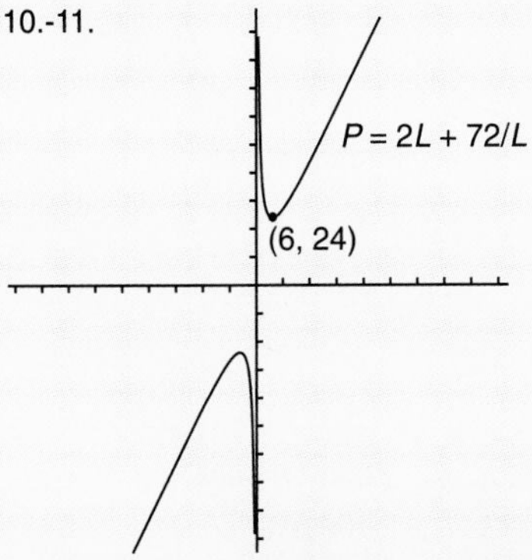

11. The lowest point is (6, 24). It means that the length that gives the minimum perimeter is 6, and the corresponding perimeter is 24.

12. Explanations will vary.

13. Answers will vary. Reasoning, using a table like the one below, may be helpful.

L	W	P
1	36	74
2	18	40
3	12	30
4	9	26
6	6	24
9	4	26
12	3	30
18	2	40
36	1	74

(Solutions continued on page 529)

PERIMETER AS A FUNCTION OF LENGTH

This section would be enriched by the use of graphing calculators.

Students should already have the key insights about minimizing perimeter from the previous section, where the symmetry of the graphs was a powerful hint. So the focus in this section is a more open-ended exploration of new mathematical territory. The function we study is a rational function, not one traditionally studied at this level. However, it is not too difficult in the context of this activity.

It is useful for students to see a function having a minimum that is not a parabola, and in fact does not have mirror symmetry. It is also an opportunity to see a graph having asymptotes that is not an inverse variation.

In problem 13 you may extend the discussion by considering large values for x. Then the answer to the question is that for an increase of one foot in the length, the perimeter increases by almost two feet. This is true because for large enough values of the length, the width does not contribute much to the perimeter. For example:

Length	Perimeter
100	200.18
101	202.178
102	204.176

Algebraically, this is because as x gets large, the function gets closer and closer to $y = 2x$, and its slope gets closer and closer to 2.

Students enjoy discussions of infinity and of asymptotes, and you may even use the latter word here, as long as you don't expect them to master the idea.

NUMBER PUZZLES

These ask the same questions without the context of the pen problem.

THINKING WRITING 13.A Business Applications

Core Sequence: none of the lesson

Suitable for Homework: 1-8

Useful for Assessment: 8

What this Assignment is About:

- Optimization
- Using tables, graphs, and equations to make decisions

*T*his optional assignment covers the same mathematical ground as the first four lessons, but in a different context.

THINKING WRITING 13.A Business Applications

MAXIMUM PROFIT

The Widget Company was trying to sell a widget for \$24, but no one was buying. They decided to try to attract customers by reducing their prices. They found that for every \$1 they lowered the price, they attracted ten customers.

Price Reduction	Price	# of Customers	Gross Profit
\$0	\$24	0	\$0
\$1	\$23	10	\$230
\$2	\$22	20	\$440

1. a. Copy and extend the table for at least eight possible price reductions.

b. If the price is \$14, how many people will buy a widget? What will the gross profit be?

c. If the price is lowered by \$$x$, how many people will buy a widget? What will the gross profit be?

d. Make a graph showing how the gross profit depends on the price reduction. Put the price reduction on the x-axis and the profit on the y-axis.

e. Interpret your graph. What price gives the most profit? Explain.

f. Write an equation for your graph.

The Widget Company was trying to sell an item for P dollars, and no one was buying it. They found that for every \$1 they lower the price, they gain C customers.

2. If they lower the cost by x and the gross profit is y, write an equation for y in terms of x.

3. Write an algebraic expression for:

a. the amount by which the price should be reduced in order to maximize the profit;

b. the maximum profit possible.

MINIMUM COST

The Widget Company would like to ship 2000 widgets. They must be packaged in boxes of equal weight. (Each widget weighs one pound.) The L.A. Barge Company charges a basic rate of \$100 per box for shipping. It also adds a surcharge to the total cost of the shipment that depends on the weight of the individual boxes, at the rate of \$1 per pound.

Example: If the widgets are packed in 10 boxes, each will weigh 200 lbs.

Basic charge	Surcharge	Total
10 boxes · \$100 per box	\$200	\$1200

4. Explain, using examples of possible ways to package the 2000 widgets, how the L.A. Barge Company's policy guarantees that customers will not ship their goods in too many boxes, or in boxes that are too heavy.

5. Write an algebraic expression for the cost of shipping the 2000 widgets, in terms of the number of boxes.

6. What is the number of boxes that would be the cheapest way to ship the widgets? Explain how you get your answer. (Hint: You may use trial and error or graphing.)

7. Using the cheapest way, how much does it cost per widget?

8. Report Imagine you work for the Widget Company. Prepare an illustrated report to other employees about:

a. the pricing of widgets and how to maximize profits, and

b. the shipping of widgets and how to minimize cost.

13.A SOLUTIONS

1. a. Tables will vary. A sample is given.

Price Reduction	Price	# of Customers	Gross Profit
\$0	\$24	0	\$0
\$1	\$23	10	\$230
\$2	\$22	20	\$440
\$3	\$21	30	\$630
\$4	\$20	40	\$800
\$5	\$19	50	\$950
\$6	\$18	60	\$1080
\$8	\$16	80	\$1280
\$10	\$14	100	\$1400
\$12	\$12	120	\$1440
\$14	\$10	140	\$1400

b. If the price is \$14, the price reduction was \$10, so there will be 100 customers. The gross profit is the price multiplied by the number of customers, or \$14(100) = \$1400.

c. If the price is lowered by \$$x$, the number of people who will buy is $10x$ and the price is $24 - x$, so the gross profit is $10x(24 - x)$ dollars.

d.

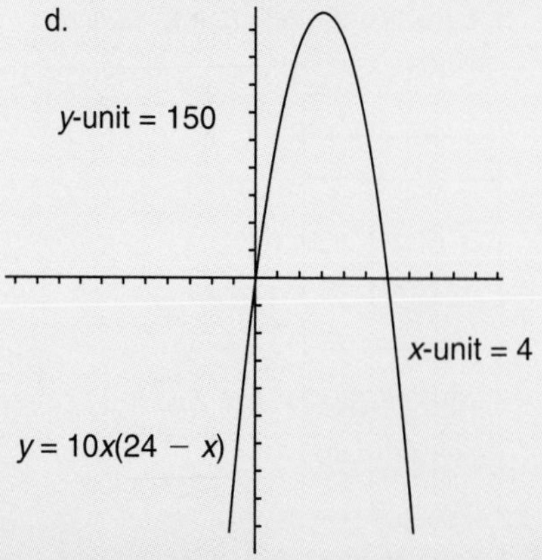

e. The highest point on the graph is (12, 1440). This means that if the price is reduced by 12, the gross profit is \$1440, and this is the maximum gross profit possible.

f. $y = 10x(24 - x)$

2. $y = Cx(P - x)$

3. a. $P/2$ b. $C(P/2)(P/2) = CP^2/4$

4. Answers will vary. Consider the extremes. If you were to use 2000 one-pound boxes, the basic charge would be \$100(2000), or \$200,000. The surcharge would be very small (only \$1) but the total cost would be high (\$200,001). If you were to use one 2000-pound box, the basic charge would be only \$100, but it would be offset by a huge surcharge of \$2000, for a total charge of \$2100.

(Solutions continued on page 529)

LESSON 13.5

Packing and Mailing

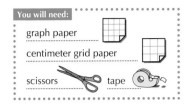

You will need:
- graph paper
- centimeter grid paper
- scissors
- tape

MAXIMIZING VOLUME

You can make cardboard trays to hold 1-cm^3 cubes. Start with an 18-cm-by-18-cm piece of grid paper. Cut a square out of each corner and fold up the sides to form a tray.

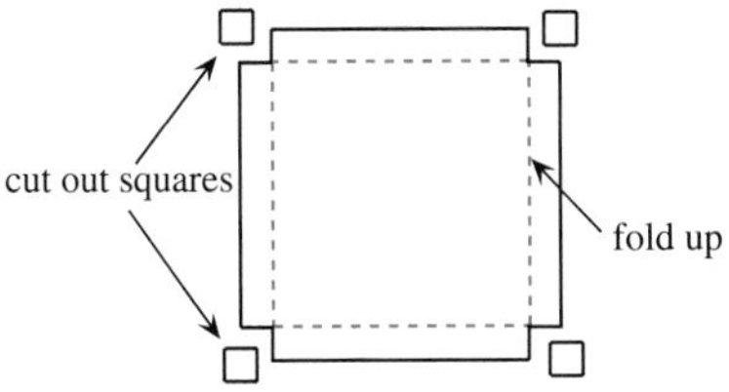

1. **Exploration** Work with other students to make as many different trays as you can by cutting square corners out of an 18-cm-by-18-cm piece of paper or cardboard. Figure out which tray holds the most cubes.

2. Make a table showing the side of the square corner that was cut out, the area of the base, and the number of cubes the tray would hold. (For example, if a 2-by-2 square is cut out at each corner, the area of the base should be 196 cm^2, and the tray should hold 392 cubes.)

3. If the side of the square cut out of the corner is x,
   a. what is the area of the base?
   b. what is the volume of the tray?

4. Make a graph of the volume of the tray as a function of x. Include some fractional values of x.

5. What is the height of the tray that will give the maximum volume?

6. What are the x-intercepts of the graph? Interpret them in terms of this problem.

7. Draw a vertical line through the highest point on the graph. Are the x-intercepts equidistant from it?

8. Extend the graph in both directions by using a few more values for x beyond the x-intercepts.

9. Explain why the points you added in problem 8 do not represent the tray problem.

10. Is the graph a parabola? Explain, giving as many reasons as you can for your answer.

11. **Generalization** Find the height which would give the maximum volume if the initial piece of paper had the following dimensions. You may want to use tables of values.
   a. 12 by 12 b. S by S

13.5 SOLUTIONS

1. Answers will vary. See solution to #5.

2.

Height (x)	Dimensions of Base	Area of Base	# of Cubes (Volume)
1	16 by 16	256	256
2	14 by14	196	392
3	12 by 12	144	432
4	10 by 10	100	400
5	8 by 8	64	320
6	6 by 6	36	216
7	4 by 4	16	112
8	2 by 2	4	32

3. a. $(18 - 2x)(18 - 2x)$
   b. $V = x(18 - 2x)(18 - 2x)$

4.-8.

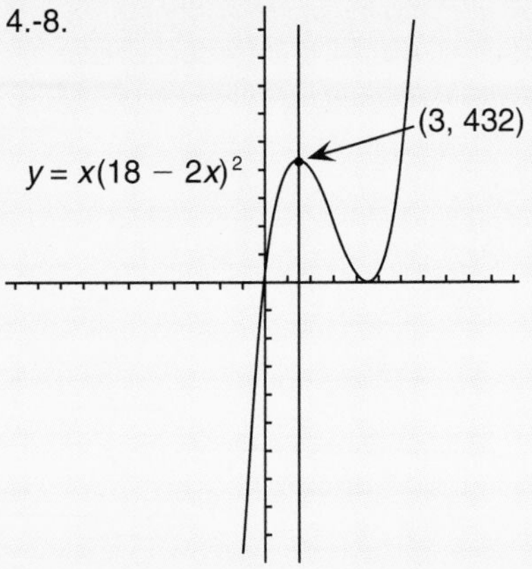

5. 3 cm

6. 9 and 0. If the side of the cut-out square is 0, the tray will have no height, so its volume will be 0. If the side of the cut-out square is 9, there will be no cardboard left to form the base.

13.5 Packing and Mailing

Core Sequence: 1-11

Suitable for Homework: 4-19

Useful for Assessment: 3, 9-10, 18

What this Lesson is About:
- Three-dimensional optimization problems
- Constraints
- Preview of cubic functions

This lesson takes the geometric optimization problems of the first half of the chapter into three dimensions.

MAXIMIZING VOLUME

It is important to start with the hands-on Exploration in problem 1, so students understand what the problem is about. Of course, you will not actually have enough cubes to fill the trays, but physically making the trays will be very important to students being able to understand the rest of this section.

Note that in problem 3, the focus moves away from the unit cubes and towards a more general question of volume, allowing the introduction of fractional dimensions.

Students may expect the patterns to be identical to the ones in the pen problems, but since the equation is a third-degree equation, the graph is not a parabola. This is to a great extent what this section is about, and the question is asked directly in problem 10.

For problem 11 students need not cut and fold papers, nor do they need to make extensive tables and graphs. A graphing calculator would help, but it is not necessary, as students may notice that the maximum volume occurs for a height that is one sixth of the side of the original square.

The tray problem can be generalized to start with a rectangle, but then a pattern is harder to detect.

STORING CUBES

POSTAL REGULATIONS

Do not assign both of these sections in one sitting. They each require a substantial amount of exploration. Either is suitable for use as *problem of the week*. They could also be worked on by pairs of students or groups.

For problems 12-14 "the least cardboard" refers to the cardboard in the final tray, but one could also research the dimensions that require the least cardboard in the original square or rectangle, prior to cutting off the corners. The results of such an investigation would be different.

For problems 15-19 there may be many divergent approaches and interpretations. Make sure groups present their interpretations and solutions to the class.

STORING CUBES

Suppose you want to make a cardboard tray for storing 100 centimeter cubes. The base does not have to be square.

12. Exploration What should the dimensions of the tray be so it will contain the least cardboard? Explain.

13. Repeat problem 12 for:

a. 50 cubes; b. 200 cubes;
c. 500 cubes; d. 1000 cubes.

14. Project Write an illustrated report explaining a strategy for solving this problem for *N* cubes.

POSTAL REGULATIONS

The U.S. Postal Service will not mail by Priority Mail™ anything that weighs more than 70 pounds or exceeds 108 inches in combined length and girth. (The girth is the distance around, as shown in the figure.)

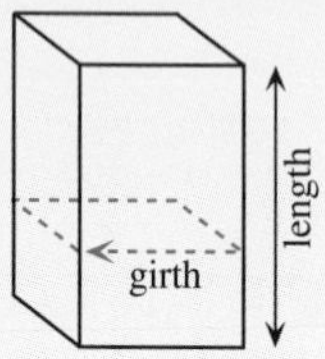

15. Exploration Find the dimensions for a box that would satisfy the Priority Mail™ requirements and would hold as large a volume as possible.

16. Suppose you want to mail a box full of 20-inch-long dowels. What are the dimensions of the rectangular box having the largest volume that would satisfy postal regulations and would accommodate the dowels?

17. Repeat problem 16, this time for 12-inch-long dowels.

18. Project A lumber company needs to pack dowels in boxes that can be sent by Priority Mail™. Boxes need to be designed to ship dowels of each length. Explain, with examples, how to find dimensions for such boxes that will allow the packing of the maximum number of dowels.

19. A shipping company has the following rules:

- maximum length: 108 inches
- maximum length plus girth: 130 inches

In addition, they recommend two inches cushioning on all sides for fragile items. What is the largest volume possible for the contents of the package in the case of fragile items?

13.5 SOLUTIONS

7. no
8. See the answer for #4.
9. The maximum value of x is 9 and the minimum is 0, for the reason given in #6.
10. No. The function is of degree 3 in x, and parabolas are graphs of quadratic (degree 2) functions. The highest point is not halfway between the x-intercepts. (Students may have additional reasons.)
11. a. $x = 2$ (This gives a volume of 128.)
    b. $x = S/6$ (This gives a volume of $2S^3/27$.)
12. The solution can be found by trial and error. From the work in two dimensions, we know that the rectangle of minimum perimeter for a fixed area is a square. Here, we might expect the minimum surface area for a fixed volume to be a cube. However, a cube in this case would not allow us to pack 100 centimeter cubes because it would not have integer dimensions. Instead, we search for three integers whose product is 100, such that the differences among the integers is minimized. By trial and error, this can be found to be 5 by 5 by 4. Just to be sure, we might want to check something like 5 by 10 by 2. The tray would not necessarily have a top, so we might expect to save some cardboard by making the base as large as possible, since this piece would not be duplicated on top. A 5 by 5 by 4 with no top would have surface area 105. A 5 by 10 by 2 would have surface area 110, so the original idea was correct.
13. a. 5 by 5 by 2 b. 8 by 5 by 5
    c. 10 by 10 by 5 d. 10 by 10 by 10
14. Answers will vary.
15. Note: Answers to #15-#19 will depend partly on assumptions students make. We have given our best answers, but your students' answers will vary.
    A 36-in.-by-18-in.-by-18-in. box will have a volume of 11,664 cubic inches.
16. A 40-in.-by-17-in.-by-17-in. box will have a volume of 11,560 cubic inches, as will a 34-in.-by-17-in.-by-20-in. box.

(Solutions continued on page 529)

LESSON 13.6

Solving with Squares

You will need:

the Lab Gear

In this chapter you have used quadratic functions to solve problems involving finding a maximum area. In the next chapter you will be faced with problems for which it will be useful to solve quadratic equations. In this lesson we start to prepare for this.

EQUAL SQUARES

In Chapter 7, Lesson 7, you solved quadratic equations using the equal squares method. Some problems are easy to solve this way. For example,

$$x^2 - 10x + 25 = 16$$

can be written

$$(x - 5)^2 = 4^2$$

with a perfect square on each side.

1. Solve this equation. (Remember: There are two solutions.)

It is not necessary for the number on the right to be a perfect square, since you can take the square root of any nonnegative number.

Example:

$$x^2 - 10x + 25 = 7$$
$$(x - 5)^2 = 7$$
$$x - 5 = \sqrt{7} \text{ OR } x - 5 = -\sqrt{7}$$
$$x = 5 + \sqrt{7} \text{ OR } x = 5 - \sqrt{7}$$

Using your calculator, you can find decimal approximations for the two solutions:

$$x \approx 7.646 \text{ or } x \approx 2.354.$$

Solve these equations using the equal squares method. First give exact answers (using radicals if necessary); then find decimal approximations. Not all are possible.

2. $x^2 - 10x + 25 = 8$
3. $y^2 + 6x + 9 = 15$
4. $x^2 - 24x + 144 = 12$
5. $4r^2 - 4r + 1 = 6$
6. $9s^2 + 12s + 4 = 21$
7. $y^2 - 14y - 49 = -20$

COMPLETING THE SQUARE

In this section you will learn how to turn certain quadratic equations into equal squares equations that you know how to solve.

8. Write the equation shown by this figure.

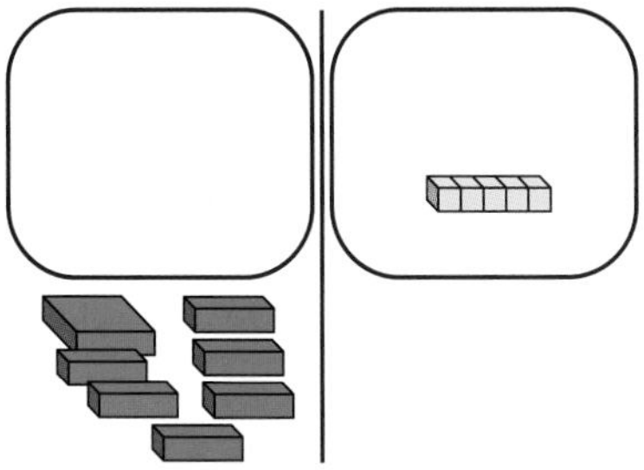

We will add the same quantity to both sides, so that the left side is a perfect square. This is called *completing the square*.

9. a. What number was added to both sides of the figure on the next page to make the left side a perfect square?
   b. Write the resulting equation.

13.6 Solving with Squares

*This lesson starts our concentrated work on quadratic equations, which will extend into the next chapter. The main point of this work is not efficient solving of quadratic equations, and therefore we are not interested in deciding which method is the "best" one to teach students. In fact, it is by using multiple approaches and seeing the relationships between them that students will develop an understanding of quadratic equations and expressions.

In Lessons 6-8 we limit ourselves to quadratic expressions in the form $x^2 + bx + c$. We present a varied approach, including manipulatives, graphing, and symbol manipulation. In Chapter 14 we will tackle the more general case of $ax^2 + bx + c$, including the introduction of the quadratic formula.

If you are interested solely in solving quadratic equations efficiently, with no regard for developing the students' grasp of algebraic structure, you do not need to do Lessons 6-8. Instead, if you have access to graphing calculators, continue to use the graphical method discussed in Chapter 7, Lesson 7, and skip to **Thinking/Writing 13.B**, and then the beginning of Chapter 14. (For example, you may feel that the symbolic work in these lessons is best left to a future course, and that you would rather use what time you have left to reinforce more basic ideas by going back to parts of the book that you skipped.)

Core Sequence: 1-35

Suitable for Homework: 17-37

Useful for Assessment: 17

What this Lesson is About:

- Review of equal squares
- Completing the square
- Review of factoring to solve quadratic equations
- Preview of the quadratic formula

This lesson is critical, because it introduces completing the square, which is the key technique for understanding much about quadratic expressions.

EQUAL SQUARES

Equal squares equations were introduced in Chapter 7, Lesson 7. Here we extend the idea to include numbers that are not perfect

13.6 S O L U T I O N S

1. $x = 9, x = 1$
2. $x = 5 \pm \sqrt{8}$
   Approximation: $x = 2.17$ or 7.83
3. $x = -3 \pm \sqrt{15}$
   Approximation: $x = -6.87$ or 0.87
4. $x = 12 \pm \sqrt{12}$
   Approximation: $x = 15.46$ or 8.54
5. $x = 0.5[1 \pm \sqrt{6}]$
   Approximation: $x = 1.72$ or -0.73
6. $x = (1/3)[-2 \pm \sqrt{21}]$
   Approximation: $x = 0.86$ or -2.19
7. no solution
8. $x^2 + 6x = -5$
9. a. 9
   b. $(x + 3)^2 = 4$
10. $(x + 3)^2 = 2^2$
    $x + 3 = -2$ or $x + 3 = 2$
    $x = -1$ or $x = -5$
11. $x = 1$ or $x = -3$
12. $x = -1$ or $x = -11$
13. $x = 0$ or $x = -4$
14. $x = 1$ or $x = -11$
15. $x = -10$ or $x = 2$
16. $x = 2$ or $x = -8$

squares. Of course, this previews the quadratic formula, since we end up with expressions in the form $\frac{b}{2} \pm \sqrt{\ldots}$. (There is no need to dwell on this now; we will return to it.)

COMPLETING THE SQUARE

It is worthwhile to bring out the Lab Gear for this section even if you have not used the blocks in a long time. Actually seeing and building the square that is being completed does wonders for students' understanding of the procedure. We limit ourselves to positive, even values of b in this section.

This was previewed in Chapters 5 and 6 in **Make a Square** Lab Gear activities and in Chapter 7, Lesson 5, when working with binomial squares.

Problem 17 is very important and deserves a full class discussion, with examples.

SQUARE PRACTICE

Here students get a chance to expand what they have learned to negative and odd values for b. There are many problems here, and you may want to spread this work out over a couple of days, perhaps combining it with puzzles or applications you may have skipped in previous lessons or chapters.

QUADRATIC EQUATIONS CHECKPOINT

Problems 30-33 can all be solved by completing the square, but we ask students to choose two to solve by factoring. (Problem 30 is certainly easier to solve by factoring. Problem 33 can be factored, but if students do not see it, let them use any method they choose.)

Problem 34 is easiest to solve by using the form $(x - p)(x - q)$. Problem 35 could be solved the same way, but students are more likely to try to reverse the process of completing the square.

Problems 36-37 could make for a good class discussion. For problem 36, an alternate approach goes like this:

$$\begin{aligned}&(x - (4 + \sqrt{3}))(x - (4 - \sqrt{3}))\\ &= (x - 4 - \sqrt{3})(x - 4 + \sqrt{3})\\ &= ((x - 4) - \sqrt{3})((x - 4) + \sqrt{3})\\ &= (x - 4)^2 - 3\end{aligned}$$

Problem 37, of course, requires no work, since the solutions can be read in problem 36, by the zero product property.

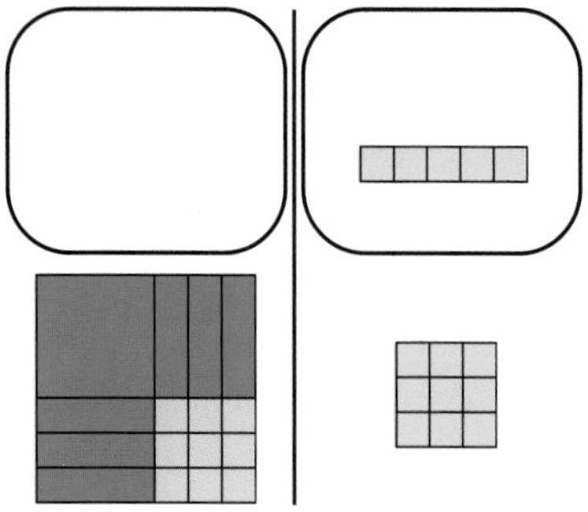

10. The right side can be simplified. The resulting equation is shown in the next figure. Write and solve this equation using the equal squares method. You should get two solutions.

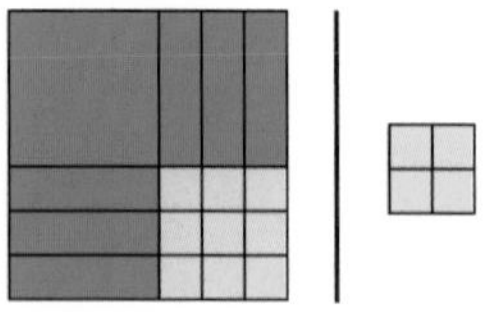

Complete the square to solve these equations. You will need to rearrange blocks and add or subtract the same amount on both sides in order to get equal squares.

11. $x^2 + 2x - 3 = 0$
12. $x^2 + 12x = -11$
13. $x^2 + 4x = 0$
14. $x^2 + 10x - 6 = 5$
15. $x^2 + 8x = 20$
16. $x^2 + 6x + 9 = 25$

17. **Generalization** Explain how to figure out what number to add to both sides of an equation of the form $x^2 + bx = k$ in order to get an equal squares equation. Use sketches and examples.

SQUARE PRACTICE

Solve these equations by completing the square. Show all your work. Include a sketch showing the equal squares.

18. $x^2 + 8x = 33$
19. $x^2 + 4x = 96$
20. $x^2 + 6x = 55$
21. $x^2 + 10x = 56$

Solve these equations. Show your work.

22. $x^2 - 8x = 33$
23. $x^2 - 4x = 96$
24. $x^2 - 4x = -96$
25. $x^2 + x = 6$

Solve these equations. Show your work. Give exact answers, then find decimal approximations to the nearest hundredth.

26. $x^2 - 8x + 3 = 0$
27. $x^2 - 5x - 8 = 0$
28. $x^2 - 4x + 1 = 6$
29. $x^2 - 7x - 4 = 0$

QUADRATIC EQUATIONS CHECKPOINT

Solve two of these equations by factoring (and the zero product property), and two by completing the square.

30. $x^2 + 18x = 0$
31. $x^2 + 5x = 2.75$
32. $x^2 + 2x - 8 = 0$
33. $x^2 + 7x + 12 = 0$

While it is somewhat cumbersome, completing the square is an important technique when dealing with quadratic expressions. Unlike factoring, you can use it to solve any quadratic equation. In addition, we will use completing the square repeatedly to get more understanding of quadratic functions and to develop more efficient ways to solve quadratic equations.

34. Find a quadratic equation having solutions 5 and -2.
35. Find a quadratic equation having solutions $2 + \sqrt{5}$ and $2 - \sqrt{5}$.
36. Multiply. $(x - (4 + \sqrt{3}))(x - (4 - \sqrt{3}))$ (Hint: Carefully remove the inside parentheses and then set up a three-by-three multiplication table.)
37. You should have obtained a quadratic expression in problem 36. Set it equal to zero, and solve the equation.

13.6 SOLUTIONS

17. Divide b in half. Square it to find the amount that must be added to complete the square. Examples will vary.

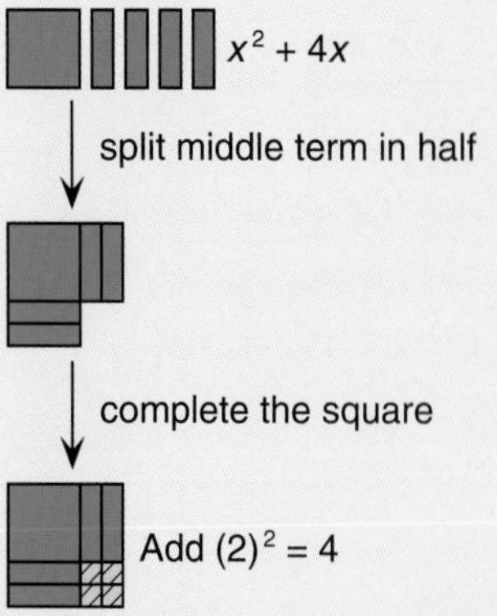

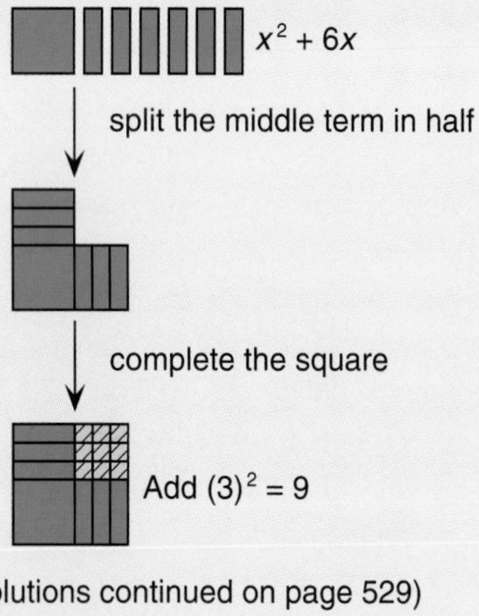

(Solutions continued on page 529)

LESSON

13.7 Finding the Vertex

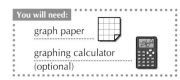

You will need:
- graph paper
- graphing calculator (optional)

In this lesson you will learn how to find the vertex of graphs of quadratic functions. This will help you solve quadratic equations.

TRANSLATING A PARABOLA

Graph these functions on the same pair of axes. Use graph paper, even if you have a graphing calculator. For each one:

a. Graph the parabola.

b. Indicate the axis of symmetry with a dotted line, and label it with its equation.

c. Label the vertex with its coordinates.

1. $y = x^2 - 5$ **2.** $y = x^2 - 4x + 4$

3. $y = x^2 - 4x - 1$

> **Definition:** The graphs obtained by shifting the location of a given graph without changing its shape are called *translations* of the original graph.

The graphs you drew in problems 1 through 3 are all translations of the graph of $y = x^2$.

4. Which of the graphs you drew in problems 1 through 3 was obtained by shifting $y = x^2$

a. horizontally? b. vertically?

c. both horizontally and vertically?

VERTEX FORM

The vertex of the graph of $y = x^2$ is (0, 0). When the graph is shifted, the vertex is (H, V).

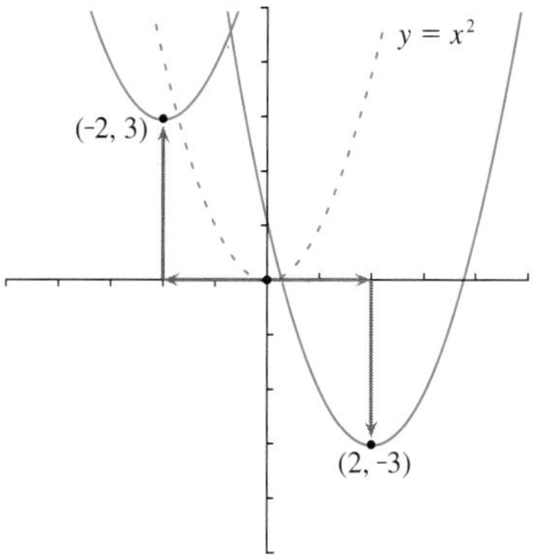

- If V is positive, the parabola $y = x^2$ has been shifted up; if V is negative, it has been shifted down.
- If H is positive, the parabola $y = x^2$ has been shifted to the right; if H is negative, it has been shifted to the left.

The graph of each function below is a translation of $y = x^2$. For each function:

a. Make a rough sketch of the graph.

b. Show the translation with arrows, as in the preceding figure.

c. Label the vertex with its coordinates.

(If you have a graphing calculator, use it for these problems. However, you should record the graphs with sketches on graph paper.)

5. $y = x^2 + 4$ **6.** $y = (x - 6)^2 - 4$

7. $y = (x + 6)^2 - 4$ **8.** $y = (x + 6)^2 + 4$

9. $y = (x - 6)^2$ **10.** $y = (x - 6)^2 + 4$

13.7 SOLUTIONS

1.

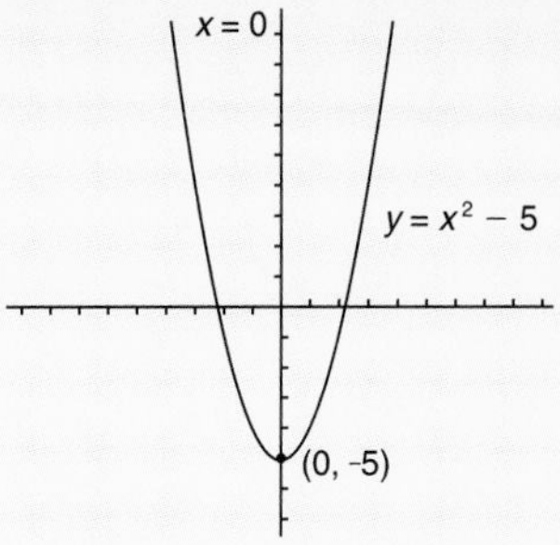

2.

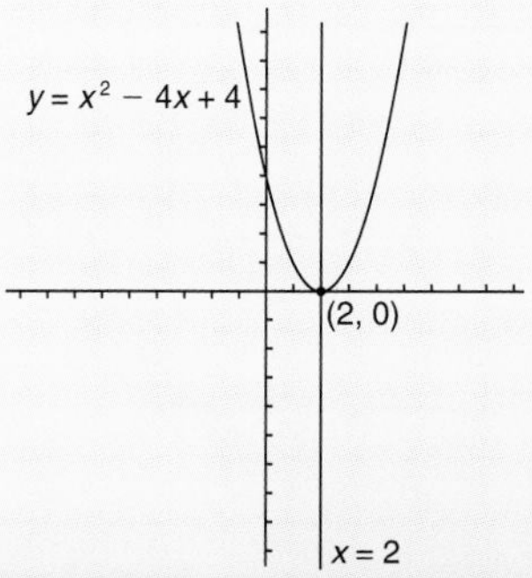

3.

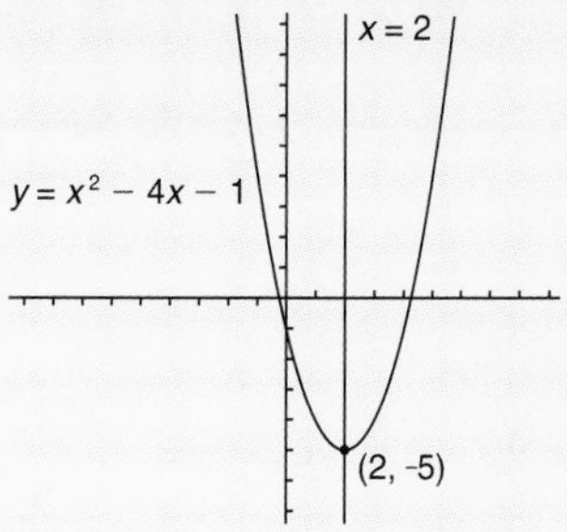

4. a. #2
b. #1
c. #3

▼ 13.7 Finding the Vertex

Core Sequence: 1-29

Suitable for Homework: 1-4, 29

Useful for Assessment: 12-14, 17-18, 21, 24, 26, 28-29

What this Lesson is About:
- Translations of the graph of $y = x^2$
- Vertex form and the parameters H and V
- The position of the vertex for the parabola with equation $y = x^2 + bx + c$
- Review of $y = (x - p)(x - q)$
- Preview of the quadratic formula

If you did not do **Thinking/Writing 12.B**, consider doing it before this lesson.

This lesson requires a great deal of both graphing and discussion. We recommend you do not assign any of it as homework, except perhaps the first section and the final Report. As usual for lessons of this type, if graphing calculators are not available, students should share the graphing work, or you should display the graphs on transparencies.

To motivate this lesson, you may remind students of the importance of the minimum or maximum of a function when solving applied optimization problems.

We limit ourselves to translations of the graph of $y = x^2$, or in other words to equations $y = ax^2 + bx + c$ with $a = 1$. We will address the more general case in Chapter 14. This lesson and the following serve as a preview of that chapter.

TRANSLATING A PARABOLA

If you have graphing calculators, you may precede this section by challenging the students to find equations of quadratics whose graphs are translations of $y = x^2$

a. horizontally only;

b. vertically only.

Of course this would have to be done before opening the book.

VERTEX FORM

The main point of this section is to familiarize students with the parameters H and V. (We use these letters instead of the more traditional h and k because they are easier to associate with the horizontal and vertical shifts.)

*T*he idea has been previewed in the context of absolute value graphs, in **Thinking/Writing 12.B**.

*P*roblem 13 is intended to bring students' attention to the signs preceding the *H* and the *V*. How they explain it is not important at this stage, so accept any answers here.

*P*roblem 14 helps preview Lesson 8, where we turn our attention to the *x*-intercepts. As it turns out, *H* has no influence on the number of *x*-intercepts, but *V* does.

SITTING ON THE *x*-AXIS

STRADDLING THE *y*-AXIS

*T*hese sections help prepare students to see how to see *H* and *V* in the quadratic expression if it is in standard form. They also prepare students to see the relationship between completing the square and the algebraic transformation of standard form into vertex form. (This will be done in Lesson 8.)

*T*he reason for the Lab Gear illustrations is to give an additional visual foundation to *H* and *V*. You may use blocks on the overhead when leading a discussion of these sections.

*I*n a way, both *H* and *V* are related to the arranging of Lab Gear blocks into a square, or if that is impossible, into an arrangement that is as close to a square as possible. *V* measures how far the quadratic expression is from being a perfect square. In fact it is the difference between *c* and the constant term in the corresponding perfect square trinomial.

11. Write the equation of a parabola that is a translation of $y = x^2$ and has

a. a vertical distance of 8 and a horizontal distance of -3 ($H = -3$, and $V = 8$);

b. a vertical distance of -4 and a horizontal distance of 5;

c. 6 units to the left and 5 units down;

d. 3 units to the right.

Earlier in this chapter you looked at equations of parabolas having the form $y = a(x - p)(x - q)$. That form was convenient for finding *x*-intercepts.

12. Explain why the equations in problems 5-10 are in a form that makes it convenient to find the vertex by just looking at the equation.

The quadratic function $y = (x - H)^2 + V$ is said to be in *vertex form*.

13. Explain why the *H* in the vertex form equation is preceded by a minus, while the *V* is preceded by a plus.

14. The graph of $y = x^2$ meets the *x*-axis in one point. Give examples of translations of $y = x^2$ that meet the *x*-axis in the given number of points. Include explanations of how you chose different values of *H* and/or *V*.

a. 0 points

b. 1 point

c. 2 points

SITTING ON THE *x*-AXIS

The quadratic function $y = x^2 + bx + c$ is said to be in *standard form.*

For problems 15-21, consider these five equations:

$y = x^2 + 6x$

$y = x^2 + 6x + 5$

$y = x^2 + 6x + 8$

$y = x^2 + 6x + 9$

$y = x^2 + 6x + 12$

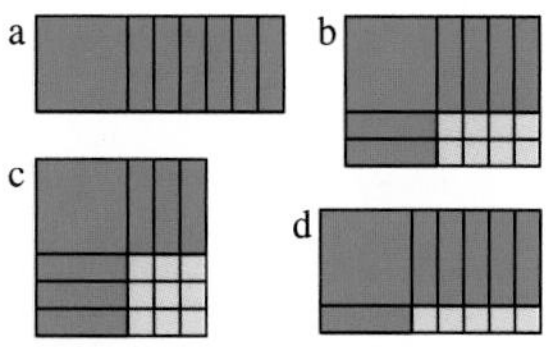

15. Match each Lab Gear figure with an equation from the list of five.

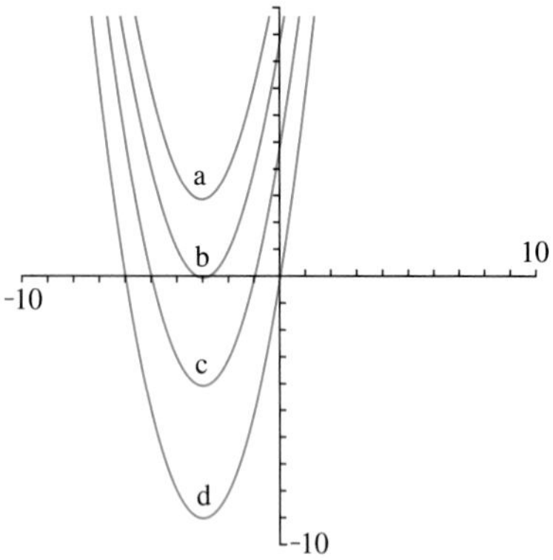

16. Match each parabola with an equation from the list of five.

17. Explain how to identify the parabolas with the help of:

a. the *y*-intercepts;

b. the Lab Gear figures, combined with the *x*-intercepts and the zero product property.

18. Explain why the graphs of perfect square quadratic equations have their vertices on the *x*-axis. (Hint: What is *V*?)

13.7 SOLUTIONS

5.

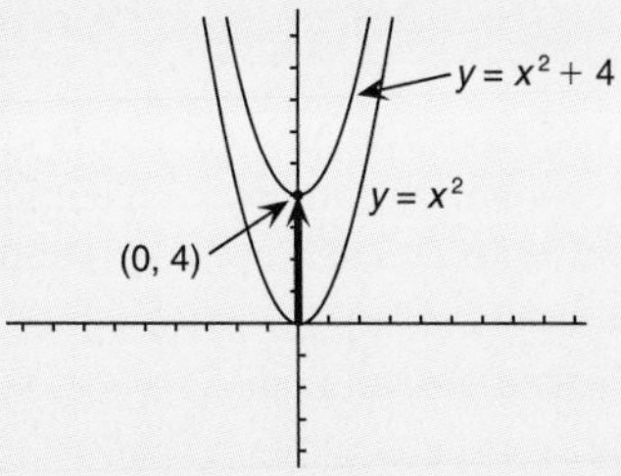

6.

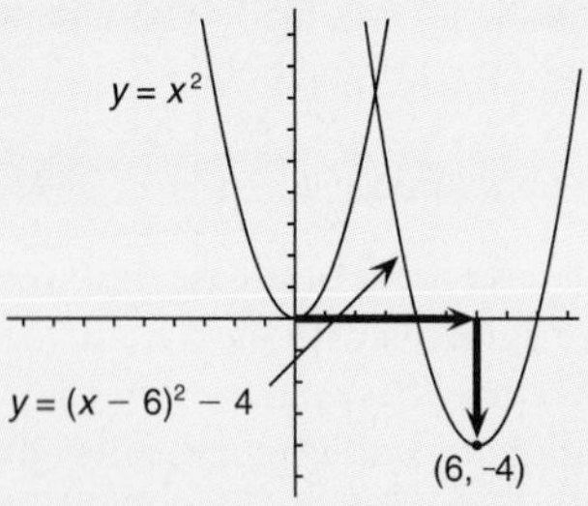

7.

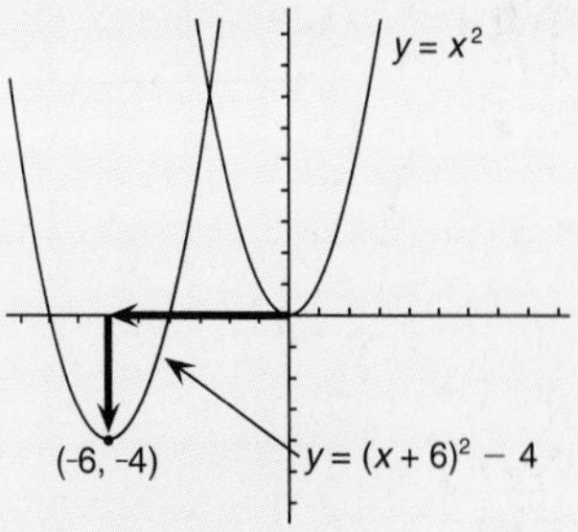

8.

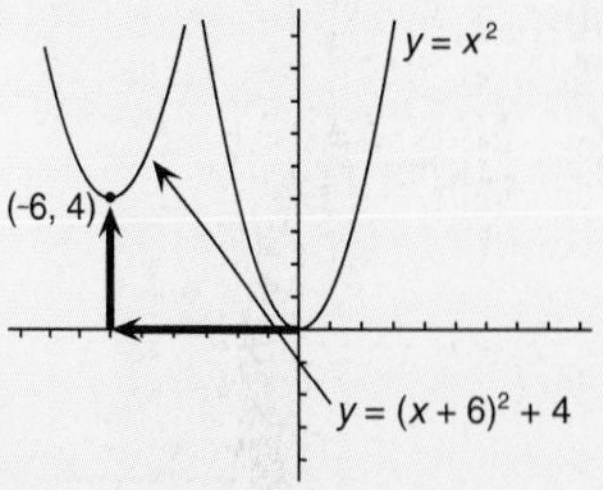

9.

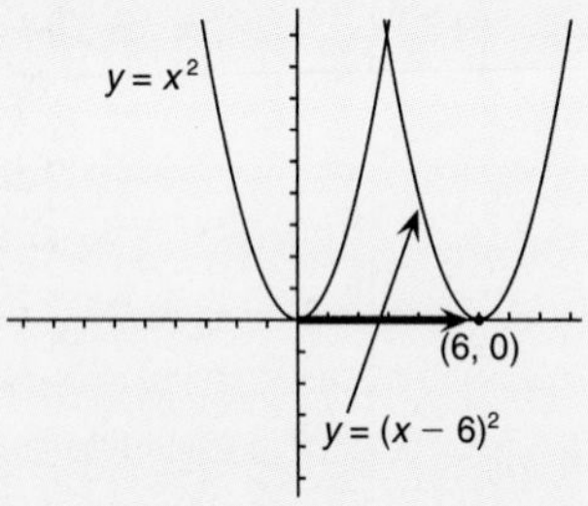

10.

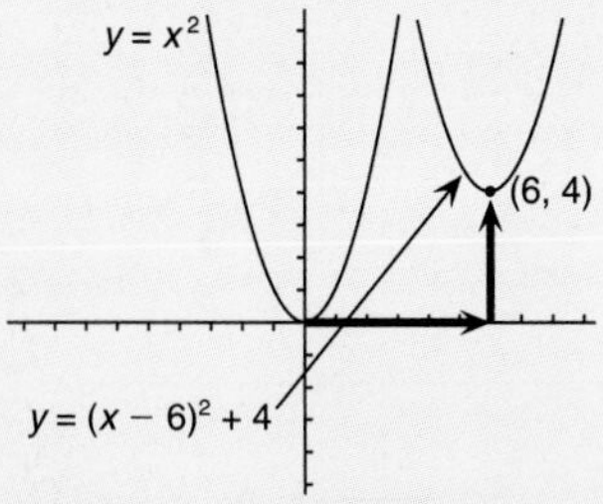

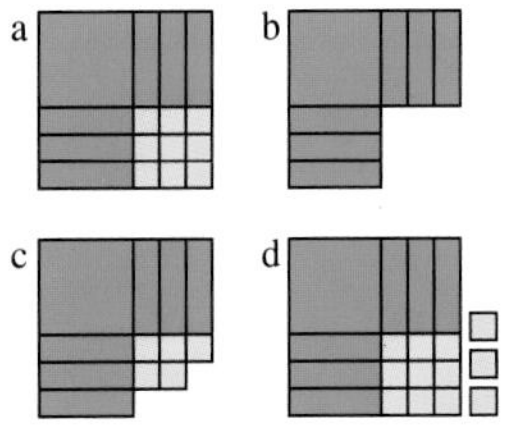

19. Match each Lab Gear figure with the corresponding equation from the five given earlier.

20. Find V for each equation of the five.

21. Explain how you can find V,

a. by looking at the Lab Gear figure;

b. by looking at the equation.

STRADDLING THE y-AXIS

For problems 22-27, consider these four equations:

$y = x^2 + 4$ $\qquad$ $y = x^2 + 2x + 4$

$y = x^2 + 4x + 4$ $\qquad$ $y = x^2 + 6x + 4$

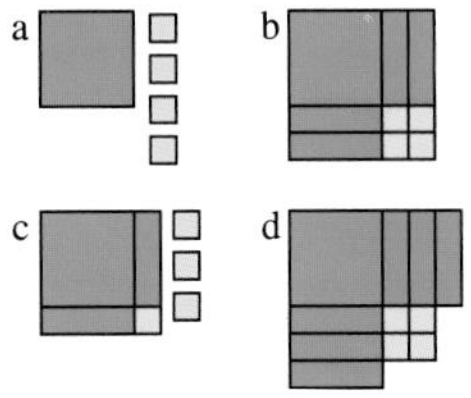

22. Match each Lab Gear figure with the corresponding equation from the four.

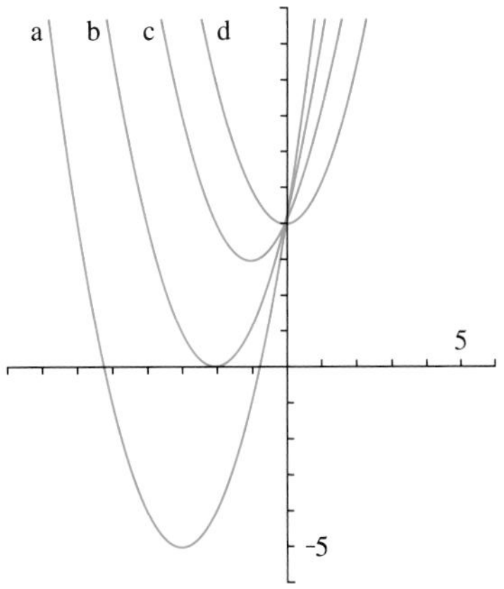

23. Match each equation with the correct graph.

24. Explain why the graphs of equations of the form $y = x^2 + c$ have their vertex on the y-axis. (Hint: What is H?)

25. Find H for each equation in the list of four.

26. Explain how you can find H,

a. by looking at the Lab Gear figure;

b. by looking at the equation.

27. a. What is H for any graph of an equation of the form $y = x^2 + 16x + c$?

b. What is H for any graph of an equation of the form $y = x^2 - 16x + c$?

28. **Generalization** Explain why, for graphs of equations in the form $y = x^2 + bx + c$, $H = -(b/2)$.

29. **Report** Write an illustrated report explaining how to find the vertex of a parabola if the equation is in:

a. the form $y = (x - p)(x - q)$;

b. vertex form; $\qquad$ c. standard form.

In problem 20 students should see that for a given b, the parameter V depends on c. In fact, for a given b, the perfect square requires a constant term equal to $(b/2)^2$. V represents how far the expression is from being a perfect square, so it is equal to $\left(\frac{b}{2}\right)^2 - c = \frac{b^2 - 4c}{4}$. Do not discuss this with your students now, except perhaps as an extra credit problem. (We will save this kind of discussion for Chapter 14.)

In problem 23 note that all the parabolas have the same y-intercept.

In problems 26 and 28 students may have trouble seeing that H is the opposite of the number of x's needed in each dimension to arrange the blocks into a (possibly incomplete) square. This makes H equal to the opposite of half of the coefficient of x, or $-(b/2)$. Note that c is not involved.

Class discussion is essential prior to assigning problem 29. Note that the Report includes a review of equations of the form $y = (x - p)(x - q)$, which was analyzed in Lesson 3.

13.7 SOLUTIONS

11. a. $y = (x + 3)^2 + 8$
b. $y = (x - 5)^2 - 4$
c. $y = (x + 6)^2 - 5$
d. $y = (x - 3)^2$

12. They are in the form $y = (x - H)^2 + V$, so the vertex can be read directly from the equation.

13. Answers will vary. This problem is intended to raise this issue for discussion. Students should have a better understanding of this idea after finishing this lesson.

14. Answers will vary. Sample answers are given. To get zero x-intercepts, use a parabola that opens upward and has $V > 0$. To get one x-intercept, use $V = 0$. To get two x-intercepts, use a parabola that opens upward and has $V < 0$. In all three cases, the choice of H does not affect the number of x-intercepts.
a. $y = (x - 5)^2 + 4$
b. $y = (x - 5)^2$
c. $y = (x - 5)^2 - 4$

15. a. $y = x^2 + 6x$
b. $y = x^2 + 6x + 8$
c. $y = x^2 + 6x + 9$
d. $y = x^2 + 6x + 5$

16. a. $y = x^2 + 6x + 12$
b. $y = x^2 + 6x + 9$
c. $y = x^2 + 6x + 5$
d. $y = x^2 + 6x$

17. a. The y-intercept is the value of c.
b. The Lab Gear figures show the factored form of the expression on the right side. This allows us to find the x-intercepts easily.

18. A perfect square can be written in the form $y = (x - H)^2$, so $V = 0$ and the vertex is $(H, 0)$.

19. a. $y = x^2 + 6x + 9$ $\quad$ c. $y = x^2 + 6x + 5$
b. $y = x^2 + 6x$ $\quad$ d. $y = x^2 + 6x + 12$

20. For $y = x^2 + 6x$, $V = -9$.
For $y = x^2 + 6x + 8$, $V = -1$.
For $y = x^2 + 6x + 12$, $V = 3$.
For $y = x^2 + 6x + 5$, $V = -4$.
For $y = x^2 + 6x + 9$, $V = 0$.

21. a. By looking at the Lab Gear figure, you can see how far it is from a perfect square. For example, if it needs 4 more one-blocks to make a perfect square, V must be -4. If it has 3 more one-blocks than is necessary to make a perfect square, V must be 3.

(Solutions continued on page 530)

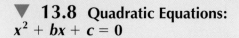

▼ 13.8 Quadratic Equations: $x^2 + bx + c = 0$

Core Sequence: 1-25

Suitable for Homework: 10-25

Useful for Assessment: 8-10, 13, 18

What this Lesson is About:

- Graphic preview of the quadratic formula
- Vertex methods of solving quadratics
- Preview of the quadratic formula
- Review of all quadratic solution methods to this point

This lesson applies what was learned in the last two lessons to the solving of quadratic equations. It serves to review all the work on this subject that we have done so far and to preview the next chapter.

FINDING THE x-INTERCEPTS

This is a Cartesian representation of the quadratic formula, at least in the special case where $a = 1$. We will return to work of this type in the general case in Chapter 14.

Problem 1 is challenging, but it provides a good review of the work of the past few lessons. It should definitely be worked on in groups and then perhaps as a class discussion.

LESSON 13.8

Quadratic Equations: $x^2 + bx + c = 0$

You will need:

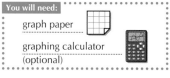

- graph paper
- graphing calculator (optional)

FINDING THE x-INTERCEPTS

Earlier in this chapter you learned how to find the vertex after finding the x-intercepts. In this section you will learn how to find the x-intercepts after finding the vertex.

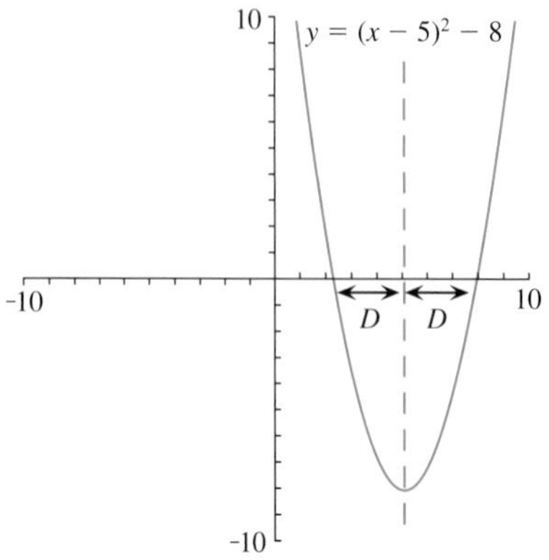

1. **Exploration** As the figure shows, the x-intercepts are equidistant from the axis of symmetry. How can you tell how far they are from it? That distance is indicated by D on the figure. Is it possible to know the value of D by looking at the equation? Try several values for H and V in equations having the form $y = (x - H)^2 + V$. Look for a pattern.

The graph of each of the following quadratic functions is a translation of $y = x^2$. For each function:

a. Make a rough sketch of the graph. Draw and label the axis of symmetry.
b. Find H and V.
c. Find exact values, not approximations, for the x-intercepts. (Set $y = 0$ and use the equal squares method.)
d. Find D, the distance of each x-intercept from the line of symmetry.

2. $y = x^2 - 9$
3. $y = (x - 5)^2 - 9$
4. $y = (x - 9)^2 - 5$
5. $y = (x + 9)^2 - 5$
6. $y = (x + 9)^2 + 5$
7. $y = (x - 9)^2$
8. 🔑 Use patterns in problems 2-7 to explain how D and V are related.

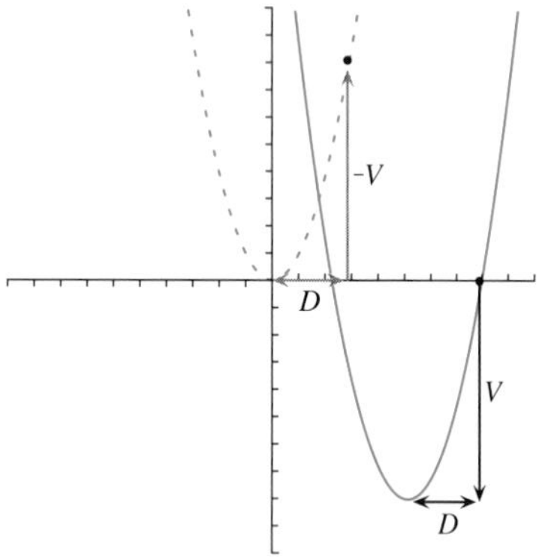

This figure shows D and V on a parabola that was translated from $y = x^2$. In this example, V was a negative number, and the translation was in a downward direction. The arrows representing D and V are also shown on the original

13.8 SOLUTIONS

1. Answers will vary. See the solution to #9.
2. a.

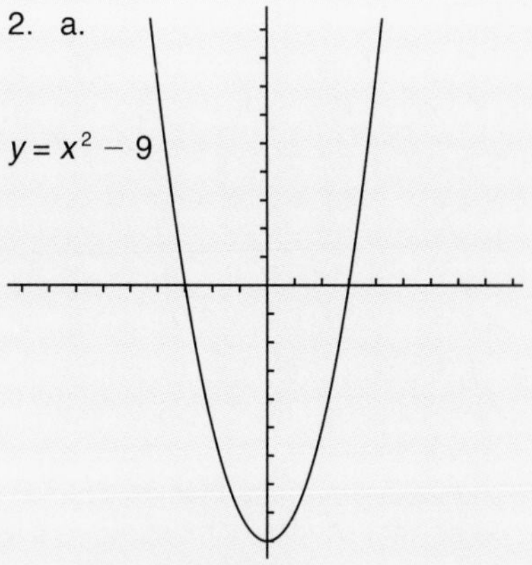

b. $H = 0$, $V = -9$
c. $x = 3$, $x = -3$
d. $D = 3$

3. a.

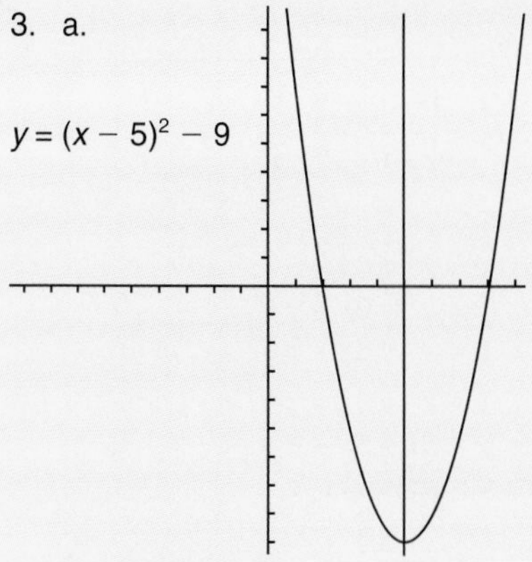

b. $H = 5$, $V = -9$
c. $x = 2$, $x = 8$
d. $D = 3$

4. a.

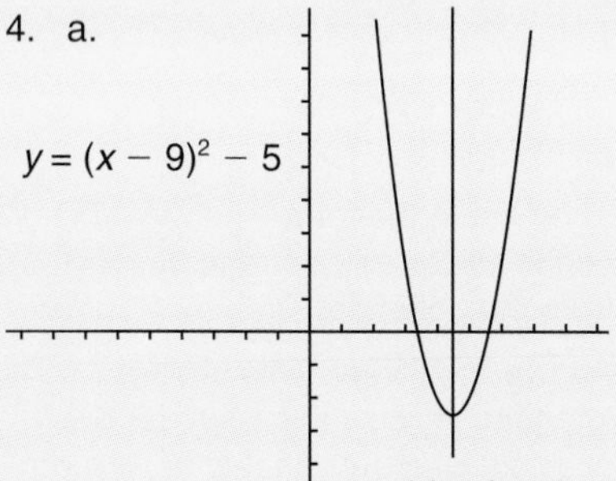

b. $H = 9$, $V = -5$
c. $x = 9 \pm \sqrt{5}$
Approximation: $x = 11.24$ or $x = 6.76$
d. $D = \sqrt{5}$

parabola. (On $y = x^2$, the direction of the arrow for V was reversed. What is shown is actually the opposite of V. This is indicated by the label $-V$. Since V is negative, $-V$ is positive.)

9. Use the figure to explain why $-V = D^2$, and therefore $D = \sqrt{-V}$.

10. **Summary** Explain why the x-intercepts, when they exist, are equal to $H - \sqrt{-V}$ and $H + \sqrt{-V}$.

SOLVING QUADRATIC EQUATIONS

One way to solve the equation $x^2 + bx + c = 0$ is to find the x-intercepts of $y = x^2 + bx + c$. You can use a graphing calculator to find an approximate answer that way. For a precise answer, you can use what you learned in the previous section about how to find the x-intercepts from the vertex.

Example: Solve $x^2 + 4x + 1 = 0$.

The solutions to the equation are the x-intercepts of $y = x^2 + 4x + 1$. We have shown that they are equal to $H - \sqrt{-V}$ and $H + \sqrt{-V}$. So all we have to do is find the values of H and V. There are two ways to do that, outlined as follows:

First method: Find H and V by rewriting the equation $y = x^2 + 4x + 1$ into vertex form. This can be done by completing the square.

$$y = x^2 + 4x + 1 = (\text{a perfect square}) - ?$$
$$y = x^2 + 4x + 1 = (x^2 + 4x + \ldots) - ?$$
$$y = x^2 + 4x + 1 = (x^2 + 4x + 4) - 3$$

11. a. Explain the algebraic steps in the three preceding equations.
b. Write $y = x^2 + 4x + 1$ in vertex form.
c. Give the coordinates of the vertex.

Second method: Find H and V by first remembering that $H = -(b/2)$. In this case, $b = 4$, so $H = -(4/2) = -2$. H is the x-coordinate of the vertex. Since the vertex is on the parabola, we can find its y-coordinate, V, by substituting -2 into the equation.

12. a. Find V. Check that it is the same value you found in problem 11.
b. Now that you have H and V, solve the equation.

13. What are the advantages and the disadvantages of each method? Explain.

For each equation, find H and V for the corresponding function. Then solve the equations. There may be zero, one, or two solutions.

14. $y = x^2 + 6x - 9$ **15.** $y = x^2 - 6x + 9$

16. $y = x^2 - 6x - 9$ **17.** $y = x^2 + 6x + 12$

18. How does the value of V for the corresponding function affect the number of solutions? Explain.

QUADRATIC EQUATIONS CHECKPOINT

As of now you know five methods to solve quadratic equations in the form $x^2 + bx + c = 0$. They are listed below.

I. *On Graphing Calculators:* Approximate solutions can be found by looking for the x-intercepts of $y = x^2 + bx + c$.

II. *Factoring* and the zero product property can sometimes be used.

III. *Equal Squares:* First complete the square, then use the equal squares method.

IV. *Using Vertex Form:* Complete the square to get into vertex form, then use the fact that the solutions are equal to $H - \sqrt{-V}$ and $H + \sqrt{-V}$.

V. *Using the Vertex:* Remember that for the function $y = x^2 + bx + c$, $H = -b/2$. Substitute into the equation to find V. Then use the fact that the solutions are $H - \sqrt{-V}$ and $H + \sqrt{-V}$.

Problems 2-8 guide students by experimentation to discover that $D = \sqrt{-V}$. Problem 9 provides a geometric argument based on the translation of the parabola $y = x^2$. The methods complement each other.

Problem 10 is a preliminary version of the quadratic formula and the key idea of this lesson.

SOLVING QUADRATIC EQUATIONS

The two methods presented here both depend on the previous section, but they also bring into play information from Lesson 6 (completing the square) and Lesson 7 (H expressed in terms of b; effect of V on the number of solutions).

13.8 SOLUTIONS

5. a.

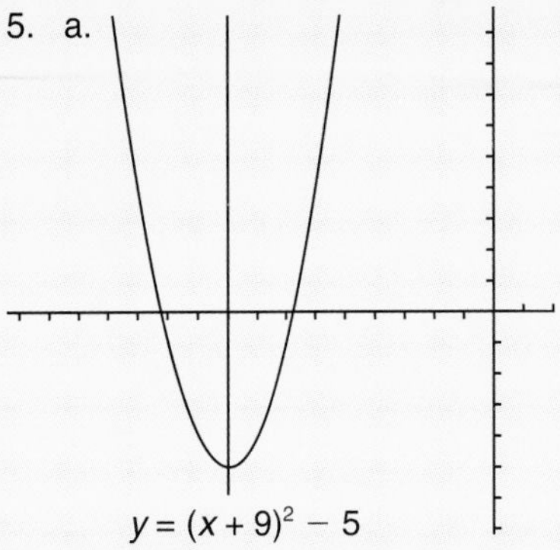

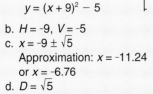

b. $H = -9$, $V = -5$
c. $x = -9 \pm \sqrt{5}$
Approximation: $x = -11.24$ or $x = -6.76$
d. $D = \sqrt{5}$

6. a.

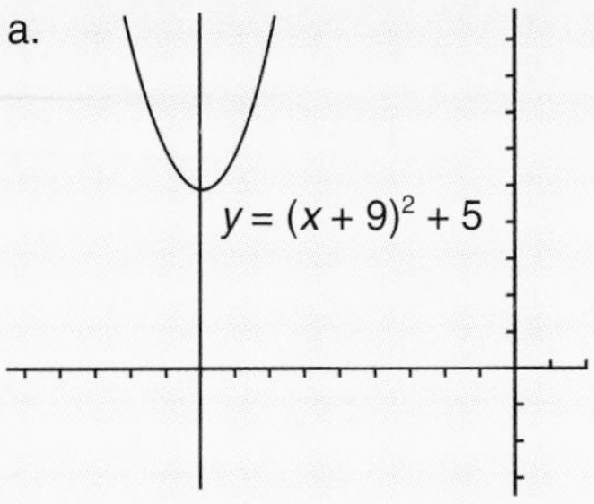

b. $H = -9$, $V = 5$
c. no x-intercepts
d. no x-intercepts

7. a.

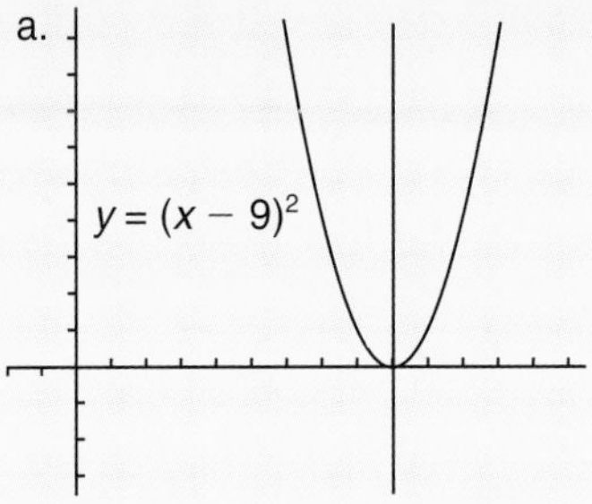

b. $H = 9$, $V = 0$
c. $x = 9$
d. $D = 0$

8. If $V \leq 0$, it seems to be true that $D = \sqrt{-V}$. If $V > 0$, then $\sqrt{-V}$ is undefined. However, in this case, there are no x-intercepts.

9. The graph is $y = x^2$. Since $-V = y$ and $D = x$, then $-V$ must equal D^2.

QUADRATIC EQUATIONS CHECKPOINT

*T*his is a review of all the work on quadratic equations so far.

Caution: In the next chapter you will learn another way to solve quadratic equations in the more general form $ax^2 + bx + c = 0$. Meanwhile you can solve them by dividing every term by a.

Example: Find an exact solution for:

$$x^2 - 6x + 2 = 0.$$

This does not seem to factor easily, which rules out Method II, and an exact solution is required, which rules out Method I. Luckily, Methods III-V always work on problems of this type. Using Method III:

$$x^2 - 6x + 2 = 0$$
$$(x^2 - 6x + 9) - 7 = 0$$
$$(x - 3)^2 - 7 = 0$$
$$(x - 3)^2 = 7$$

So $x - 3 = \sqrt{7}$ or $x - 3 = -\sqrt{7}$, and the solutions are $3 + \sqrt{7}$ and $3 - \sqrt{7}$.

19. Solve the same equation with Method IV or V. Check that you get the same answer.

Solve these equations. Use each of Methods II-V at least once. Give exact answers. The equations may have zero, one, or two solutions.

20. $x^2 - 4x + 2 = 0$

21. $x^2 + 8x - 20 = 0$

22. $x^2 - 14x + 49 = 0$

23. $x^2 - 16x + 17 = 0$

24. $x^2 + 9x = 0$

25. $x^2 + 9 = 0$

10. The axis of symmetry is $x = H$. To find the x-intercepts, move an equal distance to the right and to the left of the axis of symmetry. This distance is D. Since we showed above that $D = \sqrt{-V}$, the x-intercepts must be at $H \pm \sqrt{-V}$.

11. a. To write the equation in vertex form, first complete the square. Since $b = 4$, the amount needed to complete the square is $(4/2)^2$, or 4. This differs from the constant term by 3.
    b. $y = (x^2 + 4x + 4) - 3 = (x + 2)^2 - 3$
    c. The vertex is (-2, -3).

12. a. $y = (-2)^2 + 4(-2) + 1 = 4 - 8 + 1 = -4 + 1 = -3$
    This confirms the solution to #11c.
    b. The solutions are $H \pm \sqrt{-V} = -2 \pm \sqrt{3}$.

13. Answers will vary.

14. $H = -3$, $V = -18$, $x = 3 \pm 3\sqrt{2}$

15. $H = 3$, $V = 0$, $x = 3$

16. $H = 3$, $V = -18$, $x = 3 \pm 3\sqrt{2}$

17. $H = -3$, $V = 3$, no x-intercepts

18. For parabolas of the form $y = x^2 + bx + c$, the number of x-intercepts will be two if $V < 0$, one if $V = 0$, and none if $V > 0$.

19. By Method IV: $H = 3$ and $V = -7$, so the solutions are $3 \pm \sqrt{7}$.
    By Method V: $b = -6$. so $-b/2 = 3$. Substitute 3 into the expression $x^2 - 6x + 2$ to get V, which is -7. Hence the solutions are $H \pm \sqrt{-V} = 3 \pm \sqrt{7}$.

20. $x = 2 \pm \sqrt{2}$

21. $x = -10$, $x = 2$

22. $x = 7$

23. $8 \pm \sqrt{47}$

24. $x = 0$, $x = -9$

25. no solution

THINKING WRITING

13.B Find the Dimensions

You have 40 square feet of artificial turf and 28 feet of fencing. Is it possible to use all your materials to build a rectangular pen?

1. Find the dimensions of a rectangle having area 40 and perimeter 28. (Hint: You may use trial and error, tables, or graphs.)

Problems like this one can be solved using algebra. The first step is to write some equations.

$$\begin{cases} LW = 40 \\ 2L + 2W = 28 \end{cases}$$

2. Explain how these equations express the given conditions for the pen.

3. Divide all the terms in the second equation by two, to make it simpler.

4. Use algebra to show how the equations can be combined into one of the following equations having just one variable:

a. $L(14 - L) = 40$, or

b. $L + \frac{40}{L} = 14$

5. Explain the following steps to transform the equation in problem 4b:

$$L + \frac{40}{L} = 14$$
$$L^2 + 40 = 14L$$
$$L^2 - 14L + 40 = 0$$

6. a. Use algebra to transform the equation in problem 4a into the same equation.

b. Solve the equation.

7. a. The perimeter of a rectangle is 50. Write the area in terms of the length.

b. The area of a rectangle is 60. Write the perimeter in terms of the width.

For each problem, 8-11, find the dimensions of the rectangle. Show your work and explain your method. Include a sketch labeled with the variables you use.

8. A rectangle has area 180 and perimeter 64.

9. A rectangle has area 126. The length is 25 more than the width.

10. A rectangle has perimeter 35, and its length is 4 times its width.

11. A rectangle has area 25, and its length is 4 times its width.

12. Report Hyru has 40 square feet of artificial turf. Valerie has 40 feet of fencing. They decide to use all their materials to build a rectangular pen. Write them a letter explaining as many methods as possible for finding appropriate dimensions for such a pen.

13.B SOLUTIONS

1. Solution methods will vary. The dimensions of the rectangle are 4 and 10.
2. The first equation says that the length times the width is 40, which is a statement about area. The second equation says that twice the width plus twice the length is 28, which is a statement about perimeter.
3. The resulting equation is $L + W = 14$.
4. a. We can rewrite the equation in #3 as $W = 14 - L$. Then substitute $14 - L$ for W in the first equation to get $L(14 - L) = 40$.
   b. Solve for W in the first equation to get $W = 40/L$. Then substitute $40/L$ for W in the equation from #3 to get $L + 40/L = 14$.
5. First step: Multiply both sides by L. Second step: Subtract $14L$ from both sides.
6. a. Distribute the L: $14L - L^2 = 40$ Subtract 40 from both sides and rearrange terms: $-L^2 + 14L - 40 = 0$. Multiply both sides by -1: $L^2 - 14L + 40 = 0$
   b. One easy method for solving the equation is by factoring. $L^2 - 14L + 40 = 0$ $(L - 10)(L - 4) = 0$ $L = 10$ or $L = 4$
7. a. If the perimeter is 50, $L + W = 25$. The width can be written in terms of the length: $W = 25 - L$. Hence $A = L(25 - L)$.

(Solutions continued on page 530)

THINKING WRITING

13.B Find the Dimensions

Core Sequence: 1-12

Suitable for Homework: 1-12

Useful for Assessment: 12

What this Assignment is About:

- Using equations to solve a real-world problem
- Review of the substitution method for simultaneous equations
- Simultaneous equations that lead to a quadratic equation
- Equations involving fractions that lead to a quadratic equation

This lesson ties together the beginning and the end of the chapter, by applying equation-solving techniques to the perimeter/area problems of fencing and artificial turf.

Problem 1 is not too difficult to solve by trial and error. The main point of problems 2-7 is to prepare students to solve tougher ones like problems 8 and 12, in a problem where the final answer is already known.

If you have graphing calculators, you may approach problems like 1, 8, and 12 in other ways.

- Graphing length as a function of width in two ways, one based on the area equation, and the other on the perimeter equation—The intersection of the graphs provides the answer.
- Graphing the perimeter as a function of length, and perimeter as the given number—The intersection of the graphs provides the answer.
- Finally, graphing the area as a function of length, and the area as the given number—The intersection of the graphs provides the answer.

Essential Ideas

PERIMETER AND AREA

1. A rectangle has width $2x + 5$ and length $3x + 1$. What is the area, when the perimeter is 30?

2. The width of a rectangle is five less than the length. Write a formula for:

a. the length in terms of the width;

b. the width in terms of the length;

c. the area in terms of the width;

d. the perimeter in terms of the length.

3. The perimeter of a rectangle is 50.

a. Find the dimensions that will give an area of 46.

b. Find the dimensions that will give the largest possible area.

4. The circumference of a circle is 50. What is the area? (Hint: First find the radius.) Is it bigger or smaller than the area of the largest possible rectangle having perimeter 50?

5.

a. Find the dimensions and the area of the largest possible rectangle that can be made with P feet of fencing.

b. Find the area of the circle that is surrounded by P feet of fencing. (Hint: Start by expressing the radius in terms of P.)

c. Which has greater area, the rectangle or the circle? Explain.

FARES

6. A bus company takes people from a small town to and from a large city where they work. The fare is $4.00 per day, round trip. The company wants to raise its fare and has done a survey to find out if this will cause people to stop riding the bus. They estimate that for every 50 cents that they raise the fare, they will lose approximately 1000 customers. They now have 14,000 customers. Do you think they should raise their fare? If so, by how much? Explain.

7. A spaceship company charges its customers a basic fare of $50 million per light year for trips outside the solar system. However, to encourage long trips, it reduces the fare by $1 million for every light year a customer travels. For example, if a tourist travels five light years, her fare is reduced by $5 million. Her cost will be $45 million per light year for five light years, or $225 million. What is the most a person could ever pay for a trip on this spaceship? Explain.

PARABOLAS AND INTERCEPTS

8. Which graphs have the same x-intercepts? Explain.

a. $y = x(8 - x)$ b. $y = 2x(8 - x)$

c. $y = x(2 - x)$ d. $y = x(8 - 2x)$

e. $y = 3x(8 - 4x)$ f. $y = x(16 - 2x)$

9. Graph the following three functions on the same axes. Label x-intercepts, y-intercept, and the vertex of each parabola.

a. $y = x(25 - 2x)$ b. $y = x(25 - x)$

c. $y = 2x(25 - x)$

10. Pick one of the three functions in problem 9 and describe a real situation that would lead to the function. Tell what the variables represent. Make up at least two questions about the real situation that could be answered by looking at the graph you made in problem 9.

SOLUTIONS

1. $2(2x + 5) + 2(3x + 1) = 30$
   $4x + 10 + 6x + 2 = 30$
   $10x + 12 = 30$
   $x = 1.8$
   Hence the width is 8.6 and the length is 6.4, so the area is 55.04.
2. a. $L = W + 5$
   b. $W = L - 5$
   c. $A = W(W + 5)$
   d. $P = 2(L - 5) + 2L = 2L - 10 + 2L = 4L - 10$
3. Solution methods will vary.
   a. length = 23, width = 2
   b. A square of side 12.5 will give the largest area, which is 156.25.
4. $C = 2\pi r$
   $2\pi r = 50$
   $r = 25/\pi$
   Area $= \pi(25/\pi)^2 = 625/\pi = 198.94$ approximately
   This area is larger than that of the largest rectangle, whose area was found in #3b.
5. a. The rectangle with largest area will be a square with side $P/4$ and area $P^2/16$.
   b. The circle will have radius $P/2\pi$ and area $\pi(P/2\pi)^2 = \pi P^2/(4\pi^2) = P^2/(4\pi)$.
   c. To answer this we must compare $P^2/16$ with $P^2/(4\pi)$. The expression with the smaller denominator has the larger value. Since $16 = 4^2$, it is larger than 4π. Therefore, the area of the circle is larger.
6. One approach is to make a table. The table shows that the gross profit increases until the fare is $5.50. Then it begins to decrease.

Fare Increase	Fare	# of Customers	Gross Profit
$0	$4	14,000	$56,000
$0.50	$4.50	13,000	$58,500
$1.00	$5.00	12,000	$60,000
$1.50	$5.50	11,000	$60,500
$2.00	$6.00	10,000	$60,000
$2.50	$6.50	9,000	$58,500
$3.00	$7.00	8,000	$56,000
$3.50	$7.50	7,000	$52,500

Another approach is to write an equation for the gross profit (P) as a function of the number of $0.50 increases ($x$). The graph of the equation $P = (4 + 0.50x)(14{,}000 - 1000x)$ has x-intercepts at $x = -8$ and $x = 14$. The x-coordinate of the vertex is $(-8 + 14)/2 = 3$. This means that the maximum profit would occur with 3 fare increases of $0.50. This would

11. Write the equation of a parabola having x-intercepts at:
   a. (0, 0) and (2, 0); b. (-4, 0) and (0, 0);
   c. (-4, 0) and (1, 0).

12. Compare the graphs of $y = 4x(x - 1)$, $y = 2x(2x - 2)$, and $y = x(4x - 4)$. Explain what you observe.

13. a. Find the equation of a parabola that has no x-intercepts.
   b. Find the equation of a parabola that has only one x-intercept.
   c. Find the equation of a graph that has three x-intercepts.

14. How many x-intercepts? Explain.
   a. $y = 2x + 1$ b. $y = x(4 - x)$
   c. $y = x^2 + 1$ d. $y = 3(x + 1)^2$

15. How many x-intercepts? Explain.
   a. $y = 8x - x^2$ b. $y = x^2 - x + 2$
   c. $y = 2x^2 + 12x + 18$

16. How many x-intercepts? Explain.
   a. $y = a(x - H)^2$ b. $y = a(x - H)^2 + 3$
   c. $y = a(x - H)^2 - 3$

THE VERTEX

17. a. Write the equation of any parabola that crosses the x-axis at (2, 0) and (4, 0).
   b. Write the equation of any other parabola that crosses the x-axis at these two points.
   c. Find the coordinates of the vertices of both parabolas. Compare them. What is the same? What is different?

18. a. Write the equation of any parabola that crosses the x-axis at (0, 0) and (3, 0).
   b. Write the equation of a parabola that crosses the x-axis at (0, 0) and (3, 0) and has 9 as the y-coordinate of its vertex.
   c. Find an equation of any other parabola that has 9 as the y-coordinate of its vertex.
   d. Compare the three equations. What is the same? What is different?

19. Write three equivalent equations for the parabola that crosses the x-axis at (2, 0) and (0, 0) and has 6 as the y-coordinate of its vertex.

20. Find the equation of a parabola having:
   a. intercepts: (6, 0), (-2, 0), (0, 4);
   b. vertex (-1, -4); one intercept at (1, 0);
   c. vertex (-2, 0); one intercept at (0, 2).

21. Find the coordinates of the vertex of the graph of:
   a. $y = -2(x - 5)(x + 8)$;
   b. $y = (x + 3)^2 - 6$;
   c. $y = x^2 + 4x - 7$.

22. Find the equation of a parabola that has a vertex having the following coordinates:
   a. (2, 8)   b. (8, 64)

23. 💡
   a. Write the equation of a parabola that has x-intercepts $(p, 0)$ and $(-r, 0)$. How can you check that your answer is correct?
   b. What are the coordinates of the vertex?

QUADRATIC EQUATIONS

24. Solve.
   a. $(x - 8)^2 + 6 = 0$ b. $(x - 8)^2 - 6 = 0$
   c. $(x + 8)^2 + 6 = 0$ d. $(x + 8)^2 - 6 = 0$

Solve.

25. $x^2 - 6 = 0$ 26. $x^2 - 6x = 0$

27. $x^2 - 6x = -9$ 28. $x^2 + 6x = -9$

29. $x^2 + 6x - 4 = 0$ 30. $-4x + 2 = -x^2$

31. $-x^2 = 8x + 7$ 32. $8x - x^2 = 7$

◆ SOLUTIONS

result in a fare of \$5.50, which is the same result obtained by making a table. If the bus company's only objective is to maximize profit, they should raise the fare to \$5.50. However, they may want to maximize the number of people they serve and figure out ways to cut costs. Maximum profit should probably not be their sole criterion for making decisions.

7. One approach is to make a table.

Trip Distance (Light-years)	Fare Reduction (Millions)	Fare per Light Year (Millions)	Total Fare (Millions)
1	\$1	\$49	\$49
5	\$5	\$45	\$225
10	\$10	\$40	\$400
14	\$14	\$36	\$504
16	\$16	\$34	\$544
18	\$18	\$32	\$576
20	\$20	\$30	\$600
22	\$22	\$28	\$616
25	\$25	\$25	\$625
26	\$26	\$24	\$624
27	\$27	\$23	\$621

Another approach is to write the fare (F) as a function of the trip distance (d). $F = (50 - d)d$. The graph of this function is a parabola, whose axis of symmetry is at $d = 25$. The maximum fare is \$625 million dollars, a real bargain.

8. The graphs of $y = x(8 - x)$, $y = 2x(8 - x)$, and $y = x(16 - 2x)$ all have the x-intercepts (0, 0) and (8, 0). They can all be written in the form $y = ax(8 - x)$. The graphs of $y = x(2 - x)$ and $y = 3x(8 - 4x)$ have the same x-intercepts because they can both be written in the form $y = ax(2 - x)$.

(Solutions continued on page 531)

Chapter 14
RATIOS AND ROOTS

Overview of the Chapter

*T*his chapter begins and ends with problems involving similar rectangles. The dynamic rectangle problems in Lesson 1 can be solved without too much trouble. The following two lessons concentrate on algebraic fractions. Then in Lessons 4-7 we continue the work on quadratics that has been started in Chapter 13. Finally, with Lesson 8 and **Thinking/Writing 14.B** we see applications of fractions and quadratics.

*M*uch of the chapter covers somewhat technical work with algebraic fractions and the quadratic formula. You may prefer to postpone some of this material until a more advanced course. If so, you can still try to do Lessons 1, 8, and **Thinking/Writing 14.A** and **14.B**. These lessons are applications that can be done with other techniques, such as the use of graphing calculators to solve equations, or with the use of the quadratic formula as a black box.

*T*he last section of Lesson 7 also does not require a heavy technical background. It provides an interesting end-of-course discussion.

*O*n the other hand, if you successfully covered Lessons 6-8 in Chapter 13, you will probably want to try to assign as much of this chapter as you have time for, as it completes the work we started there. The quadratic formula constitutes the endpoint of the chapter and, in a sense, of the book. This is because it affords the opportunity to do some interesting work that ties together many ideas in the course: interpretation of intercepts, geometric connections, equation solving, real-world applications, and so on.

CHAPTER 14

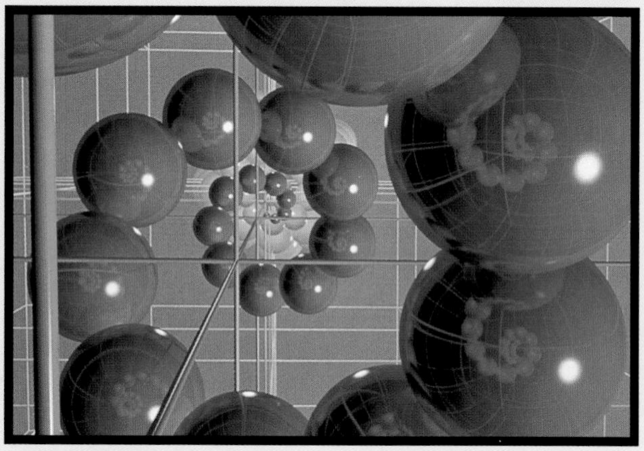

A futuristic spiral

Coming in this chapter:

Exploration Make a paper rectangle that is similar to the smaller rectangle obtained by the following method:

a. cutting the original rectangle in two equal parts;
b. cutting off a square from the original rectangle.

What is the exact ratio of length to width for each of your rectangles?

RATIOS AND ROOTS

1. New Uses for Tools:

- Cartesian graphs to help derive the quadratic formula

2. Algebra Concepts Emphasized:

- Equivalent algebraic fractions
- Simplifying algebraic fractions
- Common denominators
- Solving quadratic equations
- The role of the parameter a
- Finding the vertex
- Derivation of the quadratic formula
- Completing the square
- Number of x-intercepts of a quadratic function
- Number of solutions of a quadratic equation
- The discriminant
- The sum and product of the solutions to a quadratic equation
- The golden ratio

3. Algebra Concepts Reviewed:

- Similarity and proportional thinking
- Square roots
- Division by zero
- Fractions
- Eliminating fractions from equations
- Equal squares
- Geometric sequences
- Fibonacci-like sequences
- Distance, rate, time

4. Algebra Concepts Previewed:

- From natural numbers to complex numbers
- Limits

5. Problem-Solving Techniques:

- Trial and error
- Using an equation

6. Connections and Context:

- Art and design
- Optimization of area
- Area computation techniques
- Diagonal of a square
- Up and down stream, head wind and tail wind problems

14.1 Rectangle Ratios

Core Sequence: 1-13

Suitable for Homework: 11-20

Useful for Assessment: 6-7, 11, 13-14

What this Lesson is About:

- Review of similarity
- Review of square roots
- Connection to art and design
- More work with reciprocals

HALF RECTANGLES

THE INTERNATIONAL PAPER STANDARD

Problem 1 is intended to provide an opportunity to review the idea of similar rectangles. The diagonal test for similar rectangles, as well as the calculator division test, were introduced in Chapter 3, Lesson 12.

Students may want to try to do problem 2 by using trial and error with actual pieces of paper. If anyone finds a reasonably accurate answer that way, have him or her show the procedure to the class. Most likely, this problem will be solved by the method suggested in the hint: trial and error on a calculator. By problem 7, however, students should be able to see that an exact answer can be obtained by solving an equation.

Note that problem 5 could be tedious. The work should be distributed among the members of a group.

LESSON 14.1

Rectangle Ratios

You will need:

scissors

graph paper

HALF RECTANGLES

1. Take two identical rectangular pieces of paper. Fold one in half. Place it on top of the other piece. Is the folded half-rectangle similar to the original rectangle? Check with the diagonal test.

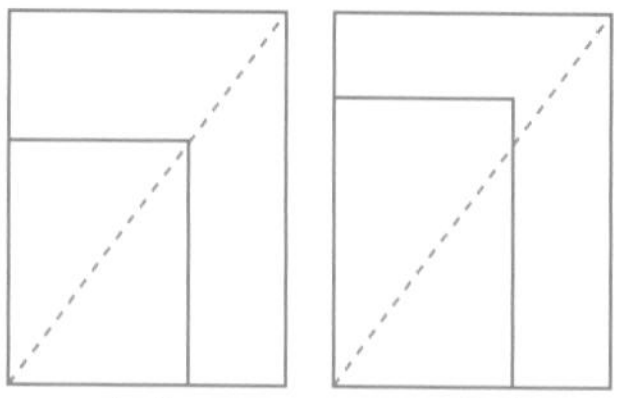

2. **Exploration** Make a paper rectangle, such that the rectangle you get by folding it in half is similar to the original rectangle. What are the dimensions of your rectangle? (Hint: Remember that if two rectangles are similar, their length-to-width ratio must be the same. You may use trial and error on your calculators for different sizes.)

3. a. Sketch a 16-unit-by-12-unit rectangle on graph paper. What is the length-to-width ratio?

b. Divide the rectangle in half to get one having length 12 and width 8. (The width of the original rectangle becomes the length of the new rectangle.) What is the length-to-width ratio?

c. Continue to divide the rectangle in half, calculating the ratio of length to width. Make a table like this one to record your data.

Length	Width	*l/w* Ratio
16	12	—
12	8	—

4. Describe any patterns you notice in your table.

5. a. Repeat problem 2 for three more rectangles. Keep a careful record of your data in tables. Look for patterns.

b. Find some rectangles for which the length-to-width ratios do not change when you cut them in half.

6. A rectangular sheet of paper is 1 foot wide and x feet long. It is cut into two rectangles, each of which is $(1/2)x$ feet wide and 1 foot long.

a. Illustrate this in a diagram.

b. What is the length-to-width ratio in the original rectangle?

c. What is the length-to-width ratio in each of the two new rectangles?

d. If the rectangles are similar, we can write an equation setting the original ratio equal to the new ratio. Do this, and find the value of x. Show your calculations.

7. **Report** Summarize your findings from problems 1 through 6. Include sketches and examples. Describe any patterns you noticed. For the rectangles you found in problem 5b, what was the common ratio? What was the common ratio for the rectangle you found in problem 2?

14.1 SOLUTIONS

1. Answers will vary.
2. Answers will vary.
3. a. 4/3

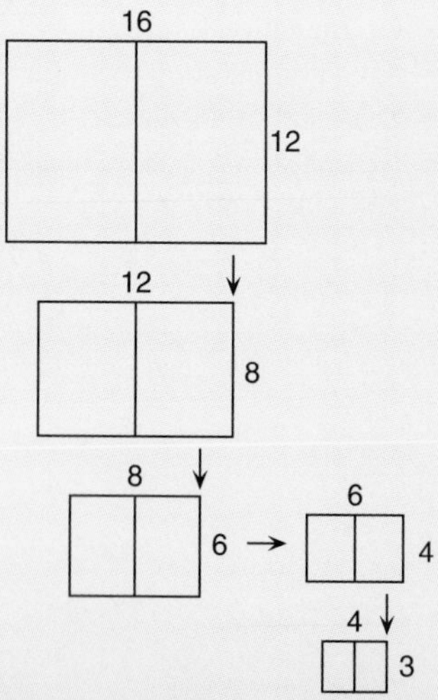

b. 3/2

c.

Length	Width	*l/w* Ratio
16	12	4/3
12	8	3/2
8	6	4/3
6	4	3/2
4	3	4/3

4. Answers will vary. The most striking pattern is probably that the ratios alternate between 4/3 and 3/2.
5. a. Answers will vary.
   b. Answers will vary, but all will have a length-to-width ratio of $\sqrt{2}$.
6. a.

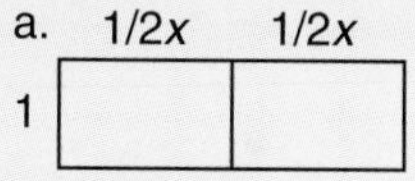

b. x to 1

c. 1 to $0.5x$

d. $\frac{x}{1} = \frac{1}{0.5x}$

$0.5x^2 = 1$

$x = \sqrt{2}$

7. Reports will vary. All rectangles for which the length-to-width ratio does not change will have a length-to-width ratio of $\sqrt{2}$.

THE INTERNATIONAL PAPER STANDARD

In 1930 an international standard was established for paper sizes, called the *A-series*. The basic size is A0, which is one square meter in area. If you fold it in half, you get paper of size A1. You can fold A1 in half to get A2, fold A2 in half to get A3, etc. The dimensions of A0 were chosen so that *all paper sizes in the series are similar to each other and to A0.*

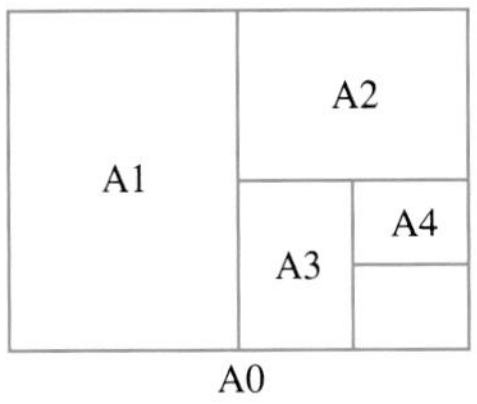

8. Find the dimensions, to the nearest millimeter, of A0 and A1.

DYNAMIC RECTANGLES

The special rectangles you discovered in the previous section each have the property that half of the rectangle is similar to the whole. They are examples of a group of rectangles, called *dynamic rectangles*, that are very useful to artists and designers. Dynamic rectangles have the property that when you cut them into a certain number of equal parts, each of the parts is similar to the whole.

The rectangle below is divided into three parts, each one of which is similar to the original rectangle.

We can express this similarity by writing two equal ratios.

$$\frac{L}{W} = \frac{W}{\frac{1}{3}L}$$

Multiplying both sides of the equation by W:

$$W\left(\frac{L}{W}\right) = W\left(\frac{W}{\frac{1}{3}L}\right)$$

$$L = \frac{W^2}{\frac{1}{3}L}$$

and then by $\frac{1}{3}L$, we get the equation:

$$\frac{1}{3}L^2 = W^2$$

9. Show how to find L, the length of the original rectangle, if the width is the following:

a. 1 b. 2 c. W

10. What is the ratio of length to width in each of the rectangles in problem 9?

Dynamic rectangles are named for their ratio of length to width. These two rectangles are both called $\sqrt{5}$ rectangles because the ratio of length to width in each of them is $\sqrt{5}$.

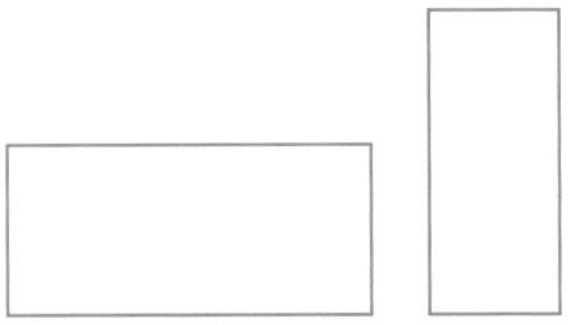

11. Into how many equal parts would you divide a $\sqrt{5}$ rectangle in order to make each of the parts similar to the original rectangle? Explain how you figured this out, showing your work.

Students may need help with the symbol manipulation in problem 6d. Stress that the equation allows us to find an exact value for the ratio ($\sqrt{2}$). In problem 8, students must apply the results of problem 6d. They can use trial and error and their calculators, and/or set up an equation. The unknown is not the same as in problem 6. Instead of 1, the short side of the rectangle should now be x, and the long side $x\sqrt{2}$. Students may be intimidated by the need to take the square root of a square root, but with a calculator it's straightforward.

DYNAMIC RECTANGLES

This section generalizes the work in the previous ones.

For problem 14, one good book about the connection between art and mathematics is *Universal Patterns: The Golden Relationship Book 1*, by Martha Boles and Rochelle Newman (Pythagorean Press, 1990).

14.1 S O L U T I O N S

8. Solution strategies will vary. An algebraic solution is given.
   $LW = 1$
   $W = 1/L$
   $\frac{L}{1/L} = \frac{1/L}{0.5L}$
   $0.5L^2 = 1/L^2$
   $L^4 = 2$
   $L = 1.189$ approximately
   Since the area is one square meter, $W = 0.841$ approximately.
   The dimensions of A0 are approximately 118.9 cm by 84.1 cm. The dimensions of A1 are approximately 84.1 cm by 59.5 cm.
9. Using the equation $(1/3)\,L^2 = W^2$, we can conclude that $L = \sqrt{3}W$.
   a. $L = \sqrt{3}$
   b. $L = 2\sqrt{3}$
   c. $L = \sqrt{3}W$
10. $\sqrt{3}$
11. Divide it into five parts. An algebraic argument is given.
    $\frac{L}{W} = \frac{W}{0.20L}$
    $0.2L^2 = W^2$
    $L^2 = 5W^2$
    $L = \sqrt{5}W$

DISCOVERY *INTERESTING NUMBERS*

Let students try to solve these problems by trial and error with their calculators. If some students write an equation and solve it, have them compare their solutions with those who used trial and error. The answer to both problems is the golden ratio, which will be the subject of Lesson 8.

12. A rectangle is divided into seven parts, each of which is similar to the original rectangle.

a. Give possible dimensions (length and width) for the rectangle.

b. Give another set of possible dimensions.

c. What is the ratio of length to width?

13. A rectangle having width one unit is divided into n equal parts, each of which is similar to the original rectangle.

a. To find the length x of the original rectangle, Tara wrote:

$$\frac{x}{1} = \frac{1}{\frac{1}{n}x}$$

Explain why Tara wrote this proportion.

b. Solve this equation for x.

c. Summarize your results in words.

14. Research Many artists and designers use mathematics. Do some research to find out why dynamic rectangles are so useful in art and design. Then make your own design based on dynamic rectangles.

DISCOVERY *INTERESTING NUMBERS*

15. Find a number that is one more than its reciprocal.

16. Find a number that is one less than its square.

REVIEW *NUMBERS AND THEIR RECIPROCALS*

If possible, find or estimate the number described. Explain how you found it. (If there is more than one number that fits the description, try to find as many as possible.)

17. The number equals its reciprocal.

18. The number is four more than its reciprocal.

19. The number is one more than twice its reciprocal.

20. The number does not have a reciprocal.

14.1 SOLUTIONS

12. a. $W = 1$ and $L = \sqrt{7}$
 b. $W = 2$ and $L = 2\sqrt{7}$
 c. $\sqrt{7}$

13. a. The rectangle was divided into n equal parts, each of which has length 1 and width x/n. Its length-to-width ratio is the same as that of the original rectangle.
 b. $x^2 = n$
 $x = \sqrt{n}$
 c. The rectangle is a $\sqrt{n}$ rectangle. The length-to-width ratio for the original rectangle and its subdivisions is $\sqrt{n}$.

14. No solution is necessary.

15. Solve the equation $1 + 1/x = x$, or use trial and error. Solution: $x = \frac{1 \pm \sqrt{5}}{2}$

16. Solve the equation $x^2 - 1 = x$ or use trial and error. Solution: $x = \frac{1 \pm \sqrt{5}}{2}$

17. Solve the equation $x = 1/x$; solution: $x = 1$ or -1

18. Solve the equation $x = 4 + 1/x$; solution: $2 \pm \sqrt{5}$

19. Solve the equation $1 + 2/x = x$; solution: $x = -1$ or 2

20. 0

LESSON 14.2

Simplifying Algebraic Fractions

You will need:

Lab Gear 

ADDING OR SUBTRACTING EQUAL AMOUNTS

1. **Exploration** What happens if you add or subtract equal amounts to or from the numerator and the denominator of a fraction? How can you tell whether the value of the fraction will increase, decrease, or remain the same? Make up several examples to see what happens, then make a generalization.

To model fractions with the Lab Gear, you can use the workmat turned on its side. Instead of representing an equals sign, the straight line in the middle now represents the fraction bar.

Edith and Anna modeled the fraction $\frac{4x + 16}{4x}$ with the Lab Gear, as shown below.

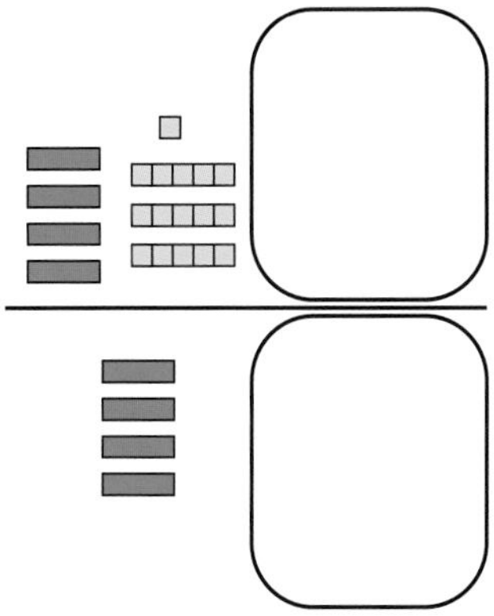

"This is an easy problem," said Edith. "There's a 4*x* in both the numerator and the denominator, so I can get rid of them. The simplified fraction is 16."

Anna didn't think Edith's method was right. She decided to check Edith's answer by substituting.

2. Calculate the value of the expression $\frac{4x + 16}{4x}$ for several different values for *x*. Do all values of *x* make this fraction equal to 16? Does any value of *x* make it equal to 16? Explain.

3. Explain why you cannot simplify a fraction by subtracting the same number from the numerator and the denominator. Give examples.

COMMON DIMENSIONS AND DIVISION

As you know, to simplify a fraction, you *divide numerator and denominator by the same number*. This is still true of algebraic fractions.

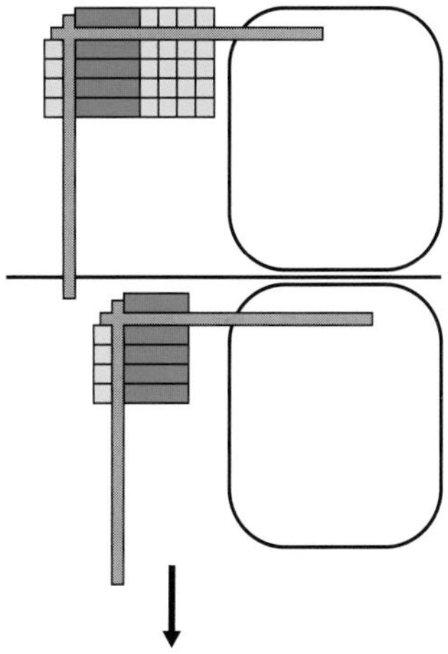

▼ 14.2 Simplifying Algebraic Fractions

Core Sequence: 1-7, 9-13

Suitable for Homework: 9-26

Useful for Assessment: 3, 9, 18-19

What this Lesson is About:

- Equivalent algebraic fractions
- Simplifying algebraic fractions
- Review of division by zero

At this stage in the course, many students may be able to do the work without actually using the Lab Gear. Nevertheless, they will still gain from an exposure to the Lab Gear method which will provide a visual anchor to their understanding.

ADDING OR SUBTRACTING EQUAL AMOUNTS

This section takes head-on a common student mistake of simplifying fractions. Another approach to the same question was taken in Chapter 5, Lesson 3.

Of course, students should use their calculators for problem 1. You may hint that they should consider fractions in three groups: less than 1, equal to 1, and greater than 1. You can also encourage discussion of what happens to the fractions when the amount added or subtracted becomes very large.

14.2 SOLUTIONS

1. Generalizations will vary. See Teacher's Notes.
2. Only one value will make the two expressions equal. This can be found by trial and error or algebraically, by solving the equation as shown.

   $\frac{4x + 16}{4x} = 16$

   $4x + 16 = 64x$

   $x = 4/15$
3. Answers will vary. See Teacher's Notes.

COMMON DIMENSIONS AND DIVISION

SIMPLIFYING FRACTIONS

*T*hese sections show two (equivalent) Lab Gear methods for simplifying fractions. In the second Lab Gear method especially, it appears that, when simplifying the fractions, we are subtracting from numerator and denominator. And in fact we are, but we are not subtracting *equal* amounts, which would not lead to an equivalent fraction. We are subtracting *proportional* amounts. Algebraically:

$$\text{If } \frac{a}{b} = \frac{c}{d}, \text{ then } \frac{a}{b} = \frac{a-c}{b-d}$$

(This need not be discussed with the class, but it can be if the question comes up.)

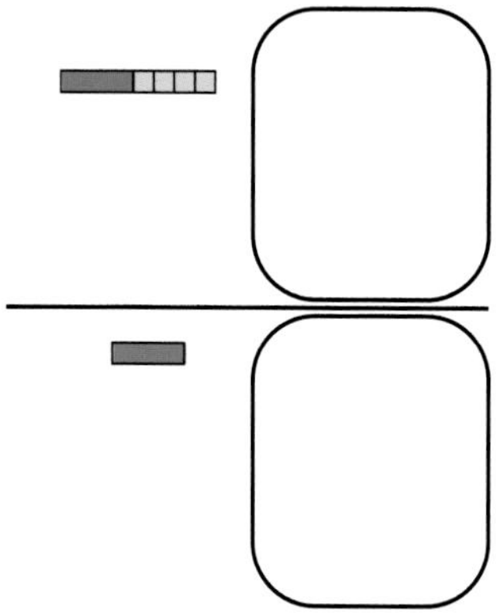

4. Study the previous figure.
   a. What are the numerator and the denominator divided by?
   b. What is the simplified fraction?

Sometimes, as in the figure below, the numerator and denominator rectangle are seen to have a common dimension, which is the common factor we divide by to get the simplified fraction.

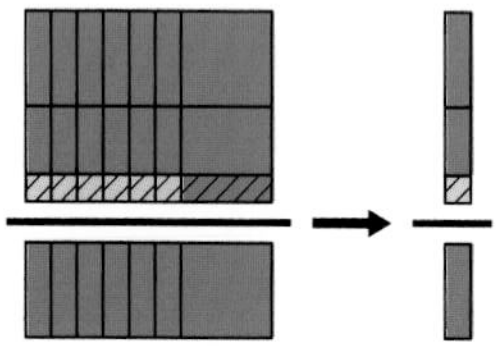

5. Study the preceding figure.
   a. Write the original fraction.
   b. Show what the numerator and denominator must be divided by to simplify the fraction.
   c. Write the simplified fraction.

Repeat problem 5 for the following figures.

6.

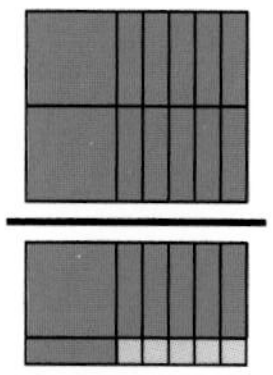

7.

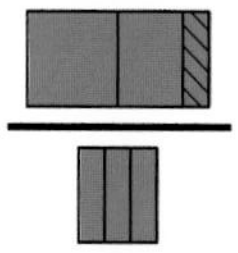

8.

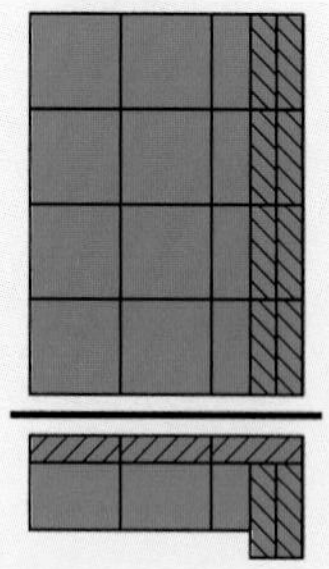

SIMPLIFYING FRACTIONS

Sometimes it is necessary to factor the numerator and the denominator in order to see the common factors.

Example: Simplify: $\frac{x^2 + 3x + 2}{x^2 + 5x + 6}$

Factor: $\frac{(x+2)(x+1)}{(x+2)(x+3)}$

Divide both numerator and denominator by the common factor, $(x + 2)$. The simplified fraction is: $\frac{x+1}{x+3}$.

14.2 SOLUTIONS

4. a. 4
   b. $\frac{x+4}{x}$

5. a. $\frac{(x+6)(2x-1)}{(x+6)x}$
   b. $x+6$
   c. $\frac{2x-1}{x}$

6. a. $\frac{2x(x+5)}{(x+1)(x+5)}$
   b. $x+5$
   c. $\frac{2x}{x+1}$

7. a. $\frac{x(2x-1)}{3x}$
   b. x
   c. $\frac{2x-1}{3}$

8. a. $\frac{4x(3x-2)}{(x-1)(3x-2)}$
   b. $3x-2$
   c. $\frac{4x}{x-1}$

The following example is done with the Lab Gear.

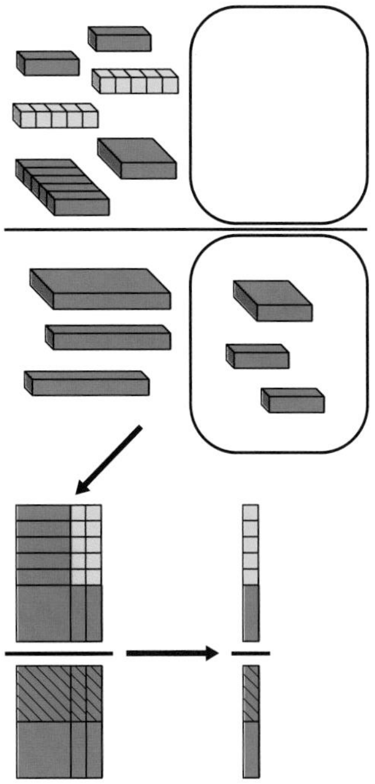

9. Explain the process shown in the figure, using words and algebraic notation.

If possible, simplify these fractions.

10. $\frac{3x + 12}{x^2 + 4x}$

11. $\frac{x^2 + 10x + 25}{2x + 10}$

12. $\frac{7x + 5}{7x}$

13. $\frac{2d + 3}{d + 3}$

ZERO IN THE DENOMINATOR

When we substitute 2 for x in the fraction $\frac{3x - 1}{x - 2}$, the denominator has the value zero. Since division by 0 is undefined, we say that the fraction is undefined when $x = 2$.

For what value or values of x (if any) is each fraction undefined?

14. $\frac{2x}{x - 6}$

15. $\frac{x - 6}{x + 6}$

16. $\frac{3}{2x + 6}$

17. $\frac{x^2 + 2}{x^2 - 6x + 8}$

ALWAYS, SOMETIMES, NEVER

Since $\frac{x^2 + 12x + 20}{x + 2}$ can be written

$$\frac{(x + 10)(x + 2)}{x + 2},$$

we can write:

$$\frac{x^2 + 12x + 20}{x + 2} = x + 10$$

18. Explain why the preceding equality is not true when $x = -2$.

19. Explain why it's true when $x \neq -2$.

20. For what value(s) of x is

a. $\frac{2x - 3}{8x - 12} \neq \frac{1}{4}$?

b. $\frac{x^2 - 9}{x - 3} = x + 3$?

Tell whether each equation 21-23 is always true or only sometimes true. If it is only sometimes true, give the values of x for which it is *not* true.

21. $\frac{8x}{4} = 2x$

22. $\frac{x^2 - 1}{8x - 8} = \frac{(x + 1)}{8}$

23. $\frac{5 - 5x}{2x^2 - 2} = \frac{-5}{2x + 2}$

Tell whether each equation 24-26 is always, sometimes, or never true. If it is sometimes true, give the values of x that make it true.

24. $\frac{5x - 5}{5} = 5x$

25. $\frac{5x - 5}{5} = x - 5$

26. $\frac{x^2 - 10}{5} = x^2 - 2$

ZERO IN THE DENOMINATOR

ALWAYS, SOMETIMES, NEVER

These sections serve mainly as preview for future courses.

14.2 SOLUTIONS

9. The original fraction is $\frac{x^2 + 7x + 10}{xy + 2y - x^2 - 2x}$. The blocks in the numerator are made into a rectangle having length $x + 2$ and width $x + 5$. The blocks in the denominator are made into another rectangle of length $x + 2$ and width $y - x$. The common dimension is $x + 2$. When both numerator and denominator are divided by $x + 2$, the result is $\frac{x + 5}{y - x}$.

10. $\frac{3}{x}$

11. $\frac{x + 5}{2}$

12. cannot be simplified

13. cannot be simplified

14. $x = 6$

15. $x = -6$

16. $x = -3$

17. $x^2 - 6x + 8 = (x - 4)(x - 2)$ The fraction is undefined if $x = 4$ or $x = 2$.

18. If $x = -2$, the denominator is 0.

19. This can be shown by substitution, or by reasoning that both sides can be multiplied by $(x + 2)$ to get an identity.

20. $x = 3/2$

21. $x = 3$

21. always

22. not true if $x = 1$

23. not true if $x = 1$ or $x = -1$

24. true if $x = -1/4$

25. never true

26. true if $x = 0$

▼ 14.3
Fractions and Equations

Core Sequence: 1-24

Suitable for Homework: 14-24

What this Lesson is About:

- Equivalent algebraic fractions
- Common denominators
- Solving quadratic equations by trial and error
- Review of eliminating fractions from equations
- Review of solving quadratic equations

The first two sections of this lesson concentrate on the manipulation of algebraic fractions, and the last two make a connection with quadratic equations.

Problem 1 gives students a chance to think about fractions, both algebraic and numerical. Making the connection between the two through substitution should help make it easier to work with algebraic fractions, but only for students who have some understanding of numerical fractions.

COMPLICATING FRACTIONS

This section is a necessary prerequisite to common denominators, and therefore to adding and subtracting algebraic fractions, which we will need to do more than once in the rest of Chapter 14.

Be sure to have a class discussion of problem 3, comparing different students' solutions.

COMMON DENOMINATORS

This section gives students an opportunity to practice with common denominators, with examples that look a little bit like the a's, b's, and c's that come up in the derivation of the quadratic formula.

LESSON 14.3

Fractions and Equations

1. **Exploration** Wanda always enjoyed the math tests Mr. Stevens gave every Friday. She especially liked the tests on fractions. Here is the test she took on Friday the 13th. Try to find the problems she did wrong. If necessary, substitute numbers. If you can, show her how to do them correctly.
   a. $\frac{2x}{5} - \frac{x}{3} = \frac{x}{2}$
   b. $\frac{x}{5} + \frac{x}{5} = \frac{2x}{10}$
   c. $\frac{x}{5} \cdot \frac{x}{5} = \frac{x^2}{25}$
   d. $\frac{2x}{5} \cdot \frac{5}{2x} = 1$
   e. $\frac{x}{5} + \frac{5}{x} = 2$
   f. $\frac{M}{5} = \frac{10M}{50}$
   g. $\frac{2M + 4}{M + 2} = 2$

COMPLICATING FRACTIONS

Sometimes it is useful to *complicate* fractions instead of simplifying them. For example, here are some more complicated fractions that are equivalent to $\frac{2x}{5}$.

a. $\frac{4x^2}{10x}$ b. $\frac{2xy}{5y}$ c. $\frac{8x + 2x^2}{20 + 5x}$

2. What was $\frac{2x}{5}$ multiplied by to give each one of the fractions? Sketch a Lab Gear fraction for part (a).
3. Write three fractions that are equivalent to $2/(x - 3)$. Check the correctness of a classmate's fractions.
4. Write a fraction that is equivalent to $\frac{x + 2}{5}$ that has the following:
   a. a denominator of 10
   b. a denominator of $5x + 15$
   c. a numerator of $4x + 8$
   d. a numerator of $3x^2 + 6x$
5. If possible, write a fraction that is equivalent to $\frac{y + x}{4x}$ that has the following:
   a. a denominator of $8xy$
   b. a denominator of $6x^2$
   c. a numerator of $-2y - 2x$
   d. a numerator of $3y + x$
6. Write a fraction equivalent to 2 that has $5a^2$ as a denominator.
7. Write a fraction equivalent to 1 that has b as a denominator.
8. Write a fraction equivalent to b that has b as a denominator.
9. Write a fraction equivalent to x that has x^2 as a denominator.

COMMON DENOMINATORS

To add or subtract fractions having unlike denominators, you first have to find a common denominator.

10. a. Write a fraction equivalent to $\frac{b}{3}$ having a denominator of $6a^2$.
    b. Add $\frac{b}{3} + \frac{c}{6a^2}$.
11. Write two fractions whose sum is $\frac{2x + 5}{10x}$.
12. a. Write a fraction equivalent to $\frac{bc}{5a}$ having a denominator of $5ac$.
    b. Add $\frac{bc}{5a} + \frac{2}{c}$.
13. Find a common denominator and add or subtract.
    a. $\frac{1}{4x} + \frac{1}{10x^2}$ b. $\frac{5}{xy} - \frac{1}{x^2}$

14.3 SOLUTIONS

1. a. Get a common denominator.
   $\frac{6x}{15} - \frac{5x}{15} = \frac{x}{15}$
   b. Use the common denominator instead of adding the denominators. The sum is $2x/5$.
   e. Get a common denominator.
   $\frac{x^2}{5x} + \frac{25}{5x} = \frac{x^2 + 25}{5x}$
2. a. $2x/2x$

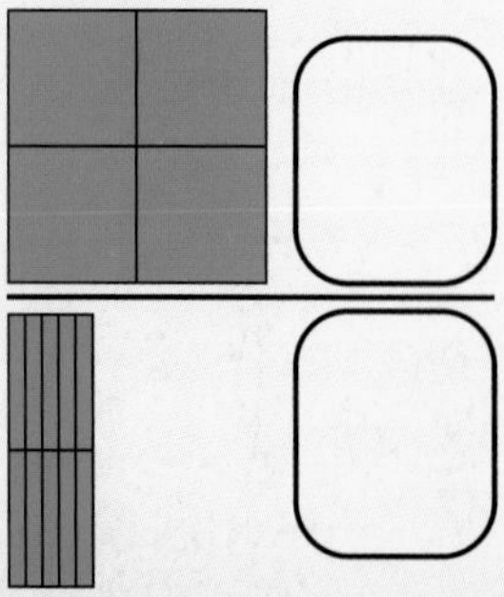

   b. y/y
   c. $(4 + x)/(4 + x)$
3. Answers will vary.
4. a. $\frac{2x + 4}{10}$
   b. $\frac{x^2 + 5x + 6}{5x + 15}$
   c. $\frac{4x + 8}{20}$
   d. $\frac{3x^2 + 6x}{15x}$
5. a. $\frac{2y^2 + 2xy}{8xy}$
   b. $\frac{1.5xy + 1.5x^2}{6x^2}$
   c. $\frac{-2y - 2x}{-8x}$
   d. impossible
6. $\frac{10a^2}{5a^2}$

FROM QUADRATICS TO FRACTIONS

Tara was trying to solve $x^2 + 4x - 6 = 0$ with the zero product property. She couldn't figure out a way to factor the trinomial. Then she had an idea. She wrote:

$$x^2 + 4x = 6$$
$$x(x + 4) = 6$$

Tara was still thinking about the zero product property. She wrote:

$$x = 6 \text{ or } x + 4 = 6$$

14. Explain why Tara's reasoning is incorrect. (Why does this method work when one side of the equation is 0?)

When Tara saw her mistake, she tried another method. She divided both sides by x.

$$x(x + 4) = 6$$
$$x + 4 = \frac{6}{x}$$

Then she was stuck. Her teacher suggested that she use trial and error, so she made this table.

x	$x + 4$	$\frac{6}{x}$
1	5	6
2	6	3
1.5	5.5	4
1.25	5.25	4.8
1.13	5.13	5.31

15. Continue the table and find a value of x that, when substituted into both sides of the equation, will give the same value

a. to the nearest tenth;

b. to the nearest hundredth.

16. The quadratic equation that Tara was solving has two roots. Approximate the other root to the nearest hundredth.

17. Solve the equation $x^2 + 5x - 3 = 0$ using trial and error. (You do not need to do it in the same way as Tara.) Approximate each solution to the nearest hundredth.

18. Confirm your solution by using a method you learned in Chapter 13.

FROM FRACTIONS TO QUADRATICS

Rewrite each equation as an equivalent quadratic equation. Then try to solve it. Show each step.

19. $x + 4 + \frac{3}{x} = 0$ **20.** $2m + \frac{4}{m} = 9$

21. $4x = \frac{1}{x}$ **22.** $L - 4 = \frac{20}{L}$

23. $\frac{1}{x} = x + 1$ **24.** $\frac{4}{x} = x + 1$

FROM QUADRATICS TO FRACTIONS

This section starts by addressing common student attempts at solving quadratics: the misuse of factoring and the limitations of linear equation techniques.

In addition, students are asked to use trial and error. Organized trial and error is helpful in developing students' sense of what's happening in a problem like this. Of course, it is quite inconvenient as an everyday approach to solving quadratic equations. The use of a programmable calculator or appropriate computer software (such as the Logo language or a spreadsheet) makes it possible to make trial and error more efficient.

If you have access to graphing calculators, you may have the students graph the two sides of the equation Tara was working on, in both forms: first $x^2 + 4x - 6 = 0$, and then $x + 4 = \frac{6}{x}$.

FROM FRACTIONS TO QUADRATICS

This section offers extra practice with fractions and with solving quadratics. Refer back to **Thinking/Writing 13.B** for similar problems. For problem 20, after putting the equation in standard form, students can either factor or divide through by 2.

14.3 SOLUTIONS

7. $\frac{b}{b}$

8. $\frac{b^2}{b}$

9. $\frac{x^3}{x^2}$

10. a. $\frac{2a^2b}{6a^2}$

b. $\frac{2a^2b}{6a^2} + \frac{c}{6a^2} = \frac{2a^2b + c}{6a^2}$

11. $\frac{x+5}{10x} + \frac{x}{10x}$

12. a. $\frac{bc^2}{5ac}$

b. $\frac{bc^2}{5ac} + \frac{10a}{5ac} = \frac{bc^2 + 10a}{5ac}$

13. a. $\frac{10x}{40x^2} + \frac{4}{40x^2} = \frac{10x+4}{40x^2} = \frac{5x+2}{20x^2}$

b. $\frac{5}{xy} - \frac{1}{x^2} = \frac{5x}{x^2y} - \frac{y}{x^2y} = \frac{5x-y}{x^2y}$

14. It works for zero because of the Zero Product Property. There is no such property about products for numbers other than zero.

15.

x	$x + 4$	$\frac{6}{x}$
1	5	6
2	6	3
1.5	5.5	4
1.25	5.25	4.8
1.13	5.13	5.31
1.14	5.14	5.26
1.15	5.15	5.217
1.16	5.16	5.172
1.162	5.162	5.1635

a. 1.15 or 1.16

b. 1.162

16. $x = -5.16$

17. approximate solutions: $x = 0.542$ or $x = -5.542$

18. Methods will vary.

19. $x^2 + 4x + 3 = 0$
$x = -3$ or $x = -1$

20. $2m^2 - 9m + 4 = 0$
$m = 0.5$ or $m = 4$

21. $x = \pm 0.5$

22. $x = 2 \pm 2\sqrt{6}$

23. $x = \frac{-1 \pm \sqrt{5}}{2}$

24. $x = \frac{-1 \pm \sqrt{17}}{2}$

14.4 Finding the Vertex

Core Sequence: 1-20

Suitable for Homework: 1-16, 18-20

Useful for Assessment: 5-6, 8, 11-12, 14-15, 18-21

What this Lesson is About:

- The role of the parameter a
- Review of finding the vertex in intercept form
- Finding the vertex in standard form

This lesson continues the work we started in Chapter 13, which will eventually lead to the quadratic formula.

DIFFERENT SHAPES

While the main point of the section is to clarify the role of the parameter a in affecting the shape of the parabola, a secondary and vital point is the review of the relationship between the fact that a point is on the graph on the one hand, and the fact that its coordinates satisfy the equation, on the other hand.

Since a determines whether the parabola is a frown or a smile, one student called a the *mood* of the parabola.

INTERCEPT FORM

This section reviews material from the beginning of Chapter 13.

LESSON 14.4

Finding the Vertex

You will need:

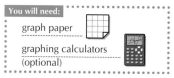

- graph paper
- graphing calculators (optional)

Knowing more about quadratic functions and their graphs will help you understand and solve quadratic equations. In particular, it is useful to know how to find the vertex and the x-intercepts of quadratic functions in the following two forms:

- *Intercept form:* $y = a(x - p)(x - q)$
- *Standard form:* $y = ax^2 + bx + c$

DIFFERENT SHAPES

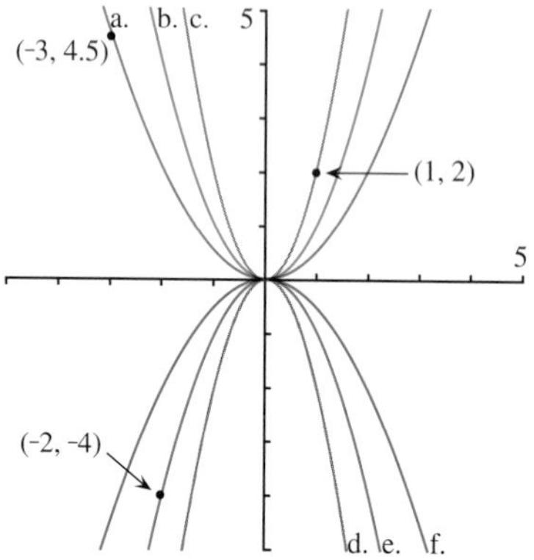

1. The figure shows several parabolas whose x-intercepts, y-intercept, and vertex are all (0, 0). Match each one with an equation:
   $y = x^2$ $y = 0.5x^2$ $y = 2x^2$
   $y = -x^2$ $y = -0.5x^2$ $y = -2x^2$
2. What is the value of a for the parabolas on the following figure?

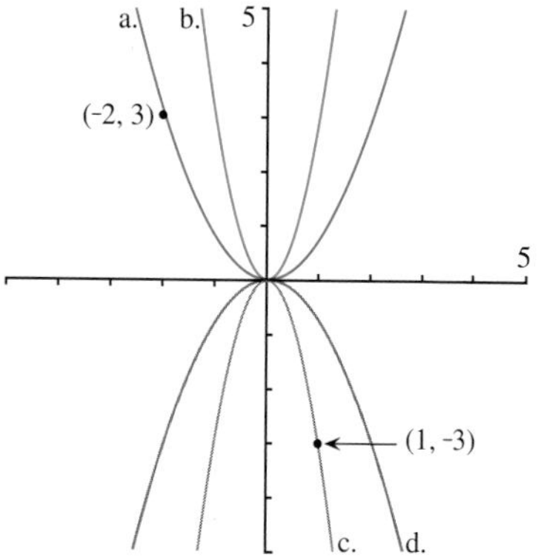

3. Which among the parabolas in problems 1 and 2 is most open? Most closed? How is this related to the value of a?
4. Write the equation of a parabola that lies entirely between parabolas 1a and 1b.
5. Describe the graph of:
   a. $y = -0.01x^2$; b. $y = 100x^2$.
6. **Summary** Explain the effect of the parameter a, in the function $y = ax^2$, on the shape and orientation of the graph.

INTERCEPT FORM

As you learned in Chapter 13, when the equation is in intercept form, you can find the vertex from the x-intercepts, which are easy to locate.

7. Try to answer the following questions about the graph of $y = 2(x - 3)(x + 4)$ without graphing.
   a. What are the x- and y-intercepts?
   b. What are the coordinates of the vertex?

14.4 SOLUTIONS

1. a. $y = 0.5x^2$
   b. $y = x^2$
   c. $y = 2x^2$
   d. $y = -2x^2$
   e. $y = -x^2$
   f. $y = -0.5x^2$
2. a. $y = 0.75x^2$
   b. $y = 3x^2$
   c. $y = -3x^2$
   d. $y = -0.75x^2$
3. The most open are $y = 0.5x^2$ and $y = -0.5x^2$. The most closed are $y = 3x^2$ and $y = -3x^2$.
4. $y = 0.75x^2$
5. a. below the x-axis, very open, almost coinciding with the x-axis
   b. above the x-axis, very closed, almost coinciding with the y-axis
6. A very large (or very large in absolute value) value of a will make the graph very closed. A very small (or small in absolute value) value of a will make it very open. As the value of a increases in absolute value, the graph becomes steeper. As it decreases in absolute value, the graph becomes more open. Negative values of a make the graph open downward into a "frown." Positive values make it open upward into a "smile."
7. a. The intercepts are (3, 0), (-4, 0) and (0, -24).
   b. The vertex is (-0.5, -24.5).

8. **Generalization**

a. What are the x- and y-intercepts of $y = a(x - p)(x - q)$? Explain.

b. Explain in words how to find the vertex if you know the intercepts.

9. The figure shows the graphs of several parabolas. Write an equation for each one. (Hint: To find a, use either the y-intercept or the vertex and algebra or trial and error.)

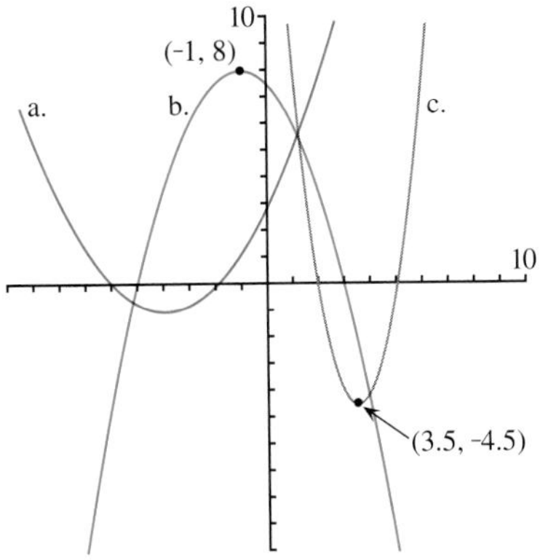

10. For each equation, tell whether its graph is a smile or a frown parabola, without graphing. Explain your reasoning.

a. $y = 9(x - 8)(x - 7)$

b. $y = -9(x - 8)(x - 7)$

c. $y = 9(8 - x)(x - 7)$

d. $y = 9(8 - x)(7 - x)$

11. If you know all the intercepts and the vertex of $y = 3(x - p)(x - q)$, explain how you would find the intercepts and the vertex of $y = -3(x - p)(x - q)$.

STANDARD FORM

When the equation is in standard form, $y = ax^2 + bx + c$, it is more difficult to find the location of the vertex. One particularly easy case, however, is the case where $c = 0$.

12. Explain why when $c = 0$, the parabola goes through the origin.

13. Find the vertex of $y = 2x^2 + 8x$. (Hint: Factor to get into intercept form.)

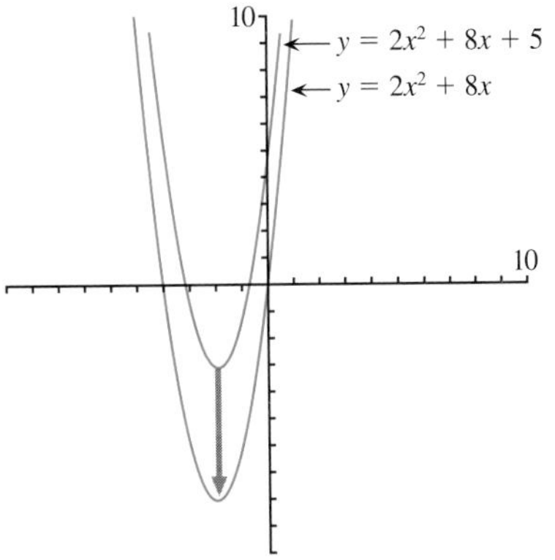

14. How are the two graphs related? Compare the axis of symmetry and the y-intercept.

15. How is the graph of $y = 2x^2 + 8x - 3$ related to them?

16. Find the equation of any other parabola whose vertex is directly above or below the vertex of $y = 2x^2 + 8x$.

FINDING *H* AND *V*

Example: Find the coordinates (H, V) of the vertex of the graph of $y = 3x^2 - 18x + 7$.

- $y = 3x^2 - 18x$ is the vertical translation for which $V = 0$. By factoring, we see it is equal to $y = x(3x - 18)$.
- To find the x-intercepts of $y = 3x^2 - 18x$, we set $y = 0$. By the zero product property, one x-intercept is 0. To find the other, we solve the equation $3x - 18 = 0$, and get $x = 6$.
- Since the x-intercepts are 0 and 6, and the axis of symmetry for both parabolas is halfway between, it must be 3. So $H = 3$.

Students are likely to have trouble with issues of signs in problem 10. Be sure you discuss this in class.

STANDARD FORM

FINDING *H* AND *V*

The idea of graphs through the origin was first seen in Chapter 4, Lesson 4. Parabolas through the origin were the subject of much of Chapter 13, Lessons 1 and 2. Here we use the fact that parabolas through the origin have equations that are easy to put in intercept form (through factoring). This turns out to be the key to a strategy that leads to finding H, the x-coordinate of the vertex, for any parabola in standard form.

14.4 SOLUTIONS

8. a. The vertex is halfway between the x-intercepts, so $x = (p + q)/2$. To find y, substitute this into the expression $a(x - p)(x - q)$. The value of y is $-a(p - q)^2/4$.
   b. Find the x-intercepts. Add them and divide by 2. This is the x-coordinate of the vertex. Substitute the result for x and solve for y to find the y-coordinate of the vertex.

9. a. $y = 0.25(x + 2)(x + 6)$
   b. $y = -0.5(x + 5)(x - 3)$
   c. $y = 2(x - 2)(x - 5)$

10. a. smile. It can be written in the form $y = a(x - p)(x - q)$ where $a > 0$.
    b. frown. It can be written in the form $y = a(x - p)(x - q)$ where $a < 0$.
    c. frown. Factor -1 out of the factor $(8 - x)$ and rewrite as $y = -9(x - 8)(x - 7)$.
    d. smile. Factor -1 out of the factor $(8 - x)$ and also out of the factor $(7 - x)$ and rewrite as $y = (-1)(-1)9(x - 8)(x - 7)$, which simplifies to $y = 9(x - 8)(x - 7)$.

11. The x-intercepts are the same. The y-intercepts are opposites. The vertex has the same x-coordinate, but the y-coordinates are opposites.

12. If $c = 0$, the equation is $y = ax^2 + bx$. Substituting 0 for x in this equation gives the value of 0 for y.

13. In intercept form, the equation is $y = 2x(x + 4)$. The x-intercepts are 0 and -4, so the x-coordinate of the vertex is $H = -2$. Substituting $x = -2$, find that the y-coordinate of the vertex is $V = -8$.

14. They have the same axis of symmetry, but $y = 2x^2 + 8x + 5$ has a y-intercept of (0, 5), compared to a y-intercept of (0, 0) for the first equation.

15. It will have the same axis of symmetry, but the y-intercept will be (0, -3). The graph is a vertical translation (down 3) of the graph of $y = 2x^2 + 8x$.

16. Answers will vary. Any answer of the form $y = 2x^2 + 8x + k$ is correct.

The procedure outlined in the example preceding problem 17 may seem daunting, but it is based on very strong visual foundations, and for students who understand the material about intercept form, vertical translation, and symmetry, it should not require any memorizing or present any conceptual difficulties.

SAME SHAPE

You should discuss the idea in this section even if you do not assign problem 21, which is challenging, and probably best done at the overhead projector or chalkboard.

- Substitute 3 into the original equation to see that the y-coordinate of the vertex is:

  $V = 3(3)^2 - 18(3) + 7 = -20.$

  So the coordinates of the vertex for the original parabola are (3, -20).

17. For each equation, find H and V. It may help to sketch the vertical translation of the parabola for which $V = 0$.

a. $y = x^2 + 6x + 5$
b. $y = 2x^2 + 6x + 5$
c. $y = 3x^2 - 6x + 5$
d. $y = 6x^2 - 6x + 5$

Generalizations

18. What is the equation of a parabola through the origin that is a vertical translation of $y = ax^2 + bx + c$?

19. Show how to find the axis of symmetry of:

a. $y = ax^2 + bx$;
b. $y = ax^2 - bx$.

20. Explain why the x-coordinate of the vertex of the parabola having equation $y = ax^2 + bx + c$ is

$$H = -\frac{b}{2a}.$$

SAME SHAPE

The parameter a determines the shape of the parabola. The graphs of all equations in standard form that share the same value for a are translations of the graph of $y = ax^2$.

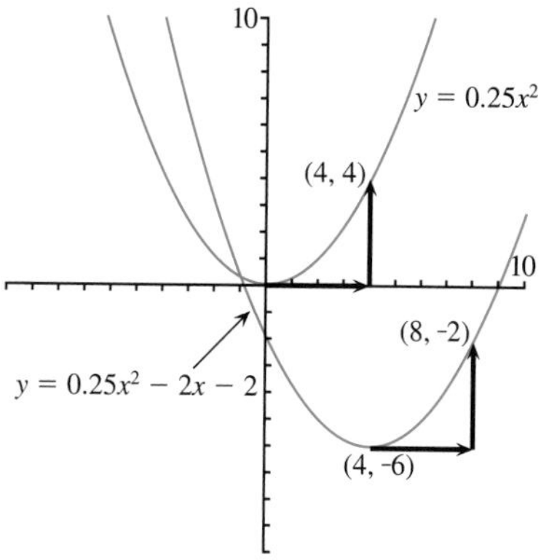

For example, the two parabolas in the figure have equations with $a = 0.25$. Therefore they have the same shape, as the following exercise shows.

21.

a. Show algebraically that starting at the vertex, and moving 4 across and 4 up, lands you on a point that satisfies the equation in both cases.
b. If you move 2 across from the vertex, show that you move up the same amount to get to the parabola in both cases.

14.4 SOLUTIONS

17. Strategies for solving these problems will vary. One approach is to find the vertex of the graph of the related equation with $c = 0$, and then move it 5 units up. Students may use other strategies from Chapter 13 as well.
    a. (-3, -4)
    b. (-1.5, 0.5)
    c. (1, 2)
    d. (0.5, 3.5)
18. $y = ax^2 + bx$
19. a. Strategies will vary. One approach follows: Factor to get $y = x(ax + b)$. The intercepts are $x = 0$ and $x = -b/a$. Average these to find that $H = -b/(2a)$. Substitute to get the y-coordinate of the vertex, $V = -b^2/(4a)$.
    b. $\left(b/(2a), -b^2/(4a)\right)$
20. It is a vertical translation of $y = ax^2 + bx$, so it has the same value for H.
21. a. The vertex of $y = 0.25x^2$ is (0, 0). By substitution, we can show that (4, 4) satisfies the equation. The vertex of $y = 0.25x^2 - 2x - 2$ is (4, -6). By substitution, we can show that (8, -2) satisfies the equation.
    b. The point (2, 1) is on the graph of $y = 0.25x^2$ If the graph of $y = 0.25x^2 - 2x - 2$ has the same shape, we should be able to get from the vertex to another point on the parabola by moving over 2 and up 1. This would get us to the point (6, -5). By substituting, we can confirm that this (x, y) pair satisfies the equation $y = 0.25x^2 - 2x - 2$.

THINKING WRITING

14.A In the Gutter

You have a long rectangular sheet of metal, having width L inches. You intend to fold it to make a gutter. You want to find out which of the folds shown in the figure will give the maximum flow of water. This depends on the area of the cross-section of the gutter; a bigger area means better flow.

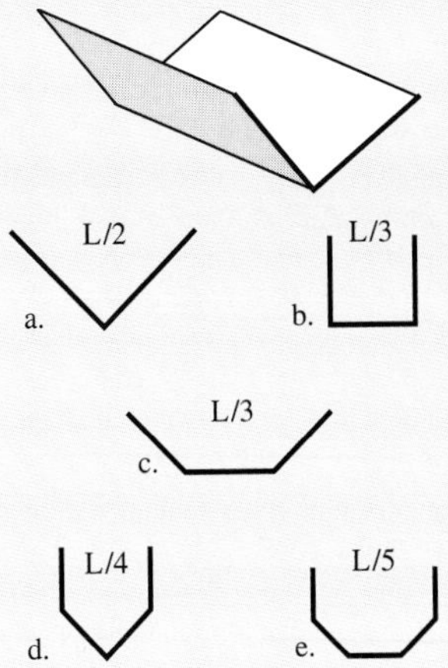

1. Find the area of the cross-section for the examples shown in the figure. (All angles are 90 or 135 degrees. All sides in each cross-section are of equal length. Hint: Divide the areas into rectangles and right triangles that are half-squares.) Which cross-section has the greatest area?
2. You may try the same shapes with different dimensions. For example, for cross-section b, you could have a height of $L/4$, and a width of $L/2$. Try to increase the areas for cross-sections b, c, d, and e by choosing different values for the different segments. (Remember that the sum of all the lengths must be L.)
3. **Report** Figure out the best design for a gutter. Write an illustrated report on your research, explaining clearly how you arrived at your conclusions. You need not limit yourself to the shapes given here.

14.A SOLUTIONS

1. a. $0.125L^2$
   b. $0.111L^2$
   c. $0.134L^2$
   d. $0.120L^2$
   e. $0.145L^2$
2. The following are our solutions. Better ones may be possible for (d) and (e).
   b. This is identical to the problem of the pen against the garage. The best answer is with a width of $L/2$ and a height of $L/4$. It yields an area of $0.125L^2$.
   c. $L/4$ for the bottom side, and $3L/8$ for the other sides, is close to the optimal solution. Area: $0.137L^2$
   d. $L/6$ for the vertical sides, and $L/3$ for the others gives an area of $0.134L^2$.
   e. $L/8$ for the vertical sides, and $L/4$ for the other ones gives an area of $0.151L^2$.
3. Changing the angles makes the problem too difficult to work on without trigonometry. A good analysis is possible based solely on the given shapes: cross-section e as described in the solution to #2e gives the best solution we found with rectilinear sides and angles of 90 and 135 degrees. It can be improved upon with a semi-circle, which yields an area of $0.159L^2$.

THINKING WRITING

14.A In the Gutter

Core Sequence: none of the lesson

Suitable for Homework: 3

Useful for Assessment: 3

What this Assignment is About:

- Optimization of area
- Review of area computation techniques
- Review of the diagonal of a square
- Review of fractions

These problems are difficult, as they entail working with the variable L, and with area calculations without the support of dot or graph paper. (You could make the lesson more accessible by choosing a value for L, for example 60 cm.)

You may consider having students work in groups on this assignment, and/or giving them several days to complete it.

To do these problems, students will need to remember how to find the length of the diagonal of a square when the side is known. You may review this with the help of the Pythagorean theorem or by using the area approach we used in Chapter 6, Lesson 12.

The best solution to the problem is actually a semi-circular cross-section. Do not give this away, or even hint at it, because it would undercut students' exploration of the given figures. (Besides, it might be easier to build cross-section e physically than to build a semi-circular one, with only a 5% loss in area.)

14.5
A Famous Formula

Core Sequence: 1-19

Suitable for Homework: 1-4, 15-22

Useful for Assessment: 5-7, 19

What this Lesson is About:

- Solving quadratic equations
- Graphic derivation of the quadratic formula
- Symbolic derivation of the quadratic formula
- Review of rectangles

STANDARD FORM OF A QUADRATIC

This reviews material from Chapter 13, Lessons 6-8.

FINDING THE x-INTERCEPTS

Note that dividing by a is legitimate in the case of an equation, but not in the case of a function. This is because the solutions of the equation are not changed when dividing all terms by the same amount, but all points on the graph except for the x-intercepts move when the terms are divided.

This section follows the same approach as Chapter 13, Lesson 7, but of course the solution is different because $a \neq 1$.

LESSON 14.5

A Famous Formula

You will need:

- graph paper
- graphing calculators (optional)

STANDARD FORM OF A QUADRATIC

Definition: A quadratic equation is said to be in *standard form* if it is in the form:

$$ax^2 + bx + c = 0.$$

In Chapter 13 you learned several methods to solve quadratics in the case where $a = 1$. If you divide all the terms of a quadratic equation in standard form by a, you can solve it with those methods.

Example: Solve $3x^2 + 5x - 4 = 0$.
Divide both sides by 3:

$$x^2 + \frac{5}{3}x - \frac{4}{3} = \frac{0}{3}$$

$$x^2 + \frac{5}{3}x - \frac{4}{3} = 0.$$

Since $a = 1$, the solutions are $H \pm \sqrt{-V}$. In this case:

$$H = -b/2 = -5/6.$$

Find V by substituting H for x in the equation.

$$V = \left(\frac{-5}{6}\right)^2 + \left(\frac{5}{3}\right)\left(\frac{-5}{6}\right) - \frac{4}{3}$$

$$= \frac{25}{36} - \frac{25}{18} - \frac{4}{3}$$

$$= \frac{25}{36} - \frac{50}{36} - \frac{48}{36}$$

$$= \frac{-73}{36}$$

So the solutions are:

$$-\frac{5}{6} + \sqrt{\frac{73}{36}} \text{ or } -\frac{5}{6} - \sqrt{\frac{73}{36}}$$

The two solutions can be written as one expression:

$$-\frac{5}{6} \pm \sqrt{\frac{73}{36}}$$

where the symbol $\pm$ is read *plus or minus*. It is also possible to write it as a single fraction:

$$-\frac{5}{6} \pm \sqrt{\frac{73}{36}} = -\frac{5}{6} \pm \frac{\sqrt{73}}{6} = \frac{-5 \pm \sqrt{73}}{6}$$

Solve. (Hint: You may divide by a, then use any of the methods from Chapter 13.)

1. $2x^2 + 4x - 8 = 0$
2. $-x^2 + 4x + 8 = 0$
3. $3x^2 + 4x - 4 = 0$
4. $-3x^2 + 8x + 8 = 0$

FINDING THE x-INTERCEPTS

You already know how to find the vertex of a quadratic function in standard form. In this section you will learn how to find the x-intercepts from the vertex.

The following figure shows the graph of the function $y = ax^2 + bx + c$, which is a translation of $y = ax^2$, whose graph is also shown. The coordinates of the vertex are (H, V). D is the distance from the x-intercepts to the axis of symmetry. When $a = 1$, we found that $D = \sqrt{-V}$. What is D in the general case?

14.5 SOLUTIONS

1. $x = 1 \pm \sqrt{5}$
2. $x = 2 \pm \sqrt{12}$
3. $x = -2$ or $x = 2/3$
4. $x = \frac{4 \pm 2\sqrt{10}}{3}$

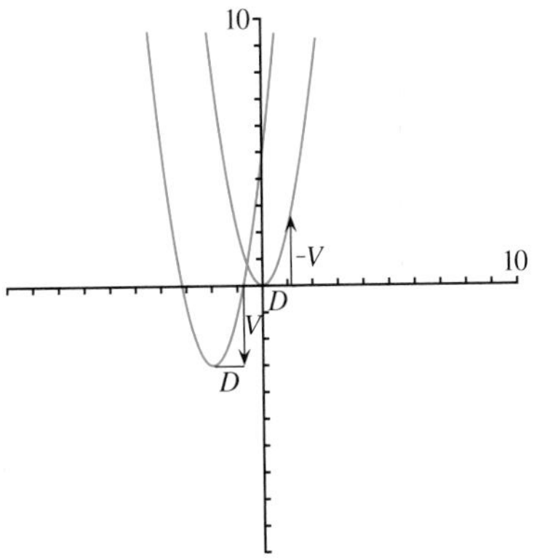

The figure shows D and V on a parabola that was translated from $y = ax^2$. In this example, V was a negative number, and the translation was in a downward direction. The arrows representing D and V are also shown on the original parabola. (On $y = x^2$, the direction of the arrow for V was reversed. What is shown is actually the opposite of V. This is indicated by the label $-V$. Since V is negative, $-V$ is positive.)

5. Use the figure to explain why $-V = aD^2$.

6. Express D in terms of V and a.

7. This formula is different from the one we had found in the case where $a = 1$. Explain why this formula works whether $a = 1$ or $a \neq 1$.

SOLVING QUADRATIC EQUATIONS

The x-intercepts, when they exist, are equal to $H \pm D$. It follows from the value of D found in the previous section that the solutions to the quadratic equation $ax^2 + bx + c = 0$ are given by the formula:

$$H \pm \sqrt{-\frac{V}{a}}.$$

Therefore, one way to solve a quadratic equation in standard form is first to find H and V. In Lesson 2 you learned how to express H in terms of a and b. Then V can be found by substituting H into the equation.

> **Example:** Solve $2x^2 + 8x - 7 = 0$.
> $H = -b/(2a) = -8/4 = -2$
> $V = 2(-2)^2 + 8(-2) - 7 = -15$

Solutions:

$$H \pm \sqrt{-\frac{V}{a}} = -2 \pm \sqrt{-\frac{-15}{2}} = -2 \pm \sqrt{7.5}$$

Solve.

8. $2x^2 + 6x - 8 = 0$

9. $-x^2 + 6x + 8 = 0$

10. $3x^2 + 6x + 1 = 0$

11. $-3x^2 + 6x + 8 = 0$

THE QUADRATIC FORMULA

As you know, $H = -b/(2a)$. The following problem uses that fact to find a formula for V in terms of a, b, and c.

12. Substitute $-b/(2a)$ into $ax^2 + bx + c$ to find the y-coordinate of the vertex as a single fraction in terms of a, b, and c.

If you did problem 12 correctly, you should have found that:

$$V = \frac{-b^2 + 4ac}{4a}.$$

13. To find a formula for the solutions of the quadratic equation in standard form in terms of a, b, and c, substitute the expressions for H and V into the expression

$$H \pm \sqrt{-\frac{V}{a}}.$$

If you did this correctly, you should have found that the solutions are:

$$-\frac{b}{2a} \pm \sqrt{\frac{b^2 - 4ac}{4a^2}}$$

SOLVING QUADRATIC EQUATIONS

This section extends the work from the previous section and the previous lesson. At the same time, it helps preview the next section by giving students experience with numbers, in a process that will be done with letters.

THE QUADRATIC FORMULA

This section is very difficult and should definitely be done in class. Many students will have trouble working strictly at the symbolic level, though comparisons with the previous section's work with numbers should help.

Note also that this derivation of the quadratic formula is preferable to the traditional approach based on completing the square, which we will see in the next lesson. It is preferable for two reasons: on the one hand it is more meaningful, as it is based on a graphical representation; and on the other hand the symbolic manipulation is substantially easier.

14.5 SOLUTIONS

5. The equation of the quadratic is $y = ax^2$. Since $y = -V$ and $x = D$, as shown in the figure, $-V = aD^2$.
6. $D = \sqrt{-V/a}$
7. If $a = 1$, $D = \sqrt{-V}$
8. $x = -4$ or $x = 1$
9. $x = 3 \pm \sqrt{17}$
10. $x = -1 \pm \frac{\sqrt{6}}{3}$
11. $x = -1 \pm \frac{\sqrt{33}}{3}$
12. $a\left(\frac{-b}{2a}\right)^2 + b\left(\frac{-b}{2a}\right) + c =$

$\frac{ab^2}{4a^2} + \frac{-b^2}{2a} + c =$

$\frac{b^2}{4a} + \frac{-2b^2}{4a} + \frac{4ac}{4a} =$

$\frac{-b^2 + 4ac}{4a}$

13. $H = \frac{-b}{2a}$

$V = \frac{-b^2 + 4ac}{4a}$

$$H \pm \sqrt{\frac{-V}{a}} = \frac{-b^2}{2a} \pm \sqrt{\frac{-\left(\frac{-b^2 + 4ac}{4a}\right)}{a}}$$

$$= \frac{-b}{2a} \pm \sqrt{\frac{b^2 - 4ac}{4a^2}}$$

14. Show that this simplifies to:

$$\frac{-b \pm \sqrt{b^2 - 4ac}}{2a}$$

This expression is the famous *quadratic formula.* It gives the solutions to a quadratic equation in standard form in terms of a, b, and c. You will find it useful to memorize it as follows: "The opposite of b, plus or minus the square root of b squared minus $4ac$, all over $2a$."

Solve these equations. (If you use the quadratic formula, you are less likely to make mistakes if you calculate the quantity $b^2 - 4ac$ first.)

15. $2x^2 + 6x - 4 = 0$
16. $-x^2 + 6x + 4 = 0$
17. $3x^2 + 6x - 4 = 0$
18. $-3x^2 + 7x - 4 = 0$

19. **Report** What are all the methods you know for solving quadratic equations? Use examples.

DISCOVERY *A TOUGH INEQUALITY*

On Friday night when Mary and Martin walked into the G. Ale Bar, Ginger gave them a challenging inequality. "This stumps some calculus students," she said, "but I think you can figure it out."

20. Solve Ginger's inequality: $3 < 1/x$. Check and explain your solution.

REVIEW *RECTANGLES*

21. The length of a rectangle is 10 more than the width. Write a formula for:
    a. the width in terms of the length;
    b. the area in terms of the length;
    c. the perimeter in terms of the width.

22. A rectangle has width $3x + 1$ and length $6x + 2$. Find the perimeter when the area is 200.

14.5 SOLUTIONS

14. $\frac{-b}{2a} \pm \sqrt{\frac{-b^2 - 4ac}{4a^2}} = \frac{-b}{2a} \pm \frac{\sqrt{b^2 - 4ac}}{\sqrt{4a^2}}$
$= \frac{-b}{2a} \pm \frac{\sqrt{b^2 - 4ac}}{2a} = \frac{-b \pm \sqrt{b^2 - 4ac}}{2a}$

15. $x = \frac{-3 \pm \sqrt{17}}{2}$

16. $x = 3 \pm \sqrt{13}$

17. $x = -1 \pm \frac{\sqrt{21}}{3}$

18. $x = 1$ or $x = 4/3$

19. Reports will vary. Students should include at least the five methods listed in Lesson 13.8 as well as the quadratic formula.

20. This can be solved by graphing $y = 1/x$ and $y = 3$ on the same axes. The solution is $0 < x < 1/3$.

21. a. $W = L - 10$
    b. $A = L(L - 10)$
    c. $P = 4W + 20$

22. Solve the quadratic equation $(3x + 1)(6x + 2) = 200$ to get $x = 3$. The perimeter when $x = 3$ is $2(10) + 2(20) = 60$.

LESSON 14.6 Translations of $y = ax^2$

You will need:

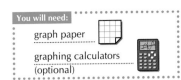

- graph paper
- graphing calculators (optional)

VERTEX FORM

In Chapter 13 you learned that the parameters H and V in the equation $y = (x - H)^2 + V$ represent the coordinates of the vertex of a parabola which is a translation of the one with equation $y = x^2$. This is easy to generalize to any equation in the form $y = a(x - H)^2 + V$, even when $a \neq 1$.

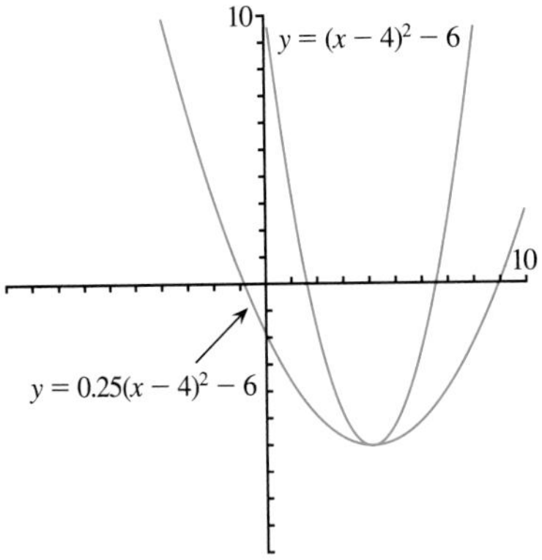

The two parabolas shown in the figure have the same vertex.

1. Write the equation of a parabola having the same vertex as both in the figure that is
a. more open than either;
b. more closed than either;
c. between the two.

2.
a. Explain why the lowest value for the quantity $(x - 4)^2$ is 0.
b. Explain how it follows that the lowest point for both parabolas must be for $x = 4$.

3. Write the equation of the parabola that has the same shape as $y = 0.25x^2$ having vertex (-3, 2).

4. Find the equation of a parabola that is a translation of $y = 5x^2$ having vertex (4, -2).

5. The following questions are about the function $y = 6(x + 5)^2 - 4$.
a. What are the coordinates of the vertex of its graph?
b. What is the equation of the parabola of the same shape having the vertex at the origin?
c. What is the equation of the frown parabola having the same shape, and the vertex at the origin?
d. What is the equation of the frown parabola having the same shape and vertex?

6. **Summary** What do you know about the shape and vertex of the graph of $y = a(x - H)^2 + V$?

MORE ON EQUAL SQUARES

Use the equal squares method to solve each equation. Notice how the solutions of the first equation in each pair differ from the solutions of the second equation.

7. a. $x^2 - 9 = 0$
b. $4x^2 - 9 = 0$

▼ 14.6 Translations of $y = ax^2$

Core Sequence: 1-11

Suitable for Homework: 1-11, 16-22

Useful for Assessment: 2, 6, 11

What this Lesson is About:

- Vertex form
- Review of the role of the parameter a
- Review of equal squares
- Derivation of the quadratic formula by completing the square
- Patterns with fractions

VERTEX FORM

This section generalizes some of the work done in Chapter 13, Lesson 7, while reviewing the effect of different values of the parameter a.

MORE ON EQUAL SQUARES

This section serves to review the equal squares technique from Chapter 13, Lesson 6, and the approach to the quadratic formula from Chapter 14, Lesson 5.

14.6 SOLUTIONS

1. Answers will vary.
   a. Any equation of the form $y = a(x - 4)^2 - 6$ where $0 < a < 0.25$. Example: $y = 0.125(x - 4)^2 - 6$.
   b. Any equation of the form $y = a(x - 4)^2 - 6$ where $a > 1$. Example: $y = 3(x - 4)^2 - 6$.
   c. Any equation of the form $y = a(x - 4)^2 - 6$ where $0.25 < a < 1$. Example: $y = 0.5(x - 4)^2 - 6$.
2. a. A square must have a nonnegative value.
   b. When 4 is substituted for x, the value of the expression $(x - 4)^2$ is 0, which is the smallest possible value of that expression.
3. $y = 0.25(x + 3)^2 + 2$
4. $y = 5(x - 4)^2 - 2$
5. a. (-5, -4)
   b. $y = 6x^2$
   c. $y = -6x^2$
   d. $y = -6(x + 5)^2 - 4$
6. The shape is the same as $y = ax^2$. The sign of a determines whether the parabola opens up or down. The vertex is (H, V).
7. a. $x = \pm 3$
   b. $x = \pm 3/2$

COMPLETING THE SQUARE

THE QUADRATIC FORMULA, AGAIN

These sections present the traditional approach to the quadratic formula. It is here for completeness and does not need to be assigned, especially if your students have done Lesson 5.

8. a. $x^2 - 6 = 0$
b. $9x^2 - 6 = 0$

9. a. $(x - 3)^2 - 5 = 0$
b. $16(x - 3)^2 - 5 = 0$

10. a. $(x + 2)^2 - 7 = 0$
b. $3(x + 2)^2 - 7 = 0$

11. **Generalization**
a. Describe how the roots of the second equation in each pair differ from the roots of the first equation.
b. Use the equal squares method to find a general formula for the solutions of the equation $a(x - H)^2 + V = 0$. Explain.

If you did problem 11 correctly, you should have found the same formula as in Lesson 5.

$$H \pm \sqrt{-\frac{V}{a}}$$

COMPLETING THE SQUARE

You can change a quadratic equation from standard form to vertex form by completing the square. When $a \neq 1$, it is more difficult, but it can still be done.

Example: Write $y = 3x^2 + 6x - 9$ in vertex form.
Start by factoring out the 3:
$$y = 3(x^2 + 2x - 3)$$
Then complete the square for the quantity inside the parentheses:
$$y = 3(x^2 + 2x + 1 - 1 - 3)$$
$$= 3((x + 1)^2 - 4)$$
Finally, distribute the 3:
$$y = 3(x + 1)^2 - 12$$

So $H = -1$ and $V = -12$. You can check that this was done correctly by finding H and V using the method from Lesson 4:
$$H = -b/(2a) = -6/6 = -1$$
$$V = 3(-1)^2 + 6(-1) - 9 = -12$$

The same method for completing the square is used even when a is not a common factor.

Example: Write $y = 3x^2 + 5x - 7$
Factor the 3:
$$y = 3\left(x^2 + \frac{5}{3}x - \frac{7}{3}\right)$$
Complete the square:
$$y = 3\left(x^2 + \frac{5}{3}x + \frac{25}{36} - \frac{25}{36} - \frac{7}{3}\right)$$
$$= 3\left(\left(x + \frac{5}{6}\right)^2 - \frac{109}{36}\right)$$
Distribute the 3:
$$y = 3\left(x + \frac{5}{6}\right)^2 - \frac{109}{12}$$
So $H = -5/6$ and $V = -109/12$.

12. Check that H and V were found correctly.

Complete the square.

13. $y = 3x^2 + 6x + 9$

14. $y = -2x^2 + 5x + 8$

15. $y = 2x^2 - 5x + 3$

THE QUADRATIC FORMULA, AGAIN

Let us write $y = ax^2 + bx + c$ in vertex form by completing the square.

Factor the a:
$$y = a\left(x^2 + \frac{b}{a}x + \frac{c}{a}\right)$$
Complete the square:
$$y = a\left(x^2 + \frac{b}{a}x + \frac{b^2}{4a^2} - \frac{b^2}{4a^2} + \frac{c}{a}\right)$$
$$= a\left(\left(x + \frac{b}{2a}\right)^2 + \frac{-b^2 + 4ac}{4a^2}\right)$$
Distribute the a:
$$y = a\left(x + \frac{b}{2a}\right)^2 + \frac{-b^2 + 4ac}{4a}$$

14.6 SOLUTIONS

8. a. $x = \pm\sqrt{6}$
b. $x = \pm\sqrt{6}/3$

9. a. $x = 3 \pm \sqrt{5}$
b. $x = 3 \pm \sqrt{5}/4$

10. a. $x = -2 \pm \sqrt{7}$
b. $x = -2 \pm \sqrt{7/3}$

11. a. In each pair, the roots of the first equation are of the form $x = H \pm R$. (In #7 and #8, $H = 0$.) The second equation has roots of the form $x = H \pm R/\sqrt{a}$.
b. $a(x - H)^2 + V = 0$
$a(x - H)^2 = -V$
$(x - H)^2 = -V/a$
$x - H = \pm\sqrt{-V/a}$
$x = H \pm \sqrt{-V/a}$

12. $H = -b/(2a) = -5/6$
$V = 3(-5/6)^2 + 5(-5/6) - 7 = 25/12 - 25/6 - 7 = (25 - 50 - 84)/12 = -109/12$

13. $y = 3(x + 1)^2 + 6$

14. $y = -2(x - 1.25)^2 + 11.125$

15. $y = 2(x - 1.25)^2 - 0.125$

So $H = \frac{-b}{2a}$, and $V = \frac{-b^2 + 4ac}{4a}$ as we saw in Lesson 5.

Finally, if we solve the equation

$$a\left(x + \frac{b}{2a}\right)^2 + \frac{-b^2 + 4ac}{4a} = 0$$

by the equal squares method, we get:

$$a\left(x + \frac{b}{2a}\right)^2 = \frac{b^2 - 4ac}{4a}$$

$$\left(x + \frac{b}{2a}\right)^2 = \frac{b^2 - 4ac}{4a^2}$$

So:

$$x + \frac{b}{2a} = \pm\sqrt{\frac{b^2 - 4ac}{4a^2}}$$

$$x = \frac{-b}{2a} \pm \frac{\sqrt{b^2 - 4ac}}{2a}$$

$$x = \frac{-b \pm \sqrt{b^2 - 4ac}}{2a}$$

DISCOVERY EGYPTIAN FRACTIONS

The ancient Egyptians used only those fractions having 1 for the numerator.

16. Find the sum. Look for patterns.

a. $\frac{1}{5} + \frac{1}{20} = \frac{1}{?}$ b. $\frac{1}{3} + \frac{1}{6} = \frac{1}{?}$

c. $\frac{1}{4} + \frac{1}{12} = \frac{1}{?}$

17. Use the above pattern to predict these missing denominators.

a. $\frac{1}{7} + \frac{1}{?} = \frac{1}{6}$ b. $\frac{1}{?} + \frac{1}{30} = \frac{1}{5}$

c. $\frac{1}{10} + \frac{1}{90} = \frac{1}{?}$

18. Write three more problems having the same pattern as above.

19. Generalization

a. Write an algebraic statement to describe the pattern you found in #16. Use expressions in terms of D for m and n in the equality.

$$\frac{1}{m} + \frac{1}{n} = \frac{1}{D}$$

b. Use algebra to check that your statement is an identity.

20. Find x. Look for patterns.

a. $\frac{1}{2} + \frac{1}{3} + \frac{1}{6} = \frac{1}{x} + \frac{1}{x}$

b. $\frac{1}{4} + \frac{1}{5} + \frac{1}{20} = \frac{1}{x} + \frac{1}{x}$

21. Use the above pattern to express the following fractions as a sum of Egyptian fractions. Check your answers.

a. $\frac{2}{5}$ b. $\frac{2}{7}$

22. Generalization

a. Write an algebraic statement to describe the pattern.

b. Use algebra to check that your statement is an identity.

14.6 SOLUTIONS

16. a. 1/4
    b. 1/2
    c. 1/3

17. a. 42
    b. 6
    c. 9

18. Answers will vary.

19. a. $\frac{1}{D+1} + \frac{1}{D(D+1)} = \frac{1}{D}$

    b. Get a common denominator.

$$\frac{D}{D(D+1)} + \frac{1}{D(D+1)} = \frac{D+1}{D(D+1)} = \frac{1}{D}$$

20. a. $x = 2$
    b. $x = 4$

21. a. $\frac{1}{5} + \frac{1}{6} + \frac{1}{30} = \frac{2}{5}$

    b. $\frac{1}{7} + \frac{1}{8} + \frac{1}{56} = \frac{2}{7}$

22. $\frac{1}{a} + \frac{1}{a+1} + \frac{1}{a(a+1)} = \frac{2}{a}$

▼ 14.7
Equations and Numbers

Core Sequence: 1-11, 17-22

Suitable for Homework: 1-11, 17-20, 23

Useful for Assessment: 2, 10-11

What this Lesson is About:

- Number of x-intercepts of a quadratic function
- Number of solutions of a quadratic equation
- The discriminant
- The sum and product of the solutions to a quadratic equation
- From natural numbers to real numbers

HOW MANY x-INTERCEPTS?

HOW MANY SOLUTIONS?

In this section students use what they know about a, c, and V to predict the number of x-intercepts of a parabola, and therefore the number of solutions of the corresponding equation.

For problem 1 students will need to remember that c is the y-intercept and that a determines whether the parabola is a frown or a smile.

Problems 3-9 provide reasons for the significance of the sign of the discriminant. Of course, a simple explanation based on the quadratic formula is possible, as indicated in problem 10.

LESSON

14.7 Equations and Numbers

In this lesson we will discuss quadratic functions and equations in standard form, $y = a^2 + bx + c$ and $ax^2 + bx + c = 0$.

HOW MANY x-INTERCEPTS?

A quadratic equation may have 2, 1, or 0 real number solutions, depending on the number of x-intercepts on the graph of the corresponding function.

1. Sketch a parabola for whose equation:
   a. $a > 0$ and $c < 0$
   b. $a < 0$ and $c > 0$

2. (key) Explain why a parabola for which a and c have opposite signs must intersect the x-axis.

3. Sketch a parabola to explain why if $a > 0$ and $V < 0$ there are two x-intercepts.

4. Fill the table with the number of x-intercepts for a quadratic function with the given signs for a and V. Justify each answer with a sketch.

	$V < 0$	$V = 0$	$V > 0$
$a > 0$	2	—	—
$a < 0$	—	—	—

(We do not consider the case $a = 0$, since then the function is no longer quadratic.)

5. How many x-intercepts are there if:
   a. $V = 0$?
   b. V and a have the same sign?
   c. V and a have opposite signs?

In Lesson 6 you found that $V = \dfrac{-b^2 + 4ac}{4a}$.

Definition: The quantity $b^2 - 4ac$, which appears under the radical in the quadratic formula, is called the *discriminant*, which is sometimes written Δ (the Greek letter *delta*).

6. Explain why we can write $V = -\Delta/(4a)$.

HOW MANY SOLUTIONS?

It turns out that the discriminant allows us to know the number of solutions of a quadratic equation. Refer to the table in problem 4 to answer the following questions.

7. If $\Delta = 0$, what is V? How many solutions are there?

8. If $\Delta > 0$,
   a. and $a > 0$, what is the sign of V? How many solutions are there?
   b. and $a < 0$, what is the sign of V? How many solutions are there?

9. If $\Delta < 0$,
   a. and $a > 0$, what is the sign of V? How many solutions are there?
   b. and $a < 0$, what is the sign of V? How many solutions are there?

The quadratic formula can be written:

$$\frac{-b \pm \sqrt{\Delta}}{2a}$$

10. **Summary** Using the quadratic formula, explain why,
    a. if $\Delta = 0$ there is only one solution;
    b. if $\Delta < 0$ there are no real solutions;
    c. if $\Delta > 0$ there are two real solutions.

11. (key) Explain why if a and c have opposite signs, the discriminant cannot be negative.

14.7 SOLUTIONS

1. a.

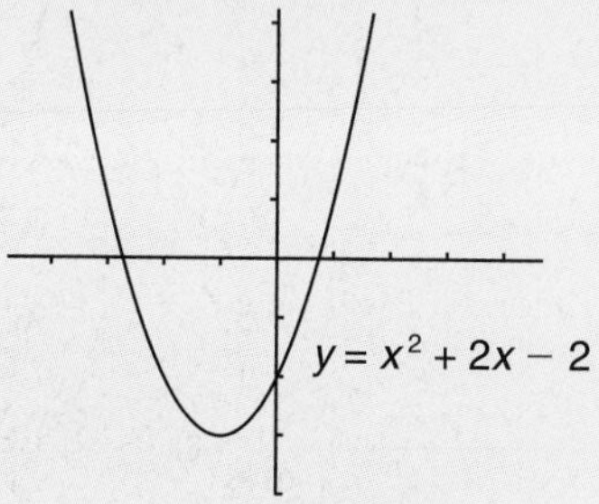

b.

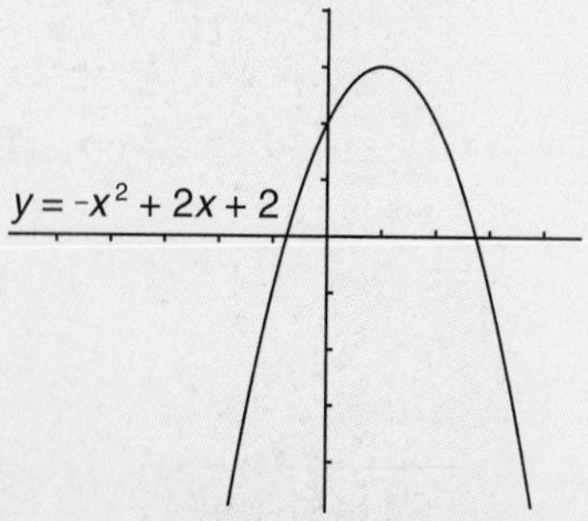

2. If $a < 0$ and $c > 0$, the parabola has a y-intercept above the x-axis and opens down, so it must cross the x-axis. If $a > 0$ and $c < 0$, the parabola has a y-intercept below the x-axis and opens up, so it must cross the x-axis.

3.

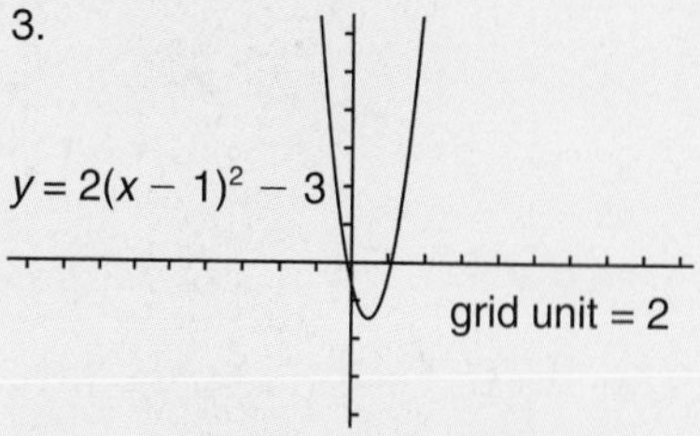

4.

	$V < 0$	$V = 0$	$V > 0$
$a > 0$	2	1	0
$a < 0$	0	1	2

5.

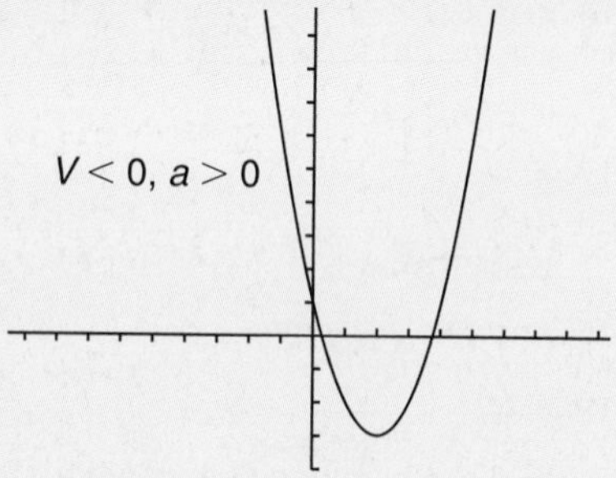

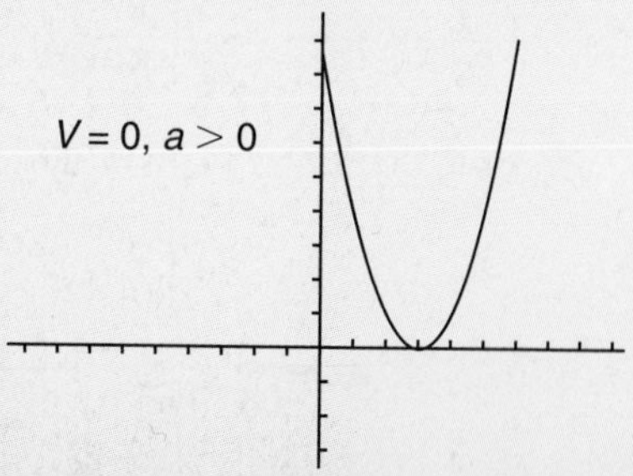

SUM AND PRODUCT OF THE SOLUTIONS

12. In the case where there are two solutions

$x_1 = \frac{-b+\sqrt{\Delta}}{2a}$ and $x_2 = \frac{-b-\sqrt{\Delta}}{2a}$,

a. what is $x_1 + x_2$?

b. what is the average of x_1 and x_2? (How is this related to the axis of symmetry?)

c. what is $x_1 \cdot x_2$?

The sum of the solutions of a quadratic equation is $S = -b/a$, and the product is $P = c/a$. This provides a quick way to check the correctness of the solutions to a quadratic.

> **Example:** Phred solved the quadratic equation $2x^2 + 5x - 8 = 0$ and got $\frac{-5 \pm \sqrt{89}}{2}$. To check the correctness of the answer, he added the two roots, hoping to get $S = -b/a = -5/2$. Conveniently, the $\sqrt{89}$ disappeared:
>
> $$\frac{-5+\sqrt{89}}{2} + \frac{-5-\sqrt{89}}{2} = \frac{-10}{2}$$
>
> Since $-10/2 \neq -5/2$, Phred must have made a mistake.

Solve, and check the correctness of your answers, with the help of S and P (or by substituting in the original equation).

13. $2x^2 + 5x - 8 = 0$

14. $2x^2 - 8x + 5 = 0$

15. $-8x^2 + 3x + 5 = 0$

16. $-2x^2 - 5x - 1 = 0$

KINDS OF NUMBERS

The first numbers people used were whole numbers. It took many centuries to discover more and more types of numbers. The discovery of new kinds of numbers is related to the attempt to solve more and more equations. The following equations are examples.

a. $x + 2 = 9$ b. $x + 9 = 2$

c. $2x = 6$ d. $6x = 2$

e. $x^2 = 9$ f. $x^2 = 10$

g. $x^2 = -9$

17. Pretend you know about only the *natural numbers*. (These are the positive whole numbers.) List the equations a-f that can be solved.

18. Pretend you know about only the *integers*. (These are positive and negative whole numbers and zero.) List the equations a-f that can be solved. Find one that has two solutions.

19. Pretend you know about only the *rational numbers*. (These are all fractions, positive, negative, and zero. Of course, integers are included, since for example $3 = 6/2$.) List the equations a-f that can be solved.

20. The *real numbers* include all rational and irrational numbers. Which equations can be solved if you know about all the real numbers?

Natural numbers, integers, rational numbers, and real numbers can all be found on a one-dimensional number line. However, to solve equation (g), you need to get off the number line. The solution is a *complex number*, and it is written $3i$. The number i is a number one unit away from 0, but off the number line. It is defined as a number whose square is -1:

$$i^2 = -1.$$

Complex numbers cannot be shown on a line. They require a two-dimensional number plane. You will learn more about them in future math classes.

21. Create an equation whose solution is

a. a natural number;

b. an integer, but not a natural number;

c. a rational number, but not an integer;

d. an irrational number.

22. Create an equation that has no real number solution.

23. Research Find out about complex numbers.

SUM AND PRODUCT OF THE SOLUTIONS

This section leads to a useful method to check the correctness of solutions to quadratic equations. It requires less calculation than substituting the answer in the original equation. However using a programmable calculator or computer program to check the solutions is even easier.

It is interesting to note that if S is the sum of the solutions, we have $H = S/2$, which makes sense, since the x-coordinate of the vertex is equal to the average of the x-coordinates of the x-intercepts, and therefore half their sum.

KINDS OF NUMBERS

This is the basis for an interesting discussion at the end of the year, as it provides a bird's eye view of students' mathematical careers, from the point of view of equations and their solutions. Problem 23 points to the future.

14.7 SOLUTIONS

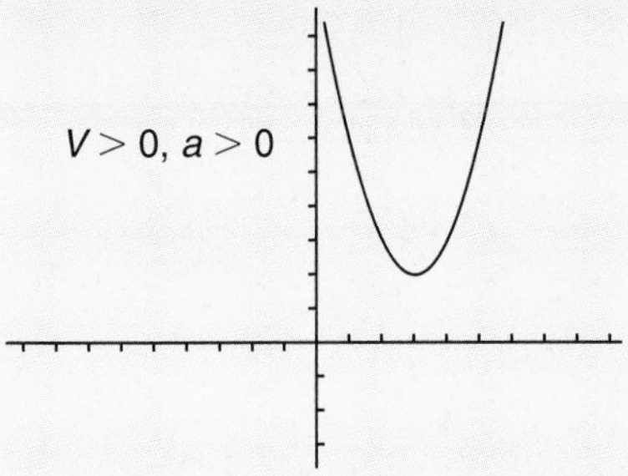

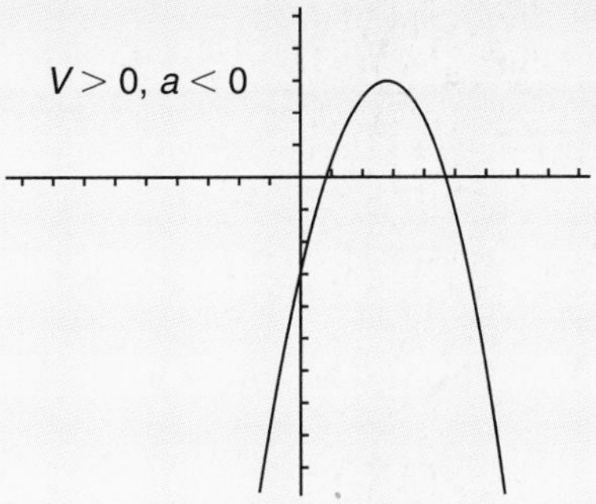

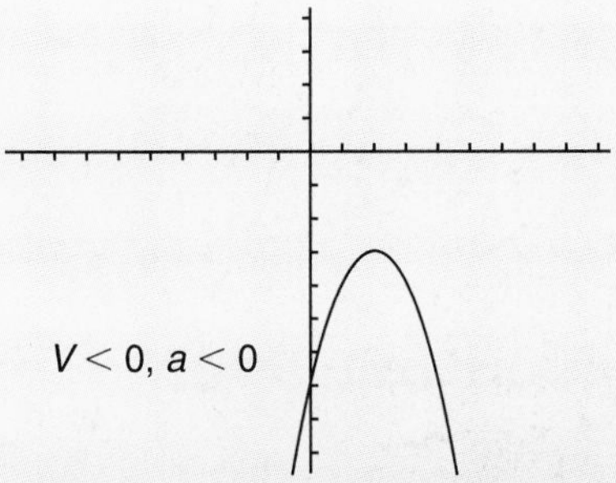

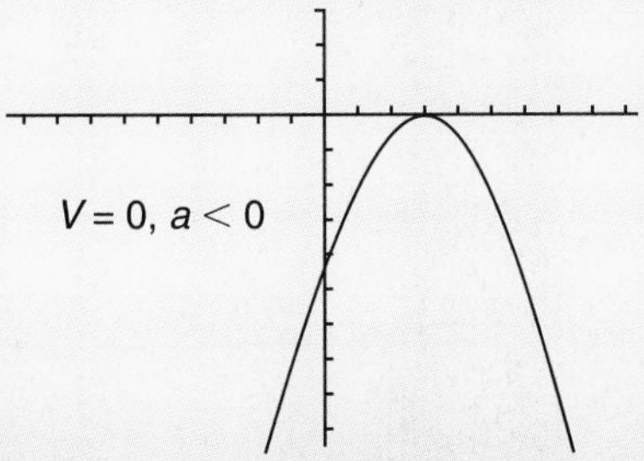

a. 1 b. 0 c. 2

6. $-(b^2 - 4ac) = -b^2 + 4ac$, which is the numerator in the expression for V.

7. $V = 0$. There is 1 solution.

8. We can find the sign of V by using the expression for V in terms of Δ and a that was given in #6. We can find the number of solutions by using the chart made in #4.
   a. Since $a > 0$ and $V < 0$, there are two solutions.
   b. Since $a < 0$ and $V > 0$, there are two solutions.

9. a. Since $a > 0$ and $V > 0$, there are no solutions.
   b. Since $a < 0$ and $V < 0$, there are no solutions.

(Solutions continued on page 531)

▼ 14.8 The Golden Ratio

Core Sequence: 1-17

Suitable for Homework: 12-18

Useful for Assessment: 4, 9-10, 13

What this Lesson is About:

- Review of similar rectangles
- The golden ratio
- Application of quadratic equations
- Review of geometric sequences
- Review of Fibonacci-like sequences
- Preview of limits

This lesson reviews many ideas from the course.

THE GOLDEN RECTANGLE

This activity is somewhat similar to the one that opened the chapter in Lesson 1.

LESSON 14.8

The Golden Ratio

You will need:
- scissors
- graph paper

THE GOLDEN RECTANGLE

1. Take two identical rectangular pieces of paper. Cut a square off one end of one of them, as shown in the figure. Is the remaining rectangle similar to the original one? Check with the diagonal test.

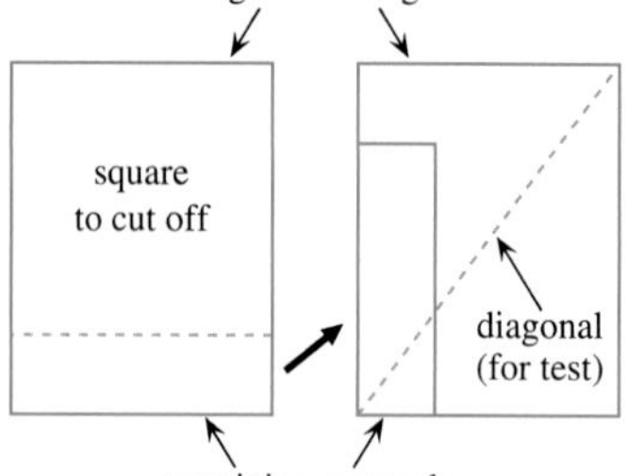

2. Exploration Make a paper rectangle, such that the rectangle that remains after cutting off a square is similar to the original rectangle. What are the dimensions of your rectangle? (Hint: Remember that if two rectangles are similar, their length-to-width ratio must be the same. You may use trial and error on your calculators for different sizes, or write and solve equations.)

Definitions:
- A *golden rectangle* is one that satisfies the following property: If you cut a square off one end of the rectangle, the remaining rectangle is similar to the original one.
- The ratio of the longer to the shorter side of a golden rectangle is called the *golden ratio.*

Golden rectangles and the golden ratio are used frequently in art, design, and architecture.

3. What is the length-to-width ratio of the rectangle you found in problem 2? Compare your answer with your classmates' answers.

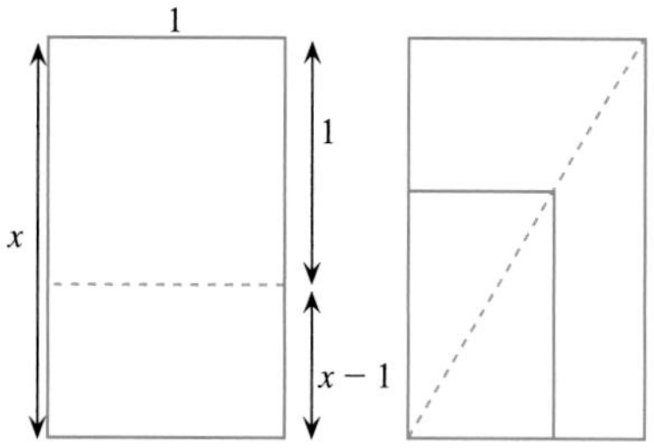

This figure shows a golden rectangle (on the left). To find the exact value of the golden ratio, we will write and solve an equation about the similar rectangles shown (on the right).

4. Explain why $\frac{x-1}{1} = \frac{1}{x}$.

5. Solve the equation.

There should be two solutions. The positive one is the golden ratio.

6. What is the exact value of the golden ratio?

7. What is the golden ratio, rounded to the nearest one thousandth?

8. What is the reciprocal of the golden ratio, rounded to the nearest one thousandth?

Notation: The golden ratio is often represented by the Greek letter φ (*phi*).

14.8 SOLUTIONS

1.-2. Answers will vary. If the rectangles are similar, they will have the same diagonal.

3. Answers will vary. It should be about 1.6.

4. The triangles are similar, by the diagonal test. One has $L = 1$, $W = x$. The other has $L = x - 1$, $W = 1$. The ratio of width to length is the same because they are similar.

5. $\frac{1 \pm \sqrt{5}}{2}$

6. $\frac{1 + \sqrt{5}}{2}$

7. 1.618

8. 0.618

A SPECIAL SEQUENCE

A Fibonacci-like sequence is one in which each term is the sum of the previous two. A geometric sequence is one in which the ratio of consecutive terms is constant. We will try to create a sequence that is geometric and Fibonacci-like at the same time.

9. Consider the sequence $1, k, k^2, k^3, \ldots$. Explain why it is a geometric sequence. What is its common ratio?

10. Explain why, if $1, k, k^2, k^3, \ldots$ were a Fibonacci-like sequence, we would have $1 + k = k^2$.

11. Find a number k that satisfies the equation $1 + k = k^2$. Explain your reasoning.

In problems 9-11, you have shown that the sequence $1, \varphi, \varphi^2, \varphi^3, \ldots$ is geometric and starts out as a Fibonacci-like sequence, since its third term is the sum of the first two. It remains to show that if you add the second and third terms, you get the fourth, if you add the third and fourth, you get the fifth, and so on. More generally, we need to show that if you add the $(n + 1)^{\text{th}}$ term and the $(n + 2)^{\text{th}}$ term, you get the $(n + 3)^{\text{th}}$ term.

12. Use algebra to explain why if $1 + k = k^2$, then $k + k^2 = k^3$.

13. Multiply both sides of $1 + k = k^2$ by k^n. Use the result to show that the sequence $1, \varphi, \varphi^2, \varphi^3, \ldots$ is Fibonacci-like.

GOLDEN WINDOWS

Some architects think that rectangular windows look best if their sides are in the ratio of approximately φ.

14. Imagine that you must make "golden windows" out of square panes. Since the sides must be whole numbers, you will not be able to have an exact golden rectangle, so try to find the dimensions of a few windows having whole number sides in a ratio close to φ.

Many architects use consecutive numbers in the Fibonacci sequence: 1, 1, 2, 3, 5, 8, 13, … as the dimensions of windows and other rectangles. (Example: 3 by 5, or 5 by 8.)

15. Make a sequence of the ratios of consecutive Fibonacci numbers: 1/1, 2/1, 3/2, 5/3, 8/5, 13/8, …. Are the ratios greater or less than the golden ratio? What is the trend in the long run?

16. a. Plot the points (1, 1), (1, 2), (2, 3), (3, 5), (5, 8), (8, 13), ….

b. Graph the line $y = \varphi x$.

c. Describe the position of the points in relation to the line.

17. Plot the points $(1, \varphi), (\varphi, \varphi^2), (\varphi^2, \varphi^3), \ldots$ and the line $y = \varphi x$. Compare the graph with the one in problem 16.

18. **Research** Read about the golden ratio, the golden rectangle, and the Fibonacci sequence. Write a report on what you learn.

A SPECIAL SEQUENCE
GOLDEN WINDOWS

These sections show the intimate relationship between the golden ratio and the Fibonacci sequence. Another relationship is that the nth Fibonacci number is given by the formula:

$$F_n = \frac{\varphi^n - \phi^n}{\sqrt{5}}$$

where φ is the golden ratio and ϕ is the other solution to the same quadratic: $\frac{1 - \sqrt{5}}{2}$. (This formula is too difficult to derive at this level.)

There are many possible references for problem 18, including the book mentioned in the notes to Lesson 1.

14.8 SOLUTIONS

9. k

10. The third term of a Fibonacci-like sequence is obtained by adding the first two terms.

11. This is the same as solving the quadratic equation $1 + x = x^2$, or $x^2 - x - 1 = 0$. By a remarkable coincidence, this is the same equation we solved in #5, so the two solutions are $\frac{1 \pm \sqrt{5}}{2}$.

12. Multiply both sides by k.

13. $k^n(1 + k) = (k^2)k^n$
$k^n + k^{n+1} = k^{n+2}$
This means that each term is the sum of the two previous terms.

14. Answers will vary. (See #15.)

15. Some are greater, some are less. However, they converge quickly to the golden ratio.

16. a & b.

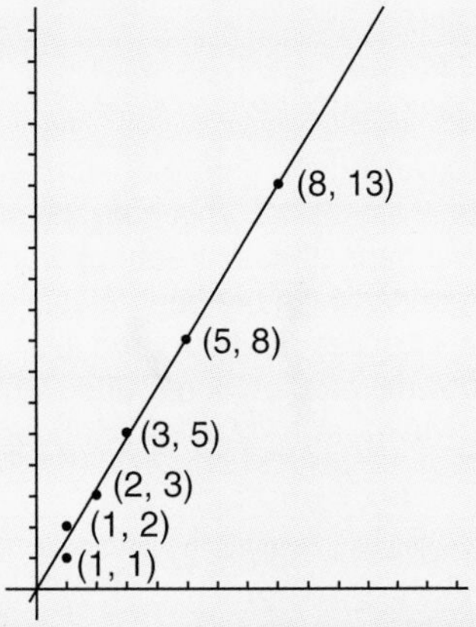

c. The points get closer and closer to the line.

17. These points are on the line. The ratio of y to x is the golden ratio for every point.

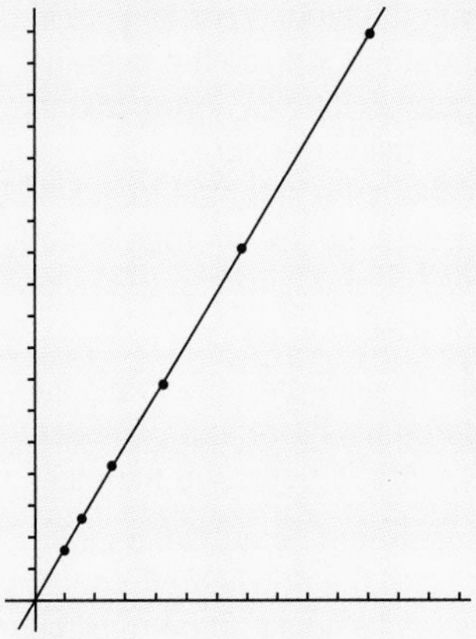

THINKING WRITING **14.B**
Up and Down Stream

Core Sequence: 1-9

Suitable for Homework: 1-9

Useful for Assessment: 9

What this Assignment is About:

- Applying fractions and quadratic equations to a real-world problem
- Review of distance, rate, time problems

This lesson allows students to apply the ideas of this chapter to real-world problems.

Problems 1-4 involve solving problems with numbers. Problems 5 and 6 introduce the use of variables. In problems 7 and 8 students must set up and solve equations. You may need to remind them of the work in **From Fractions to Quadratics** (Lesson 3) and the techniques learned in **Thinking/Writing 13.B**.

THINKING WRITING

14.B Up and Down Stream

BOATS AND CURRENTS

The L.A. Barge Company operates boats on canals, lakes, and rivers. One of their boats, the *Huck Finn*, moves at a maximum rate of 11 mi/hr in still water. The boat regularly does a round trip on the Leumas River, going 32 miles upstream, and returning. The river flows at a rate of 2 mi/hr.

To calculate the total time for the round trip, you need to use the formula

$$\text{distance} = \text{rate} \cdot \text{time}.$$

Assuming the boat goes at its maximum rate, it goes upstream at a rate of $(11 - 2)$ mi/hr, and it goes downstream at a rate of $(11 + 2)$ mi/hr.

1. What is the total time for the round trip? Assume a one-hour stop before heading back.

2. What is the average speed
   a. with a stop?
   b. without a stop?

3. True or False? Since the boat goes upstream on the way there, and downstream on the way back, the effect of the current is cancelled, and the trip takes as long as it would on a lake. Explain.

4. How long does the upstream portion of the trip take? How about the downstream portion?

For problems 5 and 6 assume the boat moves at a rate of r miles per hour in still water.

5. What would its rate be in terms of r,
   a. going upstream if the river is moving at 2 miles per hour?
   b. going downstream if the river is moving at c miles per hour?

6. If the river is moving at 3 miles per hour,
   a. how long does the upstream portion of the trip take in terms of r?
   b. how long does the downstream portion of the trip take in terms of r?
   c. how long does the whole trip take in terms of r?

7. How fast should the boat go (still water rate), if the L.A. Barge Co. wants to conserve fuel, but needs to make the round trip (including a one-hour stop) in:
   a. 13 hours?   b. 8 hours?

AIRPLANES AND WINDS

An airplane flies from Alaberg to Bergala with a headwind of 20 miles per hour and returns with a tailwind of 20 miles per hour. The plane stopped in Bergala for an hour. The whole trip took 4 hours. The towns are 500 miles apart.

8. How long did each portion of the trip take?

YOUR OWN PROBLEM

9. Create a problem involving currents, winds, or moving sidewalks that requires solving a quadratic equation. Solve your problem.

14.B SOLUTIONS

1. $32/9 + 32/13 + 1 = 7$ hours (approximately)
2. The total distance is 64 miles.
   a. With the stop, the total time is about 7 hours, so the average speed is 64/7 or approximately 9.14 miles per hour.
   b. Without the stop, the total time is 6 hours, so the average speed is 64/6 or about 10 and 2/3 miles per hour.
3. False. In still water, the total time would be 64/11, or approximately 5.82 hours (5 hours, 49 minutes).
4. The upstream portion takes 32/9 hours and the downstream portion takes 32/13 hours. If the maximum rate in still water were r, the upstream portion would take $32/(r - 2)$ hours and the downstream portion would take $32/(r + 2)$ hours.
5. a. $r - 2$
   b. $r + c$
6. a. $32/(r - 3)$
   b. $32/(r + 3)$
   c. $32/(r - 3) + 32/(r + 3)$
7. a. Excluding the one-hour stop, the total time is 12. This consists of two parts, the upstream portion (during which the boat travels at $r - 2$ miles per hour) and the downstream portion (during which it travels at $r + 2$ miles per hour).
   $$\frac{32}{r-2} + \frac{32}{r+2} = 12$$
   $$32(r + 2) + 32(r - 2) =$$
   $$12(r - 2)(r + 2)$$
   $$12r^2 - 64r - 48 = 0$$
   The positive solution to this quadratic is 6. This checks in the original equation. (The boat would go 4 mph upstream and 8 mph downstream.)
   b. This can be solved using the same reasoning as in part (a).
   $$\frac{32}{r-2} + \frac{32}{r+2} = 7$$
   Solving the resulting quadratic yields a possible solution of about 9.56 miles per hour.
8. The total flying time of 3 hours can be divided into the time with the head wind and the time with the tail wind.
   $$\frac{500}{r-20} + \frac{500}{r+20} = 3$$
   Multiplying both sides by $(r + 20)(r - 20)$ yields the quadratic equation $3r^2 - 1000r - 1200 = 0$.

Essential Ideas

WINDOWS AND PANES

1. The A.B. Glare Window Store sells a two-pane window, especially designed so that the panes have the same dimensions as each other, and the whole window has the same proportions as each pane. If the horizontal dimension of the window is 36 inches, what is the vertical dimension, to the nearest inch? Make a sketch and show your work.

2. The A.B. Glare Window Store sells two models of two-pane windows, such that one pane is square and the other is rectangular. The rectangular pane has the same proportions as the whole window. Both models have a horizontal dimension of 36 inches. Make a sketch and show your work as you answer the following question: What are the dimensions of the rectangular pane, if its longer dimension is
   a. horizontal? b. vertical?

ALGEBRAIC FRACTIONS

3. Dwight was simplifying $\frac{x+2}{x}$. He said, "I can't get rid of the x's in the numerator and denominator." He wrote $\frac{x+2}{x} = 2$.
   Did Dwight correctly simplify $\frac{x+2}{x}$? Is his statement always, sometimes, or never true?

If possible, simplify the fractions.

4. $\frac{xy + y}{y}$ 5. $\frac{3x + 3y}{x^2 - y^2}$

6. $\frac{3a + 3b}{4a + 4b}$ 7. $\frac{6}{6x - 6}$

8. $\frac{x^2 + 5x}{x^2 + 4x}$ 9. $\frac{2x + 2y}{3x + 3y}$

ALWAYS, SOMETIMES, NEVER

Tell whether each expression is always, sometimes, or never true.

10. $\frac{3x + 5}{3x} = 5$ 11. $\frac{3x + 3y}{x + y} = 6$

12. $\frac{3x + 3y}{x + y} = 3$ 13. $\frac{3x + y}{y} = 3x$

EQUIVALENT FRACTIONS

14. Write a fraction having a denominator of $6y$ that is equivalent to:
    a. 1/6 b. x

15. Write a fraction having a denominator of y that is equivalent to:
    a. $6x$ b. $6xy$

16. a. Write a fraction equivalent to $3/x$ having xy as a denominator.
    b. Write a fraction equivalent to $5/y$ having xy as a denominator.
    c. Add $3/x$ and $5/y$. (Hint: To add, you need a common denominator.)

17. a. Write a fraction that is equivalent to x having x as a denominator.
    b. Add $x + 1/x$. (Hint: Find a common denominator.)

Put on the same denominator.

18. $x^2 + \frac{b}{a}x + \frac{c}{a}$ 19. $-\frac{b^2}{4a^2} + \frac{c}{a}$

DIVISION BY ZERO?

On a test Joel solved the quadratic equation $6x^2 = 12x$ using this method:

Divide both sides by x:	$\frac{6x^2}{x} = \frac{12x}{x}$
Simplify fractions:	$6x = 12$
Divide both side by 6:	$\frac{6x}{6} = \frac{12}{6}$
The answer is	$x = 2$.

◆ S O L U T I O N S

(14.B Solutions continued)

It has 334.53 as a positive solution. This can be substituted to find the time for each portion of the trip.

$\frac{500}{334.53 - 20} = 1.59$ hours, or about 1 hour and 35 minutes

$\frac{500}{334 + 20} = 1.41$ hours, or about 1 hour and 25 minutes.

9. Answers will vary.

1. As shown in the figure:
   $\frac{y}{x} = \frac{x}{2y}$
   If $x = 36$, $y = 25.46$, approximately. Hence the vertical dimension, to the nearest inch, is 51 inches. Note that the ratio 51/36 is approximately the square root of 2.

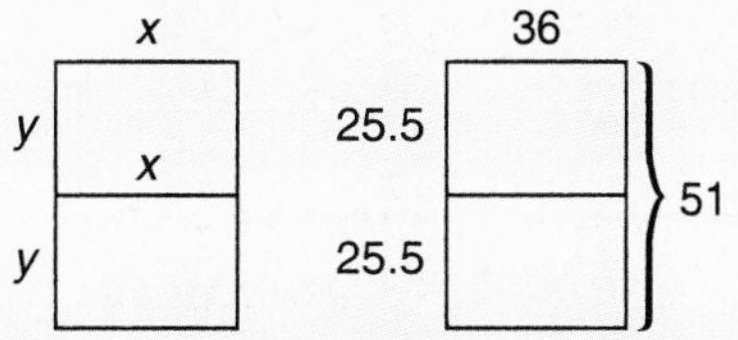

2. a. Solve the equation $\frac{36 + y}{36} = \frac{36}{y}$.
   The positive solution is 22.25, so the rectangular pane is 36 by 22.25. Note that the ratio 36/22.25 is approximately the golden ratio.

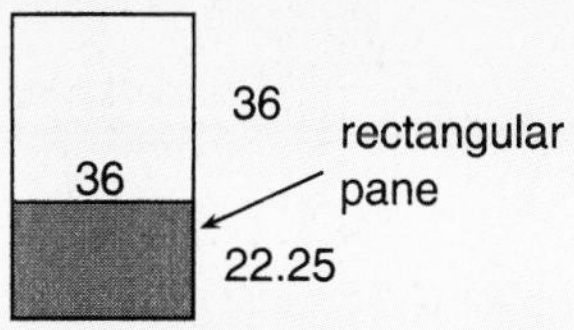

longer dimension horizontal

b. Solve the equation $\frac{y}{36 - y} = \frac{36}{y}$.
   The positive solution is 22.25, so the rectangular pane is 22.25 by (36 − 22.25), or 22.25 by 13.75. Note that the ratio 22.25/13.75 is approximately the golden ratio.

Joel's teacher, Mr. Letter, wrote this on his paper:

> There are two solutions to this equation. You missed one of them because you divided by 0.

Joel was puzzled. "I divided by x, and then by 6," he thought. "I never divided by 0."

20. Can you explain what Mr. Letter meant? Can you solve the equation correctly?

MYSTERY PARABOLAS

Make a rough sketch showing two parabolas having the features described. Some of your parabolas should be frowns and others smiles; some should be more open, some less. Label each parabola with:

a. its equation;
b. its axis of symmetry;
c. its x-intercepts (exact values);
d. its vertex.

21. The parabola has x-intercepts at 2 and -4.

22. The parabola has vertex (3, -5).

23. The parabola has an x-intercept at $\sqrt{5}$ and is symmetric with respect to the y-axis.

24. The parabola has an x-intercept at $1 - \sqrt{6}$ and has the line $x = 1$ as its axis of symmetry.

25. The parabola has an axis of symmetry at $x = 5$ and y-intercept 3.

PARABOLA FEATURES

26. Give the vertex, x-, and y-intercepts of:

a. $y = 2(x + 3)^2 - 9$
b. $y = 4(x - 5)(x + 1)$
c. $y = 6x^2 - 7x - 8$

27. How many x-intercepts?

a. $y = -2(x + 3)^2 - 9$
b. $y = -4(x - 2)^2$
c. $y = 6x^2 + 7x + 8$

FROM FRACTIONS TO QUADRATICS

Rewrite each equation as an equivalent quadratic equation. Then solve the equation. Show your work.

28. $w + 9 = \frac{10}{w}$ **29.** $L + 3 = 2 + \frac{6}{L}$

30. $L - 4 = \frac{32}{L}$ **31.** $\frac{1}{x} = x - 1$

Solve these equations. They have zero, one, or two solutions.

32. $\frac{4}{x} + x = -4$ **33.** $\frac{1}{x} + \frac{2}{x} = \frac{3}{x}$

34. $1 = \frac{1}{x} + \frac{1}{x^2}$

WRITE AN EQUATION

35. Write a quadratic equation that has the following solutions:

a. 4 and -2
b. $\sqrt{5}$ and $-\sqrt{5}$
c. $1 + \sqrt{5}$ and $1 - \sqrt{5}$

36. Write a quadratic equation that has the solution -6.

37. Write a quadratic equation that has no real number solutions.

SOLUTIONS

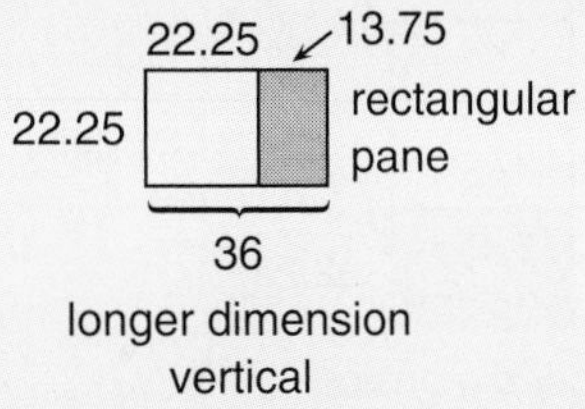

3. He did not simplify it correctly. His statement is true only when $x = 2$.
4. $x + 1$
5. $\frac{3}{x - y}$
6. 3/4
7. $\frac{1}{x - 1}$
8. $\frac{x + 5}{x + 4}$
9. 2/3
10. sometimes true (true when $x = 5/12$)
11. never true
12. always true
13. sometimes true—true for any (x, y) pair such that $x = \frac{y}{3y - 3}$
14. a. $\frac{y}{6y}$
    b. $\frac{6xy}{6y}$ $\frac{6x}{y}$
15. a. $\frac{6xy}{y}$
    b. $\frac{6xy^2}{y}$
16. a. $\frac{3y}{xy}$
    b. $\frac{5x}{xy}$
    c. $\frac{3y}{xy} + \frac{5x}{xy} = \frac{3y + 5x}{xy}$
17. a. $\frac{x^2}{x}$
    b. $\frac{x^2 + 1}{x}$
18. $\frac{ax^2}{a} + \frac{bx}{a} + \frac{c}{a} = \frac{ax^2 + bx + c}{a}$
19. $\frac{-b^2}{4a^2} + \frac{4ac}{4a^2} = \frac{4ac - b^2}{4a^2}$
20. One of the possible values of x is 0. Since Joel divided by x, he was assuming implicitly that $x \neq 0$. Mr. Letter meant that since x can be 0, Joel was dividing by 0 when he divided by x. The equation can easily be solved by factoring:
    $6x^2 - 12x = 0$
    $6x(x - 2) = 0$
    $x = 0$ or $x = 2$

(Solutions continued on page 532)

1.A (Solutions for page 14 continued.)

7. Answers will vary.
   - The graph of x-by-x rectangles is a curve, whereas the graphs of the other rectangles are diagonal lines going up from left to right.
   - The area for the x-by-x rectangles increases very fast (it's an exponential function) but the areas for the other graphs increase by a constant number.
   - The first three are lines with different steepness. The steeper the line, the faster the area grows.
   - The graphs do intersect and the intersections represent where the rectangles have the same area. These rectangles will be the same squares or they will have their lengths and widths interchanged.
   - If the graphs are extended, they will all cross the origin. This means that the rectangle will have one side of zero.
   - The fourth graph crosses the others when the rectangles have their lengths equal to their widths.
   - The area of the x-by-x grows the fastest since it is x^2.

2.9 (Solutions for page 68 continued.)

15. Since the coordinates are switched, the lines on the mirror image diagram are literal mirror images of the original function. If $y = mx + b$ is the original function, then the mirror image function will be $y = (x - b)/m$.

16. Analyzing $y = x + b$: If $b = 0$ then the lines are all horizontal. If $b < 0$ then the lines are all parallel going down from left to right. If $b > 0$ then the lines are all parallel going up from left to right.

    We can analyze $y = x - b$ in the same way as above except we switch $b < 0$ with $b > 0$ in reference to describing how the lines go. See #8 for a description of $y = mx$.

If $m < 0$, the function diagram looks something like:

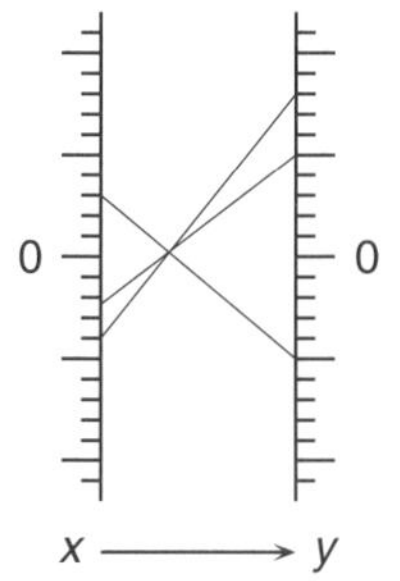

$y = mx$

If $m > 0$, the function diagram looks something like:

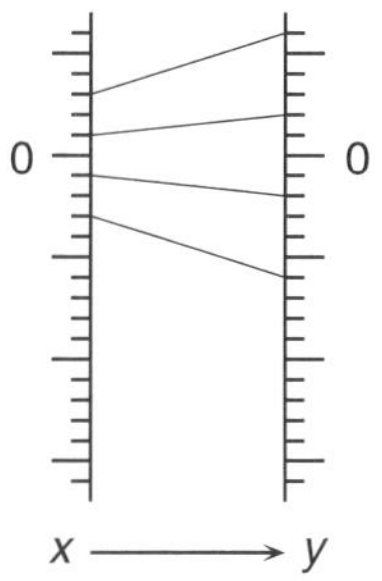

$y = mx$

If $0 < m < 1$, the function diagram looks something like:

If $y = x/m$ and m is an integer, we have the same case as $y = mx$ when $0 < m < 1$.

If $y = x/m$ and $0 < m$, we have the same case as $y = mx$ when $m > 0$.

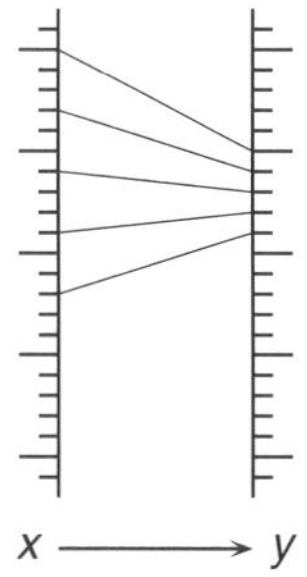

$y = x/m$

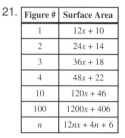

We can now analyze y = x/m. If m > 1 then this function is just like y = mx when 0 < m < 1. If 0 < m < 1 then this is like y = mx when m > 1. If -1 < m < 0 then this is like y = mx when m < -1. And finally, if m < -1 then this is like y = mx when -1 < m < 0.

17. An example of $y = b - x$ and $y = x - b$ when $b = 3$.

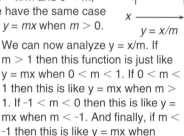

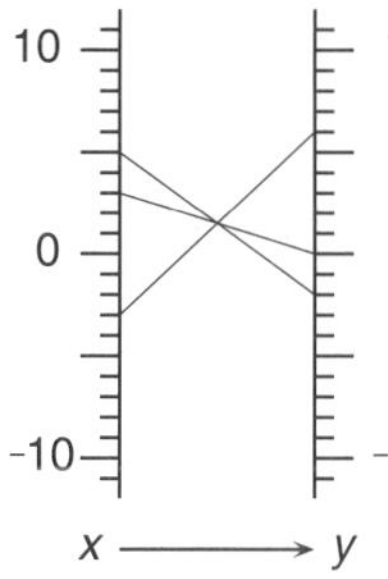

$y = 3 - x$

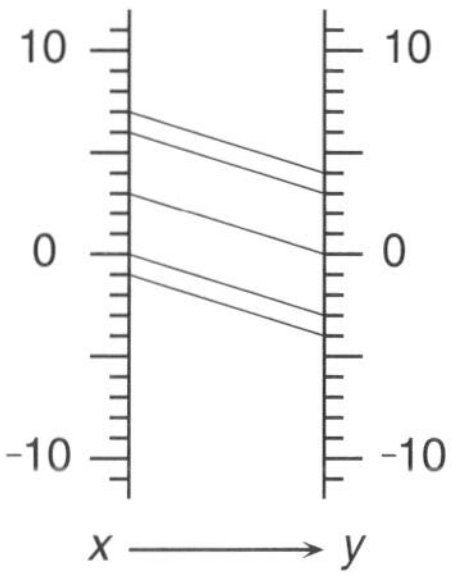

$y = x - 3$

2.10 (Solutions for page 71 continued.)

19.

Figure #	Surface Area
1	$4x + 2$
2	$6x + 4$
3	$8x + 6$
4	$10x + 8$
10	$22x + 20$
100	$202x + 200$
n	$2nx + 2n + 2x$

This is a similar explanation to #18, except we have $n(4x + 2) - (n - 1)(2x) = 2nx + 2n + 2x$.

20.

Figure #	Surface Area
1	$12x + 10$
2	$24x + 10$
3	$36x + 10$
4	$48x + 10$
10	$120x + 10$
100	$1200x + 10$
n	$12nx + 10$

Similar explanation to #18, except we have $n(12x + 10) - (n - 1)(10) = 12nx + 10$.

21.

Figure #	Surface Area
1	$12x + 10$
2	$24x + 14$
3	$36x + 18$
4	$48x + 22$
10	$120x + 46$
100	$1200x + 406$
n	$12nx + 4n + 6$

Similar explanation to #18, except we have $n(12x + 10) - (n - 1)(6) = 12nx + 4n + 6$.

22. xy-block.

2.E.I. (Solutions for page 79 continued.)

20.

Figure #	Perimeter
1	$2x + 10$
2	$4x + 12$
3	$6x + 14$
4	$8x + 16$
10	$20x + 28$
100	$200x + 208$
n	$2nx + 2n + 8$

The explanation is similar to #16 except we have $n(2x + 10) - (n - 1)8 = 2nx + 2n + 8$.

21. Figure #44.

22. a. Problems 17 and 18
    b. Problem 16
    c. None

23. a. $2x + 2y$

    b.

y	Perimeter
1	$2x + 2$
2	$2x + 4$
3	$2x + 6$
4	$2x + 8$
10	$2x + 20$

    c. It's the same as #17. This is true since $2x + 2y$ corresponds exactly to problem #17 when you substitute $y = 1, 2, \ldots$ into this formula.

24. Answers will vary.

25. Answers will vary. One possible answer is given.

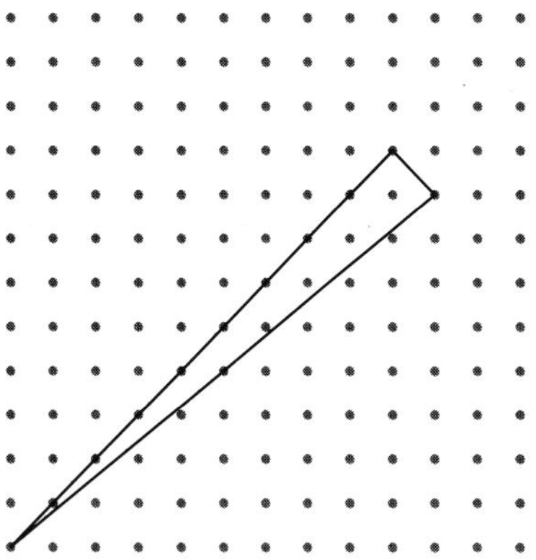

3.1 (Solutions for page 83 continued.)

11. Answers will vary.
    e.g., 99.01 and 100.01, 99.99 and 100.99
    At the end of 6 months, the balances will be \$64 apart. Because the investments differ by \$1 and are doubled every month for 6 months, the result is 2^6 dollars. If the investments differ by \$$y$ and they multiply by A times each month, in M months the result is $y \cdot A^M$ dollars.
12. People who invest more than \$100 will benefit, and people who invest less than \$100 will lose their money or be in debt. Those who invest \$100 will neither gain nor lose money.
13. a. They should invest more than \$50.
    b. They should invest more than \$200.
14. For #12, people who invest more than \$200 will benefit, and people who invest less than \$200 will lose their money or be in debt. Those who invest \$200 will neither gain nor lose money.
    For #13b, same as above, except the threshold amount is \$400.
15. Answers will vary.

3.B (Solutions for page 105 continued.)

5. b.

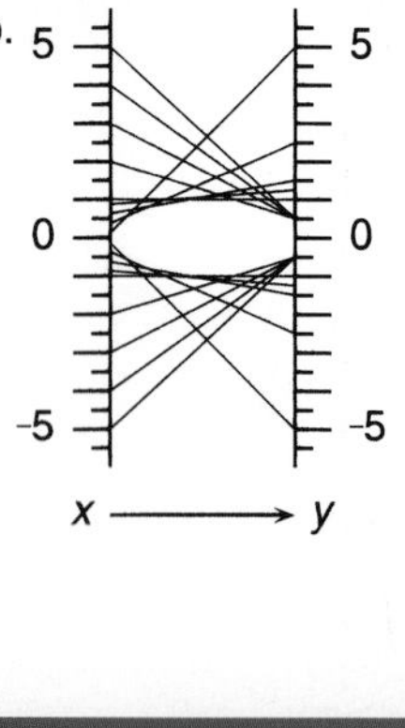

6. a. y decreases.
   b. Yes, at 1 and -1
7. a. y is a negative number close to 0.
   b. y moves down slowly towards -1.
   c. y moves down fast from -1 to smaller negative numbers.
   d. y moves down faster and approaches extremely large negative numbers.
   e. y moves down fast from a large positive number.
   f. y moves down slowly approaching 1.
   g. y moves down slowly approaching 0.
   h. y is a small positive number close to 0.

4.1 (Solutions for page 126 continued.)

14.

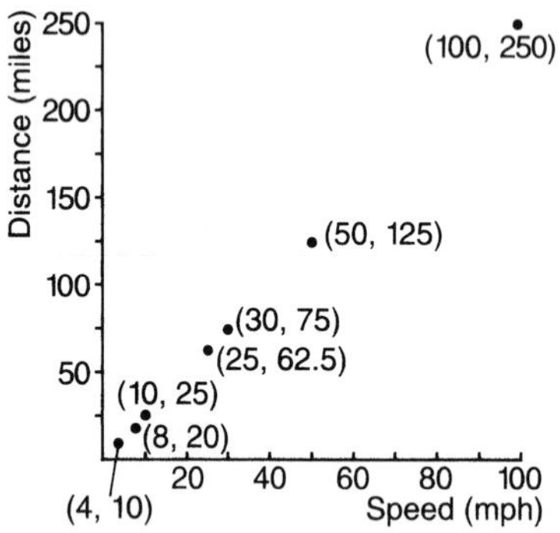

15. If travel time were greater the line would be steeper. Each speed (for example 50 mph) would be paired with a greater distance.
16. Number 4 graphs speed vs. time, #6 graphs time vs. distance, and #14 graphs speed vs. distance.
17. $S = D/T$; $ST = D$; $T = D/S$.
18. a. Student drawing
    b. The frame is 4 in. by 5 in.
    c. No. The side corresponding to the 2 in. side is doubled to 4 in. but the side corresponding to the 3 in. side is not doubled.
19. The new height of the photo is 10 inches. The height of the original photo is 3 inches. $3 \cdot (10/3) = 10$. So we multiply the original width by 10/3 as well, to get $2(10/3) = 20/3$. Width of the new frame is $20/3 + 2 = 26/3$.
20. No, the new frame is not similar to the new photo. The dimensions of the new frame are 26/3 in. by 12 in. and the new photo's are 20/3 in. by 10 in. The ratio of heights is 12/10. The ratio of the widths is (26/3)/(20/3), which is not equal to 12/10.

4.2 (Solutions for page 128 continued.)

3. d. $y = -x$

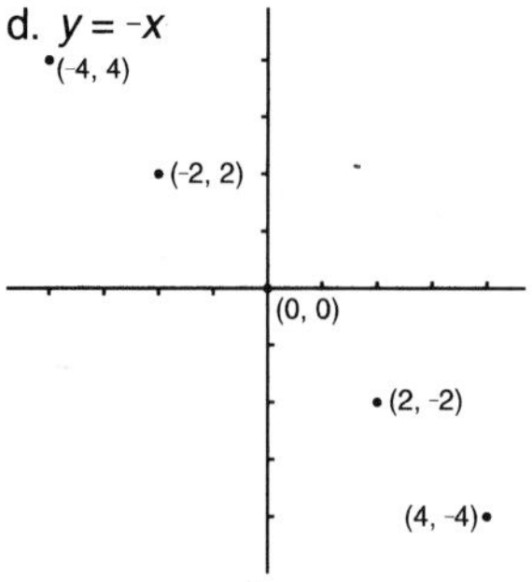

   e. $y = x^2$

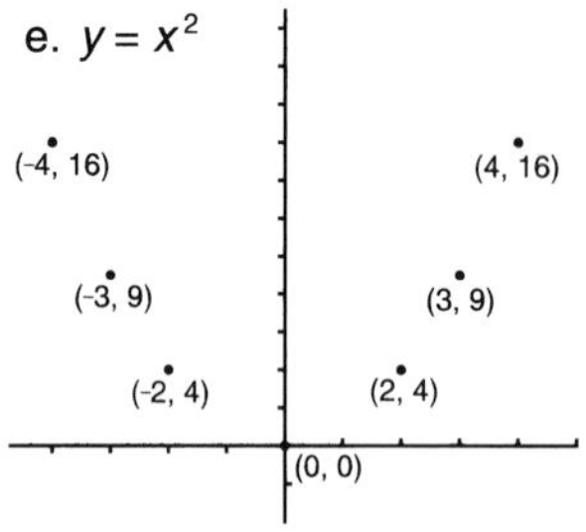

4. See the equation on each of the graphs for problem 3.
5. a. One possible table of values is:

x	y
-3	9
-1	7
0	6
2	4

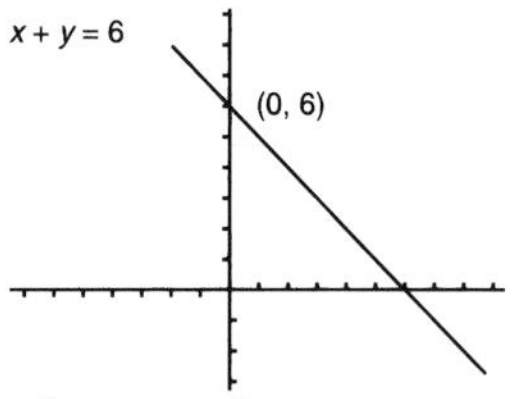

   d. $x + y = 6$
6. a. One possible table of values is:

x	y
1/2	5.5
2.6	3.4

   Yes, they lie on the line.
   b. Sample point (1, 1). No, 1 + 1 is not equal to 6.
   c. Sample point (4, 7). No, the point is not on the line.
7. a. Square the x-value and subtract 9 to get the resulting y-value
   b. One possible table of values is:

x	y
-2	-5
1	-8
3	0

   c. $y = x^2 - 9$

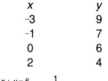

8. a. Add 3.5 to each x-value to get the resulting y-value.
   b. One possible table of values is:

x	y
-1	2.5
1	4.5
2	5.5

   c. $y = x + 3.5$

9. a. The product of x and y is 36.
   b. One possible table of values is:

x	y
-1	-36
1	36
2	18

   c. $xy = 36$ or $y = 36/x$

10. a. y is always 1.25 no matter what value of x is given.
   b. One possible table of values is:

x	y
4	1.25
1	1.25
-1.25	1.25

   c. $y = 1.25$

11. No, (7, 32) is not on $y = 4x + 5$ because $4(7) + 5 = 28 + 5 = 33$, which is not equal to 32.

12. $y = 17$ because when $x = 3$, $y = 4(3) + 5 = 12 + 5 = 17$.

13. $x = 1/4$ because when $y = 6$ we have $6 = 4x + 5 = 4(1/4) + 5 = 1 + 5 = 6$.

4.3 (Solutions for page 130 continued.)

8. a. $y = 2x^3$
   i. A sample table of values is:

x	y
-2	-16
-1.5	-6.75
-1	-2
-0.5	-0.25
0	0
0.5	0.25
1	2
2	16

   ii. $y = 2x^3$

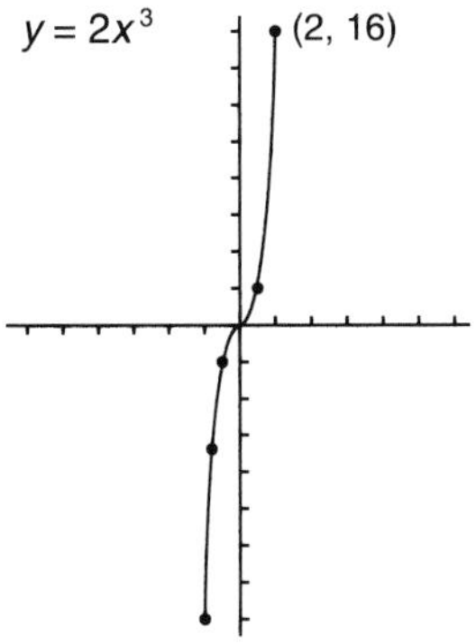

   b. $y = x^3 + 1$
   i. A sample table of values is:

x	y
-2.5	-14.625
-2	-7
-1.5	-2.375
-0.5	0.875
0	1
0.5	1.125
1	2
2	9

   ii. $y = x^3 + 1$

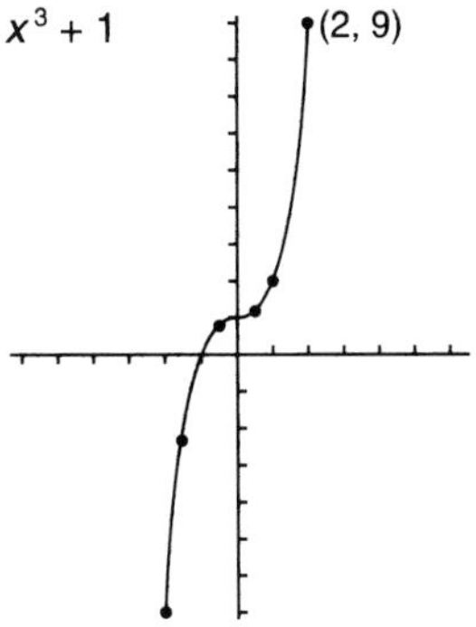

   c. $y = -x^3 - 2$
   i. A sample table of values is:

x	y
-2	6
-1.5	1.375
-1	-1
-0.5	-1.875
0	-2
0.5	-2.125
1	-3
2	-10

   ii. $y = -x^3 - 2$

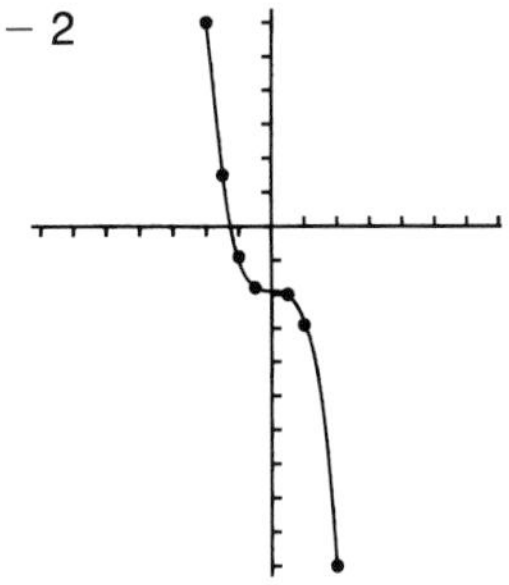

9. a. $y = x^2 - 1$
   i. A sample table of values is:

x	y
-2	3
-1.5	1.25
-1	0
-0.5	-0.75
0	-1
0.5	-0.75
1	0
2	3

   ii. $y = x^2 - 1$

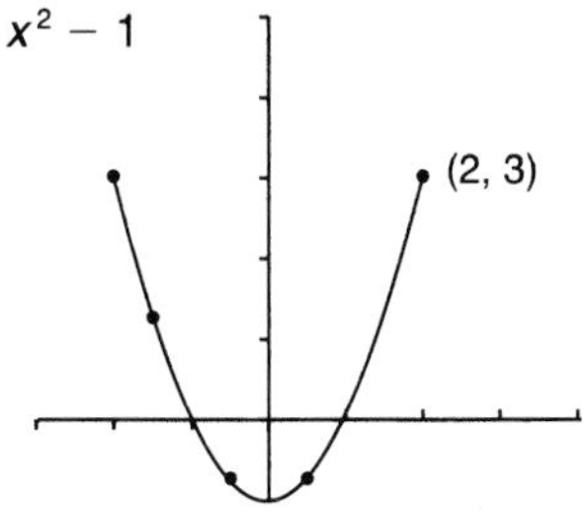

   b. $y = -3x^2$
   i. A sample table of values is:

x	y
-2	-12
-1.5	-6.75
-1	-3
-0.5	-0.75
0	0
1	-3
1.5	-6.75
2	-12

   ii. $y = -3x^2$

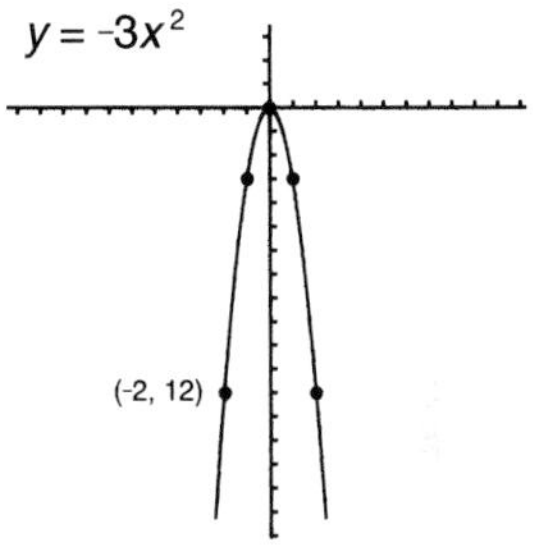

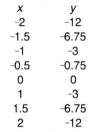

   c. $y = -x^2 + 2$
   i. A sample table of values is:

x	y
-2	-2
-1.5	-0.25
-1	1
-0.5	1.75
0	2
0.5	1.75
1	1
2	-2

   ii. $y = -x^2 + 2$

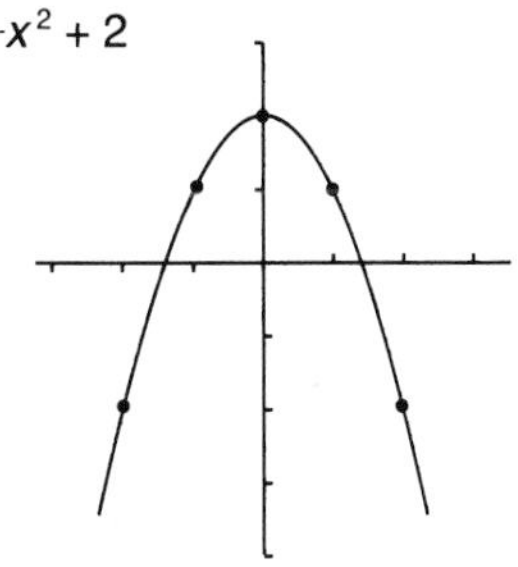

10. $y = 5x$

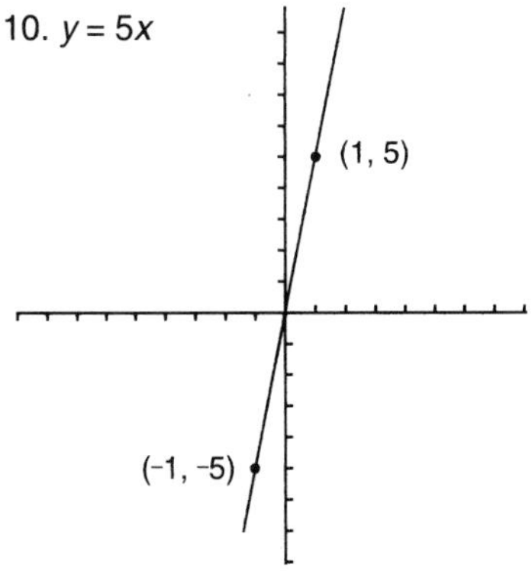

b. $y = x$

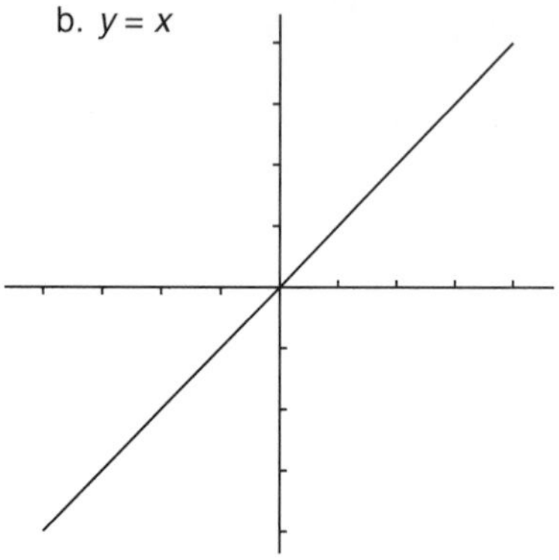

c. $y = -2x + 1$

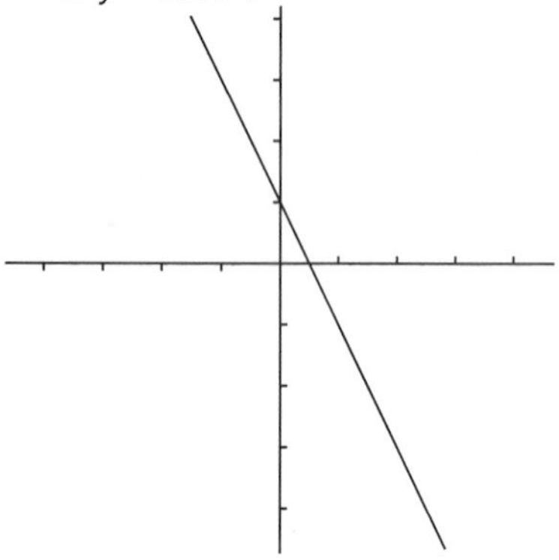

11. a. $y = 4$

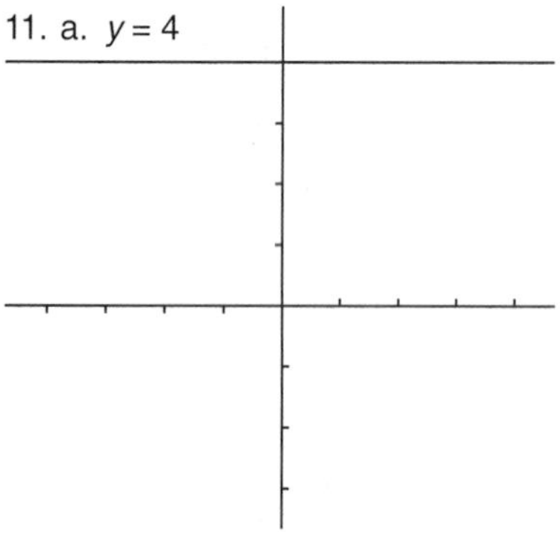

b. $y = -3$

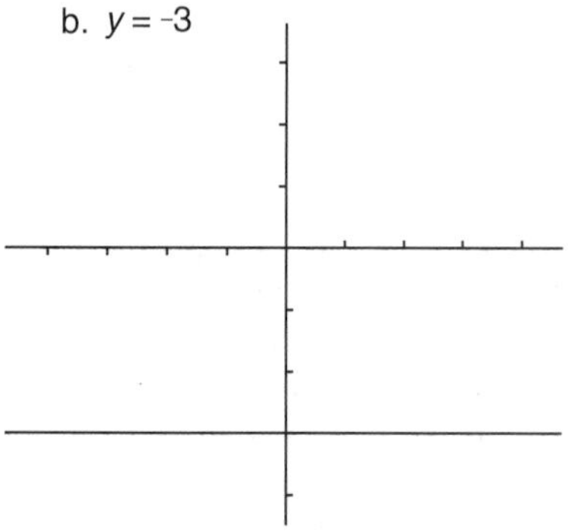

c. $y = 0$

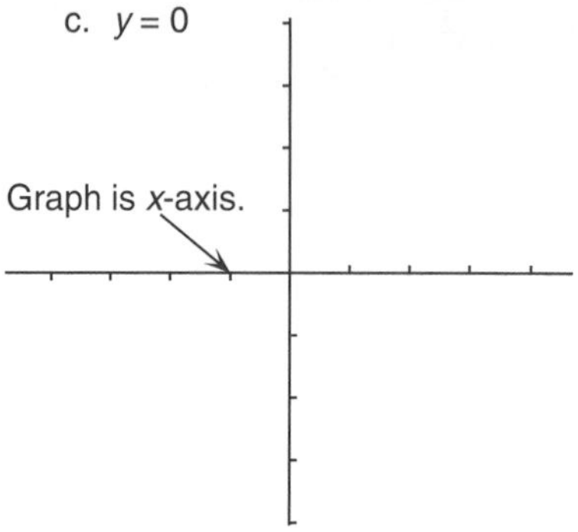

12. a. Zero or first degree
    b. Second or third degree
13. a. Zero, first, second, or third degree
    b. Zero or second degree
    c. Impossible. Zero, first, second, and third-degree polynomial functions all cross the *y*-axis.
14. a. First or third degree
    b. First or third degree
    c. Zero or second degree
15. Ideas to look for: Zero and first-degree polynomial functions are straight lines where second- and third-degree functions are curves. Zero-degree polynomial functions are horizontal lines which pass through quadrants I and II, III and IV, or are on the *x*-axis. Second-degree polynomials are parabolas passing through all four quadrants or just I and II, or III and IV. First-degree equations are straight lines passing through quadrants I and III and the origin, or II and IV and the origin, or through any three quadrants. Third-degree equations are curves which have the same quadrant properties as first-degree equations.
16. a. $y = 24/x$

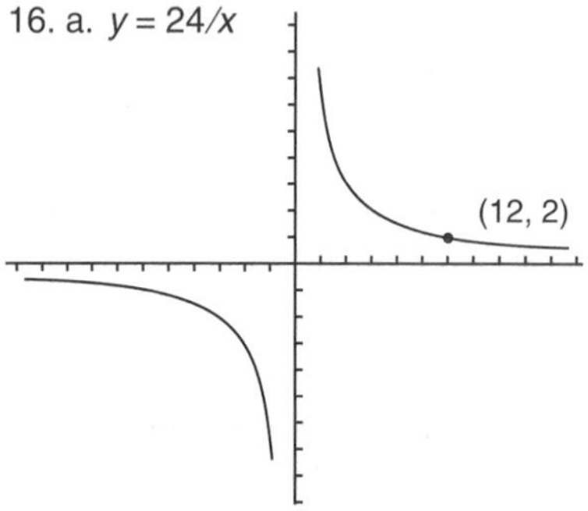

    b. No, this is not a polynomial function because the variable *x* is in the denominator of $24/x$.
17. a. Possible: $-3 - (-10) = 7$
    b. Possible: $-7 - (-3) = -4$
    c. Possible: $10 - (-5) = 15$
    d. Impossible: The result is always positive. Subtracting a negative number has the same result as adding the negative number's opposite. For example, $10 - (-5) = 10 + 5 = 15$. So, subtracting a negative number from a positive number has the same result as adding a positive number (the negative's opposite) to a positive number.
    e. Possible: $-10 - 1 = -11$
    f. Impossible: The result is always negative. Subtracting a positive number has the same result as adding the positive number's opposite. For example, $-10 - (5) = -10 + (-5) = -15$. So subtracting a positive number from a negative number has the same result as adding a negative number (the positive number's opposite) to a negative number.

4.4 (Solutions for page 132 continued.)

d. (0, 8)

9. a. See graph on #8a.
   b. Yes, they intersect at (4, 0)
10. a. One possible table for each function is given:

$y = 2x$

x	y
-2	-4
-1	-2
0	0
1	2
2	4
0.5	1

$y = 0.5x$

x	y
-2	-1
-1	-0.5
0	0
1	0.5
2	1
0.5	0.25

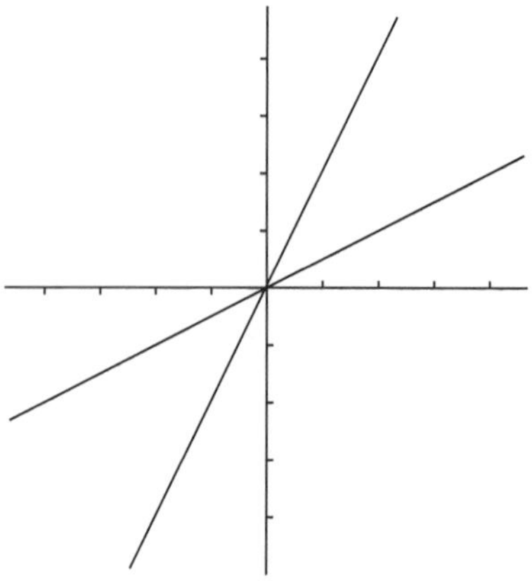

    c. (0, 0)
    d. Answers will vary. One possible solution is (2, 2).
    e. Answers will vary. One possible solution is (2, -1).

11. a. One possible table for each function is given.

$y = x$

x	y
-2	-2
-1	-1
0	0
1	1
2	2
0.5	0.5

$y = x + 2$

x	y
-2	0
-1	1
-0.5	1.5
0	2
1	3
1.5	3.5

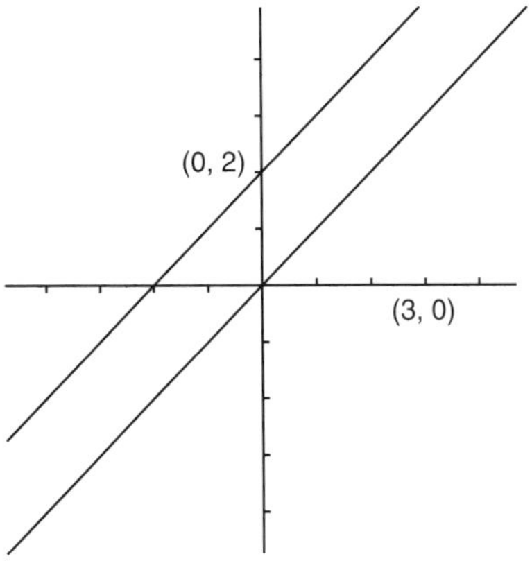

c. None

d. Answers will vary. One possible solution is (0, 1).

e. Answers will vary. One possible solution is (0, -2).

12. a. One possible table for each function is given.

$y = x^2$

x	y
-3	9
-2	4
-1	1
0	0
1	1
2	4
0.5	0.25

$y = x^2 - 3$

x	y
-3	6
-2	1
-1	-2
0	-3
1	-2
2	1
0.5	-2.75

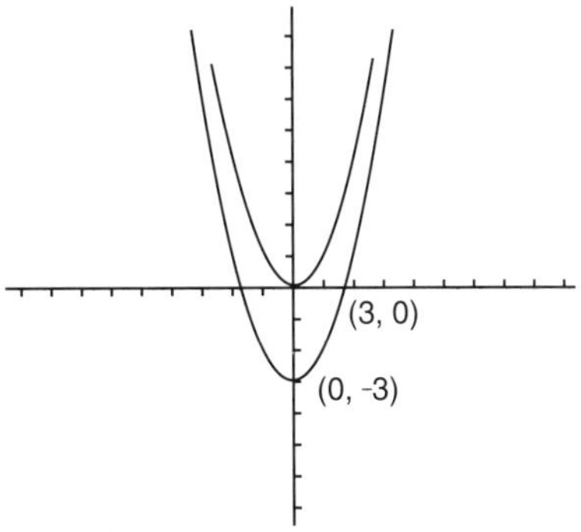

c. None

d. Answers will vary. One possible solution is (0, -1).

e. (0, -5)

13. Answers will vary. One possible solution for each problem is given. #10: $y = 0.75x$. #11: $y = x + 1$. #12: $y = x^2 - 1$.

14. $y = x^2$

15. $y = x^2 + 1$

16. $y = x^3 - 1$

17. $y = x$

18. a. $y = x + 1$

b. $y = x^2 + 1$

c.

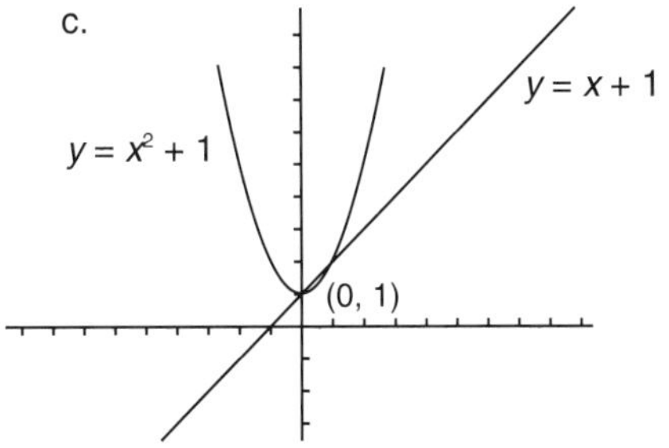

Intersection points: (0, 1) and (1, 2)

19. a. One can choose a value for one of the variables, substitute it into the equation and solve for the second variable. This results in the coordinates for one point on the graph of the equation. Repeating this procedure produces a set of points which lie on the graph.

b. When a pair of x- and y-values are substituted into an equation resulting in a valid equation, then the point with those coordinates lies on the graph of the equation. When the substituted values of x and y do not satisfy the equation, then the point does not lie on the graph. One can also graph the equation and point.

20. The origin has coordinates (0, 0). If substituting these coordinates into the equation results in a valid equation then the graph goes through the origin.

a. No b. Yes c. No

21. Answers will vary. Some possible solutions are given.

a. $y = x$, $y = x^2$, $y = x^3$

b. $y = x + 1$, $y = x^2 + 1$, $y = x^3 + 1$

22. Answers will vary. Some possible solutions are given.

a. $y = x$

b. $xy = 1$

23. Substitute coordinates (0, 0) into the equation. If a valid equation results, then the graph goes through the origin.

4.A (Solutions for page 133 continued.)

3. a. Sally rode about 25 mph on the first leg, which implies the second leg had the slowest speed of 20 mph, so she may have gone uphill there. The final leg must have been downhill because she traveled at about 50 mph.

b. Sally may also have been tired during the 20 mph leg. Perhaps she ate lunch during her 11:30-12:15 break and was feeling sluggish. Perhaps she did not eat lunch and was low in energy. During the last 50 mph leg, she might have been so excited to be nearing the end of the trip that she gave her best effort.

4. Neil drove 50 mph for the first 37.5 miles, 40 mph during the next 20 miles, and 50 mph for the final 12.5 miles.

5. The train began its trip 80 miles away from the staging area at noon. It traveled 40 mph for 2 hours until it arrived at Chapley. It passed Berkhill at 12:15 P.M., Sally at about 12:50 P.M., when they were 48 miles away from the staging area, and Neil at about 12:55 when they were 44 miles away from the staging area.

6. Sally was on her second leg and about 42 miles away from Chapley. Neil was on a break 37.5 miles away from Chapley. The train was about 60 miles away from Chapley.

7. Sally was 20 miles away from the staging area at about 10:50 A.M., Neil at about 11:25 A.M. and the train at 1:30 P.M.

8. a. Sample: (2, 80) (3, 40) (4, 0)

One example of a check by taking

the point (2, 80): 80 = 160 − 40(2) = 160 − 80 = 80.

b. Sample: Sally at (2.75, 48) and Neil at (2.9, 44).
44 = 160 − 40(2.9) = 160 − 116 = 44.

9. a. A horizontal line represents a particular distance away from the staging area. Two points are on the same horizontal line when they represent the same distance away from the staging area. Two points are on the same vertical line at the same time represented by the vertical line.
b. The parts of the graph that go up show the position and time of someone traveling away from a chosen place (such as the staging area). The horizontal segments show that the person is not moving but has stopped. The parts that go down show the position and time of someone traveling toward the chosen place (such as the staging area). A vertical segment is impossible because it would show someone moving a certain distance without any elapsed time. It takes time to travel so time must change when position changes.
c. A point that is shared by two different people shows that they are the same distance away from a chosen place at the same time. If they are on the same path or road, it means they meet one another.

10. Students might consider these possibilities: Was Sally thirsty and hungry and growing impatient while she waited 15 minutes for Neil's arrival on the sweep vehicle? Did she speak about it to Neil because he arrived at the next stopping point at exactly the same time as Sally? Or did Sally have an accident at 1:25? So Sally and Neil stopped for 15 minutes while Neil patched up Sally's scratches? Is this why he stuck close to her for the final leg? Why did Sally's speed slow down after her 45-minute stop? Was she sluggish after lunch or preoccupied and distracted by her 15-minute wait for Neil in the sweep vehicle? Was it uphill? Why was her speed the fastest of the whole trip at the very end? Was it downhill? Was she excited to be nearing her destination?

4.5 (Solutions for page 136 continued.)

19. See equations on lines in graphs for problems 15 and 18.

20. a. An example of a speed is 65 miles per hour. This represents the ratio of 65 miles to 1 hour. Speed is given by a distance divided by the time it took to travel that distance. Speed is therefore a ratio of distance to time.
b. By finding each traveler's distance-to-time ratio one can find each traveler's speed. The larger ratio is the faster speed. On a graph, the steeper the line, the faster the speed.

21. The seventeen happy two-digit numbers are 10, 13, 19, 23, 28, 31, 32, 44, 49, 68, 70, 79, 82, 86, 91, 94, 97.

22. Answers will vary.

4.7 (Solutions for page 141 continued.)

14. About 17%

15. No. The percentage varies. The lowest value seems to be 15% but for a bill of $2.00, the percentage would be 25% and for a bill of $0.01, the percentage would be 5000%.

16. a. $3.10
b. 15%

17. Yes. 10% of the bill plus 20% of the bill is 30% of the bill. Half of 30% of the bill is 15%.

18. Answers will vary. One possible explanation is: The first method varies the percentage of the tip. For bills above $5, the tip is in the 15% to 21% range. The second method always gives 15% and because of its reliability and less complicated calculation is probably the preferred method.

19. 15% is an appropriate tip, 20% for exceptional service. One method for figuring 15% is divide the bill by 10 to get 10% then divide that 10% by 2 to get 5%. Add the 10% and the 5% to get 15%.

4.8 (Solutions for page 145 continued.)

18. No, it is not an example of direct variation because the diameter to area ratio is not a constant (or because the graph is not a straight line through the origin).

19. Answers will vary. The following is one possible table:

Diameter (cm)	Area of circle (cm)	Area of square (cm^2)
3.9	12	3.8
6.8	38	11.56
7.8	48	15.21
9	66	20.25
10	83	25
0	0	0

20.

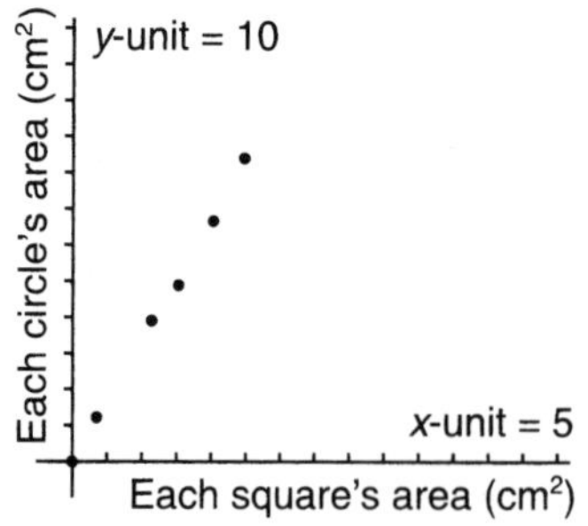

21. Answers will vary. The relationship of the area of the circles to the area of the squares is a direct variation relationship because the circle area to square area is always approximately 3.2. The equation is $C = 3.2S$ where C is the area of a circle and S is the area of a square.

22. Yes. The data gives a graph approximating a straight line through the origin. The circle area to square area ratio is close to a constant.

23. Answers will vary, but should be close to 3.

24. Answers will vary in the constants used. The relationship between the area of a circle and the square of its radius is a direct variation function.The equation for #21 is $C = 3.2S$ which could be rewritten $C = 3.2(R^2)$. The graph of data for #20 is a straight line through the origin showing that the square of the radius and the area of the circle have a constant ratio and are in a direct variation. (Of course we are aiming for $C = 3.14R^2$.) The relationship between the area of a circle and the square of its diameter is not a direct variation function. A is not equal to mD but $A = 0.8D^2$

25. Some calculators truncate digits. Others round off correctly to fit the display screen.

26. The grandfather was right because the product of 7 and its reciprocal should be exactly 1.

27. The reciprocal is $0.\overline{142857}$

28. Letters will vary but may include the following: Students can explore many more questions using a calculator because long division is time consuming and tedious. Using a calculator, students can discover patterns and formulas more easily because they can compute many calculations in less time than it would take with just a pencil and paper. One must work through related solutions several times to recognize a pattern or formula. There is always the question: What is close enough? Both Lyn's and Phil's answers give products very close to 1. By using a calculator carefully you can look for repeating decimals. Rather than writing the calculator's answer of 0.333333333..., for example, one can interpret it and write 1/3 to give the exact answer. In the example of Phil's or Lyn's reciprocal of 7, Phil's answer gives a product closer to 1 than Lyn's answer.

29. The horizontal axis is the numerator, and the vertical axis is the denominator. (see table below)

30. The repeating digits are the same digits in much the same order 142857, 285714, 428571, 571428.... Digits of 142857 that are dropped appear at the end. For example 285714 has the digits 1 and 4 at the end rather than the beginning.

31. Student investigation

4.C. (Solutions for page 159 continued.)

11. i. a. y
b. yz
c. yz
ii. The elements of the yz group are e, y, yy, z, yz, and zy.
iii. a. yz
b. zy
c. yy
iv. a. yz
b. yy
c. yz
v. All powers of y above y^2 can be simplified to y, y^2, or e.
vi. e is the only power of e. The powers of y are y, y^2, and e. The powers of yy are y^2, y and e. The powers of z are z and e. The powers of yz are yz and e. The powers of zy are zy and e.
vii. a. y
b. yz
viii.

	e	y	yy	z	yz	zy
e	e	y	yy	z	yz	zy
y	y	yy	e	yz	zy	z
yy	yy	e	y	zy	z	yz
z	z	zy	yz	e	yy	y
yz	yz	z	zy	y	e	yy
zy	zy	yz	z	yy	y	e

ix. The element e works like 1 for multiplication, because e combined with any element of the group results in that element.
x. The reciprocal of e is e. Y and yy are reciprocals of one another. Z is its own reciprocal. Zy and yz are reciprocals of one another.

12. Should include each group's rules, elements, powers, table, identity element, reciprocals for each element, and a discussion of commutativity.

	0	1	2	3	4	5	6	7	8	9	10
0	–	–	–	–	–	–	–	–	–	–	–
1	0	1	2	3	4	5	6	7	8	9	10
2	0	0.5	1	1.5	2	2.5	3	3.5	4	4.5	5
3	0	$0.\overline{3}$	$0.\overline{6}$	1	$1.\overline{3}$	$1.\overline{6}$	2	$2.\overline{3}$	$2.\overline{6}$	3	$3.\overline{3}$
4	0	0.25	0.5	0.75	1	1.25	1.5	1.75	2	2.25	2.5
5	0	0.2	0.4	0.6	0.8	1	1.2	1.4	1.6	1.8	2
6	0	$0.1\overline{6}$	$0.\overline{3}$	0.5	$0.\overline{6}$	$0.8\overline{3}$	1	$1.1\overline{6}$	$1.\overline{3}$	1.5	$1.\overline{6}$
7	0	$0.\overline{142857}$	$0.\overline{285714}$	$0.\overline{428571}$	$0.\overline{571428}$	$0.\overline{714285}$	$0.\overline{857142}$	1	$1.\overline{142857}$	$1.\overline{285714}$	$1.\overline{428571}$
8	0	0.125	0.25	0.375	0.5	0.625	0.75	0.875	1	1.125	1.25
9	0	$0.\overline{1}$	$0.\overline{2}$	$0.\overline{3}$	$0.\overline{4}$	$0.\overline{5}$	$0.\overline{6}$	$0.\overline{7}$	$0.\overline{8}$	$0.\overline{9}$	$1.\overline{1}$
10	0	0.1	0.2	0.3	0.4	0.5	0.6	0.7	0.8	0.9	1.0

4.E.I. (Solutions for page 162 continued.)

18. b. Paul drove his car away from home and may have turned around and come back (because he forgot something?). He drove at about the same speed going and returning. He then drove to a destination on a route which at first took him away from home and then closer to home. (Did he drive around a lake or mountain?) Paul's speed was a little slower on the second part of his trip.
c. Paul drove away from home. At first he drove one speed, then he increased his speed, and then slowed down to his first speed.
d. Paul drove a distance from home and stopped for a while. He then continued to drive away from home.

19. 5 ≤ width ≤ 11.5

20. a. width = 5; height = 3.5; area = 17.5
b. width = 11.5; height = 6.125; area = 70.4375
c. width = 5; height = 6.125; area = 30.625
d. width = 11.5; height = 3.5; area = 40.25

21. through 26.

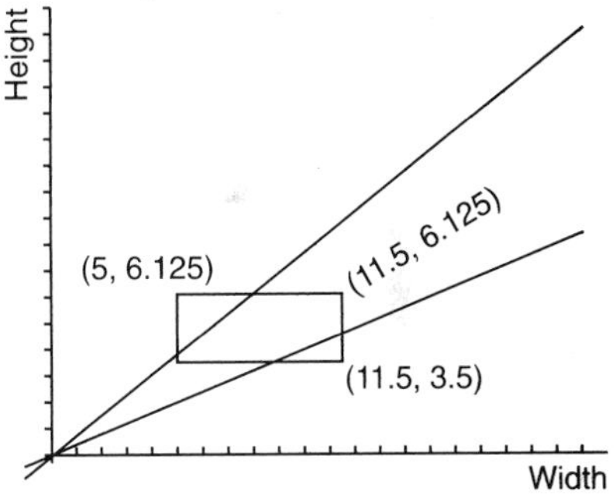

22. $y = 6.125$ and $y = 3.5$ are the horizontal lines. $x = 11.5$ and $x = 5$ are the vertical lines.

23. Answers will vary. One possible solution is: Points inside the rectangle are (7, 4), (8, 4), and (9, 4). Points outside the rectangle are (5, 1), (4, 4), and (2, 1). Points on the rectangle are (6, 3.5), (7, 3.5), and (11.5, 4). Allowable dimensions are represented by points on or inside the rectangle because the widths are between 5 inches and 11.5 inches, and the heights are between 3.5 inches and 6.125 inches.

24. 1.3 ≤ (width/height) ≤ 2.5

25. a. $w/h \approx 1.43$
 b. $w/h \approx 1.878$
 c. $w/h \approx 0.816$
 d. $w/h \approx 3.29$

The first two letters (a & b) meet the new requirement.

26. a. See graph for #21. Answers vary for coordinates of ordered pairs.
 b. Answers vary. Sample: (7.8, 6) & (5.2, 4). (7.8)/6 = (5.2)/4 = 1.3. The width to height ratio for each pair is 1.3.
 c. Answers will vary. Sample: (8.75, 3.5) & (10, 4). (8.75)/(3.5) = (10)/4 = 2.5. The width to height ratio for each pair is 2.5.

27. Points used to check will vary. Sample:
 a. Between the two lines: (5, 2.5). Ratio is 5/(2.5) = 2.
 b. Above the two lines: (6, 5). Ratio is 6/5 = 1.2.
 c. Below the 2 lines: (5, 1). Ratio is 5/1 = 5.

28. a. To satisfy all the rules choose dimensions that not only fall within or on the rectangle, but also on or between the two lines through the origin.
 b. To satisfy the first two rules choose points on or inside the rectangle.
 c. To satisfy the ratio rule choose points that fall on or between the two lines through the origin.

29. The height to width ratio is the reciprocal of 1.3 which is about 0.7692308.

30. The equations of the lines are $h = (10/13)w$ and $h = 0.4w$. Since these equations are in the form $y = mx$, they are examples of direct variation.

5.4 (Solutions for page 175 continued.)

7. a. $(x + 12)(x + 1)$
 b. $(x + 2)(x + 6)$
 c. $(x + 3)(x + 4)$

8. There are no more trinomials if we consider only positive whole numbers, since we have used all the positive whole number pairs whose product is 12. However, if we allow negative integers in the blank, these trinomials are possible:
 $(x - 12)(x - 1) = x^2 - 13x + 12$
 $(x - 2)(x - 6) = x^2 - 8x + 12$
 $(x - 3)(x - 4) = x^2 - 7x + 12$

 Moreover, there is an infinite number of possibilities if we allow nonintegers. Example:
 $(x + 0.6)(x + 20) = x^2 + 20.6x + 12$

9. a. $y(x + 2)(x + 3)$
 b. $x(x + 2)(x + 3)$
 c. $y(y + 2)(y + 3)$
 d. $x(y + 2)(y + 3)$

10. Answers will vary. (Students will learn about factoring out a common monomial factor in Lesson 6.) Sample answer: Find a monomial that is common to all three terms. Divide this factor out of all the terms and factor the resulting second-degree trinomial.

11. First rearrange this expression into two trinomials that are familiar:
 $(x^2y + 5xy + 6y) + (x^2 + 5x + 6)$
 Then factor:
 $y(x + 2)(x + 3) + (x + 2)(x + 3) =$
 $(y + 1)(x + 2)(x + 3)$.

 (Another strategy is to use the Lab Gear to make a box.)

12. a.

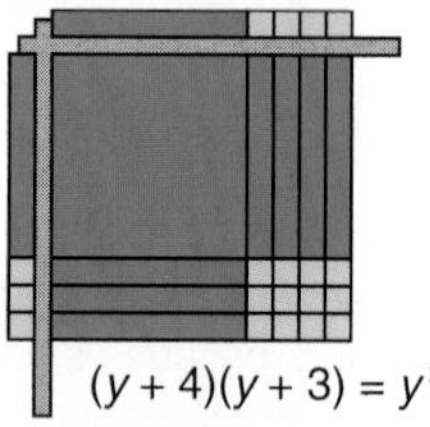

$(y + 4)(y + 3) = y^2 + 7y + 12$

 b. one y^2-block, seven y-blocks, twelve one-blocks

13. a.

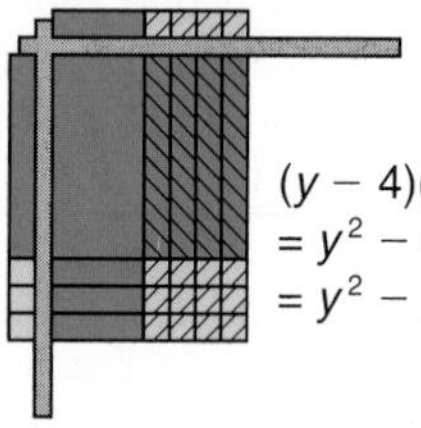

$(y - 4)(y + 3)$
$= y^2 - 4y + 3y - 12$
$= y^2 - y - 12$

 b. one y^2-block, seven y-blocks, twelve one-blocks

14. One possibility is $(y + 4)(y - 3)$, as shown in the figure. There is another possibility, $(y - 4)(y - 3)$, which most students will not be aware of since they have not studied how to model this kind of expression with the blocks. You may want to raise the question of whether or not this is another possibility, and leave it unresolved until Lesson 7.

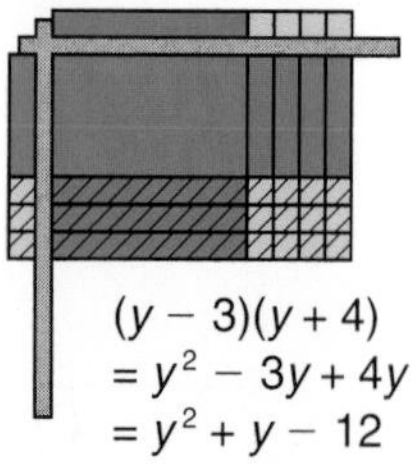

$(y - 3)(y + 4)$
$= y^2 - 3y + 4y - 12$
$= y^2 + y - 12$

15. Answers will vary. If only positive whole numbers are used, the possible answers are:
 $(x + 1)(x + 14) = x^2 + 15x + 14$
 $(x + 2)(x + 13) = x^2 + 15x + 26$
 $(x + 3)(x + 12) = x^2 + 15x + 36$
 $(x + 4)(x + 11) = x^2 + 15x + 44$
 $(x + 5)(x + 10) = x^2 + 15x + 50$
 $(x + 6)(x + 9) = x^2 + 15x + 54$
 $(x + 7)(x + 8) = x^2 + 15x + 56$

16. Answers will vary.

17. Answers will vary.

18. $(x - 7)(x - 1) = x^2 - 8x + 7$. This is the only answer, if you specify that you can fill in the blanks with positive whole numbers only. If not, there is an infinite number of answers.

19. If only positive whole numbers are allowed, #18 has only one answer since 7 is prime. However, if any numbers can be used, they all have more than one answer.

20. a. $(x + 2)(x + 3)$
 b. $(a + 6)(a + 5)$
 c. $(m + 10)(m + 10)$
 d. $(p + 1)(p + 1)$

21. a. $(x - 3)(x - 2)$
 b. $(x - 12)(x - 1)$
 c. $(x - 5)(x - 3)$
 d. $(x - 3)(x + 3)$

22. a. $(2x + 1)(3x + 1)$
 b. $(2x + 1)(3x - 1)$
 c. $(2x - 1)(3x + 1)$

23. a. $(x^2 - 5)(x^2 - 3)$
 b. $(x^2 - 4)(x^2 - 4) = (x - 2)(x + 2)$
 $(x - 2)(x + 2)$

24. Answers will vary.

5.A (Solutions for page 176 continued)

5.

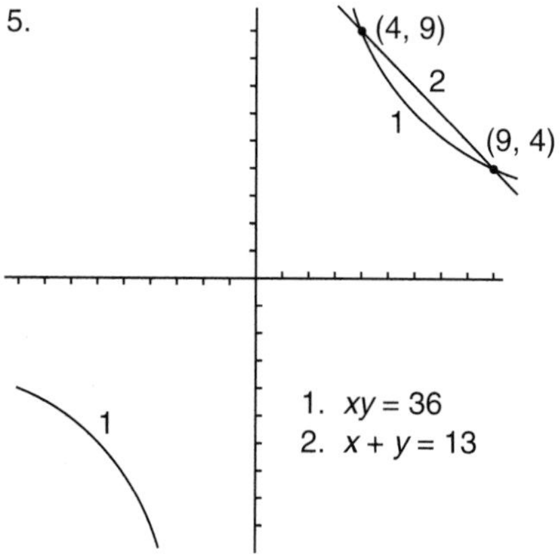

6. Answers will vary. The figure shows some possibilities.

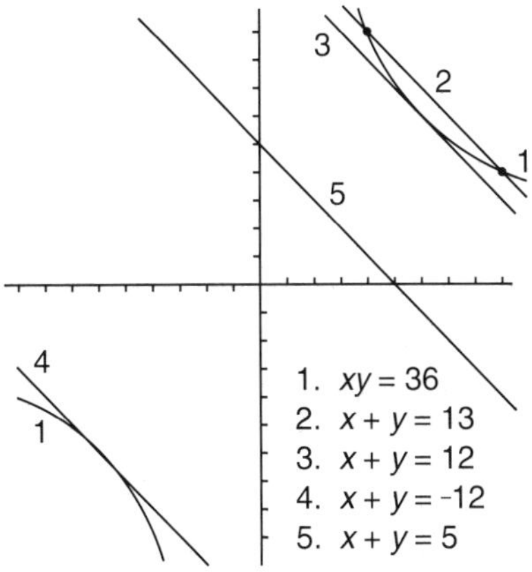

7. Answers will vary. If only positive whole numbers are considered, the possibilities are 37, 20, 15, 13, and 12. If negative integers are allowed, the possibilities are these numbers and their opposites. If any numbers are allowed, there is an infinite number of possibilities. (All numbers except those between -12 and 12 will work. This can be seen graphically.)

8., 9.

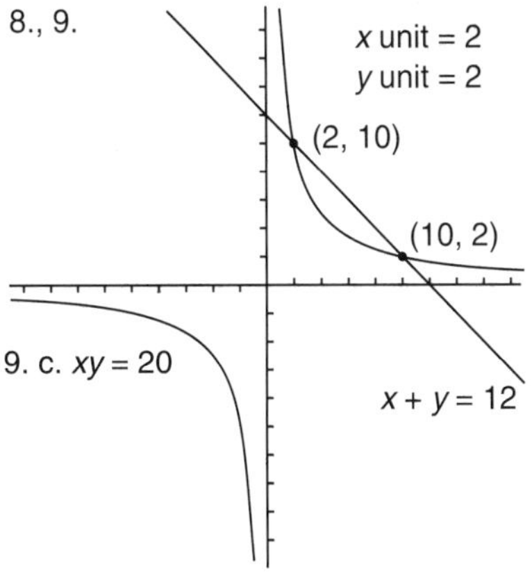

10.

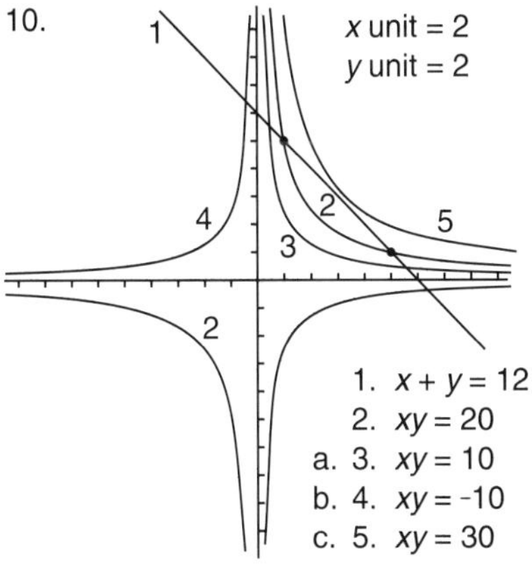

11. Answers will vary. If you consider only positive whole numbers, the possibilities are 11, 20, 27, 32, 35, 36. If positive noninteger values are allowed, any number less than 36 will work. If negative integers are allowed, there is an infinite number of possibilities. This can be seen graphically, since all constant product graphs in the second and fourth quadrants will intersect $x + y = 12$.

12. Answer will vary. (Some of the main ideas were given in #3, #7, and #11. Most student reports will be more specific. Do not expect most students to give a general statement of these ideas.)

5.5 (Solutions for page 179 continued.)

12. Answers will vary. One possibility is $y = x^2 + 5x - 4$. Substituting 0 for x gives a y-value of -4.

13. a. $b = -(p + q)$ and $c = pq$
    b. The x-intercepts are the values of x that make y equal to zero, so they are p and q. They are easily seen in the factored form. The y-intercept is the value of y when x is 0, which is c.
    c. The x-coordinate of the vertex is the number halfway between the two x-intercepts, that is $(p + q)/2$. Once this number is found, it can be substituted into the equation to find the y-coordinate of the vertex.

14.

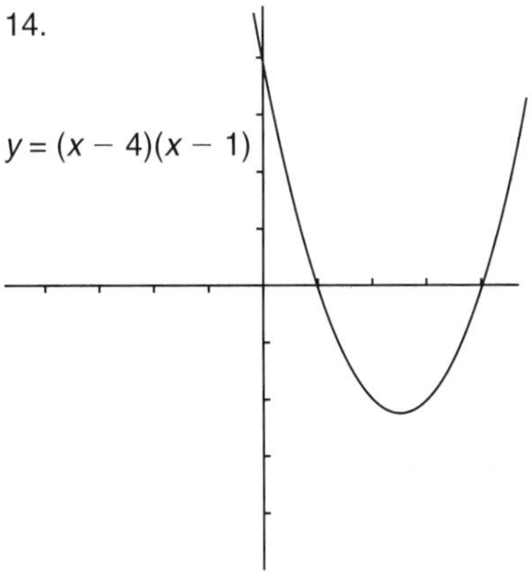

15.

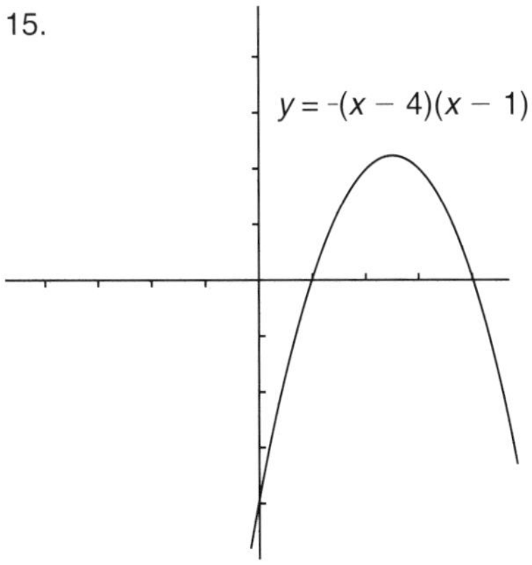

16. The graphs are mirror images, or reflections, of one another over the x-axis. They have the same x-intercepts. The x-coordinates of their vertices are the same, but the y-coordinates are opposites. The y-intercepts are opposites.

17. Answers will vary. One possible answer is given for each part.
    a. $y = (x - 3)(x + 2)$
    b. $y = -(x - 3)(x + 2)$
    c. $y = (x + 3)(x + 2)$
    d. $y = -(x + 3)(x + 2)$

18. Answers will vary.

19. $y = x(x - 5)$ and $y = -x(x - 5)$ are two possible answers. Any parabola of the form $y = ax(x - 5)$ will have these x-intercepts, since substituting either 0 or 5 for x will make y equal 0.

20. Answers will vary. One possibility is given for each problem.
    a. $y = (x - 1)(x - 3)$
    b. $y = -(x - 1)(x - 3)$
    c. $y = -2(x - 1)(x - 3)$

21.

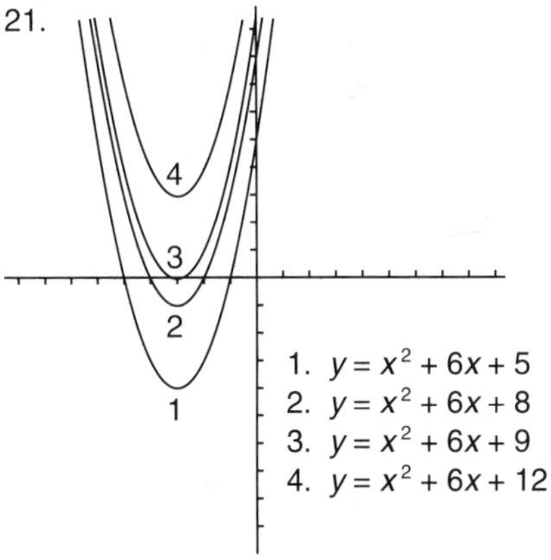

22. The parabola in (a) has two x-intercepts, (-5, 0) and (-1, 0). The parabola in (b) has the x-intercepts (-2, 0) and (-4, 0). The parabola in (c) rests on the x-axis, having one x-intercept at (-3, 0). The parabola in (d) has no x-intercepts, and hangs three units above the x-axis. All the parabolas have the same x-coordinate of the vertex, which is -3. I might have been able to predict the number of x-intercepts before graphing if I had thought about these equations using the perfect square $y = x^2 + 6x + 9$ as my reference point. Comparing the other equations to this one, I would expect those with c values greater than 9 to have no x-intercepts, and those with c values less than 9 to have two x-intercepts.

23. a. 4
  b. Any number less than 4 is a possible answer.
  c. Any number greater than 4 is a possible answer.

24. Answers will vary. The main point is that the perfect square serves as a reference to which other parabolas are compared, as explained in #22.

25. 1 dime, 2 nickels, 4 pennies

26. 19 nickels, 4 pennies; 23 coins

27. Since $ab = 0$, then either $a = 0$ or $b = 0$. Since $bc = 0$, then $b = 0$ or $c = 0$. Since $ac = 1$, neither a nor c is 0. Hence $b = 0$.

28. Since $abc = 0$, then a, b, or c must be 0. Since $bcd = 1$, none of those three variables could be 0. Hence $a = 0$.

29. 1-15, 2-14, 3-13, 4-12, 5-11, 6-10, 7-18, 8-17, 9-16

5.6 (Solutions for page 181 continued.)

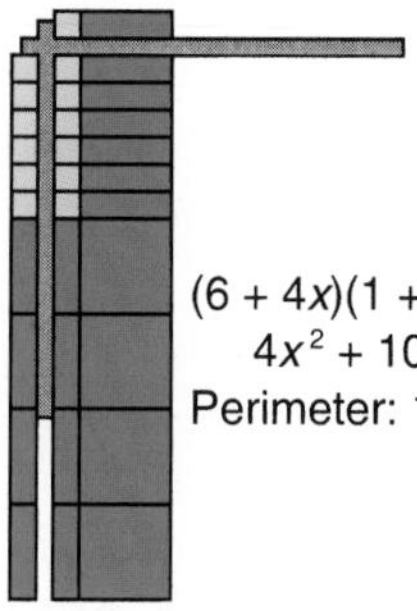

$(6 + 4x)(1 + x) =$
$4x^2 + 10x + 6$
Perimeter: $10x + 14$

In #7 through #12, answers will vary. Some will be possible to show with the Lab Gear; others will not. Sample answers are given. (All those given here can be shown with the Lab Gear.)

7. $24 = 1 \cdot 24 = 2 \cdot 12 = 3 \cdot 8 = 4 \cdot 6 = 2 \cdot 2 \cdot 6 = 2 \cdot 3 \cdot 4$

8. $6y^2 = 2y \cdot 3y = 6y \cdot y$

9. $(2x + 4)(3x + 6) = 6 \cdot (x + 2) \cdot (x + 2) = 3 \cdot (2x + 4) \cdot (x + 2)$

10. $12x^3 = 4x^2 \cdot 3x = 4x \cdot 3x^2 = 12x^2 \cdot x = 12x \cdot x^2 = 6x^2 \cdot 2x = 6x \cdot 2x^2 = 6 \cdot 2x^3 = 2 \cdot 6x^3$

11. $12x^2 + 4x = 4x(3x + 1) = x(12x + 4) = 4(3x^2 + x)$

12. $2x(6x + 18) = 6x(2x + 6) = 12x(x + 3) = x(12x + 36) = 2(6x^2 + 18x) = 6(2x^2 + 6x) = 12(x^2 + 3x)$

13. $2x^2(x + 4 + y)$

14. $2x(x - 3)$

15. impossible

16. $x(3x + 2 + 4y)$

17. $3xy(x - 1 + 2y)$

18. $3y(y + 3 - 2y^2 + x^2 + 2xy + 3x)$

19. $6(x + 3)(x + 2)$

20. $4(x + 2)(x + 3)$

21. $4(x + 8)(x + 2)$

22. $2(x + 2)(x + 2)$

23. $3(x + 2)(x + 5)$

24. $2(x + 9)(x + 4)$

25. $x(x + 3)(x + 2)$

5.7 (Solutions for page 185 continued.)

27. a.

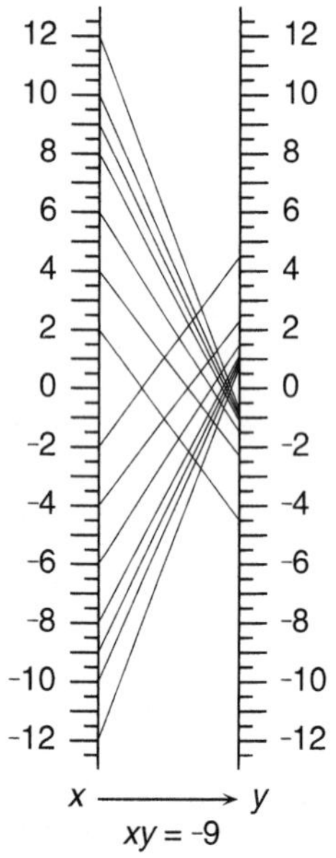

  b. No, the in-out lines do not meet at the same point.
  c. There are no horizontal lines.
  d. y moves up as x changes from -12 to 12 and jumps at zero. y moves fast for values of x close to zero.

28. $x = 1.2, 1.5, 2, 3, 6$

5.9 (Solutions for page 191 continued.)

7. a.

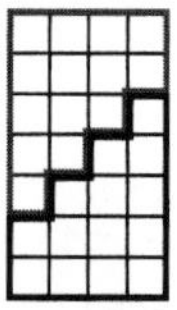

  b. length = 7 units, width = 4 units, area = 28 square units.

8. a. length = 133, width = 100.
  b. The number of tiles needed is $(133 \cdot 100)/2 = 6650$ tiles

9. a. $\frac{(55 + 5) \cdot 51}{2} = 1530$ tiles
  b. $\frac{(100 + 1) \cdot 100}{2} = 5050$ tiles.

10. $(101 \cdot 100)/2 = 5050$. The last step is to divide by two since each pair of numbers gets added up twice. This is the same answer as 9b.

11. Gauss's table would look like:

1	2	3	4	5	6	7	8	9	10
100	99	98	97	96	95	94	93	92	91

In this case we would have 100 columns and each sum would be 101, instead of having 101 columns and each sum being 100. Since multiplication is commutative, the product would be the same.

12. Answers may vary. Sample summary: In the rectangle method, find the length and width of the rectangle. The length equals 89 + 5 which is 94 and the width equals the number of steps in the staircase which is 85. The sum of the staircase is simply the area of the rectangle divided by two which is $(94 \cdot 85)/2$ which equals 3995. Using Gauss's method, you will construct a table like the following:

5	6	7	8	9	10	11	12	13...
89	88	87	86	85	84	83	82	81...

Each pair adds up to 94 and there are 85 columns. So Gauss's calculations would look like: $(94 \cdot 85)/2 = 3995$ which is the same as the rectangle method.

13. $4x + 6$

14. a. 22   b. 402

15. a. $27x + 351$. We use Gauss's method to add $1 + 2 + 3 + ... 26 = (1 + 26) \cdot 26/2 = 351$ and we have 27 xs.
  b. $84x + 3570$ since we have 84 xs and $(1 + 84)(84)/2 = 3570$.

16. a. $(n + 1)n/2$
  b. $(n + 1)x + (n + 1)n/2$
  c. $nx + (n + 1)n/2$

5.C (Solutions for page 200 continued.)

9. c.

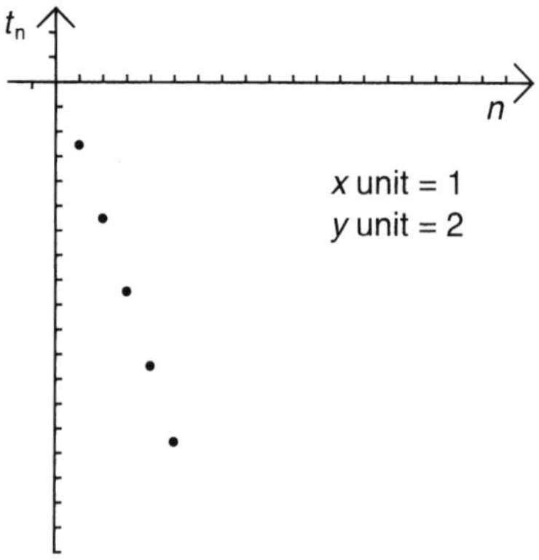

10. a.

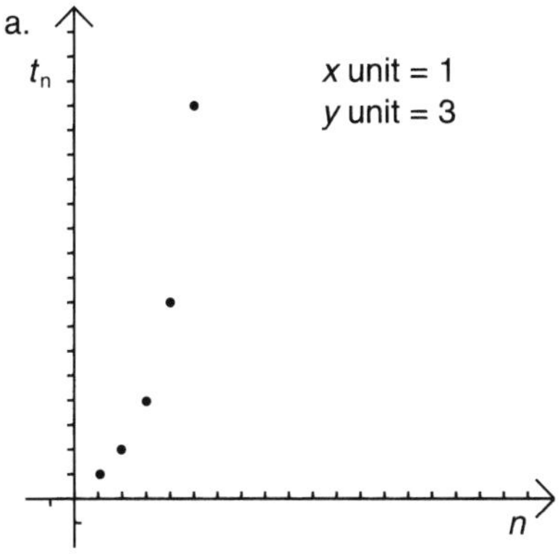

b.

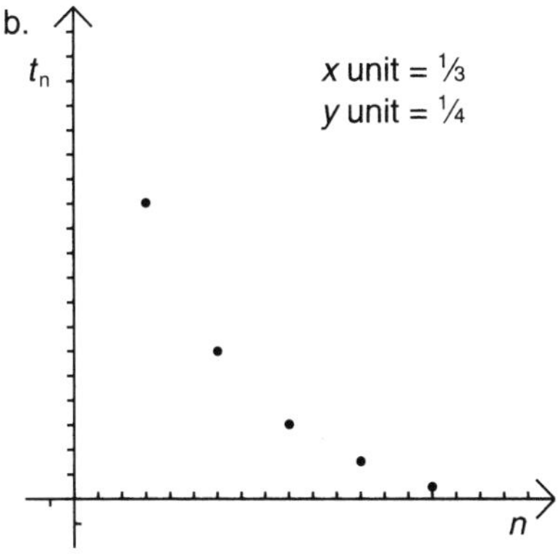

c.

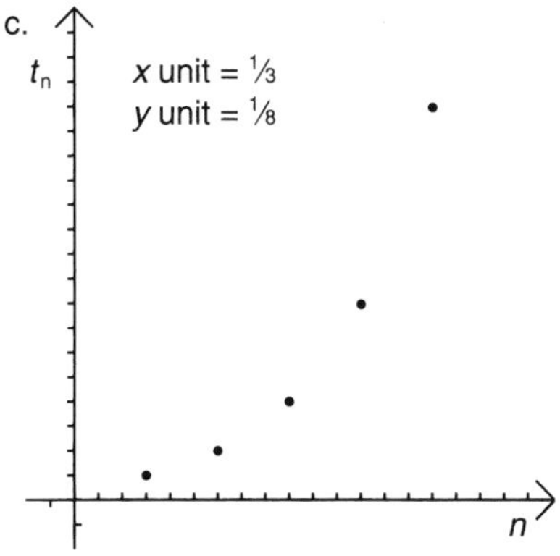

11. a.

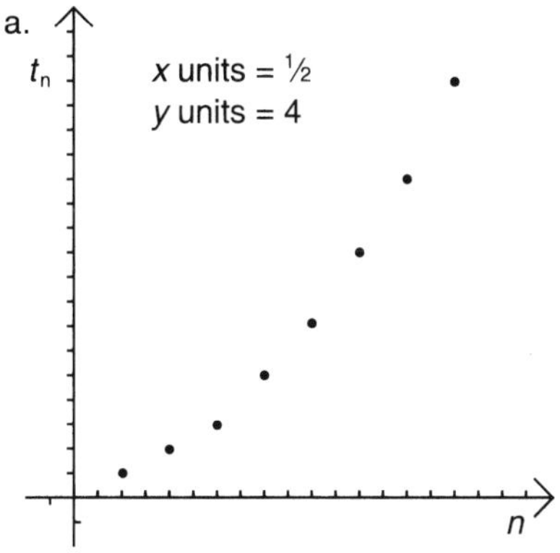

b.

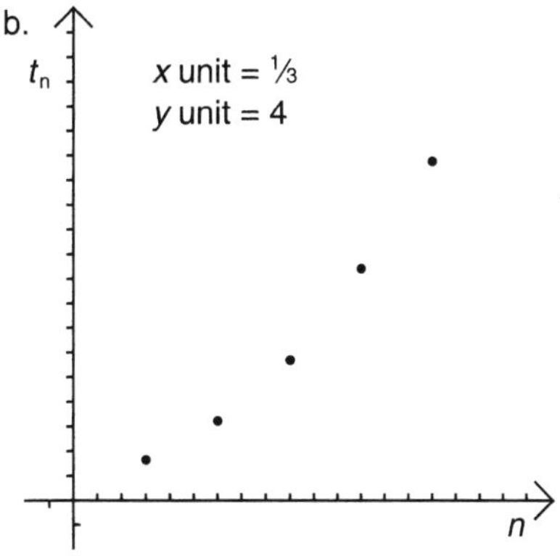

c.

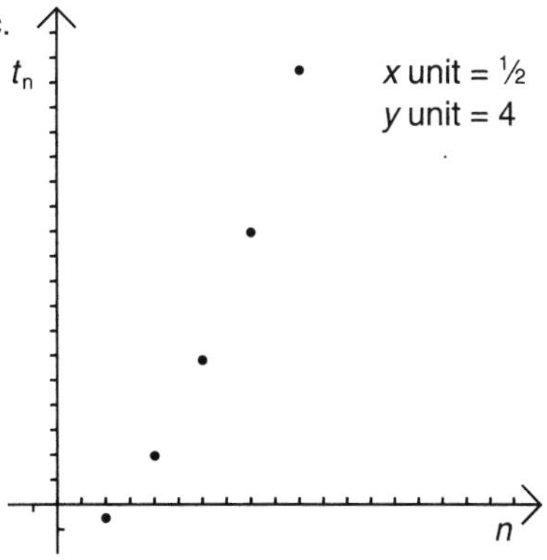

12. Answers will vary. (The sequences are quadratic.)

13. Reports will vary. Some key points follow: When an arithmetic sequence is graphed, the points will fall in a straight line. The common difference determines the steepness of this line. (The greater the common difference, the steeper the line.) The geometric sequences and the mystery sequences have curved graphs. (Students may recognize that the graphs of the mystery sequences fall along a parabolic curve.) If the common ratio in a geometric sequence is less then 1, the terms decrease and the graph curves downward from left to right. However, if the common ratio is greater than 1, the terms increase and the graph curves upward from left to right. (Both these statements about geometric sequences assume that the first term is positive.)

6.4 (Solutions for page 216 continued.)

13. b.

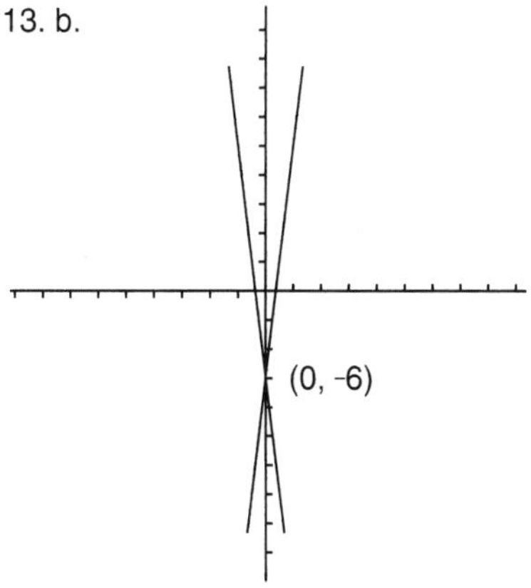

d.

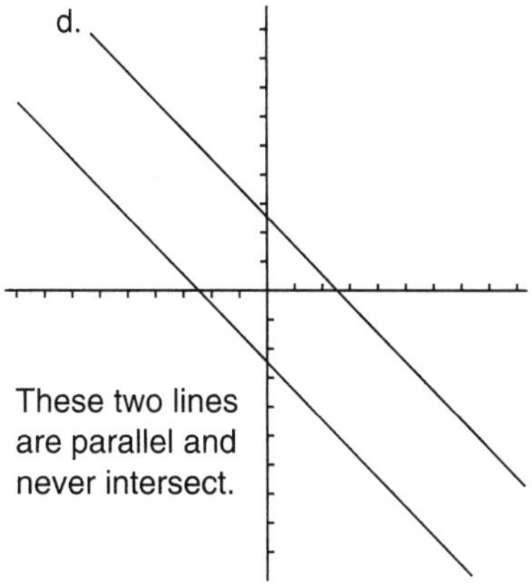

14. $y = 5 - x$ and $y = -x - 5$ from 12d do not have a point of intersection because they are parallel.

15. For the same line, the tables will be identical. For parallel lines, the tables will be entirely different. No pairs of values will be on both tables. For a particular value of x, corresponding y-values will differ by the same constant. For two lines that intersect, the tables will have exactly one identical pair of values.

16. a. This is never true since the equation simplifies down to $5 = 1$.
    b. This is sometimes true since the equation simplifies down to $-x = 0$ which is true for $x = 0$.
    c. This is sometimes true since the equation simplifies to $10x = 0$ which is true when $x = 0$.
    d. This is always true since the equation simplifies to $7x + 1 = 7x + 1$.

17. #16b is true when $x = 0$ and false for $x = 1$.
    #16c is true when $x = 0$ and false when $x = 1$.

18. a.

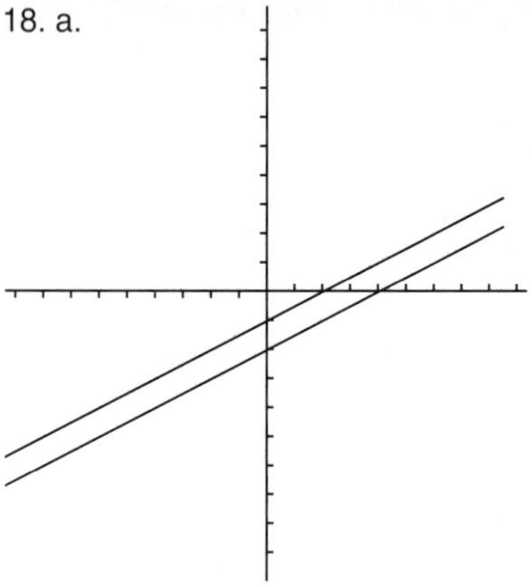

b. Never true. The lines are parallel.

19. a.

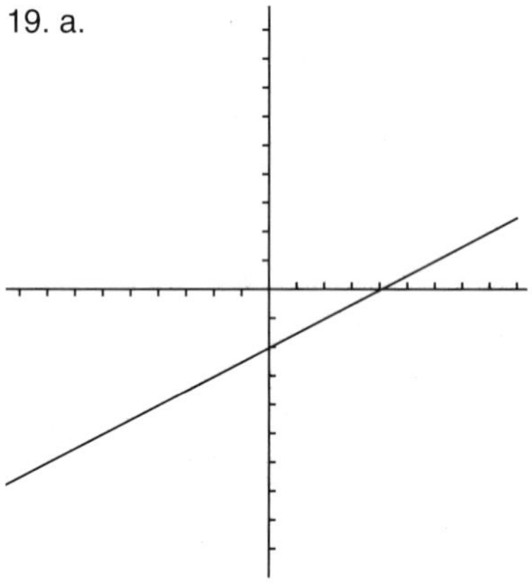

b. Always true. The lines are the same. The expressions are equal for any value of x.

20. a.

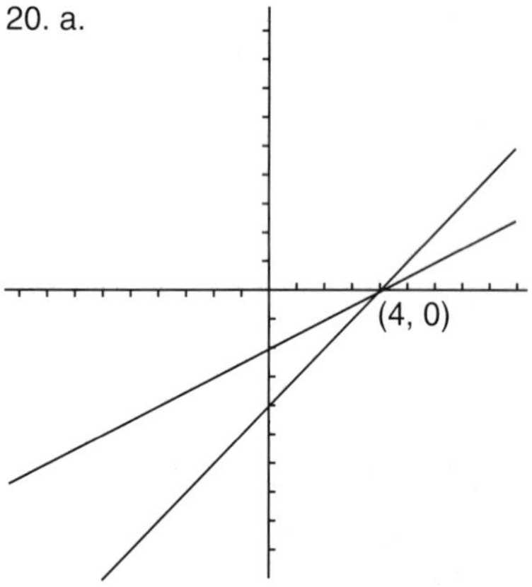

b. Sometimes true. The lines intersect at (4, 0). When $x = 4$ the expressions both equal 0.

21. a.

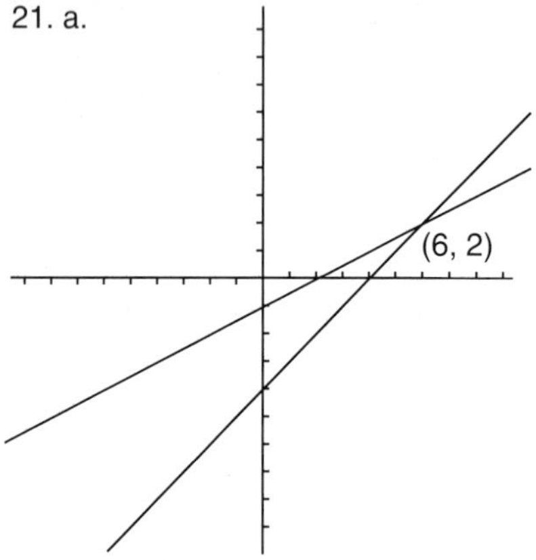

b. Sometimes true. The lines intersect at (6, 2). When $x = 6$ the expressions both equal 2.

22. Reports will vary. Identity: an equation that is true for all values of the variable. The left and right sides of the identity can be set equal to y to form two equations. When the two equations are graphed, they are the same line. Lab Gear shows that when both sides of the identity are simplified they are the same.

Graphing: Given two linear equations, one can graph each equation to see if they form the same line (always true), parallel lines (never true), or intersecting lines (sometimes true).

Lab Gear: Given two equations set equal to y, one can model the non-y sides with Lab Gear. One can see if each side simplifies to the same blocks (always true), blocks which establish one value for x (sometimes true), or blocks that could never be equal, such as 4 on one side and 6 on the other (never true).

23. a. $-2x + 7$ is always greater than $-2x$ since the line $y = -2x + 7$ is parallel to and 7 units above the line $y = -2x$.

b. $6x + 4$ is always greater than $6x - 4$ since the line $y = 6x + 4$ is parallel to and 8 units above the line $y = 6x - 4$.

c. This depends on the value of x. When x is not equal to zero, x^2 is greater than $-x^2$. x^2 is greater because it is positive whereas $-x^2$ is its opposite and always negative. When $x = 0$, the two expressions are equal to zero.

d. This depends on the value of x. When x is not equal to zero, $(-x)^2$ is greater than $-x^2$ because $(-x)^2$ is positive and $-x^2$ is negative. When $x = 0$, both expression are equal to zero.

24. $x^2 + 10x + 25 = (x + 5)^2$

25. $4x^2 + 8x + 4 = (2x + 2)^2$

26. $9x^2 + 6x + 1 = (3x + 1)^2$

27. $x^2 + 2x + 1 = (x + 1)^2$

28. $4x^2 + 12x + 9 = (2x + 3)^2$

29. No. Evenly distributing the x-blocks on two sides of a square made of x^2-blocks determines a fixed number of yellow blocks.

30. $x^2 + 10x + 25 = (x + 5)^2$

31. $4x^2 + 20x + 25 = (2x + 5)^2$

32. $x^2 + 12x + 36 = (x + 6)^2$

33. $9x^2 + 6x + 1 = (3x + 1)^2$

34. $x^2 + 6x + 9 = (x + 3)^2$

35. No. The yellow blocks determine the number of x-blocks. By making a square out of the yellow blocks, one can begin to see how many x-blocks are needed because they line up with 2 sides of the yellow square.

36. Note: Students may describe the pattern from the trinomial to the square of the binomial or vice-versa. Answers may vary. Sample:

Lab Gear: Given a quadratic trinomial, one first makes a square from the second-degree trinomial (or x^2-blocks). Next one evenly distributes half the x-blocks to the right of the square and half the x-blocks along the lower side of the square. Then one makes a square of the yellow 1-blocks in the lower right corner to complete the square. Now given the square of a binomial, with one or more x^2-blocks, make a square whose sides are the first term of the binomial. Multiply the second term of the binomial by itself and make a square of this many yellow 1-blocks so that its upper left corner (vertex) touches the lower right corner of the square made of x^2-blocks. The x-blocks can be filled in above and to the left of the yellow square to complete the square.

Algebraic Symbols:
$(x + y)^2 = x^2 + 2xy + y^2$

6.A (Solutions for page 217 continued.)

5., 6.a., & 6.b.

Month	Balance on the first of the month	Balance on the 15th of the month
1	790	660
2	750	620
3	710	580
4	670	540
5	630	500
8	510	380
n	$830 - 40n$	$700 - 40n$

7. Letters should include the fact that Lara will run out of money on the 15th of the twentieth month because $700 - 40(20) = -\$100$. On the first of the twentieth month she has a balance of $830 - 40(20) = \$30$. Because she earns \$260 a month and has a total of \$80 + 220 = \$300 a month in expenses her balance dwindles to nothing during the twentieth month. One suggestion might be to increase her work hours to cover the \$80 per month cash expenses.

6.B (Solutions for page 230 continued.)

5. Answers will vary.

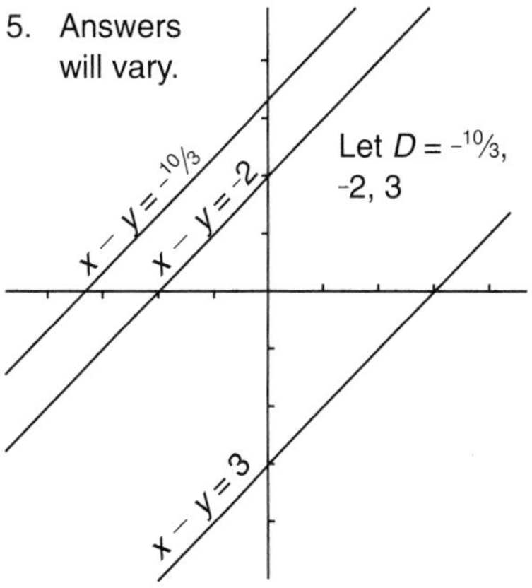

$x - y = D$ and $y - x = D$ are parallel lines that slope up from left to right. The graph of $y - x = D$ crosses the y-axis at $(0, D)$ but $x - y = D$ crosses the y-axis at $(0, -D)$.

6. $x \neq 0$

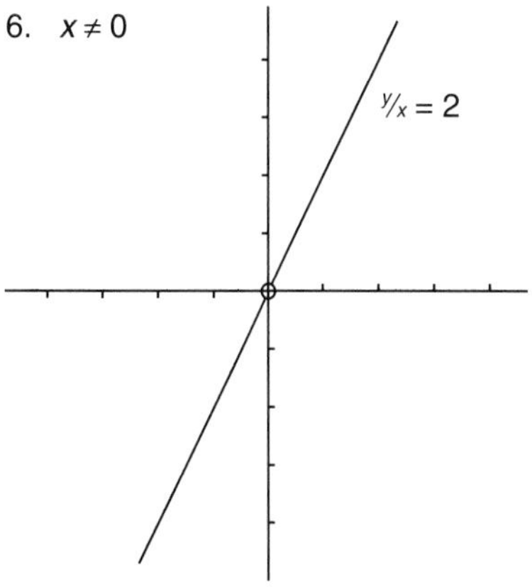

7. Answers will vary. Let $R = 5$, $x \neq 0$

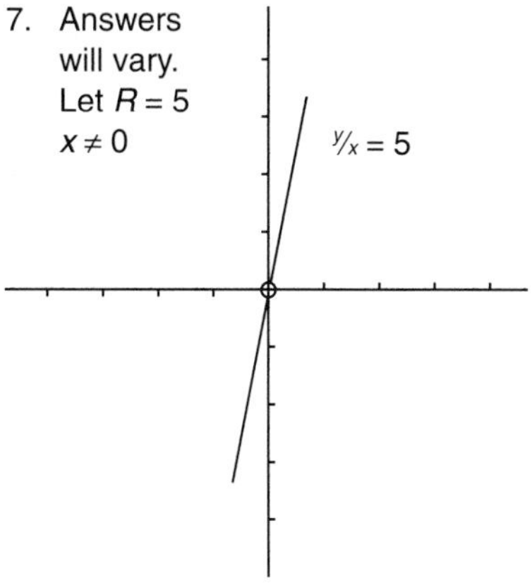

8. Sample graphs $x \neq 0$

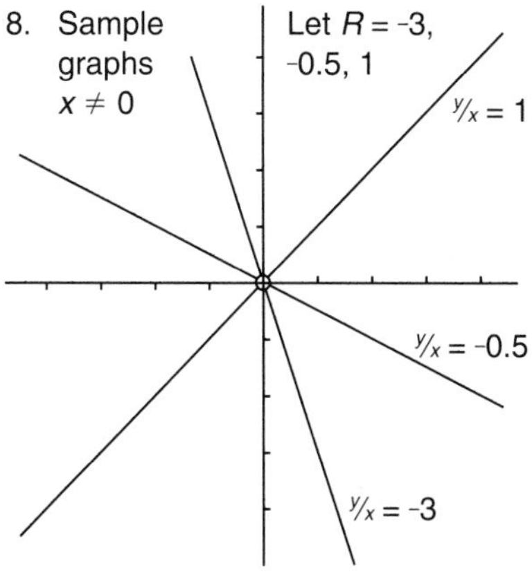

9. Sample graphs $y \neq 0$

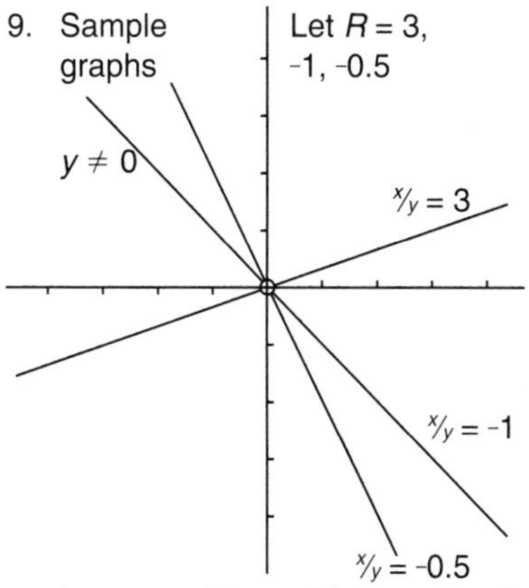

Answers will vary. The graphs of $y/x = R$ and $x/y = R$ are lines through quadrants I and III or II and IV or they could also be the x-axis, $y/x = 0$, or the y-axis, $x/y = 0$. All graphs of $y/x = R$ and $x/y = R$ have a hole at the origin, because (0, 0) does not satisfy the equation. For both, the farther D (D in the equation $x - y = D$ or $y - x = D$) is away from zero, the steeper the line.

10. Reports will vary. Constant Difference: $y - x = D$ and $x - y = D$ slope up regardless of the value of D. If $D > 0$, then $y - x = D$ is in quadrants I, II, and III. D is the y-intercept and $-D$ is the x-intercept. $x - y = D$ is in quadrants I, III, and IV. $-D$ is the y-intercept and D is the x-intercept. If $D = 0$, then $y - x = D$ and $x - y = D$ are equivalent equations passing through the origin and quadrants I and III. This is (except for the origin) the constant ratio graph with $R = 1$. If $D < 0$, then $y - x = D$ is in quadrants I, III, and IV. D is the y-intercept. $-D$ is the x-intercept. $x - y = D$ is in quadrants I, II, and III. $-D$ is the y-intercept and D is the x-intercept.

Constant Ratios: $y/x = R$ and $x/y = R$ are in quadrants I and III if $R > 0$. For $R > 1$, $y/x = R$ is steeper than $x/y = R$. For $0 < R < 1$, $x/y = R$ is steeper than $y/x = R$. If $R = 1$ then the ratios become constant difference graphs as well ($y - x = 0$ and $x - y = 0$) as long as $x \neq 0$. The graphs of $y - x = 0$ and $x - y = 0$ include the origin but $y/x = 1$ and $x/y = 1$ have a hole at (0, 0). $y/x = 1$ is not defined at $x = 0$ because division by zero is undefined. $x/y = 1$ is not defined when $y = 0$ because division by zero is not defined. $x/y = 1$ is not defined when $y = 0$ for the same reason. For $R < 0$, $y/x = R$ and $x/y = R$ are in quadrants II and IV. For $R < -1$, $y/x = R$ is steeper than $x/y = R$. When $-1 < R < 0$, $x/y = R$ is steeper than $y/x = R$.

6.C (Solutions for page 241 continued.)

inverse element: 0 does not have an inverse. (From the table, we can see that all the other elements do have inverses.) Hence the set is not a group under this operation.

c. In part (b), we showed that the set satisfied the properties of a group except that 0 did not have an inverse. Since we have removed 0 from the set, it is now a group under this operation.

5. a. yes
   b. No. Most integers do not have inverses that are elements of the set of integers. For example, the multiplicative inverse of 7 is 1/7, but 1/7 is not an element of the set of integers.

6. The rational numbers are not a group under multiplication since zero does not have an inverse. (That is, it does not have a multiplicative reciprocal.) If we remove zero from the set, then it will be a group. The set is closed, it has a multiplicative identity element, which is 1, and all elements have

inverses which are members of the set. (The inverse of an element is its reciprocal in this case.)

7.

⊕	0	1	2	3
0	0	1	2	3
1	1	2	3	0
2	2	3	0	1
3	3	0	1	2

⊗	0	1	2	3
0	0	0	0	0
1	0	1	2	3
2	0	2	0	2
3	0	3	2	1

From the tables, we can see that it is a group under the operation ⊕ but not under the operation ⊗. The second table shows that under ⊗, there are two elements (2 and 0) that do not have inverses. (3 and 1 are their own inverses.) Hence, we could not make it a group by removing only one element.

8. Answers will vary.

6.E.I. (Solutions for page 243 continued.)

19. Tables will vary. A sample is given for part (a) only.

a. Sample table:

x	y
1	5.56
10	6.05
20	6.60
40	7.70
90	10.45
100	11.00

This table shows that the answer must be between 90 and 100, so another table can be made to get a more accurate answer:

x	y
90	10.45
91	10.51
95	10.73
96	10.78

Therefore, if the customer makes more than 95 local phone calls a month, the Community Plan is better.

b. If a customer makes more than 42 local calls a month, the Community Plan is better.

c. If a customer makes more than 27 local calls a month, the Community Plan is better.

d. If a customer makes more than 19 local calls a month, the Community Plan is better.

20.

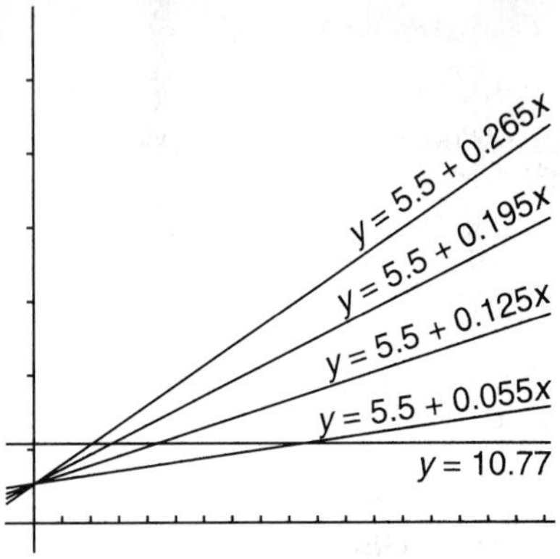

21. $y = 5.50 + [0.055 + 0.035(t - 1)]x$
$y = 5.50 + [0.055 + 0.035t - 0.035]x$
$y = 5.50 + [0.02 + 0.035t]x$

22. a. $5.50 + (0.02 + 0.035t)x = 10.77$
$(0.02 + 0.035t)x = 5.27$
$x = \frac{5.27}{0.02 + 0.035t}$

b. Substituting the various values for t in the above equation and simplifying, confirms the answers obtained by making tables in problem 19.

23. He can multiply the number of one-minute calls by 1, the number of five-minute calls by 5, the number of ten-minute calls by 10, and the number of thirty-minute calls by 30. He then finds the sum of these numbers to find the total number of minutes on the phone. He divides the total number of minutes on the phone by the total number of calls made. The result is the average duration of the phone calls.

7.2 (Solutions for page 250 continued.)

10. She would have to add 4 edge panes and 1 inside pane. (These are the shaded panes shown in the figure.)

2×2 3×3

11. a. 4 edge panes and 7 inside panes (shaded in the figure)

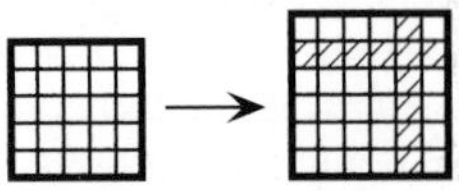

5×5 6×6

b. 4 edge panes and 13 inside panes

12. 0 corner panes, 4 edge panes, and $2N - 3$ inside panes
The figure shows the pattern. She would need to add an edge pane to each side, for a total of 4. (These are marked with an X.) She would also need to add a strip of length $N - 1$ in both directions, as shown by the shaded region. There is one pane that overlaps, so the total number is $2(N - 1) - 1$ or $2N - 3$.

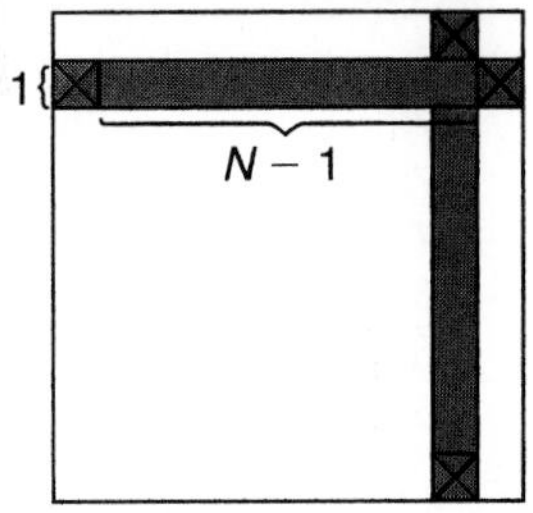

An $N + 1$-by-$N + 1$ foot window

13. $4M$ edge panes and $M^2 + 2MN - 4M$ new inside panes
The figure shows the pattern. M edge panes need to be added to each side, for a total of $4M$. (These are marked with an X.) A strip is added to increase both dimensions that will be of length $N + M - 2$. (The 2 comes from subtracting the edge panes on either end.) This strip is of width M, so the total number is $M(N + M - 2) = MN + M^2 - 2M$. There are two of these strips, so we double this amount and subtract the amount of overlap, which is M by M: $(2MN + 2M^2 - 4M) - M^2 = M^2 + 2MN - 4M$.

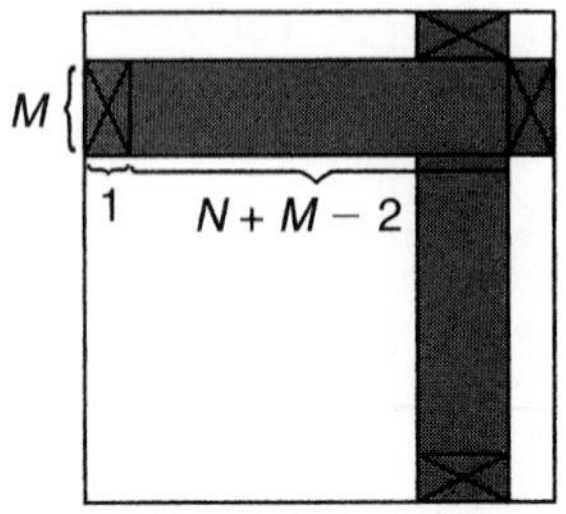

An $N + M$-by-$N + M$ foot window

Note that these formulas reduce to those in #12 in the case of $M = 1$.

14. a. A 5-by-5 window requires 4 corner panes, 12 edge panes, and 9 inside panes, so there would be 8 corner, 0 edge, and 3 inside panes left over.

b. A 2-by-2 window requires 4 corner, 0 edge, and 0 inside panes so there would be 4 corner, 0 edge, and 3 insides left over. A second 2-by-2 window could be made with 4 corner panes, leaving 0 corner, 0 edge, and 3 inside panes left over. Hence, in total, one could make one 5-by-5 and two 2-by-2 windows with 3 inside panes left over.

15. a. There are 20 of each kind. Since we will need the greatest number of interior panes, figure out what the largest window is that can be made with 20 interior panes. We are looking for the largest value of n such that $(n - 2)^2 < 20$. Solve $(n - 2)^2 = 16$ to get $n = 6$. Therefore, we start with a 6-by-6 window, which uses 4 C, 16 E, and 16 I. With the remaining 16 C, 4 E, and 4 I, we can make a 3-by-3 window which uses up 4 C, 4 E, and 1 I. Since that used up all the remaining edge panes, we can make only 2-by-2 windows. We have 12 C, which is enough to make three 2-by-2 windows. There will be 3 I left.
    b. One 12-by-12 and twenty-four 2-by-2 windows, leaving 60 edge panes left over.

16. One solution is six 6-by-6, one 3-by-3, and eighteen 2-by-2. Other solutions with three panes left over are possible.

17. a.

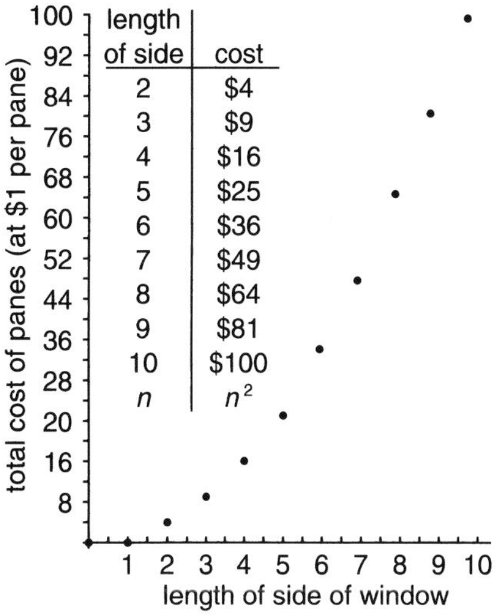

length of side	cost
2	$4
3	$9
4	$16
5	$25
6	$36
7	$49
8	$64
9	$81
10	$100
n	n^2

    b. An n-by-n window costs n^2 dollars. A 16-by-16 window costs $256, which is not 2 times $64.
    c. A 16-by-16 window costs 4 times as much as an 8-by-8 window.

7.3 (Solutions for page 253 continued.)

27. a. $m = 7$ and $n = 5$
    b. $m = 2$ and $n = 33$
    c. $m = 35$ and $n = 0$

28. Answers will vary. Sample answers:
    $N = 100$, $m = 14$
    $N = 30$, $m = 4$
    $N = 51$, $m = 7$
    N must be 2 more than a multiple of 7.

7.A (Solutions for page 257 continued.)

painted on 3 sides). So $12(n - 2)$ is the expression for blocks painted on 2 sides. All cubes have 8 vertex blocks which are painted on three sides. The interior cube is made up of $(n - 2)$-by-$(n - 2)$-by-$(n - 2)$ unpainted blocks.

5. 8

6. a. 64   b. 27
   c. 8   d. 1
   e. 100

7. one-by-one-by-one: $5^3 = 125$
   two-by-two-by-two: $4^3 = 64$
   three-by-three-by-three: $3^3 = 27$
   four-by-four-by-four: $2^3 = 8$
   five-by-five-by-five: 1
   Total: 225

8. Strategies will vary.
   Generalization: n-by-n-by-n has:
   n^3 1-by-1-by-1 cubes
   $(n - 1)^3$ 2-by-2-by-2 cubes
   $(n - 2)^3$ 3-by-3-by-3 cubes
   $(n - 3)^3$ 4-by-4-by-4 cubes
   and so on ...
   2^3 $(n - 1)$-by-$(n - 1)$-by-$(n - 1)$ cubes
   1 n-by-n-by-n cube
   For a 7-by-7-by-7, there are:
   one-by-one-by-one: $7^3 = 343$
   two-by-two-by-two: $6^3 = 216$
   three-by-three-by-three: $5^3 = 125$
   four-by-four-by-four: $4^3 = 64$
   five-by-five-by-five: $3^3 = 27$
   six-by-six-by-six: $2^3 = 8$
   seven-by-seven-by-seven: $1^3 = 1$
   Total: 784 cubes

7.6 (Solutions for page 263 continued.)

21.

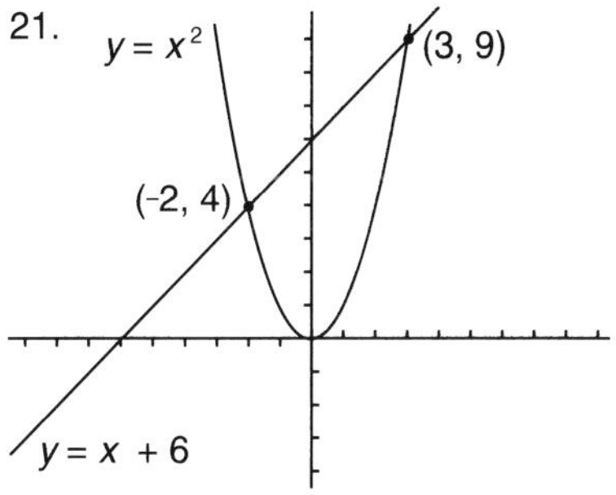

22.

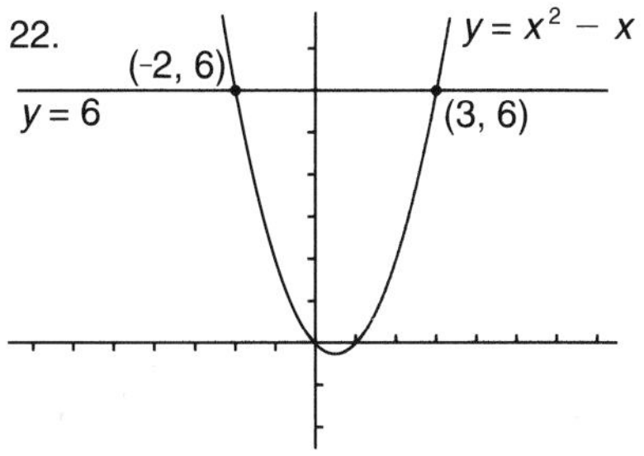

23.

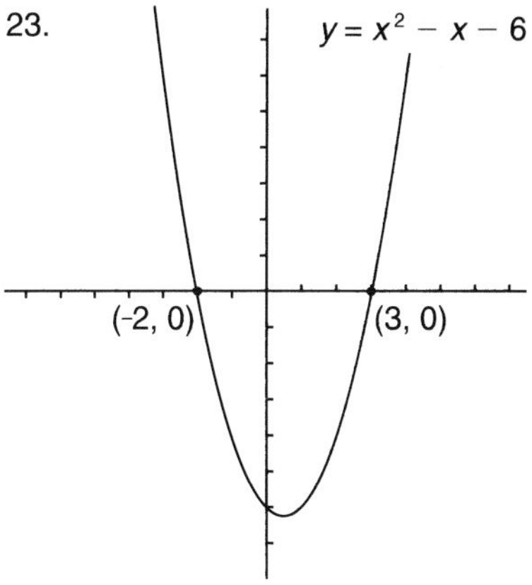

24. a. $x = -2$ or $x = -3$
    b. Answers will vary.

25. Graphs will vary. For example, the solution to (a) could be obtained by graphing and finding the intersection for any of these pairs:
    $y = x^2$ and $y = 3x + 4$
    $y = x^2 - 3x$ and $y = 4$
    $y = x^2 - 4$ and $y = 3x$
    $y = x^2 - 3x - 4$ and $y = 0$
    a. $x = -1$ or $x = 4$
    b. $x = -5$ or $x = 1$
    c. $x = 3$ or $x = -3$

26.

number	last digits
0^{100}	0
1^{100}	1
2^{100}	6
3^{100}	1
4^{100}	6
5^{100}	5
6^{100}	6
7^{100}	1
8^{100}	6
9^{100}	1

7.12 (Solutions for page 280 continued.)

$5 = 2^2 + 2^0$
$6 = 2^2 + 2^1$
$7 = 2^2 + 2^1 + 2^0$
etc. (Think about binary representations of numbers.) This is also possible for large numbers.

19. $1 = 3^0$
    $2 = 3^1 - 3^0$
    $3 = 3^1$
    $4 = 3^1 + 3^0$
    $5 = 3^2 - 3^1 - 3^0$
    $6 = 3^2 - 3^1$
    etc. This is also possible for large numbers.

8.4 (Solutions for page 298 continued.)

15. It is in slope-intercept form.
    a. $m = 5$, $b = -6$
    b. Not applicable (N/A)

16. It's not in slope-intercept form.
a. N/A
b. $y = -4x + 28$; $m = -4$, $b = 28$

17. It's not in slope-intercept form.
a. N/A
b. $y = (5/3)x - 2$; $m = 5/3$, $b = -2$

18. It's not in slope-intercept form.
a. N/A
b. $y = (-1/4)x + 7/4$; $m = -1/4$, $b = 7/4$

19. It's not in slope-intercept form.
a. N/A
b. $y = 15x - 18$; $m = 15$, $b = -18$

20. It is in slope-intercept form.
a. $m = -4$, $b = -7$
b. N/A

21. It's not in slope-intercept form.
a. N/A
b. $y = x - 4$; $m = 1$, $b = -4$

22. It's not in slope-intercept form.
a. N/A
b. $y = -x + 4$; $m = -1$, $b = 4$

23. a. When two lines have the same slope but different *y*-intercepts, then they do not intersect. These two lines have $m = 2$ and their *y*-intercepts are 8 and 10. So they are parallel and they do not intersect.
b. These lines intersect because one slopes down through point (0, 8) and the other slopes up through point (0, 10). They must intersect at a point to the left of the *y*-axis.
c. These two lines do not intersect because they are both horizontal, one through point (0, -2) and the other through point (0, 10).
d. These lines do not intersect. They are parallel lines with slope of 1/4 (which equals 0.25). One goes through point (0, 0) and the other through point (0, 10).
e. These lines do not intersect. They are parallel lines having slope 10. One goes through point (0, -6) and the other through point (0, 0).

24. a. Answers will vary. Sample: $y = x - 2$. ($y = mx - 2$, $m > 0$)
b. $y = (-3/2)x$
c. Answers will vary. Sample: $y = -1.5x$ ($y = -1.5x + b$, $b \geq 0$)

25. Answers will vary for each of the three equations given.
$y = x + 4$:
a. 1 b. 5 c. *K*
$y = 2x + 4$
a. 1/2 b. 5/2 c. *K*/2
$y = -3x + 4$
a. -1/3 b. -5/3 c. -*K*/3
Note: When $y = mx + b$
a. $1/m$ b. $5/m$ c. K/m

26. The answers depended on the parameter *m*.

27. a. $m \leq 0$, $b \leq 0$
b. $m \geq 0$, $b \leq 0$
c. $m \leq 0$, $b \geq 0$
d. $m \geq 0$, $b \geq 0$

28. For $y = mx + b$: When $x = 0$, $y = b$. When *x* increases by 1, *y* increases by *m*. When *x* increases by *d*, *y* increases by *md*. If two lines are parallel, they have the same *m* parameter. If two lines meet on the *y*-axis, they have the same *b* parameter. The slope-intercept form is useful for graphing lines quickly because one can graph without having to substitute values into the equation to calculate coordinates of points. One point on the line is (0, *b*). From there, a second point can be found by using the slope's rise and run.

29. a.

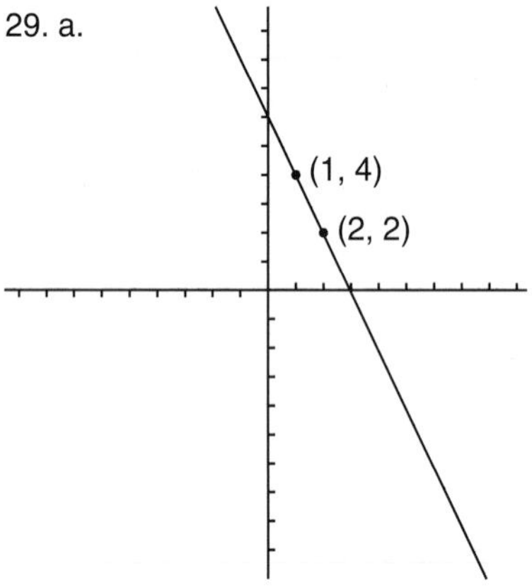

b. (0, 6)
c. $y = -2x + 6$

30. a. Answers will vary. Sample $y = 2x + b$, $b \neq -5$. ($y = 2x + 3$)
b. $y = 2x$
c. $y = 2x + 2$

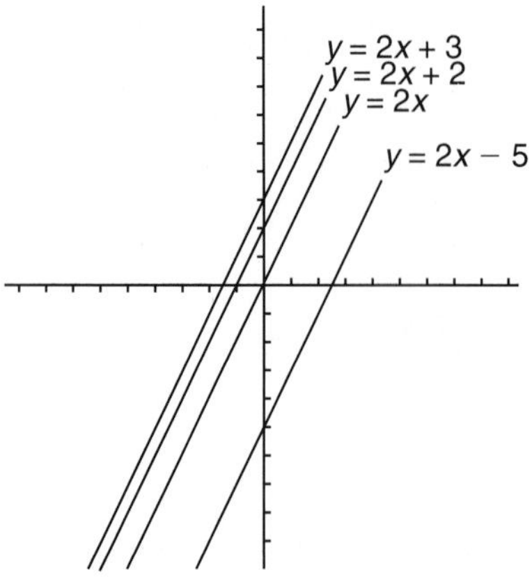

8.5 (Solutions for page 302 continued.)

18. a. When multiplying powers with the same base, keep the base and add the exponents. When dividing powers with the same base, keep the base and subtract the exponents.
b. Answers will vary. Samples:
1. $3^5 \cdot 3^6 = 3^{11}$
2. $(2^6)/(2^2) = 2^4$
c. No, the patterns described in part (a) do not work when bases are different. $3^5/2^2 = 243/4 = 60.75$ which does not equal 3^3 or 2^3.

19. a. 5^{x+y} b. a^{x+y}
c. 3^{y-x} d. 6^5
e. 6^{2x} f. 6^x

8.9 (Solutions for page 314 continued.)

19. $(4^5)^3 = (4^5)(4^5)(4^5) = 4^{15}$

20. a. x^6 b. $(y^2)^2$
c. $(y^5)^2$ d. $(y^3)^2$
e. x^{12}

21. a. y^{2x} b. y^{3x}
c. x^{4y} d. $(y^x)^a$

22. If the base is a power of a smaller number, then the power can be written with a smaller base and larger exponent. For example, $4^3 = (2^2)^3$. This uses the power of a power law of exponents. If the exponent is even, the power can be written with a larger base and smaller exponent. For example, $2^4 = (2^2)^2 = 4^2$. If the exponent is a multiple of *n*, then the power can be written with a new exponent $(1/n)^{th}$ as large. For example, if $n = 3$ then $7^{21} = (7^3)^7$ or $B^{nx} = (B^n)^x$ when $B \neq 0$.

8.11 (Solutions for page 319 continued.)

21. Answers will vary. Some students may prefer the percentage method because all scores remain higher. Others may prefer the subtraction method because they know their schedules will prevent them from handing in early papers, so they want fewer points awarded to those who can submit early papers.

22. Students will give one of these equations:
Subtracting method: $S = 100 - 10x$
or
Percentage method: $S = 100(0.9)^x$.

23. They are equal.

24. $(0.70)(0.70)x = 0.49x$ and $x - 0.050x = 0.50x$.

When $x > 0$ then $0.50x$ is greater than $0.49x$. For example, when $x = 10$, $0.49x = 4.9$ and $0.50x = 5$.

When $x = 0$ then $0.49x$ and $0.50x$ equal zero. So they are equal.

When $x < 0$ then $0.49x > 0.50x$.

25. $(0.90)^3x = 0.729x$ and $x - 0.10x - 0.10x - 0.10x = 0.70x$

When $x > 0$ then $0.729x > 0.70x$. For example, when $x = 10$ then $0.729x = 7.29$ and $0.70x = 7.0$.

When $x = 0$ then $0.729x = 0$ and $0.70x = 0$, so they are equal.

When $x < 0$ then $0.70x > 0.729x$. For example, when $x = -10$ then $0.70x = -7$ and $0.729x = -7.29$.

26. a. $x = 36$
 b. $x = 200$
 c. $x = 625$

27. $x = 25$

28. $x = 1$

29. a. $m = 1$; $y = x + 1$
 b. $m = -20$; $y = -20x + 4$
 c. $m = 7.625$; $y = 7.625x + 7$

30. a. The y-intercept is the value of y when x is zero. Each question in #29 begins with coordinates where the x-value is zero so the corresponding y-value is the y-intercept. For example, given point (0, 4) on the line, the y-intercept is 4.
 b. You find the slope by calculating the change in the y-values divided by the change in x-values.

31. a. $y = 0.9x - 2.8$
 b. $y = 3.4x - 13.78$
 c. $y = \frac{74}{67}x - 6\frac{56}{67}$

8.E.I. (Solutions for page 325 continued.)

term employment, which many first, post-graduation jobs are, the flat increase of \$1200 added to the beginning salary of \$22,000 yields a higher salary for the first 12 years.

13. a. not possible
 b. 4^6 c. 4^3
 d. 4^6 e. 4^5

14. a. not possible b. 6^5
 c. 6^{14} d. 6^0

15. a. 3^9 b. 3^9
 c. not possible d. 3^{24}

16. a. $-154a^{12}$
 b. Cannot be written as a single monomial

17. a. Answers will vary. Any positive values of a, b, and c such that $a > 1$, $b > 1$, $c > 1$, and $a > b$ will satisfy this inequality.
 b. Answers will vary. Sample: $a = 1$, $b = 2$, $c = 3$.
 c. Answers will vary. Sample: $a = 1/2$, $b = 1/3$, $c = 2$.

18. a. 3^4 b. 5^3 c. 4^3

19. a. 2
 b. $2^5 = 32$
 c. The answers are different because in (a), 5 is the exponent whose base is x. In (b), 5 is the exponent whose base is $2x$. $(2x^5)$ is $2 \cdot x \cdot x \cdot x \cdot x \cdot x$ and $(2x)^5$ is $2x \cdot 2x \cdot 2x \cdot 2x \cdot 2x = 2^5x^5$

20. a. 2^5 b. 2^7 c. 2^{10}

21. a. 3^5 b. 3^7 c. 3^{10}

22. Answers may vary in form.
 a. $14^{-1}x^{-3}y^{-3}$ b. $-3^{-1}a^{-5}$ c. $3b^2$

23. a. $3 \cdot 10^5$ b. $10^2/3$
 c. $3 \cdot R^5$ d. $6y^2/5$

24. a. 5^{x+3} b. 5^{-x-3}

25. 4^{6x}

26. The proton is $1.838 \cdot 10^3$ times heavier than the electron. $(1.674 \cdot 10^{-24})/(9.110 \cdot 10^{-28}) = 1.838 \cdot 10^4$

27. a. 48 kilograms = $48 \cdot 10^3$ grams. $(48 \cdot 10^3 g)/(9.11 \cdot 10^{-28} g) = 5.27 \cdot 10^{31}$. So Ann weighs the same as $5.27 \cdot 10^{31}$ electrons.
 b. $(48 \cdot 10^3 g)/(1.674 \cdot 10^{-24} g) = 2.867 \cdot 10^{28}$
 Ann weighs the same as $2.867 \cdot 10^{28}$ protons.

28. 1 AU/1 angstrom = $(1.50 \cdot 10^{11} m)/(10^{-10} m) = 1.5 \cdot 10^{21}$
 There are $1.5 \cdot 10^{21}$ angstroms in one AU.

9.A (Solutions for page 339 continued.)

5. These problems can be solved by looking at either algebraic or geometric patterns in the table and extending these patterns to the 20-by-20 case.
 a. $20\sqrt{2}$
 b. $10\sqrt{5}$
 c. $6\sqrt{10}$

6. 1

7. a. The table is symmetric with respect to the diagonal.
 b. One has slope 2/1 and the other has slope 1/2. In either case, roots of 5 are obtained because $\sqrt{1^2 + 2^2} = \sqrt{5}$.

8. a. 3/1 and 1/3
 b. 4/1 and 1/4

9. a. $\sqrt{26}$ and $2\sqrt{26}$ (Note that the slope is 5/1, and $\sqrt{26}$ is obtained from $\sqrt{5^2 + 1^2}$.
 b. 5 and 10 (These are both multiples of $\sqrt{25}$. The slope is 3/4, and $\sqrt{25}$ is obtained from $\sqrt{3^2 + 4^2}$.

10. Reports will vary.

9.7 (Solutions for page 347 continued.)

17. Most calculators will respond with "E" for "Error." Negative numbers are not in the domain of the square root function.

18. equal 19. equal

20. $2\sqrt{3}$ is greater

21. $\sqrt{3} + \sqrt{3}$ is greater

22. equal 23. equal

24. equal 25. $49^{.5} = 7$

9.E.I. (Solutions for page 365 continued.)

30. about 71%

31. R is 6
 R^2 is 36, so 36 times as much material

32. R^3 is 216, so 216 times as much food

10.1 (Solutions for page 370 continued.)

16. a. $y = 2x$
 b. Each adult's ticket costs twice as much as each child's ticket.

17. Plot (1.88, 0.94) on the line $6x + 3y = 14$. (This yields \$14.10, so it will be slightly off the line.)
 Plot (2, 1) on the line $6x + 3y = 15$
 Plot (2.40, 1.20) on the line $6x + 3y = 18$

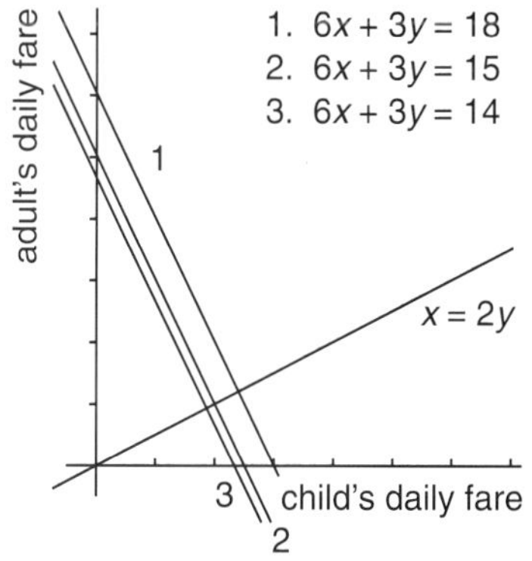

The line passing through all the points is the line $x = 2y$. It means that each child's fare is twice as much as each adult's fare.

18. a. $4c = 6$, so $c = 1.5$. Use 1.5 cups of concentrate.
    b. $4c = 10$, so $c = 2.5$. Use 2.5 cups of concentrate.

19. $15p = 160$, so p is 10 2/3 cups. Use 4 times this amount ($4p$), or 42 2/3 cups each of the iced tea, apple juice, and cranberry juice. Use twice this amount ($2p$), or 21 and 1/3 cups of orange juice. Use (p) 10 2/3 cups of lemon juice. (These amounts are awkward to use, so in real life one would probably convert to quarts or gallons and do a little rounding.)

20. a. If you had 3/4 cup of lemon juice, you could use only 2(3/4) cups of orange juice and 4(3/4) cups of each of the three other ingredients.
    12/4 + 12/4 + 12/4 + 6/4 + 3/4 = 45/4 = 11.25 cups of Piano Recital Punch, which would be sufficient for a very small piano recital.
    b. If you had 3 cups of orange juice, one part would equal 1.5 cups, so the total amount would be:
    4(1.5) + 4(1.5) + 4(1.5) + 3 + 1.5 = 22.5 cups of PRP.

21. a. 4^3x^6 or $64x^6$
    b. $4^3x^6y^3$ or $64x^6y^3$

22. a. $20 \cdot 2^2 = 80$
    b. 1/10
    c. 1/40

23. For $x = 1$, they are equal. For $x < 1$, $3 \cdot 2^x$ is greater. For $x > 1$, $2 \cdot 3^x$ is greater. (Some students will do this using trial and error. If they cannot get a complete solution, they should at least be able to find a value of x satisfying each of the three conditions.)

10.2 (Solutions for page 372 continued.)

11. Answers will vary for the last two rows. Two possible answers are given.

Apple juice		Cranberry-apple		Total	
apple	cran	apple	cran	apple	cran
15	0	2.5	2.5	17.5	2.5
8	0	6	6	14	6
6	0	7	7	13	7
4	0	8	8	12	8
1	0	9.5	9.5	10.5	9.5
x	0	0.50y	0.50y	x+0.50y	0.50y
14	0	3	3	17	3
10	0	5	5	15	5

12. If Nelson used all cranberry-apple and no apple juice, he would have a mixture that is 50% of each juice, containing 10 cups of cranberry juice and 10 cups of apple. This is the minimum amount of apple and the maximum amount of cranberry. If he used any apple juice at all, he'd have more than 10 cups of apple and less than 10 of cranberry. He could increase the amount of apple as much as he wanted, even to the point of using all apple juice. To summarize:
    minimum cranberry: 0 cups
    maximum cranberry: 10 cups
    minimum apple: 10 cups
    maximum apple: 20 cups

13. The cranberry is 2.5/20 or 12.5% of the total mixture.

14. Answers will vary for the last two rows. Two possibilities are given.

Apple juice		Cranberry-apple		Mixture		
apple	cran	apple	cran	apple	cran	%cran
15	0	2.5	2.5	17.5	2.5	12.5%
8	0	6	6	14	6	30%
6	0	7	7	13	7	35%
4	0	8	8	12	8	40%
1	0	9.5	9.5	10.5	9.5	47.5%
x	0	0.50y	0.50y	x+0.50y	0.50y	25% of y or 0.025y
14	0	3	3	17	3	15%
10	0	5	5	15	5	25%

15. The smallest percentage of cranberry is 0%, since he could use all apple if he wanted to. The largest percentage of cranberry is 50%, which would come from using all cranberry-apple. The smallest percentage of apple is 50%, and the largest is 100%.

16. x = number of cups of pure apple juice
    y = the number of cups of cranberry-apple juice
    Since the cranberry-apple juice is 50% cranberry, 0.50y represents the amount of apple juice in y cups of cranberry-apple. So, the total amount of apple juice in the final mixture is x (from the pure apple juice) plus 0.50y (from the cranapple juice).

17. The only cranberry juice in the mixture is the amount that is contributed by the cranberry-apple juice. Since 50% of that is cranberry, the amount of cranberry in the mixture is 0.50y. Notice in the table that the amounts of apple and cranberry are equal in the column for cranberry-apple.

18. The variables x and y represent the amount, in cups, of the two juices used in the mixture. Since Nelson is making 20-cup batches, $x + y$ is always equal to 20.

19. The equation $x + 0.50y = 10$ means that the total amount of apple juice in the mixture is 10 cups. The (x, y) pair that satisfies this is (0, 20), which corresponds to using no pure apple juice and all cranberry-apple juice to make the mixture.

20. a. Half of the cranberry-apple juice is 4 cups.
    b. $y = 8$. Since x and y add up to 20, $x = 12$

21. a. The amount of apple juice in the mixture is 15 cups.
    b. $x = 10$, $y = 10$
    Note: Tables may help students find solutions to #19, #20b, and #21b.

x		y		20	
apple	cran	apple	cran	apple	cran
0	0	10	10	10	10
12	0	4	4	16	4
10	0	5	5	15	5
x	0	0.50y	0.50y	x + 0.50y	0.50y

22. a. There are 4 cups of apple juice in the total mixture.
    b. This is impossible. There would have to be 16 cups of cranberry juice in the final mixture to make 20 cups. If there are 16 cups of cranberry, then 32 cups of the cranberry-apple mixture must have been used, which is too much.

23. a. There are 11.5 cups of apple juice in the total mixture.
    b. $x = 3$, $y = 17$.

24. a. The apple juice is 75% of the total mixture. Another way of writing this is $x + 0.50y = 0.75(20)$ or $x + 0.50y = 15$. This is the same as #21.
    b. From #21b, $x = 10$ and $y = 10$.

25. a. The apple juice is 25% of the total mixture. This equation is equivalent to $x + 0.50y = 0.25(20)$, or $x + 0.50y = 5$.
    b. This is impossible because there would have to be 30 cups of cranberry apple juice (y) and there can be no more than 20 cups in the total mixture.

26. #22 and #25 were impossible. To see if they would be possible to solve if the total mixture contained 30 cups, we could make a table.

x		y		30	
apple	cran	apple	cran	apple	cran
0	0	?	26	4	26
0	0	?	25	5	25

The table shows that these cases would also be impossible with 30 cups total. If there were 4 cups of apple, there would have to be 26 cups of cranberry. However, that would require 52 cups of cranberry-apple. Likewise, if there were 5 cups of apple in the final mixture, there would have to be 25 cups of cranberry, which would require the use of 50 cups of cranberry-apple.

10.A (Solutions for page 380 continued.)

14. a. Nelson is now making 25-cup batches of juice.
    b. This is impossible to solve if $x + y = 20$. Nelson cannot simultaneously make 20-cup batches and 25-cup batches.
15. a. There are 10 more cups of Fruity Flavor than Berry Blend in the 20-cup mixture.
    b. (15, 5)
16. Reports will vary. The amount of each kind of juice possible in the mixture is determined by the percentage of each juice in each of the components (FF and BB) and the total amounts of FF and BB used. The percentage of each kind of juice possible is determined by the minimum and maximum percentages in each of the components. To solve problems like #4 and #6, first find the number of cups of each juice. For example, if the final mixture were 45% cranberry, then this is (0.45)(20) or 9 cups. Write an equation that describes this in terms of the components, i.e., $0.50x + 0.20y = 9$. Write an equation that describes the total number of cups, i.e., $x + y = 20$. These can easily be solved simultaneously.

10.5 (Solutions for page 383 continued.)

14. c.

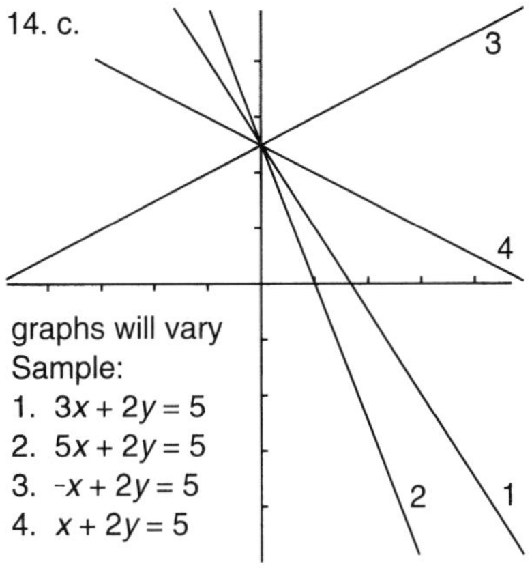

graphs will vary
Sample:
1. $3x + 2y = 5$
2. $5x + 2y = 5$
3. $-x + 2y = 5$
4. $x + 2y = 5$

15. a. When A changed and B and C remained fixed at 2 and 5 respectively, the steepness and x-intercept changed, and the y-intercept stayed the same. The closer the value of A was to zero, the farther away the x-intercept was from the origin.
    b. In problem #14, graphs with positive values of A had positive x-intercepts. Graphs with negative values of A had negative x-intercepts.
    c. When $A = 0$, the line is horizontal. When A is very large, the x-intercept is very close to the origin and the line looks vertical. It is not possible to choose a value of A to make the line vertical. When $B = 0$, the line is vertical.
16. a. The line is close to being vertical.
    b. The line is close to being vertical.
    c. The line is close to being horizontal.
    d. The line is close to being horizontal.
17. a., b.

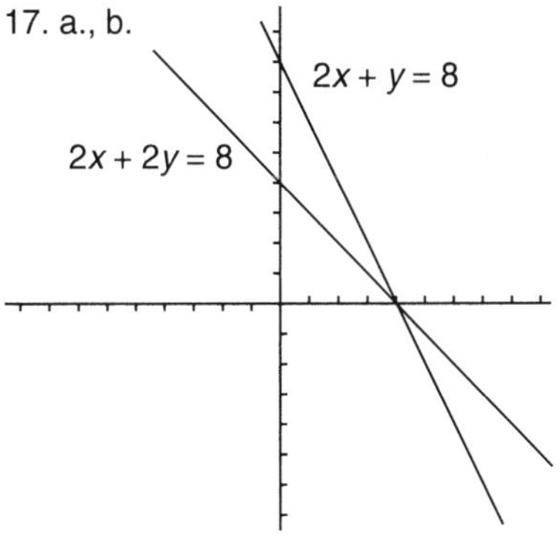

c.

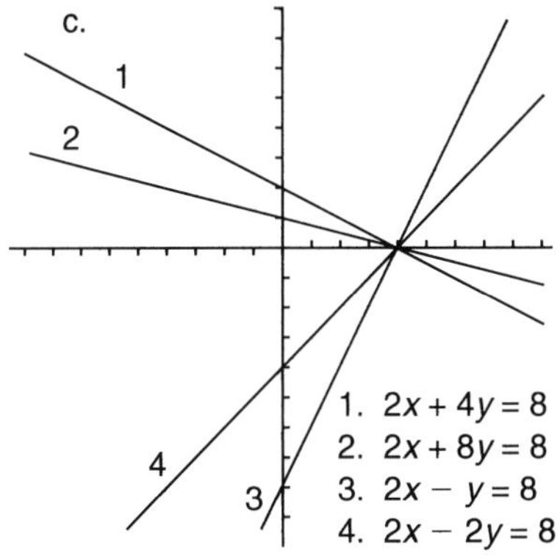

1. $2x + 4y = 8$
2. $2x + 8y = 8$
3. $2x - y = 8$
4. $2x - 2y = 8$

18. a. When B alone was changed, the steepness and y-intercept changed while the x-intercept stayed the same. The closer the value of B was to zero, the farther the y-intercept was from the origin.
    b. In #17, graphs with positive values of B had positive y-intercepts. Graphs with negative values of B had negative y-intercepts.
    c. No value of B can be found that will make the graph horizontal. (However, when B is very large, the y-intercept is close to the origin and the line looks horizontal.) A horizontal line would have $A = 0$. When $B = 0$, the line is vertical.
19. a. negative slope, close to horizontal
    b. positive slope, close to horizontal
    c. negative slope, close to vertical
    d. positive slope, close to vertical
20. They do not intersect. Since A and B are the same in both equations, the lines will have the same slope.
21. Graphs will vary. Some samples are given.

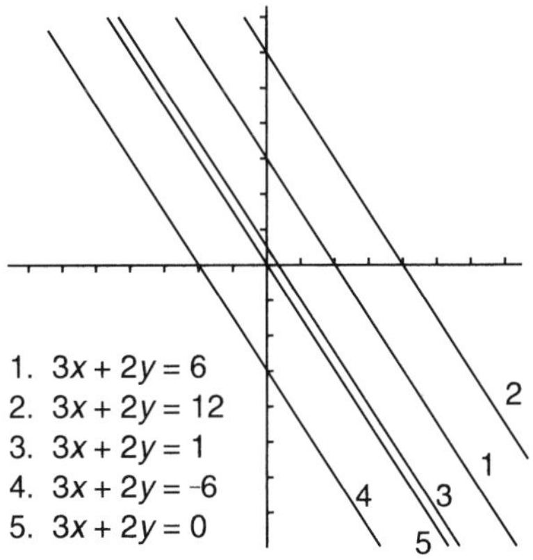

1. $3x + 2y = 6$
2. $3x + 2y = 12$
3. $3x + 2y = 1$
4. $3x + 2y = -6$
5. $3x + 2y = 0$

Conclusion: When C is changed and A and B remain constant in $3x + 3y = 6$, the resulting line has the same slope but different x- and y-intercepts. If $c > 0$, the larger its value, the further the intercepts are from the origin. If $c < 0$, the smaller its value, the farther the intercepts are from the origin. When $c = 0$, the line goes through the origin.

22. Reports will vary. Some sample points that should be included:
Changing A changes a graph's x-intercepts and slope. The y-intercept does not change. When $A = 0$, the graph is a horizontal line.
Changing B changes a graph's y-intercept and slope. The x-intercept does not change. When $B = 0$, the graph is a vertical line.
Changing C changes a graph's intercepts but not the slope. When $C = 0$, the graph goes through the origin.
23. No solution necessary. See Notes to the Teacher.
25. a. the second square
b. the first square
26. a. the square
b. the square
27. a. the square
b. the square

10.6 (Solutions for page 386 continued.)

23. (1, 1)
24. Begin with the first equation ($2x + 3y = 5$) and add to it -2 times the second equation. This will eliminate x and result in the horizontal equation $y = 3$.
25. (-2, 3)
26. Horizontal lines, of the form $y = k$, and vertical lines, of the form $x = k$, have only one variable. When solving a system of equations, one eliminates one variable and solves for the other in the form $y = k$ or $x = k$. This one variable solution is either a horizontal or vertical line through the point of intersection of the system's equations.
27. a. infinite number — some solutions: 7 and 3, 8 and 2, 9 and 1
b. one solution, (8, -2)
c. no solution
28. a. at (0, -1)
b. You are at (3, 1), which is a point on the graph. Since the slope is 2/3, every time you move up 2 units and 3 units to the right, you will be at another point on the graph. (Another way of showing this is to show that the point satisfies the equation.)
c. You are at (6, 3) which is also on the graph. Once again, you know that without graphing, either by reasoning about slope or showing algebraically that the point satisfies the equation.
d. The variable m must be 9. You can figure this out by trial and error, or find m such that $6/m$ equals 2/3.
29. First plot the y-intercept. Then move over and up from the y-intercept the amount specified by the slope. Example: To graph $y = (3/5)x + 2$, first plot the y-intercept (0, 2). Then count up 3 and to the right 5 from the y-intercept to find a second point on the line. This will get you to (5, 5). Draw a line through (0, 2) and (5, 5).
30. a. $y = -(4/3)x + 8/3$
b. $y = -3x + 6$
c. $y = 3x - 2$
d. $y = -(4/3)x + 2/3$

11.3 (Solutions for page 405 continued.)

6. d.

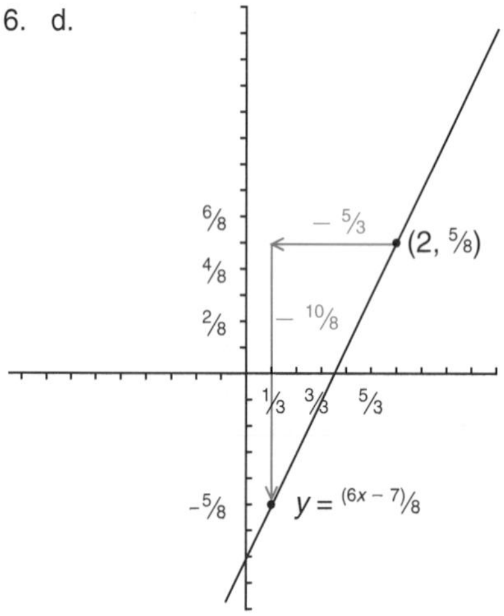

6. e.

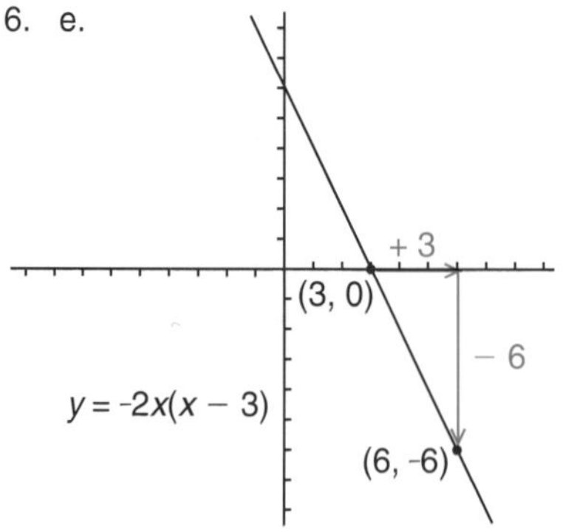

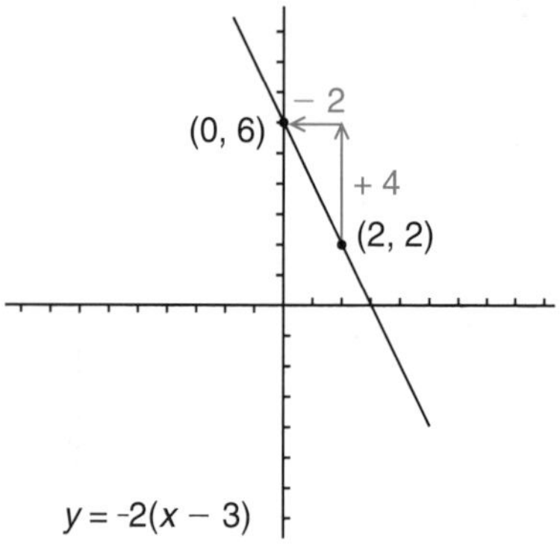

7. Answers will vary. Sample answers are given.
a. rise: -7.5 run: 1
b. rise: 2.5 run: -5
8. a. $y = (2/3)x + 8$
b. $y = (2/3)x + 8$
9. Answers will vary. Sample answers are given.
a. (1, 7), (2, 14)
b. (3, 2), (6, 4)
c. (2, 9), (4, 18)
d. (100, 678), (200, 1356)
10. a. (2, 3) and (-2, -3)
b. All points of the form ($2n$, $3n$), where n is an integer.
c. $y = (3/2)x$
11. This problem is for discussion. Students will be able to answer it after completing Lesson 11.4.
12. q/p
13. All points of the form (qn, pn), where n is an integer will be on the line. If p and q are not relatively prime, find a fraction r/s that is equivalent to p/q. All points of the form (sn, rn), where n is an integer will also be on the line.
14. Answers to the Exploration will vary. Students will be guided to the correct answer in the following problems.
15. a. $q - 1$ horizontal
b. $p - 1$ vertical
16. a. none
b. It crosses $n - 1$ lattice points between (0, 0) and (p, q).
17. a. $p + q - 1$
b. $p + q - (n + 1)$
18. Reports will vary. They should use the results from #15 - #17.

11.B (Solutions for page 421 continued.)

Measured number of seconds	Actual number of seconds	Estimated speed in mi/hr	Actual speed in mi/hr	Error
43	45	83.72	80.00	3.72
45	45	80.00	80.00	0
47	45	76.60	80.00	3.4
83	85	43.37	42.35	1.02
85	85	42.35	42.35	0
87	85	41.38	42.35	0.97

The error is obviously higher if you are going faster. The maximum error for the speeds shown in the table in #7 is 3.7 miles/hour.

10. If the car were going 80 miles per hour, the maximum error would be two seconds in starting and stopping the stopwatch. With the maximum error, the measured number of seconds would be 178 seconds in four miles. 178/4 = 44.5, so the estimated speed in miles per hour would be 3600/44.5 or 80.90 miles per hour, which would be off by 0.90 miles per hour.

11. Reports will vary.

11.E.I. (Solutions for page 423 continued.)

b. This is fair. There are 2^3 or 8 possibilities in all. If necessary, make a table to show that there are 4 possibilities with 0 or 2 heads and 4 possibilities with 1 or 3 heads.
c. fair

23. 1 pound = 0.454 kg, so 1 kg = (1/0.454) pounds or about 2.2 pounds

24. a. 1/144 $ft^2/in.^2$
b. 144 $in.^2/ft^2$
c. $(2.54)^3 = 16.387\ cm^3/in.^3$
d. (1/16.387) = 0.061 $in.^3/cm^3$

25. 62.4 lbs/ft^3

12.B (Solutions for page 452 continued.)

15. a. The graph would be a V with a vertex at (2, 600).
b. The equation would be $y = {}^-300\,|x - 2| + 600$.

16. $({}^-10/3)x$

17. $3.08\overline{3}x + 0.875$

18. $0.1x + 0.4$

12.E.I. (Solutions for page 455 continued.)

21. The amount immediately before taking the next dose will be $0.4x_a$. When she takes the next dose, the amount in her body will be 360 mg more than that, or $0.4x_a + 360$.

22. The amount immediately after taking the dose is $x_b + 360$. Just before taking the next dose, 40% of the drug will remain in her body, or $0.40(x_b + 360)$.

23. Using equations, solve for x_a in the equation $x_a = 0.4x_a + 360$. The highest amount approaches the stable level of 600 mg. Solve for x_b in $x_b = 0.40(x_b + 360)$ to find the lowest amount, which is 240 mg. (Notice that these are 360 mg apart, which is exactly the dose.)

13.1 (Solutions for page 460 continued.)

22. a. $y = {}^-0.25x(x - 8)$
b. $y = {}^-4x(x - 2)$
c. $y = {}^-1x(x + 4)$
d. $y = (2/3)x(x + 6)$

23. $x = {}^-1.6$

24. $x = {}^-1.6$, $y = {}^-1.6$

25. The fixed point is the point for which the input equals the output. Therefore, $y = x$.

26. The graphs of $y = x^2$ and $y = x$ intersect at (0, 0) and (1, 1). These are indeed the fixed points of $y = x^2$.

13.4 (Solutions for page 467 continued.)

We can see from the table that a 1-unit increase in length leads to a different amount of increase or decrease in perimeter, depending on the length. The change is not constant. This is what might be expected, since perimeter is not a linear function of length.

14. a. Divide 36 by the length to find the width. Add the width and the length and double the result to find the perimeter.
b. $P = 2[L + 36/L]$
c. The length and width would be 6 and the perimeter would be 24. This is a square. This figure is represented by the lowest point of the curve graphed in #10.

15. a. W = A/L
b. $P = 2[L + A/L]$

16. The minimum perimeter can be obtained by making a square. The square will have side $\sqrt{A}$ and hence perimeter $4\sqrt{A}$.

17. 5 and 15 (Methods will vary.)

18. They should have two points of intersection: (5, 15) and (15, 5). This is the same problem as #17, stated in terms of graphs.

19. 20 and 3.75

20. We can achieve the smallest sum by making the two numbers equal. The two numbers are $\sqrt{75}$ and $\sqrt{75}$, so their sum is $2\sqrt{75}$.

13.A (Solutions for page 468 continued.)

5. Let x be the number of boxes.
y = basic charge + surcharge
= $100x + 2000/x$

6. By graphing or trial and error, the correct answer is found to be between 4 and 5. Check both:
4 boxes: basic charge = 4($100) = 400
surcharge = $2000/4 = 500
Total = $900
5 boxes: basic charge = 5($100) = 500
surcharge = $2000/5 = 400
Total = $900
Either works.

7. Per widget, the cost is $900/2000, or 45 cents per widget.

8. Reports will vary.

13.5 (Solutions for page 470 continued.)

17. A 24-in.-by-24-in.-by-18-in. box will have a volume of 10,368 cubic inches.

18. Solutions will vary.

19. With 2 inches of cushioning, the maximum length plus girth would be 116 inches. A box with dimensions 19 by 19 by 40 would have volume of approximately 14,440 cubic inches.

13.6 (Solutions for page 472 continued.)

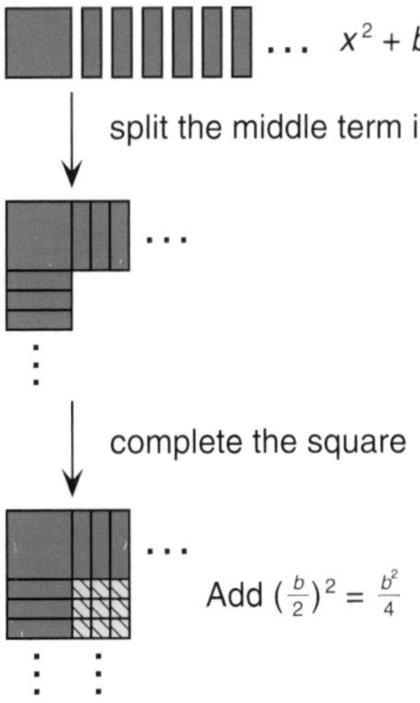

18. Add 16 to both sides. Sketch of equal squares should show $(x + 4)^2$ on one side and 7^2 on the other side. Then $x + 4$ must equal 7 or -7. The solutions are 3 or -11.

19. Add 4 to both sides. Sketch of equal squares should show $(x + 2)^2$ on one side and 10^2 on the other side. Then $x + 2$ must equal 10 or -10. The solutions are 8 or -12.

20. Add 9 to both sides. Sketch of equal squares should show $(x + 3)^2$ on one side and 8^2 on the other side. Then $x + 3$ must equal 8 or -8. The solutions are 5 or -11.

21. Add 25 to both sides. Sketch of equal squares should show $(x + 5)^2$ on one side and 9^2 on the other side. Then $x + 5$ must equal 9 or -9. The solutions are 4 or -14.

22. $x = 11$ or $x = -3$

23. $x = 12$ or $x = -8$

24. no solution

25. Add 1/4 to both sides to get $x^2 + x + 1/4 = 6.25$, so $(x + 0.5)^2 = 2.5^2$. Hence $x = 2.0$ or $x = -3.0$.

26. Exact answer: $4 \pm \sqrt{13}$
    Approximations: $x = 7.61$ or $x = 0.39$

27. Exact answer: $2.5 \pm \sqrt{14.25}$
    Approximations: $x = 6.27$ or $x = -1.27$

28. Exact answer: $x = -1$ or $x = 5$

29. Exact answer: $0.5[7 \pm \sqrt{65}]$
    Approximations: $x = -0.53$ or $x = 7.53$

30. $x = 0$ and $x = -18$

31. $x = -5.5$ and $x = 0.5$

32. $x = -4$ and $x = 2$

33. $x = -4$ and $x = -3$

34. Answers will vary. Any equation that can be written in the form $a(x + 2)(x - 5) = 0$ will have roots -2 and 5.

35. Answers will vary. One possible solution is $(x - 2)^2 = 5$, or $x^2 - 4x - 1 = 0$.

36. $x^2 - 8x + 13$

37. $x^2 - 8x + 13 = 0$
    We know the solution, because we obtained the expression on the left side by multiplying a factored expression. The solutions are $x = 4 \pm \sqrt{3}$.

13.7 (Solutions for page 475 continued.)

b. Look at the value of c in the equation and determine how far it is from 9, since 9 is the value that will make the expression a perfect square. $V = c - 9$

22. a. $y = x^2 + 4$
    b. $y = x^2 + 4x + 4 = (x + 2)^2$
    c. $y = x^2 + 2x + 4 = (x + 1)^2 + 3$
    d. $y = x^2 + 6x + 4 = (x + 3)^2 - 5$

23. a. $y = x^2 + 6x + 4$
    b. $y = x^2 + 4x + 4$
    c. $y = x^2 + 2x + 4$
    d. $y = x^2 + 4$

24. Since $H = 0$, the vertex is $(0, c)$.

25. $y = x^2 + 4 = (x + 0)^2 + 4$, so $H = 0$
    $y = x^2 + 4x + 4 = (x + 2)^2$, so $H = -2$
    $y = x^2 + 2x + 4 = (x + 1)^2 + 3$, so $H = -1$
    $y = x^2 + 6x + 4 = (x + 3)^2 - 5$, so $H = -3$

26. a. H is the opposite of half the number of x-blocks.
    b. H is the opposite of half of b.

27. a. $H = -0.5b = -0.5(16) = -8$
    b. $H = 8$

28. As the Lab Gear figures show, you must have half the number of x-blocks on each side to make a square. This corresponds to taking half the coefficient of the middle term. To see that it is necessary to take the opposite of $b/2$, compare the Lab Gear figures and the graphs.

29. Reports will vary. The main ideas follow.
    a. The x-intercepts are p and q. The x-coordinate of the vertex is halfway between the x-intercepts, or $(p + q)/2$. To find the y-intercept of the vertex, substitute this number into the equation for x and solve for y.
    b. The vertex can be read directly from an equation in vertex form.
    c. The x-coordinate of the vertex is $-b/2$. To find the y-intercept of the vertex, substitute $-b/2$ for x in the equation and solve for y.

13.B (Solutions for page 479 continued.)

b. If the area is 60, $LW = 60$. The length can be written in terms of the width: $L = 60/W$. Since $P = 2L + 2W$, we can write $P = (120/W) + 2W$.

8. Solution methods will vary. One possible method is given.

8. 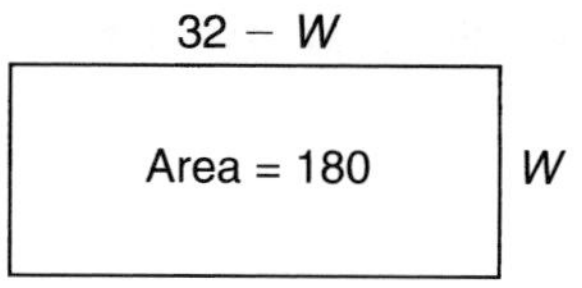

$W(32 - W) = 180$
$(32 - W)W = 180$
$W^2 - 32W + 180 = 0$
$H = 16$, $V = (16)^2 - 32(16) + 180 = -76$
The solutions are $16 \pm \sqrt{76} = 16 \pm 8.72 = 7.28$ or 24.72
The dimensions of the rectangle are approximately 7.28 by 24.72.

9. Solution methods will vary. One possible method is given.

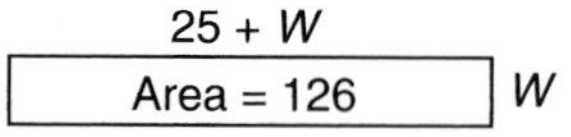

$W(25 + W) = 126$
$W^2 + 25W - 126 = 0$
$H = -12.5$, $V = (-12.5)^2 + 25(-12.5) - 126 = -282.25$
The solutions are $-12.5 \pm \sqrt{282.25} = -12.5 \pm 16.8$. Only the positive solution, which is 4.3, will work. The other dimension of the rectangle must be $25 + 4.3 = 29.3$. Check by multiplying 4.3 by 29.3. The result is very close to 126.

10. Solution methods will vary. One possible method is given.

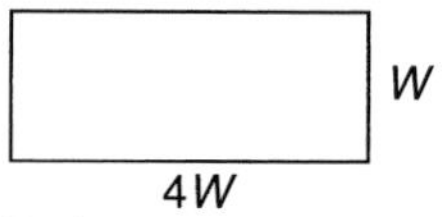

Perimeter = 35
The length is $4W$, so the perimeter is $8W + 2W = 10W$. The perimeter is given to be 35, so
$10W = 35$.
$W = 3.5$
$L = 4(3.5) = 14$

11. It is given that the length is four times the width, so we can write the equation $L = 4W$. The area is $4W \cdot W$.

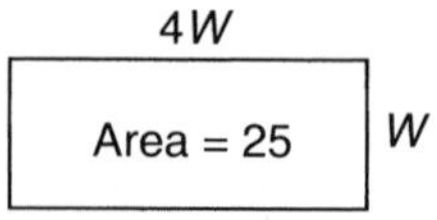

$4W^2 = 25$

$4W \cdot W = 25$
$W^2 = 25/4$
$W = 5/2$
Hence the width is 2.5 and the length is 10.

13.E.I. (Solutions for page 481 continued.)

9. x-unit = 4
y-unit = 40

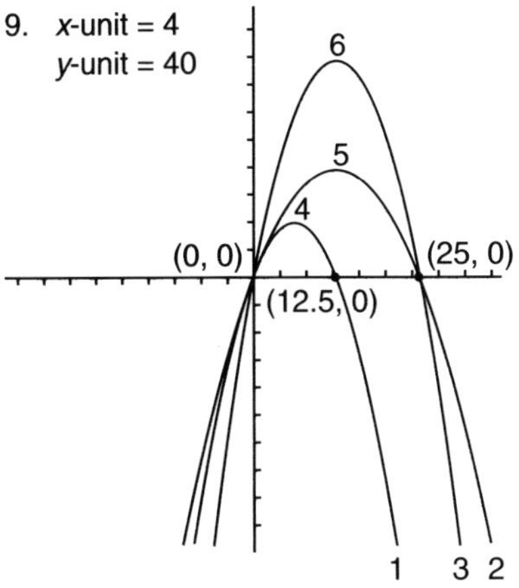

1. $x(25 - 2x)$
2. $x(25 - x)$
3. $2x(25 - x)$
4. (6.25, 78.125)
5. (12.5, 156.25)
6. (12.5, 312.5)

10. Answers will vary.
11. Answers will vary. Sample answers are given.
 a. $y = 3x(x - 2)$
 b. $y = -6x(x + 4)$
 c. $y = -99(x - 1)(x + 4)$
12. The graphs should all be the same, since all the equations can be written in factored form as $y = 4x(x - 1)$.

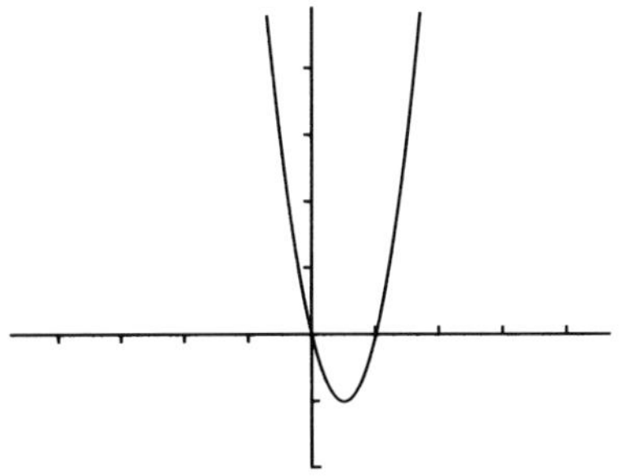

13. Answers will vary. Sample answers are given.
 a. $y = x^2 + 4$
 b. $y = (x - 3)^2$
 c. $y = (x - 3)(x + 2)(4x + 5)$
14. a. There is one x-intercept, since there is one solution to the equation, $0 = 2x + 1$.
 b. There are two x-intercepts, since by the zero product property either $x = 0$ or $4 - x = 0$.
 c. There are no x-intercepts, since there is no real number such that $x^2 = -1$.
 d. There is one x-intercept, since the parabola sits on the x-axis on $x = -1$.
15. a. The equation can be written $y = x(8 - x)$ in factored form, so by the zero product property $x = 0$ or $8 - x = 0$. Hence there are two x-intercepts.
 b. By completing the square, one can see that this can be written in the form $y = (x - 0.5)^2 + 1.75$, which has a graph that is entirely above the x-axis. Hence there are no x-intercepts.
 c. The equation can be written in factored form as $y = 2(x + 3)(x + 3)$, so there is only one x-intercept, since the two factors are the same.
16. a. If $a > 0$, there is one x-intercept, since the parabola sits on the x-axis at $(H, 0)$. If $a < 0$, there is also one x-intercept, since the parabola hangs down from the x-axis at $(H, 0)$.
 b. There are no x-intercepts if $a > 0$, since the graph is a smile parabola with its vertex above the x-axis at $(H, 3)$. There are two x-intercepts if $a < 0$, since the graph has a vertex above the x-axis but opens down into a frown.
 c. If $a > 0$, there are two x-intercepts, since the graph has a vertex below the x-axis at $(H, -3)$, and opens up into a smile. If $a < 0$, there are no x-intercepts, since the graph has a vertex below the x-axis at $(H, -3)$, and opens down into a frown.
17. Answers will vary. Sample answers are given.
 a. $y = 5(x - 2)(x - 4)$
 b. $y = -3(x - 2)(x - 4)$
 c. The vertex of the first parabola is (3, -5). The vertex of the second parabola is (3, 3). The vertices have the same x-coordinate, but different y-coordinates.
18. Answers will vary. Sample answers are given.
 a. $y = x(x - 3)$
 b. $y = -4x(x - 3)$
 c. $y = x^2 + 9$
 d. Answer will depend on the form (standard, vertex, or factored) in which students have given their answers to (a), (b), (c).
19. Answers will vary. Three possible equations are: $y = -6x(x - 2)$, $y = -6x^2 + 12x$, $y = 3x(-2x + 4)$.
20. a. The equation must be of the form $y = a(x + 2)(x - 6)$. Substituting (0, 4) into the equation, we can show that $x = -1/3$, so the equation is $y = (-1/3)(x + 2)(x - 6)$.
 b. The other x-intercept must be at (-3, 0), since the vertex is halfway between the x-intercepts. The equation must be of the form $y = a(x + 3)(x - 1)$. Substituting (-1, -4) into the equation, we can show that $a = 1$, so the equation is $y = (x + 3)(x - 1)$.
 c. Since the vertex is on the x-axis, it is the only x-intercept. The equation is of the form $y = a(x + 2)(x + 2)$. Substituting (0, 2) into the equation, we can show that $a = 1/2$, so the equation is $y = (1/2)(x + 2)^2$.
21. a. Find the x-coordinate of the vertex by averaging the x-coordinates of the x-intercepts. The x-coordinate is $(5 + -8)/2 = -3/2$. Substitute for x in the equation to get the y-coordinate of the vertex. The vertex is (-1.5, 84.5).
 b. The vertex is (-3, -6).
 c. The x-coordinate is $-b/2 = -2$. The y-coordinate can be found by substituting: $y = (-2)^2 + 4(-2) - 7 = 4 - 8 - 7 = -11$. The vertex is (-2, -11).
22. Answers will vary. Sample answers are given.
 a. $y = 3(x - 2)^2 + 8$
 b. $y = -4(x - 8)^2 + 64$
23. a. Answers will vary. Any answer that can be written in the form $y = a(x - p)(x + r)$ will work. Check by substituting p and $-r$ for x.
 b. The x-coordinate is $(p - r)/2$, which was found by averaging the x-intercepts. The y-coordinate is $-a(p + r)^2/4$.
24. a. no solution
 b. $x = 8 \pm \sqrt{6}$
 c. no solution
 d. $x = -8 \pm \sqrt{6}$
25. $x = \pm \sqrt{6}$
26. $x = 0$ or $x = 6$
27. $x = 3$
28. $x = -3$
29. $x = -3 \pm \sqrt{13}$
30. $x = 2 \pm \sqrt{2}$
31. $x = -7$ or $x = -1$
32. $x = 7$ or $x = 1$

14.7 (Solutions for page 503 continued.)

10. a. Since $\sqrt{0} = 0$, the number being added and subtracted is 0.

b. The number under the radical is a negative number, so there are no real solutions.
c. The number under the radical is a positive number, so one solution is obtained by adding its square root and the other is obtained by subtracting it.

11. If a and c have opposite signs, the related parabola must cross the x-axis, as explained in #2. Therefore, there must be two solutions, which would mean that the discriminant would be positive.

12. a. $-b/a$
    b. $-b/(2a)$
    c. c/a

13. $x = \frac{-5 \pm \sqrt{89}}{4}$
    sum of roots: -5/2
    product of roots: -4

14. $x = \frac{4 \pm \sqrt{6}}{2}$
    sum of roots: 4
    product of roots: 5/2

15. $x = 1$ or $x = -5/8$
    sum of roots: 3/8
    product of roots: -5/8

16. $x = \frac{-5 \pm \sqrt{17}}{4}$
    sum of roots: -2.5
    product of roots: 1/2

17. a, c

18. a, b, c, e

19. a, b, c, d, e

20. a, b, c, d, e, f

21. a. $3x = 12$
    b. $3x = -12$
    c. $12x = 3$
    d. $x^2 = 12$

22. $x^2 + 1 = 0$

23. No solution is necessary.

14.E.I. (Solutions for page 508 continued.)

21. a. Any equation of the form $y = a(x - 2)(x + 4)$ is correct.
    b. $x = -1$
    c. (2, 0)(-4, 0)
    d. $H = -1$ $V = -9a$

22. a. Any equation of the form $y = a(x - 3)^2 - 5$ is correct.
    b. $x = 3$
    c. $(3 + \sqrt{5/a}, 0)(3 - \sqrt{5/a}, 0)$
    d. (3, -5)

23. a. Any equation of the form $y = a(x + \sqrt{5})(x - \sqrt{5})$ is correct.
    b. $x = 0$
    c. $(\sqrt{5}, 0)$ and $(-\sqrt{5}, 0)$
    d. $(0, -5a)$

24. a. Any equation of the form $y = a[x - (1 + \sqrt{6})][x - (1 - \sqrt{6})]$ is correct.
    b. $x = 1$
    c. $(1 + \sqrt{6}, 0)$ and $(1 - \sqrt{6}, 0)$
    d. $(1, 6a)$

25. a. One possible equation is $y = x^2 - 10x + 3$. Answers will vary.
    b. $x = 5$
    c. Answers will vary.
    d. Answers will vary.

26. a. vertex: (-3, -9)
    x-intercepts: $-3 \pm \frac{3}{\sqrt{2}}$
    y-intercept: 9
    b. vertex: (2, -36)
    x-intercepts: 5 and -1 y-intercept: -20
    c. vertex: (0.583, -10.041)
    x-intercepts: $\frac{7 \pm \sqrt{241}}{12}$
    y-intercept: -8

27. a. 0 b. 1 c. 0

28. $w^2 + 9w - 10 = 0$
    solution: $w = -10$ or 1

29. $L^2 + L - 6 = 0$
    solution: $L = 2$ or -3

30. $L^2 - 4L - 32 = 0$
    solution: $L = 8$ or -4

31. $x^2 - x - 1 = 0$
    solution: $\frac{1 \pm \sqrt{5}}{2}$

32. $x = -2$

33. identity

34. $x = \frac{1 \pm \sqrt{5}}{2}$

35. Answers will vary. Sample answers are given.
    a. $3(x - 4)(x + 2) = 0$
    b. $x^2 = 5$
    c. $(x - 1)^2 = 5$

36. Answers will vary.
    Sample answer: $-5(x + 6)^2 = 0$

37. Answers will vary.
    Sample answer: $x^2 + 1 = 0$

TOPICS COVERED IN THIS BOOK

*F*or the most part this book is not organized by topics. The most important ideas and techniques appear again and again in different chapters, instead of being confined to a small set of consecutive lessons. This allows students to see topics from many points of view, over a longer stretch of time, and leads to better retention of the central concepts of the course. The following list includes the main algebra topics in the book. Even though they play an essential role in the course, topics from geometry, probability, and number theory, as well as real-world applications, are *not* listed here.

ALGEBRA TOPICS

Numbers

- Fractions and decimals
- Square roots
- Scientific notation: very large and very small numbers
- Working with numbers between 0 and 1
- Real numbers and their subsets: rational and irrational numbers, integers, natural numbers

Variables

- Like terms
- Substitution and evaluation
- Polynomials

Functions

- Input-output tables
- Function diagrams
- Cartesian graphs
  - intercepts
  - effect of parameters
  - rate of change
  - relationship of graphs, ordered pairs, and equations
- Linear functions
  - slope-intercept form
  - standard form
  - constant sum, constant difference
- Quadratic functions
  - intercept form
  - standard form
  - vertex form
- Other functions
  - exponential functions
  - constant products
  - rational functions
  - step functions
  - absolute value functions
- Iterating linear functions
- Definitions of function, domain, range

Sequences

- Arithmetic
- Geometric
- Fibonacci-like

Structure

- Operations
  - order of operations
  - geometric and graphic models for operations
  - laws of exponents
  - rules for radicals
- The Distributive Law
  - minus and parentheses
  - identities
  - multiplying
  - dividing
  - factoring
- Inverses
  - opposites and reciprocals
  - inverse operations
  - inverse functions
- Algebraic fractions
  - equivalent fractions
  - lowest terms
- Abstract algebra

Equations and Inequalities

- Solving equations graphically
- Solving equations by trial and error
- Linear equations
- Quadratic equations
  - the zero product property
  - completing the square
  - the quadratic formula
- Inequalities
- Simultaneous equations
- Finding the equation of a line

Proportion, Ratio, and Slope

- Similarity and proportions
- Direct variation
- Slope

Working with Data

- Using graphs and tables
- Averages
- Fitting a line to data

INDEX OF SELECTED TOPICS AND TOOLS

INDEX OF SELECTED TOPICS

To help you navigate through the course, we provide the following index for selected topics. For each topic we provide a listing of some of the lessons where it appears. At any particular time when teaching or planning your course, this can help you get a sense of what's coming next in a given strand and of what has come before. Topics that appear in one or two chapters only are not listed here. Look for them in the index to the textbook.

The lessons shown in **bold type** emphasize the given topic. Other lessons provide preview or review.

INDEX OF SELECTED TOOLS

While the Lab Gear, Cartesian graphing, and tables of values are used repeatedly in almost every chapter, the following two tools are used only sporadically. Since these tools play an essential role in the development of key ideas, you may want to use these lists as a reference.

Course Overview

Chapters 1-4 are introductory. They serve to acquaint the students with the big ideas of the course, the tools, writing, and group work. (In a standard one-year course, you cannot afford to get bogged down here. Keep forging ahead!)

Chapters 5-8 develop the basic concepts for a first-year algebra course: the distributive law, equations and inequalities, linear and exponential growth. This is the central and most important part of the course.

Chapter 9 is where students learn about radicals, and key geometric connections are made. (Only the first two-thirds of the chapter are essential to do in a one-year course.)

Chapters 10-14 consist of more advanced topics: simultaneous equations, mathematical modeling, and quadratics. In a standard one-year course you need to decide which of the topics you want to cover, and distribute the remaining days among them. Note that these chapters are shorter: 8 lessons and 2 Thinking/Writing assignments, instead of 12 and 3 respectively.

Pacing Guides

The following tables provide a rough schedule for the course. The key to effective pacing is to plan ahead. Look over each chapter and set a rough chapter timetable. Select which core and noncore sections you want to cover, and estimate how much time you can afford to spend on each. Be aware that all important ideas keep coming back, so that if you skip a certain section, you will probably get a chance to tackle those ideas later. Use the Notes to the Teacher and the Essential Ideas to determine when specific skills and concepts need to be mastered, and avoid trying to achieve mastery by giving lots of extra practice the first time a concept or skill is introduced, since this will slow you down. Keep in mind that we preview difficult concepts early in the course and return to them several times before we expect mastery.

The Standard Course timetable is appropriate for most algebra classes in grades 8 and 9.

Standard Course

	Days per Chapter	
Chapter	**One-year course**	**Two-year course**
1	12	20
2	12	20
3	16	24
4	16	24
5	16	30
6	20	30
7	16	30
8	20	32
9	16	32
10	(12)	20
11	(12)	20
12	(12)	22
13	(12)	20
14	(12)	20
Total	**180***	**344**

* assumes coverage of 3 of the last 5 chapters

Minimum Course

	Days per Chapter	
Chapter	**One-year course**	**Two-year course**
1	16	25
2	16	25
3	16	25
4	20	25
5	20	35
6	20	35
7	20	35
8	20	35
9	20	30
10	(12)	(20)
11	(12)	(20)
12	(12)	(22)
13	(12)	(20)
14	(12)	(20)
Total	**180****	**350*****

** assumes coverage of 1 of the last 5 chapters
*** assumes coverage of 4 of the last 5 chapters

END-OF-YEAR OPTIONS

It is not likely that you will have time to complete the entire book in one year. After Lesson 9.9, you can choose from among several options, depending upon what you want to emphasize.

Geometric Connections
(parts of Chapter 9): Lessons 9.10, 9.11, 9.12, and 9.C concern perimeter, area, and volume of similar figures. Although there are only four lessons, they involve substantial hands-on exploration and can be time-consuming. These four lessons, combined with some of the optional geometric puzzles and challenges from other lessons in Chapter 9, can make a good two-week unit for the end of the year.

Sequences
(parts of Chapters 5, 11, and 12): Lessons 5.9, 5.10, 5.11, and 5.C are an introduction to sequences. Lessons 11.1 and 11.2 concern geometric sequences. The issue of convergence can be further explored by work with iterating linear functions in Lessons 12.7 and 12.8. These last two lessons also wrap up the work with function diagrams.

Simultaneous Equations
(Chapter 10 and parts of Chapter 12): For a solid introduction to simultaneous equations, you will want to do most of Chapter 10. This chapter also covers finding the equation of a line and ends with a problem on fitting a line to data. If time permits, you may want to follow this with Lesson 12.2 on the median-median line and perhaps other applications from Chapter 12.

Mathematical Modeling
(Chapter 12 and parts of Chapters 10 and 11): Chapter 12 gives students the opportunity to apply algebra in several interesting contexts. If you have time to do Chapter 10 before Chapter 12, that is best. If not, you should at

least do some work on finding the equation of a line (Lessons 10.8 and 10.B). Previous work on unit conversion (Lessons 11.8 and 11.B) will also be helpful, since students use this skill in the motion applications in Chapter 12.

Ratios
(Chapter 11 and parts of Chapters 5 and 14): Chapter 11 presents several uses and interpretations of ratios, including an introduction to probability. Lessons 11.1 and 11.2 involve geometric sequences, so you will want to give a brief introduction to sequences by doing some of the lessons in Chapter 5 first. (See Sequences, above.) You can follow Chapter 11 with some work on algebraic fractions in Lessons 14.1, 14.2, and 14.3.

Quadratic Equations and Functions
(Chapters 13 and 14): You can skip directly to these two chapters after Chapter 9. However, students might be more successful if they do a bit of work with simultaneous equations in Chapter 10 first, since they need to be comfortable with the idea of substitution. If you want to emphasize the quadratic formula, you will need to do all of Chapters 13 and 14. If not, you can emphasize applications and skip some of the more theoretical lessons leading to the quadratic formula. This is especially feasible if students have access to graphing calculators to allow for graphical solutions of quadratics.

THE TEACHER'S ROLE

As the teacher, you are the key to the success of this book. Your role is more that of "the guide on the side" than that of "the sage on the stage." In order to foster independence and self-confidence, you should as much as possible help students by questioning, rather than by telling. When speaking to the whole class, you should model problem-solving techniques and attitudes.

Because the book works very much in a discovery style, you should encourage risk-taking. Students should not be penalized for being wrong when discussing or exploring new material. Being wrong is a necessary part of the process. Conversely, those who venture conjectures should be praised whether or not they are right.

On the other hand, be aware of the fact that unguided discovery of the concepts of algebra is not likely to happen. It took hundreds of years and the world's greatest minds to develop algebra, and your students are not likely to succeed at doing this unaided in the course of one school year. Your leadership is essential. Due to their lack of experience and understanding, student explorations may or may not lead to better understanding. Sometimes students explore and are no clearer on the subject than they were at the beginning.

However, with your leadership, a discovery-based classroom can be an exciting and empowering environment for learning. To provide the leadership that makes this possible, you can

- introduce new topics with pointed questions
- compare various answers to open-ended questions
- encourage students to come up with more solutions to open-ended questions
- help students make connections between different representations of the same concept
- encourage and help the process of generalization
- encourage and help students to summarize what they have learned
- provide hints if students are getting frustrated

DISCOVERING AND INVESTIGATING

▶ Using Explorations

One way of promoting a discovery-oriented environment in your class is to make good use of the problems labeled Exploration. These problems stimulate exploration of a problem without providing too much structure or guidance. Teachers should provide support and encouragement, or even hints, but should not completely structure that part of the lesson. Explorations are often large in scope and cannot usually be solved by a single student in a few minutes. They are geared to group work, followed and/or preceded by whole-class discussion.

Use your judgment as to how much time to allow for Explorations. On the one hand, it is usually wrong to stop students from exploring a question if they have gotten started and they are continuing to make progress. On the other hand, if students are having difficulty, it may be good to leave the Exploration unfinished and to come back to it after having done more structured work.

If an Exploration goes well (generates enthusiasm, hard work, and interesting discoveries) it may take a whole period. It may also lead to other questions, formulated by the class. Do not expect this, but be open to it.

You may prefer to conduct the Explorations with the book closed, so as to remove the temptation to "look ahead" for a solution. Or you may develop a more flexible style which allows groups who get frustrated with the Exploration to go on with the more structured part of the lesson.

Explorations serve as motivation for the work that follows. By grappling with them, even if they do not completely solve them, students start to understand what the question is that the lesson will answer, and why this particular algebraic question is important or interesting. This helps make the guided investigation that follows more meaningful and effective.

▶ Emphasizing Problem Solving

This book is designed to help students develop algebraic ideas through problem solving. Problem solving is an integral part of the course every day, not a once-a-week adjunct.

To help your students become better problem solvers, you can

- avoid teaching cookbook recipes for solving different types of problems
- bring out different student solutions to the same problem
- discuss whether other solutions exist for a given problem
- lead discussions of difficult problems
- model your own problem-solving strategies
- encourage and model persistence — not all problems can be solved at once.

▶ Using Guided Discovery

While the big problems in the Explorations help put the lesson's question in focus, the small problems in the guided investigation help students take small steps in their understanding of these questions.

In some cases the investigations are simply a guide to one way of solving the preceding Exploration. If your class has been able to go far with the Exploration, you may be able to skip part of the next investigation. Or, you can assign problems from the investigation as homework for reinforcement and to insure that more students get the idea.

Discussing, Explaining, and Practicing

▶ The Importance of Discourse

Part of the reason group work is important is that it allows students to verbalize mathematics. It is by talking that students separate what they understand from what they don't understand. It is by explaining a concept that they deepen their understanding of it. It is by learning to ask the right question that they prepare to understand the answer.

The other vital verbalizing activity is writing. Beyond a certain point, drill loses its effectiveness, as students are turned into unthinking automatons. At that point, they will learn more from writing than from continuing the drill. We often ask students to "explain" their answers. This goes beyond merely "showing work," and can include writing sentences, paragraphs, or drawing sketches. This is not easy for most students, and your coaching and coaxing is particularly important. It is worth the effort, because what they can explain they surely understand.

Because writing is so important, we will discuss it at length a little later.

▶ Reading

We have tried to write a book that students can read. If your students are not used to reading in math class, you will have to insist that they *always* read the problems and their introductions. Some students enjoy reading aloud to their groups, others prefer to read to themselves. Do not discourage either approach. Perhaps group assignments such as Explorations should be read aloud, while other problems are read individually. The important thing is that students read everything.

If you have students who do not know English well, or are weak readers, make sure they get help. Remember: It is more important to learn to read and write than to learn algebra, and math class can help in this process.

▶ Mastery and Skill Development

Because learning is not smooth and linear, students need frequent repetition of important activities, and rethinking about important ideas. Mastery is not immediate. In fact for any important concept, the appearance of quick mastery often masks an underlying lack of understanding. Abstraction is a process that takes time. Rushing it leads to the memorization of poorly understood material as a substitute for understanding.

Our belief is that practice is important, but that it is most effective in the context of worthwhile and interesting work. Even though it may not be obvious at first glance, the lessons of this book entail continuous application of the basic skills of algebra. On the other hand, we have tried to avoid long stretches of repetitive drill. We do provide short bursts of it here and there for those of you who feel that your students need more practice. However we discourage you from using all of the drill at the expense of the more central material.

One way to provide additional practice at a more interesting, less mechanical level is to ask students to create problems of the type you think they need to practice. The process of creating problems for each other does a lot more than solving many problems of the same type, since it requires a better understanding of the problems.

In fact, you should be alert to the fact that the book often asks students to do just that. The basic idea is that students should be able to do everything in every possible direction. For example, they should know

- not just how to simplify expressions, but how to complicate them;
- not just how to solve equations, but how to create equations with a given solution;
- not just how to graph a function, but how to recognize a function from its graph.

This level of understanding is far more meaningful and durable than the mere ability to follow a given algorithm in a narrowly defined situation, which is all that can be gained from repetitive drill.

▶ Homework

This book is written with the expectation that students will have daily homework. In some cases, students can simply move ahead in the text at home. But some work should be done in class, not as homework, for example:

- new material
- material that requires the use of manipulatives
- material that is labor-intensive where the work should be shared

- material that is difficult enough to require group work or teacher guidance

Such assignments are the ones omitted from the *Suitable for Homework* list in the Teacher's Notes. (However, keep in mind that even homework material may need some discussion in class the next day, and that one night's assignment may be more or less than the problems flagged as suitable in a given lesson.)

When you cannot assign the next section for homework, be prepared to assign the Essential Ideas, below-the-line problems, or Thinking/Writing from previous chapters. For more ideas on organizing homework, see below, under *Two Sequences*.

WRITING

▶ Why Write in Math Class?

Writing enhances thinking and learning. When students explain their ideas during group work and class discussion, they have to think more deliberately. Writing requires even more clarity. As students struggle to put their ideas in writing, they have to come to grips with what they don't understand. They find a need for new vocabulary. They look for good examples. They search for the combination of drawings, mathematical symbols, and words that will communicate what they know.

Writing in math class can change the way students think about math as a discipline. Their daily routine in math class in the past might have consisted of providing answers to routine exercises. Both exercise and answer consisted solely of numbers and other mathematical symbols, with the terrifying exception of "word problems." In this book, many of the problems and answers involve a combination of words and symbols. As students work to understand and answer them, their goals shift from simply getting an answer to achieving an understanding. As they write, they summarize, generalize, and resolve contradictions. Writing also gives them the opportunity to raise questions, because as they try to write about a topic they become conscious of gaps in their own understanding. They become more aware of their own thinking.

Writing is not a specialized skill that can be mastered only by the creative few who have a special talent for it. The ability to write in a clear, direct, logical way is a basic skill, and one of the most valued in the workplace. Likewise, teaching writing is not in the purview of the English teacher alone. Writing can enrich your math teaching and add a new dimension to discourse in your class.

▶ How This Book Supports Writing

When students are led by the hand through discovery work, they can sometimes lose sight of the whole idea, even if they competently answer specific questions along the way. They may not be seeing the staircase for the steps. Writing explanations of their work helps students remain alert.

This book is designed so that writing can play a central role in the course. The Key Questions, Summaries, and Generalizations encourage informal, daily writing. They help students see what big ideas should be emerging from all the details. If you are having students build a reference section in their notebooks, entries can be chosen from these problems.

The Reports are intended to be more extensive and formal, but you can vary the format of these to keep students' interest. (See below.) The Thinking/Writing assignments (each of which contains one or sometimes two Reports) are intended to be used as a major assessment tool. Some teachers occasionally use these like problems of the week, requiring a polished, individual report.

Projects and Research provide other opportunities for larger writing assignments. You will not be able to assign all of these to all students, but they are there to be used as major independent assignments once or twice per semester, or as extra credit assignments. It is nice for students to present what they found to the class, via bulletin boards, or oral presentations. If you are not used to assigning this kind of work or have trouble evaluating it, you can get help from librarians and teachers in other departments. These kinds of assignments help show that math is connected to the world. The sources can be almanacs, newspapers, calls made to businesses or other institutions, visits to the library, whatever. Try to have a few resource books in your classroom, such as an almanac and a dictionary.

▶ Finding a Good Balance

By flagging the problems involving writing, and by providing frequent opportunities for both formal and informal writing, we communicate our belief in its importance. The prominence of the Thinking/Writing assignments allows you to emphasize these lessons as much as chapter tests. Students take writing seriously if they know it is as important a part of their grade as traditional tests. Parents and school administrators who think math class means only symbol manipulation are readily convinced of the power of writing assignments in math when they look at actual student work, and see how these lessons develop competence in problem solving and writing along with understanding of algebraic concepts.

Although we want to encourage writing, students quickly tire of it if they are asked to write too many reports. Varying the format of reports will maintain students' interest and provide an alternate creative outlet for students who find writing difficult. For example, instead of writing individual reports, groups can summarize their findings by drawing and writing with colored markers on posters or butcher paper. These can be displayed around the room and provide a focus for oral group reports and class discussion. Many students are hesitant to speak to the whole class, and doing group presentations on a regular basis will help them develop confidence. Reports need not always be written. You can ask students to prepare oral Reports and Projects, as well as bulletin board displays. Some teachers have even allowed student projects to be video documentaries, computer programs, skits, or dioramas.

▶ Informal Writing

Writing gives teachers a window into the students' minds. By giving students plenty of opportunities for informal writing, we can watch them reflect, analyze, clarify, interpret, evaluate, discuss, question, and conjecture.

Students using this book will do a lot of writing. Almost daily, they will write Summaries or Generalizations, and answer key questions. This informal writing will be in their notebooks, and need not be polished. It is there to help students get familiar with the material and to give you insights on a particular student should you need information beyond that provided by tests and formal writing assignments.

Informal writing can be used frequently as a diagnostic tool at key points in the discussion. You can ask each student (or in some cases, each group) to spend a few minutes writing. The directions might be quite open, ("Summarize what you learned from this discussion," or "Write down a question you have about our discussion,") or very specific, ("Describe one method for solving linear equations."). You can have students share their results orally, walk around the room for a quick look at several students' papers, or collect them to look at later to get an idea of the class's understanding of a concept. This technique is especially helpful in getting responses from students who are reluctant to speak up in class.

A frequent question from students who used the preliminary version of this book was, "What do they mean when they ask us to explain?" To help students get used to this, you can write student responses on the board or overhead so that they can see examples and compare explanations. Write an explanation and ask what students would add to it or delete from it to make it clearer. Ask the members of each group to compare their explanations and come up with one group explanation. Explaining will soon become a natural part of doing math problems for your students.

Some students resist writing not because they are afraid of writing itself, but because they are reluctant to confront uncertainties in their understanding and reasoning. This is particularly true of students who have always done well in the kind of math class in which the goal was to follow the teacher's step-by-step instructions and get the right answer. "If I can do it, why do I have to explain it?" is a common question at first. If the atmosphere in your class is one of accepting partial understanding and welcoming the questions that arise from them, such students will become more receptive. Informal writing is a record of the work of the class as it moves together toward a clearer understanding. If you value this process, students will soon see writing as natural and central rather than peripheral to the learning process.

Because we explicitly encourage daily writing, it will be relatively easy for you to incorporate other types of informal writing into the course, such as freewriting, learning logs, and journals. For more information on using these techniques, see Countryman (1992).

▶ Formal Writing

Do not be discouraged if students complain at the beginning of the year that, "This is more writing than my English class." As they see the benefits of writing, the complaints rapidly diminish. Most students soon begin to take pride in the quality of their formal written work, and to value the opportunity to revise it. As an assessment tool, writing has the potential to create a more positive climate in the classroom. Students, who often feel that tests reveal what they don't know, welcome the opportunity to communicate in writing what they do know.

A few students will have done extensive writing in previous math classes, particularly if they have done problems of the week. Others will have had little experience writing in math and may be very anxious about it. You need to communicate from the very beginning that

- you have high standards for the finished product, and
- you will provide support for learning how to create a high-quality finished product.

Student groups of four may work well for day-to-day problem solving and working on assignments, but pairs of two often work better when there is something to polish or publish. In the beginning, the Thinking/ Writing assignments guide student writing with a series of questions. Students can work on these for homework, then work in pairs in class the next day, comparing answers. The second night's homework can be to write up the work in a more polished form. The following day, students read each other's work and make editorial comments. The third night's homework is to write the final report. This works well as a three-day homework assignment while you continue to move ahead with new material in class.

Among the reproducible pages at the end of this Teacher's Guide, we have provided some general guidelines for Thinking/ Writing assignments. We suggest that you use these guidelines (or similar ones) to get students started. The four stage process described here is one suggestion for how to work through the early writing assignments. You may want to revise it to fit your own needs. Students will also have suggestions for tailoring the process to the needs of your class. As students become more skilled, you may be able to compress this process and spend less class time on it. We have also included a suggested format for the final version of the report. You may want to begin with this format and revise it as you and your class come up with other ideas.

Organizing the Material

▶ Providing Access and Challenge

Mathematical thinking among the students, not any particular activity, tool, or technique, should be the primary goal of instruction in math class. This is valid not only among the top students, but even more so among average and weaker students. All students can think, even the ones whom we have in the past classified as unable to engage in abstract thinking. In fact, a thinking approach, combined with the themes and tools described above, is the best approach to involving average and weaker students.

All algebra classes are somewhat heterogeneous. Some are very heterogeneous. The way to work with a mixed group is not to "teach to the middle," "teach to the top," or "teach to the bottom." Teach to *all* students by mixing the approaches, the tools, and the levels of difficulty. *If the material is varied enough, you will get everyone involved.*

This book was written for heterogeneous classes. We have tried to have something "too difficult" (for some students), and something "too easy" (for some students) in each lesson. We also offer open-ended questions and projects as often as possible. All this means that the course provides *access* and *challenge* at the same time.

We provide something "too difficult" because not every student needs to master every idea in the course. If they did, the course would be too easy for the top students, who would resent it. The top students' needs are as important as those of any member of the class. Besides, they are your crucial allies in a heterogeneous class, the engine that drives discovery lessons, and potentially your colleagues in teaching their peers. You need to keep them (and their parents) satisfied that they are not being hurt by working in a classroom with students who are less talented in math.

We provide something "too easy" because not every problem needs to be profound. There must be some entryway into the ideas of the lesson for all students. Those who cannot get in through one door should have other options. Easy, step-by-step questions are helpful to such students, and in fact benefit the rest of the class as well, by helping them organize and consolidate their ideas.

We provide **open-ended questions and projects** because in these, students find their own level. To the simple open-ended problem *Find two numbers that add up to 10*, one could provide a number of different answers. Similarly, in a project such as the newspaper article in *Instant Riches*, (Chapter 3, Lesson 1) some students will produce a multi-page, coherent, well-illustrated, original, and mathematically sound paper, while others will barely manage to turn in a sketchy paper that rehashes some of the ideas in the text.

For open-ended questions and projects, make sure students get a chance to share their work with their classmates if they wish. This helps enrich all students' experience.

The material in this book can be appreciated at many levels simultaneously. Do not expect all students to get the same thing out of any given lesson. Some ideas should be mastered by most, but others will be grasped by only a few. A good model of your role is that of a sports coach or drama teacher, who encourages each student to perform at the best of his or her ability, without expecting all students to be at the same level.

▶ Two Sequences

This book contains many rich problems on which you could spend a very long time. It would be easy to get involved in solving interesting problems and to discover at the end of the year that you had completed far too little of the course. For this reason, we recommend that you continually forge ahead, and one way of doing this is to organize your assignments in two parallel sequences.

The Forward Motion Sequence: This is the main sequence. It consists mostly of the main body of the core Lessons, some of the Thinking/Writing assignments (the ones mentioned in the Teacher's Notes as necessary to the sequence), and any below-the-line Preview assignments. Much of this work is done in class, and some as homework as needed. All of it needs to be done more or less in the order it appears in the book.

The Review and Extension Sequence: This is the support sequence and is just as important. It consists primarily of below-the-line Review or Discovery material, most of the core Thinking/Writing assignments, and the Essential Ideas.

The Essential Ideas, for example, are almost always suitable for homework, can be used as preparation for an end-of-chapter test or can be saved for later review of the chapter. They need not be assigned right at the end of the chapter and are perfect elements to include in the Review and Extension sequence.

One payoff of the two-sequences approach is that when you get to a section that just cannot be assigned as homework, or when you are engaged in an interesting but time-consuming digression in class, you can assign Review and Extension material for homework. For example, a geoboard lesson at the end of a chapter, which is likely to require more than one day of in-class time, might be followed by a lesson or two involving the Lab Gear at the beginning of the following chapter. This is a good time to draw on the reservoir of Review and Extension assignments as a source of homework assignments.

▶ Pacing

Because of the spiral approach of the book, which incorporates preview of difficult ideas early on, and review long after the ideas are first encountered, it is not necessary (or possible) to wait until everyone in the class has mastered an idea to move on. Mastery often takes a long time for many students and, especially in a heterogeneous class, it is important to keep constant forward motion. You can use the Essential Ideas to find out what mastery is expected at the end of a chapter.

If mastery is not expected, do not waste time by assigning extra practice from other sources. For example, students will solve linear equations in various ways for six whole chapters before they are expected to have mastered them. Teaching them everything you know about equation solving in Chapter 1 will undermine the work on equations that is built into the next five chapters, and rob the students of worthwhile discoveries.

If you are teaching a one-year Algebra 1 course, be careful not to linger too long on the first three chapters. These chapters are designed to get students involved in problem solving, and they contain many rich, open-ended activities. Teachers who used the preliminary version of this book found that students sometimes got so interested in a problem that they did not want to move on to the next section before they had completely explored it. If you have more than a year to teach the course, or are using the first part of it in Pre-Algebra, you can use this feature to your advantage to promote problem solving and encourage the practice of delving deeply into problems. However, in a one-year course, you will have to make some compromises, so don't spend more than about two and one-half weeks on each of the first three chapters.

▶ Challenge and Enrichment

Do not routinely skip challenge (light bulb) problems. A small amount of frustration is not bad, and success at these problems can be thrilling. Make clear that you do not expect everyone to be able to do these problems, but that they should be tried. They are important for the stronger students to work on and are well suited to group work.

If you are concerned that your top students are not being challenged enough, there is plenty of optional material you can use as "extra for experts."

▶ What to Skip

It is not likely you can "cover" this entire book in one year with an algebra class. Do as much as you can, but remember that your goal is to help students *uncover* and *discover* material, not "cover" it. There's a whole ocean of mathematics out there — all you can do is take the students to the beach. At this level, generating interest and confidence in algebra is more important than mastering particular algebraic topics.

To help you select what to skip, and as a first approximation, we have marked some material as optional by displaying it on a light beige background.

However this is only an approximation. What we included in the optional work is

- some less traditional topics
- some time-consuming problems
- some particularly difficult problems
- some puzzles
- some material that previews future courses such as Geometry, Algebra 2, Pre-Calculus, and Abstract Algebra

You need not agree with us on these choices, and you should feel free to make your own decisions. In particular you should skip work that seems to provide repetitive drill in areas where your students do not need more practice.

You will have to use your judgment about how much time you can devote to optional activities and when you do them. They are often the least traditional part of the book, but they can be the most interesting and valuable. As you get more familiar with this book and its approach, and as the math reform process leads to changes in the list of what you must "cover," you can use more and more of them. In our own classes, we intend to use as much of the optional work as we can.

The best overall guideline on skipping is to skip material you don't enjoy teaching. However, be cautious about skipping core lessons. The most likely core lessons to skip are the ones that seem to be hammering an already-familiar topic into the ground. You may also be tempted to skip lessons that you yourself do not fully understand. However, remember that the best way to learn something is to teach it.

▶ A Use for Skipped Material

A good use for optional material you do skip is to assign it to speed demons, those students who want to "get ahead in the book." Getting ahead should be discouraged, because it makes students less available to their group, and because it often leads to superficial understanding. Instead, demand more depth from these students: higher-quality work on reports and projects and extra work on optional material. (Of course, assign material to them that you are sure you will not want to assign to the whole class later.)

Creating a Community of Learners

▶ Student Involvement

We need to get away from the image of the student as passive receptor of information, and the teacher as the source of the information. Teacher explanation, no matter how clear and patient, does not usually succeed in getting across difficult ideas. Instead, we need to think of the student as explorer, collaborator, question-poser, evaluator of the validity of statements, and peer teacher. Everything we do must put student involvement at the center, because math is not a spectator sport. One learns math by doing math.

▶ Groups of Four

Groups of four is an arrangement that maximizes student involvement. This does not mean that all work needs to be done in a group, but it does mean that students should routinely sit in such a way as to be able to work in a group.

You probably have your own way of selecting groups. Teacher-organized groups (as opposed to randomly selected ones) can backfire. Students are quick to jump to conclusions like, "I am the stupid person in this group," or "I am the smart person in this group," neither of which is helpful.

You may try random groupings that change every two to four weeks. Random groupings are sometimes homogeneous, and sometimes heterogeneous, which allows you to take advantage of both types of arrangements. In a heterogeneous group the stronger student can take the lead, or serve as a resource. In a homogeneous group of stronger students there is the excitement of being able to do really fancy work fast. In a homogeneous group of weaker students there is the comfort of not "feeling stupid" and not having to compare oneself to some star student. As long as the groupings are temporary, the students do not feel trapped, even if they do not like some of the students in the group.

▶ Cooperative Learning

Like most algebra books, this book is probably too hard for an average student to work through individually. However, it is not too hard for an average or even weak student working in a cooperative learning group in the presence of a teacher.

There are many approaches to cooperative learning, and we cannot present them all here. We have had success with an informal approach.

Students work individually much of the time, but can ask each other for help whenever they need or want to.

Large or tedious tasks can be split between members of the group.

Difficult problems can be read aloud, then discussed.

Class can start each day with groups going over their homework.

The purpose of the math class is not to teach cooperation. Rather, the purpose of cooperation is for the students to learn math. Do not expect the students to start the year knowing how to work in groups. Give them as much structure as necessary to help them get off the ground, but don't spend too much time discussing how groups *should* run.

Instead, circulate among the groups and use modeling or direct intervention to redirect the group in the direction you want. For example, if one student is being left out, involve him or her in the work. If a capable student is not being asked for help, or is reluctant to give it, you can ask him or her to answer a tricky question someone else is struggling with. If a group is losing focus, get them back on task, and so on.

We have found that external rewards for effective group work are less necessary if,

- group work is used only for activities for which it is well suited rather than for activities which are better done individually;
- students understand the goal of group work is to help them learn math, not fit some incomprehensible teacher agenda;
- group work is part of the department and school culture.

Certain problems are especially suited to group work, perhaps because they are open-ended Explorations, or because a lot of data need to be collected. Such problems are mentioned in the Teacher's Notes. Finally, it is sometimes useful or necessary to have students work in pairs, for example when working with the graphing calculators or the Lab Gear.

▶ Whole-Class Discussions

You will find that sometimes the groups cannot handle some part of the work. A problem may be too difficult, a concept may have been insufficiently clarified, and one or more groups grind to a halt. Or, you may feel the class needs a change of pace. At such times, it is good to have a whole-class, teacher-led, discussion. The idea is to lead the class to a discovery or understanding through well-asked questions.

At times you may even use a mini-lecture to explain a particularly tricky idea. The key is for your lecture to answer questions your students have as a result of working on problems. Then, students will listen. Answering questions they don't have is a waste of everyone's time, as they are not likely to listen to or absorb what you have to say.

It is not wrong to start a class with a lecture or chalkboard demonstration, especially if it concerns real questions based on the previous day's work. (This is sometimes necessary if you have trouble getting the class back to a single point of focus once group work has started.)

Keep in mind that when you ask questions of the class, you cannot judge what the whole class is thinking by the answers of a few. This is one of the main limitations of whole-class work, but it can be compensated for periodically by making it a point to ask all students to write down answers to a question, or to ask a question for group discussion.

▶ Individual Work and Responsibility

The purpose of group work and of whole-class work, is to develop mathematical power *in the individual*. Students should generally do at least their homework and quizzes or tests individually. Of course, it is fine to have exceptions to this, but make sure that students have some work they do on their own every day. This will allow them to "know whether they're getting it." In fact, there should be a record of all work in each student's notebook, even when the work is done collaboratively.

Much of the work in this book can be done by students individually. Certainly most of the work labeled *Suitable for Homework* fits in that category. However, when working on new ideas or challenging problems, students should be able to ask other members of their group for help (except during tests)!

▶ Dealing with Absences

Absences are more difficult to make up in a class where cooperative work and the use of tools is essential. Here are a few suggestions.

Make a set of Lab Gear blocks and a geoboard available for checkout from the school library.

Allow students who have been absent to borrow your Teacher's Edition to correct their work.

Arrange for peer tutoring, by members of their group, for students who have been absent.

CREATING AN ALGEBRA LABORATORY

This book provides the basis for turning your classroom into a laboratory for learning algebra. Many students will come into your class unaccustomed to the idea of using tools to learn math. Adolescents can be a conservative bunch, and some, particularly those who are good at memorizing and following rules, will resist the new approach at first. Teachers who used the preliminary edition found that a slight rearrangement of their classrooms to promote the notion of laboratory learning not only enhanced their teaching but helped eliminate student resistance as well.

These teachers placed manipulatives and other materials, such as scissors, graph paper, and dot paper, on shelves around the room, making them easily accessible to students. Colored markers and butcher paper were available for making group reports. When possible, graphing calculators were also available at all times. After a couple of months students had become familiar with all the tools and began to use them spontaneously, even when the lesson did not specifically call for them. Some even chose to use the Lab Gear to check their work on tests.

▶ Calculators and Computers

The only electronic tool absolutely required for this course is a calculator. If your students cannot afford to purchase their own calculators, you should try to secure funding for the purchase of a class set.

A graphing calculator is ideal. If these are not available, you can use any calculator which has the following capabilities:

- negative numbers ([+/−] or [(−)])
- squaring ([x^2])
- powers of ten, scientific notation ([10^n], or [EXP], or [EE])
- reciprocals ([1/x] or [x^{-1}])
- exponentiation ([y^x] or [x^y])
- square roots ([√]) and ([π])

The ability to deal with fractions is a major advantage ([$a^b/_c$]), but trigonometric, log, and exponential functions are not needed.

There are many lessons in this book that are greatly enhanced by the use of an electronic grapher. The ideal situation is to have a graphing calculator for at least every pair of students. If these are not available, having students work with graphing software in a computer lab or having a teacher-run demonstration with a computer can be effective alternatives. If you have no access at all to an electronic grapher, students can do the graphing by hand, sharing the calculations and graphing, so that they can still see a number of graphs without the tedium of constructing every single one. Remember in this case that the goal is to see and use the graphs, not to become skillful at constructing them.

We are careful not to create situations where technology is used for its own sake. The lessons involving graphing are constructed to insure students have had some experience doing pencil-and-paper graphing so that they understand the concept before using a graphing calculator. We also give you suggestions in the Teacher's Notes about where to introduce the graphing calculator.

A few lessons in the book would be enhanced by the use of a computer spreadsheet, a grapher that will graph lines given in the form $ax + by = c$, or simple statistical software. We indicate this in the Teacher's Notes, but once again you will find that these technological enhancements, while desirable, are not necessary.

If you have access to graphing calculators or computers, but are reluctant to use them because of lack of familiarity with new technology, remember that your students are your allies. Many of them are more technologically literate than their teachers, and you can use this to your advantage. One way of challenging bright students who finish early is to ask them to learn how to use the calculator or computer to do something that is needed for a future lesson. When they have learned, they can teach you and the rest of the class.

In one class that used this book, two students discovered how much time they could save by using the programming capabilities of the graphing calculators. They had soon taught the entire class. This example illustrates the importance of encouraging students to use tools as much as they like, and in their own way. In this book, we make suggestions only for their use. As you and your students become more familiar with them, you will discover many more uses.

▶ The Algebra Lab Gear®

Each pair of students will need one set of Lab Gear. In most cases it is best for students to work with their partner. However do not allow students to avoid work by letting their partner do all the manipulation of blocks, or conversely, all the record keeping. Students should take turns so as to develop competence in all aspects of the work.

It is, of course, important that students respect the materials. A little time must be allotted at the end of each period for putting the Lab Gear away. Improper use of the blocks, such as throwing them, should not be tolerated. Some teachers threaten students who misuse the blocks with having to do all the Lab Gear problems without blocks, instead sketching what they would do with them.

Sometimes, you will need to get the whole class to pay attention to a discussion at the overhead. At such times, ask students to have "no plastic" in their hands. (We tell our students that scientific studies have shown that plastic in student hands impairs their ability to hear.) Students who want to explain something to the class can come up to the overhead projector and demonstrate, or can talk while you demonstrate.

Keep in mind that the Lab Gear is not intended to be used as a mechanical "do-as-I-do" representation. Instead think of it as a creative medium, which can be used by you and your students to explore, model, and illustrate many algebraic ideas. You and your students should feel free to question the way the Lab Gear model is presented in the textbook and to create your own variations on it or extensions to it.

▶ Student Resistance

While we have found the Lab Gear to be popular with a wide range of students, there are a few who do resist it. If this happens, keep in mind that the manipulatives are a means, not an end. If students can demonstrate competence with the ideas, it is not essential that they use the Lab Gear. However, most students will gain from using it, if only when communicating with their classmates. Some encouragement on your part at the beginning of the year may help them overcome their anxiety. Often the biggest resistance is before students have had a chance to use the Lab Gear, before the blocks actually grow on them.

The biggest factor determining whether students will enjoy the work with the Lab Gear is your own attitude. Do not use the blocks in cases where you do not think there is much to be gained, because your ambivalence will be transmitted to your students. Use the blocks only if you are comfortable with the lesson. On the other hand, do not promote the use of the Lab Gear as "fun." Students may wonder, "Fun, compared to what?" The use of manipulatives is intended to provide an arena for tackling difficult ideas. It is a part of learning algebra, not a break from it.

Later in the year you can be more flexible and acknowledge individual differences by allowing those students who still need it to use the Lab Gear, while letting those who don't to work just on paper. The student who can execute the algorithms, but cannot model them with the Lab Gear, does not have as full an understanding as the student who can do both, though he or she may be able to manage well enough.

▶ The Lab Gear® as a Map

When in a new city, to get from one place to another, one may rely on instructions like these: "…take 80 south to the bridge, cross the bay, then take 101 north. Get off at Fell…(etc.)." The problem with this approach in a new city is that even if you remember the instructions, a single mistake along the way means you're lost. If you miss a turn, you may look up at the street signs and not recognize them. At that point all you can do is ask someone for help.

Being able to use a map is a more effective method of finding your way. It allows you to choose among alternate routes, for example, if road work is being performed somewhere along the way.

The usual algorithm-driven way to teach algebra corresponds to the giving of directions. "First you get rid of the fractions, then…(etc.)." Students who get lost have no recourse but to ask the teacher for help. The Lab Gear constitutes a map of much of the territory. Students can use it to check the validity of a statement, or as a strategy to solve a problem, without having to resort to asking the teacher. Like learning to use a map, there is a certain initial investment of effort, but it pays off in increased independence and self-confidence.

The eventual goal is to know the city of algebra well enough to find your way without a map or directions. Someone who already knows algebra has no need for the Lab Gear or for following any particular algorithm. The aim is for our students to get to the point where they just *know* their way around elementary algebra and its applications.

ASSESSMENT

▶ Grading or Assessment?

Assessment and grading are not synonymous. In order to teach a class effectively, you need to have a sense of where the class is as a whole. You also need warning flags about students who may be having trouble with the material. Informal assessment of the class as a whole, of groups, and of individuals, should be going on at all times.

Observing group work is a very effective way to see where students are. Work with the Lab Gear in particular, being extremely visual, allows you to spot immediately the students who are having trouble with the material. When new groups are formed, you should try to identify in the first day or two which ones will need most attention and support from you and make sure to spend more time with them.

You can periodically ask groups to make impromptu presentations to the class on what they have discovered. This can take the form of an oral presentation, but it usually works better if it is accompanied by supporting materials in the form of student-created transparencies or butcher-paper-and-marking-pen posters.

When conducting a whole-class discussion, make sure to ask students frequently to work problems on paper. Then circulate around the room to see their work. Finally, you can use random checks of student notebooks as yet another informal assessment method.

The move toward more writing in all parts of the curriculum is part of a larger movement to encourage and assess authentic achievement. There is a variety of formal assessment methods that you can use to assess student understanding and to help students monitor their own progress. These are designed to be integral to the learning process, rather than simply a source of grades. In the following sections, we will describe some of these in more detail.

If it is at all possible in your school culture, you should gradually move away from an over-emphasis on grades as the motivator, and add as much as possible to the part of the work students do without external rewards. Much of the work students do should not be graded on the basis of "right" and "wrong." Specifically:

- participation in class discussion,
- participation in group work,
- reliably doing one's homework,
- keeping a neat and organized notebook.

All these behaviors are essential to a student's success in the course, and should favorably affect the grade, *no matter whether the work is correct*. Because mistakes, partial understandings, and confusion are a normal part of the learning process, they should not be penalized.

Not everything needs to be graded. On the other hand, the goal of the course is competence in algebra, and parents, students, colleagues, colleges, and society in general expect that to be measured with grades. To arrive at those, you can use a combination of reports and tests, as described below.

▶ Evaluating Reports

Writing assignments are a very important part of a fair grading policy, because they give you a chance to evaluate students' understanding without some of the limitations of tests. (See below.) It is important to establish high expectations early. Although you may be disappointed with the quality of students' written work at first, do not give up. If you give students the message that reports and projects are just as important as tests, and you assign them on a regular basis, you will find that most students will improve. This requires you to start with small assignments, and perhaps to ask for rewrites, but the extra effort is worth it in the long run.

Formal writing assignments are essential, but be realistic in the number you assign, as they are time consuming for both student and teacher. As a rule of thumb, plan on using one large writing assignment every three or four weeks if you give in-class tests frequently, or every two weeks if you do not.

Using a holistic scoring method will enable you to assign more writing without being inundated by a sea of papers. Most teachers begin by first quickly dividing papers into three piles: *exceeded expectations*, *got the point*, and *missed the point*. Among the reproducible pages in the back of this Teacher's Guide, we have included a *Writing Assignment Evaluation*. Students need to know from the beginning how their work will be evaluated. For more ideas on rubrics and holistic scoring see Pandey (1991) and Stenmark (1991).

▶ Tests and Quizzes

Some reformers have advocated completely eliminating tests, but we disagree. Tests and quizzes have three important functions.

- They help students know what they know.
- They help you know what students can do by themselves without the help of a group.

- They send the message that the purpose of the group is to help everyone learn, not to allow some people to loaf while others work. In the end, everyone is individually accountable.

On the other hand, tests and quizzes should not be overemphasized because, for many students, performance under time pressure is not an accurate reflection of their ability.

Be sure that the tests and quizzes you give reflect the skills being developed in this book. Great speed in computation and accuracy in algebraic manipulation should not be emphasized to the detriment of such skills as using graphing to solve problems, writing clear explanations, and so on. Tests should evaluate students' ability to use what they learned, not primarily their ability to remember facts. You should also use some open-ended questions on occasion. Calculators and other tools should definitely be allowed.

The Essential Ideas can be used as a source of ideas for a chapter test.

It is a good idea for tests to be cumulative as much as possible. One approach is to keep bringing back on tests new versions of problems that proved to be difficult in previous tests. This very effectively gives students the message that they'd better learn it.

Another variation on the traditional test is to ask students to do a Thinking/Writing assignment, minus the Report, in preparation for the test. The test then includes questions of the type that would have been answered in the Report, and students have to write detailed answers.

Note: A set of reproducible tests, with solutions included, is available from Creative Publications. Please see a current Creative Publications catalog for ordering information.

▶ Notebooks

All students in this course should keep a notebook. Since many definitions and generalizations are developed by the students themselves, it is essential that they keep an organized written record of their work.

Enforcing neat notebooks is difficult at first, but well worth the effort. It is best to decide exactly what format you want for the notebooks and insist that students follow it. Otherwise, many will keep a notebook that is much too chaotic to be of much help to them. (A sample notebook assignment with a suggested format appears among the reproducible pages at the end of this Teacher's Guide.)

Notebooks can be checked periodically. One method is to pick one or two names at random every day and check those students' notebooks. Let the students know that their notebooks are part of what they are being evaluated on. Since the notebook contains a record of almost all of a student's work, it can be used to check on many things, such as:

- completeness of homework
- understanding of certain ideas (especially by looking at the problems marked *Useful for Assessment* in the Teacher's Notes.)
- quality of the writing: The "Reports" section of the notebook can serve as a ready-made portfolio of student writing. (You may ask students to indicate which reports reflect their best work and make sure to look at those.)

▶ Portfolios

A portfolio is a selection of student work that gives a comprehensive summary of a student's work in the course. Portfolios provide another alternative for assessment.

You might check notebooks merely for organization rather than content. They can be thought of as working portfolios in which students keep a record of all their work.

Every two to eight weeks, depending upon how significant portfolios are as a part of your assessment program, students should choose material from their notebooks and create a portfolio for assessment. You may wish to choose some of the assignments to be included, but at least some of them should be chosen by the student. Students should also be encouraged to revise some of the work they choose to meet a higher standard. The portfolio should provide not only a chance to show their best work but also a record of their progress. (Because of the importance of showing progress, all entries in a portfolio should be dated.)

For assessment, portfolios can be far superior to notebooks for several reasons. First, they put more responsibility on the student. Students generally have some choice in what is included in the portfolio. Portfolios provide a record of student progress. Students are required to look over their work, to reflect on what they have done well and what needs improvement, to select what represents their best work, and to provide evidence of progress.

Many teachers ask students to include a cover letter each time they add a new set of papers to their portfolios. The cover letters may include a brief description of the items in the portfolio, perhaps accompanied by an explanation of why they where chosen. They may also include a summary of the main concepts covered during the time period. The cover letters give students a chance for self-assessment, and their reflections on their progress are often very revealing. Self-assessment will be new for many students, and it may take some time before they can be honest and thoughtful about it. Be patient and encouraging.

At the end of the semester, you may want students to cull their portfolios and put together semester portfolios. Some teachers allow students to use their portfolios as a reference during the final exam.

As with written reports, the standards by which portfolios will be evaluated should be clear to the students in advance. Some possible criteria for evaluating portfolios can be found in the reproducible pages in the back of this Teacher's Guide. You will want to discuss criteria with students and revise them as the year progresses. We suggest that you use only a few criteria each time you look at portfolios. For example, you may want to concentrate on how students are using different problem-solving strategies and ask them to choose items for their portfolios to illustrate that they can use more than one strategy.

For more information on using and evaluating portfolios, see Stenmark (1991).

■ References

Countryman, Joan. *Writing to Learn Mathematics*. Portsmouth, NH: Heinemann Educational Books, 1992.

Davidson, Neil, ed. *Cooperative Learning in Mathematics*. Menlo Park, CA: Addison-Wesley, 1990.

Johnson, David. *Every Minute Counts*. Palo Alto, CA: Dale Seymour Publications, 1982.

Pandey, Tej, et al. *A Sampler of Mathematics Assessment*. California Department of Education, 1991.

Stenmark, Jean Kerr, ed. *Mathematics Assessment: Myths, Models, Good Questions, and Practical Suggestions*. Reston, VA: National Council of Teachers of Mathematics, 1991.

NOTEBOOK ASSIGNMENT

You will need some supplies and an organized notebook for your Algebra course.

By _________________, you should have assembled all the items below.

Check off each one as you complete it.

■ Supplies

____ a three-ring notebook

____ five notebook dividers

____ a scientific calculator

____ lined, three-hole notebook paper

____ graph paper, hole-punched

____ a ruler, showing both inches and centimeters

____ pencils

____ a red and a blue colored pencil

____ eraser

■ Organization

____ Label the dividers for your notebook as follows:

- Assignment Sheets
- Daily Work and Notes
- Reports and Projects
- Tests and Quizzes
- Reference

____ Put this sheet at the front of the Daily Work and Notes section of your notebook.

Here are some suggestions on how to do a good job on writing assignments.

■ Getting Started

When you first start, don't worry about writing the final report. Concentrate on solving the problem. Keep a record of everything you do, including false starts, but don't worry about being neat or explaining what you are doing.

■ The Outline

Decide how you will organize your report. Make a note of any questions that you do not understand or cannot answer completely. Discuss them with other students or with a teacher.

■ The Rough Draft

Make a rough draft of your report. Ask at least one person to read and critique it. This could be a parent, a student, or a friend. Your goal is not only to give correct solutions and explanations, but to communicate them clearly to someone who may not be familiar with this topic.

■ The Final Report

Make changes based on the critique of your rough draft. Your final report should represent your best work.

SUGGESTED REPORT FORMAT

Although reports sometimes require you to solve a single problem, usually you will be summarizing an investigation that may include solving several problems. In either case, you can use this three-part format for your final report.

1. Problem Statement

- State the problem, topic, or main idea clearly.
- If you are summarizing the results of an investigation, you may be answering several questions. Look for the main idea that encompasses all the sub-problems.
- If it will help the reader to understand the problem, use a sketch as part of your explanation.

2. The Strategy and Solution

- If you are solving a problem, describe your approach. If you tried something that didn't work, include a brief explanation of it as well.
- If you are summarizing the results of an investigation, describe how you conducted the investigation.
- Show your calculations and explain them.
- Include graphs and tables, carefully labelled.
- Tell what variables stand for, and use units if appropriate. (Don't just write *w*. Let the reader know whether it stands for *width*, *water*, or *widget*.)

3. The Conclusion

- Explain the answer to the problem or summarize the results of your investigation.
- Write about any unresolved questions you still have.
- Comment on the problem or topic. If possible, suggest generalizations, applications, or extensions.

WRITING ASSIGNMENT EVALUATION

Writing assignments are equal to tests in the evaluation of your work in this class. Here is what your teacher will be looking for when reading the assignments.

■ The Math

- Did you understand the problem?
- Did you express yourself clearly?
- Did you summarize all that you learned about the problem?
- Did you answer all the questions?
- Did you think about the problem beyond what was asked?
- Were you creative in your approach?

■ The Presentation

- Do you have an introduction that states what the paper is about?
- Did you organize your paper into paragraphs?
- Did you illustrate the paper adequately?
- Did you avoid repeating yourself?
- Is the paper neat and legible? Is it beautiful?
- Were you creative in your presentation?

CHAPTER PORTFOLIO ASSIGNMENT

Include the following items in your portfolio.

1. Cover Letter

Write your teacher a letter about the chapter, including answers to these questions.

- What were the main important ideas in math that you studied in this chapter?
- What did you learn? Give examples of each of the main topics.
- What did you enjoy the most? The least?
- What do you understand the best? What would you like to learn better?

2. Table of Contents

Make a table of contents for your portfolio, including a brief description of each entry and why you chose to include it.

3. Favorites

Write *Favorite* at the top of each one.

- Your favorite lesson
- Your favorite Thinking/Writing assignment

4. Important Problems

Choose five problems that you think represent important ideas in this unit. For each one, copy the problem and show the solution neatly. Explain why you chose the problem.

5. Revisions and Corrections

- Include your original paper for Thinking/Writing _____. Revise and improve the assignment on a separate sheet of paper.
- Make corrections to your chapter test on a clean sheet of paper. Include both the original test and the corrections.

Include the following items in your portfolio.

1. Cover Letter

Write your teacher a letter about the semester, including answers to these questions.

- What were the main important ideas in math that you studied this semester?
- What did you learn? Give examples of each of the main topics.
- Write about your strengths and weaknesses. Describe the progress you have made this semester. What are you especially proud of? What are some concrete ways you can improve?
- What were the high points and low points for you mathematically?
- What did you enjoy the most? The least?
- What do you understand the best? What would you like to learn better?

2. Table of Contents

Make a table of contents for your portfolio, including a brief description of each entry and why you chose to include it.

3. Favorites

Write *Favorite* at the top of each one.

- Your two favorite lessons
- Your favorite Thinking/Writing assignment

4. Progress

Write *Progress* at the top of each one. Choose several pieces of work that show the progress you have made. You should include at least two writing assignments in this section of your portfolio.

5. Test Corrections

Make corrections to these tests on a clean sheet of paper. Include both the original tests and the corrections.

- Test ___
- Test ___
- Test ___

6. Semester Exam Preview

Complete Lesson ___, through problem ___. The semester exam will include some questions on this section. You may bring your notes on it to the semester exam.

7. Extra Credit

Do the project described in Lesson ___, problem ___.

CRITERIA FOR EVALUATING A PORTFOLIO

These are some of the criteria your teacher may use to evaluate your portfolio.

■ General

- Is the portfolio complete? Does it include a cover letter and all the specific components (or specific assignments, if asked for) that were requested?
- Is there evidence, either from self-assessment in the cover letter, or from group work included, of being able to work effectively in a group?
- Does the student have a good sense of the level of his or her own work, the direction it is necessary to go in, and strengths and weaknesses?
- Has the student revised and improved work when given the opportunity?
- Is there evidence that the student is well-organized and is keeping track of his/her work?
- Does the portfolio show a variety of different work?
- Does the portfolio show progress over time?
- Is there evidence of enthusiasm for the course and for mathematics?

■ Competence in Mathematics and Communication

- Does the student use mathematical vocabulary and notation appropriately?
- Is there evidence of the student's ability to communicate effectively in writing? Does he or she elaborate sufficiently?
- Is there evidence of the student's ability to formulate problems?
- Is there evidence of the student's ability to develop and apply different problem-solving strategies?
- Has the student shown an ability to generalize?
- Is there evidence that the student can analyze and interpret results and make connections to what was learned previously?
- Is there any evidence of particular ways that this student learns best? (use of hands-on materials, visual strategies, facility with words, sketches, or with using the calculator?)

■ Specific Content

- Does the cover letter show that the student has a grasp of the main ideas from the period included?
- Are particular strengths or weaknesses in terms of specific content revealed by the table of contents?
- Does the student show particular weaknesses in background or problem-solving strategies that make understanding of certain content particularly difficult?

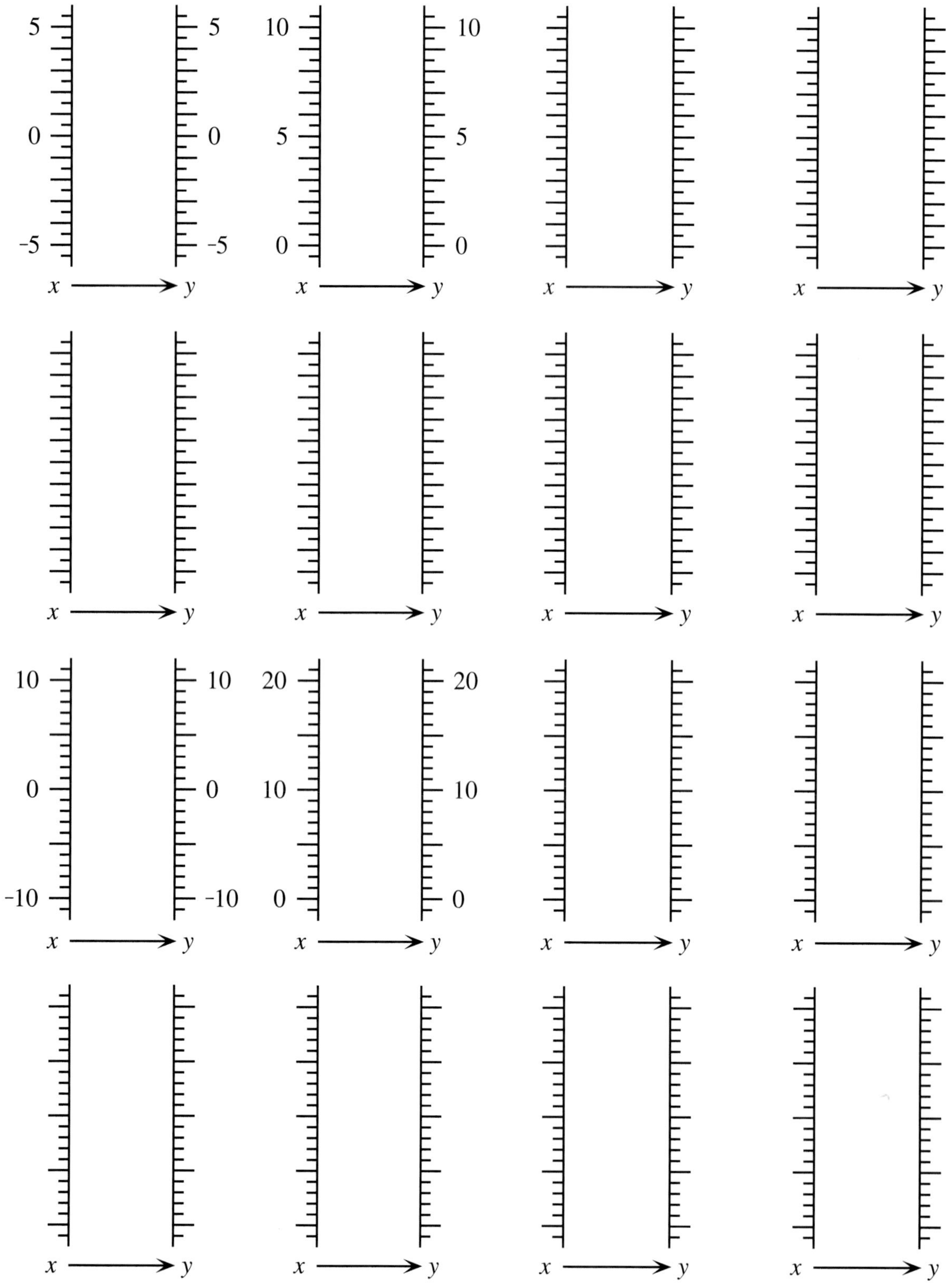
5
0
-5
5
0
-5
10
5
0
10
5
0
x
y
10
0
-10
10
0
-10
20
10
0
20
10
0
x
y

GLOSIAN MONEY ADDITION TABLE

+	d	e	f	d+e	d+f	e+f	d+e+f
d							
e							
f							
d+e							
d+f							
e+f							
d+e+f							

+	Mo	Tu	We	Th	Fr	Sa	Su
Mo							
Tu							
We							
Th							
Fr							
Sa							
Su							

CALENDAR MATH MULTIPLICATION TABLE

×	Mo	Tu	We	Th	Fr	Sa	Su
Mo							
Tu							
We							
Th							
Fr							
Sa							
Su							

LINKED FUNCTION DIAGRAMS

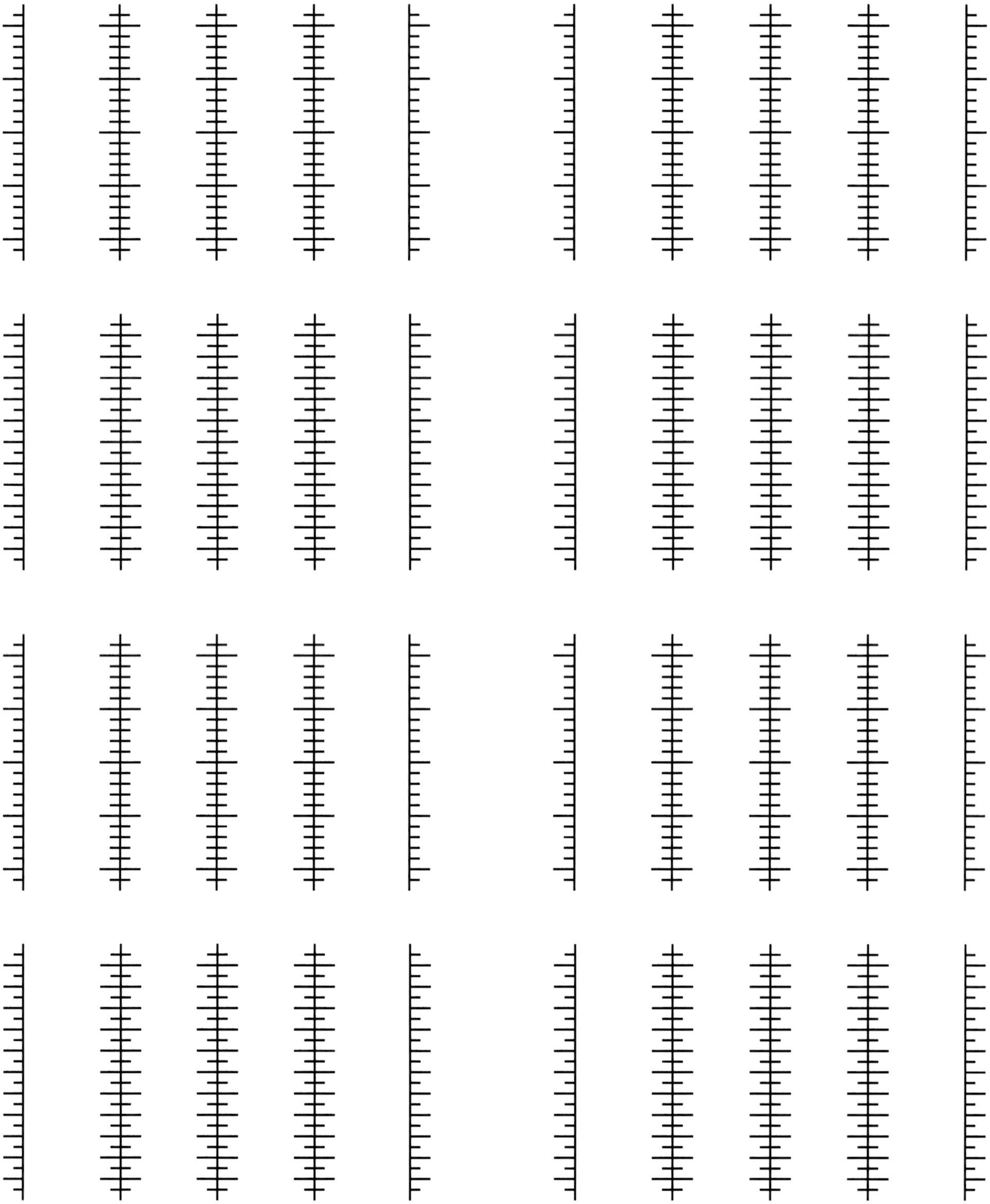

The YZ Game

↔	E	Y	YY	Z	YZ	YYZ
E						
Y						
YY						
Z						
YZ						
YYZ						

The yz Game

Then…

First…

↔	e	y	yy	z	yz	zy
e						
y						
yy						
z						
yz						
zy						

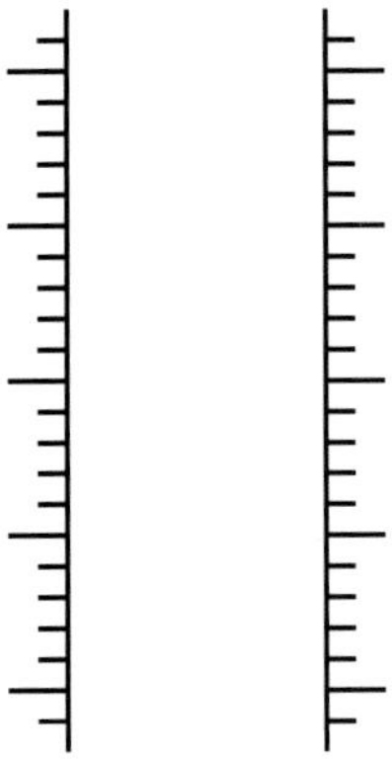

x	y

$x \longrightarrow y =$ ____________

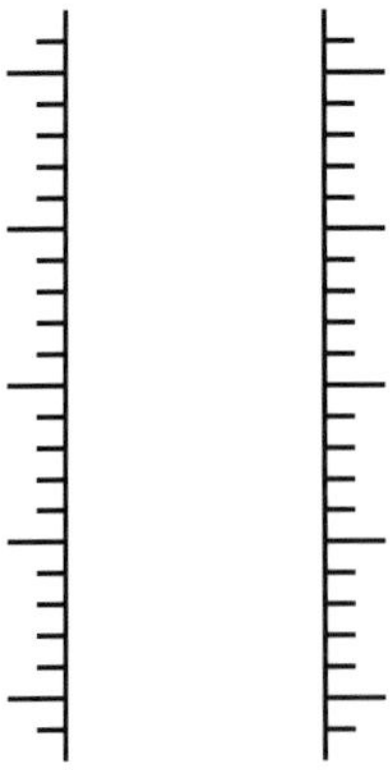

x	y

$x \longrightarrow y =$ ____________

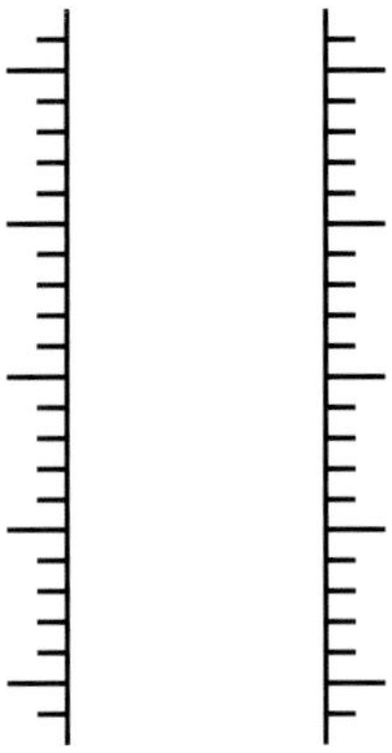

x	y

$x \longrightarrow y =$ ____________

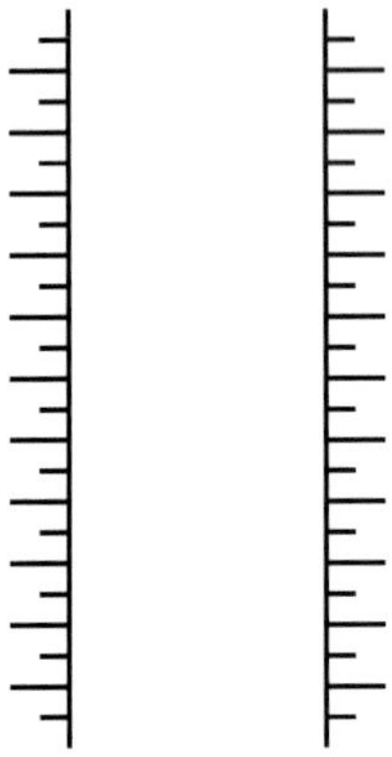

x	y

$x \longrightarrow y =$ ____________

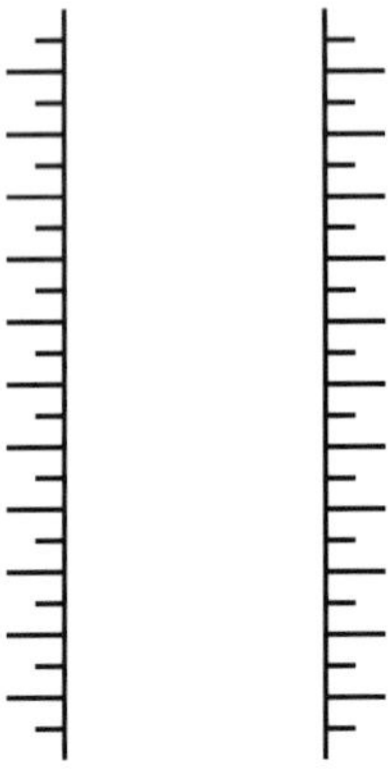

x	y

$x \longrightarrow y =$ ____________

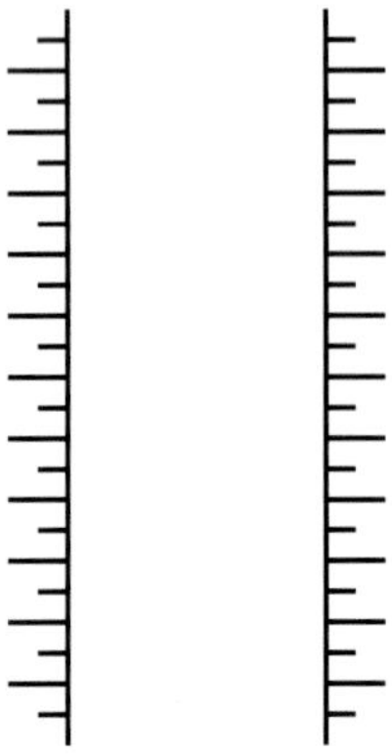

x	y

$x \longrightarrow y =$ ____________

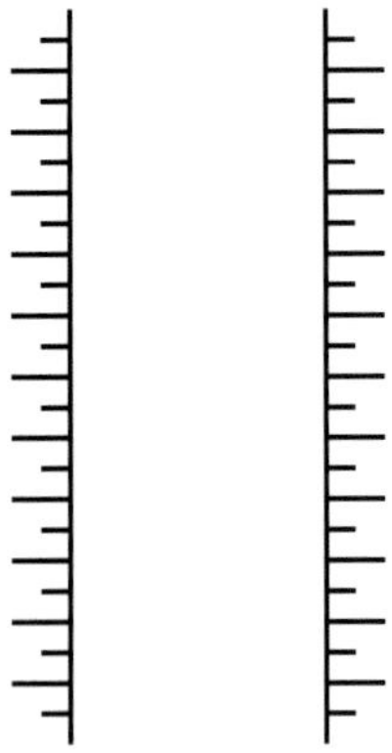

x	y

$x \longrightarrow y =$ ____________

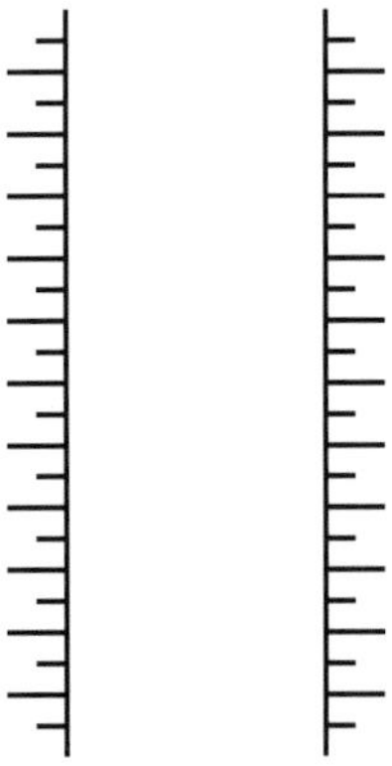

x	y

$x \longrightarrow y =$ ____________

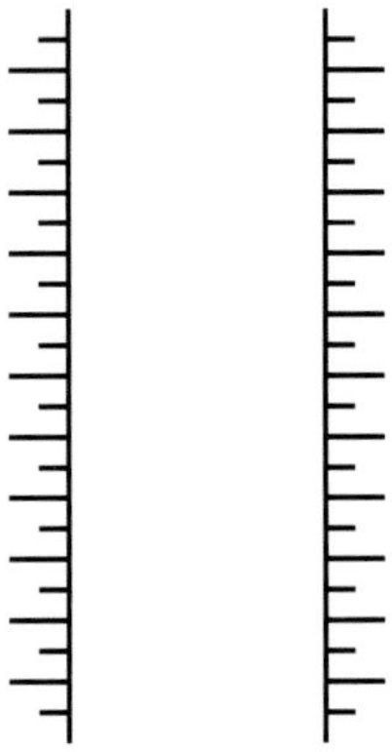

x	y

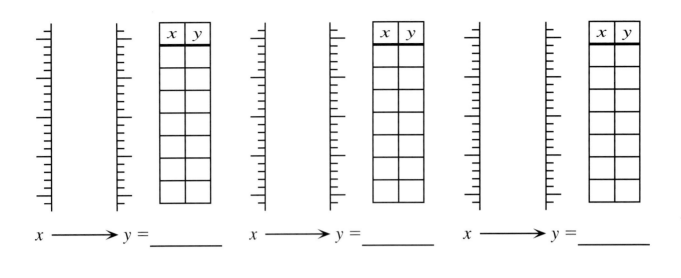

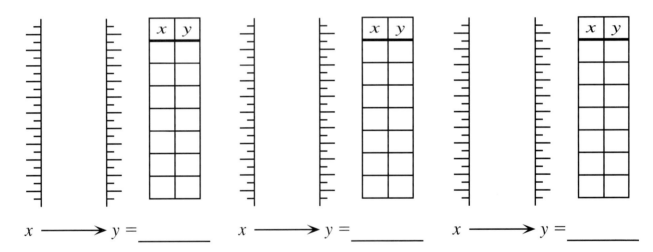

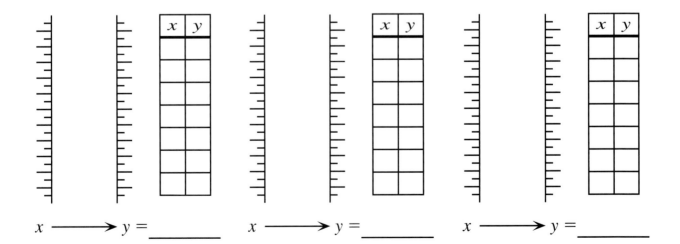

$x \longrightarrow y =$ ____________

Paste these on the two sides of a cardboard triangle

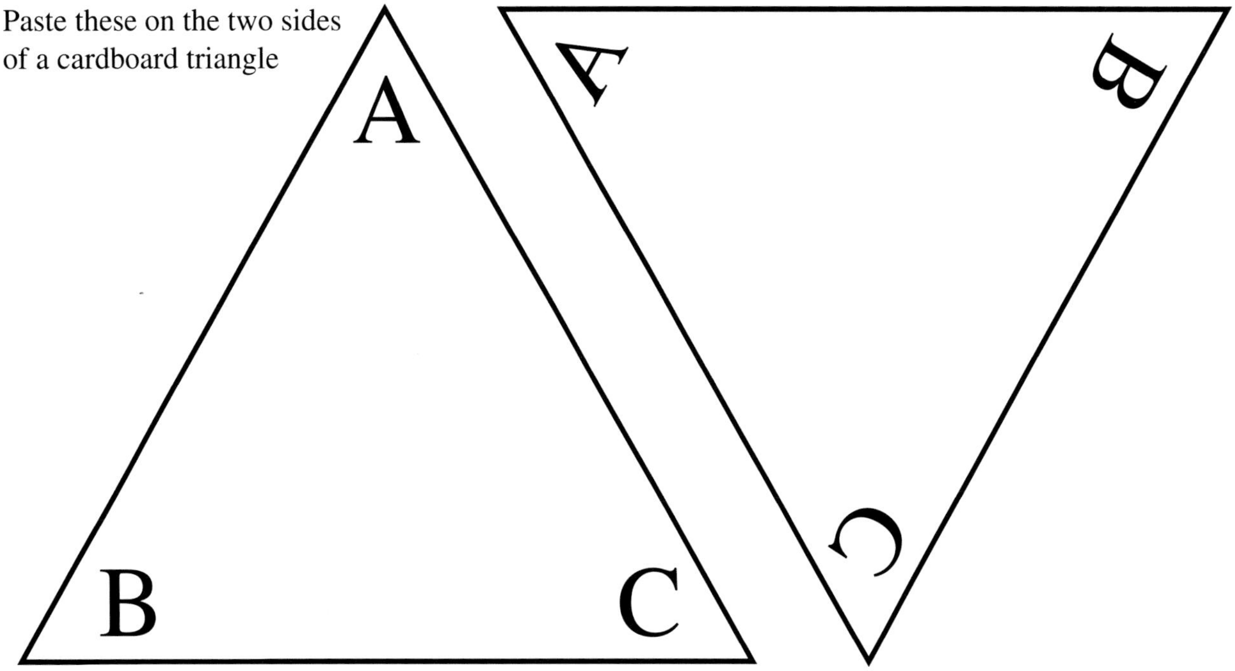

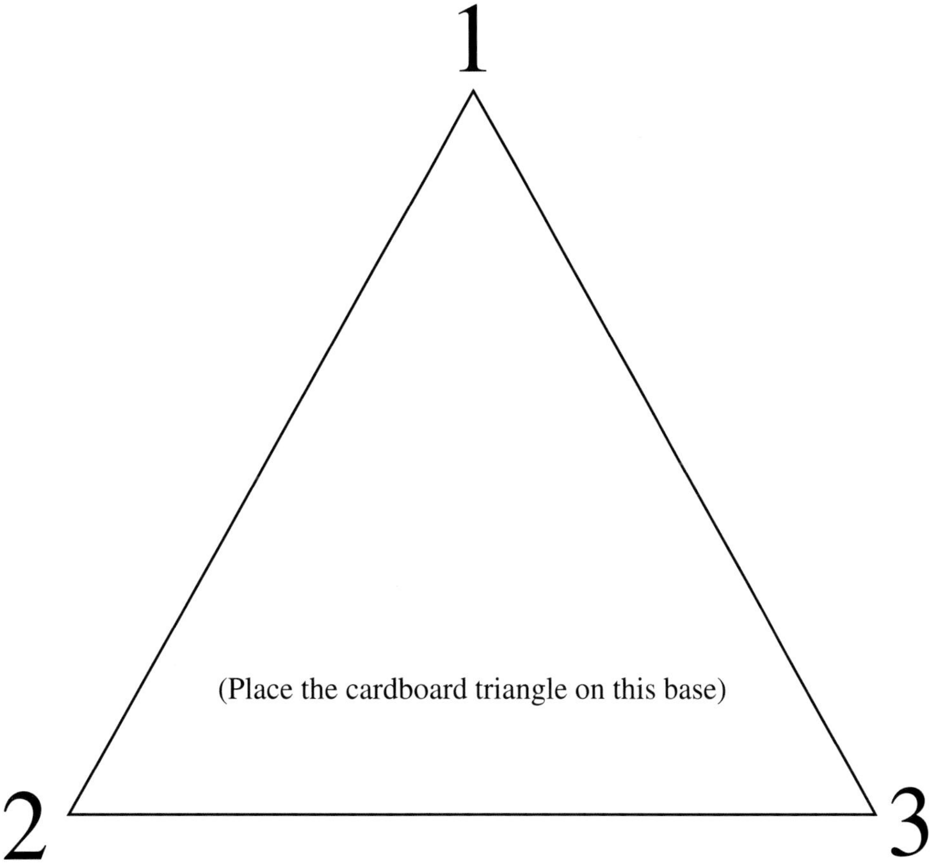

Mod 5 Clock

⊕	0	1	2	3	4
0					
1					
2					
3					
4					

⊗	0	1	2	3	4
0					
1					
2					
3					
4					

SIXTEEN FUNCTION DIAGRAMS

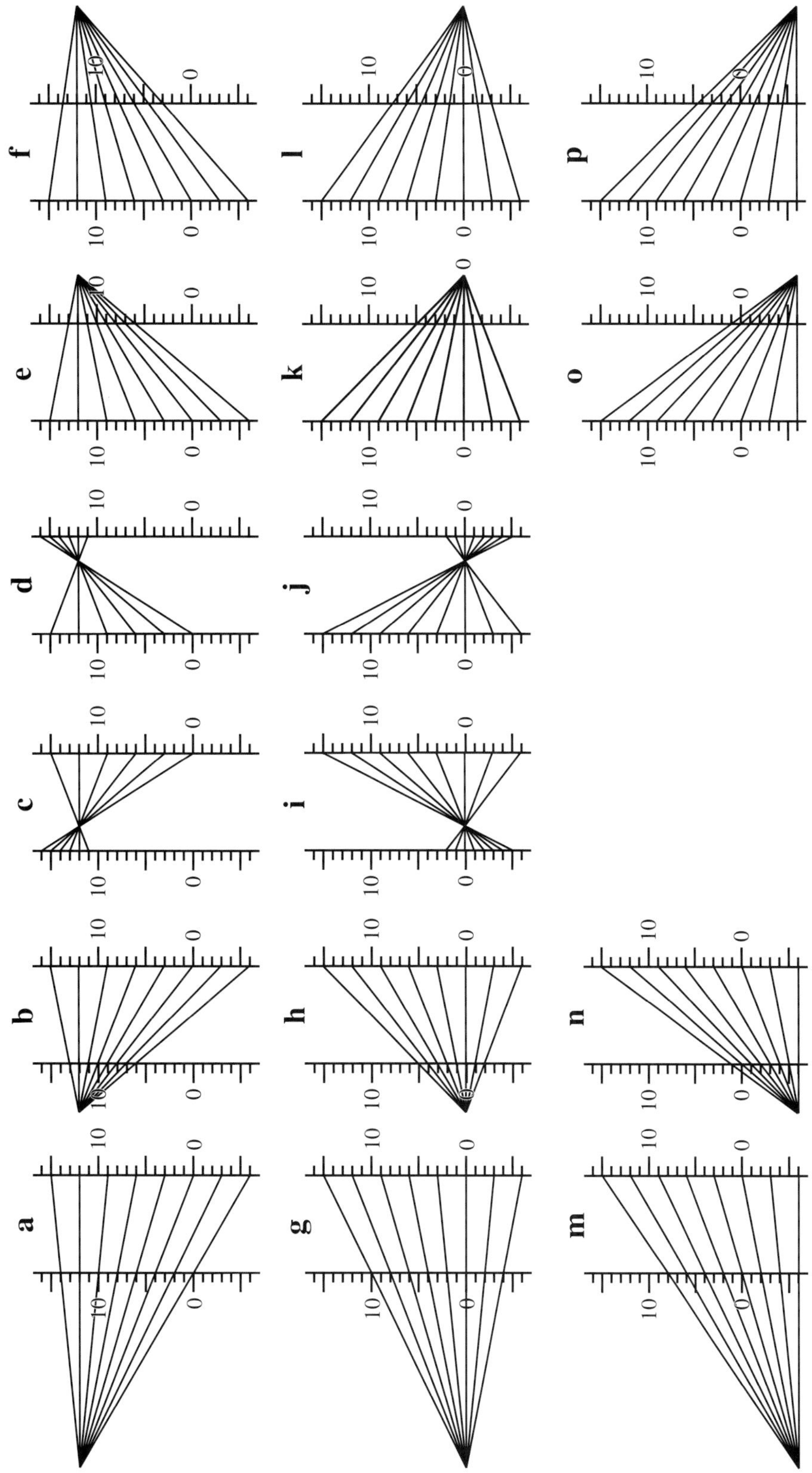

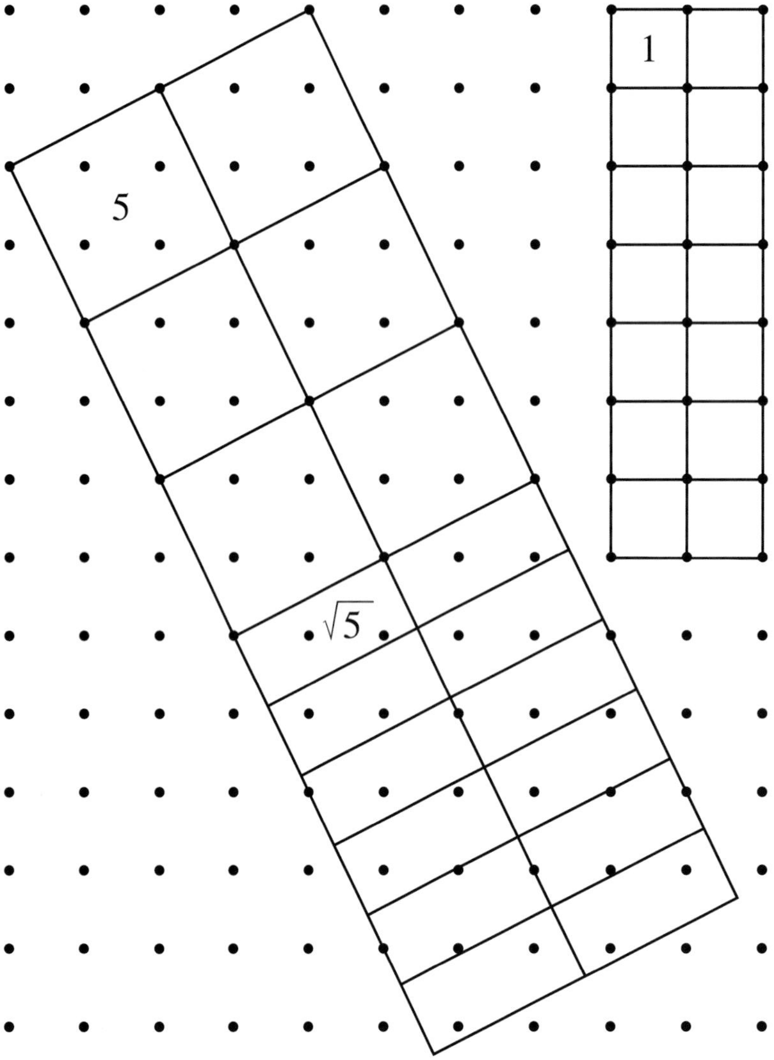
5
$\sqrt{5}$
1

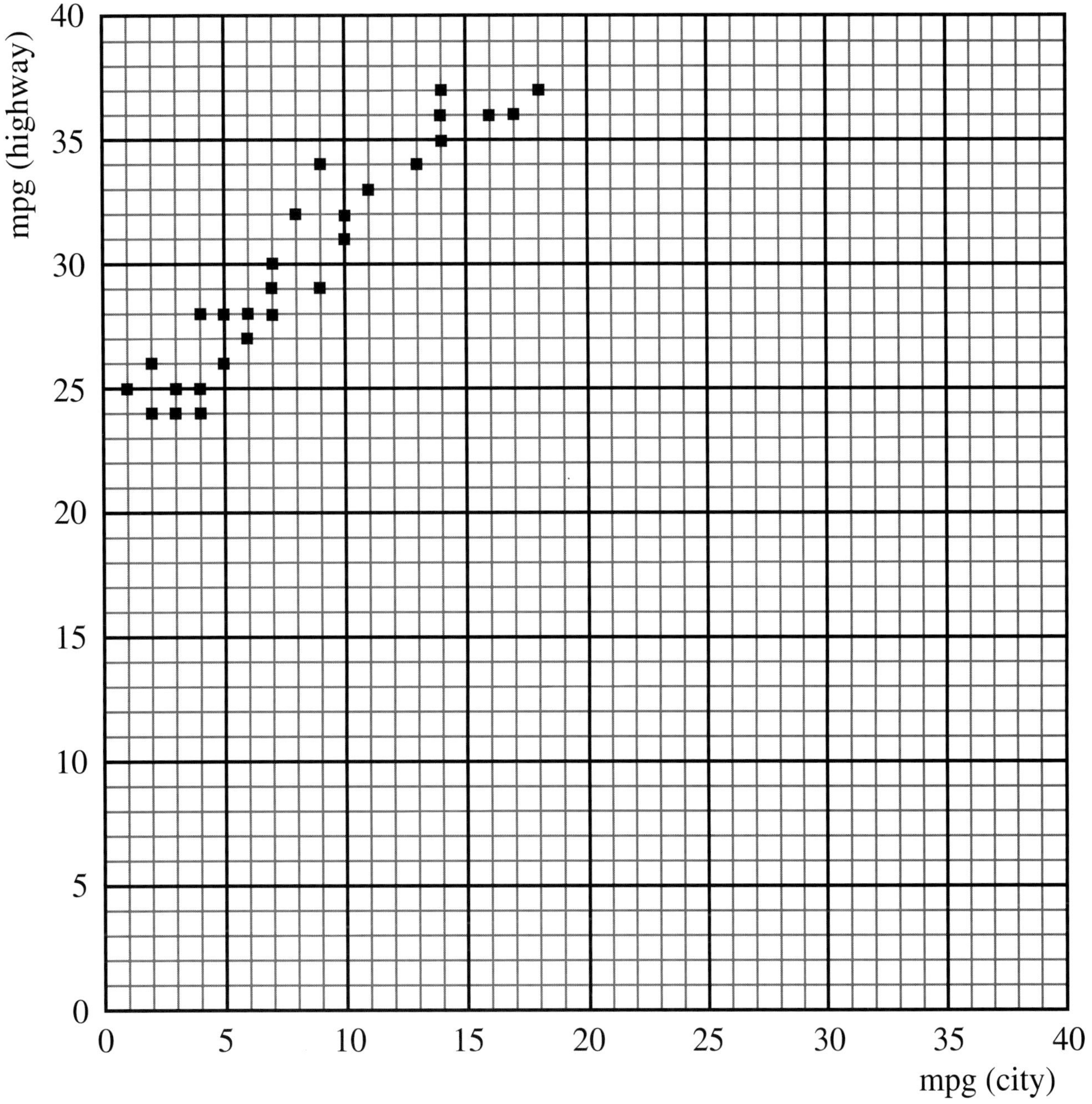
mpg (highway)
40
35
30
25
20
15
10
5
0
0
5
10
15
20
25
30
35
40
mpg (city)

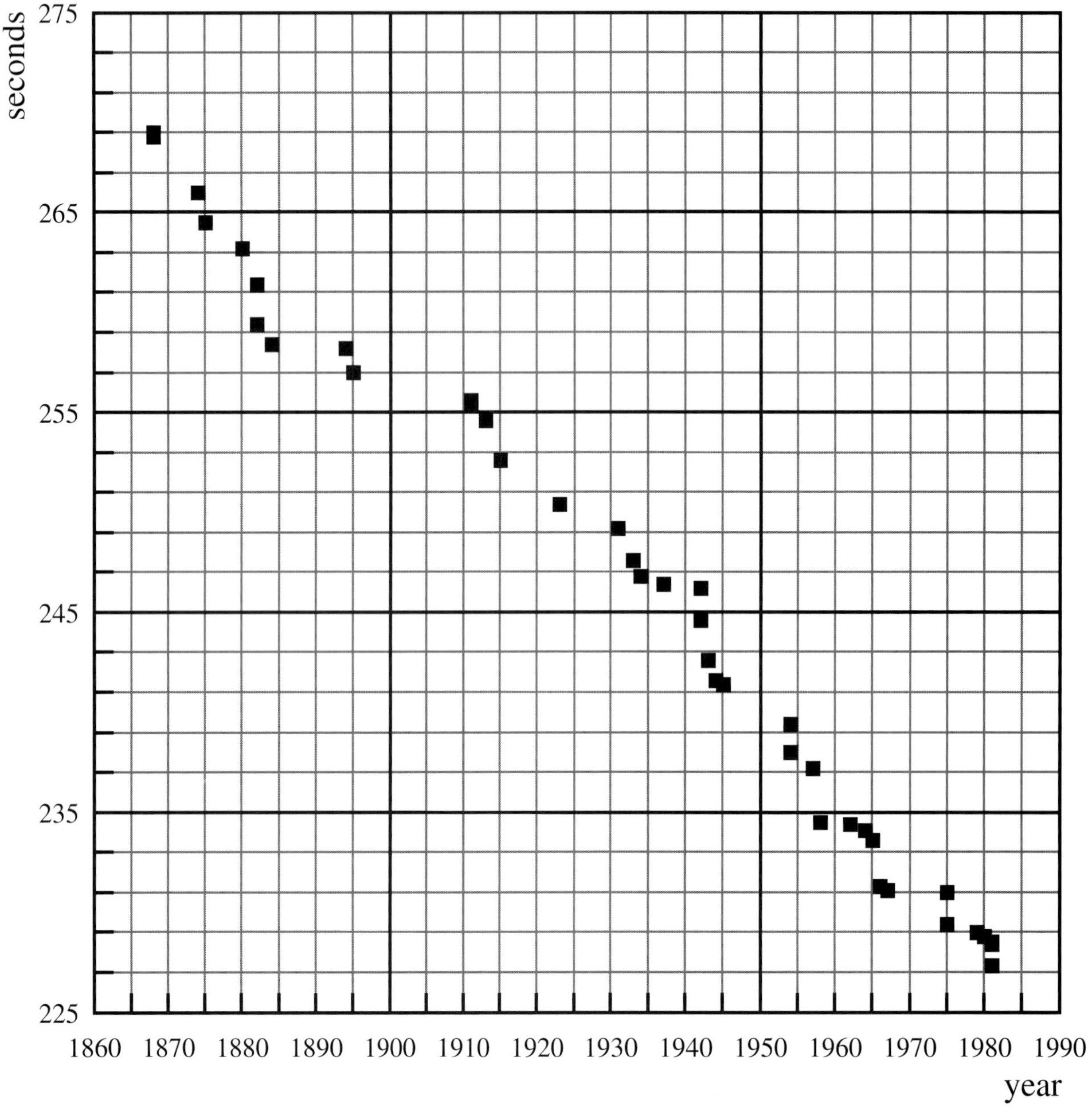
seconds
275
265
255
245
235
225
1860
1870
1880
1890
1900
1910
1920
1930
1940
1950
1960
1970
1980
1990
year

CENTIMETER DOT PAPER

CENTIMETER GRAPH PAPER

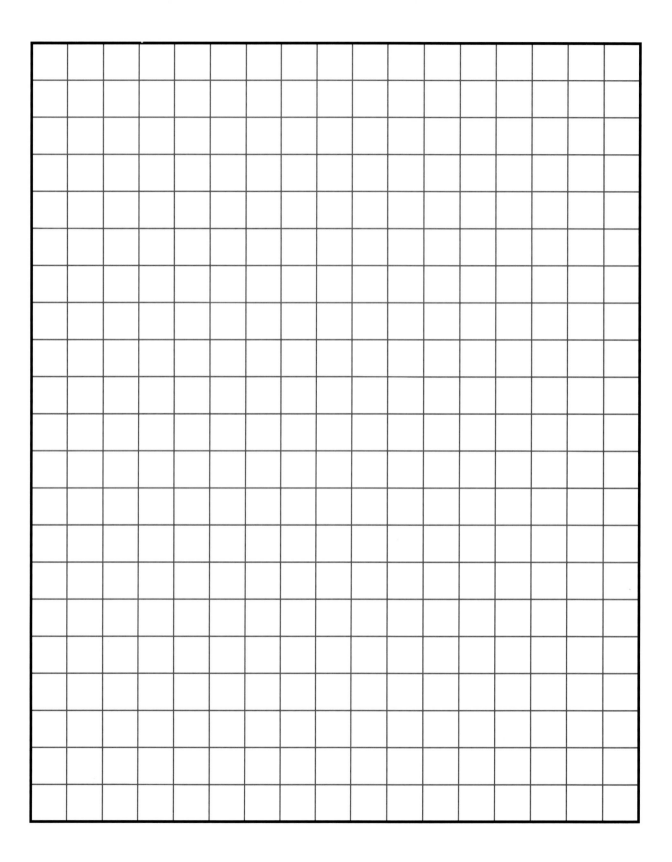

We do not believe it is constructive to put too much emphasis on signed number arithmetic in an algebra class, because students have spent so much time on this in the preceding years. Certainly, it is inappropriate and demoralizing to start the school year with it.

You may disagree with us, especially if you teach in a middle school. If you want to work on signed numbers, you may use the following pages, where we have reproduced Chapter 2 of the *Algebra Lab* (High School) binder, published by Creative Publications, which addresses operations on signed numbers. More practice can easily be created by you or your students.

The following summarizes the Lab Gear approach to signed number arithmetic.

The Basics

Start with zero (an empty mat)

It's OK to remove zero (opposites)

It's OK to add zero (opposites)

The Operations

Addition: put down, put down, (remove zero?)

Subtraction: put down, (add zero?), take away

Multiplication: put down sets

or: add zero, take away sets

What's Wrong with the Two-Color Model for Minus?

As you know, with the Lab Gear, color distinguishes numbers from variables. This is particularly useful early on, and when making rectangles. We prefer the Lab Gear model of minus to the two-color model of signed numbers with which you may be familiar.

In the two-color model for minus, one color represents positive numbers, and another represents negative numbers. The operations are carried out much in the same way as they are with the Lab Gear. However, the model is much weaker when it comes to algebra. First of all, the use of two colors for variables reinforces the widespread student misconception that ^{-}x is negative, since it is the same color as $^{-}1$. In fact, of course, ^{-}x is just as likely to be positive.

Moreover, the two-color model does not provide a smooth transition to the use of manipulatives in algebra. Specifically:

> In the rectangle model of multiplication, the two-color model represents $(x + 1)(x - 2)$ with the same rectangle as $(x + 1)(x + 2)$. The only difference is the color. However the rectangles should differ in size, since $x - 2$ is less than $x + 2$! This works out correctly with the Lab Gear approach (using upstairs, the minus area, or both to show minus, depending on the context.)

The Lab Gear approach to signed number operations is consistent with the workmat introduction to inequalities and equations. The two-color model is not, nor do we know of any effective way to extend it in the direction of a manipulative approach to equation solving.

Note: One limitation of the Lab Gear model of minus is that while it works well with the area model of multiplication and the workmat model of equations, it does not work well with the 3-D blocks. When using the 3-D blocks, use only plus!

Using the Reproducible Pages

The usual approach to work with signed numbers (teaching of rule, sometimes combined with number line techniques) is often frustrating, because so many students seem to forget the rules, even though they are given endless practice. On the other hand, the students who "get it," quickly get bored with the drills.

We suggest a different approach. Instead of being taught signed number arithmetic, present the students with a model for the four operations. The model is easy to learn, because it is a natural extension of concrete models most students have already mastered for these operations. In fact, once learned, the model is almost impossible to forget, unlike the rules and number line techniques, which are confusing and easy to mangle. Moreover, the work with the blocks keeps more students motivated, at all levels of proficiency.

The commutative law is not mentioned by name in the following reproducible pages, but students are asked to observe what happens when switching the order of the terms for each operation.

After working with the blocks for a while, you will find that many students discover the rules for themselves, or learn them from each other. Knowledge that is earned the hard way by one's own thinking and interaction with peers is much more securely anchored than techniques that have been learned by rote.

If your students already know signed number arithmetic, there is little point in working through these pages with the exception of *Square Numbers* and the Exploration on that page. An interesting approach with such students is to ask them to figure out a way to use the Lab Gear to explain the rules of signed number arithmetic. If they cannot figure it out, show them the models, but do not assign too many drill problems.

ADDITION WITH SIGNED NUMBERS

To model addition with the Lab Gear, *put on* the first number, *put on* the second number, *cancel* what you can, and *count*.

Look at this example, -6 + 2.

- *Put on* the first number. To show -6, put 6 in the minus area.

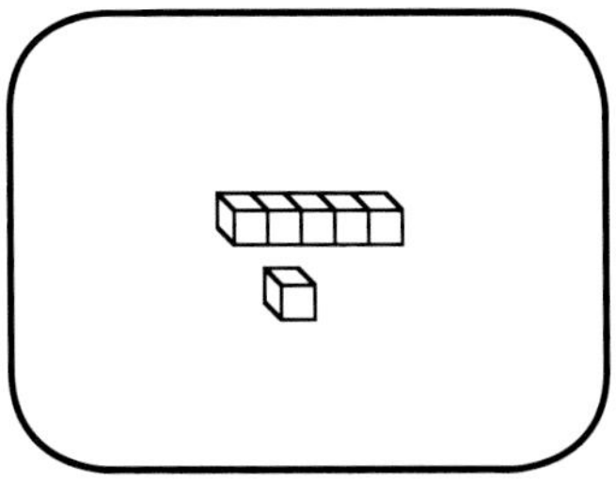

- *Put on* the second number. To show 2, put 2 outside the minus area.

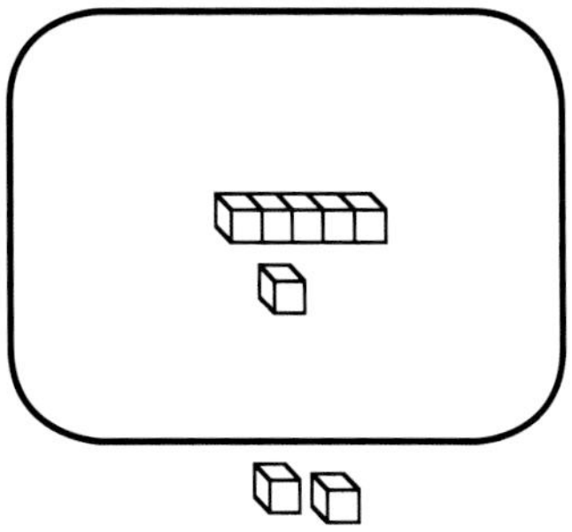

- *Cancel* 2 and -2.

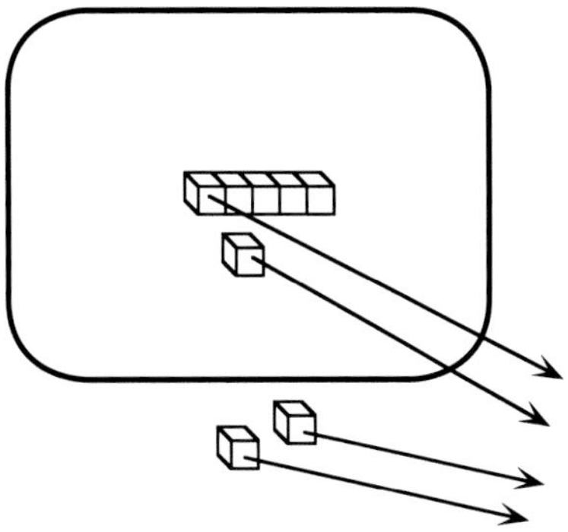

- *Count* to find the answer.
  -6 + 2 = -4

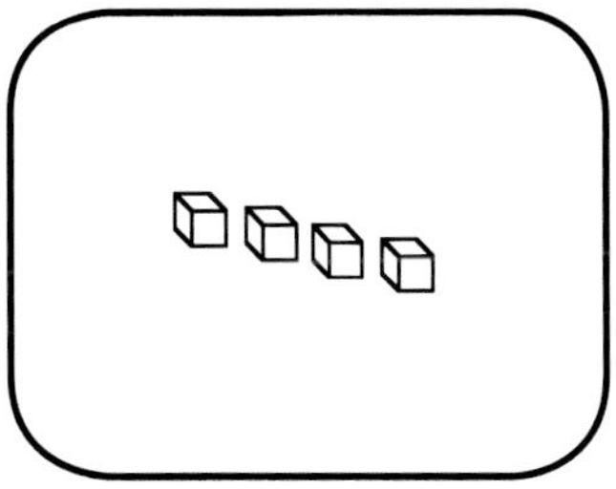

1. Does the order that you put on the numbers matter? Try it by modeling 2 + -6, and compare the result.

Sometimes, there is nothing to cancel.

2. Write the addition shown by this figure.

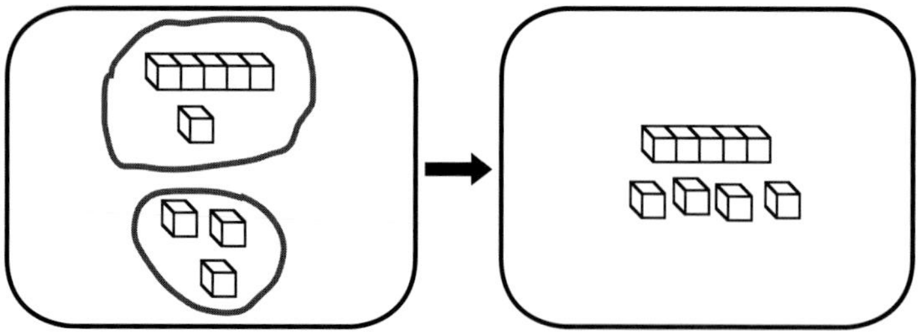

If you are adding several numbers, just put them all on the mat, cancel, and count.

3. Write the addition shown by this figure.

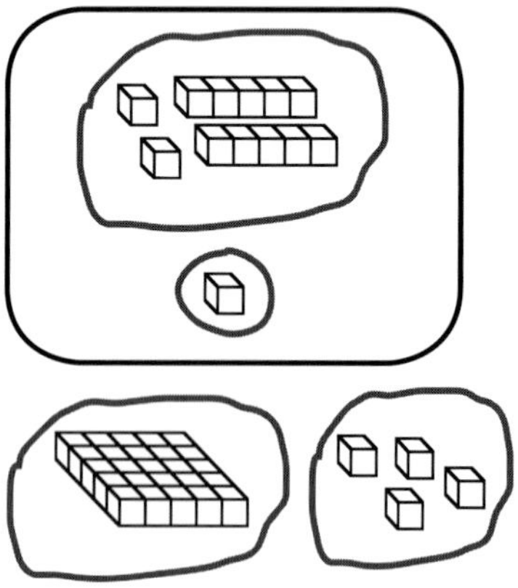

Use the Lab Gear to model these additions. Sketch the process in four steps (put on first number / put on second number / cancel / final solution). The sketches should include the minus area. You can sketch the blocks in two dimensions.

4. -5 + 2
5. -15 + (-3)
6. -8 + 9

Use the Lab Gear to find these sums.

7. 10 + -4
8. -25 + 5
9. -12 + -6
10. 10 + (-8) + 3
11. -25 + 11 + (-4)
12. -15 + 20 + (-7) + 2

 Algebra: Themes • Tools • Concepts

SUBTRACTION WITH SIGNED NUMBERS

To model subtraction with the Lab Gear, *put on* the first number, *take off* the second number, and *count*.

This example shows that -8 − (-2) = -6.

- Put on -8.

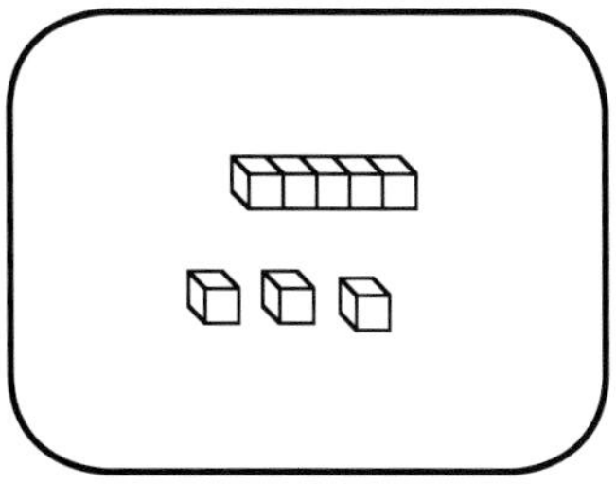

- Take off -2.

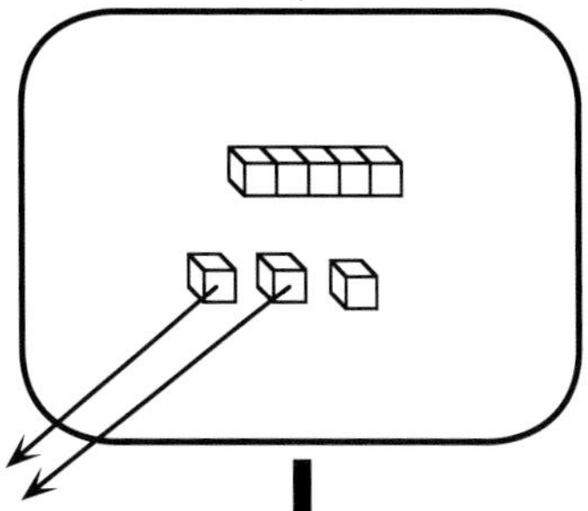

- Count to find the answer. -6

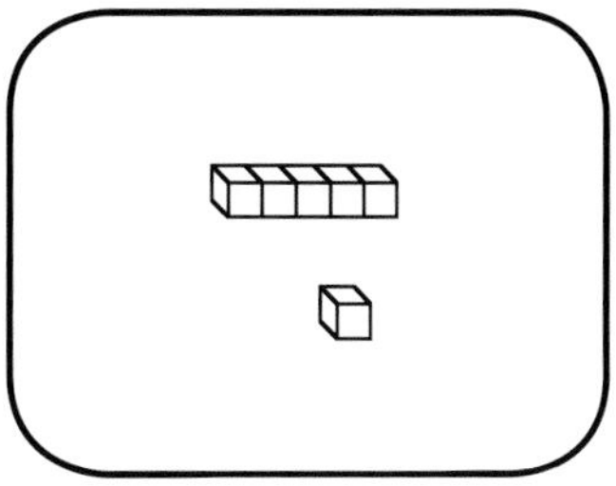

Sometimes, there are not enough blocks to take off. For example, 4 − 5. The solution is to show 4 differently by *adding zero.*

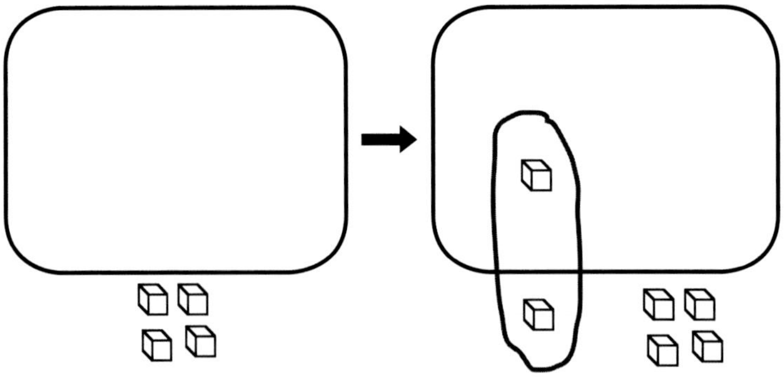

As long as you add the same amount inside the minus area and outside it, you have not changed the quantity on the workmat. If you cancelled the blocks you put on, you would be back to the original amount. (Adding zero could be called "uncancelling.")

Notice that now it is possible to take off 5, and you can see that the answer is -1.

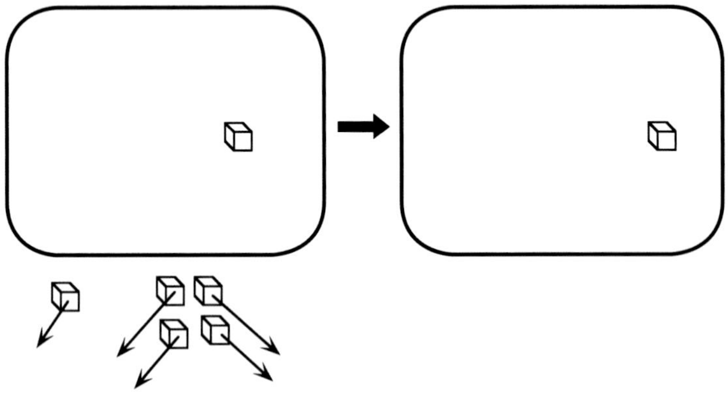

Perhaps you knew what the answer was going to be, and you are asking yourself, why do so much work to get it? Keep in mind that the point of working with the Lab Gear is not just to get the answer, but to understand why it turns out the way it does. Work these easy problems carefully; you will soon be doing similar ones with variables. You will then see how working with variables is just an extension of the work you're doing now with integers.

Use the Lab Gear to model these problems.

1. -7 − (-3)

2. -3 − (-7)

3. In problem 2, the order of the numbers was reversed. How did that affect the answer?

The adding zero trick should help you do some of these problems. For problems 4-7, sketch the process in four steps (put on / add zero (if you need to) / take off / final solution).

4. -2 − 8

5. -4 − (-2)

6. -8 − 3

7. 7 − (-6)

8. -5 − 9

9. 11 + (-6)

10. -1 + 10

11. 20 − 25

12. 13 − 3

13. -17 + 3

14. -2 − 21

15. -15 − 5

16. -5 − (-15)

17. 6 − 17

18. 18 − 9

For the first example, consider the multiplication 3 (-4).

- Look at the first number. If the first number is positive, *put on* the second number the number of times indicated by the first number. Here you put on three sets of -4.

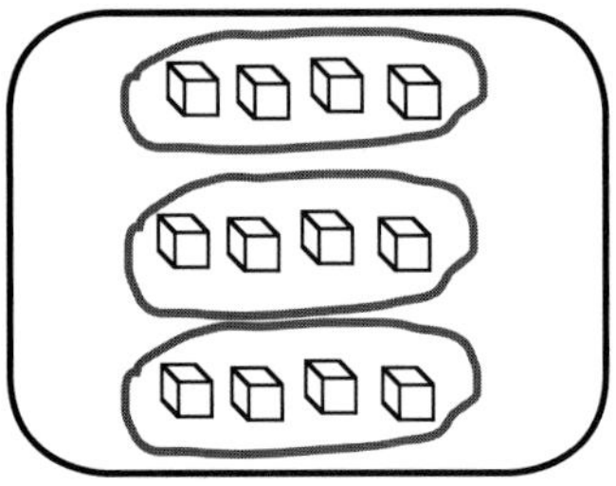

- *Count* to get the final result. -12

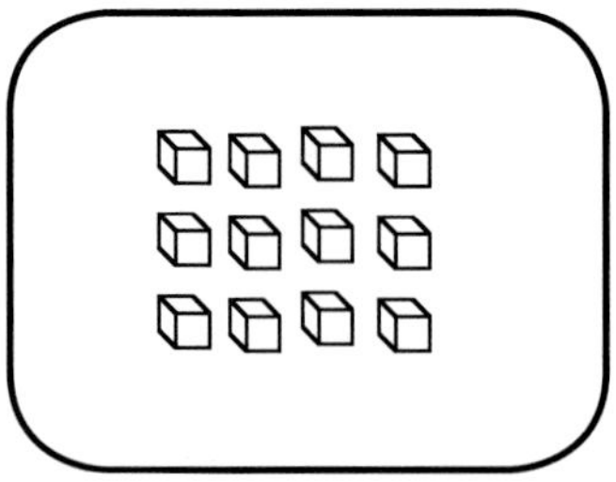

- *Make a rectangle* to show multiplication. 3 (-4) = -12

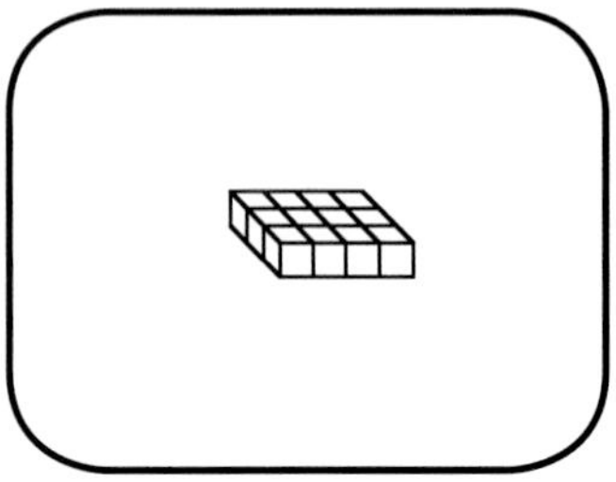

For the second example, consider the multiplication -2 (-5).

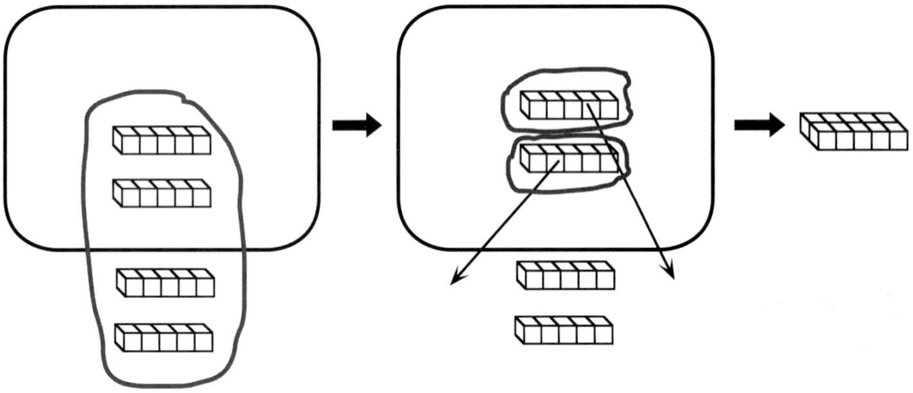

- If the first number is negative, *take off* the second number the number of times indicated by the first number. However, since you're starting with an empty mat, there is nothing to take off, so you must use the adding zero trick. In this case, add 10 and -10, then *take off* two sets of -5.
- *Count* to get the final result.
- *Make a rectangle*. -2 (-5) = 10.

Look at the preceding examples. Use the Lab Gear in the same way to model problems 1 and 2. Notice that the order of the numbers has been reversed.

1. -4 (3)
2. -5 (-2)
3. Tell how changing the order affects the answer.

Notice that at the end of a multiplication problem, you can always arrange the blocks into a rectangle.

Use the Lab Gear to model these multiplications. For problems 4-6, sketch the process in two or three steps. (Put on / make a rectangle; or, add zero / take off / make a rectangle.)

4. 2 (-4)
5. -3 (2)
6. -4 (-5)
7. -6 (-2)
8. -10 (2)
9. 7 (-3)

Compute:

10. -9 + 6
11. 2 − (-4)
12. -3 − 2
13. -3 (-2)
14. Copy and complete this sentence: Problem 12 is a subtraction, while problem 13 is a __________.

MULTIPLYING BY -1

Use the Lab Gear to model these multiplications.

15. -1 (-2)
16. -1 (3)
17. 4 (-1)
18. -5 (-1)
19. Explain what happens when a number is multiplied by -1.
20. What happens *to the blocks* when you multiply a number by -1?
For each example above, sketch the blocks that represent the number *before* and *after* multiplying by -1. Describe what happens in each case.

A special case of multiplication is the multiplication of a number by itself. Use the Lab Gear to model these multiplications. At the end of each problem, check whether the answer is positive or negative, and try to arrange the blocks into a square.

1. $(-3)(-3)$

2. $5 \cdot 5$

3. $(-2)(-2)$

4. $(-6)(-6)$

Multiplying a number by itself is called *squaring* the number. Instead of writing $5 \cdot 5$, you can write 5^2, which is read *five squared.* Instead of writing $(-5)(-5)$, you can write $(-5)^2$. This is read *negative five, squared,* or perhaps more clearly, *the square of negative five.* The parentheses tell us that we are squaring -5. The answer is 25.

Be careful! If you write -5^2, without the parentheses, that will be read as *the opposite of five squared,* in other words, the opposite of 25, or -25. In conclusion, $(-5)^2$ and -5^2 are not the same! In fact, they are opposite. If you want to indicate squaring -5, you must use parentheses.

Write how to read each of the following expressions.

5. 2^2

6. $(-4)^2$

7. -3^2

8. $(3x)^2$

9. $(-3x)^2$

10. $-3x^2$

11. In problems 8, 9, and 10, which expressions are equal to each other? Explain your answer. Hint: Work out the numerical value for each one if $x = 2$, and then if $x = -2$.

When writing 5^2, the 2 is called the *exponent*, and the 5 is called the *base*. When writing $6x^2$, the 6 is called the *coefficient.*

12. In the expression 7^2, what do you call the 2? The 7?

13. In the expression $3xy$, what do you call the 3?

Exploration Positive or Negative?

Look at these expressions. For each one, indicate with 0, P, and/or N, if the value of the quantity is zero, positive, or negative. If it is impossible to tell, write *a* ?.

14. 2^2

15. $(-4)^2$

16. -3^2

17. $(3x)^2$

18. $(-3x)^2$

19. $-3x^2$

You may be wondering how division is performed with the Lab Gear. Later, you will learn to use the Lab Gear to divide some expressions that involve variables. For integers, the best method is to use the fact that division is the inverse operation of multiplication.

For example, to divide 8 by 2, you could ask, "What times 2 equals 8?" Remember that for multiplication, you start with an empty mat. How many sets of 2 should you *put on* to get 8? It is easy to see that the answer is 4.

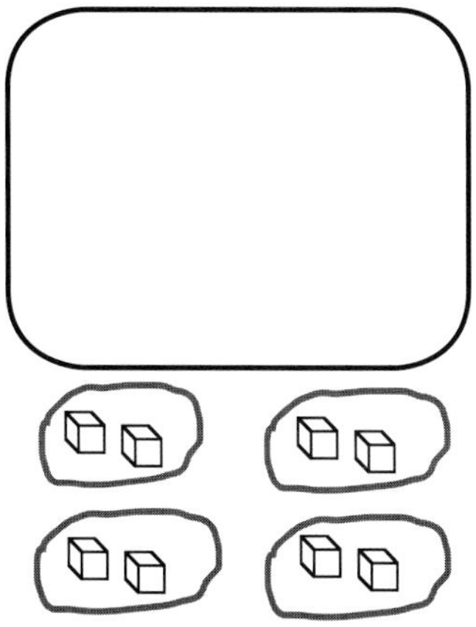

1. Consider the division -8 ÷ -2. What is the multiplication question to ask? How would you solve it on the workmat? Write the answer.

Now consider dividing 8 by -2. Ask yourself, "What times -2 equals 8?" Start with an empty workmat. How many sets of (-2) should you *put on* to get 8? Clearly that question has no answer, since no matter how many times -2 is *put on* you will only get negative numbers.

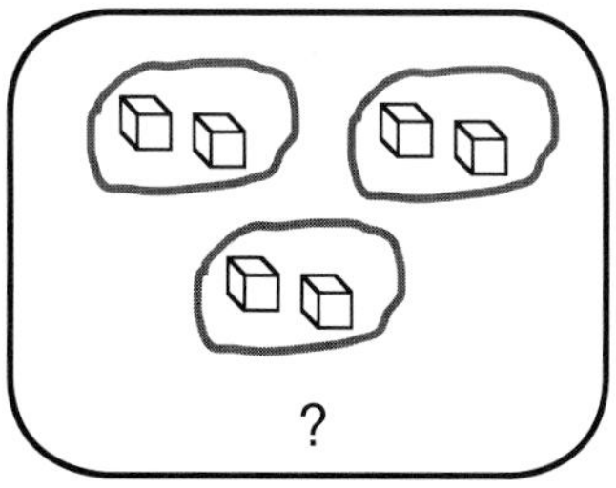

Try another approach. How many sets of (-2) should you *take off* to get 8? Start with an empty workmat and add zero in the form of 8 and -8. Now try *taking off* four sets of -2 to leave 8. This works. So the answer to "What times -2 equals 8?" is -4. So, 8 ÷ -2 = -4.

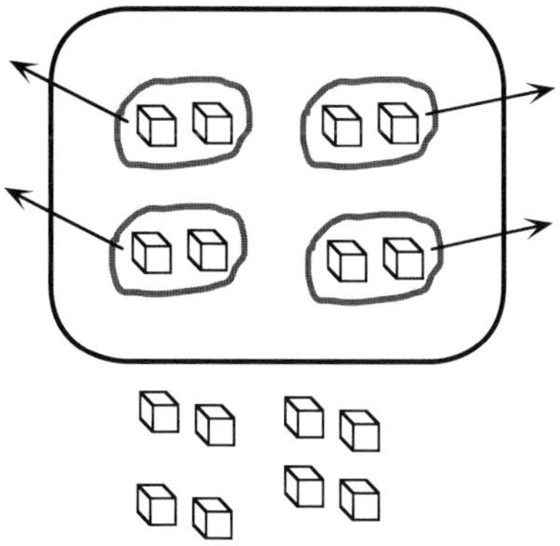

2. Consider the division -8 ÷ 2. What is the multiplication question to ask? How would you solve it on the workmat? Write the answer.

3. Using the method shown in the examples, try to figure out rules for division. How do negative numbers in the numerator and/or denominator affect the result? Give examples.

4. Compare these rules to the ones for multiplication.

5. What happens when a number is divided by -1?

6. Which of these divisions are equal?

a. $\frac{8}{-2}$

b. $\frac{-8}{2}$

c. $\frac{-8}{-2}$

d. $\frac{8}{2}$

While using the Lab Gear to do integer arithmetic, you may have discovered some rules, tricks, or patterns that will help you deal with minus signs when doing arithmetic without the blocks. Write down any such rules or patterns.

1. Addition rules, tricks, or patterns
2. Subtraction rules, tricks, or patterns
3. Multiplication rules, tricks, or patterns
4. Squaring rules, tricks, or patterns

You have been working with integers. However, the rules for integer arithmetic still apply when working with decimals and fractions. For example, the square of a negative fraction, just like the square of a negative integer, is always positive. Try to do the following computations without pencil or calculator:

5. $^{-}5.2 + 11.36$

6. $^{-}2.2 - 0.06$

7. $^{-}3.07(1000)$

8. $-\frac{2}{3} + \frac{1}{6}$

9. $-\frac{2}{3} - \frac{1}{6}$

10. $-\frac{2}{3} \cdot \frac{1}{6}$

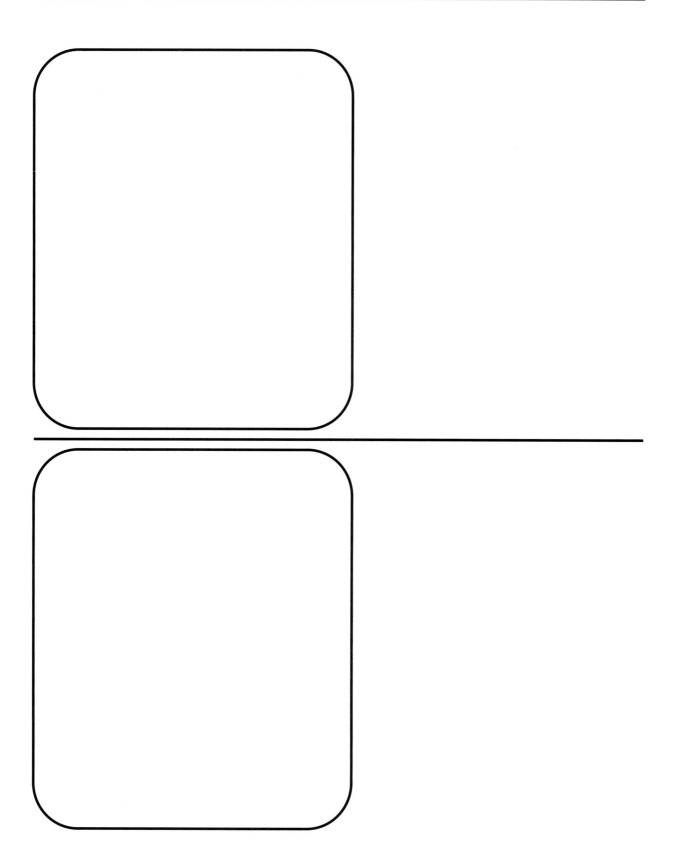

GLOSSARY

Absolute value The absolute value of a number x is the distance from x to 0 on the number line.

Absolute zero The temperature for which the volume (of gases) would be zero—the lowest possible temperature.

Acute angle An angle whose measure is less than a right angle.

Acute triangle A triangle that contains three acute angles.

Adding zero Adding the same quantity to both sides of an equation, or to the plus and minus area on a workmat, is the technique of adding zero.

Area The size of a surface expressed in square units.

Arithmetic sequence In an arithmetic sequence the difference between consecutive terms is always the same. It is called the *common difference*.

Associative Law For all real numbers a, b, and c,
Addition: $a + (b + c) = (a + b) + c$, i.e., quantities can be grouped in any way.
Multiplication: $a \cdot (b \cdot c) = (a \cdot b) \cdot c$, i.e., factors can be grouped in any way.

Average speed The total distance traveled divided by total travel time.

Axis In the Cartesian coordinate system, the horizontal number line is the x-axis. The vertical number line is the y-axis.

Axis of symmetry If the graph of a parabola is folded so that its two sides coincide, the line on which the fold occurs is the axis of symmetry.

Bounce ratio The bounce-height to drop-height ratio.

Cadence The pace of pedaling (a bicycle).

Cartesian coordinate system The Cartesian coordinate system is the technique of using horizontal and vertical axes and graph points to make geometric representations of algebraic equations. It is named for Descartes, the French mathematician and philosopher.

Chunking The process of grouping bits of information into a single piece of information. Also treating an entire algebraic expression as one variable.

Coefficient In a term, the coefficient is the numeric factor of the term or number that is multiplied by the variable.

Commutative Law For any real numbers a and b,
Addition: $a + b = b + a$.
Multiplication: $ab = ba$.

Completing the square When you add the same quantity to both sides of a quadratic equation (and make a perfect square), you are completing the square.

Complex number A complex number cannot be shown on a number line. It requires a two-dimensional number plane.

Compound inequality An inequality that contains more than one inequality symbol.

Constant A term having no variables.

Constraints A constraint is a condition necessary when solving an equation.

Conversion factor In the case of unit conversion, the proportionality constant (the number by which you multiply) is the conversion factor.

Coordinates In the Cartesian coordinate system, the numbers in an ordered pair, i.e., (x, y) are used to locate a point on a plane.

Degree of an expression The degree of an expression, in terms of the Lab Gear, is the lowest dimension in which you can arrange the blocks.

Density Density is equal to weight per unit of volume.

Discriminant The discriminant is the quantity $b^2 - 4ac$ that appears under the radical in the quadratic formula, sometimes written as the Greek letter delta, Δ.

Distributing the minus sign When you write an equivalent expression without parentheses you are distributing the minus sign.

Distributive Law For any real numbers a, b, and c,
of multiplication over addition: $a(b + c) = ab + ac$ and $(b + c)a = ba + ca$.
of multiplication over subtraction: $a(b - c) = ab - ac$ and $(b - c)a = ba - ca$.

Domain (of a function) The set of values that the input can take.

Dynamic rectangles Dynamic rectangles have the property that half of such a rectangle is similar to the whole.

Equivalent equations If equations in two variables have the same graph on the Cartesian coordinate system, they are called equivalent equations.

Euclidean distance The straight-line distance between two points.

Evaluating expressions When you evaluate an expression, you replace each variable in it by a given value and then simplify the result.

Experiment An example of an experiment would be one roll of a pair of dice. Each different possibility of a result is an *outcome*. An *event* is one or more outcomes.

Exponential growth Involves repeated multiplication by a number.

Exponentiation or **Raising to a power** The operation of multiplying a number by itself repeatedly. The number multiplied is the *base*. The number of factors is the *exponent*.

Extrapolation When you know data points and use them to predict data values at a later or earlier time, the process is called extrapolation.

Eyes The points of intersection of the grid lines inside a polyomino are eyes.

Factor (noun), Common A common factor divides each term in a polynomial evenly.

Factor (verb) To write as a product.

Fair A game is fair if each of the players is equally likely to win.

Family (of functions) A group of functions that share a certain attribute.

Fixed point If an in-out line is horizontal, its input is a fixed point.

Focus Point where all in-out lines meet, if extended to the left or right.

Function A relation that assigns to each member of its *domain* exactly one member, its *range*.

Gear The gear ratio multiplied by the diameter of the rear wheel (of a bicycle).

Gear ratio The ratio of the number of teeth on the chainwheel (of a bicycle) to the number of teeth on the rear sprocket.

Geometric sequence In a geometric sequence each term is obtained from the previous term by multiplying by a constant amount, the common ratio.

Golden ratio The ratio of the longer to the shorter side of a golden rectangle is the golden ratio.

Golden rectangle A golden rectangle satisfies this property: If you cut a square off one end of the rectangle, the remaining rectangle is similar to the original rectangle.

Group A set of elements, together with an operation, that satisfies certain rules.

Hypotenuse The side of a right triangle that is opposite the right angle.

Identity An equation that is true for all values of the variables.

Inequalities An inequality is a mathematical sentence that contains an inequality symbol between two expressions, e.g. $2 < 6, x + 4 > 5$.

Input-Output Tables In such tables, x is the number that is put in, and y is the number that comes out. Each table has a rule that allows you to get y from x.

Integer Any positive or negative whole number and zero.

Intercepts of graphs
x-intercept: The point where it crosses the x-axis.
y-intercept: The point where it crosses the y-axis.
Intercept form: $y = a(x - p)(x - q)$

Interpolation When you know data points and use them to determine data values between those points, the process is called interpolation.

Inversely proportional You can say that y is inversely proportional to x if the product of x and y is constant. Algebraically, $xy = k$ or $y = k/a$ for some constant k.

Iterating functions To iterate a function means to use its output as a new input.

Lattice line A line having equation $x = b$ or $y = b$, where b is an integer.

Lattice point A point on the Cartesian plane having integer coordinates.

Legs The two sides of the right angle in a right triangle.

Like terms Terms whose variable factors are the same.

Linear combination The equation obtained by adding constant multiples of two equations together.

Magnification In function diagrams that have a focus, changes in y can be found by multiplying the changes in x by a number, called the magnification. Also called *rate of change*.

Mean The average of a set of values.

Median The middle value of a set of values.

Numbers
Rational: A rational number is any number that can be expressed as the ratio of two integers in the form a/b where $b \neq 0$.
Irrational: An irrational number is a real number that cannot be written in the form a/b where a and b are integers.
Natural: Natural numbers are the numbers we count with: 1, 2, 3, 4,…etc.
Real: Real numbers include all rational and irrational numbers.

Observed probability Can be represented graphically by the slope of the line through the origin and the corresponding data point.

Obtuse angle An obtuse angle is greater than a right angle.

Obtuse triangle An obtuse triangle contains an obtuse angle.

Order of operations A rule for the order in which operations are to be done.
1) Compute within grouping symbols;
2) Compute powers;
3) Multiply and divide in order from left to right;
4) Add and subtract in order from left to right.

Origin The point at which the axes of a graph cross; point (0, 0) in the Cartesian coordinate system.

Parabola The graph of a quadratic equation $ax^2 + bx + c = 0$; $a \neq 0$ is a parabola.

Parameter A constant or variable in a mathematical expression which distinguishes specific cases. In $y = a + bx$, a and b are the parameters.

Perimeter The perimeter of a figure is the distance around it.

Pi Pi, π, is approximately equal to the number 3.1415926536. The formula for the area of a circle is πr^2. (r is the radius of the circle.)

Plaintext The text of a message, before it is encoded.

Polycubes You can create polycubes by joining cubes together face-to-face. Polycubes are the three-dimensional equivalent of *polyominoes*.

Polynomial function A function of the form $y =$ a polynomial.

Polynomials A polynomial is a monomial or a sum of monomials.
Monomial: An expression that is the product of numerals and variables.
Binomial: A polynomial having two terms.
Trinomial: A polynomial having three terms.

Polytans Shapes created by combining tans.

Power A number that can be named using exponential notation.

Power of a product law It states that $x^a y^a = (xy)^a$ as long as x and $y \neq 0$.

Power of a ratio law It states that $x^a/y^a = (x/y)^a$ as long as x and $y \neq 0$.

Prime factorization Prime factorization occurs when you write a whole number as a product of prime factors.

Prime number An integer greater than one that has no factors other than one and itself.

Probability The probability of an event is interpreted to mean the relative frequency with which an event occurs if the experiment is repeated many times.

Product of powers law States that $x^a \cdot x^b = x^{a+b}$ as long as $x \neq 0$.

Pythagorean theorem In all right triangles, if a and b are the lengths of the legs and c is the length of the hypotenuse, then $a^2 + b^2 = c^2$.

Quadrant In the Cartesian coordinate system, the axes divide the system into four parts, called quadrants.

Quadratic formula A formula for finding the solutions of a quadratic equation $ax^2 + bx + c = 0$. The formula is $x = \frac{-b \pm \sqrt{b^2 - 4ac}}{2a}$

Quadratic function A second-degree polynomial function.

Radical
Radical sign: The symbol $\sqrt{\ }$.
Radical expression: An expression written under the radical sign.

Range (of a function) The set of values the output can take.

Rate of change of a function The rate of change of a function is the ratio between the change in y and the change in x.
rate of change = change in y/change in x
It is often called *magnification*.

Ratio of powers law It states that $x^a/x^b = x^{a-b}$ as long as $x \neq 0$.

Rational expression The quotient of two polynomials.

Rationalizing the denominator Simplifying a radical expression so that there are no radicals in the denominator and only whole numbers or variables in the radicand.

Reciprocals Two expressions are reciprocals if their product is one. Also called the *multiplicative inverse*.

Relative frequency The relative frequency of successes is the ratio of successes to trials.

Repeating decimal A decimal in which the same number or group of numbers repeats endlessly.

Right triangle A right triangle contains one angle of 90 degrees.

Rise The units of altitude gained for every 100 units moved in a horizontal direction (the run).

Run Distance moved in the horizontal direction when dealing with grade and slope.

Scientific notation A number expressed as the product of a power of 10 and a numeral greater than or equal to 1 but less than 10.

Sequence An ordered list of numbers or expressions, called *terms*.

Similarity Two figures are similar if all the dimensions of one can be obtained by multiplying the dimensions of the other by the same number. This number is called the *ratio of similarity*.

Simple radical form Writing the square root of a whole number as a product of a whole number and the square root of the smallest possible whole number.

Simultaneous equations Two or more equations for which you must find a common solution.
Slope A number telling how steeply a line slants; the ratio of rise to run.
Slope-intercept form $y = mx + b$
Solving an equation When you find all the values of a variable that make an equation true, you are solving an equation.
Standard form equation $ax^2 + bx + c = 0$
Step function May be shown by a graph. The end points of the steps may be filled in (closed circles) or hollow (open circles).
Subjective probability Subjective probability is assigned to an event according to a person's own knowledge, beliefs, or information.
Surface area The surface area of a figure (for example, a cube) is the number of unit squares it would take to cover all its faces.
Tan In the world of geometric puzzles, a tan is half a unit square (cut along the diagonal).
Tangent A line that touches a graph at only one point is tangent to the graph.
Taxicab distance The taxicab distance between two points in the Cartesian plane is the length of the shortest path between them that consists of only horizontal and vertical segments.
Terminating decimal A decimal that can be written in decimal form with a finite number of digits.
Terms An expression that is the product of numerals and variables.
Theoretical probability Can be represented graphically as a line through the origin.
Translations (of groups) A graph obtained by shifting the location of a given graph without changing its shape is called a translation of the original graph.
Variable A letter or other symbol used to represent a number or numbers.
Vertex of an angle The "corner" of a geometric figure is the vertex. The plural is *vertices.*
Vertex form of quadratic function The quadratic function $y = (x - H)^2 + V$ in vertex form.
Volume of solids The volume of a solid is the number of unit cubes it would take to build it.
Zero product property It states that when the product of two quantities is zero, one or the other quantity must be zero.

INDEX

Q

R

S